31/8/94.

Electric Cables Handbook

Second Edition

Edited by
E. W. G. Bungay
Formerly Chief Engineer,
BICC Power Cables Limited

and

D. McAllister
Formerly Assistant Chief Engineer,
BICC Power Cables Limited

OXFORD
BSP PROFESSIONAL BOOKS
LONDON EDINBURGH BOSTON
MELBOURNE PARIS BERLIN VIENNA

BSP Professional Books
A division of Blackwell Scientific
Publications Ltd
Editorial Offices:
Osney Mead, Oxford OX2 0EL
25 John Street, London WC1N 2BL
23 Ainslie Place, Edinburgh EH3 6AJ
238 Main Street, Cambridge,
MA 02142, USA
54 University Street, Carlton
Victoria 3053, Australia

Other Editorial Offices:
Librairie Arnette SA
1, rue de Lille
75007 Paris
France

Blackwell Wissenschafts-Verlag GmbH
Düsseldorfer Str. 38
D-10707 Berlin
Germany

Blackwell MZV
Feldgasse 13
A-1238 Wien
Austria

First published by
Granada Publishing 1982
Reprinted 1983, 1984, 1987
Second edition published by
BSP Professional Books 1990
Reprinted 1992, 1994

Set by Setrite Typesetters Ltd, H.K.
Printed and bound in Great Britain at
the University Press, Cambridge

DISTRIBUTORS

Marston Book Services Ltd
PO Box 87
Oxford OX2 0DT
(*Orders*: Tel: 0865 791155
Fax: 0865 791927
Telex: 837515)

USA
Blackwell Scientific Publications, Inc.
238 Main Street,
Cambridge, MA 02142
(*Orders*: Tel: 800 759-6102
617 876-7000)

Canada
Oxford University Press
70 Wynford Drive
Don Mills
Ontario M3C 1J9
(*Orders*: Tel: 416 441–2941)

Australia
Blackwell Scientific Publications Pty Ltd
54 University Street
Carlton,
Victoria 3053
(*Orders*: Tel: 03 347-5552)

British Library
Cataloguing in Publication Data

Electric cables handbook. – 2nd ed.
1. Electric cables
I. Bungay, E.W.G. II. McAllister,
D. (Donald)
621.31934

ISBN 0–632–02299–X

Contents

Preface to Second Edition

The good reception of the first edition, and the knowledge from many reprintings that the book has continued to be found useful, prompted a request for a revised edition to reflect the changes which have taken place during the last nine years.

Examination of the text showed that it required more than superficial treatment and that it would be beneficial to have a complete review to ensure that the new edition should be as up to date as possible.

Mr E. W. G. Bungay consented to become co-editor with a major role in ensuring continued support from experts in the BICC organisation, as well as providing his own detailed knowledge of the whole national and international situation.

Where the original contributors have either been long retired or moved to new technical fields, other contributors have been brought in to revise the text. Some of the changes have been relatively small and others quite significant.

In the previous preface, reference was made to the difficulty in deciding which types of cable should be excluded. As the interest in telecommunication cables tends to be quite separate from that of other types of cable they were left out. Within the last decade, however, largely due to the explosion in electronics applications, another large category of cables has emerged to cater for such requirements. Although much allied with data communications, it also overlaps significantly with some of the cables traditional to the general wiring field. To indicate the designs and types of cable now available a new chapter has been added to this edition.

The acknowledgements previously made continue to be applicable and the editors would particularly like to record appreciation for the invaluable support from the management of BICC Cables Ltd together with present and former members of staff. Special mention is due to Mr R. T. Brown who has played the major part in the review and updating of part 2 on wiring cables etc. As before, Mr C. A. Arkell has been a focus for part 4.

D. McAllister

Preface to First Edition

Comparatively few books on electric cables have been published and those available have become somewhat dated. This has been particularly unfortunate in view of the important changes in practice which have occurred in the 1960s and 1970s.

Retirement, and the encouragement of BICC management, presented the opportunity to make good the lack of up-to-date material by the present book, which provides comprehensive coverage of all types of insulated cable, from wiring and flexible cables for general use, to distribution, transmission and submarine cables. Current designs and practices are commented on against a background of how the present situation has evolved and what changes can be foreseen in the future.

Apart from the cables themselves, practical information has been provided on the materials used, design principles, installation aspects and Standards. The Appendices also contain tables of data on all commonly used cable types.

It is hoped that the book will be a valuable reference aid for university students, electrical engineers in factories, electrical engineering consultants, contractors, supply authorities and cable manufacturers – in short, anyone professionally involved with cables.

In covering a wide field from lighting flexibles to future 750 kV a.c. transmission cables, some difficulty was encountered in the breakdown to specific subjects and chapters, especially as it was clearly obvious that the assistance of many specialist contributors would be necessary. The very willing response to the Editor's requests for such assistance was most gratifying. Sincere thanks are due to all the contributors, not only for their texts, but for their ready collaboration in dealing with the problems arising in working to a synopsis for a subject which could easily give rise to difficulties with overlap, as discussed in chapter 1.

Thanks are also due to many others, without whose help the book could not have been produced. Firstly, grateful appreciation must be expressed to the directors and mangement of BICC for provision of the many facilities required for the preparation of a manuscript. Three operating companies were involved; whilst the greatest contribution came from BICC Power Cables Limited, much assistance has also been received from BICC Supertension Cables Limited and BICC General Cables Limited.

So many individuals have helped in various ways that it is difficult to name them all. The work has undoubtedly been a team effort. However, particular tribute must be expressed to Mr E. W. G. Bungay whose helpful advice was so often sought and so willingly given throughout all stages. Grateful thanks are also due to Mr W. L. Town, Mr B. E. Roberts and Mr C. A. Arkell who respectively did much to coordinate parts 2, 3 and 4 of the book. Mr E. W. G. Bungay, Mr J. D. Endacott and Mr S. Verne all read the finished text and provided very helpful comments.

Appreciative acknowledgement is also due to the International Electrical Commission and the British Standards Institution for permission to refer to the requirements of various publications and standards. Illustrations have been provided by a number of companies and institutions and these are gratefully acknowledged in the relevant caption.

So far as is practicable SI units have been used in the text but attention is drawn to the adoption of 'bar' for pressure. As gauge pressure is always implied, 'bar g' should perhaps have been adopted as some readers may interpret 'bar' as absolute pressure.

D. McAllister
Wrexham (September 1981)

Contributors

C. A. Arkell, BSc, CEng, MIEE
Chief Engineer, BICC Cables Limited, Power Division, Supertension Cables (33, 35, 40, 41, 44)

H. Baker, BA, FInstP
Chief Engineer, BICC Pyrotenax Limited (16)

V. A. A. Banks, BSc
Senior Projects Engineer, BICC Cables Limited, Power Division, Mains Cables (25)

Z. Bonikowski, BSc, CEng, MIMechE, FIEE,
Technology and Planning Manager, BICC Cables Limited (16)

R. T. Brown, BSc
Formerly Cable Assessment Manager, BICC Elastomeric Cables Limited (11, 12, 13, 14, 15)

E. W. G. Bungay, BSc, CEng, MIEE
Formerly Chief Engineer, BICC Power Cables Limited (7, 10, 19, 29, 31, 36)

G. R. M. Dench, TEng(CEI), MITE
Formerly Specifications Engineer, BICC Supertension Cables Limited (34, 45)

A. W. Field, PhD, CEng, FPRI
Chief Engineer, BICC Cables Limited, Power Division, Mains Cables (3, 6, 25)

A. Friday, BSc, MSc, PhD
Research and Development Manager, BICC Components Limited (28)

P. F. Gale, BTech, PhD, CEng, MIEE
Formerly Chief Engineer, Biccotest Limited (30, 43)

S. G. Galloway, BSc
Systems Installation Engineer, BICC Cables Limited, Power Division, Supertension Cables (45)

B. Gregory, BSc, CEng, MIEE
Chief Development Engineer, BICC Cables Limited, Power Division, Supertension Cables (38)

J. E. Hawkes, TEng(CEI), MIEE
High Voltage Laboratory Engineer, BICC Cables Limited, Power Division, Supertension Cables (42)

J. T. Henderson, BSc, CEng, FIEE
Formerly Marketing Manager (Far East and Pacific), BICC Supertension Cables Limited (2)

S. H. Jagger, BSc, CEng, FIEE
Formerly Contracts Manager, Balfour Beatty Power Limited, Traction and General Division (27)

D. McAllister
Formerly Assistant Chief Engineer, BICC Power Cables Limited (1, 3, 4, 5, 7, 8, 9, 20, 21, 22, 23, 24, 26, 29, 32, 33, 35)

P. L. Mayhew, BSc, CEng, MIEE, MIIM
Formerly Site Director and General Manager, Elastomeric Cables Unit, BICC Cables Limited (39)

D. Pollard, CEng, FIEE
Formerly Technical Manager, Leigh Works, BICC General Cables Limited (11, 12, 13, 14, 15)

I. B. Riley, BSc
Projects Manager, BICC Cables Limited, Construction and Wiring Division (28)

B. E. Roberts, BEng, CEng, FIEE
Director and General Manager, BICC Cables Limited, Power Division, Mains Cables (25, 36)

D. G. Roberts, CChem, MRSC
Senior Project Engineer, BICC Cables Limited Power Division, Mains Cables (6)

G. J. Smee
Commercial Manager, BICC Cables Limited, Power Division, Supertension Cables (37)

N. H. Waterhouse, BSc
Formerly Engineering Manager, Submarine Cables Unit, Balfour Kilpatrick Limited (46)

G. R. Williams
Contracts Manager, BICC Cables Limited, Power Division, Supertension Cables (39)

A. J. Willis, CEng, MIEE
Chief Engineer, Electronics Business, BICC Cables Limited, Communications and Electronics Division (17)

W. J. Willis, BSc
Sales Engineer, Biccotest Limited (30, 43)

H. S. Wood, CEng, MIEE
Development Engineering, Merseyside and North Wales Electricity Board (17)

D. E. E. Woolmer, CEng, MIEE
Chief Cabling Engineer, Balfour Kilpatrick Limited (46)

Chapter 1

Introduction

The first edition of the book covered all types of insulated cable for the supply of electricity for voltages from about 100 V to 525 kV, a.c. or d.c., the cable types excluded being mainly those for telecommunication purposes and for specialised applications. Because of the subsequent extensive growth in the field of newly developed cables for electronic equipment, this second edition includes a chapter on such applications at lower voltages.

FORMAT

The field is very wide and the division into suitable chapters posed a number of problems. Having decided on a presentation to conform with the existing manufacturing and marketing patterns, a need was apparent for specialist contributors in the various fields. There was then a further difficulty in providing a synopsis with the object of making each chapter a complete entity but without too much overlap and repetition. This was not easy, and for the benefit of readability and reference most emphasis has been placed on making each chapter reasonably self-contained. This has been done at the expense of allowing a measure of repetition and it is hoped that the overlap will assist clarity rather than cause distraction.

Organisation of the book and the cable industry

The problems in chapter sequence arise primarily because, whatever headings are selected, there is no sharp line of demarcation and considerable merging occurs in practice. The operating voltage provides a rough guide but is very far from representing a clear division between different cable types. For example, pressure-assisted cables are generally considered to be a well defined group which divorces transmission cables from distribution cables. However, they are commonly used in the 33–132 kV range, which is now in the field of distribution cables in the UK.

Similarly, cables for such applications as mining where flexibility is required, and ships or offshore oil installations, are generally dealt with by manufacturers and users as belonging to the group containing general wiring cables, even though the voltages may extend into the range representative of distribution cables for public supply.

A further aspect is that the cable making industry, together with its relationships with users and standardising authorities, is largely built up on a pattern of specific factories and liaison staff for some established groupings of cable types. The factories are often at separate locations but may also be subdivisions on a common site. Historically these groupings arose because of the materials used in the cables and the types of manufacturing plant adopted. To some degree, the average size and weight of the cables can be allied with the same pattern.

Likewise, specialist personnel became associated with the same groupings. As the book has been compiled with the aid of such personnel it was found convenient to arrange the chapters in accordance with such groupings. Some aspects arising are considered below.

Part 1

Trends in material usages are towards elimination of the older distinctions and also many facets of cable design are common to all types. Part 1, therefore, deals with materials and design features which are reasonably applicable to most cables.

Part 2

A group of cables traditionally known as 'wiring and general' emerged and grew historically around cables predominantly having rubber insulation, in contrast with power distribution cables having impregnated paper insulation. Whereas paper cables were usually bought directly by the user, the wiring cables were commonly marketed through wholesalers. Nowadays, although the main product types still remain, the insulants used in the two fields are often similar, i.e. thermoplastics and thermoset materials (rubbers and crosslinked thermoplastics).

This group of cables is often still further subdivided and segregated into different factories, e.g. (a) cables having thermoset insulation and/or sheaths, (b) cables which are produced in large quantity for specific applications such as PVC insulated cables for fixed wiring, (c) flexible cables and (d) cables for electronic applications.

Part 3

This part caters for a much smaller number of cable types than part 2 and essentially embraces the cables required for public supply and heavy industrial distribution. However, industrial distribution covers a wide range of power requirements and causes some overlap with part 2. For example the British Standard for PVC armoured cables for industrial use is a common one for cables covered by parts 2 and 3 of the book and in such cases a common but somewhat arbitrary pattern is for cables with conductor sizes of 25 mm^2 and above to come within the power distribution ambit.

Part 4

This part essentially covers cables for public supply transmission systems, but in the voltage range 33–132 kV there is some overlap with part 3. In this book the non-pressure-assisted cables in this voltage range, which now includes important developments with crosslinked polyethylene insulation, are generally covered in part 3. Historically, transmission cables have been of the pressure-assisted paper insulated type. However, polyethylene (PE) and crosslinked polyethylene (XLPE) are now showing potential as insulants for voltages of 132 kV upwards and have to be included as an extension of their use covered by earlier sections. Gaseous dielectrics may also find application in this field.

Appendices

Much of the tabular data presented is aimed towards providing information on the ranges of cables available in the most widely used fields, and on the properties of the cables. Those engineers dealing with cables on a regular basis, and placing orders for them, will no doubt have manufacturers' catalogues available which give other more detailed information.

HISTORICAL SURVEY

The book endeavours to give an account of the present position on the current types of cable used and their applications, together with a forecast of changes which can be anticipated in the not too distant future. To explain how the existing situation has been reached, an outline is also given of the various stages which have led to present practices.

In the latter context it may be of interest to note some of the more important dates or periods which have been significant in past developments. These are indicated in table 1.1.

DIFFERENCES IN CABLE DESIGN THROUGHOUT THE WORLD

Transmission cable practices are fairly similar throughout the world. For wiring type cables many individual countries have preferences for particular designs or materials but the differences are not fundamental.

Similar preferences apply to distribution cables but in addition there are some major differences allied with the systems, which may be divided into two categories: those countries following British and European practice, and those which have adopted the USA system designs.

There is a certain amount of overlap between the distribution practices but the differences are such that it has not been found possible to produce a book which would be sufficiently clear and concise to do justice to both. Hence the coverage is essentially for British practice and this also reasonably represents usage in Europe and the majority of countries throughout the world.

The USA practices are followed in countries and areas that have been more geared to the American economy, such as South America and the Philippines. The most notable difference in such systems is that in urban areas, apart from the relatively newer concept of underground residential distribution (URD), the vast majority of the distribution is overhead and undergrounding is only adopted in relatively small areas in the innermost parts of cities and large towns. Even in such areas the concept is frequently different from undergrounding in the European sense, as it often comprises the use of conductors similar to those used overhead but having insulation, i.e. single-core cables, which are installed in ducts. The transformers also follow similar lines and often consist of small single-phase types, in contrast with the larger 3-phase transformers used elsewhere. The use of single-core cables in ducts has an effect on cable designs, particularly concerning the neutral and/or protective conductor and armour.

In the early stages of development, the American systems clearly favoured rubber rather than paper insulation and paper insulation was never developed to the same extent as in Europe. The introduction of thermoplastic and thermoset insulation, coupled with the huge output from the American chemical industry, also favoured the development of single-core polymeric insulated cables and this has led the way to changes which are steadily being adopted throughout the world.

Table 1.1 Significant dates in cable developments

1880s	First gutta percha electric cable followed by rubber and vulcanised bitumen insulation
1890	Ferranti 10 kV tubular cable and the introduction of paper insulation
1914	Hochstadter development of screening which enabled distribution voltage to be increased to 33 kV
1926	Emanueli provided the principle of pressurisation with oil-filled paper cables for voltages of 66 kV upwards
1930s	PVC insulation first tried out in Germany
1943	First 3-core 132 kV pressure cable in service
1949	Introduction of the mass-impregnated non-draining cable in the UK to overcome the problems of drainage of oil–rosin impregnant with cables installed on slopes
1950s	(a) Full commercial introduction of PVC and later thermoset insulation for wiring cables. PVC for power cables followed at the end of the decade (b) Successful development of aluminium sheaths, initially for pressure-assisted cables, and gradual adoption of aluminium conductors for power cables (c) First 275 kV OF cable (1954), operational use in 1959
1960s	(a) Significant distribution economies obtained by the use of combined neutral and earth cables (b) England/France ±100 kV submarine d.c. link inaugurated in 1961 (c) First 400 kV OF cable, operational in 1969
1970	Metrication of British Standards
1970s	Gradual extension of the use of thermoset insulation, mainly XLPE, as an alternative to paper insulation. Large commercial applications up to 15 kV but also experimental installations at higher voltages, including transmission up to 132 kV
1980s	Rapid extension in the proportion of cable used for electronic applications. Very widespread use of XLPE in the 11–33 kV range with significant quantities installed for transmission voltages of 66–240 kV Development and growing use of cables designed to alleviate the effects when cables are involved in fires. Properties include reduced flame propagation, low smoke emission, reduced emission of noxious fumes and corrosive gases and combinations of these characteristics

Throughout the century a feature of the British/European system has been that in built-up areas the distribution cables have been placed underground – hence the avoidance of unsightly poles, wires and overhead transformers. Details are given in chapter 18 and the successful experience obtained has led, over the years, to a large measure of export business. This not only includes cables and equipment but also engineering practice from specialised consultants.

In 1987 the UK production of insulated wires and cables amounted to about £1500 million, of which 13% was exported. For the more highly developed types of cable, e.g. as covered in parts 3–5 of the book, the export proportion is very much higher and also increases fairly directly with voltage rating.

PART 1

THEORY, DESIGN AND PRINCIPLES COMMON TO ALL CABLE TYPES

Chapter 2

Basic Electrical Theory Applicable to Cable Design

In all engineering undertakings, economical, technical and practical aspects are taken into consideration to establish the optimum solution or design. For the transmission, distribution and utilisation of electrical power, the choice normally lies between the use of overhead lines and underground cables.

For economic reasons, overhead lines are used extensively for the transmission and distribution of electricity in rural areas where environmental or practical considerations do not dictate otherwise. However, in urban areas it is more usual to install insulated cables which, in the main, are buried underground. The utilisation of electricity in factories, domestic premises and other locations is also mainly by cables as they present the most practical means of conveying electrical power to equipment, tools and appliances of all types. Cable designs vary enormously to meet the diverse requirements but there are certain components which are common to all.

All types of electric cable consist essentially of a low resistance conductor to carry the current except in special cases, such as heating cables, and insulation to isolate the conductors from each other and from their surroundings. In several types, such as single-core wiring cables, the two components form the finished cable, but generally as the voltage increases the construction becomes much more complex.

Other main components may include screening to obtain a radial electrostatic field, a metal sheath to keep out moisture or to retain a pressuring medium, armouring for mechanical protection, corrosion protection for the metallic components and a variety of additions extending, for example, to internal and external pipes to remove the heat generated in the cable.

This chapter contains some of the electrical theory applicable to all cable types. Further details of individual cable designs and components are given in later chapters.

VOLTAGE DESIGNATION

In the early days of electric power utilisation, direct current was widely used, but little now remains except for special applications and for a few interconnections in transmission networks. Alternating current has many advantages and 3-phase alternating current is used almost exclusively throughout the world.

So that suitable insulation and cable construction can be specified for the required 3-phase a.c. service performance, the design voltages for cables are expressed in the form U_0/U (formerly E_0/E). U_0 is the power frequency voltage between conductor and earth and U is the power frequency voltage between conductors for which the cable is designed, U_0 and U both being r.m.s. values.

Power cables in British Standards are thus designated 600/1000 V, 1900/3300 V, 3800/6600 V, 6350/11000 V, 8700/15000 V, 12700/22000 V and 19000/33000 V. For transmission voltages above this it is normal to quote only the value of U and thus the higher standard voltages in the UK are 132, 275 and 400 kV. The maximum voltage can be 10% greater than the above values for voltages up to and including 275 kV and 5% greater for 400 kV.

Although the local distribution voltage in the UK is 240/415 V, the cables are designed for 600/1000 V, largely because during manufacture and installation this grade of cable requires an insulation designed on mechanical rather than electrical parameters.

Standardisation of system voltages has not been achieved worldwide although there is some move towards this. IEC has published voltage designations which are approaching universal acceptance.

D.C. system voltages, by which is meant d.c. voltages with not more than 3% ripple, are designated by the positive and negative value of the voltage above and below earth potential. The symbol U_0 is used for the rated d.c. voltage between conductor and the earthed core screen.

Many references will be found to cables described as low voltage (LV), medium voltage (MV), high voltage (HV) and even EHV or UHV. Apart from low voltage, which is defined internationally, these terms do not have generally accepted precise meanings and can be misleading. In some countries MV has in the past applied to 600/1000 V cables (these now fall clearly within the LV designation), whereas others have taken it to mean 6/10 kV or 8.7/15 kV and misunderstanding could arise. For precision it is best to use the actual voltage rating of the cable.

CONDUCTOR RESISTANCE

D.C. resistance

Factors affecting d.c. conductor resistance in terms of material resistivity and purity are discussed in chapter 3 and those relating to conductor design in chapter 4. The latter are associated with the fact that the prime path of the current is a helical one following the individual wires in the conductor. Hence if an attempt is made to calculate the resistance of a length of stranded conductor a factor must be applied to cater for the linear length of wire in the conductor to allow for extra length caused by the stranding effect. In a multicore cable an additional factor must be applied to allow for the additional length due to the lay of the cores.

The d.c. resistance is also dependent on temperature as given by

$$R_t = R_{20}\,[1 + \alpha_{20}\,(t - 20)] \tag{2.1}$$

where R_t = conductor resistance at t°C (Ω)
R_{20} = conductor resistance at 20 °C (Ω)
α_{20} = temperature coefficient of resistance of the conductor material at 20 °C
t = conductor temperature (°C)

A.C. resistance

If a conductor is carrying high alternating currents, the distribution of current is not evenly disposed throughout the cross-section of the conductor. This is due to two independent effects known as the 'skin effect' and the 'proximity effect'.

If the conductor is considered to be composed of a large number of concentric circular elements, those at the centre of the conductor will be enveloped by a greater magnetic flux than those on the outside. Consequently the self-induced back e.m.f. will be greater towards the centre of the conductor, thus causing the current density to be less at the centre than at the conductor surface. This extra concentration at the surface is the skin effect and it results in an increase in the effective resistance of the conductor. The magnitude of the skin effect is influenced by the frequency, the size of the conductor, the amount of current flowing and the diameter of the conductor.

The proximity effect also increases the effective resistance and is associated with the fields of two conductors which are close together. If each carries a current in the same direction, the halves of the conductors in close proximity are cut by more flux than the remote halves. Consequently, the current distribution is not even throughout the cross-section, a greater proportion being carried by the remote halves. If the currents are in opposite directions the halves in closer proximity carry the greater density of current. In both cases the overall effect results in an increase in the effective resistance of the conductor. The proximity effect decreases with increase in spacing between cables.

Mathematical treatment of these effects is complicated because of the large number of possible variations but Arnold[1] has produced a comprehensive report (see also chapter 8).

Skin and proximity effects may be ignored with small conductors carrying modest currents. They become increasingly significant with larger conductors and it is often desirable for technical and economic reasons to design the conductors to minimise them. The Milliken conductor, which reduces skin and proximity effects, is described in chapter 4.

A.C. resistances are important for calculation of current carrying capacity. Values for standard designs of distribution and transmission cables are included in the tables in appendices 12–16.

INDUCTANCE

The inductance L per core of a 3-core cable or of three single-core cables comprises two parts, the self-inductance of the conductor and the mutual inductance with other cores. It is given by

$$L = K + 0.2 \log_e \frac{2S}{d} \text{ (mH/km)} \qquad (2.2)$$

where K = a constant relating to the conductor formation (table 2.1)
S = axial spacing between conductors for cables in trefoil spacing (mm)
= 1.26 × phase spacing for single-core cables in flat formation (mm)
d = conductor diameter or for shaped designs the diameter of an equivalent circular conductor (mm)

For 2-core and 3-core cables the inductance obtained from the formula should be multiplied by 1.02 if the conductors are circular and by 0.97 for 3-core oval conductors.

REACTANCE

The reactance X of each core of a 3-core cable or three single-core cables may be

Table 2.1 Typical values for constant K for different stranded conductors (at 50 Hz)

Number of wires in conductor	K
3	0.0778
7	0.0642
19	0.0554
37	0.0528
61 and over	0.0514
Hollow-core conductor, 12 mm duct	0.0383

obtained from the formula

$$X = 2\pi f L \times 10^{-3} \ (\Omega/\text{km}) \tag{2.3}$$

where f = frequency (Hz)
L = inductance (mH/km)

IMPEDANCE

The impedance Z of each core of a 3-core cable or a circuit of three single-core cables is given by

$$Z = (R^2 + X^2)^{1/2} \ (\Omega/\text{km}) \tag{2.4}$$

where R = a.c. resistance at operating temperature (Ω/km)
X = reactance (Ω/km)

INSULATION RESISTANCE

Insulation resistance is the resistance to the passage of direct current through the dielectric between two electrodes. In the case of an electric cable it is the value of the resistance between the conductor and the earthed core screen, metallic sheath, armour or adjacent conductors.

Consider a unit length of single-core cable with conductor radius r and radius over insulation R (fig. 2.1). The surface area of a ring of insulation of radial thickness δx

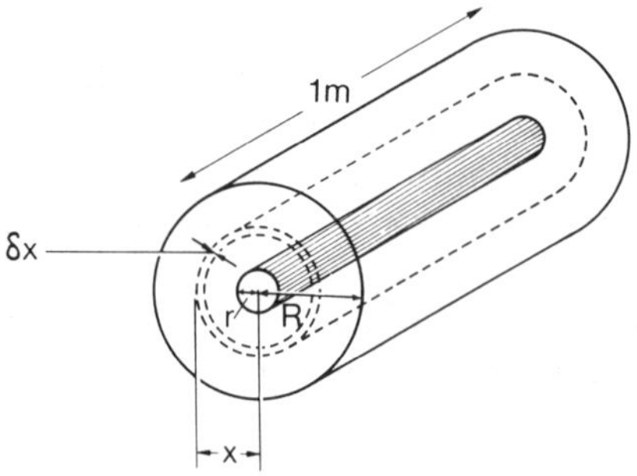

Fig. 2.1 Calculation of insulation resistance of an insulated conductor

at radius x is $2\pi x$ times the unit length. The insulation resistance D_R of this ring is given by

$$D_R = \frac{\rho \delta x}{2\pi x} \ (\Omega) \tag{2.5}$$

where ρ is the specific resistivity (Ω m).

Thus the insulation resistance of radial thickness $R - r$ for 1 m cable length is given by

$$D_R = \frac{\rho}{2\pi} \int_r^R \frac{\mathrm{d}x}{x} \ (\Omega) \tag{2.6}$$

which evolves to

$$D_R = \frac{\rho}{2\pi} \log_e \frac{R}{r} \ (\Omega)$$

or for cable length l

$$\frac{\rho}{2\pi \, l} \log_e \frac{R}{r} \ (\Omega) \tag{2.7}$$

Correction for temperature may be made according to

$$\rho_t = \rho_{20} \exp(-\alpha t)$$

where ρ_{20} = specific resistivity at 20 °C
α = temperature coefficient of resistance per degree Celsius at 20 °C
t = temperature (°C)

Specific resistivity is also dependent on electric stress and hence the above derivation is a simplification. However, the effect is much less than that of temperature and in most cases it can be neglected. It can be of importance in the design of high voltage d.c. cables and this is dealt with in chapter 41. In making measurements of insulation resistance it is necessary to maintain the d.c. test voltage for sufficient time to ensure that any transient currents associated with electrification of the cable are of negligible value.

In a.c. cables there will be additional currents flowing through the insulation due to the capacitance of the insulation and for high voltage d.c. cables an extra factor is introduced to take account of the variation of resistivity with applied voltage (see chapter 41).

CAPACITANCE

Single-core cables

Single-core cables used for power transmission and distribution are generally screened by an earthed metallic sheath. The electric field of the single-core cable is therefore contained within the earthed envelope and is substantially radial.

Consider a single-core cable with a smooth conductor of radius r (m) and an internal sheath radius of R (m) (fig. 2.2). Assume that the conductor carries a charge of q (coulomb/m), then the electric flux emanates from the conductor radially,

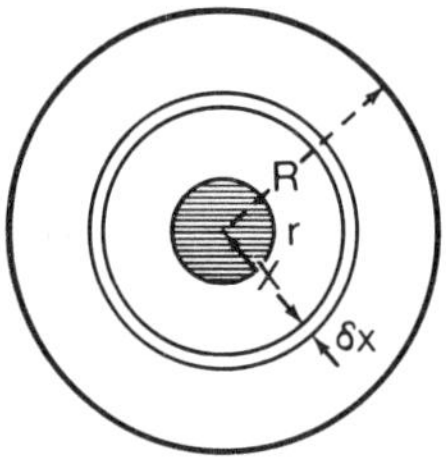

Fig. 2.2 Cross-section of cable core for derivation of capacitance

giving a flux density at radius X (m) from the centre of the conductor of

$$D_x = \frac{q}{2\pi X} \text{ (coulomb/m}^2\text{)}$$

The electric field intensity at radius X is

$$E_x = \frac{D_x}{\epsilon_0 \epsilon_r} = \frac{q}{2\pi X \epsilon_0 \epsilon_r} \tag{2.8}$$

where ϵ_0 = permittivity of free space, $10^{-9}/36\pi$
ϵ_r = relative permittivity of the insulation

The work done in moving a unit positive charge the distance dx in an electric field of intensity E is given by

$$\mathrm{d}W = -E\,\mathrm{d}x$$

i.e. the change in potential along dx is

$$\mathrm{d}V = -E\,\mathrm{d}x$$

Therefore the work done in moving unit charge from the conductor surface to the outer surface of the insulation is governed by

$$V = \int_R^r -E\,\mathrm{d}x$$

$$= -\frac{q}{2\pi\epsilon_0\epsilon_r}\int_R^r \frac{\mathrm{d}_x}{X}$$

$$= \frac{q}{2\pi\epsilon_0\epsilon_r}\log_e\left(\frac{R}{r}\right) \text{ (V)} \tag{2.9}$$

The capacitance of the cable per metre length is given by

$$C = \frac{q}{V}$$

$$= \frac{2\pi\epsilon_0\epsilon_r}{\log_e(R/r)} \text{ (F/m)}$$

$$= \frac{2\pi\epsilon_r \times 10^{-9}}{36\pi \log_e(R/r)} \text{ (F/m)}$$

or

$$= \frac{\epsilon_r}{18 \log_e(D/d)} \ (\mu F/km) \qquad (2.10)$$

where D = diameter over the insulation (m)
d = diameter over the conductor (m)
ϵ_r = relative permittivity

The relative permittivity is charateristic of the insulation material and is dependent on temperature and frequency. For power frequencies and normal operating temperatures the effect is small and can be ignored for most engineering calculations.

Three-core belted type cables

The equation for calculating the capacitance of a belted type cable is not readily formulated (see later for field theory for paper insulated cables), but an approximation of the capacitance between one conductor and the other conductors bonded to the lead sheath can be obtained from equation (2.10) if D is taken as

D = diameter of one conductor plus the thickness of insulation between conductors plus the thickness of insulation between any conductor and the metal sheath

The various other capacitances of a belted type cable may be obtained, to a close approximation, by calculating C by equation (2.10) and using the following factors:

$C_1 = 1.2C$ = equivalent star capacitance (capacitance to neutral)
$C_2 = 0.6C$ = conductor-to-conductor capacitance (other conductors and sheath free)
$C_3 = 1.8C$ = capacitance of all conductors (bunched) to sheath

DIELECTRIC POWER FACTOR (DIELECTRIC LOSS ANGLE)

It is of great importance that the power factor of the dielectric of cables for voltages of 33 kV and above is of a very low value. The power factor of a dielectric is the ratio

$$\frac{\text{loss in dielectric (watt)}}{\text{volts} \times \text{amps}}$$

Referring to fig. 2.3, when a voltage is applied to a cable with a 'perfect' dielectric, a charging current I_C flows which is in leading quadrature with the voltage. In such a 'perfect' dielectric there would be no component of the current in phase with U. However, perfection in dielectrics has not been achieved and there is

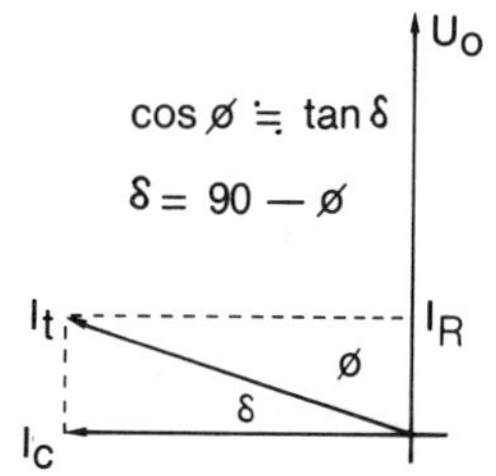

Fig. 2.3 Vector diagram to represent dielectric loss angle

a small current I_R which is in phase with U. (See later section on dielectric losses.) This current causes losses $I_R U$ in the dielectric which generate heat. The losses in the dielectric are proportional to the cosine of the angle between the resultant current I_t and applied voltage U.
Now

$$I_t = (I_R^2 + I_C^2)^{1/2}$$

$$I_R U = I_t U \cos \phi$$

and

$$\cos \phi = \frac{I_R}{(I_R^2 + I_C^2)^{1/2}} \qquad (2.11)$$

As ϕ is close to 90°, cos ϕ equates approximately to tan(90 − ϕ), i.e. equates (approximately) to tan δ, and the dielectric power factor of a cable is frequently referred to as tan δ, where δ is known as the dielectric loss angle (DLA).

The dielectric loss in watts per kilometre per phase is given by

$$D = 2\pi f\, C\, U_0^2 \tan \delta\ 10^{-6} \text{ (watt/km per phase)} \qquad (2.12)$$

It will be seen from this equation that, for a specified design of cable in which values of f, C and U_0 are fixed, the dielectric loss angle must be kept to an absolute minimum to achieve low dielectric losses.

In addition to establishing the dielectric loss angle of the cable to determine the dielectric losses for cable rating purposes, valuable information can be obtained by testing the power factor of the cable in discrete voltage steps within the voltage range $0.5U_0$–$2U_0$. Such a test gives information on the ionisation which takes place in the insulation since ionisation increases with increase in applied voltage (see later under 'Mechanism of breakdown').

In the case of paper insulated cables the DLA is a function of the density of the paper and the contamination in the oil and paper. The oil can readily be cleaned and the contaminants arise mostly from the paper as ionisable salts. To obtain the lowest DLA in transmission cables at high temperature, deionised water is used in paper manufacture.

ELECTRICAL STRESS DISTRIBUTION AND CALCULATION

The flux distribution in a.c. belted cable insulation is complex and is shown diagrammatically in fig. 2.4. The stress is a maximum at the conductor surface and varies throughout the insulation, decreasing with distance from the conductor surface, but not in a clearly defined manner because of the differing permittivities of the components and the distribution of the flux at various times during the voltage phase rotation. The screened cable used for alternating voltages has a clearly defined stress pattern, while that of cables used on d.c. transmission has a changing pattern depending on temperature due to cable loading.

A.C. stress distribution in single-core and screened multicore cables

The stranding effect of unscreened conductors gives a slight unevenness of stress distribution around the periphery of the conductor because of the small radius of the

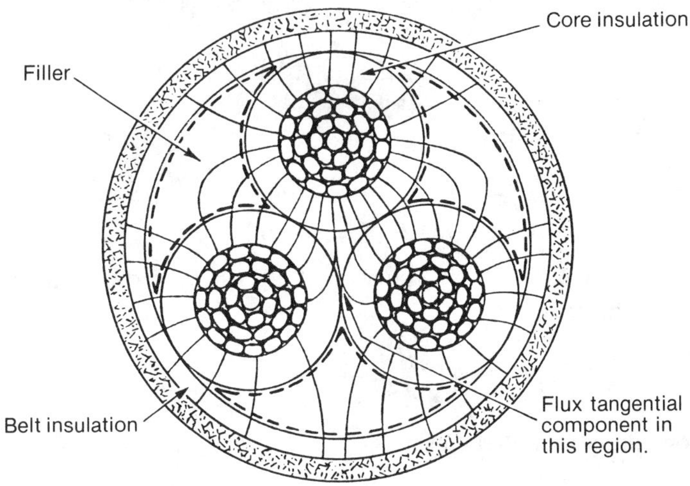

Fig. 2.4 Paper insulated belted cable with top conductor at peak potential

wires. Neglecting this effect, a screened core consists of a cylindrical capacitor with the conductor as the inner electrode and the core screen as the outer electrode. Assuming a uniform permittivity, the radial stress distribution curve of a circular core is derived as below. It will be seen to be maximum at the conductor surface, reducing in a hyperbolic curve (fig. 2.5). As the permittivity of the dielectric is substantially constant throughout the operating temperature range of the cable, the stress distribution remains constant at all operating conditions.

Using the notation given previously, i.e.

r = radius of conductor (m)
R = internal radius of sheath (m)
ϵ_0 = relative permittivity of free space
ϵ_r = relative permittivity of the dielectric
V = potential of conductor relative to the sheath (V)
q = charge (coulomb/m of axial length)

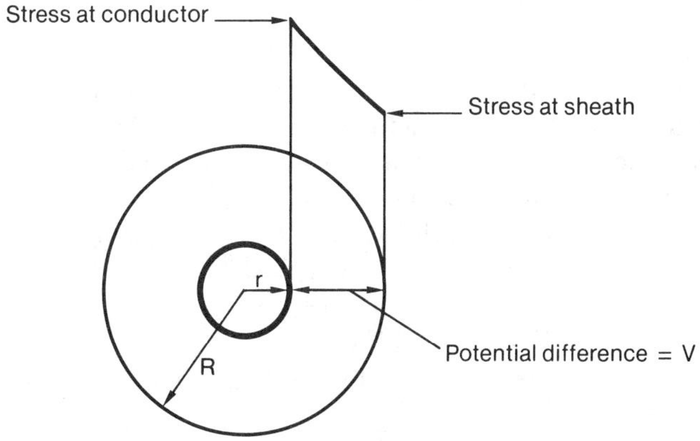

Fig. 2.5 Electrostatic stress in single-core cable

from equation (2.9)

$$V = \frac{q}{2\pi\epsilon_0\epsilon_r} \log_e\left(\frac{R}{r}\right) \text{ (V)}$$

Therefore

$$\frac{q}{2\pi\epsilon_0\epsilon_r} = \frac{V}{\log_e(R/r)}$$

Stress may be calculated from equation (2.8) which showed the electric field intensity E_x at radius x to be

$$E_x = \frac{q}{2\pi x \epsilon_0\epsilon_r}$$

By substitution, the stress at radius x is

$$E_x = \frac{V}{x\log_e(R/r)} \text{ (MV/m)} \tag{2.13}$$

It will be noted that the range is

$$\text{maximum} = \frac{V}{r\log_e(R/r)} \text{ at conductor surface}$$

$$\text{minimum} = \frac{V}{R\log_e(R/r)} \text{ at sheath inner surface}$$

Several features arising from this are as follows.

Stress at conductor surface

In the above derivation of the stress distribution it was assumed that the conductor surface was smooth. However, the effects of the radius of the wires in a stranded, uncompacted conductor may increase the stress substantially. In high voltage cables it is therefore usual to apply a thin metallic or semiconducting tape over a stranded conductor to obtain a smooth surface.

Conductor diameter

The equation (2.13) derived for the stress within the cable dielectric showed the stress to be a maximum at the conductor surface. The equation may be developed further to obtain the ratio of the diameter over the conductor to that over the insulation and hence the conductor diameter which gives the minimum stress at the conductor surface for a specified voltage and diameter over the insulation:

$$E_r = \frac{V}{r\log_e(R/r)}$$

For minimum stress at the conductor for constant values of V and R

$$\frac{dE_r}{dr} = 0$$

i.e.

$$\frac{d}{d_r}\left[\frac{V}{r\,\log_e(R/r)}\right] = 0$$

$$\frac{d}{d_r}\left[\frac{V}{r\,\log_e R - r\,\log_e r}\right] = 0$$

$$\frac{-\,V\,(\log_e R - \log_e r - 1)}{(r\,\log_e R - r\,\log_e r)^2} = 0$$

Therefore

$$\log_e R - \log_e r - 1 = 0$$

$$\log_e(R/r) = 1$$

and

$$R/r = \mathrm{e} \qquad (2.14)$$

The stress at the conductor is at a minimum when the ratio R/r equals e. By substituting this in the stress equation it will be seen that the value of the stress is V/r. This is illustrated in fig. 2.6.

The conductor cross-sectional area is determined by the current which has to be carried. When designing cables, particularly for the higher transmission voltages, it is possible that the radius of the conductor size needed to give the current carrying capacity called for will be smaller than that to give optimum ratio of diameter over conductor to diameter over insulation. This necessitates the application of thicker insulation to maintain an equal maximum stress. Frequently the smaller conductors within a specific voltage range have a greater insulation thickness than the larger sizes. An alternative design procedure is to increase the conductor diameter to attain the optimum ratio. For example, in the case of oil-filled cables, the diameter of the central oil duct may be increased.

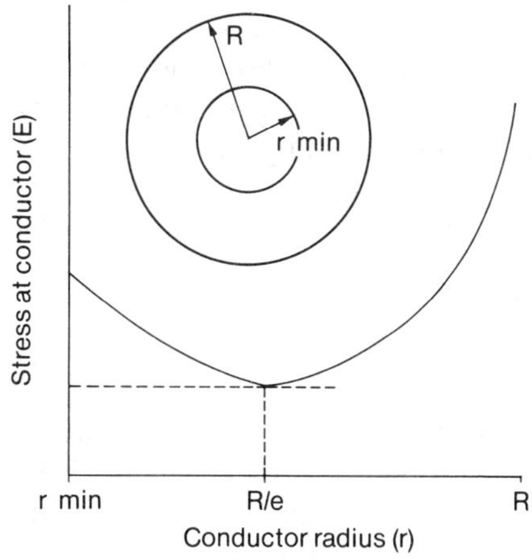

Fig. 2.6 Variation of stress with conductor radius

Grading of insulation
In high voltage impregnated paper insulated cables it is an advantage to have material of high electric strength near the conductor to reduce the total insulation thickness. This is normally achieved by having thinner high quality, higher density papers in this region. The use of graded insulation also gives improved bending properties (chapter 20).

D.C. stress distribution

The stress distribution within a d.c. cable is determined, *inter alia*, by insulation resistivity, which, as indicated previously, is influenced by the temperature of the insulation and also the stress. The stress pattern within a d.c. cable thus alters with the load. This is discussed in chapter 41.

FIELD THEORY FOR PAPER INSULATED CABLES

In the early days of electrical power transmission the belted type cable was used extensively but, with the increase in system voltage to 33 kV in the early 1920s, the shortcomings of the belted construction became apparent and the screened type (sometimes called H or Hochstadter type) cable was introduced and has been used successfully for this voltage to the present day. As transmission voltages increased, 'pressure-assisted' type cables using the screened construction were designed and are employed at voltages of 33 kV and above.

Belted type cables

The construction of the 3-core belted type cable is shown in fig. 2.7 (left). The insulation between conductors is twice the radial thickness of the insulation around each conductor and the insulation between any conductor and the earthed sheath is the radial thickness of the insulation around a conductor plus the thickness of the belt. As the phase to phase voltage is $\sqrt{3}$ times the phase to earth voltage, the total thickness of insulation between conductors and that between conductors and sheath are designed in approximately the same ratio.

For voltages up to 22 kV the belted construction has been used as the electrical stresses are acceptably low. For cables used at higher voltages it is necessary to raise the operating stresses for economical and practical reasons and this brought to light defects in the belted cable design which are described in a later section on the mechanism of insulation breakdown in paper insulated cables. Nowadays screened cables are generally used at 15 kV and above.

Screened or H type cable

To eliminate the weaknesses of the belted type cable a design of cable in which each core is individually surrounded by an earthed metallic layer was introduced and is shown in fig. 2.7 (right). This design of cable, first patented by Hochstadter in 1914, ensures that the stress is substantially radial and hence normal to the paper surface and is also contained within the machine lapped insulation, which is electrically

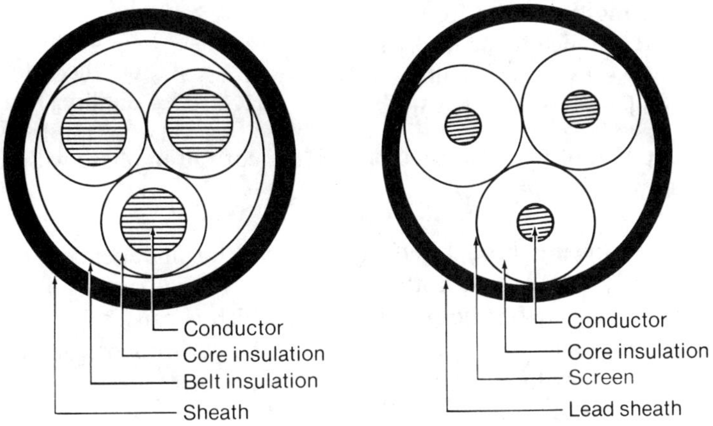

Fig. 2.7 3-core belted-type cable (*left*) and screened cable (*right*)

strong. The possibility of separation of the cores due to thermal excursions and mechanical handling, while not eliminated, does not present a hazard as all electrical flux is contained within the earthed screens.

SOURCES OF ELECTRICAL LOSSES

An electric power cable consists of three basic components, namely the conductor(s), the dielectric and the outer protective sheath. When the cable is energised and carrying load, heat, which must be dissipated to the surrounding medium, is generated by each of these components. The effects on current carrying capacity are discussed in chapter 8.

Conductor losses

The conductor losses are ohmic losses and are equal to

$$nI^2R_\theta \text{ (watt)}$$

where I = current carried by the conductor (A)
R_θ = ohmic resistance of the conductor at θ°C (Ω)
n = number of cores

When high a.c. currents are transmitted, the distribution of current is not evenly disposed throughout the cross-section of the conductor. This is due to the skin effect and the proximity effect as discussed earlier in relation to a.c. resistance.

Dielectric losses

The dielectric losses of an a.c. cable are proportional to the capacitance, the frequency, the phase voltage and the power factor. They are given by

$$D = \omega C U_0^2 \tan\delta \; 10^{-6} \text{ (watt/km/phase)} \qquad \text{(see equation (2.12))}$$

where ω = 2π multiplied by frequency
C = capacitance to neutral (μF/km)
U_0 = phase to neutral voltage (V)
$\tan \delta$ = dielectric power factor

The loss component of the power factor (i.e. the current in phase with the applied voltage) is made up of

(a) leakage current flowing through the dielectric which is independent of frequency and consequently occurs with both a.c. and d.c. voltage applications
(b) dielectric hysteresis, by far the largest effect, which is caused by the interaction of the alternating field with the molecules of the constituents of the insulation and is only present with a.c. voltage application
(c) ionisation, i.e. partial discharge in the dielectric

The power factor of the cable insulation is dependent on frequency, temperature and applied voltage. It is of a very low order and consequently for cables of up to 50 kV operating voltage the dielectric losses are small in comparison with conductor losses. However, for cables for operation above this level the losses rise rapidly with voltage and this must be taken into consideration when calculating the current carrying capacity of the cables.

Sheath losses

When single-core cables carry alternating current the magnetic field associated with the current induces e.m.f.s in the sheath of the cable and also in the sheaths of surrounding cables. Two types of sheath losses are possible resulting from such e.m.f.s as follows:

Sheath eddy currents
Eddy currents are induced by the current or currents in the conductors of the cables in close proximity to the sheath. Consider a three-phase circuit with cables R, Y and B. The flux of cables Y and B cuts the sheath of cable R. More lines of flux cut the sections of the sheath of R closer to Y and B than that section remote from Y and B. Thus a resultant e.m.f. is induced which causes current (eddy current) to flow along one side of the sheath and return along the other.

The integral of such currents over the sheath cross-section is zero. These eddy currents are independent of the type of sheath bonding which is applied and decrease with the distance between the cables.

The sheath eddy current losses are given by the following formula:

$$S_e = I^2 \left[\frac{3\omega^2}{R_s} \left(\frac{d_m}{2S} \right)^2 \times 10^{-8} \right] \text{ (watt/km per phase)} \qquad (2.15)$$

where S_e = sheath eddy current losses
I = current (A)
ω = 2π multiplied by frequency
d_m = mean diameter of the sheath (m)
S = distance between cable centres (m)
R_s = sheath resistance (Ω/km)

For single-core lead sheathed cables these losses are normally small compared with conductor losses, but are considerably higher with aluminium sheathed cables when they are in close proximity.

Sheath circuit loss

When the sheath of a single-core cable is bonded to earth or to other sheaths at more than one apoint, a current flows in the sheath due to the e.m.f. induced by the a.c. conductor current by 'transformer' action. This is because the sheath and return path, to which each end of the sheath is bonded, form a closed loop which is cut by the flux associated with the current in the conductor. The magnitude of the flux which cuts the sheath is dependent on the size of the loop which, in turn, is dependent on the spacing between the cables or between the sheath and the mean return path of the current through the earth or other medium.

The voltage induced in the sheath is given by

$$E_s = IX_m$$

where I = conductor current (A)
$X_m = 2\pi fM \times 10^{-3}$ (Ω/km)

The mutual inductance M between conductor and sheath is given by

$$M = 0.2 \log_e\left(\frac{2S}{d_m}\right) \text{ (mH/km)}$$

The impedance of the sheath Z_s (per km) is given by

$$Z_s = (R_s^2 + X_m^2)^{1/2}$$

where R_s is the sheath resistance (Ω/km). Therefore the sheath current I_s is equal to

$$I_s = \frac{E_s}{(R_s^2 + X_m^2)^{1/2}}$$

$$= \frac{IX_m}{(R_s^2 + X_m^2)^{1/2}} \text{ (A)}$$

The sheath current losses per phase are given by

$$I_s^2 R_s = \frac{I^2 X_m^2 R_s}{R_s^2 + X_m^2} \text{ (watt/km)} \qquad (2.16)$$

Therefore total sheath losses, i.e. sheath circuit losses plus sheath eddy current losses, are given by

$$I^2 R_s \left\{ \frac{X_m^2}{R_s^2 + X_m^2} + \left[\frac{3\omega^2}{R_s^2} \left(\frac{d_m}{2S} \right)^2 \times 10^{-8} \right] \right\} \qquad (2.17)$$

The heat generated by losses in the conductor, the dielectric, the sheath and armour has to pass to the surrounding medium, which may be the ground, air, water or some other material. As the current carrying capacity of an electric cable is normally dictated by the maximum temperature of the conductor, the components of the cable, in addition to meeting the electrical requirements, must also have as low a thermal resistivity as possible to ensure that the heat can be dissipated efficiently.

The subjects of heat dissipation and operating temperatures of cable components are discussed in chapter 8.

MECHANISM OF INSULATION BREAKDOWN IN PAPER INSULATED CABLES

In addition to the obvious and by far the most usual reasons for failure, such as mechanical damage to the insulation or ingress of moisture, there are three basic reasons for failure:

(a) breakdown due to ionisation
(b) thermal breakdown
(c) breakdown under transient voltage conditions

Breakdown due to ionisation

The 'perfect' belted solid type cable would be so manufactured that the impregnant would completely fill the interstices between the wires of the conductor, the fibres of the paper, the gaps between papers and the filler material. In short, the whole volume contained within the lead or aluminium sheath would be completely void free. During installation, however, the 'perfect' belted cable undergoes mechanical manipulation, and movement of the cores relative to each other takes place. Also, when the cable is loaded electrically the conductors, insulation, free impregnant and lead sheath expand, but the lead sheath does not expand with temperature to the same extent as the interior components of the cable. The sheath is thus extended physically by the pressure exerted by the inner components. On cooling, the lead sheath does not return to its original dimensions and consequently the interior of the sheath is no longer completely occupied, there being voids formed within the cable.

Installation, repeated load cycling and migration of compound on inclined routes can therefore all cause voids within the cable. Such voids are particularly hazardous when they occur within the highly stressed zones of the insulation. As transmission voltages increased, the insulation of the belted cables was increased to meet the higher stresses involved. On the introduction of 33 kV belted cables in the early 1920s, however, it was found that merely increasing the insulation thickness did not give satisfactory performance as there was a high failure rate. On studying the problem, certain weaknesses were found in the belted construction of cables for this voltage. Because of the design of the cable, part of the flux due to the 3-phase voltage, at a certain instant of time during the voltage phase rotation, passes radially through electrically strong core insulation; at other parts of the insulation there is a radial and a tangential component of the flux, and at still other parts the flux passes through the sound core insulation and into the inferior insulation (fig. 2.4).

The tangential strength, i.e. the strength along the surface of the papers, of lapped dielectric is only about one-fifteenth of the radial strength and also the filler insulation is much weaker than the normal core insulation; consequently these weaknesses were highlighted by the higher stresses involved in 33 kV cables.

A more serious weakness in the belted construction occurs, however, when the cores which were originally in close contact with each other move or are forced apart, either by mechanical manipulation or by cable loading. When this happens, the flux passes through sound core insulation, through the space between the two cores and then through the insulation of the second core. The space between the cores which is likely to be devoid of compound is therefore highly stressed, and any gas which may be present will ionise. The adjacent core insulation is thereby weakened by ionic bombardment and failure can occur.

The screened cable was introduced to eliminate the weakness of the belted type cable caused by the weak filler insulation, the spaces between cores and the tangential flux. The screen round the individual cores confines the stress to sound core insulation and also ensures that the flux is substantially radial.

With the introduction of the screened or H type cable, many of the weaknesses of the belted construction were eliminated and 33 kV solid H type cables have given extremely good service performance for many years. On increasing the transmission voltage above 33 kV, however, the one weakness remaining, though not manifestly harmful at 33 kV, had to be eliminated. This final weakness was the gaseous ionisation in voids formed within the insulation by compound migration resulting from cable loading and steep inclines.

The breakdown of paper insulation due to ionisation occurs through the formation of carbonaceous 'fronds' on the insulation papers (fig. 2.8). This is generally known as 'treeing'. The carbonaceous paths start at an almost imperceptible carbon core, generally at the conductor surface, and gradually spread outwards through the insulation, increasing in width and complexity as progression takes place.

Fig. 2.9 depicts the development of tree paths and the steps which lead to breakdown comprise the following:

(a) Ionisation takes place within a gaseous void in the gap between the paper next to the conductor and the conductor.
(b) Owing to the ionic bombardment of the second paper, the impregnant is partly pushed out and partly condensed into cable wax with the formation of more gas. Eventually, if the ionic bombardment is sufficiently severe, a carbonaceous path will penetrate between the fibres of the second paper.
(c) There is now a conducting path extending from the conductor, through the butt gap of the first paper and reaching the surface of the third paper nearest to the conductor. Neglecting the voltage drop along this path, the potential of the path front is substantially the same as that of the conductor; thus there is a point on the conductor side of the third paper which is at conductor potential, i.e. V_1 in fig. 2.9. There is a potential gradient throughout the dielectric and thus the third paper is at a potential lower than that of the conductor, i.e. V_2 in fig. 2.9. Therefore there exists a tangential stress $V_1 - V_2$ across the surface of the third paper.
(d) Ionisation due to this tangential stress sweeps away some of the compound and condenses some of the remainder, forming wax.
(e) Eventually carbonisation of the compound takes place. 'Fronds' of carbon spread out until the gap in the third paper is reached and the path proceeds through the gap where there is no fibrous barrier to the fourth paper.
(f) The treeing mechanism thus progresses, increasing in severity as the distance from the conductor increases owing to the greater tangential stress which exists.
(g) The carbon fronds at each paper continue in length along the surface of the paper until the voltage drop due to the current within the main track and the frond lowers the tangential stress to a value below ionising level.

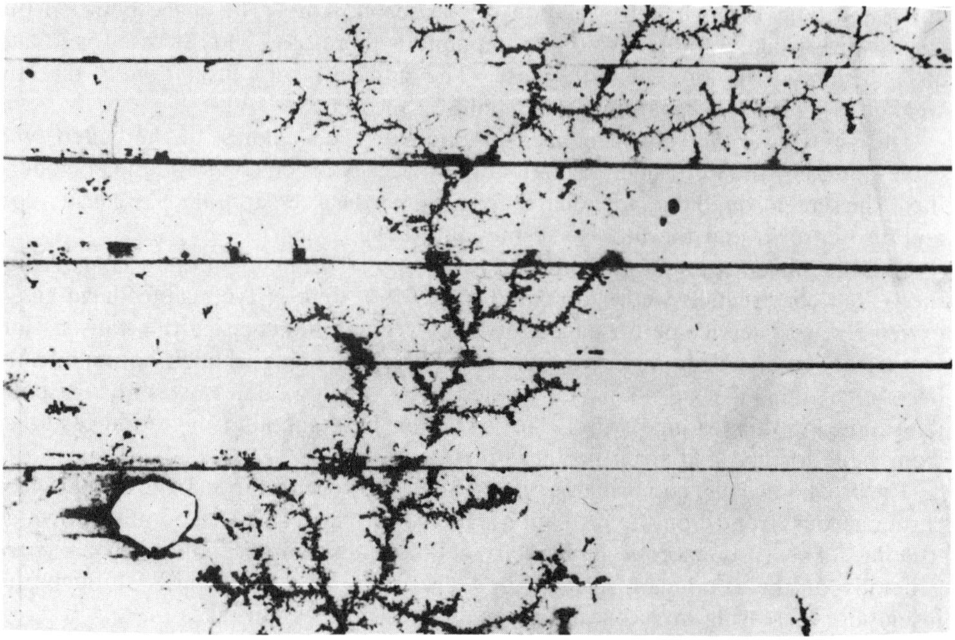

Fig. 2.8 Treeing, i.e. carbon tracking, on paper insulating tapes

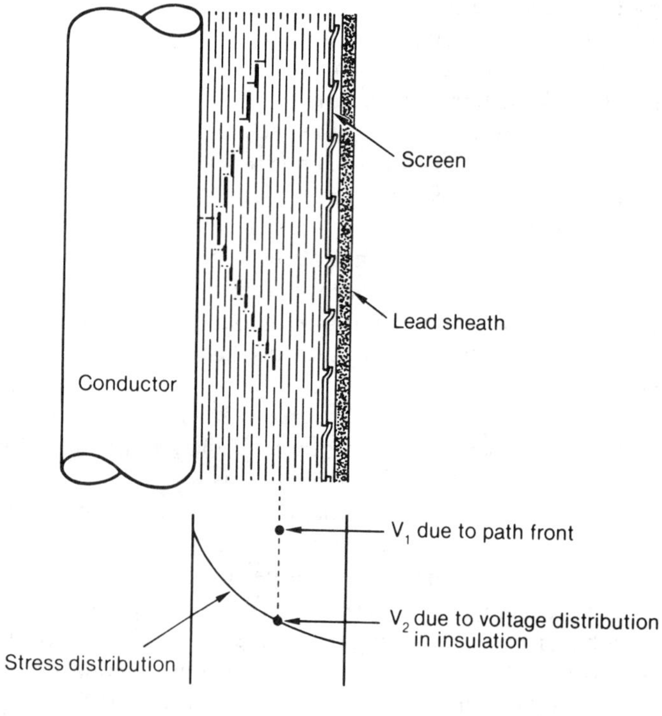

Fig. 2.9 Mechanism of breakdown of paper insulation by treeing

Several methods of controlling ionisation may be used. One method is to prevent the formation of voids throughout the life of the cable by impregnating the cable with a low viscosity oil and maintaining a positive oil pressure within the cable over the complete operating temperature range of the cable. This is attained by fitting pressurised reservoir tanks at strategic positions throughout the cable route. At periods when the cable is loaded, the components within the aluminium or reinforced lead sheath expand and the displaced oil passes along the cable via the ducts into the pressure tanks which accept the oil and retain it until the cable cools. On cooling, the pressure tanks force the oil back into the cable, thus retaining void-free insulation. Such a cable is called self-contained oil-filled cable.

Other methods of controlling ionisation are (a) to fill the voids with pressurised gas and (b) to apply sufficient pressure externally to the cable to close up the voids. The high pressure gas-filled cable controls ionisation by having the conductors and gap spaces between the pre-impregnated paper tapes filled with an inert gas under high pressure. Ionisation does not occur in the gaps because of the high pressure involved. During cable heating, the gas expands more in the gaps close to the conductor than in those at the outside of the insulation owing to the temperature differential, and the gas moves towards the aluminium or reinforced lead sheath. On cooling, the gas is forced by the differential pressure back from the outside of the insulation towards the conductor. The pressure within the cable is kept at all times at a value sufficient to prevent ionisation.

Ionisation within voids is prevented in the pipe type compression cable by the application of external pressure to the cable. In this case, the mass-impregnated single-core cables are shaped so that the sheath can be deformed under pressure. The 3-core or three single-core cables are all contained within a steel pipe and the intervening space is filled with a gas under high pressure. When the cable expands on load, the gas absorbs the expansion and on cooling the gas pressurises the cable and prevents void formation.

The pipe type high pressure oil-filled cable is constructed with three unsheathed cores within a steel pipe. The intervening space within the pipe is filled with a low viscosity oil under pressure which prevents the formation of voids.

Thermal breakdown in paper insulation

The dielectric loss angle for oil/paper insulation has a minimum value in the region of 50–60 °C. Thus, at around the operating temperature, a rise in temperature increases the dielectric loss, so giving a larger heat generation. The rise in temperature also increases the temperature gradient to the surroundings and raises the rate of heat dissipation. If the rate of rise of heat generation is greater than the rate of rise of heat dissipation, the cable temperature will continue to increase, with the result that the dielectric will overheat and fail electrically.

Fig. 2.10 illustrates the dielectric loss angle versus temperature characteristics of two types of impregnated paper. Paper A is typical of paper in use some years ago, while paper B represents paper of the type now used for very high voltage cables. Paper B exhibits comparatively little variation of DLA with temperature over the important temperature range, whereas the DLA of paper A increases considerably above 60 °C.

Fig. 2.11 indicates the effect of using these papers on the thermal stability of 400

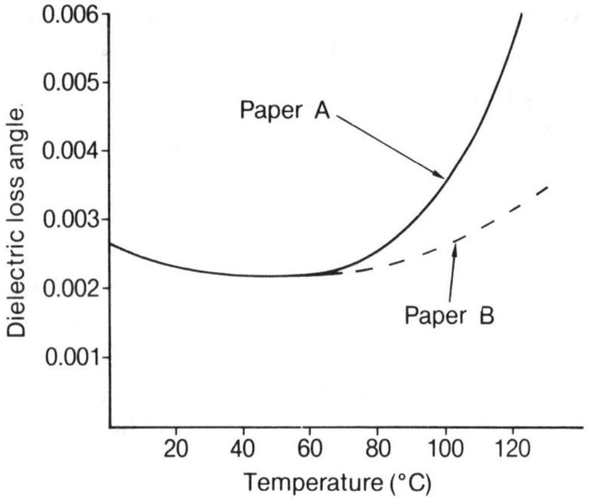

Fig. 2.10 Dielectric loss angle versus temperature characteristics of two types of impregnated paper for high voltage cables

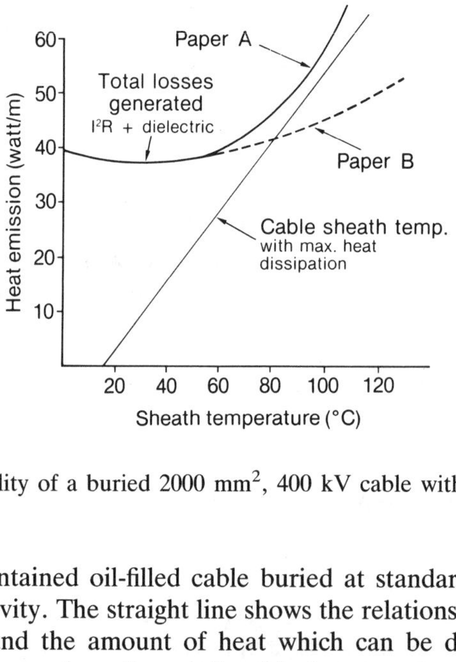

Fig. 2.11 Thermal stability of a buried 2000 mm^2, 400 kV cable with a current of 1400 A

kV 2000 mm^2 self-contained oil-filled cable buried at standard depth in ground of normal thermal resistivity. The straight line shows the relationship between the cable sheath temperature and the amount of heat which can be dissipated through the ground. The other curves show the relationship between the total losses generated within the cable and the sheath temperature. These losses comprise two main components: the I^2R loss in the conductor and the dielectric loss. The I^2R loss is approximately linearly dependent on the cable temperature, because of the increase in conductor resistance with temperature. The dielectric loss is proportional to the DLA in accordance with equation (2.12). If the current is taken to be 1400 A, applied at ambient temperature, the cable with the insulation comprising paper B would at first rise rapidly in temperature because the total losses generated would greatly exceed the amount of heat which could be dissipated from the sheath. The general cable temperature would continue to rise until the heat generation and losses were in equilibrium, i.e. at the intersection of the two lines. The temperature of the cable would then remain steady (at a temperature of 80 °C on the graph).

If the cable had insulation corresponding to paper A, the initial temperature rise would follow a similar pattern. However, when the temperature exceeded 60 °C, the rate of rise of the dielectric losses would exceed the increase in the ability of the sheath to dissipate the losses and the cable temperature would rise. The losses generated would continue to exceed the losses dissipated, with the result that the progressive temperature rise would continue until thermal breakdown of the cable occurred. In this particular example the current loading condition is somewhat exaggerated but the principle illustrates the importance of selecting paper having suitable characteristics. It has also been assumed that the sheath bonding and spacing between cables is such that sheath losses can be ignored.

Breakdown under transient conditions

Cables are designed to withstand transient conditions appropriate to their operating voltage, and this is an important aspect in the case of pressure assisted transmission cables (chapter 32). However, should the cable insulation be subjected to transient voltages such as lightning or switching surges, which are higher than the impulse voltage for which the cable is designed, a failure may occur. Such a breakdown takes the form of a puncture of the insulation and is usually very localised in nature.

BREAKDOWN OF PLASTIC INSULATION

This subject is covered in chapters 3 and 25.

REFERENCE

(1) Arnold, A.H.M. (1946) *The A.C. Resistance of Non-magnetic Conductors.* National Physical Laboratory.

Chapter 3
Materials Used in Cables

METALS

Electrical properties

Table 3.1 indicates the electrical properties of the common metals used in cables. Taking price into consideration, copper and aluminium are clearly the best choice for conductors but there has been some experience with sodium. Reference to this is made in chapter 4 which also contains information on the variation of resistance with temperature.

Table 3.1 Electrical properties of metals

Metal	Relative conductivity (copper = 100)	Electrical resistivity at 20°C (Ω m, 10^{-8})	Temperature coefficient of resistance (per °C)
Silver	106	1.626	0.0041
Copper (HC, annealed)	100	1.724	0.0039
Copper (HC, hard drawn)	97	1.777	0.0039
Tinned copper	95–99	1.741–1.814	0.0039
Aluminium (EC grade, soft)	61	2.803	0.0040
Aluminium (EC grade, $\frac{1}{2}$H–H)	61	2.826	0.0040
Sodium	35	4.926	0.0054
Mild steel	12	13.80	0.0045
Lead	8	21.4	0.0040

Physical properties

The physical properties of metals used for conductors and sheaths are given in table 3.2. Except for the conductors of self-supporting overhead cables, copper is invariably used in the annealed condition. Solid aluminium conductors are also mainly in a soft condition but stranded aluminium conductors are $\frac{3}{4}$H (hard) to H. Aluminium sheaths are now extruded directly onto cables and hence of soft temper but a small amount of work hardening occurs during corrugation.

Copper conductors

Because of the way it can readily be rolled into rod and then drawn to wire, together

Table 3.2 Physical properties of metals used in cables

Property	Unit	Copper	Aluminium	Lead
Density at 20 °C	kg/m^3	8890	2703	11370
Coefficient of thermal expansion per °C	$\times 10^{-6}$	17	23	29
Melting point	°C	1083	659	327
Thermal conductivity	W/cm °C	3.8	2.4	0.34
Ultimate tensile stress				
soft temper	MN/m^2	225	70–90	–
$\frac{3}{4}$H to H	MN/m^2	–	125–205	–
Elastic modulus	MN/m^2	26	14	–
Hardness				
soft	DPHN	50	20–25	5
$\frac{3}{4}$H to H	DPHN	–	30–40	–
Stress fatigue endurance limit (approximate)	MN/m^2	±65	±40	±2.8

with its excellent electrical conductivity, copper was virtually unchallenged as a conductor for all types of insulated cable for well over 50 years. Indeed, in the electrical world, the International Electrotechnical Commission established an International Annealed Copper Standard (IACS) with copper of resistivity of 1.724 μΩ cm at 20 °C assigned as 100%.

The grade and quality of copper is very important and the high conductivity copper used for electrical purposes comfortably exceeds the 100% IACS value. Conductivity is greatly influenced by impurities and by mechanical working. Consequently, the purity is of the order of 99.99%, which nowadays is obtained by final electrolytic refining.

Fortunately, the mechanical strength of annealed wire is adequate for nearly all types of insulated cable. If any minor working of the material occurs during conductor manufacture, e.g. in compacting to reduce the overall dimensions, allowance has to be made for work hardening by increasing the copper volume to compensate for the reduction in conductance. In an extreme case, such as the use of hard drawn copper for self-supporting overhead lines, this may amount to as much as 3%.

Almost the only unsatisfactory feature of copper is the way that the price fluctuates widely with the world supply and demand. If its use could always be justified economically it would not have competitors. However, over the last two decades aluminium has become a replacement in the power distribution field solely on the basis of cost.

Aluminium conductors

Although aluminium did not make much serious impact until the price of copper soared in the late 1950s, it is surprising to find that a relatively substantial amount was used between 1909 and 1912. Fig. 3.1 shows a sophisticated low voltage paper insulated d.c. cable made in quantity by British Insulated Cables at Prescot during this period. This particular cable was taken out of service in 1967 and was just as

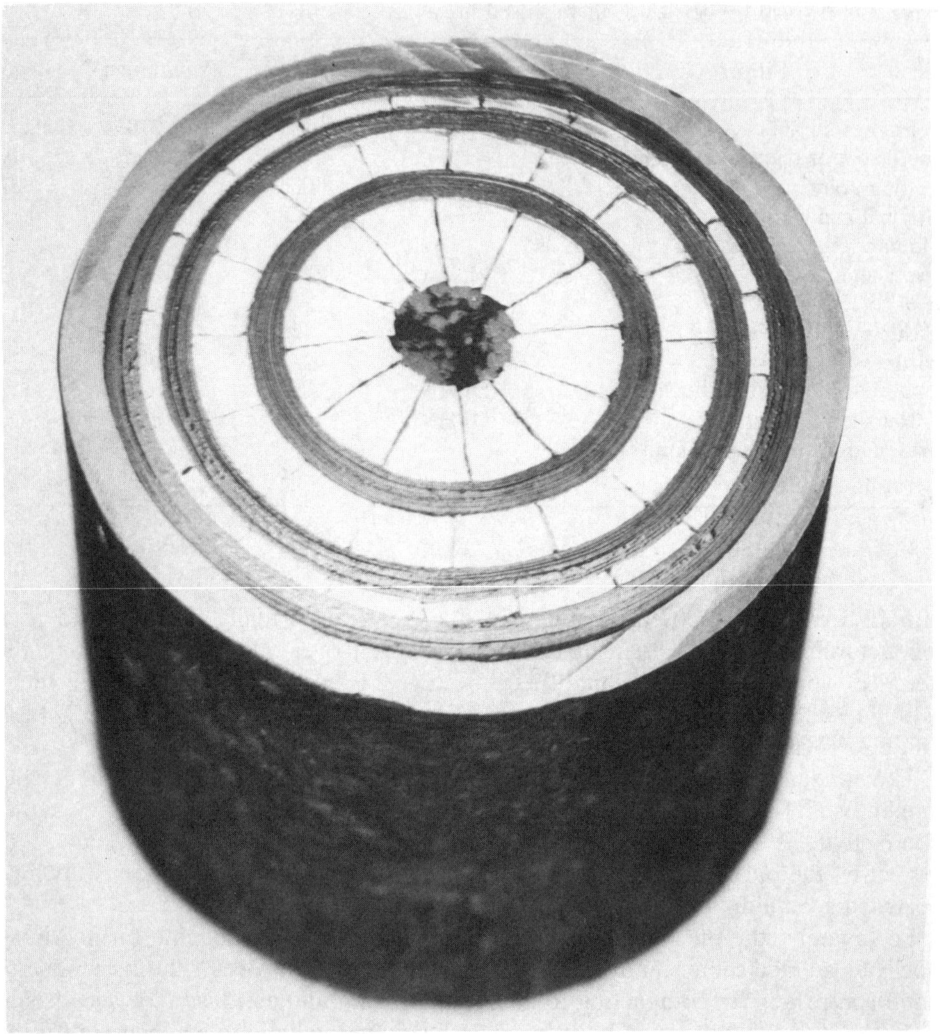

Fig. 3.1 ±230 V d.c. cable installed in London in 1911 and removed from service in 1967

perfect as when installed. Even the jointing was of interest as each shaped wire had an individual sleeve secured by pinch-screws.

Unlike copper, the mechanical strength of annealed aluminium is rather low for soft single wire or stranded conductors but fortunately conductivity is little changed by working. Consequently the temper of wire used is commonly known as a broad $\frac{3}{4}$-hard grade. Tensile strength is relatively unimportant and this grade covers ranges which in the aluminium industry spread from $\frac{1}{2}$-hard to fully hard, the main requirement being to specify a maximum of 205 MN/m^2, which avoids the use of wire having too little elongation before fracture on bending. Aluminium, however, can also be used in solid as distinct from stranded form and in this case a soft temper is desirable to keep the stiffness of the conductor to a minimum. Such conductors are mostly produced by hot extrusion, which virtually provides an annealed temper, and the upper limit of tensile strength is fixed at 80 MN/m^2 for sizes above 35 mm^2. For small sizes this limit is rather low to exclude some stretching during cable processing and also there are advantages in producing the conductors by drawing. The maximum is therefore in the range 125–165 MN/m^2 according to size.

Compared with copper, aluminium has a number of technical disadvantages, all of which can be satisfactorily overcome to benefit from its economic attraction. The advantage of a low density of one-third that of copper is partly offset by its low conductivity of 61% that of copper, but for equal conductance the weight of the expensive conductor metal required is almost exactly halved. However, the cross-sectional conductor area has to be increased by a factor of 1.6 and this means extra usage of insulation, sheathing and armouring material. With conventional paper insulated, lead sheathed and armoured constructions, there is no overall saving in cable weight but the situation is quite different if aluminium is also used for sheathing. The above is a generalisation based on cables having equal conductance. In practice there are other factors to be considered such as the cable voltage, current carrying capacity and voltage drop. In general, current ratings of aluminium cables are about 78%–80% of those of copper cables of the same conductor size.

As with copper the addition of alloying metals to provide high tensile strength has no application for insulated cables. There is a conductivity penalty which is only justified for all-aluminium overhead lines. Incidentally, steel-cored aluminium (non-alloyed) has been used for such lines for over 50 years because the economic aspects are very different from those with insulated cables and the use of massive compression jointing sleeves presented no problems.

Impurities, as distinct from alloying additions, do not greatly affect the conductivity of aluminium but a grade known as EC (electrical conductivity) is commonly accepted in the aluminium industry. The basic British Standards for wrought aluminium for electrical purposes, i.e. BS 2627, 'Wire', and BS 3988, 'Solid conductors for insulated cables', define the purity as 99.5% minimum, with limits for individual impurities.

By controlling the amounts of copper, silicon and iron and/or small amounts of other metals, it is possible to create a range of 'dilute alloys', without much sacrifice of conductivity but with particular strength properties to cater for special requirements in manufacture and jointing, e.g. for single-wire conductors for telephone cables which have been adopted by the British Post Office. No applications have been found for such compositions for power or wiring cables.

A particular disadvantage of aluminium for electrical purposes is the thin, hard protective oxide skin which is so valuable in giving corrosion protection to aluminium installed above ground. Satisfactory techniques for removing it in making soldered joints or to break it up by appropriate designs of compression or mechanical joint have long been developed, but it is always necessary to emphasise that jointers must exercise care and attention when following prescribed instructions in detail. This emphasis applied more particularly to soldering and plumbing, and modern techniques for power cable conductor jointing have been centred on mechanical methods capable of easy adoption by unskilled operatives.

Apart from the oxide film, there is another factor which has contributed to lack of success in one particular field of use, namely wiring cables. The low yield or proof stress of aluminium means that if the conductor is only held, for example, by a single pinch-screw, as is common in many wiring cable accessories, there can be relaxation and development of a high resistance joint. Overheating and failure may then follow. It is difficult to ensure that all accessories are specially designed for aluminium, and although large-scale installations have been undertaken in North America the problems have not been overcome and the use of aluminium wiring cable has been halted.

Corrosion protection is covered elsewhere and all that need be mentioned here is that, whilst claims for aluminium having excellent corrosion resistance are true if made in relation to dry indoor situations, or even outdoors if drying off is rapid after rain, cable engineers must ensure that bare aluminium is not left exposed anywhere. Cable situations are rarely dry; for example in the base of outdoor pillars corrosion can be rapid. Protection in a form such as heat-shrink sleeving should always be used.

Copper-clad aluminium conductors

Copper-clad aluminium comprises an aluminium core with a heavy layer of copper which is metallurgically bonded to the aluminium. The thickness of copper may be varied but for cable purposes it is defined by BS 4990 as 10% by volume, i.e. 27% by weight. Conductor wire may be produced in various ways but the techniques most commonly used have been to start from a composite billet with either subsequent rolling to rod and then drawing to wire or extrusion.

The whole purpose of the cladding with copper is to overcome the problems in making mechanical connections to aluminium, particularly in wiring type cable accessories, which are predominantly of the pinch-screw type. Copper-clad may be treated in the same way as copper conductors.

Superconducting and cryoresistive conductors

A major problem with cables is to dissipate the heat generated in the cable, a high proportion of which is due to the resistivity of the conductor material, and so it is advantageous to reduce the conductor losses. All metals show reduced resistivity with temperature and superconductors have no measurable d.c. resistance below critical values of temperature and magnetic field. Such critical temperatures are below 20 K and so require the use of liquid helium as coolant. (absolute zero temperature, i.e. 0 K, is $-273\,°C$). Helium also provides satisfactory electrical insulation.

At low magnetic fields the current is confined to a thin surface layer and so a foil of 25 μm thickness is practicable. Even a thickness of a few microns would carry a load of the order of 3000 MVA. However, with alternating current there are some losses and the current or magnetic field may penetrate beneath the surface. The current carrying capacity of a superconductor is dependent, therefore, on the strength of the magnetic field which it produces. Allowance has also to be made for high fault currents and it is more economic to bond the superconductor to a less expensive metal, both to deal with fault currents and to provide mechanical support. Aluminium of 99.999% purity is a suitable material for the backing as it has a d.c. resistivity of $1.5 \times 10^{-9}\ \Omega$ cm at the liquid helium boiling temperature of 4 K.

Niobium and its alloys, with a critical temperature of around 4 K, were originally the most extensively studied superconductor metals and an experimental transmission cable was made by BICC in the mid-1960s. It became apparent, however, that there was little chance of commercial success as long as it was necessary to use expensive liquid helium to obtain critical temperatures below 20 K. Alternative niobium alloys were developed which could use liquid hydrogen at 20 K and several cables were made in Europe, Japan and the USA during the 1970s and early 1980s.

Another approach during this period was to use normal metals such as aluminium instead of superconductors and to operate in the cryogenic range of liquid nitrogen (boiling point 77 K). Compared with normal ambient temperature, the resistivity of aluminium is reduced by a factor of 10 at 70 K and 1000 at 20 K, the actual values being dependent on the aluminium purity. However, although this reduced the cost of the conductor it was still not viable in relation to total cost.

For applications other than cables, a major technical advance was made in 1986 with the development of superconductors with a high critical temperature which can operate at 35–45 K, and there were promises of similar materials with a critical temperature of around 93 K. At 93 K cable construction can be greatly simplified, and cost much reduced, because of the possibility of using liquid nitrogen instead of liquid helium or hydrogen. This new generation of superconductors has been evolving around complex mixed oxides such as yttrium barium copper oxide, $YBa_2Cu_3O_7$. Such materials have a ceramic nature, with the hardness of pottery or brick, and a characteristic brittleness which makes them difficult to work. Developments are proceeding towards the use of these oxides in film form but it still remains to be seen whether they are appropriate for cable conductors.

The general situation remains that the only prospect for superconductors in cables is for transmission cables of very high current carrying capacity. There is still no apparent commercially viable need for such cables in the UK or in Europe and it is more likely that incentive will come from Japan or the USA. Further information is given in chapter 44 and D.R. Edwards has provided a comprehensive review.[1]

Lead sheaths

Lead has served the cable industry well since the end of the last century, but, because of its weight and softness and the need for good plumbing skill, few users will regret that its use is diminishing rapidly. Although the overall incidence of faults associated with the lead sheath itself has been quite small, large users are likely to have met them at some time. They can be divided into four categories:

(a) fatigue cracking
(b) extrusion defects
(c) fractures associated with internal pressure
(d) corrosion

Fatigue

Lead has comparatively low resistance to fatigue and fig. 3.2 shows a typical case of sheath fracture associated with cracks in the crystal boundaries. Fig. 3.3 indicates the effect after etching and illustrates why such failures used to be erroneously attributed to crystallisation. Most sheath fatigue fractures are caused by vibration, either during transport over a long distance to site, or by installation on bridges, in ships, alongside railways or in overhead catenary systems etc. In such cases the vibration

Fig. 3.2 Surface of lead sheath showing typical cracking due to fatigue

Fig. 3.3 Etched surface of lead sheath to show the fatigue cracks at crystal boundaries

frequency is usually high and the amplitude low. Other situations arise where the frequency is low and the amplitude high, so that the effect is more akin to repeated bending, e.g. due to thermal expansion and contraction with bodily longitudinal movement. This can occur in jointing manholes for cables in ducts or with unsecured cables on racks or trays exposed to solar heating and/or having pronounced load cycles. In all such installations it is important to prevent the expansion being accommodated in a local loop or offset.

Much can be done to prevent such failures. If long intercontinental transport is involved it is important for the cable ends to be fixed tightly so that there is no loose cable which can vibrate separately from the whole drum. Installations should also be planned to accommodate expansion and contraction uniformly along the whole length. However, the main factor is that lead alloys are available to provide increased fatigue resistance according to the requirement.

British practice is based on the use of unalloyed lead, alloy E (0.4% tin, 0.2% antimony) and alloy B (0.85% antimony), which have respective fatigue endurance limits (10^6 cycles) of 2.8, 6.3 and 9.3 MN/m^2. An exception is that $\frac{1}{2}$C (0.2% tin, 0.1% cadmium) has better properties for internal pressure cables. Unalloyed lead is quite satisfactory for most cables, including armoured cables to be shipped overseas. Alloy E should be used for unarmoured cables and when vibration is suspected. Alloy B is only required for severe cases, e.g. cables on bridges and for catenary suspension. If there is any doubt, advice should be sought from the cablemaker. The use of high purity lead is undesirable (see later).

Different alloys are often favoured in other countries. For the duct jointing manhole requirements in the USA, various combinations of lead/arsenic/tellurium/bismuth compositions have shown particularly good properties, the contents of each alloying metal varying between 0.05% and 0.15%. In continental Europe there has been some preference for alloys containing copper (0.03%–0.05%), often with an addition of tellurium (0.04%). Alloys containing antimony in proportions from 0.35% to 1.0% are also used.

Extrusion defects

When lead sheathing was carried out on hydraulic vertical ram presses, defects were sometimes caused by the entrapment of impurities as the press cylinder was refilled with molten lead. This can be overcome by the Glover tray principle in which the charging is automatic from a bowl of liquid lead on the top of the extrusion cylinder. Such presses have now largely been replaced by continuous screw type extruders which also overcame the occasional faulty stop mark that occurred when ram presses were stopped for recharging with lead.

Effects of internal pressure

Lead has no elastic limit and will deform slowly (creep) at very low stresses. The complex stress–strain relationship has an important bearing on the requirements for sheath composition of cables in which hoop stresses arise as a result of internal pressure. Even though sheaths for gas- and oil-filled cables are reinforced to withstand the pressure, the sheath itself may be subject to a low stress for a long time and therefore will need to expand by a small amount. Under high stresses lead sheaths will show considerable extensibility and burst with a knife-edge fracture, but at low stresses the fracture with some alloys may be of a blunt intercrystalline type with little expansion. Ageing effects such as recrystallisation, precipitation of impurities and alloying metals in grain boundaries, and change of creep rate in circumferential zones due to bending also have an important influence and affect the choice of alloy. In the case of oil-filled cables it is important to select an alloy which is not subject to grain growth during the heating period that occurs with one method of impregnation.

Correct choice of alloy for all internal pressure cables is therefore vital. Much testing is required with conditions relating not only to cable design and processing but also to the particular type of extruder to be used for sheathing. Extrusion temperature, grain size and segregation effects all have a bearing on subsequent stability. Nowadays most cables in this category are of the oil-filled type, lead sheathed on a screw press, and ½C alloy has given outstanding service.

Corrosion

Some lead water pipes have survived since Roman times but lead may corrode in peaty or highly alkaline soils. Protection in the form of bitumen or bituminised hessian tape plus bitumen is normally adequate. Where corrosion does occur the analysis of corrosion products will normally show the cause and over the years the main source of trouble has been stray direct currents, e.g. from tramways, leaving the sheath.

Purity

Some cable users had a vogue for specifying high purity virgin lead. Much commercial lead is now refined to 99.99% purity and such a material is really best avoided as it can lead to very large grain size with a single crystal across the sheath. Such a structure is particularly weak in fatigue and creep properties. BS 801 allows a maximum impurity content of 0.1% and some alloying metals such as tin or antimony are often added with advantage up to this limit. While being convenient for the utilisation of manufacturing scrap it also provides a better sheath than very high purity lead.

Aluminium sheaths

Following some early developments and trials in Germany during the Second World War, initiated because of a shortage of lead, a similar stimulus arose in the UK in the early 1950s. Marketing of 1 kV paper cables was commenced with utilisation of a novel and successful sheathing procedure involving pulling the insulated cores into a length of oversize aluminium tubing and then drawing either through a die to reduce the diameter or through a rotating nut to form a cable sheath with a corrugated rib.

Unfortunately initially it was not appreciated that the apparently good corrosion resistance of aluminium in free air did not apply to buried conditions. Moreover it had not then been established that relatively short time tests on small buried samples were not representative of the differential concentration cell type of corrosion mechanism which applied with long lengths of aluminium. Consequently the bituminous type finishes, satisfactory for lead sheaths, were used with somewhat disastrous consequences.

Nevertheless, it was immediately apparent that aluminium sheaths were quite practicable for handling, up to at least 100 mm diameter, and that they had an economic attraction for internal pressure cables because of the lack of need for sheath reinforcement. The corrosion problem was first overcome by the use of plastic and rubber tapes (chapter 5). Extruded PVC was then coming in as an insulating material and was an obvious choice for providing a reasonably tough protective jacket for aluminium sheaths. The combination became an accepted alternative to lead sheaths in the late 1950s and within a decade had become the preferred choice for pressurised cables.

For solid type cables there was little further activity until the later 1960s when, following experience in Germany, interest developed in the use of combined neutral/earth distribution cables. The Consac cable (chapter 23) used the aluminium sheath as a conductor and created an economic design which was soon used in large quantity. By this time sheathing by direct extrusion was replacing the tube sinking process, with the advantages of reduced cost and a lower permissible sheath thickness. The latter arose because thickness is determined by the ability of the sheath to bend without any serious buckling and the softer extruded material is more favourable in this respect.

In the early 1970s the economic advantage of aluminium was extended to 11 kV paper insulated cables, as used by the UK Electricity Boards. A price saving of the order of 20% was obtained at the time.

Sheath composition and properties

The extrusion pressures and temperatures (approximately 500 °C) are quite critical because of the high stress on the extrusion tools. To keep stresses to a minimum, aluminium of 99.7% minimum purity was formerly used but the standard grade of 99.5% minimum has since been proved to be acceptable. At the temperature used the resultant sheath mechanical properties are equivalent to those of material of annealed temper.

Compared with lead sheaths, the most notable difference in properties of aluminium is the greater force that can be developed owing to thermal expansion. As a result of load cycles this can give rise to increased thrust and mechanical stresses in joints. If the sheath is of the corrugated design no problems arise but in the case of solid type cables with smooth sheaths some strengthening may be necessary if operation to full rating is required. Use of a cast resin filling material suffices.

Corrosion

Much may be written and indeed has been published about the vulnerability of aluminium to corrosion and the mechanism by which it may be quickly penetrated by pinholes. Various aspects are the formation of corrosion cells by differential concentration and aeration conditions, crevice attack and avoidance of contact with more electropositive metals. For cables, however, discussions can be avoided by stipulating that aluminium must never be left exposed and sheaths must always have appropriate protective finishes. Extruded PVC, polyethylene and high density polyethylene (chapter 5) have been proved by experience.

Armour for distribution cables

Power cables are usually armoured to carry earth fault currents and to give some protection against mechanical damage both during installation and in service. However, it is difficult to define an optimum requirement or how long it should last in service before the armour material is destroyed by corrosion. National practices vary widely but the materials used consist mainly of steel tape or strip and galvanised steel wire.

Steel tape
This is mild steel of thickness 0.5 mm to 0.8 mm according to cable diameter. The smaller sizes are cold rolled and the larger hot rolled. They are coated with bitumen by the supplier and again subsequently during the armouring process. On the basis that most external damage to cables occurs in the first few years of life it probably does not matter that corrosion may be severe after a few more years. On the other hand it can be argued, as it was with CNE cables (chapter 23), that at 0.5 m depth of burial most damage is due to heavy mechanical plant and the cable would suffer severely whether armoured or not, i.e. steel tape armour fulfils little purpose.

Continental European practice tends to favour narrow flat steel strip instead of wire armour but this is probably due to history rather than to any technical or economic difference. If there is a good case for ensuring that either strip or tape armour has long life then galvanising is possible and, although much more expensive, such material is often preferred in the Middle and Far East.

Galvanised steel wire
Wire to BS 1442 is used for cables having no metallic sheath and is usually preferred to steel tape for solid type lead sheathed cables for 11 kV upwards. If higher tensile strength is required, e.g. for submarine cables, the requirements for carbon steel wire are covered by BS 1441.

Non-magnetic armour
For single-core cables in a.c. circuits, it is usually preferable to use non-magnetic material. Wire rather than tape is generally adopted to secure adequate mechanical protection. Stainless steel is difficult to justify on cost grounds and aluminium is the normal choice.

BS 6346 caters for PVC cables with aluminium strip armour. Whilst useful if it is necessary to carry high earth fault currents, the degree of mechanical protection obtained is not as good as with steel wire armour. Such strip armour now also tends to be more expensive and is little used.

Mechanical protection for wiring cables

Metal tapes and even helically applied wires are not suitable for very small cables, especially when good flexibility is required. Braided constructions using plain or tinned copper wire are usually adopted.

IMPREGNATED PAPER INSULATION

Paper

Paper for cable making consists of a felted mat of long cellulose fibres derived by chemical treatment of wood pulp, which mostly comes from North America and Scandinavia. Digestion with sodium sulphide and caustic soda at high temperature and pressure removes impurities such as lignin and resins. The paper construction is generally of 2-ply form, but some 3-ply is used at the highest voltages. The important physical properties required are controlled by the amount of beating of the pulp, together with the quantity of thin pulp (93%–95% water) fed to a rotating wire mesh on which the paper is formed and the amount of subsequent calendering. These factors determine the thickness, apparent density and impermeability, all of which have to be adjusted according to the cable type and voltage.

The thicknesses of paper normally used are from 65 to 190 μm. The density varies from 650 to 1000 kg/m^3, and as the density of the actual fibres is around 1500 kg/m^3 a considerable volume of the space within the fibres is available for filling with impregnating compound. The impermeability, i.e. the porosity, of the paper can be adjusted independently of density and can have important effects on final mechanical and electrical properties. Tensile strength and, more particularly, tearing resistance also have to be controlled according to application and bending requirements and may have to take account of the width of the tape which is used. The tensile strength in the longitudinal and transverse directions is in a ratio of about 2:1.

Vast quantities of water are used in paper making, up to 200 or even 300 tonnes per tonne of paper, and the quality of the water is important for obtaining the required electrical properties of the paper. For very high voltage transmission cables, the water has to be of deionised quality to achieve the highest degree of purity.

The actual properties of the paper selected by the cable manufacturer have also to be related to the paper–impregnant combination and this is discussed later. Among many important factors is the ability to obtain a good cable bending performance because individual layers must slide over each other. Insulation thicknesses vary from 0.6 to over 30 mm according to voltage and electrical stress and the bending problems increase progressively with thickness. In addition, to achieve strict control over the individual paper tape widths and application tensions, the surface finish of the paper is highly important, as is the tensile strength and thickness, these being increased towards the outside of the insulation from mechanical considerations. Adjacent to the conductor, where the electrical stress is highest, thinner papers may be used.

Impregnating oils and compounds

Paper has good electrical properties only when dry and the impregnation with suitable oils and compounds, which is necessary for electrical reasons, also helps to reduce moisture absorption. Impregnation, which is covered in chapter 26, is preceded by heating to 120 °C and evacuation to a pressure of the order of 10–20 N/m^2 so as to remove both air and moisture from the paper web and ensure that the whole of the matrix is filled with impregnant. The initial moisture content of the paper of around 2–7% is reduced to of the order of 0.01%–0.5% according to voltage. For voltages of 6.6 kV and above, where partial discharge in any vacuous voids could be important, the impregnation treatment must also ensure that the butt-gap spaces between tapes are full of impregnant. When the compounds exhibit a change of state, with highly increased viscosity as temperature is reduced, very slow cooling is necessary and preferably the compound should be circulated through a heat exchanger to achieve uniform cooling.

The impregnant for solid type distribution cables is based on refined mineral oil derived from petroleum crudes. According to compound formulation these may be of basically paraffinic or naphthenic type. After final distillation the oil, and subsequently the mixed compound, are subjected to clay treatment (Fullers' earth) to remove remaining impurities which affect electrical quality.

In the conventional oil–rosin impregnant, the mineral oil is thickened by the addition of refined gum rosin to increase the viscosity in the cable working temperature range. Gum rosin is a material which exudes from pine trees and after initial distillation is selected according to shade of colour before further refining to high quality. In addition to its function for viscosity control, the addition of rosin increases electric strength and it gives substantial improvements in resistance to oxidation. This is of importance in the manufacturing process, where large quantities of impregnants are held in tanks for long periods with frequent cycles of heating.

The increase in viscosity which can be obtained by addition of rosin is still insufficient to prevent drainage of impregnant from cables installed vertically or on steep slopes and the development of non-draining compounds for this purpose is discussed in chapter 20.

The fundamental characteristic of mass-impregnated non-draining (MIND) compounds is that while they have the same fluidity as oil–rosin compounds, at the impregnating temperature of 120 °C, and therefore good impregnating properties, they set to a waxy solid at maximum cable operating temperature. The formulation is controlled to produce a plastic consistency which provides good cable bending behaviour. The somewhat greater stiffness of MIND compounds at very low temperature is no handicap to normal installation but excessively severe bending at such temperatures would cause more damage than with oil–rosin impregnant. Satisfactory bending test performance at −10 °C can be achieved but demands a higher standard of manufacture in which the quality of paper and paper lapping application play an important part.

The gelling of the mineral oil to a consistency akin to that of petroleum jelly is achieved by the addition of such materials as microcrystalline waxes, polyethylene, polyisobutylene and a small amount of rosin. These constituents possess high electrical strength and the properties are chosen to give an elevated softening temperature with suitable plasticity over the operational temperature range.

Some forms of microcrystalline waxes are obtained from the residues resulting from the distillation of crude petroleum oils after a solvent extraction process. Others are derived when the Sasol technique is used in the production of petrol from coal, principally at present in South Africa. The important feature of microwaxes is their ability to hold or occlude oil, i.e. to stop the oil from separating from the mixture. This property is not possessed by macrowaxes such as paraffin wax or the common mineral waxes, which have a much more coarse crystal structure. Because non-draining compounds are of complex composition, there may nevertheless be some slight movement of some of the constituents at elevated temperatures just below the set point of the compound and consequently a slight loss of relatively fluid impregnant when a vertical sample of cable is heated in an oven for a drainage test. The total amount is quite small and together with the expulsion due to thermal expansion of the compound an amount of 1% −3% is permitted by cable specifications.

Progressive improvements to MIND compounds were made during the 1950s and 1960s. The early compounds contained a high proportion of microcrystalline waxes having a high coefficient of expansion. This meant that during the impregnation cooling process, after the compound had reached its set point, no further compound could feed into the insulation and in the final cooling to room temperature some very small contraction voids were formed. Fig. 3.4 shows that the problem was overcome by later developments using different waxes. The coefficient of expansion has been much reduced and the shape of the expansion coefficient–temperature relationship has been changed so that more expansion occurs above the set point temperature of the compound. As the compounds were patented, full details have not been published and this is probably the reason that statements have been made in other countries that non-draining cables suffer from lower breakdown strength and short-circuit performance. UK experience has shown that, although the earlier compounds also had somewhat lower impulse and a.c. breakdown strength than oil–rosin compounds, the long-term performance has been much better because the insulation remained fully impregnated with no loss of impregnant.

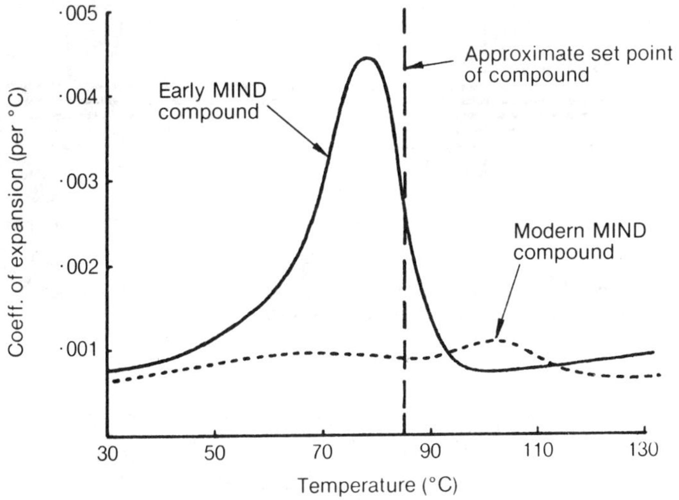

Fig. 3.4 Typical coefficient of expansion versus temperature relationships for mass-impregnated non-draining compound

Different circumstances apply to high voltage pressure type cables because of the better electrical quality necessary and the fact that the drainage problem does not arise. The pre-impregnated paper construction for gas-filled cables uses compounds with petroleum jelly and polyisobutylene for viscosity control. For oil-filled cables, the oil must be very fluid so that it readily flows from the cable into pressure tanks during heating and back on cooling. Resistance to gas evolution under electrical stress and to oxidation are other key properties necessary. Although highly refined mineral oils were used for many decades, the increasing stress requirement for modern cables has led to a change to the use of synthetic alkylates of dodecylbenzene type.

Impregnated paper dielectrics

Although various important characteristics have been mentioned it is ultimately the electrical properties of the complete dielectric which are paramount. In this respect the effects in the butt-gap spaces between the layers of paper tapes are a critical feature as voltage increases. Such spaces are necessary so that individual papers may slide as the cable is bent but, except for low voltage cables, should be well filled with impregnating compound by careful control of impregnating conditions, particularly to ensure slow cooling. They are inevitably a source of electrical weakness and hence the registration of paper tapes compared with underlying layers should be chosen so that a minimum of gaps is superimposed in a radial direction. Fig. 3.5 compares a registration of 35:65 (35% of the tape lying in front of and 65% behind the trailing edge of the tape beneath it) with a registration of 50:50, in which the butt gaps are superimposed every alternate layer. Theoretically, 20:80 registration would be better than 35:65 but as a tolerance is necessary there is a danger of some drift towards 100:0, with a butt gap of double depth.

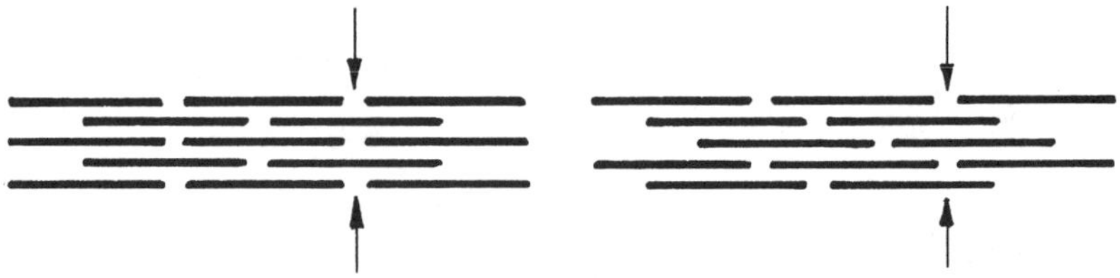

Fig. 3.5 Effect of paper layer registrations on butt-gap alignment: one paper between aligning gaps with 50/50 registration and two papers with 35/65

The electric strength of impregnated paper in sheet form is very high. Impulse strength increases with density, and with impermeability up to an optimum value, and also increases as paper thickness is reduced. A level of 200 MV/m can readily be obtained. Similarly, a.c. strength also increases with density and a level of 50 MV/m is possible. However, other factors have to be considered for high voltage cables, particularly the effects in butt-gap spaces, the relationship between density and dielectric losses and the moisture content.

The relevant requirements also have to be aligned with the operating voltage of the cable. A moisture content up to 1% can be tolerated at 1 kV and 0.2% is satisfactory for the 10–30 kV range but for transmission cables it needs to be kept below 0.1%. Increase in paper density increases the dielectric losses and also the differential between the permittivity of the paper and the impregnant, so causing greater stresses in the latter. Effects of partial discharge in butt gaps and dielectric losses are of particular importance for transmission cables and are considered in greater detail in chapters 31 and 36.

Fig. 3.6 illustrates typical examples of the dielectric loss angle versus temperature relationship for dry paper, impregnating compounds and impregnated paper for various types of cables. The actual values may be somewhat displaced according to moisture content. The loss angle and permittivity of the composite dielectric are

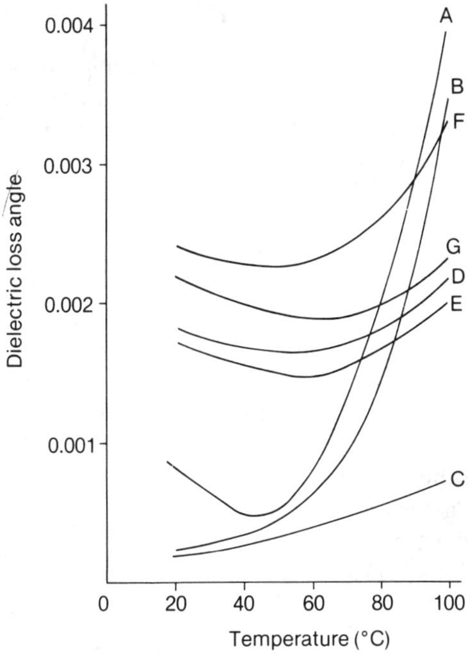

Fig. 3.6 Typical dielectric loss angle versus temperature characteristics of oil–rosin compound (curve A), MIND compound (curve B), OF cable oil (curve C), paper for solid type cables (curve D), paper for OF cables (curve E), impregnated paper for solid cables (curve F), impregnated paper for OF cables (curve G)

related to the density of the paper. As the density of the paper increases, and the space occupied by the impregnant decreases, the higher loss angle and permittivity of the paper predominate and hence they increase in the composite material. However, other factors are also involved such as the purity of the paper pulp, to which reference has been made.

Table 3.3 gives similar data for permittivity. The relative permittivity of dry paper is related to the ratio of paper fibres and air, as the permittivity of the fibres is of the order of 5.5 compared with 1.0 for air. With increasing density of paper the fibre ratio increases, and the permittivity of a paper tape is within the range 1.7–3.2 according to density.

Table 3.3 Permittivities of cable components

Material	Temperature 20°C	100°C
Oil–rosin compound	2.5	2.4
MIND compound	2.4	2.2
OF cable oil	2.2	2.0
Impregnated paper		
low density	3.3	3.3
high density	3.8	3.8

POLYMERIC INSULATION AND SHEATHING MATERIALS

In tonnage terms, synthetic polymers have largely replaced natural materials such as paper, mineral oil and natural rubber for the insulation of distribution and wiring type cables and for the oversheathing of cables in general. The range of polymers available is extensive and variations in chemical composition enable specific mechanical, electrical and thermal properties to be obtained. Where appropriate, these properties may be further modified by the addition of specific fillers, plasticisers, softness extenders, colourants, antioxidants and many other ingredients.

As the variety of polymeric materials has grown, it has become increasingly difficult to place them all within easy general definitions. A polymer is a molecule, or a substance consisting of molecules, composed of one or a few structural units repeated many times. However, this definition embraces not only synthetic materials but also materials such as paper (cellulose).

In the cable industry the term polymeric material is taken to signify polymers which are plastics or rubbers. British Standards define plastics as materials based on synthetic or modified natural polymers which at some stage of manufacture can be formed to shape by flow, aided in many cases by heat and pressure. Rubbers are considered to be solid materials, with elastic properties, which are made from latex derived from living plants or synthetically and used in the manufacture of rubber products.

An elastomer is a material which returns rapidly to approximately its initial shape after substantial deformation at room temperature by a weak stress and release of that stress. In cable technology the terms 'rubber' and 'elastomer' are used synonymously and interchangeably, although 'rubber' to many implies 'natural rubber'.

Plastics may be further divided into thermoplastics, i.e. materials capable of being softened by heating and hardened by cooling, and thermosets. A thermosetting material is a plastic which does not soften significantly on heating to temperatures below its decomposition temperature and is not capable of permanent reshaping by the application of heat and pressure. Unlike thermoplastics, thermosets are insoluble and infusible, i.e they will not fuse together. Many thermoplastics may be converted to thermosets by appropriate treatment to induce 'crosslinking', e.g. by the addition of a suitable chemical crosslinking agent or by irradiation. Rubbers for cable insulation and sheath, whether natural or synthetic, are normally crosslinked.

The definition of the terms used in the plastics and rubber industries are given in BS 1755: Part 1 and BS 3558 respectively. Common names and abbreviations for plastics and rubbers are given in BS 3502: Parts 1 and 3.

Tables 3.4 and 3.5 indicate the majority of thermoplastic and thermosetting insulating materials used in cables and their typical properties.

THERMOPLASTIC MATERIALS

The major thermoplastics in use today were developed in the 1930s and although some were used for specialised applications during the 1940s it was not until the early 1950s that poly(vinyl chloride) (PVC) and polyethylene (PE) came into widespread use for electric cables.

Table 3.4 Physical properties of polymeric materials

Material	Type	Tensile strength (min) (N/mm^2)	Elongation at break (min) (%)	Limiting temperature[a] Rating (°C)	Installation (°C)
Thermoplastic[b]					
poly(vinyl chloride)	TI 1	12.5	125	70	0
poly(vinyl chloride)	2	18.5	125	70	0
poly(vinyl chloride)	TI 2	10	150	70	−10
poly(vinyl chloride)	4	7.5	125−150	85	0
poly(vinyl chloride)	5	12.5	125	85	0
polyethylene LD	PE 03	7	300	70	−60
polyethylene LD	PE 2	7	300	70	−60
polyethylene HD		37	500	80	−40
polypropylene		37	400	80	−10
Elastomeric[c]					
general purpose GP rubber	EI 1	5.0	250	60	−45
heat-resisting GP rubber	GP 1	4.2	200	85	−45
heat-resisting GP rubber	GP 2	4.2	200	85	−45
heat-resisting MEPR rubber	GP 4	6.5	200	90	−45
flame-retardant rubber	FR 1	5.5	200	85	−30
flame-retardant rubber	FR 2	5.5	200	85	−30
OFR rubber	OR 1	7.0	200	85	−30
silicone rubber	EI 2	5.0	150	150	−55
ethylene−(vinyl acetate)	EI 3	6.5	200	105	−25
hard ethylene−propylene rubber		8.5	200	90	−40
crosslinked polyethylene		12.5	200	90	−40
Fluorocarbons					
polytetrafluoroethylene		24	300	260	−75

[a] Maximum temperature for sustained operation and minimum temperature for installation
[b] BS 6746 for PVC types and BS 6234 for polyethylene types
[c] BS 6899 for GP rubber types, EPR types and crosslinked polyethylene

Poly(vinyl chloride) (PVC)

The basic unit which is repeated in the PVC chain is

$$
\begin{array}{c}
-CH_2-\underset{\substack{|\\ Cl}}{CH}-
\end{array}
$$

PVC polymer cannot be processed by extrusion without the addition of materials which, *inter alia*, act as processing aids, e.g. plasticisers and lubricants. PVC is also strongly polar, because of the C—Cl dipole moment, and the addition of plasticisers also shifts the electrical loss peaks to a lower temperature at constant frequency.

Table 3.5 Electrical properties of polymeric materials

Material	Type	Volume resistivity (min) at 20 °C (Ω m)	Permittivity at 50 Hz	Tan δ at 50 Hz
Thermoplastic[a]				
poly(vinyl chloride)	TI 1	2×10^{11}	6–7	0.1
poly(vinyl chloride)	2	1×10^{12}	4–6	0.08–0.1
poly(vinyl chloride)	TI 2	2×10^{11}	6–7	0.09–0.1
poly(vinyl chloride)	4	1×10^{9}	5–6	0.07–0.13
poly(vinyl chloride)	5	5×10^{11}	6	0.9
polyethylene LD	PE 03	1×10^{16}	2.35	0.0003
polyethylene LD	PE 2	1×10^{16}	2.35	0.0003
polyethylene HD		1×10^{16}	2.35	0.0006
polypropylene		1×10^{16}	2.25	0.0005
Elastomeric[b]				
general purpose GP rubber	EI 1	2×10^{12}	4–4.5	0.01–0.03
heat-resisting GP rubber	GP 1	7×10^{12}	3–4	0.01–0.02
heat-resisting GP rubber	GP 2	1×10^{13}	3–4	0.01–0.02
heat-resisting MEPR rubber	GP 4	7×10^{12}	3–4	0.01–0.02
flame-retardant rubber	FR 1	5×10^{12}	4.5–5	0.02–0.04
flame-retardant rubber	FR 2	1×10^{13}	4–5	0.015–0.035
OFR rubber	OR 1	1×10^{10}	8–11	0.05–0.10
silicone rubber	EI 2	2×10^{12}	2.9–3.5	0.002–0.02
ethylene–(vinyl acetate)	EI 3	2×10^{12}	2.5–3.5	0.002–0.02
hard ethylene–propylene rubber		2×10^{13}	3.2	0.01
crosslinked polyethylene		1×10^{14}	2.3–5.2	0.0004–0.005
Fluorocarbons				
polytetrafluoroethylene		1×10^{16}	2	0.0003

[a] BS 6746 for PVC types and BS 6234 for polyethylene types
[b] BS 6899 for GP rubber types, EPR types and crosslinked polyethylene

Apart from the plasticisers, other additions to the PVC resin to produce compounds for electrical applications include fillers and stabilisers. The resin itself is characterised by its molecular weight and freedom from impurities. The most common plasticiser for general purpose compounds is dioctyl phthalate and it is often used in conjunction with a secondary plasticiser such as a chlorinated extender (e.g. Cereclor).

A common filler is calcium carbonate, usually whiting, and it may be coated with a lubricant such as calcium stearate to aid extrudability. It is not just a diluent but increases the resistance of the compound to hot deformation. The most common general purpose stabilizers are lead carbonate and dibasic lead sulphate.

The whole formulation is optimised for mechanical and electrical properties, ease of processing and cost. The requirements for PVC insulation and sheathing compounds are given in BS 6746. In the IEC format they are included in the standards for the particular cable types, e.g. IEC 502.

In addition to the general purpose compounds, other formulations are available for particular applications. Where higher temperature resistance is required, e.g. for the oversheathing of cables with thermosetting insulation, a less volatile plasticiser such as didecyl phthalate is beneficial. For high temperature insulation, di-tridecyl phthalate may be used. For low temperature applications, PVC can be compounded to be flexible at −40 °C by omitting fillers and substituting sebacate or adipate ester plasticisers for part of the normal phthalates. However, it is now more usual to use rubber or other thermosetting materials for such situations.

Compounds with improved electrical properties are required for power distribution cables operating above 3 kV. IEC 502 requires the product of permittivity and dielectric loss angle to be below 0.75 within the temperature range from ambient to 85 °C (chapter 21). In addition the DLA at 80 °C must not exceed the value at 60 °C. For such cables a smaller amount of a selected filler is used. This also reduces susceptibility to water under service conditions. Secondary plasticiser is also omitted.

The major reason for these electrical requirements is that when a length of open circuited PVC cable is energised, provided that the voltage is sufficiently high, the insulation will become warm even though no current is passing through the conductor. The effect is caused by dielectric heating and the energy loss is given by the equation

$$\text{power loss per phase} = 2\pi f\, C\, U_0^2 \tan\delta \qquad (3.1)$$

where f = supply frequency (Hz)
C = capacitance per core (F/m)
U_0 = voltage to earth (V)
$\tan\delta$ = dielectric loss angle (DLA)

There are significant differences between PVC, XLPE and EPR in this respect. Typical values of relative permittivity and tan δ are as follows:

	PVC	XLPE	EPR
Permittivity (at 50 Hz)	6–8	2.3	3.5
Tan δ	0.08	0.0003	0.004

The heat generated in this way is dissipated through the cable into the surroundings and a condition of equilibrium exists between the two. However, if the voltage is increased or if excessive current is allowed to flow through the conductor, or part of the cable is lagged, it may not then be possible to maintain the balance with the result that the temperature of the dielectric continues to rise until the dielectric fails.

Fig. 3.7 depicts the relationship between the dielectric loss and temperature. Curves A and B are idealised DLA–temperature curves. As the rate of dissipation of heat to the surroundings is more or less proportional to the temperature rise, lines C and D relate to this condition, starting from two different ambient temperatures. Considering cable A and the rate of heat dissipation shown in C, the rate of heat dissipation will exceed the rate of heat generation until the two curves intersect at (1). Above this temperature heat is generated faster than it can be dissipated and, as the losses further increase, a runaway condition develops. Ultimately, the dielectric will fail. In these circumstances the characteristics of cable B are totally unsatisfactory. Similarly, cable A can only operate at an ambient temperature of 40 °C if the cable is derated. It is for these reasons that the selection of materials for use at high voltage requires careful consideration. The DLA–temperature curves of PVC compounds suitable for low voltage and high voltage use are illustrated in fig. 3.8.

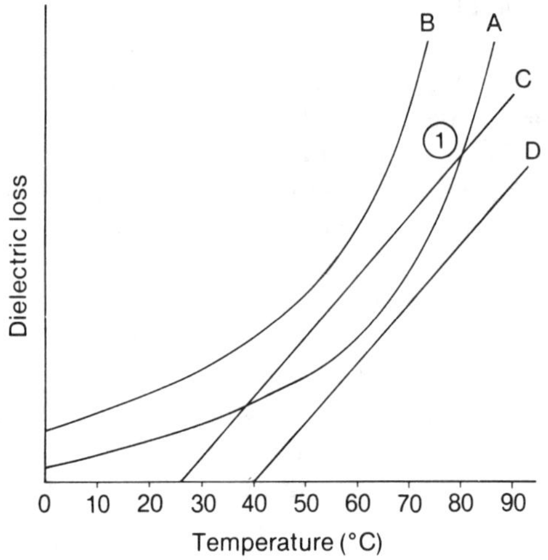

Fig. 3.7 Thermal stability of high voltage PVC compounds illustrated by dependence on the dielectric loss–temperature relationship

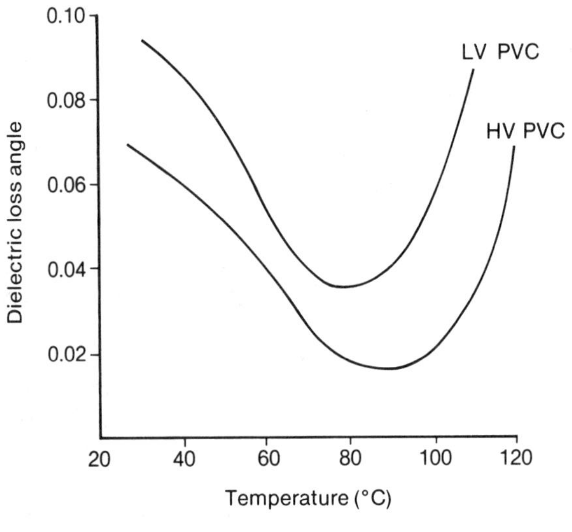

Fig. 3.8 Relationship between DLA and temperature for PVC compounds suitable for low voltage and high voltage uses

Coloured oversheaths are sometimes used in accordance with an identification code, and when buried they may darken or change to a black colour. This is caused by a reaction between sulphur compounds in the ground and lead stabilisers, with the formation of lead sulphide. The problem may be overcome by the use of the more expensive calcium/barium/cadmium stabiliser systems. While PVC is not as susceptible to degradation by ultraviolet light as the polyolefins it is recommended that black compound should be used wherever possible for service involving exposure to sunlight.

An important field of development has been the formulation of PVC compounds with modified burning characteristics (chapter 6). Resistance to flame propagation can be improved by the use of fillers such as aluminium trihydrate and antimony trioxide, and phosphate and halogenated plasticisers. The concentration of hydrogen chloride released during burning can be reduced by the use of calcium carbonate filler of very fine particle size. These are known as acid-binding PVC compounds. Reduction of smoke generation can be achieved by the use of certain metal salts, but unfortunately a compromise of properties is always necessary.

Polyethylene

Polyethylene is a semicrystalline polymer with the repeat unit —CH_2—CH_2—. It is available in a variety of grades, differing in molecular weight and density, which are obtained by the use of different methods of polymerisation. High density polyethylenes (HDPE), with densities of 945–960 kg/m^3, have fewer and shorter chain branches than low density polyethylenes (LDPE) having densities of 916–930 kg/m^3. A higher density is a direct consequence of higher crystallinity resulting from reduced chain branching. Among other properties which increase with crystallinity are stiffness and melting point. The crystalline melting point increases from 110 to 130 °C as the density increases from 916 to 960 kg/m^3. The crystallinity of LDPE is typically 45%–55% while that of HDPE is 70%–80%.

A newer class of polyethylenes which is now being used for cable sheathing is linear low density polyethylene (LLDPE). It is made by a low pressure process similar to that used for HDPE.

Polyethylene is a non-polar material with excellent electrical characteristics. Much of the small electrical loss (DLA approximately 10^{-4}) is due to impurities such as oxidation products generated during processing or residues from the polymerisation process. LDPE is used for both insulation and oversheathing. HDPE finds fewer applications and is used mainly for oversheathing (chapter 5). When polyethylene was first introduced for oversheathing some failures occurred due to environmental stress cracking but this problem was overcome by the incorporation of 5% butyl rubber. More recently the use of copolymers and higher molecular weight polymers having melt flow indices (MFI) of 0.3 or less (2.16 kg load at 190 °C) has also been successful. For insulation grades attention is given to the molecular weight distribution and the purity of the polymers. For many applications the only compounding ingredient is a small amount of antioxidant to prevent oxidation during processing and subsequent use. The grades available in the UK are covered by BS 6234.

In the USA polyethylene insulation referred to as HMW is high molecular weight LDPE with melt flow index in the range 0.1–0.3.

In direct contact with copper conductors or screening tapes, some embrittlement may occur and this can be rapid at elevated temperatures. This is caused by oxidation, which is catalysed by copper, and is inhibited by suitable choice of antioxidant. Polymerised 1,2-dihydro-2,2,4-trimethylquinoline type is used for general purpose applications but for more severe conditions a copper inhibitor of bis-hydrazine type is also used.

Polyethylenes are also susceptible to oxidative degradation induced by ultraviolet radiation and for this reason the addition is recommended to oversheaths of 2.5% of a fine particle size (20 μm) carbon black.

A wide range of compositions can be obtained by the incorporation of other materials. The addition of fillers is limited because they lead to brittleness but small amounts of butyl or ethylene–propylene rubber may be added to maintain flexibility. An alternative approach is to use an ethylene copolymer, in which case the second component increases the flexibility. Vinyl acetate and alkyl acrylates are widely used as the comonomers and the resulting polymers, when filled with a suitable carbon black, provide a semiconducting grade with reasonable flexibility. Copolymerisation may also give considerable improvement in environmental stress cracking resistance for oversheathing applications. Like all hydrocarbons polyethylene burns readily; thus there is a requirement, especially in the USA, for grades having improved resistance to burning. A degree of improvement can be achieved through the addition of chlorinated hydrocarbons together with antimony trioxide, although the amounts which can be added are limited by the adverse effects of the additives on mechanical properties.

Normal grades of LDPE have melting points in the range 110–115 °C but begin to soften in the 80–90 °C region. For this reason the maximum continuous operating temperature of LDPE is limited to 70 °C. HDPE softens above 110 °C.

Polypropylene

The repeated basic unit of polypropylene is

$$
\begin{array}{c}
\qquad\quad CH_3 \\
\qquad\quad | \\
—CH_2—CH—
\end{array}
$$

Polypropylene is considerably harder and stiffer than polyethylene and interest arises because the commercial grades of the homopolymer do not melt until about 160 °C, in comparison with approximately 110–115 °C for LDPE and 135 °C for HDPE. However, polypropylenes are not widely used at present.

Nylon

The group of nylon materials contain units which are similar to

$$
\begin{array}{ccccccccccccc}
 & & O & & & & & & O & & & O & \\
 & & \| & & & & & & \| & & & \| & \\
— & R' & —C— & NH & — & R & — & NH— & C & —R'— & & C & —NH—
\end{array}
$$

where R and R′ are usually alkylene groups. These condensation polymers may be formed from a dibasic acid and a diamine, e.g. adipic acid and hexamethylenediamine give nylon 6,6, or by a ring opening mechanism, e.g. caprolactam gives nylon 6.

Nylons are rather rigid but extremely tough and resistant to abrasion and find applications where these properties are required (e.g. oversheathing). Some have good resistance to softening up to about 200 °C.

Polyurethanes

Polyurethanes are characterised by the urethane group

$$
\begin{array}{c} \mathrm{O} \\ \| \\ \text{—NH—C—O—} \end{array}
$$

and are manufactured by the reaction of hydroxyl terminated polyester or polyether prepolymers with isocyanate. Thermoplastic polyurethanes are used for special oversheathing applications because of their excellent abrasion resistance.

Polyester block copolymers (PEE)

Polyester block copolymers consist of a hard (crystalline) segment of polybutylene terephthalate and a soft (amorphous) segment based on long-chain polyether glycols. The properties are determined by the ratio of hard to soft segments and the make-up of the segments. They offer ease of processing, chemical resistance and wide temperature resistance whilst retaining mechanical strength and durability. The commercial name is Hytrel (DuPont).

Fluorinated polymers

Polytetrafluoroethylene (PTFE) is by far the most important member of this group and has a repeat unit of

$$\text{—}CF_2\text{—}CF_2\text{—}$$

The polymer is non-polar and has outstanding electrical properties. It cannot really be considered to be a true thermoplastic because the melt viscosity is so high that extrusion is not possible. The insulation has to be applied to conductors by a cold shaping operation followed by a sintering process to cause the polymer particles to fuse and coalesce. The good electrical properties are combined with very high resistance to chemicals and temperature: service operation up to 260 °C is possible.

Because of the high cost and difficulty in processing PTFE, much attention has been given to other fluorinated monomers which are melt processable. Commercial names of materials include FEP (DuPont, TFE copolymer with hexafluoropropylene), Tefzel (DuPont, TFE copolymer with ethylene), Halar (Allied Chemical, ethylene copolymer with chlorotrifluoroethylene), PFA (DuPont, perfluoroalkoxy branched polymers) and Dyflor (Dynamit Nobel, polyvinylidene fluoride).

Thermoplastics in tape form

Some materials are used for insulation, bedding and sheathing as tapes or strings, polypropylene being an example of the latter. Polyethylene terephthalate (PET), under the trade name Melinex (ICI) or Mylar (DuPont), is widely used as a binder tape for multicore cables and as a barrier layer to retard the migration of components such as oils and plasticisers from beddings and sheaths into insulation and to separate insulation from stranded conductors.

Polyimide, e.g. Kapton (DuPont), in tape form is being used increasingly for high temperature applications where light weight is important. It has the structure

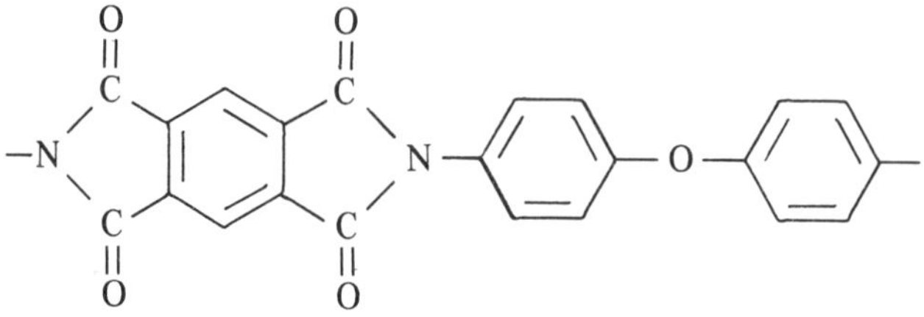

THERMOSET MATERIALS

In the cable industry thermoset polymers have two distinct fields of application. Firstly rubber type materials having intrinsic flexibility or other required property (e.g. oil resistance) need to be crosslinked to cater for the thermal conditions arising when some types of sheath are applied, as well as to provide the required service performance. Secondly crosslinking provides greater resistance to thermal deformation at higher cable operating temperature. The need for crosslinking tends to increase cost and so when a thermoplastic material such as PVC can be used satisfactorily, e.g. for domestic and industrial wiring cables, it is generally preferred.

In general, specifications are prepared for a particular polymer type but some, such as BS 6899, 'Rubber insulation and sheath of electric cables', mainly define performance characteristics. This allows the most effective material to be used.

Natural rubber (NR)

Natural rubber is a dried or coagulated solid obtained from the latex exuded from certain trees (usually *Hevea brasiliensis*). In the past, crude methods of collection and preparation caused variability in compounding and quality but natural rubber is now produced to well defined specifications, e.g. to the Standard Malaysian Rubber (SMR) scheme. This defines maximum levels for dirt, ash, nitrogen and volatiles and controls the plasticity.

In chemical terms natural rubber is *cis*-1,4-polyisoprene with the structural unit

$$\begin{array}{c} \quad\;\; CH_3 \\ \quad\;\; | \\ —CH_2—C{=}CH—CH_2— \end{array}$$

Raw rubber is difficult to extrude satisfactorily. It needs to be masticated to the required viscosity and compounded with fillers, extenders and other additives. Crosslinking of natural rubber is generally achieved by sulphur or sulphur-bearing chemicals and as these materials may react with copper such conductors are usually tinned.

Natural rubber tends to compare unfavourably with synthetic polymers in terms of maximum operating temperature (approximately 60 °C) and ageing performance. It is also susceptible to cracking in the presence of ozone. Thermal stability in air depends on the method of crosslinking and the antioxidant used. Much testing is devoted to ageing and, by experience, correlations can be obtained between natural and accelerated ageing conditions. When the logarithm of life is plotted against the reciprocal of the ageing temperature a straight line is obtained – the well known Arrhenius reaction rate equation. Some typical graphs for different types of rubber are given in fig. 3.9.

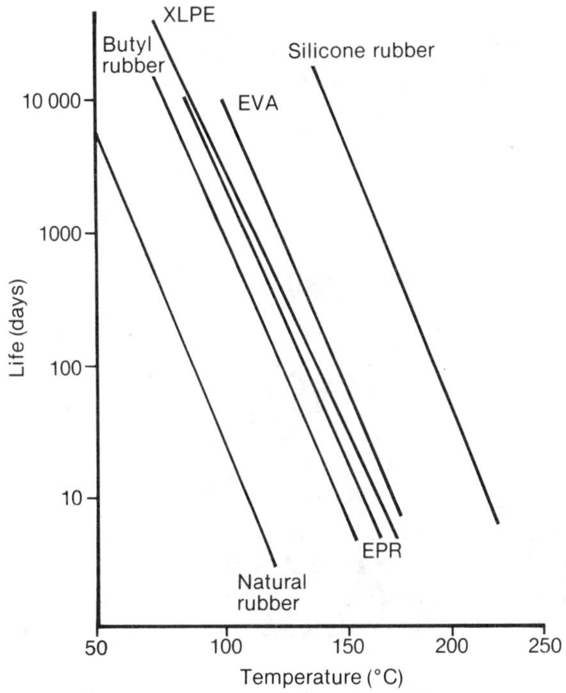

Fig. 3.9 Ageing characteristics of thermoset insulating compounds

In tests of this kind care must be taken, firstly, in choosing the failure criteria, and secondly, to ensure that the same degradation mechanism occurs over the temperature range selected. Extrapolation of operating temperature should not exceed 25 °C and allowance must be made for the effects of short duration overloads to higher temperature. Guidance on the determination of thermal endurance properties of electrical insulation materials is given in IEC 216.

Synthetic versions of *cis*-1,4-polyisoprene polymerised by transition metal catalysis in solution are available but although they are free from dirt and nitrogenous material they do not match natural rubber in all respects. They are usually used as a part replacement.

Styrene–butadiene rubber (SBR)

SBR is an amorphous rubber manufactured usually by the emulsion copolymerisation of styrene and butadiene. The structural units are

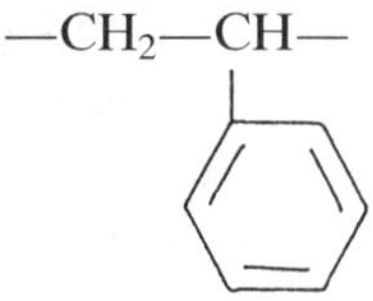

and $-CH_2-CH{=}CH-CH_2-$

or

$$\begin{array}{l} -CH_2-CH- \\ \qquad\quad | \\ \qquad\quad CH \\ \qquad\quad \| \\ \qquad\quad CH_2 \end{array}$$

The properties of SBR are affected by the styrene-to-butadiene ratio and also by the butadiene configurations (1,2, *cis*-1,4, *trans*-1,4). SBR is used for the same applications as natural rubber and the two are often used in blends according to the economic conditions.

Butyl rubber (IIR)

Butyl rubber is a copolymer of isobutylene (97%) and isoprene (3%), with a structural unit of

$$\begin{array}{c} CH_3 \\ | \\ -CH_2-C- \\ | \\ CH_3 \end{array}$$

It is manufactured in solution with an aluminium chloride catalyst. The isoprene is present to provide suitable sites for crosslinking and this may be effected either by the normal sulphur donor/accelerator systems, or preferably with the dibenzoyl quinone dioxime (dibenzo GMF)/red lead system. The latter gives improved resistance to ageing.

Because the cured butyl rubber is substantially free from unsaturation (carbon–carbon double bonds), it has excellent resistance to ozone and weathering. IIR has low resistance to radiation.

Being suitable for operation to 85 °C, compared with 60 °C for natural rubber, it has had widespread use for higher voltage cables and cables in ships but is now tending to be superseded by EPR because of the latter's ease of processing and improved performance.

Ethylene–propylene rubber (EPR)

The term EPR encompasses a range of polymers which fall into two classes. Firstly the saturated copolymers of ethylene and propylene (EPM) form a minor class in which organic peroxides have to be used for crosslinking. The structural units may be arranged randomly or in blocks:

$$-CH_2-CH_2- \text{ and } \begin{array}{r} CH_3 \\ | \\ -CH_2-CH- \end{array}$$

The second class is formed by the incorporation of a third monomer, a non-conjugated diene, to provide unsaturation for crosslinking by sulphur compounds as well as by peroxides. These materials are termed EPDM, and are available with dicyclopentadiene (DCPD), cyclooctadiene (COD), ethylidene norbornene (ENB) and 1,4-hexadiene (HD) as comonomer. The latter two are now normally preferred because of increased rate of cure.

The use of peroxides for crosslinking provides better long-term resistance to ageing and electrical properties. They decompose under the action of heat to give radicals which react with the polymer and result in stable carbon–carbon crosslinks. Improved properties are obtained through the use of coagents with the peroxides, such as ethylene glycol dimethylacrylate or triallylcyanurate. Dicumyl peroxide is a common crosslinking agent but others are available.

Calcium carbonate incorporated in larger quantities reduces the cost. Better physical properties and reduced moisture absorption are obtained by replacing calcium carbonate with calcined clay. An unsaturated silane, which binds to the filler, also improves mechanical properties. Other additives include red lead to give better water resistance and oils to help processing. These have to be selected with care to obviate reaction with peroxides.

Compounds have recently been designed which use other polymers such as polyethylene and polypropylene to provide reinforcement, and these blends when crosslinked by peroxide or the newer silane systems meet all the physical requirements of mineral filled systems but have superior electrical properties.

Because of its superior performance, with suitability for continuous operation at 90 °C, EPR has gradually displaced butyl rubber for insulation and is now being considered for oversheaths.

Crosslinked polyethylene (XLPE)

Despite its excellent electrical properties the use of polyethylene has been limited by an upper operational temperature of about 70 °C, due to its thermoplasticity. By crosslinking, this constraint is removed and the working temperature is increased to 90 °C.

For general purpose low voltage cables it is possible to incorporate up to 30% calcium carbonate into XLPE to reduce the cost. However, to maintain the best electrical properties, especially when immersed in water, the filled compound should not be used.

In the USA, compounds incorporating approximately 30% thermal carbon black are used. These have the advantage of improved resistance to hot deformation and cut-through resistance.

Crosslinking in pressurised tubes

The most common method of crosslinking is by the incorporation of peroxides into the polymer followed, after extrusion, by heating under pressure to activate the peroxide. If steam is used for heating, the pressure is correspondingly high (18–20 bar) so as to achieve a temperature of the order of 210 °C. If an electrically heated tube with inert gas atmosphere is used, the gas pressure needs to be around 5–10 bar to prevent the formation of voids due to peroxide decomposition products.

A suitable peroxide has to be selected to give fast crosslinking without precuring in the extruder, and dicumyl peroxide is widely used. For compounding in-line during the extrusion process, there are advantages in using a liquid instead of a powder. Di-*tert*-butyl peroxide, which decomposes more slowly, is frequently adopted.

The crosslinking mechanism of polyethylene with dicumyl peroxide is illustrated in fig. 3.10. Similar schemes apply to rubbers such as EPR and EVA. The diagram indicates how volatile by-products such as acetophenone, cumyl alcohol, methyl styrene and water vapour are formed. It is also important with peroxide systems to choose the antioxidant system carefully because they may react with the free radicals

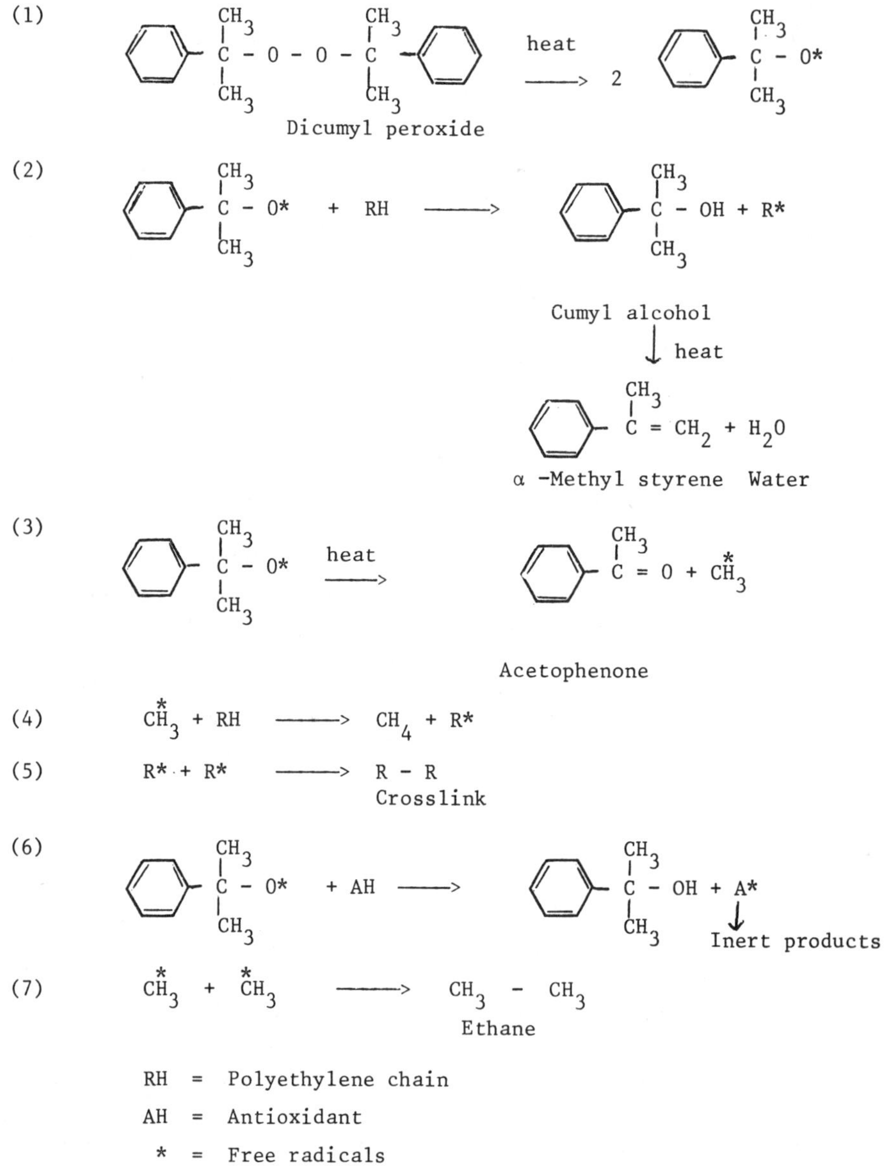

Fig. 3.10 Schematic crosslinking mechanism for polyethylene with peroxides

(reaction 6) to reduce the number of crosslinks. Phenolic antioxidants are particularly reactive and only two are in common use: Santonox R (Monsanto) and Irganox 1010 (Ciba Geigy).

A very suitable antioxidant is 1,2-dihydro-2,2,4-trimethylquinoline, e.g. Flectol H (Monsanto), but it can increase the dielectric loss angle of XLPE and the phenolic materials are preferred for high voltage cables.

Crosslinking in pressurised tubes

Irradiation with fast electrons or γ-rays produces crosslinking by a mechanism which is chemically similar to the use of peroxides. It works by a radical process with hydrogen being evolved. The material to be irradiated comprises only polyethylene with an antioxidant and so there is no problem of pre-cure in the extruder. However, the process is only economically suitable for relatively small insulation thicknesses.

Chemical crosslinking using silanes

A newer process, using the well established technology of silicones, is now replacing the conventional crosslinking procedure for low voltage cables. The basic system (Sioplas) was developed by Dow Corning in the UK in the early 1970s. This is a two-component system for which two materials are first prepared: a crosslinkable graft polymer and a catalyst master batch. These are blended together at the fabricating machine and the product is subsequently crosslinked by immersion in water or low pressure steam.

Typical reaction sequences are shown in fig. 3.11. Because the polyethylene radicals are constantly being regenerated in the (3) and (4) reaction cycles, only small amounts of dicumyl peroxide are required in comparison with peroxide linking under heat and pressure (typically 0.1% instead of 2.5%). Constraints concerning antioxidant choice apply equally. Water is the actual crosslinking agent and a relatively large amount is required (3000 ppm) but as polyethylene can only absorb about 100 ppm of water at 80 °C, and this is constantly being converted into methanol, the finished XLPE always has a low water content.

The crosslinks formed are of the Si–O–Si type common to silicone rubbers and are thus thermally and hydrolytically stable.

It is important to carry out tests to determine the degree of crosslinking achieved because this governs the physical properties of this material. At one time it was usual to use a solvent extraction technique to determine the proportion of un-crosslinked material. However, it became apparent that, because of the different crosslink structures, the alignment between extraction proportion and properties such as high temperature modulus was different for silane and peroxide crosslinked materials. For this reason the extraction method has now been superseded by an elongation test under a fixed load at 200 °C.

A further development of the Sioplas materials has been made by BICC and Maillefer.[2] This process (Monosil) introduces all the ingredients together by metering them into the extruder so that the separate grafting stage is eliminated. This ensures that the material is free from contamination and is thus suitable for cables in the 10–30 kV range. It also removes problems due to the limited storage life of the graft polymer and reduces processing costs.

Because water remains as the crosslinking agent and has to diffuse into the material, the cure time required is proportional to the square of the thickness. This

Preparation of Graft

RH = Polyethylene

(1)

$$\text{(C$_6$H$_5$)} - \overset{\overset{\displaystyle CH_3}{|}}{\underset{\underset{\displaystyle CH_3}{|}}{C}} - O - O - \overset{\overset{\displaystyle CH_3}{|}}{\underset{\underset{\displaystyle CH_3}{|}}{C}} - \text{(C$_6$H$_5$)} \xrightarrow{\text{heat}} 2 \quad \text{(C$_6$H$_5$)} - \overset{\overset{\displaystyle CH_3}{|}}{\underset{\underset{\displaystyle CH_3}{|}}{C}} - O*$$

(2)

$$\text{(C$_6$H$_5$)} - \overset{\overset{\displaystyle CH_3}{|}}{\underset{\underset{\displaystyle CH_3}{|}}{C}} - O* + RH \longrightarrow \text{(C$_6$H$_5$)} - \overset{\overset{\displaystyle CH_3}{|}}{\underset{\underset{\displaystyle CH_3}{|}}{C}} - OH + R*$$

(3)

$$R* + CH_2 = CH - \overset{\overset{\displaystyle OCH_3}{|}}{\underset{\underset{\displaystyle OCH_3}{|}}{Si}} - OCH_3 \longrightarrow R - CH_2 - \overset{*}{CH} - \overset{\overset{\displaystyle OCH_3}{|}}{\underset{\underset{\displaystyle OCH_3}{|}}{Si}} - OCH_3$$

(4)

$$R - CH_2 - \overset{*}{CH} - \overset{\overset{\displaystyle OCH_3}{|}}{\underset{\underset{\displaystyle OCH_3}{|}}{Si}} - OCH_3 + RH \longrightarrow R - CH_2 - CH_2 - \overset{\overset{\displaystyle OCH_3}{|}}{\underset{\underset{\displaystyle OCH_3}{|}}{Si}} - OCH_3 + R*$$

Crosslinking

(5)

$$R - CH_2 - CH_2 - \overset{\overset{\displaystyle OCH_3}{|}}{\underset{\underset{\displaystyle OCH_3}{|}}{Si}} - OCH_3 + H_2O \xrightarrow{\text{Catalyst}} R - CH_2 - CH_2 - \overset{\overset{\displaystyle OCH_3}{|}}{\underset{\underset{\displaystyle OCH_3}{|}}{Si}} - OH + CH_3OH$$

(6)

$$2\, R - CH_2 - CH_2 - \overset{\overset{\displaystyle OCH_3}{|}}{\underset{\underset{\displaystyle OCH_3}{|}}{Si}} - OH \xrightarrow{\text{Catalyst}} R - CH_2 - \overset{\overset{\displaystyle OCH_3}{|}}{\underset{\underset{\displaystyle OCH_3}{|}}{Si}} - O - \overset{\overset{\displaystyle OCH_3}{|}}{\underset{\underset{\displaystyle OCH_3}{|}}{Si}} - CH_2 - CH_2 - R + H_2O$$

(7)

$$R - CH_2 - CH_2 - \overset{\overset{\displaystyle OCH_3}{|}}{\underset{\underset{\displaystyle OCH_3}{|}}{Si}} - OH \xrightarrow{\text{Catalyst}} R - CH_2 - CH_2 - \overset{\overset{\displaystyle OCH_3}{|}}{\underset{\underset{\displaystyle OCH_3}{|}}{Si}} - O - \overset{\overset{\displaystyle OCH_3}{|}}{\underset{\underset{\displaystyle OCH_3}{|}}{Si}} - CH_2 - CH_2 - R + CH_3OH$$

$$+\quad R - CH_2 - CH_2 - \overset{\overset{\displaystyle OCH_3}{|}}{\underset{\underset{\displaystyle OCH_3}{|}}{Si}} - OCH_3$$

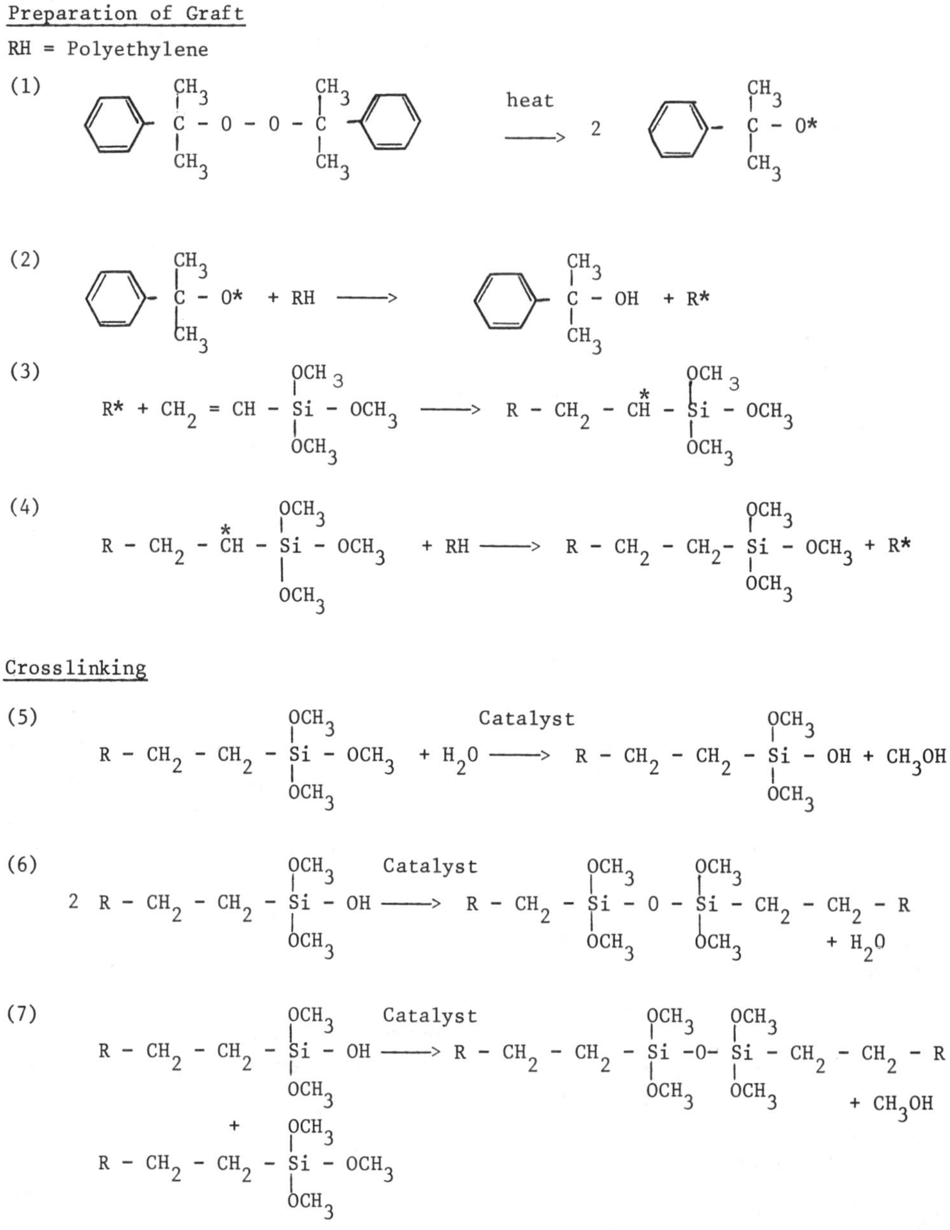

Fig. 3.11 Schematic crosslinking mechanism for polyethylene with silane

places a limitation on extrusion thicknesses which can be handled within a reasonable time scale. Currently, cure times are of the order of 4 hours at 90 °C in water for insulation of 2.5 mm thickness.

Currently XLPE is primarily used for insulation but in some countries, notably Sweden, it has some application for oversheathing as an alternative to PVC and LDPE.

Ethyl vinyl acetate (EVA)

Ethylene copolymers containing small amounts of vinyl acetate have been known for many years. More flexible grades of EVA suitable for cables became available around 1970, including amorphous polymers with vinyl acetate contents in excess of 40%. Such materials have vinyl acetate units in the form

$$-CH_2-CH-$$
$$|$$
$$O$$
$$|$$
$$CO$$
$$|$$
$$CH_3$$

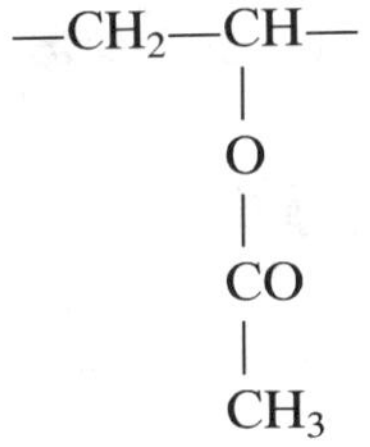

The polymers are crosslinked by peroxides or by radiation and the formulation is generally similar to that for EPR. Resistance to ageing in air is slightly superior to that of EPR, service temperatures up to 110 °C being possible, but the electrical properties such as permittivity are inferior. EVA is also used as the base for extruded semiconducting dielectric screening materials, especially those designed to be strippable from XLPE and EPR.

Silicone rubber

Silicone rubbers have the general chemical structure

$$R$$
$$|$$
$$-Si-O-$$
$$|$$
$$R$$

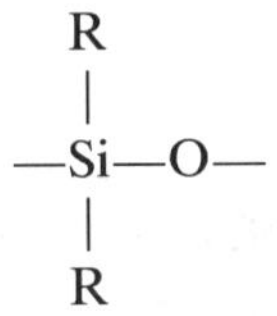

where R is usually methyl or phenyl. Some vinyl groups are also introduced to facilitate peroxide crosslinking, which with silicones, unlike other rubbers, can be carried out in hot air.

Silicones have outstanding properties, especially in resistance to high temperatures, 180 °C being the normal operating limit. However, at ambient temperatures the mechanical properties are somewhat inferior to those of the more commonly used materials, particularly for sheathing applications. Silica fillers are generally used to provide reinforcement.

Chloroprene rubber (CR or PCP)

Polychloroprene, otherwise known as neoprene, was the first commercial synthetic rubber. It has the structure

$$Cl$$
$$|$$
$$-CH_2-C=CH-CH_2-$$

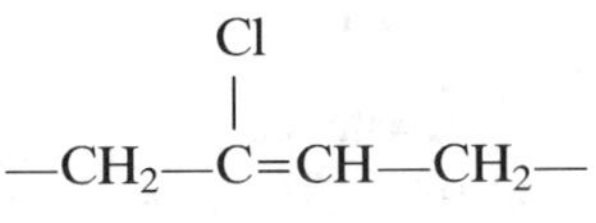

It has rarely been used by itself for insulation but is often used blended with

natural rubber. Its major use is as a very tough flexible sheathing material. Poly-chloroprene compounds have good abrasion and tear resistance together with good resistance to swelling and to chemical attack by a wide range of natural oils and aliphatic hydrocarbons. They do not normally support combustion.

Chlorosulphonated polyethylene rubber (CSP, CSM)

CSP is obtained when polyethylene is reacted in carbon tetrachloride with chlorine and sulphur dioxide. The polymer has the following units arranged randomly in the approximate ratio of A:B:C of 45:15:1:

$$-CH_2-CH_2- \qquad \underset{\underset{Cl}{|}}{-CH_2-CH-} \qquad \underset{\underset{Cl}{\underset{|}{SO_2}}}{-CH_2-CH-}$$

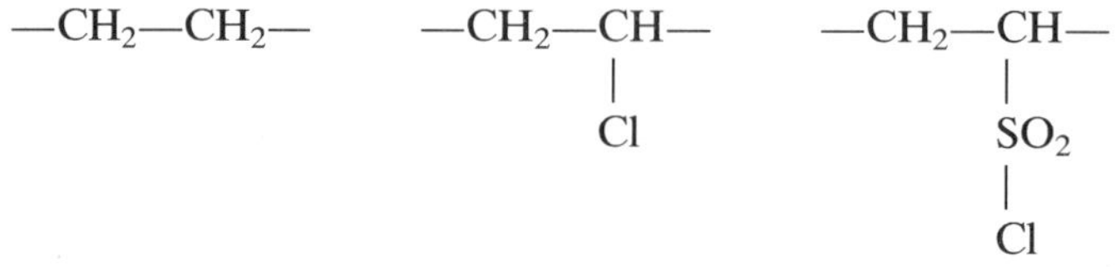

(A)	(B)	(C)

CSP compounds have superior electrical properties to compounds based on PCP and are particularly advantageous for insulation and sheathing which is required to be oil-resisting. CSP also has good resistance to ozone and weathering.

When blended with EVA or EPR and filled with a suitable carbon black, CSP compounds provide a strippable dielectric screening material for XLPE and EPR cables in the 10–30 kV range.

Acrylonitrile–butadiene rubber (NBR/PVC blends)

The copolymerisation of acrylonitrile with butadiene produces a range of polymers characterised by good oil resistance. They have the structural units

$$-CH_2-CH=CH-CH_2-$$

and

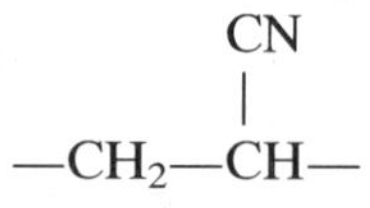

$$\underset{\underset{CH}{|}}{-CH_2-}\overset{\overset{CN}{|}}{CH}-$$

or

$$-CH_2-\underset{\underset{\overset{\|}{CH_2}}{\underset{CH}{|}}}{CH}-$$

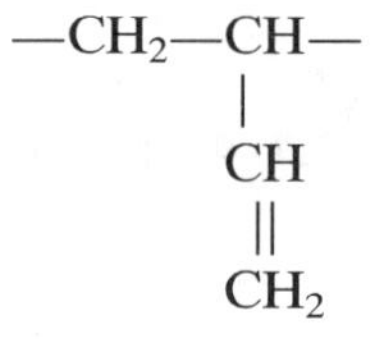

The addition of PVC improves resistance to ozone, weathering and abrasion. By suitable choice of plasticisers improved processability and flame retardance are also obtained. These materials are used solely for sheathing.

Fluorocarbon rubbers

The fluorocarbon rubbers find application for sheathing where very good resistance to oils is required at high temperatures. The best known material is a copolymer of vinylidene fluoride and hexafluoropropylene (Viton).

Ethylene–acrylic elastomers (EMA)

Ethylene–acrylic elastomers are heat- and oil-resistant non-halogen synthetic rubbers which can be compounded to resist ignition in the presence of flame and have low smoke generation when burned. They are suitable for service temperatures of 40–170 °C. The commercial name is Vamac (DuPont).

Thermoplastic elastomers

Thermoplastic elastomers are processible on thermoplastic and modified rubber equipment and have the feel and recovery of vulcanised rubber. A unique property balance includes outstanding oil resistance, heat ageing and weather resistance coupled with good general rubber properties. The commercial names are Alcryn (DuPont) and Santoprene (Monsanto).

ENVIRONMENTAL DEGRADATION OF POLYMERS

There are many factors which determine the maximum operating temperature of a material. For some thermoplastics, such as polyethylene, the main determining factor is resistance to deformation. However, for most thermosets and indeed some thermoplastics, service life is determined by the susceptibility of the material to thermal degradation at elevated temperatures. The most common form of degradation is that due to heat and oxygen. Hydrocarbon polymers oxidise thermally and, because the process is autocatalytic, large changes in mechanical and electrical properties usually accompany the onset of oxidation. The chemical process is illustrated in fig. 3.12. The number of radicals generated multiplies through the decomposition of the hydroperoxide (ROOH). The most efficient method of breaking the multiplication process is through the use of suitable antioxidants. Termination reactions can result in both polymer crosslinking and chain scission. Chain scission does not necessarily result in the destruction of radicals:

$$—CH_2—\underset{\displaystyle OOH}{\underset{|}{CH}}—CH_2 \longrightarrow —CH_2—\underset{\displaystyle O^{\cdot}}{\underset{|}{CH}}—CH_2— \longrightarrow —CH_2CHO + \cdot CH_2—$$

The oxidative stability of a polymer depends upon the availability of hydrogen atoms which can be abstracted by the peroxy ($ROO^{\cdot}$) radicals. This depends upon two factors: the carbon–hydrogen bond dissociation energies and the steric position of the labile hydrogens. Some typical bond dissociation energies of hydrocarbons are given in table 3.6. Thus polyisoprene (natural rubber) oxidises more easily than polyethylene:

A. Initiation

$$\text{Polymer} \longrightarrow \underset{\text{Polymer radical}}{R^{\cdot}}$$

B. Propagation

$$R^{\cdot} + O_2 \longrightarrow ROO^{\cdot}$$

$$ROO^{\cdot} + \underset{\text{Polymer}}{RH} \longrightarrow ROOH + R^{\cdot}$$

$$ROOH \longrightarrow RO^{\cdot} + {}^{\cdot}OH$$

C. Termination

$$ROO^{\cdot} \longrightarrow \text{unreactive products}$$

$$ROO^{\cdot} + \underset{\text{Antioxidant}}{HA} \longrightarrow ROOH + \underset{\text{Inactive product}}{A^{\cdot}}$$

Fig. 3.12 Auto-oxidation mechanism of hydrocarbon polymers

$$\text{—}CH_2\text{—}\overset{\overset{\displaystyle CH_3}{|}}{C}\text{=}CH\text{—}\underset{\underset{\displaystyle H}{|}}{CH}\text{—} \quad \text{less stable than} \quad \text{—}CH_2\text{—}\underset{\underset{\displaystyle H}{|}}{CH}\text{—}$$

Furthermore, since hydrogen abstraction is the key reaction, the most stable polymers will be those which either have no hydrogen atoms or other labile groups (e.g. PTFE) or have hydrogen atoms which are relatively inert in methyl or phenyl groups (e.g. silicones). Antioxidants have removable hydrogens, usually in amine or phenol moieties. However, the resultant antioxidant radicals are relatively stable and propagation ceases.

It is often found in practice that a plot of the logarithm of material life against the reciprocal of the absolute temperature is linear. Some idealised Arrhenius plots have been illustrated in figure 3.9. However, it is unlikely that extrapolations can be readily justified, as the physical manifestation of degradation is often the result of many reactions of differing importance at high and low temperatures. For example, at low temperatures chain scission predominates in the degradation of polyethylene in the early stages with crosslinking predominating after long time periods. At higher temperatures crosslinking occurs from the start. Also, as oxygen is mainly taken up by the amorphous regions, the life of semicrystalline polymers such as polyethylene may be considerably increased below their melting points (about 100 °C). The diffusion of air through cables is relatively slow and for this reason ageing studies on materials should always be accompanied by studies on complete cables. Contact with incompatible materials may also affect ageing performance.

Table 3.6 Bond dissociation energies

R—H	Dissociation (kcal/mole)
CH_3—H	104
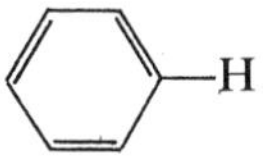	104
$CH_3CH_2CH_2$—H	98
$(CH_3)_2CH$—H	94
$(CH_3)_3C$—H	91
CH_2=CH—CH_2—H	85

In certain polymers other chemical reactions occur alongside those of chain scission and crosslinking outlined above. For example, PVC compounds evolve hydrogen chloride at high temperatures and, using time to first evolution as the failure criterion, Arrhenius plots can be constructed. In this type of polymer metallic compounds are often used as the chain terminators.

Polymers differ in their susceptibility to ultraviolet radiation. The problem is usually confined to a thin surface craze but cracks can propagate through the harder materials such as polypropylene. The addition of suitable carbon black provides adequate screening. The organic chromophore type of UV stabilizer is rarely used in cable sheathing.

Finally, one type of degradation, once common, has now almost disappeared. Cracking due to ozone is a common problem with NR as main chain scission occurs at the carbon–carbon double bonds which results in cracks under strain. The problem is much less severe with PCP and non-existent with CSP, EPR, butyl and the common thermoplastics.

REFERENCES

(1) Edwards, D. R. (Jan 1988) 'Supertension or superconducting cables. 20 years on – can the U.K. regain the lead'. *Proc. IEE, Part C* **135**(1), 9–23.
(2) British Patent 1 526 398.

Chapter 4

Conductors

Conductors are designed to conform to a range of nominal areas in graduated steps. These steps have been in three ranges:

(a) Until 1970 British procedure used imperial measure with units of square inches.
(b) Continental Europe used metric (mm^2) and this now also applies to British practice. In fact outside North and South America, and countries following their techniques, the rest of the world now adopts essentially common practices and standards based on IEC 228.
(c) American usage continues to be based on American Wire Gauge (AWG) up to 4/0, i.e. 107 mm^2, and larger sizes are in thousand circular mils (MCM). A 'mil' is 1/1000 inch and circular mils represent the area of an equivalent solid rod having a diameter expressed in mils.

It is important to bear in mind the connotation of 'nominal' as applied to the standard sizes because it is impracticable for manufacturers to produce conductors to precise areas. One factor is that in a stranded conductor the current flows essentially along the wires and as the outer wires are longer than the conductor, due to helical application of the wires, they have increased resistance. As a very large number of sizes of conductor have to be made it is uneconomic to produce special wire sizes for each conductor area and it is necessary to limit the total number of wire sizes handled. This always has to be taken into account in revision of conductor standards. Manufacturers, therefore, adjust their wire sizes and manufacturing processes to meet a specified maximum resistance rather than an area. For this purpose it is also necessary in specifications to allow manufacturers to choose the number of wires, within limits, for shaped and compacted conductors and for flexible conductors. The effective electrical areas are thus based on the maximum d.c. resistance and are slightly different from the nominal areas. The divergences are upwards and downwards on individual sizes and there is no regular pattern.

The overall system has evolved over many years with arbitrary rules. Until 1978 the IEC practice provided different maximum resistance values for single-core and multicore cables, thus allowing for the increased conductor length due to laying-up the cores. This has now changed, however, and a single maximum d.c. resistance is specified for each size of conductor of a given material. American specifications still adhere to the pattern of a 'nominal' resistance, together with a tolerance to provide a maximum resistance for single-core cable and a further tolerance for multicore cable. These tolerances also vary with conductor classification.

Table A4.1 in appendix A4 shows the standard conductor sizes for fixed wiring cables included in IEC 228 and the maximum resistances for three conductor materials.

These resistances also apply to the size range which is applicable for solid conductors, i.e. essentially 0.5–16 mm^2 for copper and 1.5–300 mm^2 for aluminium. Table A4.2 provides similar information for flexible conductors and applies to conductors having two classifications of flexibility, covered by the standard.

Table A4.3 indicates corresponding information for fixed wiring cables to a typical American specification. In trying to select cables which correspond between metric and American practice much care is necessary, however, and table A4.3 merely extracts data from one of three tables in the specification to which reference is made in the footnote. A column has been included with the heading 'equivalent metric area' and this is merely an arithmetic conversion from a 'nominal area'. As explained above the nominal area has no exactitude and in choosing corresponding sizes it is necessary to work from the specified maximum resistances.

Other points in the metric–American comparison are as follows:

(a) Table A4.3 caters only for stranded conductors and different resistances apply to solid conductors.
(b) There are many classifications of conductors in American practice, each with different standard resistances. Classes B, C and D cover power cables, C having more flexibility than B, and D still further flexibility. All three classes have 'concentric-lay' conductors (see later). Classes G, H, I, K, M cater for 'rope-lay' or 'bunch-stranded' flexible cords and cables with varying flexibility for particular applications. Table A4.3 is based on classes B to D and so illustrates only a small proportion of the total range.
(c) The tolerances between 'nominal' and 'maximum' resistances also vary with some types of conductors and cables.

For sizes up to 16 mm^2 and for higher voltages, where electrical stress at the conductor surface is important, the construction is circular. For the majority of multicore power cables up to 11 kV a sector shape is used (fig. 4.1) to keep the cable dimensions to a minimum. The corner radii are adjusted according to the cable voltage for reasons of electrical stress and influence on the dielectric during bending. A 'D' shape is frequently used for 2-core cables and an oval construction for 33 kV

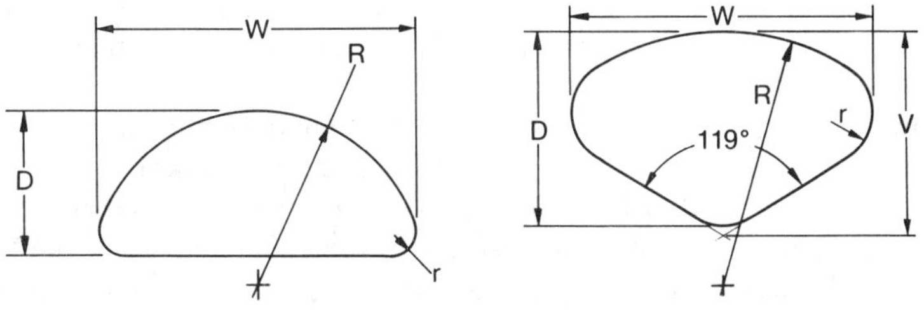

Fig. 4.1 Shapes for multicore power cables: W, width; D, depth; R, back radius; r, corner radius; V, V gauge depth

cables, the latter largely to provide better uniformity of frictional forces between layers of paper.

In this chapter the references to resistance are mainly concerned with d.c. resistance. The a.c. resistance is also very important in many applications and is covered in chapter 2.

INTERNATIONAL STANDARDISATION

British practice is based on BS 6360, 'Conductors in insulated cables', which now covers both copper and aluminium conductors. Until 1981, aluminium conductors were in BS 6791. The 1969 edition of BS 6360, which conformed to the version of IEC 228 current at the time, has now been revised to bring it into line with the 1978 edition of IEC 228 which introduced some modifications aimed at simplification of the total number of alternative groupings. As IEC 228 reflects practice throughout the world (outside the USA), it can be taken as a basis for comments.

IEC 228 covers conductors from 0.5 to 2000 mm^2 and specifies the maximum d.c. resistance values for insulated conductors and flexible cords generally but excluding pressurised transmission cables. Class 1 for solid conductors and Class 2 for stranded conductors both deal with single-core and multicore cables for fixed installations and define identical maximum resistance values for each size and type in copper, metal-coated copper and aluminium.

Class 3 and 4 of the previous editions have been deleted. Classes 5 and 6 cater for flexible copper and metal-coated copper conductors of two ranges of flexibility. The maximum resistances in the two classes are the same for each, but differ from those of conductors for fixed installations.

The wires used in stranded conductors are specified by designation of a minimum number of wires in the conductors for fixed installations. This minimum number is varied according to whether the conductor is circular (non-compacted), circular (compacted) or shaped. For circular non-compacted conductors all wires must be of the same diameter but a ratio of 2:1 is permitted for the other two types. For flexible conductors the control is by specification of the maximum diameter of the wires.

A new feature of the 1978 edition of IEC 228 was the inclusion of metal-coated aluminium, with the object of catering for copper-clad aluminium. Contrary to previous practice in British Standards, the resistance values have been made the same as for plain aluminium. The resistance values for aluminium conductors up to 10 mm^2 have also been changed to align them with the next smaller size of copper conductors.

From the fact that conductor resistances for single-core and multicore cables are the same, it may be considered that the resistances are now more arbitrary than previously (e.g. as outlined in BS 6360 in 1969). However, the change does not have any real significance. Originally the resistances were derived from the assumption that, for example in the case of stranded copper conductors, the wire had 100% International Annealed Copper Standard (IACS) conductivity and various factors were applied, e.g.

$$R = \frac{4A}{n\pi\, d^2} K_1\, K_2\, K_3 \qquad (4.1)$$

where R = conductor resistance at 20 °C (Ω/km)
A = volume resistivity at 20 °C (Ω mm^2/km)
n = number of wires in conductor
d = nominal diameter of wires in conductor (mm)

K_1, K_2 and K_3 are constants of specified values. K_1 varies with wire diameter and allows for tolerances on the nominal diameter and the effect of metal coating when appropriate. K_2 allows for the fact that in stranding the length of individual wires is longer than the length of the finished conductor. K_3 allows similarly for laying-up the cores in multicore cable.

When effects of actual wire conductivity and compacting were superimposed, the cablemaker still had to derive his own requirements for input wire diameter and number of wires and the allowances for K_1, K_2 and K_3 had limited practical significance in the published form.

The resistances of copper and aluminium vary significantly with temperature and measured values on cables need to be corrected to the specified values at 20 °C. At this temperature, the temperature coefficient of resistance per degree Celsius for copper is 0.00393 and for aluminium is 0.00403. For most purposes the value for each metal can be taken as 0.004 and table A4.4 (appendix A4) provides factors to convert to or from 20 °C over the range of 5–85 °C. More exact formulae for conversion of a measured conductor resistance to a basis of 20 °C and a length of 1000 m are as follows.

$$\text{Copper:} \quad R_{20} = R_t \frac{254.5}{234.5 + t} \frac{1000}{L} \ (\Omega/\text{km})$$

$$\text{Aluminium:} \quad R_{20} = R_t \frac{248}{228 + t} \frac{1000}{L} \ (\Omega/\text{km})$$

where t = conductor temperature (°C)
R_t = measured resistance (Ω/km)
L = cable length (m)
R_{20} = conductor resistance at 20 °C (Ω/km)

BRITISH STANDARDS

Whilst IEC 228 prescribes the basic essentials in terms of the finished resistance and control of the wire diameters used, British practice has always provided some additonal requirements. The full range of British Standards is included in chapter 7 and although, as already indicated, they were revised in 1981, the additional provisions compared with IEC 228 have continued:

(a) properties of the wire or material from which the conductor is made
(b) restrictions applicable to joints in individual wires and solid conductors
(c) control of the dimensions of shaped solid aluminium conductors so as to ensure compatibility with sleeves fitted for compression jointing.

Largely for the purpose of providing guidance to engineers involved in the preparation of standards for conductors, some further information on the principles of standardisation and the use of formula (4.1) was provided in a 1985 amendment to BS 6360. This refers to a 'conceptual' construction of conductors and provides more data on the sizes used in standards. These data comprise for non-compacted stranded conductors a number and nominal diameter of wires, nominal conductor diameters and weights. Stranded copper conductors for fixed installation and for flexible cables are included, together with plain aluminium stranded conductors for fixed installation. Further reference is also made to formula (4.1) and the values for the constants K_1, K_2 and K_3.

CONDUCTOR DIMENSIONS

When conventional practice for joining conductors and terminating them on appliances was by soldering for the larger conductors and use of pinch-screw type fitting for small conductors, no problems arose in relation to the tolerance between conductor and ferrule or tunnel diameter. However, with the introduction of compression and crimping techniques for straight ferrules and termination lugs, the clearance between conductor and fitting became important. Cases arose when conductors and fittings from one manufacturer were not compatible with those from another, e.g. the conductor was too large to enter the bore of the ferrule.

The problem was tackled nationally and internationally and the outcome was the issue in 1982 of a supplement (IEC 228A) to IEC 228 which provided what is termed a 'Guide to the dimensional limits of circular conductors'.

The 1985 amendment to BS 6360 covers all that is included in IEC 228A and additionally provides some helpful comments on shaped conductors. Nevertheless, it is still a guide to assist in ensuring that cable conductors and connectors fit together and does not cover specified requirements.

The tables included in the BS 6360 Amendment are reproduced in appendix A4, tables A4.5 and A4.6, and some further comments, largely relating to circular conductors, are printed under the tables. The Amendment also makes reference to shaped conductors in that BS 6360 has a cross-reference to BS 3988 which gives dimensional data for shaped solid aluminium conductors used in cables covered by British Standards. The data in BS 3988 apply to conductors for use in making the cables and not directly to conductors in the manufactured cables. However, the dimensions of the conductor envelope will not increase during cable manufacture and hence are a good guide for connectors to fit the conductors.

As shaped stranded copper and aluminium conductors are normally circularised before connection it is considered unnecessary to standardise dimensional limits for these conductors.

STRANDED CONDUCTORS

Conventional practice is illustrated in fig. 4.2(a) in which there is a centre wire and then concentric layers of nominally 6, 12, 18, 24, 30, 36 and 42 wires – hence the term 'concentric-lay' conductor often used in American terminology. Usually each layer is applied with alternate direction of lay as this provides the most stable construction with resistance to 'birdcaging'. For some special applications unidirectional lay may be used. Instead of one wire there may be three or four wires in the centre.

(a)

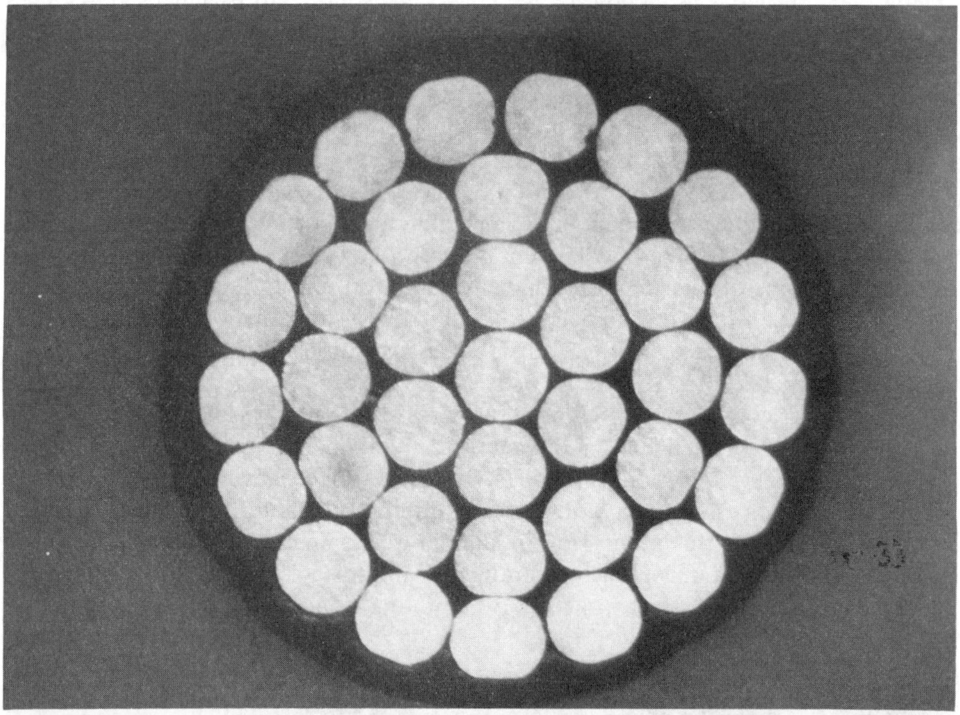

(b)

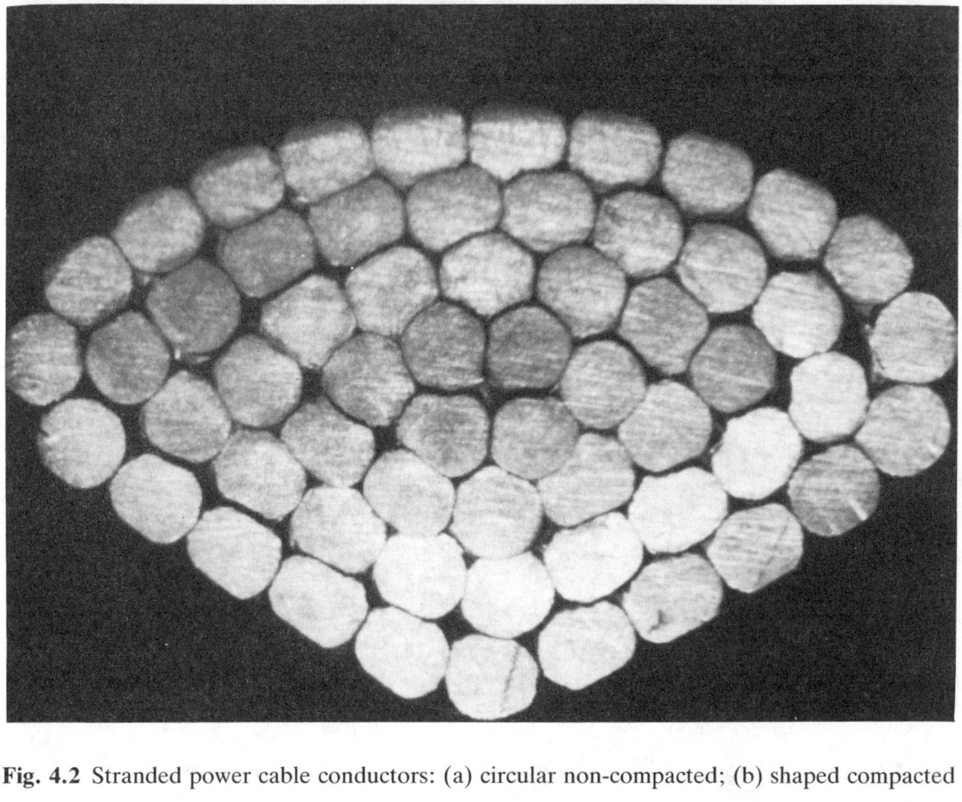

Fig. 4.2 Stranded power cable conductors: (a) circular non-compacted; (b) shaped compacted

However, it is more usual nowadays to pass such conductors through shaping rolls or pull them through a die to obtain some compacting (fig. 4.2(b)). This has the advantage of providing a smoother surface, reducing the overall size of the cable, and limiting the amount of impregnating compound present in paper insulated cables, which could contribute to flow and 'bleeding' problems. Sector conductors are basically stranded in the same way and the shape is obtained by passage through shaping rolls (fig. 4.3) preferably after application of each layer of wires. With copper conductors work hardening in compacting has to be kept to a minimum. This factor also limits the degree of compaction to a normal range of 85–90% (expressed against the volume of the circumscribing envelope). At higher degrees of compaction the extra copper required to meet the specified resistance may be greater in cost than the saving in material usage outside the insulation obtained by the reduced conductor diameter.

During compaction some stretching of the wires occurs and, because it is necessary to start with wires of somewhat larger diameter, the method of mathematical progression to be seen in fig. 4.2 no longer applies. It may even be advantageous to have a centre wire or even an outer layer of wires of different diameter from the remainder: hence the reason for this permission in standards. Compacted conductors normally have fewer wires than uncompacted conductors and this is one reason why manufacturers deprecate the former practice of denoting conductor sizes by their wire

Fig. 4.3 Rotating shaping and compacting rolls for power cable conductors

Fig. 4.4 Storage lanes for conductor wire on bobbins

formation, e.g. 37/1.78 mm. Nevertheless, as already mentioned, it is not practicable for manufacturers to use an ideal wire diameter for every single conductor and it is very important to keep the total number of wire sizes to a minimum. This applies particularly when there is a storage system for wire on bobbins. Fig. 4.4 shows an arrangement whereby drawn wire is automatically delivered by conveyor to a storage lane and similarly conveyed to a stranding machine as required. Fig. 4.5 illustrates the automatic loading onto the strander carriage.

The rolls used for shaping and compacting normally rotate around the conductor to impart a pre-spiral lay (fig. 4.6). This avoids the need to twist the cores when laying-up into the multicore form, thus providing a more stable construction with less possibility of damage to the insulation, both in manufacture and in subsequent bending.

Milliken conductors

With alternating current there is a tendency for more of the current to be carried on the outside of the conductor than in the centre (skin effect), and to overcome this problem the larger sizes of conductor are frequently of Milliken construction (fig. 4.7). Such conductors are formed from several individual sector shapes, usually four for power distribution cables and six for hollow-core OF cables. A thin layer of

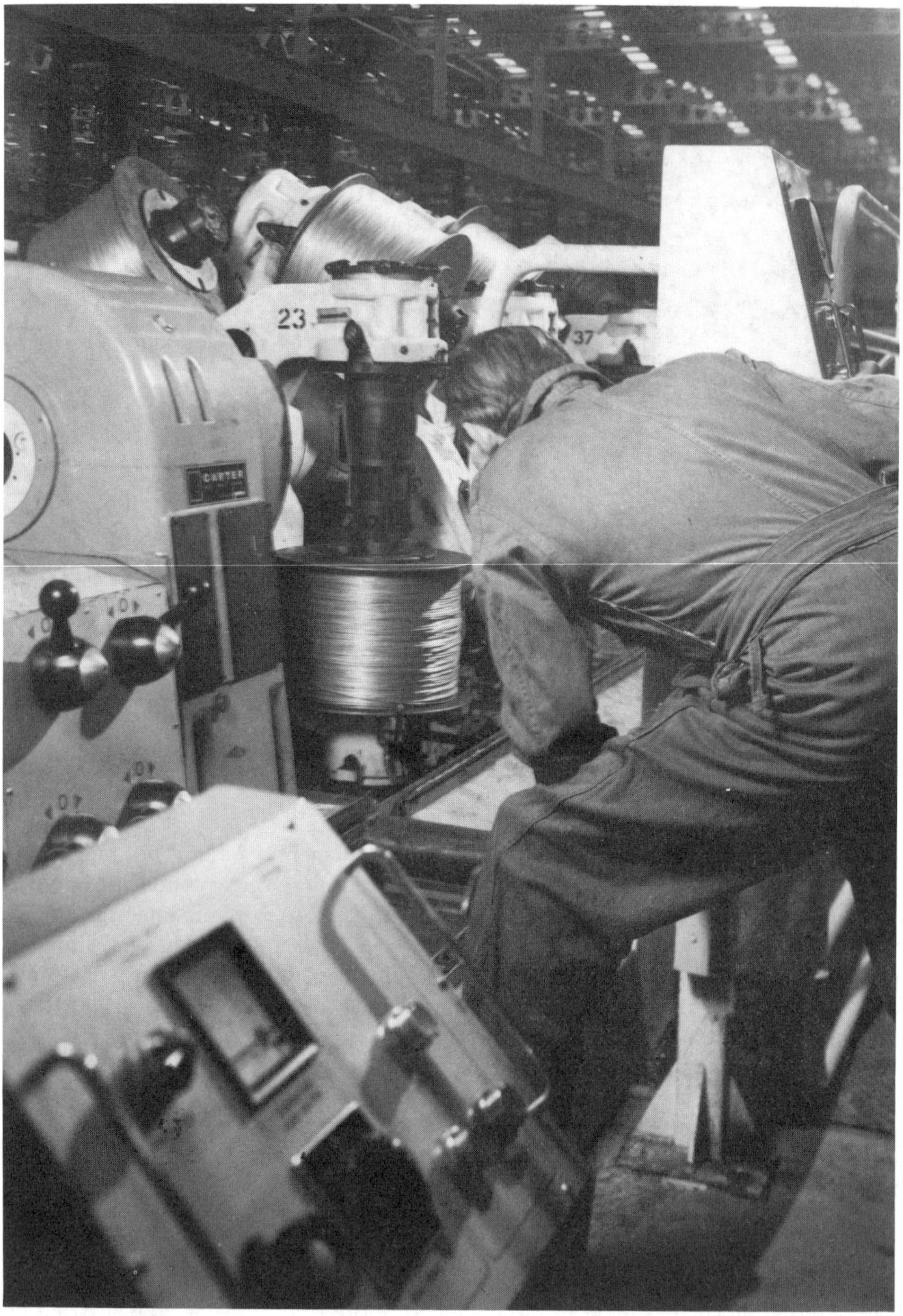

Fig. 4.5 Automatic loading of a bobbin of wire onto the head of a stranding machine

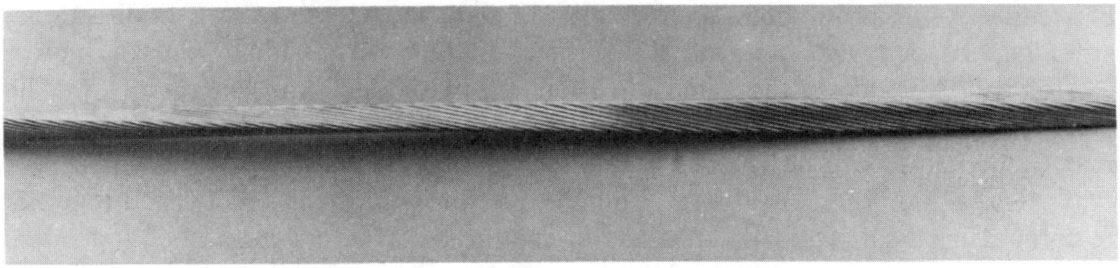

Fig. 4.6 Shaped conductor with pre-spiralled lay

Fig. 4.7 400 kV oil-filled cable with Milliken conductor

paper or other suitable insulation is applied over alternate sectors. There is insufficient economic advantage to use this construction below 900 mm^2 but the Milliken design may also be used to obtain increased conductor flexibility. In the USA such conductors are often termed 'segmental' construction.

FLEXIBLE CONDUCTORS

Flexibility may be achieved by stranding the conductors as described above and merely using a larger number of smaller diameter wires. The smaller the wire diameter for a conductor of given area, the greater is the flexibility, and hence the main specification requirement for flexibility is the maximum diameter of wire used. IEC 228 does not go beyond this but some specifications differ between concentric-lay and rope-lay or bunch-stranding.

Concentric-lay refers to the conventional stranding practice in which there is a single wire or a group of wires in the centre and then successive complete layers of wires are applied on each other. Normally the direction of application is reversed between layers but in some special cases it may be the same, i.e. unidirectional stranding. In bunched conductors the total number of individual wires is merely twisted together, all in the same direction and with the same length of lay. The position of any one wire with respect to any other is largely fortuitous. The construction may be used for both flexible cords and cables, typically with up to 56 wires.

There are limitations to the total number of wires which can be twisted together to form a single satisfactory bunch and so for the larger conductors small individual bunches are stranded together in layers, i.e. 'multiple bunch stranded'. It is common in cable conductors for the direction of lay in the bunch and in the layer to be the same and for unidirectional stranding to be used. American practice, however, is to reverse the direction of lay in alternate layers.

SOLID CONDUCTORS

Solid copper conductors are permitted up to 16 mm^2 in British Standards, but with the exception of mineral insulated cables are rarely used above 6 mm^2 because of reduced flexibility. IEC 228 caters for solid conductors up to 150 mm^2 for special applications.

The position is quite different with aluminium as used for power distribution cables. There is an economic advantage for using conductors having 100% compactness up to the maximum size which provides a cable which can be readily handled and also a technical advantage in that both soldering and compression jointing are easier and more reliable with the solid form. Solid conductors cause some increase in stiffness but this is not usually significant up to 185 mm^2 with paper insulation or 240 mm^2 with plastic insulation. In the case of paper insulated cables the use of shaped solid conductors is limited to 600/1000 V because no satisfactory way of prespiralling them has been found. Solid conductors may be circular or sector shaped up to 300 mm^2. For larger sizes of circular conductor the stiffness problem is overcome by the solid sectoral construction comprising four 90° sector shaped sections laid up together (fig. 4.8). There are six sizes between 380 and 1200 mm^2.

Fig. 4.8 PVC insulated 1 kV cable with solid sectoral aluminium conductor

The use of solid conductors, mostly of sector shape, has been extensive in the UK for 600/1000 V cables with paper and polymeric insulation, but less so throughout the rest of the world. For economic reasons the corner radii are relatively sharp. The German specification requires larger radii and this design is more suitable for 11 kV cables with XLPE insulation. Conductor shape is important because ferrules for compression fitting need to fit closely on the conductor and a current problem is to provide international cable standardisation.

CONDUCTORS FOR TRANSMISSION CABLES

Most of this chapter has been concerned with conductors for solid type cables. The special requirements for pressure cables are covered in part 4.

USE OF ALUMINIUM IN RELATION TO COPPER FOR DISTRIBUTION CABLES

Usage of aluminium has varied and still varies from country to country. After some fairly extensive initial use around 1910 in the UK there was quite wide-scale use in Germany in the 1930s and 1940s when copper was scarce, but it was abandoned after the Second World War because of jointing problems. Soldering and welding were the main techniques available until the mid-1950s and by this time soldering methods had been developed which, although entirely satisfactory, required a little more care and skill than for copper. Such skills presented no problem to large users such as UK Electricity Boards, and having rationalised on aluminium in the early 1960s they have remained with it for virtually all their cables, other than small sizes of the house-service type. The relative prices of copper and aluminium frequently vary but over many years copper cables have rarely been cheaper than aluminium. Much, of course, depends on cable type and size and the nature of the complete installation.

For industrial applications the position is similar in that large users have been better able to deal with the different circumstances arising and have adopted solid aluminium conductor cable with PVC insulation. But as the cost of joints and terminations tend to be higher than for copper cables and there are more of them in relation to cable length, small industrial users have tended to stay with copper. Space availability in terminal boxes or motors and distribution boards has also been a factor: more space is required to deal with solid aluminium conductors and it is necessary to stipulate the use of aluminium when ordering the equipment. BS 5372: 1976, 'Cable terminations for electrical equipment', was issued in an attempt to provide guidance in this respect. Many other detailed points arise such as making alternative or appropriate arrangements for dealing with pinch-screw fittings and, whilst all can be dealt with satisfactorily, it is only economic to devote the extra effort when large-scale installations are involved.

Following the successful experience in public supply systems in the UK, similar usage of aluminium became the general practice throughout Europe and today aluminium is predominant in the USA and throughout much of the world. A notable contribution to this has been the development of compression jointing instead of soldering. For industrial applications, however, comparatively little aluminium is now used and the cost incentive is not as strong as it was in the 1960s.

COPPER-CLAD ALUMINIUM CONDUCTORS

Large-scale attempts have been made in the USA, and also more particularly in India, to use aluminium conductors in general house wiring type systems. Owing to overheating in accessories having pinch-screw type connections, the results were unsatisfactory and much of the cable had to be replaced to avoid excessive maintenance cost.

Copper-clad aluminium conductors were developed mainly to overcome these problems but they have had only very limited service. They were introduced in the UK in 1970 for single-wire 1.5 mm^2 and stranded conductors from 4 mm^2 to 10 mm^2. At the time there was a cost advantage compared with copper but this subsequently diminished and they have since been withdrawn. Operational experience was satisfactory, the main disadvantage being that the increase in size over a copper cable of equal rating caused conduit occupancy to be reduced.

For power cables there is no justification for increase in conductor cost to obtain more satisfactory jointing. Another factor with stranded conductors of the larger sizes is that with the conventional plant used for stranding there is a possible danger of local damage to the copper surface and any exposure of aluminium could lead to corrosion due to the bimetallic effect.

SODIUM CONDUCTORS

Because of the low density and price of sodium, coupled with its reasonable conductivity of 35% IACS, interest developed in the early years of cable making and patents were first filed in 1905. It was not until the 1960s, however, that experimental cables were made in the UK and the USA. The significant aspect was that by then polyethylene had been developed for insulation and a convenient way to use sodium as a conductor was to inject it into a polyethylene tube at the same time as the tube was being extruded, i.e. to make a complete cable core in one operation from basic raw materials. In the USA a considerable amount of cable was put into service to obtain operating experience.

Table 4.1 indicates some of the relevant data which were applicable in the UK in the 1960s.

Table 4.1 Comparative data on conductor metals (sodium taken as 100)

	Sodium	Aluminium	Copper
Price/unit weight	100	132	246
Density	100	280	910
Weight/unit resistance	100	160	300
Cost/unit resistance	100	200	750
Diameter/unit resistance	100	74	57

The figures show that, whilst the cost of conductor metal was comparatively cheap, there was a much larger penalty than with aluminium in terms of conductor diameter. Nevertheless, for fairly simple cables, especially single-core cables, popular in the USA, there appeared to be a strong economic case. Even for 15 kV cables it was only necessary to apply some copper wires outside the insulation to obtain URD cable comparable with the design with copper conductors.

No great difficulty was found in producing the cables. Joints and terminations could also readily be made by sealing a cap onto the cables and fitting a corkscrew arrangement into the conductor to achieve good electrical contact. The performance under service conditions was quite satisfactory provided that suitable protection was used to cater for the low melting point of sodium (98 °C). Tests showed that short circuits to higher cable temperature could be sustained without dangerous effect.

However, sodium is an extremely reactive metal and when exposed to water it reacts vigorously with the formation of caustic soda. Whilst such action was not catastrophic, even if a cable was cut when immersed in water, there were obvious handling problems for cable installation and jointing personnel. Disposal of cut ends required special care and attention and difficulties arose in making repairs to damaged cable. Largely for these reasons it became apparent that in comparison with aluminium the handling difficulties exceeded what could be justified by the saving in the initial cost of cable. The use of sodium subsequently lapsed but there is a view that interest may well redevelop.[1]

SUPERCONDUCTORS

The subject of superconductivity is becoming of growing importance in many fields because there are potential economic advantages in relation to reduction of conductor size due to increased conductivity at very low temperatures. The only possible cable applications so far identified have been for very high rating transmission cables. There is little doubt that technical and engineering success could be achieved but economic viability seems related to the distant rather than the near future. Further details are given in chapters 3 and 43.

REFERENCE

(1) Graneau, P. (1979) *Underground Power Transmission*. New York: Wiley.

Chapter 5

Armour and Protective Finishes

ARMOUR

This chapter applies mainly to power distribution cables, certainly in relation to armour, as special considerations apply to wiring type cables and to transmission cables. Features relating to the design of both these groups of cables are given with the design aspects in the relevant chapters.

For lead sheathed paper insulated cables, the two universal types of armour are steel tape (STA) and galvanised steel wire (GSW), usually referred to as single wire armour (SWA). Steel tapes are applied over a cushion of bituminised textile materials which also contribute to corrosion protection. Two tapes are applied helically, each tape having a gap between turns of up to half the width of the tape and the second tape covering the gap and overlapping the edges of the first tape. By applying the two tapes from the same taping head of the armouring machine the lay length of each tape is identical and the tapes register correctly with each other. Although the tapes and the underlying bedding are flooded with bitumen during application the tapes are pre-coated by the supplier with a bitumen varnish to prevent rusting during delivery and storage and to ensure that the underside of the tape is always coated.

Although bitumen provides reasonably good protection of steel in many soils, it has to be remembered that a cable life of 40–50 years is not unusual and in some conditions severe corrosion of the steel may occur after long periods of burial. Before the introduction of extruded plastic layers for protective finishes, some cable users called for the much more expensive galvanised steel tape. This material is seldom adopted now but may still be valuable in special cases, e.g. where the metallic protection is of particular importance on polymeric insulated cables and it is not desirable to use bitumen under an extruded thermoplastic oversheath (see later).

Other users have taken the view that mechanical protection of buried cables is primarily of value during the early years in the life of the cable, e.g. in the development of the site for housing or industrial purposes. After a few years the ground is more rarely disturbed and this has been shown by fault statistics.

Wire armour consists of a layer of galvanised steel wires applied with a fairly long lay. It is more expensive than STA but has several advantages such as (a) better corrosion protection and hence longer armour life, (b) greatly increased longitudinal reinforcement of the cable, (c) avoidance of problems due to armour displacement which can occur under difficult laying conditions and (d) better compatibility with extruded thermoplastic oversheathing layers, as discussed later. It may be argued that SWA is not so resistant to sharp spikes which may pierce between armour wires but in practice it appears that such damage seldom occurs.

The longitudinal reinforcement aspect covers such advantages as the ability to withstand higher pulling loads, e.g. for cables drawn into ducts, and better support of cable in cleats or hangers, particularly if vertical runs are involved. SWA is essential for cables to be laid in ground liable to subsidence.

A further, often important, feature of armour design is to provide effective conductance of earth fault currents. If the cable has a lead sheath, the sheath alone is adequate in most cases; steel tape armour does nothing to extend the sheath current carrying capacity. In the absence of a lead sheath, as with PVC and XLPE insulated cables, it is generally desirable or necessary to use wire armour to deal with fault currents.

Before the 1970s in the UK, when PILS cables were invariably used for power distribution, it was common practice for 600/1000 V cables to have STA and the more important higher voltage cables to have SWA. Central London was an exception, because with a preponderance of installations of cables in ducts, SWA was preferred. The armour was usually left bare. Outside London the two different types of armour provided a good guide during digging operations to indicate whether any cables exposed were low or high voltage. When the PILS design disappeared it was necessary to take other steps for easy cable identification and the supply authorities standardised on a red PVC oversheath for 11–33 kV cables.

Wire armour normally comprises a single layer of wires but there are a few special applications where a double layer (DWA) is preferred to provide increased robustness. The main field is for cables in coal mines, not only for the in-coming supply cables which need to be self-supporting in the primary vertical pit shafts but also for cables which are laid along roadways. At one time all the roadway cables had DWA but this caused increased rigidity, which was a problem in coiling the cables for transport down the lift shafts. It is now often considered that SWA is adequate for fixed cables in tunnels. DWA comprises two layers of wires, with opposite directions of lay and a separator layer such as bituminised hessian tape applied between the wire layers.

Single-core cables

A problem arises with single-core cables because in their installation formation the armour is situated between the conductors and if a magnetic material is used it causes high induced currents in the armour. These result in high electrical losses. Consequently if armour is essential it is necessary to use a non-magnetic material such as aluminium. However, few single-core cables are buried directly in the ground and as the main application is for short interconnectors armour is not usually essential.

Armour conductance

Technical details of the importance of armour conductance with particular reference to wiring cables are discussed in chapter 10, and armour conductance requirements for colliery cables are detailed in chapter 19.

Armouring for polymeric insulated cables

The lower voltage (i.e. up to 3.3 kV) PVC or XLPE cables which have replaced PILS cables require mechanical protection of a similar standard. For various reasons, such as ease of cable handling and armour conductance, SWA is normally used. Such cables usually have an extruded PVC oversheath (other extruded materials are used for cables to meet certain performance requirements in fires – see chapter 6), and particularly from overseas there are users who express a preference for steel tape armour. Whilst PVC can certainly be applied over STA, and much such cable is supplied, it is more satisfactory to apply the PVC over the smooth surface provided by SWA. In extruding over the stepped surface of STA there is a tendency for thinning of the PVC to occur at the edges of the steel tape.

Nowadays a significant proportion of cables for 11 kV and upwards has XLPE insulation instead of paper and metallic sheath and it is mandatory for such cables to have an earthed screen over each core and/or collectively over the laid-up cores. SWA can serve quite well as the metallic component of the earthed screen and it has the advantage of providing good earth fault current carrying capacity. As discussed in chapter 25 a common cable design is to have an extruded PVC bedding followed by SWA and PVC oversheath. Some users overseas adopt STA and deal with earth fault currents by a thin metallic tape on each core. Tape thickness is restricted by the need to maintain intimate contact with the core surface, and some caution is necessary with such design as fault current carrying capacity is necessarily limited.

Nevertheless, with polymeric insulated HV cables, there is a greater tendency to use single-core cables, rather than multicore, and for these it is not practicable to use SWA. Furthermore, as there is no lead sheath, protection against mechanical damage and penetration of water may be of lesser importance than with PILS cables and so there is less need for increased robustness, especially as the whole cable design is more resilient. A frequently used cable design is therefore to replace armour by a layer of copper wires spaced apart round the cable (chapter 25). Nevertheless, with such cables, and for HV polymeric insulated cables generally, the design of protective finish has to take account not just of corrosion protection but also of the effects of water penetration on the electrical properties of the insulation ('water treeing' – see chapter 25).

PROTECTIVE FINISHES

Protective finishes are of particular interest for the protection of metal sheaths, reinforcement and armour in buried distribution and transmission cables. Whether the installation is below or above ground, very few cables are supplied without a protective finish. For the newer designs of the above categories of cable, an oversheath of extruded PVC has become nearly universal.

When wiring type cables need to be of robust construction, the cable design normally comprises an extruded oversheath, but one important difference is that this oversheath can be of a tougher thermoset material such as PCP, CSP or NBR/PVC. These materials are also used where special properties are required, e.g. for oil resisting and flame retardant (OFR) finishes and heat and oil resisting and flame retardant (HOFR) finishes as discussed in chapter 3. Such materials could have advantages for distribution and transmission cables but they can rarely be adopted because the high temperature required by most methods of curing would cause damage to the cable.

A special situation arises when the protective finish both has to be flame retardant and has to emit a minimum of toxic fumes and smoke in a fire. This is covered in chapter 6.

The UK attitude for distribution cables has always been that after burial the user expects to forget about them for the rest of their life, and with paper insulated cables life expectancy has steadily been extended to over 40 years. In spite of the generally good corrosion resistance of metals like lead and copper they can fail when buried in some types of ground, and in the UK such metals have rarely been left bare. Much attention has been paid to corrosion protection, and cable failures due to this cause have been rare. In the USA the practice has been somewhat different and in the case of cables having a copper concentric neutral conductor, it is not unusual to install cables without protection. Recent literature has reported a substantial level of cable failures and, although it is relatively easy with a duct system to replace the cable, the economics of savings against subsequent expenditure would seem to be finely balanced.

The protection of aluminium against corrosion is of particular importance because aluminium may corrode very quickly when buried, or even when near the surface and exposed to damp conditions, e.g. where cables descend from cabinets into the ground. At these positions, it is most important to apply protection over exposed metal right up to and over the termination.

The corrosion of aluminium usually takes the form of local pits which may quickly penetrate a sheath, although general surface attack may be quite small. The mechanism of pitting is associated with the local breakdown of the protective oxide film, in conditions which do not allow its repair, followed by cell action due to differential conditions of electrolyte concentrations or of aeration. The presence of other underground services containing metals anodic to aluminium, such as lead, steel or copper, may accelerate the attack. While some soils, such as in made-up ground, are worse than others, it is always essential to consider that any ground is aggressive and to ensure that good protection exists. Protection is also necessary for above ground installation because in damp conditions corrosion can occur in crevices, owing to differential aeration conditions, and it is difficult to avoid crevice conditions at points of support or in contact with walls.

It is convenient to review protective finishes in two categories: first, the bitumen – textile type used traditionally with lead sheathed paper cables, and second the extruded thermoplastic oversheaths which were first developed to provide satisfactory corrosion protection for aluminium sheathed cables and were then adopted for all newer cable designs as well as for paper/lead cables when improved protection was desirable. For armoured cables, the protective finish comprises a bedding under the armour and a layer over the armour, usually termed a serving when textile and an oversheath when it is extruded.

BITUMINOUS FINISHES

Constructions

The earliest paper/lead cables at the end of the last century were protected with coal tar pitch and fibrous textile materials such as cotton and jute in yarn or woven form, i.e. hessian. The basic design has changed little over the years but the once popular jute yarn roving has largely given way to woven hessian. Replacement of coal tars by bitumens provided better uniformity and enabled particular grades to be used according to their function within the construction. The introduction of two impregnated paper tapes adjacent to the lead sheath was also beneficial. For many years stray direct currents from tramway systems caused corrosion problems with underground cables due to electrolytic effects. The combination of impregnated paper and bitumen improved the consistency of the protective layer.

For armoured cables, the most common construction today is for the bedding to consist of two bituminised paper tapes plus two bituminised cotton or hessian tapes with a serving of two bituminised hessian tapes. A suitable grade of bitumen is applied over each layer and a coating of limewash is given overall to stop rings sticking together on the drum.

Bitumen

A thick layer of bitumen would give excellent corrosion protection, as it does on rigid steel underground pipes, but no method has been found of producing such a layer to withstand the bending and other conditions necessary with cable. Many grades of bitumen are available, with a wide range of viscosities and pliability. Careful selection has to be made to suit the requirement for impregnating the textiles of the particular layer in the cable and to suit the subsequent service conditions, bearing in mind that some cables have to operate in the tropics whilst others may be in polar regions. On the whole the bitumen should be as hard and rubbery as possible, but must not crack when bent at low temperatures. If the viscosity is too low, troublesome 'bleeding' may ensue at high ambient temperatures. Generally a resinous coal tar pitch is applied as a coating over the lead at the time of extrusion with residual bitumens of penetration 20–200 within the bedding and armour and blown, i.e. oxidised, bitumens over the outer layers. The general principle is to use the softer bitumens on the inside, with grading to harder bitumens on the outside. Blown bitumens have rubber-like characteristics, and whilst flowing less than residual bitumens they are also less brittle at low temperatures.

Microbiological degradation of textiles

The jute or other textiles in the finish are present largely to support the bitumen and even if they are partially rotted the bitumen layer continues to give a reasonable measure of protection. In tropical countries such rotting can develop very quickly, even to a serious extent on drums held in a stockyard for a year or so. In such areas it also became established that there was an unusually high incidence of chemical attack on lead sheathing. The attack was similar to that which had been found on old cables where coal tar products had been used. It was thought to have been associated with phenolic compounds and was termed 'phenol corrosion'. It was later established, however, that much of this type of corrosion was caused by the acidic degradation products of jute and other cellulosic constituents, namely acetic and butyric acids.

The immediate solution was to substitute PVC tapes for the paper tapes adjacent to the lead sheath, so as to create a barrier. Rot proofing of hessian, by the incorporation of a material such as zinc naphthenate, has also been popular for cables in tropical countries. In later years, however, it was realised that a much better solution was to use extruded PVC instead of bitumen–textile finishes.

Alternative materials to textiles

Much work has been done to try to find an alternative to jute, largely because occasions have arisen when it has been in short supply. Cotton is expensive and indeed this has proved to apply to all other substitutes. Fibreglass is mechanically weak unless used in woven form. However, quite satisfactory bituminised finishes can be produced using such materials as creped paper or woven fibrillated polypropylene of the type which has now largely replaced hessian for carpet backing. The main problem with all these materials is to obtain sufficient bulk and bitumen content at an economic price.

Improvements to bituminous finishes

Before the advent of extruded thermoplastic materials much development effort was expended on improved protection for expensive high voltage cables. One of the problems is the wick action caused by textiles and an early improvement was 'Packer protection'. This used a helically applied layer of ebonite strings 6 mm in diameter instead of jute.

Subsequently, rubber in tape form was introduced and a series of finishes known as 'rubber bitumen sandwich' was developed. To express the make-up it is convenient to use a shorthand notation in which C denotes cotton, R rubber, H hessian and Q PVC tape, with numerals indicating the number of tapes. The initial form was $RCRCH_2$ in which the rubber was soft and unvulcanised. It was later found possible to apply the two rubber tapes together, with sulphur in one and accelerator in the other, so that after application they formed a homogeneous self-vulcanising layer, i.e. CR_2CH_2. Finally a very good finish was developed by calendering the rubber onto PVC and then, with a special de-lining head at the taping machine, separating the PVC to form individual layers under and over the rubber, i.e. QR_2QH_2. As an alternative to the use of 'self-vulcanising' rubber tapes, another process was to apply suitably compounded rubber tapes individually and to obtain the vulcanisation by passage through a bath of hot bitumen. Whilst such finishes represented a major improvement and were very successful in service, they are inferior to extruded PVC, largely because the rubber thickness is less than is desirable and sharp flints can become entrapped in the outer hessian. A quite elaborate testing system was devised to check the performance of the rubber sandwich systems both on the finished cable and after laying. This is discussed later.

EXTRUDED THERMOPLASTIC FINISHES

PVC oversheaths

Following many years successful use on wiring cables, PVC was established as an oversheath for power distribution and transmission cables in the mid-1950s and since then PVC sheaths have become the most commonly used type of protective finish for power cables.

Grade of material

For wiring cables, flexibility and easy sheath removal are important and the grade of PVC used for sheathing is softer than that used for insulation. However, for the heavier power cables different criteria apply. Toughness and resistance to deformation both during and after installation are of greater significance and it is usual to use a similar grade of material to that used for insulation. For most purposes oversheaths are black, in order to give good resistance to sunlight, but where this is not important colours may be adopted as a means of cable identification. When red sheaths were first used for buried cables some darkening of colour occurred due to sulphides in the ground and special compositions were found to be necessary.

Whilst the amount of plasticiser in the PVC may theoretically be varied to suit a wide range of high and low ambient temperature conditions, the practical advantages are limited because of other aspects such as the resistance to deformation previously mentioned. This is of particular significance when low temperatures are encountered because at around 0 °C PVC becomes somewhat brittle and may crack either by a sudden blow or by rapid bending during handling operations. For this reason it is important not to install cables at low temperatures.

Construction

When applied over any type of cable, extruded PVC provides a clean finish which is attractive and contributes to ease of handling. Whilst the external profile is smooth if the application is over a normal metal sheath or wire armour, this is not the case with corrugated aluminium sheaths or steel tape armour. Extrusion is by the 'tubing-on technique' (chapter 25) and the external profile follows the contour of the underlying surface, thus creating small steps over steel tape armour. In the case of corrugated sheaths the oversheath tends to be slightly thicker in the troughs.

Initially, when PVC oversheaths were first applied over steel wire armour, no change was made in the use of bitumen, i.e. the oversheath was extruded directly over armour which was flooded with bitumen. Such cables are frequently installed vertically in factories. When bitumen is in contact with PVC it absorbs some plasticiser from the PVC. Whilst the amount of loss is insufficient to have much effect on the properties of the PVC, it is enough to cause considerable reduction in the viscosity of the bitumen. In fact, the bitumen may become so fluid that it can run out of the cable at terminations situated below the cable run. Subsequent practice has therefore been to omit bitumen between wire armour and PVC unless a preference for inclusion is expressed by the user. A particular example is the use of bitumen in the single or double wire armoured PVC insulated cables used underground by British Coal. The cables are usually installed horizontally and as the oversheaths may be damaged it is useful to have the benefit of bitumen as secondary protection. Similarly, in the UK, bitumen is normally applied over steel tape armoured cables, as these are invariably buried. It is not so necessary and normally not used over galvanised steel tape.

When PVC is applied directly over aluminium sheaths it is particularly desirable to have a uniform coating of bitumen on the aluminium to provide an interface seal and mitigate against spread of corrosion resulting from damage to the PVC. At one time it was a practice to include a small amount of a sparingly soluble chromate in the bitumen to serve as a corrosion inhibitor but, whilst this was undoubtedly beneficial, it is no longer used because of possible toxic effects. With corrugated sheaths the tendency is for an excess of bitumen to remain in the troughs and the corrugation effect is less visually apparent on the finished cable. Some German manufacturers aim at complete filling of the troughs on such cables and also apply a layer of a thin plastic tape to assist in maintaining a thick bitumen layer.

Characteristics of PVC

In combination with a good measure of flame retardance, and resistance to oils and chemicals, PVC contributes much to robustness and ease of handling. Very few chemicals normally found in the ground on cable routes have significant effect on PVC. Investigations have been carried out to determine whether any substances found in chemical factories and oil refineries are particularly aggressive to PVC. It was found that the only chemicals which caused attack were high concentrations of chlorinated solvents, esters, ketones, phenols, nitro compounds, cyclic ethers, aromatic amino compounds, pyridine, acetic anhydride and acetic acid. Except for perhaps occasional splashes, it is unlikely that such materials will be in contact with cables. Prolonged immersion in oils and creosote may cause swelling and softening but there is usually considerable recovery when the source is removed.

Loss of plasticiser from PVC to other materials in contact with cables may cause some problems with wiring type cables. One example of this relates to cables in roof spaces where polystyrene granules have been used for thermal insulation over ceilings. The granules in contact with the oversheath may become soft and tacky due to leaching of plasticiser from the PVC, which itself will lose some flexibility. Direct contact between the granules and cables should be avoided. Similar remarks apply to some fittings which are in contact with cables. In addition to polystyrene and expanded polystyrene, acrylonitrile–butadiene–styrene (ABS), polyphenol oxide and polycarbonate are also affected. Nylon, polyester, polyethylene, polypropylene, rigid PVC and most thermosetting plastics are little affected. Natural rubber grommets can become softened but synthetic rubber and PVC grommets are satisfactory.

With the greater thickness of oversheath on distribution and transmission cables the rate of loss of plasticiser from the body of the oversheath is much slower and in any case subsequent disturbance by bending is unlikely. Although the PVC becomes somewhat harder as plasticiser is removed, the properties of permeability to moisture and protection against corrosion are not impaired.

A special situation arises when PVC oversheathed cables are in ground which may contain hydrocarbons such as petrol. This can happen in oil refineries as a result of spillage. Although only a small amount of hydrocarbon is absorbed by the PVC, such materials can diffuse through the sheath and be taken up by materials inside, or condense in any air spaces available. The PVC itself is unaffected, except for some loss of plasticiser. However, the petrol may then flow along the cable and run out of joints and terminations. For such conditions it is general practice, therefore, for cables to have a lead sheath, even if the insulation is of PVC. By sealing the lead sheath to the equipment, no hydrocarbon will flow into the equipment. Flow will still take place along the armour, and if it is important that no leakage should occur at the armour termination this may also need to be specially sealed.

Polyethylene oversheaths

Although from the outset PVC became the established material in the UK for power cables, polyethylene has tended to be preferred in the USA and also throughout the world for telephone cables. Most of what has been stated for PVC applies equally to polyethylene but, whereas PVC has to be compounded with plasticisers and fillers etc., the only additions normally made to polyethylene are antioxidant and carbon black. Problems due to such aspects as loss of plasticiser do not arise. Furthermore, polyethylene does not suffer from effects of brittleness at low temperatures and so has a particular advantage for installation in countries where sub-zero temperatures exist for long periods. Polyethylene sheaths have to contain carbon black and this prevents their use when coloured sheaths are required.

On balance the overall advantages and disadvantages of the two materials are marginal and it is more economic for manufacturers to standardise on one material. Polyethylene is flammable and this is one of the main reasons for the preference for PVC. Another is that resistance to thermal deformation is an important characteristic for distribution cables. Whilst polyethylene may be marginally better for temperatures within the normal continuous operating range, it softens more than PVC above 80 °C, and at 130 °C it flows readily under mechanical load.

Many grades of polyethylene are available and for oversheaths it is necessary to select one which has good resistance to environmental stress cracking.

High density polyethylene oversheaths

Frequent references have been made in this chapter to the importance of damage to extruded oversheaths due to mechanical deformation. Because of the susceptibility of aluminium to corrosion, this is a matter of particular importance with heavy and expensive aluminium sheathed transmission cables. Damage to the oversheath may occur, for example, through the presence of sharp stones in the cable trench, especially when cables are being installed at high ambient temperatures in tropical conditions. To ensure freedom from damage an electrical test is carried out on the oversheath after laying and in bad conditions much time may be spent in locating and repairing faults. In general a material which is tougher than PVC or polyethylene would be desirable.

High density polyethylene (HDPE) is such a material and it is frequently used for transmission cables. It is extremely hard and difficult to damage even with a sharp spade thrown directly at the cable. It is particularly advantageous for conditions involving high ambient temperatures, e.g. in tropical and subtropical countries where, at the time of laying, PVC is much softer than it is in the UK. However, it is not suitable for universal adoption as an alternative to PVC because its very rigidity causes a penalty due to increased cable stiffness. This is not a serious disadvantage with transmission cables because the proportionate increase in stiffness is only modest and bending to small radii is not required.

HDPE oversheaths cost a little more than PVC oversheaths and this is also a factor which has restricted its use on the less expensive types of cable. Even more care has to be taken in grade selection than with PE to ensure good resistance to cracking in some environments.

A further feature which may add marginally to overall cost is that, because of the enhanced coefficient of expansion and rigidity, it is important for the oversheath to be secured rigidly at joints and terminations; otherwise retraction may occur on cooling and the metal sheath could be left exposed. No difficulties in this respect arise with OF cables because it is fairly standard practice for sheath plumbs to be reinforced by resin and glass fibre and the oversheath is readily included in the arrangement.

Although not important with the majority of oversheathing applications, another feature of HDPE is that it is notch sensitive. Cracking may occur if there is a sudden change of section due, for example, to steps in the surface on which the oversheath is applied.

FINISHES FOR PROTECTION AGAINST INSECTS

Although instances have arisen of damage caused to cables and cable drums by various insects and by gnawing from rodents, the most common form of attack is from ants, termites and teredos.

Protection against ants and termites

Termites are essentially subterranean in habit and exist only in tropical and sub-tropical regions up to 40° on each side of the equator. Most reports of damage to cables have come from Malaysia and Australia. Termites feed on cellulose, generally from wood, and attack on cables is not for food but because their path is obstructed. They have hard saw-tooth jaws capable of tearing through a soft metal such as lead but harder metals and even hard plastics are resistant.

Ants are much more common but again problems with cables are confined to warmer climates. They exist on the ground surface but may extend underground to a depth of about 120 mm in loose sandy soils. They are more readily controlled by treatment of the ground with insecticides.

Measures required for protective finishes are the same for both ants and termites, and in the areas concerned the problems arising have probably been more with telephone cables than with power cables. With modern cable constructions there are some differences which have an effect on recommended practices.

The most common advice has always been to incorporate a layer of metal in the finish, e.g. thin bronze tapes. With bituminous finishes, steel tape armour is fairly effective as gaps between the tapes are seldom large enough to allow penetration. Similarly any gaps between wire in SWA finish are usually small.

For an improved finish of bituminous type it was once a practice to incorporate a poison of arsenious oxide type but although the insects were killed others would still follow. A better solution was to mix a contact insecticide of chlorinated hydrocarbon type with the bitumen, e.g. DDT, BHC or gammaxene. However, these materials have a comparatively high vapour pressure and consequently a limited life compared with the expected cable life. Alternative materials of similar type such as aldrin and dieldrin are much more effective, especially in combination. Aldrin, being more volatile, has value in the early years and dieldrin lasts longer. However, toxicity problems on an overall environmental scale and also in relation to material availability and handling have raised complications in the use of such materials. Furthermore, the extended use of extruded plastic oversheaths has changed the problem to one of preventing damage to materials like PVC and polyethylene. A metal layer under the plastic oversheath does not then provide a solution in many cases.

Incorporation of aldrin and/or dieldrin into PVC has been proved to be very effective, and for many years a common practice by UK manufacturers has been to use 0.25% of each. The addition is made at the time of oversheathing by feeding a small quantity of a concentrated masterbatch into the main PVC flow. Only simple hygiene precautions are required by cable manufacturers and users and the only difficult area is in the production of the masterbatch. Possibly in the future it will become unavailable. With polyethylene, however, which is usually the preferred choice for telephone cables, an additional problem is that aldrin and dieldrin bloom to the surface, thus being less long lasting and creating additional handling problems. For these reasons, other solutions had to be found for such cables.

In Australia a commonly used construction has been to extrude a thin nylon skin over the main oversheath but, apart from cost, an objection to this for universal application is that it is less easy to apply the nylon on the heavier power cables. More recent research has shown that plastics with a hardness exceeding D48 on the Shore scale are also resistant. High density polyethylene is in this category and is now frequently used, especially for transmission cables. Much work has been done on special fillers for PVC, e.g. fibreglass, but the results of laboratory tests to date have not been particularly encouraging.

Protection against teredos

Teredos are a form of marine life existing in relatively shallow sea-water near to land. They were often called ship-worms because of the attack on the hulks of wooden sailing ships. The shore ends of submarine cables usually have to be protected and the standard method is to include a layer of tin–bronze tapes in the protective finish. Adequate protection under and over this layer has to be considered according to the other circumstances arising.

BRAIDED FINISHES

Braided finishes used to be popular before extruded finishes came into general use. Because of the slow manufacturing process, however, they were expensive and could only be justified when there was a need for improved abrasion resistance. For power cables, hessian, cotton and asbestos braids were superseded by extruded PVC and the special formulations for flame retardance discussed in chapter 6. Health and safety problems also arose with asbestos.

For flexible cables, braided finishes have continued to find fairly standard application for domestic appliances where there is a possibility of the cable coming into contact with hot metal and an extruded finish might be damaged, e.g. for electric irons and toasters etc. Continuous filament of the regenerated cellulose type is now the most common material for such braids. When there is justification for a more robust finish, as for aircraft cables, nylon is used.

TESTS ON PROTECTIVE FINISHES

Apart from tests on the thickness and properties of the materials used, the only tests of importance are those given in IEC 229. These cover requirements when the quality of the finish is especially significant, such as for the protection of aluminium sheaths or the sheath and reinforcement of transmission cables.

D.C. voltage test

When the requirements are onerous it is usual to check that no damage has occurred during laying and often subsequently during the life of the cable. This is done by a voltage test and for the purpose a conducting layer of graphite type varnish is applied on the outer surface of the oversheath at the time of cable manufacture. The routine test in the factory is at a voltage of $(2.5t + 5)$ kV, applied for 1 min, where t is the minimum average thickness of the oversheath.

Test for protection of aluminium

In the event of local damage to the oversheath, it is important that soil water should not penetrate beyond the exposed area and reference has been made to the application of bitumen to provide such secondary protection. The test for this purpose is carried out on a length of cable previously submitted to a bend test. Four circular pieces of oversheath 10 mm in diameter are cut out with a cork borer and the exposed aluminium is cleaned. The sample is placed in 1% sodium sulphate solution with the ends protruding and 100 V d.c. is applied between the aluminium sheath and the bath, a resistor being used so that the current is 100 mA. After 100 hours the oversheath is removed and no signs of corrosion should be visible beyond 10 mm from the initial holes.

Abrasion and penetration tests

Tests are included in IEC 229 to demonstrate that the finish has adequate resistance to abrasion and to penetration by sharp objects. They are described in chapter 42. These tests were originally developed to create a standard at the time when finishes included layers of unvulcanised or vulcanised rubber together with outer layers of hessian. They are of less significance with modern extruded oversheaths.

Chapter 6

Cables in Fires – Special Designs and Finishes for Optimum Performance

Each year fires result in thousands of fatalities worldwide with many more injured. The financial cost is large. Although cables very seldom cause fire, they are an integral part of all property and equipment and are often subjected to fire resulting from other causes. In the majority of cases the continued electrical operation of the cables during a fire is not required and they can be isolated. However, certain circuits such as those for emergency lighting or for the safe shut-down of equipment will have to remain in service and for these requirements special cables with fire survival properties are available.

During the 1960s and early 1970s many laboratory-scale tests were adopted which were believed to indicate the fire performance of cables. Many cables were considered to be fire retardant because the requirements of standard flame tests were being met. However, it is now clear that the situation is considerably more complex and that there is little correlation between small-scale tests and 'real fire' hazards. Increasingly, the evolution of smoke and toxic gases from some types of cable in fires as well as their ability to spread fire has come under scrutiny. Some significant improvements have been made by the modification of standard materials and constructions and the adoption of new materials.

LABORATORY TEST METHODS

As it has become increasingly apparent that real fires cannot be reproduced by small-scale tests, attempts have been made to confine such tests to specific hazards such as flame spread, noxious or corrosive gases and smoke. Tests may be performed either on materials or cables. Work at the National Bureau of Standards in the USA on plastics materials has been directed towards the development of a 'hazard index' which is the summation of ratings given to six properties; ease of ignition, smoke, noxious gas emission, rate of heat release, flame spread and rate of burning. There are indications that this type of approach could be used with cables for specific uses, e.g. in ships.

Oxygen index and temperature index

Oxygen index (limiting or critical oxygen index) is the most widely used and abused fire parameter in the assessment of materials. The index is the minimum concentration of oxygen in an oxygen–nitrogen mixture in which the material will burn. The major advantage of the test is that reproducible results may be obtained, provided that a standard test method is used.[1]

Air contains 21% oxygen and it is often stated that material with an oxygen index greater than about 26 will be self-extinguishing. Such statements illustrate the problem of extrapolating the results of what is essentially a quality control test to 'real fire' situations. In general a particular oxygen index value offers no guarantee of resistance to flame spread. In practice, materials with identical oxygen indices may have widely differing burning properties, especially if the base polymers or additives are of different types. The reasons for this lack of correlation are twofold. In the test configuration the flame propagation is downward, while in most fires the flame propagates upwards, heating fresh material ahead of it and increasing the rate of decomposition of the material. Secondly, in the oxygen index test the sample temperature is maintained at approximately 25 °C, whereas the extent of burning may be significantly influenced by the actual temperature involved.

To overcome this restriction the oxygen index was initially modified so that the index was measured over a range of temperatures. From the results a 'temperature index' could be obtained, usually by extrapolation, the temperature index being defined as that temperature at which the oxygen index becomes 21. Fig. 6.1 illustrates some results obtained with two PVC compounds. However, correlations carried out by Day[2] for a range of materials indicate that extrapolation from these limited data is unjustified: because of lack of linearity, the real value is lower than is obtained by extrapolation. In view of this limitation, a more valid method of determining temperature index has evolved. It simply involves maintaining the oxygen concentration at 21% and varying the temperature, the temperature index being recorded as the minimum temperature at which a material will support combustion following its ignition. Such a test is currently used by London Underground Limited and is expected to become the subject of a British Standard shortly.

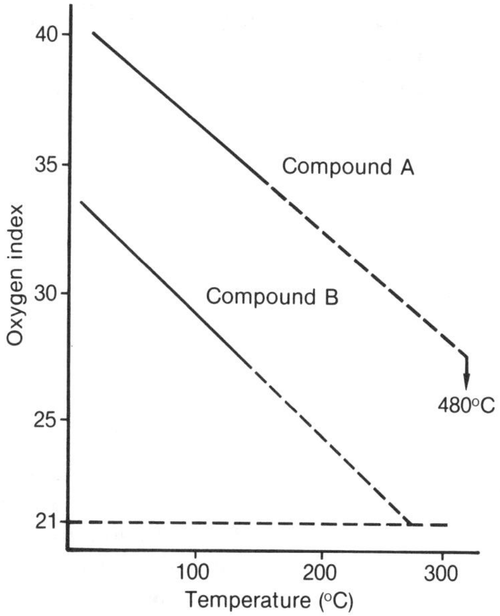

Fig. 6.1 Effect of temperature on the oxygen index of PVC compounds

Flame retardance

There are many varieties of tests involving the effect of a Bunsen flame on a single cable. The cable may be horizontal, inclined or vertical and the flame intensity may vary. The most common form of this type of test is IEC 332, Part 1 (or BS 4066: Part 1: 1980). A single cable sample, 1600 mm long, is clamped vertically. A Bunsen or similar burner is arranged at an angle of 45° to the axis of the cable sample, 475 mm below the top clamp. The flame size is specified and the temperature is regulated such that a copper wire 0.71 mm in diameter melts in 4 to 6 s. Where the cable diameter exceeds 50 mm, two burners are used, impinging at the same point, the second being displaced 90° from the first. The flame is applied for a period of T seconds, where $T = 60 + W/25$ and W is the weight in grams of a 600 mm length of the cable.

The test requirement is that after all burning has ceased the charred or affected portion shall not have reached within 50 mm from the top clamp.

IEC subcommittee SC 50D is currently looking at a new design of Bunsen burner which will be capable of giving a consistent heat output. It is likely that this burner will ultimately be used in the test to BS 4066: Part 1.

Fire resistance

A cable can be described as fire resistant when it complies with the severe test in IEC 331 in which the middle portion of a sample of cable 1200 mm long is supported by two metal rings 300 mm apart and exposed to the flame from a tube type gas burner at 750 °C for 3 hours. Simultaneously the rated voltage of the cable is applied continuously throughout the test period. Furthermore, not less than 12 hours after the flame has been extinguished, the cable is re-energised. No electrical failure must occur under these conditions.

There are many customer variations of this test in which the time and temperature are treated as variables. Test temperatures of 1000 °C are now common to simulate hydrocarbon fires. The cable is also subjected to impact during the test to simulate falling debris and application of a water deluge after the gas flame has been extinguished to simulate fire fighting.

Smoke

Tests for smoke characteristics employ either gravimetric or optical techniques. The Arapahoe smoke chamber is the best known gravimetric method. A filter is mounted in the top of a cylindrical stack 76 mm in diameter and 457 mm high fitted to a combustion chamber 127 mm in diameter and 178 mm high. A 38 mm × 13 mm × 3 mm specimen is exposed to a small propane gas flame in the base of the combustion chamber and the smoke particles are collected on the filter by drawing the combustion products through it. However, because of the problems arising from the flocculation of smoke particles and also because of the very variable nature of the types of smoke generated, optical rather than gravimetric methods are preferred.

The NBS smoke chamber[3] is 914 mm × 610 mm × 914 mm. A sample 76 mm square is exposed to a heat flux of 2.5 W/cm^2 under piloted (flaming) or non-piloted (smouldering) conditions. The effect of smoke stratification is minimised by using a vertical photometer path to measure the maximum specific optical density. The various smoke tests have been reviewed by Hilado,[4] and the ASTM Task Group.[5]

Combustion gases

Few standard test methods have been proposed for the analysis of the gases evolved by burning materials. Attention to date has concentrated on the halogen acids, especially hydrogen chloride. IEC Publication 754–1 and the corresponding British Standard, BS 6425: Part 1, specify a test method in which approximately 1 gram of material is pyrolised at 800 °C in a combustion tube and the resultant gases are analysed. Hydrogen chloride and hydrogen bromide are analysed as hydrogen chloride. A limitation is that non-halogenated acidic by-products are not determined. For this reason proposals are under consideration to modify the method to measure the pH of aqueous solutions of the combustion gases.

Large-scale tests

The relevance of tests on small samples of materials or cables to 'real fire' situations has already been questioned. Some of these problems may be overcome by using simulated installation conditions together with a realistic heat source.

Up to 1981 there had been about ten fires at power generating stations involving cables where the cables propagated the fire along ducts and tunnels, often at high speed (10 m/min). It was to retard this rate of flame spread that new cables were designed in the early 1970s and tests were developed. These examine groups of cable in vertical runs and have requirements for the maximum spread of fire damage. IEEE 383 (1974) requires a vertical ladder 2.4 m high, 305 mm wide and 76 mm deep. The centre of the tray is filled with a single layer of cables approximately one half a cable diameter apart. A ribbon type gas burner 250 mm wide with a heat input of 70 000 BTU/hour is placed 600 mm above the bottom of the tray and 76 mm from the cables for 20 min. After the flame source has been removed the flame shall not propagate to the full height of the tray. Recent work has shown that the 70 000 BTU/hour heat source may be insufficient to represent a 'worst case' fire and a level of 210 000 BTU/hour has been suggested.

A deficiency in the IEEE 383 test is that the pronounced 'chimney effect' found in duct fires is not simulated. This is overcome in the Italian (CEI–20–22) and UK (CEGB GDCD 21) specifications where the dimensions of the enclosure are specified, together with maximum wind speed. These tests use electrically heated panels at 600 °C minimum together with a pilot flame rather than the gas burner. The cable must be seen to ignite within 15 min.

The good features of both the IEEE 383 and CEGB tests were combined to produce the test standardised in IEC 332, Part 3 (BS 4066: Part 3). This test involves the use of a 70 000 BTU gas burner but with a closely defined layout of the cables and the chimney, including definition of the thermal properties of the construction materials.

Where the evolution of smoke is of prime importance, as for example in cabling mass-transit systems, an alternative test approach has been adopted. A cubical enclosure with 3 m sides has been constructed by London Underground Limited[6] in the UK and cables are burnt in a horizontal configuration using 1 litre of ethanol as the fire source. This burns for approximately 25 min with a heat output of about 15 kW. The obscuration of 5 W emergency lighting bulbs, arranged vertically in a far corner of the cube, was initially the test parameter. Now the test has been refined, and a light source and photocell are mounted on opposite faces of the cube at a height of 2.15 m to measure smoke density. The photocell is designed to have a response close to that of the human eye and is of the selenium type fitted with a green filter. To reduce the effect of smoke stratification a fan, suitably screened so as not to influence the flame, is used to distribute the smoke.

PROPERTIES OF MATERIALS

Unfortunately polymeric materials which combine good electrical properties, ease of processing at low cost and low fire risk properties with regard to flame propagation and the evolution of smoke and noxious and corrosive gases are not readily available. However, polymeric materials can be modified and in suitable cable designs offer some improved performance in fires. Invariably, because of the nature of the modifiers, physical and electrical properties are affected, but they are still acceptable for many applications. The three main properties, propagation, smoke and noxious gases, are considered below with specific reference to PVC or in comparison with it.

Flame propagation

With many objects it is debatable whether it is the ignitability, or ease of ignition, of a material or its rate of flame propagation when once ignited which is the controlling factor in its performance in a fire. Flash ignition is that which is caused by a flame or a spark. Self-ignition arises solely due to temperature. While natural materials such as paper, cotton, wood and wool have flash-ignition temperatures in the region of 200–250 °C, those of polymeric materials are generally higher than 300 °C. Also the self-ignition temperature of polymers is higher than their flash-ignition temperature, whereas for the natural materials the two temperatures are similar. Wool is an exception, having a flash-ignition temperature of 200 °C and a self-ignition temperature of 590 °C. As the provision of fuel for the fire is critical for propagation, the heat of combustion of the material is important. Some values for common materials[7] are given in table 6.1. In those cases where combustible plasticisers are used (e.g. phthalates in PVC) these values can be increased considerably.

The concept of oxygen index has already been described and some values for common natural materials and unmodified polymers are given in table 6.2.

A typical standard PVC compound composed of 100 parts of polymer together with 50 parts of dioctyl phthalate and 50 parts of calcium carbonate and the usual minor additives would have an oxygen index of approximately 25. Cables sheathed with this material would fulfil the requirements of the single cable tests (BS 4066) but probably not those of the IEEE 383 type of test. Additives can be incorporated into the PVC compound which affect the fire propagating mechanism in the following ways:[8]

(a) interference with the ultimate combustion reaction in which the gas molecules break down and combine with oxygen

Table 6.1 Heat of combustion of typical materials

Material	Heat of combustion (MJ/kg)
Wood	18.5
Wool	20
Cotton	16.7
Polyethylene	46
Polypropylene	46
Poly(vinyl chloride) (unplasticised)	19
Polystyrene	40
Polyisobutylene	47
Nylon 66	33
Polyurethane	28
CSP (Hypalon)	28
PCP (polychloroprene)	24

Table 6.2 Oxygen index of typical materials (at 25 °C)

Material	Oxygen index
Cotton	18
Wool	24
Coal	60
Polyethylene	18
Polypropylene	18
XLPE	18
Ethylene–propylene rubber	18
Poly(vinyl chloride) (unplasticised)	47
Polystyrene	18
Nylon 66	20
Polytetrafluoroethylene	95
CSP (Hypalon)	27
PCP (polychloroprene)	40

(b) alteration of the thermal degradation of the base polymer so that it yields less flammable products of pyrolysis
(c) reduction of the heat transfer from the flame to the solid, thereby reducing the rate of thermal degradation and the amount of fuel generated by the material
(d) absorbence of heat internally, thereby reducing the heat available to degrade the polymer
(e) reduction in the rate of diffusion of the pyrolysis products to the flame or in the concentration of the flammable gases by generation of non-flammable gases
(f) dilution of combustibles by non-combustibles, e.g. mineral filler

With PVC, the phthalate plasticiser may be partly replaced by a chlorinated hydrocarbon or by a phosphate ester plasticiser to provide some improvement.

However, a major benefit is obtained through addition of 3%–6% antimony trioxide which acts together with the chlorine in the PVC to suppress flame propagation. A typical compound is A in fig. 6.1. Zinc and barium borates contain water of hydration which is evolved slowly above 135 °C and are used as part replacements for antimony trioxide. The major alternative filler is aluminium hydroxide, otherwise known as alumina trihydrate. It contains about 35% water which is released above 200 °C with the absorption of heat:

$$2Al(OH)_3 \rightarrow Al_2O_3 + 3H_2O$$

The steam produced also dilutes the flammable gases.

PVC compounds incorporating these additives have much improved resistance to flame propagation. Similar techniques can be used with other polymers. For example, antimony trioxide is equally effective in CSP and PCP. However, in polyolefins alumina trihydrate can be used to obtain good flame retardance combined with low acid and noxious gas outputs.

Smoke

In many fires human escape becomes impossible because smoke obscures vision rather than because of the build-up of heat or toxic gases. However, less attention has been paid to this area, possibly because accurate reproducible test methods have been unavailable.

Plasticised PVC evolves considerable quantities of black smoke when burnt. This is primarily because of the use of aromatic plasticisers and the conversion of the resin into aromatic chemicals. In general, the higher the carbon-to-hydrogen ratio is in hydrocarbons, the blacker the smoke is. Thus in some formulations tricresyl phosphate gives more smoke than dioctyl phthalate. Also better results may be obtained with aliphatic plasticisers such as dioctyl adipate.

Fillers appear to act mainly by diluting the combustible material available. None are preferred solely from the point of view of smoke, although some claims have been made for hydrated fillers such as hydrated magnesium carbonate. Very many patents were taken out in the late 1970s to cover the beneficial effect of adding small amounts of organic compounds containing metals, especially those based on iron, nickel, vanadium and molybdenum.[9] Much experimental work has been carried out on the action of ferrocene.[10]

More attention has also been paid to the use of polymers which themselves emit little smoke when burnt, such as PE, EPR, EVA or ethylene acrylic elastomer. The use of hydrated fillers in such polymers provides materials which have some flame retardancy together with low evolution of smoke under flaming conditions.

Toxic and corrosive gases

The evolution of toxic gases is an area in which there has been considerable development work. However, it is now apparent that much of this work has been superficial and unrelated to causes of death in fires. Three approaches have developed.

Firstly it is recognised that certain materials such as PVC, CSP and PCP evolve hydrogen chloride on burning. Hydrogen chloride is corrosive and toxic. PVC compounds normally evolve 25%–30% hydrogen chloride by weight. Special compounds which evolve 15%, or even only 5%, are now available, and use of these is believed to reduce the hazard. The main technique in formulating these materials is the addition of calcium carbonate of fine particle size which reacts with the hydrogen chloride – hence the term 'acid-binding' PVC. However, while the binding may occur under standard test conditions this may not be the case in all fire situations. One further point concerning acid-binding PVC may be made by reference to compound B in fig. 6.1. This is a typical example which evolves only 12% hydrogen chloride. However, because of the acid-binding requirement, the flame retardancy is compromised. Thus in a fire more of the acid-binding PVC could burn relative to the flame-retardant PVC, and the total evolution of hydrogen chloride may then be the same in each case unless each was totally consumed.

Attempts have been made to analyse the combustion products for a range of toxic gases and then to sum the toxicities to obtain a 'hazard index'. Little is known of the toxicity of mixtures of gases and so various summing procedures have had to be adopted. While this approach is obviously superior to specifying material composition it suffers from two main disadvantages: certain toxic products or antagonists, perhaps not yet identified, will be missed and also the concentrations of the toxic products will be dependent on the test conditions. Furthermore, all organic materials can generate fatal concentrations of carbon monoxide during combustion in a reduced oxygen atmosphere.

Of course, toxicity concerns the physiological effects and it is difficult to simulate these effects through chemical analysis. What has been done is to expose animals to the pyrolysis products of burning materials. One such study exposed mice to the pyrolysis products from 1 gram of material and determined the time to incapacity and death.[11] While some sulphur-containing polymers such as polyphenylene sulphide exhibited the shortest times to death, others such as CSP exhibited the longest. Some materials exhibited short incapacitation times and highlighted that some unidentified toxicants are faster acting than others. The major problem with this type of study is the relationship between test exposure and fire conditions.

It is now clear that toxicity cannot be determined by chemical analysis alone. A new approach has been adopted by Professor Einhorn of the Flammability Research Centre of the University of Utah, USA, in a study of fires involving PVC wiring.[12] On hospital admission, fire victims are checked for their medical condition and breath and blood samples are analysed. From the chemical analysis of materials removed from site, such work provides the missing link in practical toxicity.

Further animal work has also been carried out to study behaviour and also physiological responses. Part of the study was the exposure of PVC to various heat fluxes and investigation of the effect of the resultant gases on rats. Heart and respiratory rates were determined during exposure and the condition of the brain, heart, lungs, trachea, kidney, spleen and liver were subsequently studied histopathologically.

It appears that it will be many years before the full relationship between the chemical nature of cable materials and their toxicity emerges. For more detailed study, the articles of Punderson[13,14] and the work of various task forces[15,16] are available. Although the toxic products of combustion are a common cause of death of persons trapped in a fire, they are rarely a major factor in preventing escape.

With the increasing complexity and cost of modern electronic equipment it is important that indirect fire damage is minimised. When halogenated polymers burn, clouds of acidic gas form which condense on metal surfaces, rapidly corroding contacts. In such areas halogen-free materials are becoming more popular.

In formulating materials which are incapable of generating toxicants containing halogens, nitrogen, sulphur and phosphorus, and corrosive gases, a wide range of other critical properties has to be compromised. Therefore, at present, eliminating the use of all halogenated materials in wire and cable applications where flammability is a concern is not practical.

CABLE DESIGN

As yet there are few standards which deal with the design of finished cables covering all degrees of reduced flammability. It is preferable that the cores should be designed in the normal manner so that optimum electrical performance can be obtained. In most cases the use of standard PVC, PCP and CSP oversheaths gives sufficient protection for normal use, the cables complying with the flame-retardant tests of BS 4066 and IEC 332, Part 1. Then the required cable properties can be optimised through the use of high-temperature-resistant barrier tapes, metal tapes and armour to conduct heat from the fire source, and special bedding and oversheaths.

Where large numbers of cables are bunched together, especially in vertical runs, attention to the oversheath design alone is insufficient. Beddings also need to be flame retardant, and in addition it is usual for the insulation to have some improved resistance to propagation.

Where it is necessary to minimise smoke and reduce corrosive gases, halogen-free polymer systems such as EPR, EVA, PE or ethylene acrylic elastomer are used, together with substantial loadings of fillers such as alumina trihydrate or magnesium hydroxide. Materials based on these systems are used for the bedding and oversheathing layers of a wide range of cables complying with BS 6724: 1986, which relates to armoured cables for electricity supply with low emission of smoke and corrosive gases when affected by fire.

There are many instances where limited fire survival capability is critical. In the chemical industry, processes have to be shut down and chemicals pumped away from the fire. Aircraft and ships obviously require certain circuits to continue operating. Also, emergency lighting, whether to facilitate personnel evacuation or for navigation, must always function properly. The standard cable in many of these installations has been the mineral insulated cable. This will withstand the IEC 331 fire-resistant test without difficulty. It is robust and will resist a considerable degree of maltreatment and dousing with water.

In aircraft engine compartments light weight is also of paramount importance and cables based on a combination of silicone rubber, quartz and PTFE coverings over nickel-clad conductors have been developed.

Cables with silicone rubber insulation are also used for ships, and when used together with a glass braid the requirements of the IEC 331 test can be met, the silica ash being retained by the glass. Further advances have been made in the use of EPR rather than silicone rubber in this type of cable and it is now possible to comply with the IEC 331 requirements with the test temperature at 1000 °C. Mica–glass tapes around the conductor provide high temperature insulation and cost effective alternatives to the silicone–glass and mineral insulated designs.

Detection of fire and heat

A further approach to fire protection in generating stations and warehouses has been the development of fire detector cables, or linear heat sensors. Their main features involve high tensile steel conductors, copper and tin coated to provide a low contact resistance and assembled so that they move together into physical contact when the thermoplastic insulation melts, thus causing a short circuit. They have a response time of approximately 5 s and the short circuit which occurs can be used to locate the fire and operate a variety of fire fighting devices, such as a water sprinkler system.

SUMMARY

Fire testing has two major areas of activity:

(a) The development of improved laboratory-scale 'fire performance' tests measuring such variables as ignitability, rate of mass loss, rate of heat release and rate of development of the hazardous condition in terms of smoke density, effluent toxicity and corrosivity. Such tests would be more suitable for material screening than for assessing the likely fire performance of a cable system.
(b) The application of mathematical modelling to the fire behaviour problem. More and more engineering applications of zone and field computer based fire models are to be expected which will result in fire hazard analysis of cable installations.

Cables have been developed which have a significantly reduced tendency to propagate fire even under onerous conditions and major reductions have been achieved in the emission of smoke and toxic and corrosive gases from burning cables. Cables and systems have been developed which will provide rapid detection and location of fires.

However, care must be exercised in the interpretation of the results of simulated fire tests, especially small-scale tests. Research and development is continuing to make further improvements in both cable-making materials and cable designs in an effort to reduce the risks of cables in fire.

REFERENCES

(1) BS 2782 (1978) Method 141D, or ASTM D–2863.
(2) Day, A. G. (1975) 'Oxygen index test: temperature effect and comparisons with other flammability tests'. *Plast. Polym.* **43** (164), 64.
(3) ASTM E–662–79.
(4) Hilado, C. J., Cumming, H. J. and Machado, A. M. (Jul. 1978) 'Screening materials for smoke evolution' *Mod. Plast. Int.*, 53.
(5) (Aug. 1976) 'A report on smoke test methods'. *ASTM Standardisation News.*
(6) Smith, V. H. (1979) 'Fire resistant cables for underground railways'. *Electr. Rev. Int.* **205** (9), 54.
(7) Socrates, G. (26 May 1978) 'Plastics as a fire risk'. *Plast. Rubber Weekly*, 18.
(8) Lindstrom, R. S., Sidman, K. R., Sheth, S. G. and Howarth, J. T. (Aug. 1974) 'Effects of flame and smoke retardant additives in polymer systems'. *JFF/Fire Retardant Chem.* **1**, 152.

(9) Starns, W. H. and Edelson, D. (Sep.–Oct. 1979) 'Mechanistic aspects of the behaviour of molybdenum(VI) oxide as a fire-retardant additive for poly(vinyl chloride). An interpretive review'. *Macromolecules* **12** (5), 797.
(10) Lawson, D. F. (1976) 'Investigation of the mechanistic basis for ferrocene activity during combustion of vinyl polymers'. *J. Appl. Polym. Sci.* **20** (8), 2183.
(11) Kourtides, D. A., Gilwee, W. J. and Hilado, C. J. (Jun. 1978) 'Relative toxicity of the pyrolysis products from some thermoplastic and thermoset polymers'. *Polym. Eng. Sci.* **18** (8), 674.
(12) Einhorn, I. N. and Grunnet, M. L. (1979) 'The physiological and toxicological aspects of degradation products produced during the combustion of polyvinyl chloride polymers; flammability of solid polymer cable dielectrics'. *EPRI Report No. EL–1263, TPS* 77–738.
(13) Punderson, J. O. (Sep./Oct.1977) 'Toxicity and fire safety of wire insulation: A state-of-the-art review'. *Wire Tech.*, 64.
(14) Punderson, J. O. (10–17 Apr. 1981) 'Toxic fumes – forget standards, moderate the fire'. *Electr. Rev.* **208** (14), 24.
(15) National Materials Advisory Board (1978) *Flammability, Smoke, Toxicity and Corrosive Gases of Electric Cable Materials*. Washington, DC: National Academy of Sciences, Publication No. NMAB–342.
(16) (1979) 'Flammability of solid polymer cable dielectrics'. *EPRI Report No. EL–1263, TPS 77–738.*

Chapter 7
Cable Standards and Quality Assurance

STANDARDS

The most universal standardising authority for cables is the International Electrotechnical Commission (IEC), although comparatively little commercial business is placed directly against the IEC standards. This arises because IEC standards cater for a large variety of permissible options and serve mainly as a basis for the preparation of national standards, which are usually prepared in accordance with the IEC requirements. Furthermore the IEC standards represent a consensus of national opinions and hence take several years both to prepare initially and for agreement to be reached on amendments. If all minor points were to be included, the time period for resolution would be extremely lengthy, especially in dealing with new developments. Countries such as the UK which have always been well to the fore in cable development are therefore able to issue much more comprehensive and up-to-date standards.

This can be seen from the number of items in the lists below of the relevant IEC and British Standards. Whilst it might have been of interest to include standards from other countries, these tend to be even more numerous, e.g. in the USA where in addition to national standards for materials and components there is widespread use by industry at large of cable standards issued by four bodies, Underwriter's Laboratories (UL), Association of Edison Illuminating Companies (AEIC) and jointly by the Insulated Power Cables Engineers Association and the National Electrical Manufacturers' Association (IPCEA/NEMA). In the UK some large organisations have separate specifications for their own use but many, such as the nationalised Electricity Boards, adopt the available British Standards and only add any requirements necessary for their particular purposes.

British and IEC Standards

Cables and flexible cords

BS 638	Arc welding power sources, equipment and accessories (includes cables)
BS 4553	600/1000 V PVC-insulated single-phase split concentric cables with copper conductors for electricity supply
BS 5055	PVC-insulated and elastomer-insulated cables for electric signs and HV luminous discharge tube installations
BS 5308	Instrumentation cables: Part 1 – Polyethylene-insulated cables Part 2 – PVC-insulated cables
BS 5467	Cables with thermosetting insulation for electricity supply for rated voltages up to and including 1900/3300 V

BS 5593	Impregnated-paper-insulated cables with aluminium sheath/neutral conductor and three shaped solid aluminium phase conductors (Consac), 600/1000 V, for electricity supply
BS 6004	PVC-insulated cables (non-armoured) for electric power and lighting
BS 6007	Rubber-insulated cables for electric power and lighting
BS 6116	Elastomer-insulated flexible trailing cables for quarries and miscellaneous mines
BS 6141	Insulated cables and flexible cords for use in high temperature zones
BS 6195	Insulated flexible cables and cords for coil leads
BS 6207	Mineral-insulated cables: Part 1 – Copper-sheathed cables with copper conductors
BS 6231	PVC-insulated cables for switchgear and control wiring
BS 6346	PVC-insulated cables for electricity supply
BS 6480	Impregnated-paper-insulated lead or lead alloy sheathed electric cables of rated voltages up to and including 33 kV
BS 6500	Insulated flexible cords and cables
BS 6622	Cables with extruded crosslinked polyethylene or ethylene – propylene rubber insulation for rated voltages from 3800/6600 V up to 19000/33000 V
BS 6708	Trailing cables for mining purposes
BS 6724	Armoured cables for electricity supply having thermosetting insulation with low emission of smoke and corrosive gases when affected by fire
BS 6726	Festoon and temporary lighting cables and cords
BS 6862	Cables for vehicles: Part 1 – Cables with copper conductors
BS 6883	Elastomer-insulated cables for fixed wiring in ships
BS 6977	Insulated flexible cables for lifts and other flexible connections
BS Series	Cables for aircraft use: G177 (Nyvin), G189 and G227 (Tersil), G192 and G222 (Efglas) G195 and G221 (Minyvin), G206 (Fepsil) G210 (PTFE), G212 (General requirements)
IEC 55	Paper-insulated metal-sheathed cables for rated voltages up to 18/30 kV (with copper or aluminium conductors and excluding gas pressure and oil-filled cables) 55-1 Part 1 – Tests 55-2 Part 2 – Construction
IEC 92	Electrical installations in ships: There are many parts of this standard, of which those relevant are 92-3, 92-351, 92-352, 92-359, 92-373, 92-375 and 92-376
IEC 227	Poly(vinyl chloride)-insulated cables of rated voltages up to and including 450/750 V: 227-1 Part 1 – General requirements 227-2 Part 2 – Test methods 227-3 Part 3 – Non-sheathed cables for fixed wiring 227-4 Part 4 – Sheathed cables for fixed wiring 227-5 Part 5 – Flexible cables (cords) 227-6 Part 6 – Lift cables and cables for flexible connections

IEC 245	Rubber-insulated cables of rated voltages up to and including 450/750 V 245-1 Part 1 – General requirements 245-2 Part 2 – Test methods 245-3 Part 3 – Heat-resisting silicone-insulated cables 245-4 Part 4 – Cords and flexible cables 245-5 Part 5 – Lift cables 245-6 Part 6 – Arc welding electrode cables
IEC 502	Extruded solid dielectric insulated power cables for rated voltages from 1 kV to 30 kV
IEC 541	Comparative information on IEC and North American flexible cord types
IEC 702	Mineral insulated cables and their terminations with a rated voltage not exceeding 750 V 702-1 Part 1 – Cables 702-2 Part 2 – Terminations
IEC 800	Heating cables with a rated voltage of 300/500 V for comfort heating and prevention of ice formation

Conductors

BS 2627	Wrought aluminium for electrical purposes: wire
BS 3988	Wrought aluminium for electrical purposes: solid conductors for insulated cables
BS 4109	Copper for electrical purposes: wire for general electrical purposes and insulated cables and flexible cords
BS 5714	Method of measurement of resistivity of metallic materials
BS 6360	Conductors in insulated cables and cords
IEC 228	Conductors of insulated cables 228A First supplement: Guide to the dimensional limits of circular conductors

Insulation and sheathing (non-metallic)

BS 6234	Polyethylene insulation and sheath of electric cables
BS 6746	PVC insulation and sheath of electric cables
BS 6746C	Colour chart for PVC insulation and sheath of electric cables
BS 6899	Rubber insulation and sheath of electric cables
IEC 173	Colours of the cores of flexible cables and cords
IEC 304	Standard colours for PVC insulation for low frequency cables and wires
IEC 391	Marking of insulated conductors
IEC 446	Identification of insulated and bare conductors by colour

Tests on cables and materials

BS 903	Methods of testing vulcanised rubber (in 53 parts)
BS 4066	Tests on electric cables under fire conditions: Part 1 – Method of test on a single vertical insulated wire or cable

	Part 3 – Method of classification of flame propagation characteristics of bunched cables
BS 5099	Spark testing of electric cables
BS 6387	Performance requirements for cables required to maintain circuit integrity under fire conditions
BS 6425	Methods of test for gases evolved during combustion of electric cables:
	Part 1 – Method for determination of amount of halogen acid gas evolved during combustion of polymeric materials taken from cables
BS 6469	Methods of test for insulation and sheaths of electric cables
BS 6470	Method for determination of water in insulating oils and in oil-impregnated paper and pressboard
IEC 55	See above
IEC 60	High voltage test techniques:
	60-1 Part 1 – General definitions and test requirements
	60-2 Part 2 – Test procedures
	60-3 Part 3 – Measuring devices
	60-4 Part 4 – Application guide for measuring devices
IEC 141	Tests on oil-filled and gas pressure cable and their accessories:
	141-1 Part 1 – Oil-filled, paper-insulated, metal-sheathed cables for alternating voltages up to and including 400 kV
	141-2 Part 2 – Internal gas pressure cables and accessories for alternating voltages up to and including 275 kV
	141-3 Part 3 – External gas pressure (gas compression) cables and accessories for alternating voltages up to 275 kV
	141-4 Part 4 – Oil-impregnated paper-insulated high pressure oil-filled pipe-type cables and accessories for alternating voltages up to and including 400 kV
IEC 229	Tests on cable oversheaths which have a special protective function and are applied by extrusion
IEC 230	Impulse tests on cables and their accessories
IEC 233	Tests on hollow insulators for use in electrical equipment
IEC 270	Partial discharge measurements
IEC 332	Tests on electric cables under fire conditions:
	332-1 Part 1 – Test on a single vertical insulated wire or cable
	332-3 Part 3 – Tests on bunched wires or cables
IEC 538	Electric cables, wires and cords: methods of test for polyethylene insulation and sheath
IEC 540	Test methods for insulation and sheaths of electric cables and cords (elastomeric and thermoplastic compounds)
IEC 754	Test on gases evolved during combustion of electric cables:
	754-1 Part 1 – Determination of the amount of halogen acid gas evolved during the combustion of polymeric materials taken from cables
IEC 811	Common test methods for insulating and sheathing materials of electric cables
	811-1 Part 1 – Methods for general application

	811-2 Part 2 – Methods specific to elastomeric compounds
	811-4 Part 4 – Methods specific to polyethylene and polypropylene compounds
	(The several parts of IEC 811 are themselves subdivided into sections, e.g. 811-1-1, 811-1-2, 811-2-1, with certain groups of test methods in each section. Part 3 is reserved for methods specific to PVC compounds)
IEC 815	Electrical test methods for electric cables
	815–2 Part 2 – Partial discharge tests
	(When all parts of IEC 811 and IEC 815 have been completed they will replace IEC 538 and IEC 540)
IEC 840	Tests for power cables with extruded insulation for rated voltages above 30 kV (U_m = 36 kV) up to 150 kV (U_m = 170 kV)

Jointing and accessories

BS 4579	Performance of mechanical and compression joints in electric cable and wire connectors:
	Part 1 – Compression joints in copper conductors
	Part 2 – Compression joints in nickel, iron and plated copper conductors
	Part 3 – Mechanical and compression joints in aluminium conductors
BS 5372	Cable terminations for electrical equipment
BS 6081	Terminations for mineral-insulated cables
BS 6121	Mechanical cable glands for elastomer and plastics insulated cables
IEC 702	Part 2 See above

Miscellaneous

BS 801	Composition of lead and lead alloy sheaths of electric cables
BS 1441	Galvanised steel wire for armouring submarine cables
BS 1442	Galvanised mild steel wire for armouring cables
BS 2897	Wrought aluminium for electrical purposes – strip with drawn or rolled edges
IEC 38	IEC standard voltages
IEC 71	Insulation co-ordination
	71-1 Part 1 – Terms, definitions, principles and rules
	71-2 Part 2 – Application guide
	71-3 Part 3 – Phase-to-phase insulation co-ordination: principles, rules and application guide
IEC 183	Guide to the selection of high voltage cables
IEC 287	Calculation of the continuous current rating of cables (100% load factor)
IEC 331	Fire-resisting characteristics of electric cables
IEC 364	Electrical installations of buildings. This has a number of parts, which are subdivided into chapters, and sections, of which some have a bearing on cables; the following, which supersedes IEC 448, is particularly relevant:

	364–5–523 Part 5 –	Selection and erection of electrical equipment Chapter 52 Wiring systems Section 523 Current carrying capacities
IEC 724	Guide to the short-circuit temperature limits of electric cables with a rated voltage not exceeding 0.6/1.0 kV	

Influence of CENELEC

CENELEC, the European Committee for Electrotechnical Standardisation, has an important effect on the preparation and issue of new cable standards in Europe. Membership consists of the electrotechnical standards organisations of the countries of the European Common Market together with those of the European Free Trade Association (EFTA) outside the EEC. One of the main aims of CENELEC is to harmonise national standards in order to remove technical barriers to trading. For cables the basic work is done by a technical committee, TC20, on which all countries are represented. Working groups are established for individual subjects. The activities of CENELEC embrace a wide field of electrical equipment and regulations concerning its use, including the harmonisation of rules for electrical installations, at present up to 1000 V. The latter is covered by Technical Committee TC64, and the outcome of this committee's work has an important bearing on the IEE Wiring Regulations. Generally, as for TC20 and TC64, the numbering of the CENELEC technical committees is the same as for the IEC technical committees dealing with the same subjects and, because of the correlation between the work of the two organisations, it is convenient for representation for European countries to be the same, at least in part, in the two bodies.

To achieve the aims, Harmonisation Documents or European Standards are prepared taking account of IEC requirements and they are published after approval by the technical committee and other overall committees. Subsequently, and within a limited time scale, all member countries have to bring their national specifications into line, without deviations (other than any which may be justified by special national conditions, which should be only temporary, if possible). To date, in the cable field, flexible cables and cords and some types of wiring cables have been harmonised. Harmonisation Documents have also been produced for certain components or aspects which relate to all or several types of cable, so that reference can be made to them in the documents for the cables. These include Harmonisation Documents for conductors, test methods for thermoplastic and elastomeric insulations and sheaths, the method of numbering of small cores in cables with more than five cores and a standardised system of coded designations of cables. In some fields IEC standards are adopted verbatim as Harmonisation Documents or European Standards. In the cable field this applies to the Harmonisation Documents for conductors and test methods mentioned above, which constitute endorsements of IEC 228 and IEC 540 respectively, but the Harmonisation Documents for the cables themselves, while conforming in most respects with the corresponding IEC standards, include some differences and additions agreed between the CENELEC countries.

One effect of the CENELEC procedure can be a delay in the up-dating of national standards. This arises because when work is announced on a new subject a stand-still arrangement is imposed and no changes may be made until after harmonisation has been agreed, unless special permission has been obtained from CENELEC.

Harmonised types of cable may be marketed without restriction in any of the EEC and EFTA countries and attempts are made to keep the number of types to a reasonable minimum. Provided that agreement has been obtained within CENELEC it is still possible to retain non-harmonised designs as recognised national types if they are not of interest to members of other CENELEC countries. These tend to be for a wider range of conductor sizes or for particular wiring practices which are specific to national standards. Permission would not be given to types which would inhibit the use of harmonised designs.

Individual customers may still obtain cables manufactured to their own specification but it is one of the aims to keep these to a minimum and to regard them as specials for small-scale local use.

QUALITY ASSURANCE

In general the importance of quality has always been fully recognised in the cable industry and quality assurance, which, as the term implies, comprises the planned and systematic actions designed to give confidence that a product or service will satisfy the requirements for quality, is an intrinsic feature of a cablemaker's activities, as it is of reputable suppliers of most other products or services. However, during the last decade quality has been the subject of increasing publicity, with governmental bodies lending their support to, and taking initiatives in, promoting its importance. There has been a growing emphasis on the formalising and documentation of quality assurance procedures, not only to enable the supplier to satisfy himself that his system of quality assurance is effective, but also to enable him to demonstrate this to his customers and others.

Certification

A means of providing evidence that a manufacturer's quality management system and/or his product conforms to recognised standards is through certification to that effect by a body recognised to be competent to apply examinations and tests to verify it. Similarly, for a product for which no recognised standard exists, evidence of its suitability for the function claimed for it and for its safety may be provided by an approval certificate from a body recognised to be competent to make a judgement to that effect.

There are, then, three main categories of certification related to quality.

(a) Certification of the quality management system: this is a verification that the supplier's organisation, planning and system of quality control and its operation provide confidence that he will satisfy requirements for quality.
(b) Certification of product conformity: this is a verification that, in so far as is reasonably ascertainable, the supplier's product conforms with the standard with which it is intended to comply, and is based upon the examination and testing of

actual samples of the product taken from the supplier's production or purchased in the market.

(c) Product approval certification: for products outside the scope of existing standards, this is a certification that a product can confidently be expected to perform safely and reliably as required of it. To provide certification in this category the approvals organisation needs to go beyond satisfying itself that the product meets criteria embodied in a standard: it needs to determine the criteria to be used to assess the likely operational performance and satisfy itself that these are met.

Over a long period in the UK cable industry, in addition to elements of self-certification on the part of manufacturers, 'second party' certification has been practised by some purchasers. Certification of a supplier by a purchaser of his products is often referred to as 'second party' certification. The Ministry of Defence and the CEGB are prominent examples of organisations who have long operated a practice of auditing the quality assurance systems and their operation of their suppliers. They, and several other major cable users who operate similar schemes, are concerned with the manufacturer's quality assurance as it affects the products supplied to them. However, the likelihood is that a manufacturer who applies a system to products for some customers will apply the same system to his production as a whole and those customers who have not the resources and/or the inclination to audit a supplier's quality assurance themselves might reasonably be influenced by the knowledge that the supplier is approved by one or more other purchasers who do operate an auditing scheme and dispense certificates. Indeed there has been a register of approvals, Register of Quality Assessed United Kingdom Manufacturers issued by the Department of Trade (at that time) and published by HM Stationery Office, which can be consulted to ascertain who has approved whom. In so far as purchasers are influenced by second party certification by another purchaser, the second party certification is used, in effect, as 'third party' certification.

Strictly, 'third party' certification is certification by an independent approvals organisation and not an individual purchaser. The certification may cover the supplier's quality management system and/or a product or range of products and it applies to these irrespective of who the purchasers may be. Any customer can therefore accept third party certification of a manufacturer as applying to his purchases, provided, of course, that the product he buys is within the range covered by the certification.

In the UK cable industry third party certification was little used until the 1970s and 1980s. For example, not much use has been made for cables of the Kite Mark scheme administered by the British Standards Institution (BSI). This is in contrast with many other countries. In some, such as Canada, Denmark and Sweden, there have been national approval organisations backed by government. In some instances approval has been required by law. In some other countries third party certification has been almost essential for marketing; for example, in Germany VDE (Verband Deutscher Elektrotechniker) approval is required by many cable users.

The approvals organisation which has become most widely used in the field of cables in the UK is the British Approvals Service for Electric Cables (BASEC). This organisation is linked to the BSI and utilises the BSI's laboratories at Hemel Hempstead. BASEC was the approvals organisation appointed for administration in the UK of the ◁HAR▷ mark, devised by CENELEC as a reciprocal product conformity certification scheme for harmonised cables, which is explained more fully later. As well as this, BASEC's activities now cover certification of manufacturer's quality management systems, certification of product conformity for non-harmonised cables to British Standards and product approval.

The British Standard which specifies requirements for an effective quality management system is BS 5750. This has seven parts, but several of these are guides to the use of other parts. The specified requirements appropriate to cable manufacture and supply are contained in Parts 1 and 2. Part 1 is intended to apply to the total quality management system where this covers design of a part, at least, of the products manufactured. Part 2 applies where the system is only for products to a recognised standard, where it is assumed that compliance with the standard automatically gives assurance that the design of the product is suitable for the intended use. Part 1 is therefore more demanding, in that it covers the means by which the supplier assesses the likely performance of his design, e.g. the criteria and tests he adopts for this purpose, as well as his system for ensuring compliance.

Certification of a manufacturer's quality management system by BASEC will normally be to the effect that it conforms to BS 5750, Part 1 or Part 2, as the case may be. The first such BASEC certificates were issued to a number of cablemakers in 1986.

Product conformity certification has been provided by BASEC for cables to several British Standards over a period from 1973, mainly for cables of rated voltages up to 1000 V. The schemes for appraisal include type approval and regular surveillances; they began with flexibles and wiring cables and have extended to PVC and XLPE insulated 600/1000 V mains cables.

In the field of product approval BASEC is nominated in the IEE Wiring Regulations as the body to assess whether a new type of cable, not included in a British Standard, can be regarded as providing equivalent safety to types covered by the regulations, which are all required to be to British Standards. At one time this provision in the IEE Wiring Regulations, to allow for the use of newly developed equipment not strictly in accordance with the regulations, was through the Assessment of New Techniques (ANT) scheme, but this has been abandoned and, where cables are concerned, BASEC provides the equivalent. In carrying out this function BASEC may recruit experts from outside its regular staff.

Accreditation

One facet of governmental interest in quality assurance and certification has been the setting up of the National Accreditation Council (NAC). The function of this body is to accredit certification bodies. A body which itself issues certificates to suppliers is able to apply for a certificate of its own to signify that it is accredited by the NAC. It is appraised in a way not unlike its own appraisal of its clients, the basic criteria being impartiality and competence, and is certified as accredited, if appropriate. It may be accredited to operate in one or more of the areas of certification of quality management systems, certification of product conformity and certification of product approval, but accreditation for product conformity or product approval certification is generally not given unless the certification body requires of its clients that their quality management systems be approved by an accredited certification body. BASEC was accredited by the NAC for certification of quality management systems of suppliers of electric cables in 1986.

A certification body may operate without accreditation, relying on its established prestige within the part of industry where it operates, but obviously accreditation by an official body is seen as conferring greater status.

Governmental papers on the subject of accreditation and certification envisage the possibility of more than one certification body being accredited for operation in a given product area. Indeed there is implied encouragement of this in the interests of competition. For suppliers, however, an advantage of third party certification by a body recognised in the industry and acceptable to customers generally is that this can lead to a single assessment based upon standardised criteria in place of a number of second party appraisals which may differ from each other in detail and anyway cause duplication of time spent and expense incurred in external audits. This advantage would be lost if there were too many bodies providing third party certification in the same product area and individual customers required certification of their suppliers by different third parties.

As with certification, accreditation is on-going. After the first accreditation, appraisals are carried out periodically for maintenance of the status.

The ◁HAR▷ mark

A particular and significant form of product conformity certification is a licence to use the ◁HAR▷ mark. This is a certification system devised in CENELEC to apply to harmonised cables. While harmonisation of standards is a major step in removing technical barriers to trade between the member countries, it was recognised that differences in certification procedures, with some customers in some countries insisting on certification by their own national body, could inhibit marketing by one country in others. CENELEC includes a Marks Committee to deal with this aspect of trade barriers. It has that name because certification usually confers a licence to use a mark on the product concerned. The ◁HAR▷ mark scheme for cables, drawn up in collaboration between CENELEC TC20 and the Marks Committee, is in effect a harmonised product conformity certification scheme.

Licences to use the ◁HAR▷ mark on harmonised types of cable are granted by the nominated National Approval Organisation (NAO) in each participating country. In the UK this is BASEC. The mark consists of ◁HAR▷ preceded by the mark of the NAO printed or otherwise displayed on the outside of the cable, or it may be signified by a coloured thread within the cable. The colours of the thread are yellow, red and black and the lengths of the three colours indicate the country of the NAO.

Requirements for the NAO to issue approval are common for all member countries and comprise initial inspection of manufacturing and testing facilities, the testing of samples for initial approval and subsequent surveillance by the periodic testing of samples. The numbers of samples, related to production volume, the tests to be carried out and their frequency and the bases of assessment are the same for all countries and there is reciprocal acceptance of the mark between the countries. For example, the BASEC◁HAR▷ mark would be accepted in Germany as equivalent to the VDE◁HAR▷ mark, in The Netherlands as equivalent to the KEMA◁HAR▷ mark and so on.

To achieve common safety requirements, a low voltage directive was issued at an early stage by the European Commission to establish safety standards between 50 V and 1000 V and the requirements have to be incorporated in the national laws of the EEC countries. It is accepted that the requirements of the directive will be met if there is compliance with the Harmonisation Documents and it is presumed that manufacturers' products conform if they qualify for use of the ◁HAR▷ mark.

Chapter 8

Current Carrying Capacity

To achieve maximum economy in first cost and subsequent operation of cables, an important aspect is the selection of the optimum size of conductor. Several factors are involved in this and whilst the continuous current carrying capacity is paramount, other factors such as voltage drop, cost of losses and ability to carry short-circuit currents must not be neglected. In this chapter on current rating aspects, particular emphasis is placed on data concerning supply distribution cables but the principles are equally applicable to general wiring and transmission cables. For the latter, however, other more specialised features arise and further information is given in chapter 37.

For reasons which are discussed later, the most convenient way to establish a rating for a particular cable design is to calculate an amperage which can be carried continuously (often called a sustained rating) under prescribed standard conditions. Appropriate factors may then be applied to cater for the actual installation conditions and mode of operation.

AVAILABILITY OF PUBLISHED RATINGS

As is usual with most cable matters, the basic source of reference is an IEC specification and IEC 287, 'Calculation of the continuous current rating of cables (100% load factor)', provides in great detail the theory and mathematical treatment for most situations. IEC 364, 'Electrical installations of buildings', Part 5, gives tabulated ratings for standard cable designs up to 1000 V (unarmoured only) under standard conditions. For other types of cable and installation it is necessary to look elsewhere but all recognised publications provide figures which are deduced substantially in accordance with IEC 287.

Two of the important parameters in establishing ratings for standard operating conditions for particular installations are the ambient temperature and the permissible temperature rise. Therefore in selecting or comparing figures from published sources it is important to take account of them in assessing the information provided. The most commonly used sources of tabulated ratings are as follows.

(a) The Institution of Electrical Engineers in the UK publishes the IEE 'Regulations for electrical installations' and this contains tables for most standard cable types up to 1000 V, including mineral insulated. The tabulated ratings are for cables 'in air', i.e. not buried, and are calculated for a base ambient temperature of 30 °C. In the case of general supply distribution cables most other published ratings are based on an ambient temperature of 25 °C, and hence a greater permissible temperature rise. When corrected to any specific ambient temperature there is alignment with IEC 287.

(b) Since the very early years of cable utilisation, the Electrical Research Association in the UK (now ERA Technology Ltd) has specialised in methods of calculation and practical work for verification. It has become a recognised authority and many reports of its work have been published (see Bibliography, appendix A18). Report ERA 69-30 provides ratings in Part 1 for paper insulated cables up to 33 kV, in Part 2 for 600/1000 V Consac cables, in Part 3 for PVC insulated cables up to 3.3 kV, in Part 5 for armoured cables with thermosetting insulation to BS 5467 and in Part 6 for PVC insulated cables to BS 6346 in multilayer groups on trays.
(c) Most cable manufacturers issue catalogues which contain ratings for the cables which they supply.
(d) Other sources exist for more specialised installations. Cables for ships are based on an ambient temperature of 45 °C with somewhat lower maximum temperatures for continuous operation than permitted elsewhere. Ratings are provided in the IEE 'Regulations for the electrical and electronic equipment of ships'.
(e) While all the above references apply generally throughout the world, the types of cable and systems involved with USA practice are slightly different and reference should be made to NEMA/ICEA publications such as ICEA P53-426/NEMA WL 50, which contains details for XLPE/EPR insulated cables from 15 to 69 kV, or the National Electrical Code published by the National Fire Protection Association. Another different feature of American practice is that the published data allow for limited periods of emergency overload for a specific number of hours per year to a higher cable temperature. Whilst it is recognised that such operation could have an effect on the life of a cable, the conditions are chosen to ensure that only limited ageing is likely to occur. International practice may well move in this direction in the future.

The above sources generally contain ratings for individual cable types and sizes installed under specified conditions in air, in buried ducts and buried directly in the ground. The use of multiplying factors for variations in the conditions is discussed in a later section.

TYPICAL VALUES OF SUSTAINED RATINGS UNDER STANDARD CONDITIONS

Tables in the appendices contain sustained ratings and other data such as a.c. resistance at maximum operating temperature as required for rating calculations. The ratings conform to the principles of IEC 287 and are for cables in air and directly buried in the ground. Relevant installation and operating conditions for each table are given. The types of cable covered are essentially those to British Standards, or otherwise of recognised designs as used in the UK.

GENERAL BASIS OF RATING DETERMINATION

During service operation, cables suffer electrical losses which appear as heat in the conductor, insulation and metallic components. The current rating is dependent on the way this heat is transmitted to the cable surface and then dissipated to the surroundings. Temperature is clearly an important factor and is expressed as a conductor temperature to establish a datum for the cable itself. A maximum temperature is fixed which is commonly the limit for the insulation material, without undue ageing, for a reasonable maximum life. Then, by choosing a base ambient temperature for the surroundings, a permissible temperature rise is available from which a maximum cable rating can be calculated for a particular environment.

Under steady state conditions the difference between the conductor temperature and the external ground or ambient temperature is related to the total heat losses and the law of heat flow is very similar to Ohm's law. Heat flow corresponds to current, temperature difference to voltage and the total thermal resistance in the cable and surroundings to electrical resistance. From this basis the heat losses are often referred to as ohmic losses and using this analogy it is possible to construct a circuit diagram as illustrated in fig. 8.1. This shows how the heat input at several positions has to flow through a number of layers of different thermal resistances. By measuring values for the materials, rating calculations can then be made. Thermal resistivity is defined as the difference in temperature in kelvins between opposite faces of a metre cube of material caused by the transference of 1 W of heat – hence the units K m/W.

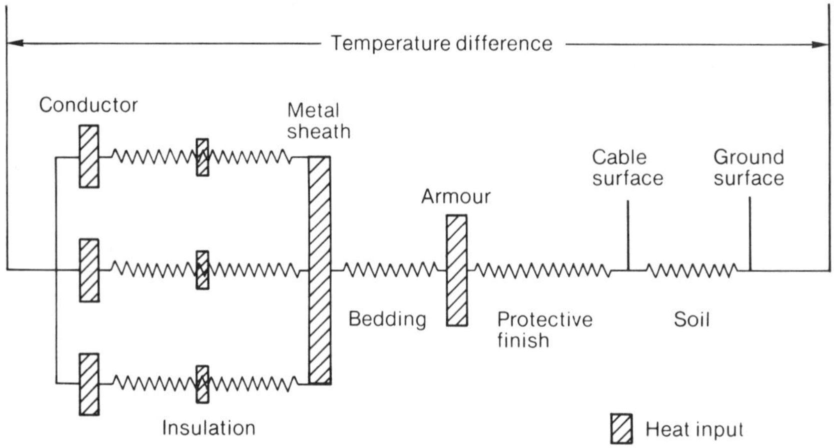

Fig. 8.1 Circuit diagram to represent heat generated in a 3-core metal sheathed cable

The heat flow within a cable is reasonably radial but externally it is not so and allowance must be made for the method of installation. Fig. 8.2, which shows the pattern of heat flow for three single-core cables, illustrates the importance of making allowance for the depth of burial and could be extended to show the effects of other cables in close proximity.

Mathematical treatment is most conveniently expressed for steady state conditions, i.e. for continuous (sustained) ratings. A small cable in air will heat up very quickly to a steady state condition but a large buried power cable may take very many hours. Hence for most types of operation for supply distribution cables laid direct, the continuous ratings may be conservative and allowance can be made for cyclic operation as discussed later.

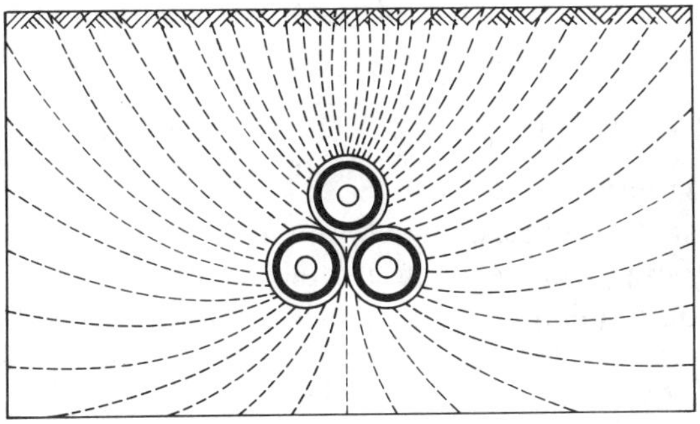

Fig. 8.2 Heat flow from a circuit of single-core cables installed in trefoil

MATHEMATICAL TREATMENT

The temperature rise in the cable is due to the heat generated in the conductors (I^2R), in the insulation (W) and in the sheath and armour (λI^2R), with allowance being made by multiplying each of these by the thermal resistance of the layers through which the heat flows (T). More detailed derivation of these components is discussed in the next section but the following formula shows how they can be used for calculation purposes for a.c. cables:

$$\Delta\theta = (I^2R + \tfrac{1}{2}W_d)T_1 + \left[I^2R\,(1 + \lambda_1) + W_d\right] nT_2 + \left[I^2R\,(1 + \lambda_1 + \lambda_2) + W_d\right] n(T_3 + T_4) \qquad (8.1)$$

where $\Delta\theta$ = conductor temperature rise (K)

I = current flowing in one conductor (A)

R = alternating current resistance per unit length of the conductor at maximum operating temperature (Ω/m)

W_d = dielectric loss per unit length for the insulation surrounding the conductor (W/m)

T_1 = thermal resistance per unit length between one conductor and the sheath (K m/W)

T_2 = thermal resistance per unit length of the bedding between sheath and armour (K m/W)

T_3 = thermal resistance per unit length of the external serving of the cable (K m/W)

T_4 = thermal resistance per unit length between the cable surface and the surrounding medium (K m/W)

n = number of load-carrying conductors in the cable (conductors of equal size and carrying the same load)

λ_1 = ratio of losses in the metal sheath to total losses in all conductors in that cable

λ_2 = ratio of losses in the armouring to total losses in all conductors in that cable

This formula may be rewritten as follows to obtain the permissible current rating:

$$I = \left\{\frac{\Delta\theta - W_d\,[\tfrac{1}{2}T_1 + n(T_2 + T_3 + T_4)]}{RT_1 + nR(1 + \lambda_1)\,T_2 + nR\,(1 + \lambda_1 + \lambda_2)\,(T_3 + T_4)}\right\}^{1/2} \qquad (8.2)$$

In using this formula account needs to be taken of the fact that it only provides ratings for the prescribed representative conditions. It does not allow for heat generation from any other source, such as other cables in close proximity, or from exposure to direct solar radiation. More detailed treatment for the latter is given in IEC 287.

In the case of 1 kV 4-core cables, n may be assumed to be 3 if the fourth conductor is neutral or is a protective conductor.

For d.c. cables some of the losses are not applicable and for up to 5 kV formula (8.2) may be simplified to

$$I = \left[\frac{\Delta\theta}{R'T_1 + nR'T_2 + nR'\,(T_3 + T_4)}\right]^{1/2} \qquad (8.3)$$

where R' = d.c. resistance per unit length of the conductor at maximum operating temperature (Ω/m)

CALCULATION OF LOSSES

Conductor resistance

It must be noted that R in the formula is the resistance at the maximum operating temperature and for a.c. operation allowance must be made for skin and proximity effects.

The d.c. resistance (Ω/km) at temperature θ is

$$R' = R_{20}\,[1 + \alpha_{20}(\theta - 20)] \qquad (8.4)$$

Values for R_{20} are given in appendix A4. The temperature coefficient per degree Celsius at 20 °C (α_{20}) for copper is 0.00393 and for aluminium is 0.00403. Reference to values for θ is made in the next section.

The a.c. resistance at temperature θ is

$$R = R'(1 + y_s + y_p)\ (\Omega/\text{km}) \qquad (8.5)$$

where y_s = the skin factor
y_p = the proximity effect factor

At power frequencies of 50–60 Hz the skin effect factor is small for conductors smaller than about 150 mm^2. Above this size it may be taken as

$$y_s = \frac{x_s^{\,4}}{192 + 0.8x_s^{\,4}} \qquad (8.6)$$

$$x_s^{\,2} = \frac{8\pi f}{R'} \times 10^{-7} k_s \qquad (8.7)$$

where f = supply frequency (Hz)
k_s = a constant for cable type (see IEC 287)

These formulae are accurate provided that x_s does not exceed 2.8.

Proximity effects are due to mutual effects between the main cable conductors themselves plus inductive currents in any metallic sheath and eddy currents in both metallic sheaths and armour. They can be neglected for small conductor sizes at power frequencies.

If detailed calculation is necessary reference should be made to IEC 287, but for standard cables figures for the total effective a.c. resistance at maximum operating temperature are included in the tables in the appendices.

Dielectric losses in a.c. cables

The dielectric loss in each phase is

$$W_d = \omega C U_0^2 \tan \delta \text{ (W/m)} \qquad (8.8)$$

where $\omega = 2\pi f$ (1/s) in which f is frequency (Hz) (s = second)
C = capacitance (F/m)
Values for $\tan \delta$ are given in table 8.1.

Table 8.1 Nominal values for relative permittivity and loss factor

Type of cable	Permittivity	$\tan \delta$
Solid type paper insulated	4	0.01
Oil-filled paper, low/medium pressure	3.3	0.004
Oil-filled paper, high pressure	3.5	0.0045
Oil pressure pipe type/paper	3.7	0.0045
External gas pressure/paper	3.5	0.004
Internal gas pressure/paper	3.4	0.0045
Butyl rubber	4	0.05
EPR	3	0.04
PVC	8	0.1
PE	2.3	0.001
XLPE	2.5	0.008

The capacitance for cables with circular conductors (F/m) is given by the formula below and this may also be applied for oval conductors if the geometric mean diameter is used:

$$C = \frac{\epsilon}{18 \log_e(D_i d_c)} \times 10^{-9} \qquad (8.9)$$

where ϵ = relative permittivity of insulation (table 8.1)
D_i = external diameter of insulation excluding screen (mm)
d_c = diameter of conductor including screen (mm)

It is not usually necessary to calculate the capacitance for cables with shaped conductors because they are only used in cables for which dielectric losses may be neglected, i.e. for values of U_0 below 26 kV for paper cables, 12 kV for butyl rubber, 15 kV for EPR, 6 kV for PVC, 110 kV for PE and 37 kV for XLPE.

Losses in metal sheaths and armour (a.c. cables)

In multicore cables, sheath and armour losses may make some contribution to total losses but the effects are not of very great significance. However, with single-core cables the situation is very different and substantial losses may result from circulating currents and eddy currents in the sheaths. Eddy current losses may be ignored when cables are bonded at both ends.

Sheath circulating currents are of particular importance but losses can be reduced to zero by single-point bonding or by carrying out cross-bonding of the sheaths as described in chapter 37. Allowance still has to be made for eddy current losses. Equations for calculations of all the losses relating to sheaths and armour are available but because of the many different possible combinations of circumstances they are difficult to summarise concisely and reference should be made to IEC 287 which contains full details.

Similar remarks apply to magnetic armour on single-core cables and in this case the effect on rating is so great that it is seldom possible to use such armour. Non-magnetic aluminium or bronze is normally adopted and the losses are then much lower, but allowance still has to be made for circulating and eddy currents.

CALCULATION OF THERMAL RESISTANCES

In order to use equation (8.2) it is necessary to calculate the thermal resistances of the different parts of the cable (T_1, T_2 and T_3). Representative values for the resistivity of the individual materials used in cables are included in IEC 287, of which table 8.2 is a summary.

In making calculations, screening layers are considered to be part of the conductor if they are metallic and part of the insulation if they are semiconducting. With cables having corrugated metallic sheaths, the thickness of insulation is based on the mean internal diameter of the sheath.

Thermal resistance between one conductor and sheath (T_1)

The equations for various cable constructions are outlined below, IEC 287 contains further information, including data for the geometric factor G and an additional screening factor which is necessary for screened cables.

Single-core cables

$$T_1 = \frac{\rho_\tau}{2\pi} \log_e\left(1 + \frac{2t_1}{d_c}\right) \qquad (8.10)$$

where ρ_τ = thermal resistivity of insulation (K m/W)
d_c = diameter of conductor (mm)
t_1 = thickness of insulation, conductor to sheath (mm)

Multicore belted cables

$$T_1 = \frac{\rho_\tau}{2\pi} G \qquad (8.11)$$

Table 8.2 Thermal resistivities of materials

Material	Thermal resistivity (K m/W)
Insulation	
Paper (varies with cable type)	5.5–6.5
PE and XLPE	3.5
PVC – up to and including 3 kV	5.0
over 3 kV	6.0
EPR – up to and including 3 kV	3.5
over 3 kV	5.0
Butyl rubber and natural rubber	5.0
Protective coverings	
Compounded jute and fibrous materials	6.0
PCP	5.5
PVC – up to and including 35 kV cables	5.0
over 35 kV cables	6.0
PE	3.5
Materials for ducts	
Concrete	1.0
Fibre	4.8
Asbestos	2.0
Earthenware	1.2
PVC	7.0
PE	3.5

where G is a geometric factor.

Multicore screened cables

$$T_1 = \frac{\rho_\tau}{2\pi} G \times \text{screening factor} \tag{8.12}$$

SL and SA type cables
These are treated as single-core cables.

Thermal resistance between sheath and armour (T_2)

Single-core and multicore cables

$$T_2 = \frac{\rho_\tau}{2\pi} \log_e\left(1 + \frac{2t_2}{D_s}\right) \tag{8.13}$$

where t_2 = thickness of bedding (mm)
D_s = external diameter of sheath (mm)

SL and SA type cables

$$T_2 = \frac{\rho_T}{2\pi} G' \tag{8.14}$$

where G' is a geometric factor from IEC 287.

Thermal resistance of outer coverings (T_3)

$$T_3 = \frac{\rho_T}{2\pi} \log_e\left(1 + \frac{2t_3}{D'_a}\right) \tag{8.15}$$

where t_3 = thickness of outer covering (mm)
D'_a = external diameter of armour (mm)

For corrugated sheaths reference should be made to IEC 287.

External thermal resistance in free air (T_4)

Assuming protection from solar radiation,

$$T_4 = \frac{1}{\pi D_e h (\Delta\theta_s)^{1/4}} \tag{8.16}$$

where D_e = external diameter of cable (mm)
h = heat dissipation coefficient from IEC 287
$\Delta\theta_s$ = excess of surface temperature above ambient (K)

Allowance can be made for exposure to solar radiation and details are given in IEC 287.

External thermal resistance for buried cables (T_4)

Single isolated buried cables

$$T_4 = \frac{\rho_T}{2\pi} \log_e[\mu + (\mu^2 - 1)^{1/2}] \tag{8.17}$$

where ρ_T = the thermal resistivity of the soil (K m/W)
$\mu = 2L/D_e$
L = distance from ground surface to cable axis (mm)
D_e = external diameter of the cable (mm)

IEC 287 contains further information for groups of cables, touching and non-touching, with equal and unequal loading, together with a reference to unfilled troughs at surface level.

The range of values for soil thermal resistivity is given later, and the subject is of considerable importance, particularly for transmission cables. For cables in buried troughs careful attention must be given to the filling medium and the value of resistivity selected.

Cables in buried ducts (T_4)

In this case T_4 is the sum of the thermal resistance of the air space between cable and duct (T_4'), the thermal resistance of the duct itself (T_4'') and the external thermal resistance (T_4''').

Thermal resistance of air space (T_4')
For cable diameters of 25 to 100 mm

$$T_4' = \frac{U}{1 + 0.1(V + Y\theta_m)D_e} \tag{8.18}$$

where U, V and Y are constants (IEC 187)
D_e = external diameter of cable (mm)
θ_m = mean temperature of the air space (°C)

Thermal resistance of the duct (T_4'')

$$T_4'' = \frac{\rho_\tau}{2\pi} \log_e\left(\frac{D_o}{D_d}\right) \tag{8.19}$$

where D_o = outside diameter of duct (mm)
D_d = inside diameter of duct (mm)
ρ_τ = thermal resistivity of duct material as given in table 8.2 (K m/W)

Thermal resistance of the external medium (T_4''')
In general this is treated as though the duct represents a cable in equation (8.17). If the ducts are surrounded by concrete, allowance has to be made for the composite surrounding of concrete and soil.

IMPORTANT PARAMETERS WHICH AFFECT RATINGS

The main factors which have effects on ratings may be split into a number of groups as follows.

Temperature
Primarily it is the temperature rise which is important but this is governed by the base ambient temperature for the given cable location and the maximum temperature applicable to the insulation and cable construction. This is discussed in the next section.

Cable design
Apart from the temperature limit, the other effect of cable design is the ability to transfer heat from the conductors to the outer surface. This varies with the materials used and the number of layers in the construction. Details have been given in the sections on mathematical treatment.

Conditions of installation
On the whole, a cable in air can dissipate heat better than a cable in the ground but in this respect the cable diameter, or more particularly the surface area, is important. Up to a certain size cables in air have a lower rating than buried cables and when cables are buried the rating decreases with depth of burial. Further details are given in a later section.

Effects of neighbouring cables
Any other heat input from hot pipes or other cables in the vicinity has to be taken into account. In the case of other cables, allowances can usually be made by the use of correction factors, as discussed later, and reference may be made to IEC 287 for the basis of calculation.

Correction factors for deviation from standard conditions
In addition to the above there are many other conditions such as ambient temperature etc. for which rating correction factors can be applied and these are given later.

AMBIENT AND CABLE OPERATING TEMPERATURES

Ambient temperature

Representative average ambient temperatures may vary within any individual country, e.g. according to whether the cables are buried or in air outdoors or within a building, and between countries according to the geographical climate. For convenience, the normal tabulated ratings in the UK are based on 15 °C for cables in the ground, 25 °C outdoors in air, 30 °C in air within buildings and 45 °C for conditions in ships. For guidance purposes IEC 287 has made an attempt to provide representative average values for other countries. These are included in table 8.3 which illustrates the general overall range throughout the world and table 8.4 which aims to provide data for individual countries. Table 8.4 is only very approximate, however, and subject to many variations.

In using information from these tables several points must be kept in mind. Cable ratings must be applicable for the worst conditions throughout the year and hence for the highest temperatures. Minimum temperatures are only of interest if specific winter ratings are being considered. Also many countries have important differences in climate across the country. Although different countries quote different values of

Table 8.3 Ambient air and ground temperature (°C)

Climate	Air temperature		Ground temperature (at 1 m depth)	
	Minimum	Maximum	Minimum	Maximum
Tropical	25	55	25	40
Subtropical	10	40	15	30
Temperate	0	25	10	20

Table 8.4 Representative conditions for various countries

Country	Ambient air temperature (°C)	Ambient ground temperature (°C)	Soil thermal resistivity (K m/W)	Depth of burial (mm)
Australia	40 summer 30 winter	25 summer 18 winter	1.2	500
Austria				
1 kV	20 average	20 maximum	0.7	700
3–6 kV	20 average	20 maximum	0.7	800
10 kV	20 average	20 maximum	0.7	1000
pressure	20 average	20 maximum	1.0	1200
Canada	40 maximum −40 minimum	20 maximum −5 minimum	1.2 ref*	
paper to 69 kV				1100
polymeric to 46 kV				900
pressure				1100
Finland	25 ref* (−20 to 35)	15 maximum 0 minimum	1.0 ref*	
below 36 kV				700
36–52 kV				1000
52–123 KV				1300
123–245 kV				1500
France	30 summer 20 winter	20 summer 10 winter	1.2 summer 0.85 winter	
West Germany	30 maximum (−20 to + 20 average)	20 maximum 0 minimum	1.0	
below 20 kV				700 ref*
above 60 kV				1200
Italy	30 ref* (0–30)	20 ref* 5 minimum	1.0 maximum	
below 12				800
12–17.5 kV				1000
17.5–24 kV				1200
24–36 kV				1500
36–72 kV				1800
72–220 kV				2200
Japan	40 summer 30 winter	25 summer 15 winter	1.0 average	
up to 33 kV				1200
pressure				1500
Netherlands	20 average (−5 to 30)	15 average (5–20)	0.5–0.8	
up to 10 kV				700
over 10 kV				1000

Table 8.4 (*cont.*)

Country	Ambient air temperature (°C)	Ambient ground temperature (°C)	Soil thermal resistivity (K m/W)	Depth of burial (mm)
Poland	25 ref*	15 ref*	0.8	
up to 1 kV				700
1–15 kV				800
over 15 kV				1000
Sweden		15 maximum 0 minimum	1.0 ref*	
up to 52 kV				700
pressure				1000–1500
Switzerland	25 ref*	20 ref*	1.0 ref*	1000
UK	25 outdoors 30 buildings	15	1.2 ref*	
1 kV				500
3.3–33 kV				800
pressure				900
USA	40 ref*	20	0.9 ref*	900

*ref signifies reference value for rating purposes

soil resistivity for calculation purposes it is important to investigate the conditions for the individual cable circuit.

It will be apparent from table 8.3 that the rating penalty, when referred to permissible temperature rise, is very high for cables at high ambient temperatures. There is clearly a considerable advantage in using a type of insulation which can sustain a high operating temperature, e.g. XLPE at 90 °C instead of solid type paper cable at 33 kV with a temperature of 65 °C.

Maximum cable operating temperature

Maximum cable operating temperatures according to insulation material, cable design and voltage have been agreed in IEC and the standard values are almost universally accepted throughout the world for continuous operation (table 8.5).

In using these values an important proviso is that attention must be given to soil resistivity. Continuous operation at cable surface temperatures above 50 °C will cause movement of moisture away from the cables and, with many types of cable, drying out of the backfill may occur and the cable could exceed the permissible temperature.

Taken at face value, the figures in table 8.5 indicate a major advantage for the materials which can be operated at high temperature but it must be remembered that there are other factors involved in the choice of cable size. For cables in

Table 8.5 Conductor temperature limits for standard cable types

Insulation	Cable design	Maximum conductor temperature (°C)
Impregnated paper (U_0/U)		
0.6/1, 1.8/3, 3.6/6	Belted	80
6/10	Belted	65
6/10, 8.7/15	Screened	70
12/20, 18/30 MIND	Screened	65
Poly(vinyl chloride)	All	70
Polyethylene	All	70
Butyl rubber	All	85
Ethylene–propylene rubber	All	90
Crosslinked polyethylene	All	90
Natural rubber	All	60

buildings in the UK (base ambient temperature of 30 °C) the permissible temperature rise for XLPE is 60 °C, compared with 40 °C for PVC. However, in such installations it is often voltage drop which is the determining factor. Furthermore, the extra cost of electrical losses due to increase in conductor resistance may not be insignificant with relatively continuous operation.

EFFECT OF INSTALLATION CONDITIONS ON RATINGS

Reference has already been made to a conductor size effect in rating differences between installation in air and in the ground, this being associated with the cable surface area. Some other aspects arising are covered below.

Depth of burial

The depth of laying is governed primarily by what is considered to be the most advisable to minimise effects of damage and generally increases with cable voltage. Values adopted in various countries have been given in table 8.4. An equation covering the effect on rating has already been quoted and for most purposes the thermal resistance of the soil may be simplified to

$$T_4 = \frac{\rho_\tau}{2\pi} \log_e\left(\frac{4L}{D_e}\right) \tag{8.20}$$

where ρ_τ = soil thermal resistivity (K m/W)
L = depth of burial to cable axis (mm)
D_e = cable external diameter (mm)

In this formula variations of ρ_τ may be extremely important but variations of laying depth have less effect. As the depth increases the temperature decreases and also the moisture content increases, so that this improves the soil resistivity. Therefore for conditions where the temperature can be taken as 15 °C and ρ_τ is around 1.2 K m/W, it is only with transmission cables that much account need be taken of depth of laying, and with these cables the subject of external thermal resistance has to be thoroughly evaluated anyway because of the need to select appropriate backfill.

Thermal resistivity of the soil

Provided that it is possible to arrive at a reasonably representative value, it is not normally necessary with supply distribution cables to devote much attention to soil thermal resistivity, unless because of fully continuous operation there is a danger of the soil drying out.

The presence of moisture has a predominant effect on the resistivity of any type of soil and so it is necessary to take the weather conditions into account. IEC 287 gives guidance as indicated in table 8.6 and ignores the make-up of particular ground types. However, the steps quoted are rather broad and certainly for transmission cables greater precision is necessary.

Table 8.6 Soil thermal resistivities

Thermal resistivity (K m/W)	Soil conditions	Weather conditions
0.7	Very moist	Continuously moist
1.0	Moist	Regular rainfall
2.0	Dry	Seldom rains
3.0	Very dry	Little or no rain

At one time it was common to take direct measurements using a needle-probe technique but such results are very difficult to interpret because judgement is necessary on whether the moisture content at the time of measurement is representative and because the resistivity is strongly dependent on the amount of compaction; this can be changed when the probe is inserted and the soil put back round the cable will be in a different condition. It is better, therefore, to adopt a more empirical approach according to whether the cable operating conditions will or will not cause drying out of the soil.

If drying out is not a problem, as with nearly all distribution cable installations, the question is the likely moisture content. In some cases it will be known that the ground will remain wet or fairly moist and in these situations it is reasonable to adopt 0.8–1.0 K m/W.

In the more general case, however, where soils are not always quite moist but the texture is of an average clay or loam type, a good representative figure is 1.2 K m/W, and in the UK this is usually taken as a standard value for the preparation of tabulated ratings. The situation is more difficult if the soil consists of sand, shingle or made-up ground, i.e. with a large air-space content after water has drained away. If such drainage can occur during some months of the year the value used should be between 2.0 and 3.0 according to circumstances.

Guidance is given in ERA Report 69–30: Part 1 on the following lines.

Type A – cables carrying constant load throughout the year
Whether the load is sustained or cyclic, allowance needs to be made for maximum values of soil resistivity which may occur in some years only and for relatively short periods in summer and autumn. Values recommended are as follows:

All soils except those below	1.5 K m/W
Chalk soil with crushed chalk backfill	1.2 K m/W
Peat	1.2 K m/W
Very stony soil or ballast	1.5 K m/W
Well-drained sand	2.5 K m/W
Made-up soils	1.8 K m/W

The value for the 'all soils' category may be reduced to 1.2 if the soil is under impermeable cover such as asphalt or concrete.

Type B – cables with varying load and maximum in summer
If the load is mixed, advantage may be taken of the fact that in all probability the maximum load in summer will not coincide with the dry periods. During the summer periods, recommended values are as follows:

All soils except those below	1.2 K m/W
Stony soils or ballast	1.3 K m/W
Well-drained sand	2.0 K m/W
Made-up soils	1.6 K m/W

The value for the 'all soils' category may be reduced to 1.0 if the soil is under impermeable cover and assumes that in chalky ground the backfill is crushed.

Type C – cables with varying load and maximum in winter
For the winter period it is safe to use rather lower values:

All soils except those below	1.0 K m/W
Clay	0.9 K m/W
Chalk soil with crushed chalk backfill	1.2 K m/W
Well-drained sand	1.5 K m/W
Made-up soil	1.2 K m/W

The value for clay soils may be reduced to 0.8 if the soil is under impermeable cover.

The drying out of soil is quite a complex subject because, in addition to the cable temperature and natural drainage, drying is also caused by tree roots and natural vegetation. A solid cover on the surface, e.g. asphalt or concrete, restricts drying out.

As already mentioned, a cable surface temperature of 50 °C is sufficient to lead to progressive drying out, and if the soil is well drained, e.g. sandy, drying out can occur at an even lower temperature. The most favourable dried out natural soil and sands are unlikely to have a thermal resistivity lower than 2.0 K m/W and values of 2.5–3.0 K m/W are probable. To obtain optimum cable rating in situations where drying out is possible, it is now general practice to surround the cable with imported material of known properties. Such material is usually known as thermal or controlled backfill and the key to successful formulation is minimum air space together with good compaction. These materials are always designed to have a good thermal resistivity when dry and measurement of the dry density at a defined compaction provides a reasonable means of evaluation. Nowadays they fall into two groups: one in which there is control of particle sizes and another using a weak mix of cement. The dry mixture is composed of blends of shingle and sand each having a wide range of particle sizes with the object of obtaining very good packing. The alternative material, now more widely used, is a 20:1 ratio of suitable mixed particle size sand and cement with optimum water content.

Further details of the importance of the use of controlled backfill material are given in chapter 37.

STANDARD OPERATING CONDITIONS AND RATING FACTORS FOR SUPPLY DISTRIBUTION CABLES

The standard conditions for the ratings given in the tables in the appendices are included with the tables and in general are as given below.

The standard conditions, and particularly the rating factors, vary with the cable design and the operating parameters. The data given apply primarily to supply distribution cables and are averages for such cables. They may be taken as a general guide for wiring type cables but some special comments on wiring type cables are given in a later section.

In the case of transmission cables it is not possible to obtain sufficient accuracy by the use of rating factors and the rating for each installation needs to be calculated directly.

Cables installed in air

Standard conditions

(a) Ambient air temperature is taken to be 25 °C for paper insulated cables and for XLPE insulated cables above 1.9/3.3 kV. 30 °C is chosen for PVC insulated cables and for XLPE cables of 1.9/3.3 kV and below in order to be in conformity with the IEE Wiring Regulations.

(b) Air circulation is not restricted significantly, e.g. if cables are fastened to a wall they should be spaced at least 20 mm from it.

(c) Adjacent circuits are spaced at least 150 mm apart and suitably disposed to prevent mutual heating.

(d) Cables are shielded from direct sunshine.

Rating factors for other ambient air temperatures

Factors to correct from a base of 25 or 30 °C to other temperatures are given in table 8.7. For the types and voltages of paper insulated cables to which the various operating temperatures apply reference should be made to table 8.5.

Group rating factors for cables in air

When groups of multicore power cables are installed in air it is necessary to have a

Table 8.7 Rating factors for ambient temperature

Cable insulation	Maximum conductor operating temperature (°C)	Ambient air temperature (°C)						
		25	30	35	40	45	50	55
Paper	65	1.0	0.93	0.85	0.77	0.68	0.58	0.47
Paper	70	1.0	0.93	0.87	0.80	0.72	0.64	0.55
Paper	80	1.0	0.94	0.89	0.84	0.77	0.72	0.65
PVC	70	1.06	1.0	0.94	0.87	0.79	0.71	0.61
XLPE (a)[a]	90	1.0	0.95	0.91	0.86	0.80	0.75	0.69
XLPE (b)[b]	90	1.04	1.0	0.96	0.91	0.87	0.82	0.76

[a] Above 1.9/3.3 kV
[b] 1.9/3.3 kV and below

sufficient air space for dissipation of heat. No reduction in rating is necessary provided that

(a) the horizontal clearance between circuits is not less than twice the overall diameter of an individual cable;
(b) the vertical clearance between circuits is not less than four times the diameter of an individual cable;
(c) if the number of circuits exceeds three, they are installed in a horizontal plane.

For smaller clearances reference should be made to ERA Report 74–27, 'Heat dissipation for cables in air', and ERA Report 74-28, 'Heat dissipation for cables on perforated steel trays'.

Further information relative to the smaller sizes of PVC and XLPE cables, as used in buildings, is given later in this chapter.

Cables laid direct in ground

Standard conditions

(a) Ground temperature	15 °C
(b) Soil thermal resistivity	1.2 K m/W
(c) Adjacent circuits	at least 1.8 m distance
(d) Depth of laying	0.5 m for 1 kV cables
	0.8 m for cables above 1 kV and up to 33 kV

Rating factors

Factors for ground temperature, soil thermal resistivity, grouped cables and depth of laying are given in tables 8.8–8.12.

Table 8.8 Rating factor for ground temperature

Cable insulation	Maximum conductor operating temperature (°C)	Ground temperature (°C)							
		10	15	20	25	30	35	40	45
Paper	65	1.05	1.0	0.95	0.89	0.84	0.77	0.71	0.63
Paper	70	1.04	1.0	0.95	0.90	0.85	0.80	0.74	0.67
Paper	75	1.04	1.0	0.96	0.92	0.88	0.83	0.78	0.73
PVC	70	1.04	1.0	0.95	0.90	0.85	0.80	0.74	0.67
XLPE	90	1.03	1.0	0.97	0.93	0.89	0.85	0.81	0.77

Table 8.9 Rating factors for thermal resistivity of soil (average values)

Conductor size (mm^2)	Soil thermal resistivity (K m/W)						
	0.8	0.9	1.0	1.5	2.0	2.5	3.0
Single-core cables							
Up to 150	1.16	1.11	1.07	0.91	0.81	0.73	0.67
From 185 to 400	1.17	1.12	1.07	0.90	0.80	0.72	0.66
From 500 to 1200	1.18	1.13	1.08	0.90	0.79	0.71	0.65
Multicore cables							
Up to 16	1.09	1.06	1.04	0.95	0.86	0.79	0.74
From 25 to 150	1.14	1.10	1.07	0.93	0.84	0.76	0.70
From 185 to 400	1.16	1.11	1.07	0.92	0.82	0.74	0.68

Cables installed in ducts

Standard conditions

(a) Ground temperature, 15 °C
(b) Thermal resistivity of ground and ducts, 1.2 K m/W
(c) Adjacent circuits, at least 1.8 m distance
(d) Depth of laying, 0.5 m, except for paper insulated cables above 1 kV and up to 33 kV, for which the value is 0.8 m

Rating factors

Factors for variation of ground temperatures are the same as in table 8.8 for cables laid directly in the ground. Factors for soil thermal resistivity, groups of cables and depth of laying are given in tables 8.13–8.16.

SUSTAINED RATINGS FOR WIRING TYPE CABLES

Ratings for the most commonly used types of cables in the UK are given in the tables in appendices A5–A11. Standard conditions vary according to cable type and

Table 8.10 Group rating factors for circuits of three single-core cables, in trefoil and laid flat touching, horizontal formation

Cable voltage (kV)	Number of circuits	Spacing of circuits (between centres of cable groups)					
		Touching		0.15 m[a]	0.3 m	0.45 m	0.6 m
		Trefoil	Laid flat				
0.6/1	2	0.77	0.80	0.82	0.88	0.90	0.93
	3	0.65	0.68	0.72	0.79	0.83	0.87
	4	0.59	0.63	0.67	0.75	0.81	0.85
	5	0.55	0.58	0.63	0.72	0.78	0.83
	6	0.52	0.56	0.60	0.70	0.77	0.82
1.9/3.3 to 12.7/22	2	0.78	0.80	0.81	0.85	0.88	0.90
	3	0.66	0.69	0.71	0.76	0.80	0.83
	4	0.60	0.63	0.65	0.72	0.76	0.80
	5	0.55	0.58	0.61	0.68	0.73	0.77
	6	0.52	0.55	0.58	0.66	0.72	0.76
19/33	2	0.79	0.81	0.81	0.85	0.88	0.90
	3	0.67	0.70	0.71	0.76	0.80	0.83
	4	0.62	0.65	0.65	0.72	0.76	0.80
	5	0.57	0.60	0.60	0.68	0.73	0.77
	6	0.54	0.57	0.57	0.66	0.72	0.76

[a] This spacing will not be possible for some of the larger diameter cables

application and the various relevant conditions applicable are included with the tables. Some of the more important aspects are given below.

Ambient temperature

The tabulated ratings are based on an ambient temperature, and hence temperature rise, according to the primary application of the cable, e.g. 25 °C where no regulations apply, 30 °C for cables in buildings subject to the IEE Wiring Regulations and 45 °C for cables in ships subject to IEE Regulations. When applying temperature correction factors it is important to choose the correct factor which takes into account the base ambient temperature and the maximum permissible conductor temperature.

Excess current protection

The IEE Wiring Regulations require that the overload protective device should operate in conventional time at 1.45 times the current rating of the cable. As discussed in chapter 10, if the protection is by semi-enclosed rewirable fuse, which may require a current up to twice its own rating to operate it in conventional time, a

Table 8.11 Group rating factors for multicore cables in horizontal formation

Cable voltage (kV)	Number of cables in group	Spacing (between cable centres)				
		Touching	0.15 m	0.3 m	0.45 m	0.6 m
0.6/1	2	0.81	0.87	0.91	0.93	0.94
	3	0.70	0.78	0.84	0.87	0.90
	4	0.63	0.74	0.81	0.86	0.89
	5	0.59	0.70	0.78	0.83	0.87
	6	0.55	0.67	0.76	0.82	0.86
1.9/3.3 to 12.7/22	2	0.80	0.85	0.89	0.90	0.92
	3	0.69	0.75	0.80	0.84	0.86
	4	0.63	0.70	0.77	0.80	0.84
	5	0.57	0.66	0.73	0.78	0.81
	6	0.55	0.63	0.71	0.76	0.80
19/33	2	0.80	0.83	0.87	0.89	0.91
	3	0.70	0.73	0.78	0.82	0.85
	4	0.64	0.68	0.74	0.78	0.82
	5	0.59	0.63	0.70	0.75	0.79
	6	0.56	0.60	0.68	0.74	0.78

Table 8.12 Rating factors for depth of laying (to centre of cable or trefoil group of cables)

Depth of laying (m)	0.6/1 kV cables			1.9/3.3 kV to 19/33 kV cables	
	Up to 50 mm^2	70 mm to 300 mm^2	Above 300 mm^2	Up to 300 mm^2	Above 300 mm^2
0.50	1.00	1.00	1.00	–	–
0.60	0.99	0.98	0.97	–	–
0.80	0.97	0.96	0.94	1.00	1.00
1.00	0.95	0.94	0.92	0.98	0.97
1.25	0.94	0.92	0.90	0.96	0.95
1.50	0.93	0.91	0.89	0.95	0.94
1.75	0.92	0.89	0.87	0.94	0.92
2.00	0.91	0.88	0.86	0.92	0.90
2.50	0.90	0.87	0.85	0.91	0.89
3.0 or more	0.89	0.86	0.83	0.90	0.88

cable with a higher rating in comparison with the fuse rating is required than for other standard protective devices.

Selection of cable size

The rating factors for ambient temperature and installation conditions are factors by

Table 8.13 Rating factor for soil thermal resistivity

Conductor size (mm^2)	Soil thermal resistivity (K m/W)						
	0.8	0.9	1.0	1.5	2.0	2.5	3.0
Single-core cables							
Up to 150	1.10	1.07	1.04	0.94	0.87	0.81	0.75
185 to 400	1.11	1.08	1.05	0.94	0.86	0.79	0.73
500 to 1200	1.13	1.09	1.06	0.93	0.84	0.77	0.70
Multicore cables							
Up to 16	1.05	1.04	1.03	0.97	0.92	0.87	0.83
25 to 150	1.07	1.05	1.03	0.96	0.90	0.85	0.78
185 to 400	1.09	1.06	1.04	0.95	0.87	0.82	0.76

Table 8.14 Group rating factors for single-core cables in trefoil single-way ducts, horizontal formation

Cable voltage (kV)	Number of circuits	Spacing (between duct centres)		
		Touching	0.45 m	0.60 m
0.6/1	2	0.86	0.90	0.93
	3	0.77	0.83	0.87
	4	0.73	0.81	0.85
	5	0.70	0.78	0.83
	6	0.68	0.77	0.82
1.9/3.3 to 12.7/22	2	0.85	0.88	0.90
	3	0.75	0.80	0.83
	4	0.70	0.76	0.80
	5	0.67	0.73	0.77
	6	0.64	0.71	0.76
19/33	2	0.85	0.88	0.90
	3	0.76	0.80	0.83
	4	0.71	0.76	0.80
	5	0.67	0.73	0.77
	6	0.65	0.71	0.76

which the tabulated ratings, as given in the appendices, should be multiplied in order to determine the rating under the applicable conditions. For distribution cables the procedure for determining the size of cable is often to make a first judgement of the size required, multiply its tabulated rating by any applicable factors and check the result against the circuit requirement. If necessary, adjacent sizes are considered.

For installations to the IEE Wiring Regulations, the Regulations recommend an alternative procedure. The rating of the overload protective device to be used, decided according to the circuit current, is divided by the applicable factors and the

Table 8.15 Group rating factors for multicore cables in single-way ducts, horizontal formation

Cable voltage (kV)	Number of ducts in groups	Spacing (between duct centres)			
		Touching	0.30 m	0.45 m	0.60 m
0.6/1	2	0.90	0.93	0.95	0.96
	3	0.82	0.87	0.90	0.93
	4	0.78	0.85	0.89	0.91
	5	0.75	0.82	0.87	0.90
	6	0.72	0.81	0.86	0.90
1.9/3.3 to 12.7/22	2	0.88	0.91	0.93	0.94
	3	0.80	0.84	0.87	0.89
	4	0.75	0.81	0.84	0.87
	5	0.71	0.77	0.82	0.85
	6	0.69	0.75	0.80	0.84
19/33	2	0.87	0.89	0.92	0.93
	3	0.78	0.82	0.85	0.87
	4	0.73	0.78	0.82	0.85
	5	0.69	0.75	0.79	0.83
	6	0.67	0.73	0.78	0.82

Table 8.16 Rating factors for depth of laying (to centre of duct or trefoil group of ducts)

Depth of laying (m)	0.6/1 kV cables		1.9/3.3 to 19/33 kV cables	
	Single-core	Multicore	Single-core	Multicore
0.50	1.00	1.00		
0.60	0.98	0.99		
0.80	0.95	0.97	1.00	1.00
1.00	0.93	0.96	0.98	0.99
1.25	0.90	0.95	0.95	0.97
1.50	0.89	0.94	0.93	0.96
1.75	0.88	0.94	0.92	0.95
2.0	0.87	0.93	0.90	0.94
2.50	0.86	0.93	0.89	0.93
3.0 or more	0.85	0.92	0.88	0.92

result is compared with the values listed in the tables to determine the cable size, i.e. the principles for wiring cables are as outlined below.

Protective device being a fuse to BS 88 or BS 1361 or a circuit breaker to BS 3871 or BS 4752: Part 1

When the protective device is a fuse or circuit breaker to the above specifications, it is necessary to ascertain the cable rating required by one of the following methods.

(a) Select a protective device rating I_n adequate for the design current I_b which the circuit is to carry.
(b) Divide the nominal current of the protective device (I_n) by any applicable correction factor for ambient temperature, if this is other than 30 °C (C_a).
(c) Further divide by any applicable correction factor for thermal insulation (C_i).
(d) Divide by any applicable correction factor (C_g) for cable grouping, when such groups are liable to simultaneous overload. (See the alternative method below for groups which are *not* liable to simultaneous overload.)
(e) The size of cable required is such that its tabulated current carrying capacity I_t is not less than the value of the nominal current of the protective device (I_n) adjusted as above, i.e. $I_t \geqslant I_n / C_a C_i C_g$.

Alternative method for cable grouping when groups are not liable to simultaneous overload
Provided that the circuits of the groups are *not* liable to simultaneous overload, the tabulated current rating I_t may be calculated by the following formulae:

$$I_t \geqslant \frac{I_b}{C_g} \tag{8.21}$$

and

$$I_t \geqslant \left(I_n^2 + 0.48\, I_b^2 \, \frac{1 - C_g^2}{C_g^2} \right)^{1/2} \tag{8.22}$$

The size of the cable required is such that its tabulated single-circuit current carrying capacity is not less than the larger of the two values of I_t given by equations (8.21) and (8.22).

Where any further correction factor is applicable, such as for ambient temperature or thermal insulation, this must be applied as a divisor to the value of I_t derived by the methods indicated above in respect of the group rating factor.

Protective device being a semi-enclosed fuse to BS 3036
When the protective device is a semi-enclosed fuse to BS 3036 (i.e. formerly coarse excess current protection) it is necessary to ascertain the cable rating required by one of the following methods.

(a) Select a fuse I_n required from BS 3036 adequate for the design current I_b which the circuit is to carry.
(b) Divide the nominal current of the protective device (I_n) by any applicable correction factor for ambient temperature, if this is other than 30 °C (C_a).
(c) Further divide by any applicable correction factor for thermal insulation (C_i).
(d) Further divide by 0.725.
(e) Divide by any applicable correction factor C_g for cable grouping when groups are liable to simultaneous overload. (See the alternative method for groups which are *not* liable to simultaneous overload.)
(f) The size of cable required is such that its tabulated current carrying capacity I_t is not less than the value of nominal current of the protective device (I_n) adjusted as above, i.e. $I_t \geqslant \dfrac{I_n}{0.725\, C_a C_i C_g}$

Alternative method for cable grouping when groups are not liable to simultaneous overload
Provided that the circuits of the groups are *not* liable to simultaneous overload, the tabulated current rating I_t may be calculated by the following formulae:

$$I_t \geqslant \frac{I_b}{C_g} \tag{8.23}$$

and

$$I_t \geqslant \left(1.9 I_n^2 + 0.48 I_b^2 \frac{1 - C_g^2}{C_g^2}\right)^{1/2} \tag{8.24}$$

The size of the cable required is such that its tabulated single-circuit current carrying capacity is not less than the larger of the two values of I_t given by equations (8.23) and (8.24).

Group rating factors
Correction factors C_g for groups of cables are given in table 8.17. With reference to the table the following should be noted.

Table 8.17 Group correction factors for PVC cables

Arrangement of cables	Number of circuits or multicore cables									
	2	3	4	5	6	8	10	12	14	16
Enclosed in conduit or trunking, or bunched and clipped direct	0.80	0.70	0.65	0.60	0.57	0.52	0.48	0.45	0.43	0.41
Single layer clipped direct to or lying on a non-metallic surface										
Touching	0.85	0.79	0.75	0.73	0.72	0.71	–	–	–	–
Spaced[a]	0.94	0.90	0.90	0.90	0.90	0.90	0.90	0.90	0.90	0.90
Single layer on a perforated metal cable tray, vertical or horizontal										
Touching	0.86	0.81	0.77	0.75	0.74	0.73	0.71	0.70	–	–
Spaced[a]	0.91	0.89	0.88	0.87	0.87	–	–	–	–	–

[a] Spaced means a clearance between adjacent surfaces of at least one cable diameter D_e. Where the horizontal clearance between adjacent cables exceeds twice their overall diameter, no correction factor need be applied

(a) The factors are applicable to uniform groups of cables, equally loaded.
(b) If, with known operating conditions, a cable is expected to carry a current of not more than 30% of its grouped rating, it may be ignored for the purpose of obtaining the rating factor for the rest of the group. For example, a group of N loaded cables would normally require a group reduction factor of C_g applied to the tabulated I_t. However, if M cables in the group carry loads which are not greater than $0.3C_gI_t$ amperes the other cables can be sized by using the group rating factor corresponding to $N - M$ cables.
(c) The factors have been calculated on the basis of prolonged steady state operation at 100% load factor for all live conductors.

Thermal insulation
For cable installed in a thermally insulating wall or installed above a thermally insulated ceiling and in contact with a thermally conductive surface on one side, in the absence of more precise information the rating may be taken as 0.75 times the current carrying capacity for that cable when clipped direct to a surface and unenclosed. For a cable likely to be totally surrounded by thermally insulating material, the applicable rating factor may be as low as 0.5.

Rating factors C_a for ambient temperature
For ambient temperatures other than 30 °C the tabulated rating may be adjusted by the temperature rating factors in tables 8.18 or 8.19 according to the type of protective device.

CABLES FOR SHIPWIRING AND OFFSHORE INSTALLATIONS

Wiring in ships usually has to comply with regulations such as the IEE Regulations for the Electrical and Electronic Equipment of Ships. As well as basing tabulated ratings on an ambient temperature of 45 °C, to which reference has been made, there is also a specified maximum cable conductor temperature of 5 °C or 10 °C below the values given earlier in table 8.5, e.g. 85 °C for EPR insulated cables. Cables of this type are now quite capable of operation to 90 °C and offshore applications in most countries are at ambient temperatures well below 45 °C. Much

Table 8.18 Factors for ambient temperature where semi-enclosed fuses to BS 3036 are used

Insulation	Ambient temperature (°C)								
	25	35	40	45	50	55	65	75	85
60 °C rubber	1.04	0.96	0.91	0.87	0.79	0.56			
PVC	1.03	0.97	0.94	0.91	0.87	0.84	0.48		
Paper	1.02	0.97	0.95	0.92	0.90	0.87	0.76	0.43	
85 °C rubber	1.02	0.97	0.95	0.93	0.91	0.88	0.83	0.58	
Thermoset	1.02	0.98	0.95	0.93	0.91	0.89	0.85	0.69	0.39
Mineral:									
70 °C sheath	1.03	0.96	0.93	0.89	0.86	0.79	0.42		
105 °C sheath	1.02	0.98	0.96	0.93	0.91	0.89	0.84	0.79	0.64

Table 8.19 Factors for ambient temperature where the protection is a fuse to BS 88 or BS 1361 or a circuit breaker to BS 3871 or BS 4752

Insulation	Ambient temperature (°C)								
	25	35	40	45	50	55	65	75	85
60 °C rubber	1.04	0.91	0.82	0.71	0.58	0.41			
PVC	1.03	0.94	0.87	0.79	0.71	0.61	0.35		
Paper	1.02	0.95	0.89	0.84	0.72	0.71	0.55	0.32	
85 °C rubber	1.02	0.95	0.90	0.85	0.80	0.74	0.60	0.43	
Thermoset	1.02	0.96	0.91	0.87	0.82	0.76	0.65	0.50	0.29
Mineral:									
70 °C sheath	1.03	0.93	0.85	0.77	0.67	0.57			
105 °C sheath	1.02	0.96	0.92	0.88	0.84	0.80	0.70	0.60	0.47

higher ratings are therefore possible for the many offshore installations for which it is considered that shipwiring regulations do not apply. Tables of ratings for a number of cable types for shipwiring and offshore installation are included in appendix A7 and details of the conditions applicable to offshore installations follow table A7.2.

SHORT TIME AND CYCLIC RATINGS

It very often happens that loads are cyclic rather than sustained. Many cables, particularly when buried, may take up to 24 hours or even longer for the temperature to build up the equilibrium conditions on which sustained ratings are based. Allowance may be made for this, therefore, together with the cooling period between loads, to derive a cyclic rating which will be higher than the value for sustained operation.

Fig. 8.3 indicates the temperature rise of the conductor of a typical buried cable. It will be noted that the heating is exponential and hence during sustained loading the temperature change when nearing equilibrium is slow.

If the loading is only at maximum for a few hours, or is at a level below maximum for a longer period, it is possible to calculate a rating to suit the circumstances.

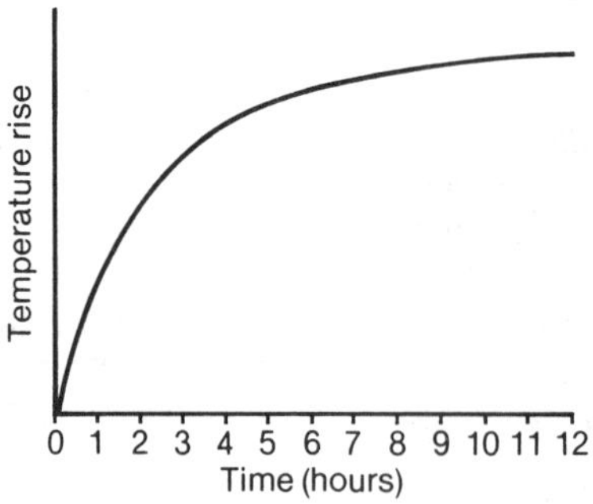

Fig. 8.3 Rate of conductor temperature rise for typical buried power cable

Public supply cables having daily cycles with morning and afternoon peaks represent one application where such treatment is beneficial. Another, of a different type, relates to requirements for machines where the loading may be for minutes rather than hours, e.g. arc welding.

Many factors have to be taken into account in calculations for such ratings. Cable diameter in relation to the environment has a major effect, because surface area increases with diameter and if the cable is in air heat may be dissipated quickly. This is the reason, for example, that small size cables have a lower rating in air than in ground, whereas the reverse applies for large cables. Cables in air heat up very quickly compared with buried cables. Cables so installed may therefore have an allowance for short time currents but not for cyclic loads over a 24 hour period.

Other factors are the type and reproducibility of the cycle, the effect of any other cables in the vicinity and the thermal resistivity of the soil. The mathematics is rather voluminous and complicated. For the last three decades a standard work of reference has been a report by Goldenberg[1] which uses the concept of a 'loss load factor' representative of the loading cycle. An IEC Committee is now investigating the subject and in 1985 issued a publication[2] covering cables up to 30 kV.

A report by Gosden and Kendall[3] deals specifically with ratings for 11 kV public supply distribution cables in the UK and explains the background to the utilisation of considerably higher ratings[4] than are published for sustained operation. Account is also taken of the fact that common practice is to install 11 kV cables in normally open rings (fig. 8.4). In such operation any point in the ring is fed by two cables and each carries half the load of the ring, i.e. the cables have only 50% utilisation. In the fairly rare occurrence of a cable fault in the ring the link is closed and the load on the cable beyond the fault is back-fed from the unfaulted cable, which thus carries an increased load until repair is completed.

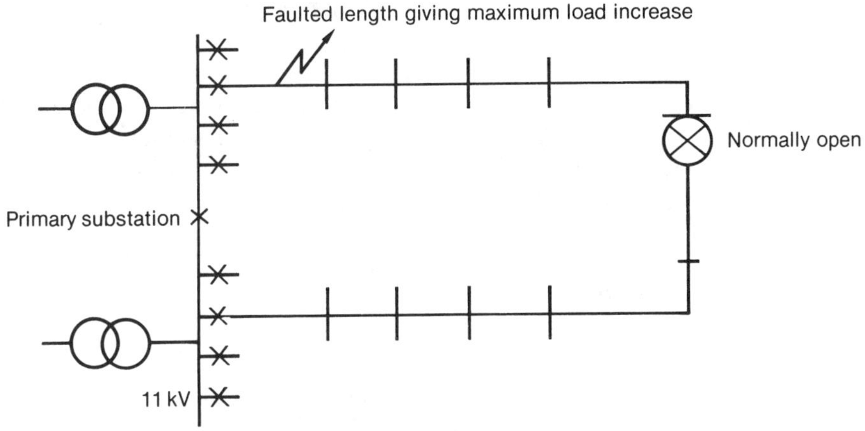

Fig. 8.4 Typical open ring system in 11 kV UK public supply distribution (Courtesy of Institution of Electrical Engineers)

Compared with sustained ratings, fig. 8.5 indicates the magnitude of the improvement possible for public supply operation. This figure also includes contributions

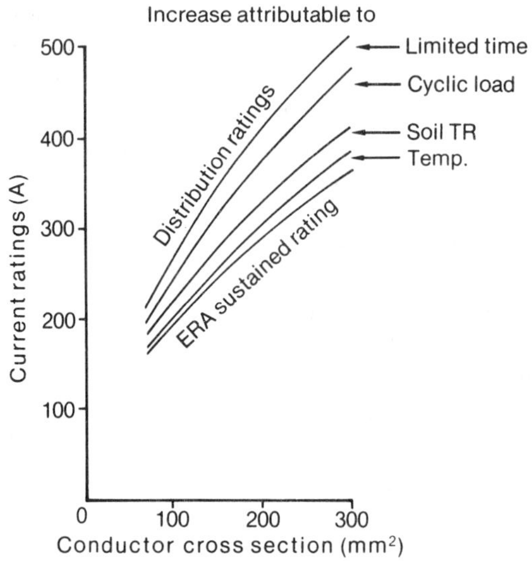

Fig. 8.5 Comparison of UK 11 kV distribution ratings and standard ratings for PILS belted cables with aluminium conductors (Courtesy of Institution of Electrical Engineers)

from other variations from standard conditions, i.e. a soil temperature and soil thermal resistivity (TR) that are lower than standard.

REFERENCES

(1) Goldenberg, H. (1958) *'Methods for the calculation of cyclic rating factors and emergency loading for cables direct in ground or in ducts'*. ERA Report No. F/T 186.
(2) IEC 853–1 (1985) 'Calculation of the cyclic and emergency current rating of cables', Part 1, 'Cyclic rating factor for cables up to and including 30 kV'.
(3) Gosden, J. H. and Kendall, P. G. (1976) 'Current rating of 11 kV cables'. *IEE Conference on Distribution Cables and Jointing Techniques for Systems up to 11 kV*.
(4) Engineering Recommendation P17 (1977) *Current Rating Guide for Distribution Cables*. London: Electricity Council.

Chapter 9
Short-circuit Ratings

It happens frequently that the conductor size necessary for an installation is dictated by its ability to carry short-circuit rather than sustained current. During a short-circuit there is a sudden inrush of current for a few cycles followed by a steadier flow for a short period until the protection operates, normally between 0.2 and 3 seconds. During this period the current falls off slightly due to the increase in conductor resistance with temperature but for calculation purposes it is assumed to remain steady.

At the commencement of the short circuit the cable may be operating at its maximum permissible continuous temperature and the increase in temperature caused by the short circuit is a main factor in deriving acceptable ratings. However, the current may be 20 or more times greater than the sustained current and it produces thermomechanical and electromagnetic forces proportional to the square of the current. The stresses induced may themselves impose an operating limit unless they can be contained adequately by the whole installation. This requires checks on cable design, joints, terminations and installation conditions.

TEMPERATURE

As the time involved is short and cooling follows rapidly, the cable insulation can withstand much higher temperatures than are allowed for sustained operation. Table 9.1 shows the values, related to a conductor temperature, used for transmission and distribution cables in the UK. These temperatures are in accordance with IEC Publication 724, 'Guide to the short-circuit temperature limits of electric cables with a rated voltage not exceeding 0.6/1.0 kV', first issued in 1982 and revised in 1984.

For convenience table 9.1 includes temperatures for materials and components other than insulation so as to indicate other constraints. Figures for oversheaths are included to allow for the fact that the material is in contact with armour wires and a higher temperature value may be assigned. In the absence of armour the oversheath should be treated as insulation. It is important to appreciate that the temperatures in table 9.1 for components cannot be adopted if the insulation dictates a lower temperature.

The difference between the maximum conductor temperatures for sustained rating, given in chapter 8, and the above temperatures, provides a maximum temperature rise which can be used in short-circuit rating calculations.

RATINGS DERIVED ON A TEMPERATURE BASIS

It is normally assumed that the whole of the energy input appears as heat which is absorbed by the conductors, i.e. the conditions are adiabatic. Further refinement is

Table 9.1 Short circuit temperature limits

Material or component	Temperature (°C)
Paper insulation	250
PVC – insulation up to 300 mm^2	160[a]
PVC – insulation above 300 mm^2	140[a]
PVC – insulation 6.6 kV and above	160[a]
PVC – oversheath	200
Natural rubber	200
Butyl rubber	220
Polyethylene – oversheath	150
XLPE and EPR	250
Silicone rubber	350
CSP – oversheath	220
Soldered conductor joints	160
Compression joints	250
Lead sheaths – unalloyed	170
Lead sheaths – alloyed	200

[a] For grades TI 1 and TI 2; not applicable to non-standard soft grades

proceeding under the auspices of IEC to allow for heat absorption by other cable components but it is likely that several years will elapse before resolution is obtained and the difference will not be greatly significant, except for conductors applied concentrically. Similarly the heat absorption could be affected by the time factor and it is assumed that the maximum short-circuit duration will be 5 s.

An equation may be derived by equating heat input (I^2RT) to the heat absorbed (product of mass, specific heat and temperature rise). Current international discussions are leading towards a formula in the following form:

$$I^2 = \frac{K^2S^2}{T} \log_e \left(\frac{\theta_1 + \beta}{\theta_0 + \beta}\right) \tag{9.1}$$

where I = short circuit current (r.m.s. over duration) (A)
T = duration of short circuit (second)
K = constant for the material of the conductor
S = area of conductor (mm^2)
θ_1 = final temperature (°C)
θ_0 = initial temperature (°C)
β = reciprocal of the temperature coefficient of resistance (α) of the conductor (per degree Celsius at 0 °C

In the above, 'conductor' refers to the current carrying component. The constants for the usual metals are given in table 9.2 in which

$$K^2 = \frac{Q_c(\beta + 20)}{\rho_{20}}$$

where Q_c = volumetric specific heat of the conductor at 20°C (J/°C mm^3)
ρ_{20} = resistivity of conductor metal at 20°C (mm)

Table 9.2 Constants for short-circuit calculation

Material	K	β	Q_c	ρ_{20}
Copper	226	234.5	3.45×10^{-3}	17.241×10^{-6}
Aluminium	148	228	2.5×10^{-3}	28.264×10^{-6}
Lead	42	230	1.45×10^{-3}	214×10^{-6}
Steel	78	202	3.8×10^{-3}	138×10^{-6}

Power distribution cables

For specific conditions of temperature rise in accordance with table 9.1 the formula may be further adapted as indicated in table 9.3. In this table, as is usual for short-circuit calculations, it is assumed that the cable is operating at maximum permissible continuous temperature when the short-circuit occurs. If the system design dictates a lower temperature, a factor may be applied.

Care must be exercised in using the figures derived on this basis, e.g. for paper cables it is assumed that the conductor joints are soldered, and hence subject to a 160°C limitation, whereas mechanical joints suitable for 250°C are adopted with XLPE and EPR. Other considerations are given in the next section.

Table 9.3 Short-circuit currents for various cables

Cable insulation/type	Conductor metal	Temperature rise (°C)	Short-circuit current (A)
Paper			
1–6 kV: belted	Copper	80–160	$108ST^{-1/2}$
	Aluminium	80–160	$70ST^{-1/2}$
10–15 kV: belted	Copper	65–160	$119ST^{-1/2}$
	Aluminium	65–160	$77ST^{-1/2}$
10–15 kV: screened	Copper	70–160	$116ST^{-1/2}$
	Aluminium	70–160	$74ST^{-1/2}$
20–30 kV: screened	Copper	65–160	$119ST^{-1/2}$
	Aluminium	65–160	$77ST^{-1/2}$
PVC: 1 and 3 kV			
Up to 300 mm^2	Copper	70–160	$115ST^{-1/2}$
	Aluminium	70–160	$76ST^{-1/2}$
Over 300 mm^2	Copper	70–140	$103ST^{-1/2}$
	Aluminium	70–140	$68ST^{-1/2}$
XLPE and EPR	Copper	90–250	$114ST^{-1/2}$
	Aluminium	90–250	$92ST^{-1/2}$

An alternative way of expressing the data available from the last column of table 9.3 is the graphical presentation given in figs 9.1 and 9.2 for paper insulated cables, figs 9.3 and 9.4 for PVC insulation cables and figs 9.5 and 9.6 for XLPE insulated cables.

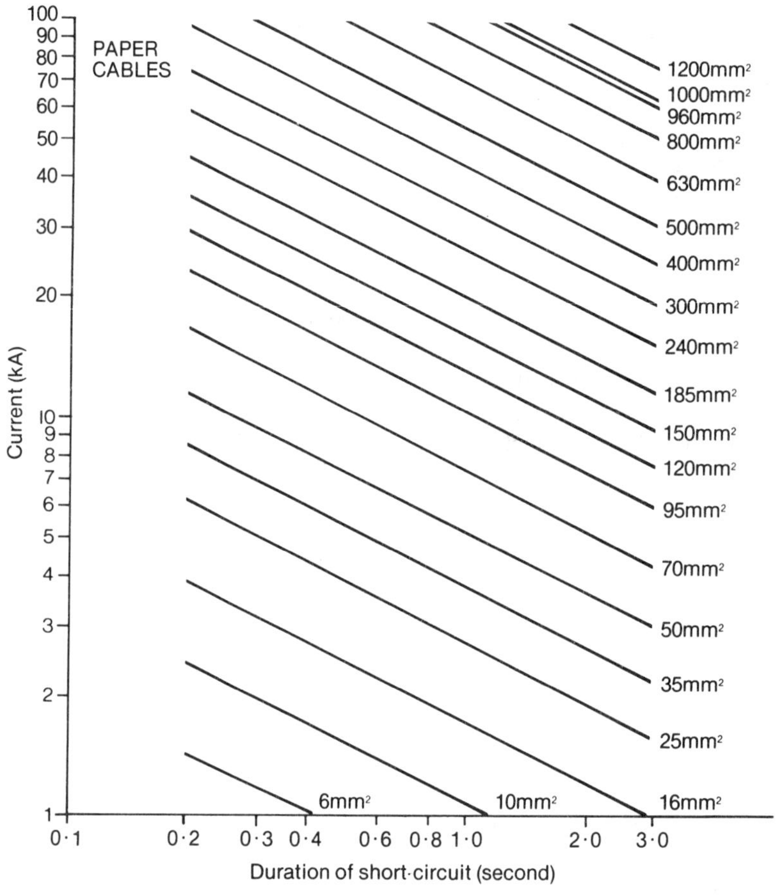

Fig. 9.1 Short-circuit ratings for paper insulated cables with copper conductors. These ratings apply to cables for voltages up to and including 3.8/6.6 kV. For higher voltages they may be increased by the factors shown below:

Cable type	*Voltage*	*Factor*
3-core (belted)	6.35/11 kV	1.10
Single- and 3-core (screened)	6.35/11 and 8.7/15 kV	1.07
Single- and 3-core	12.7/22 and 19/33 kV	1.10

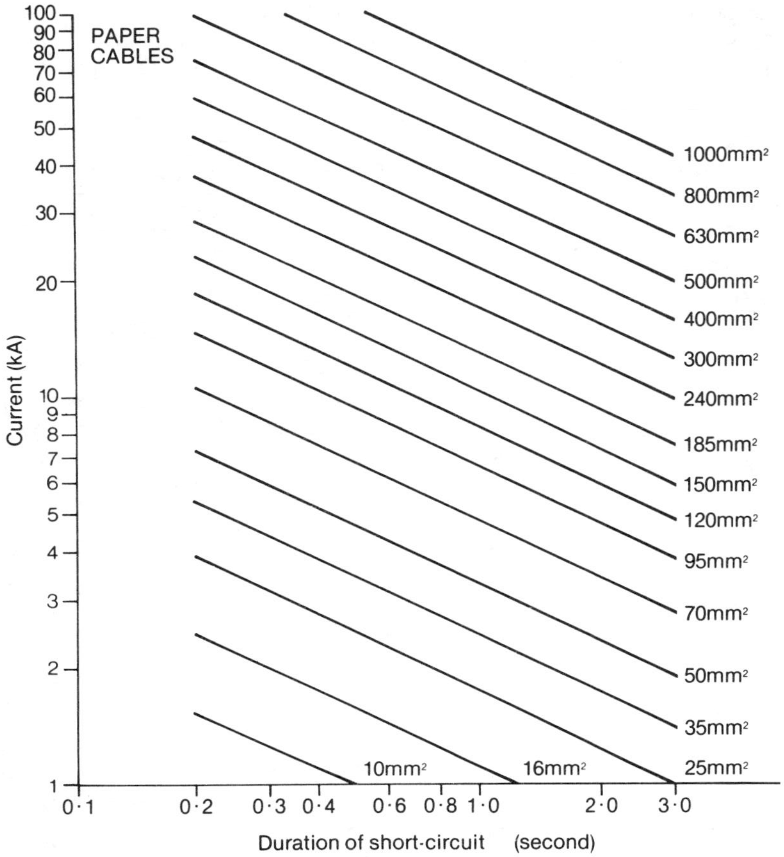

Fig. 9.2 Short-circuit ratings for paper insulated cables with aluminium conductors. The factors given under fig. 9.1 for higher voltages are applicable

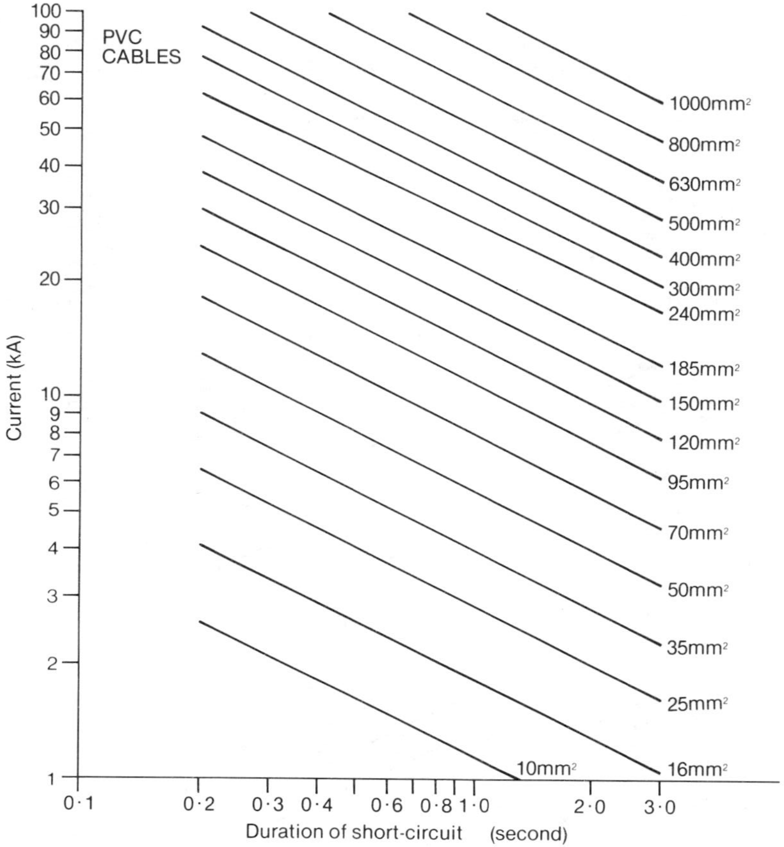

Fig. 9.3 Short-circuit ratings for 1 kV PVC insulated cables with copper conductors (based on a final conductor temperature of 160 °C for sizes up to and including 300 mm^2 and 140 °C for conductors above 300 mm^2)

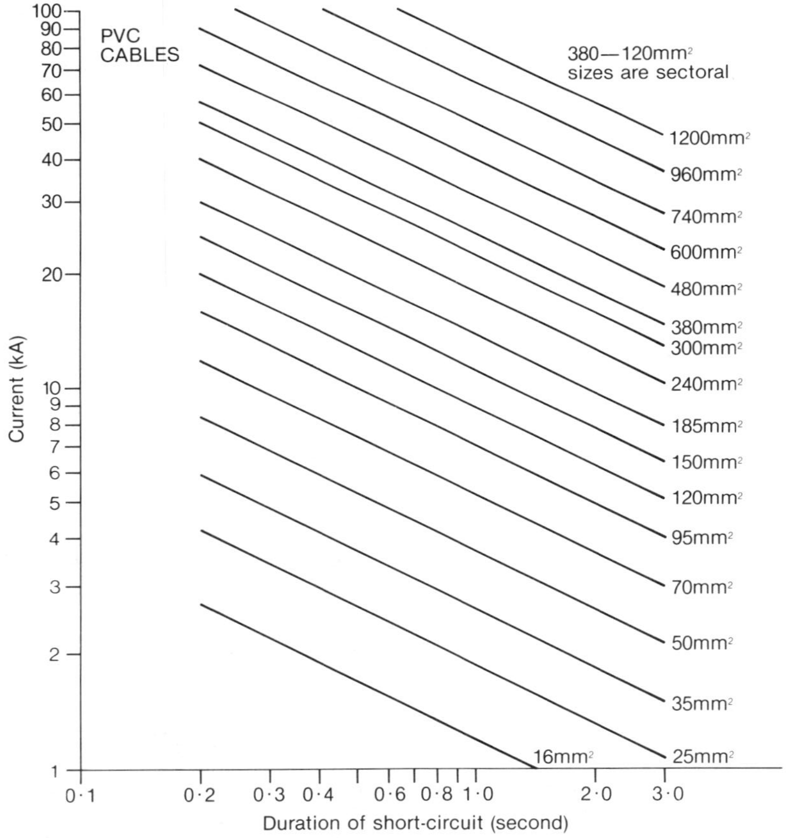

Fig. 9.4 Short-circuit ratings for 1 kV PVC insulated cables with aluminium conductors (based on a final conductor temperature of 160 °C for sizes up to and including 300 mm^2 and 140 °C for conductors above 300 mm^2)

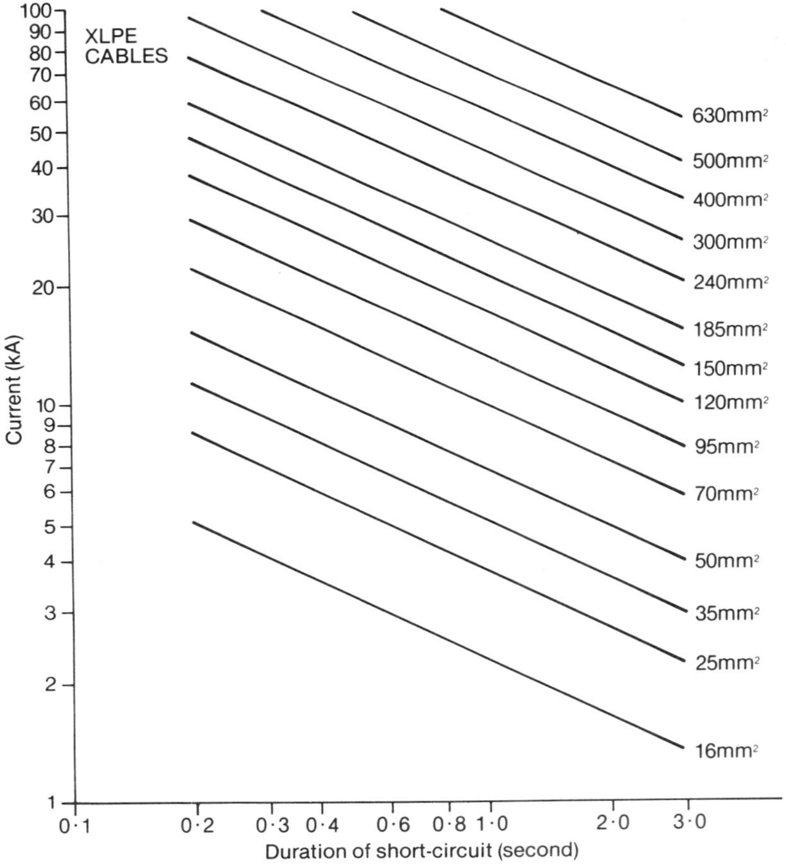

Fig. 9.5 Short-circuit ratings for XLPE insulated cables with copper conductors (based on a temperature rise from 90 to 250 °C, i.e. 160 °C)

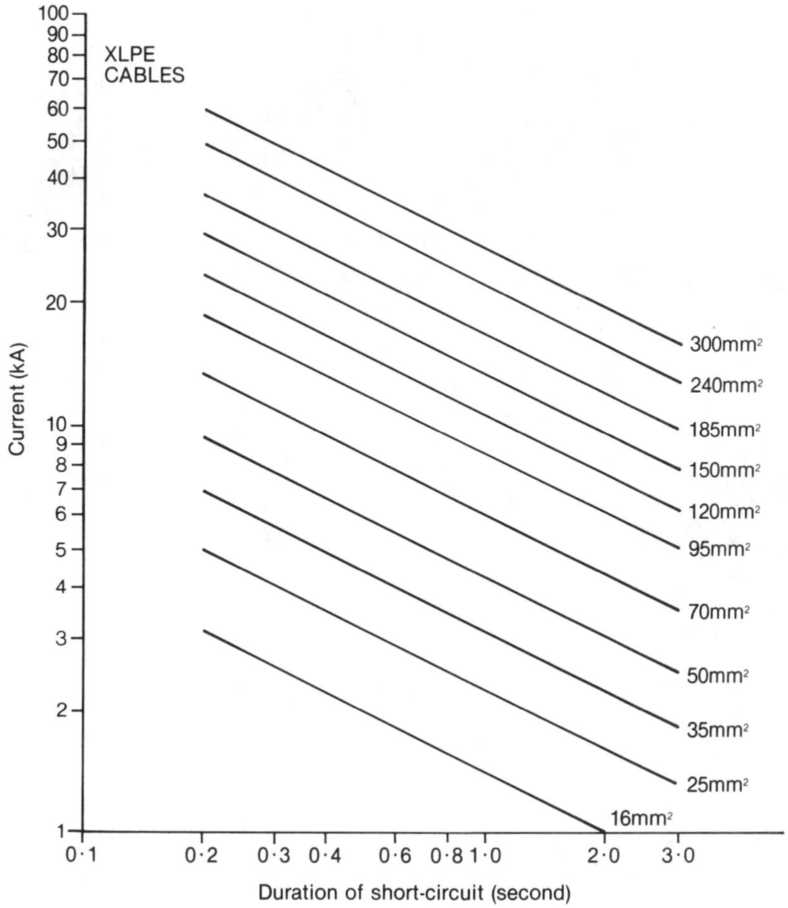

Fig. 9.6 Short-circuit ratings for XLPE insulated cables with solid aluminium conductors (based on a temperature rise of 160 °C)

Oil-filled cables

Short-circuit ratings for oil-filled cables are calculated from a temperature rise of 90–160 °C and are shown in figs 9.7–9.10 for single- and 3-core cables with copper and aluminium conductors.

Wiring cables

For wiring cables the basic method of calculation given earlier applies but the actual method of implementation is slightly different. Table 9.4, which is in the same form as table 9.3, includes data as used in the IEE Wiring Regulations. An average is taken for 65 °C rubber and 85 °C rubber (which includes EPR). Although the short-circuit temperatures for the two materials are different, so also are their operating temperatures under sustained conditions; hence the permissible temperature rise is similar in each case (see also chapter 19).

A typical graphical presentation applicable to PVC insulated conduit wires is shown in fig. 9.11.

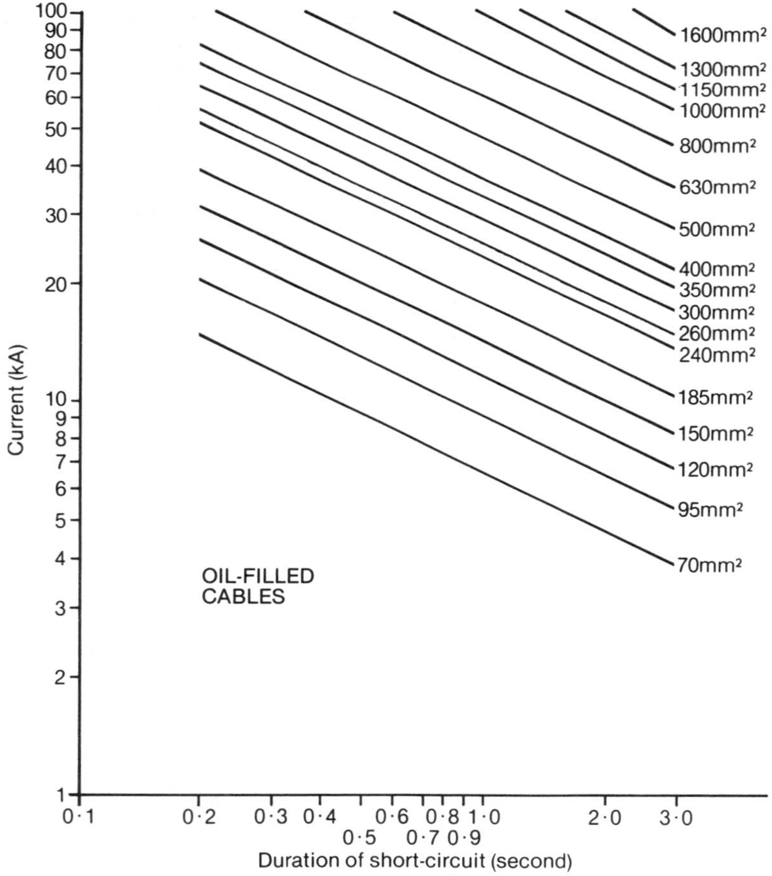

Fig. 9.7 Short-circuit ratings for single-core oil-filled cables with copper conductors (based on conductor temperature of 90 °C at start of short circuit and final conductor temperature of 160 °C)

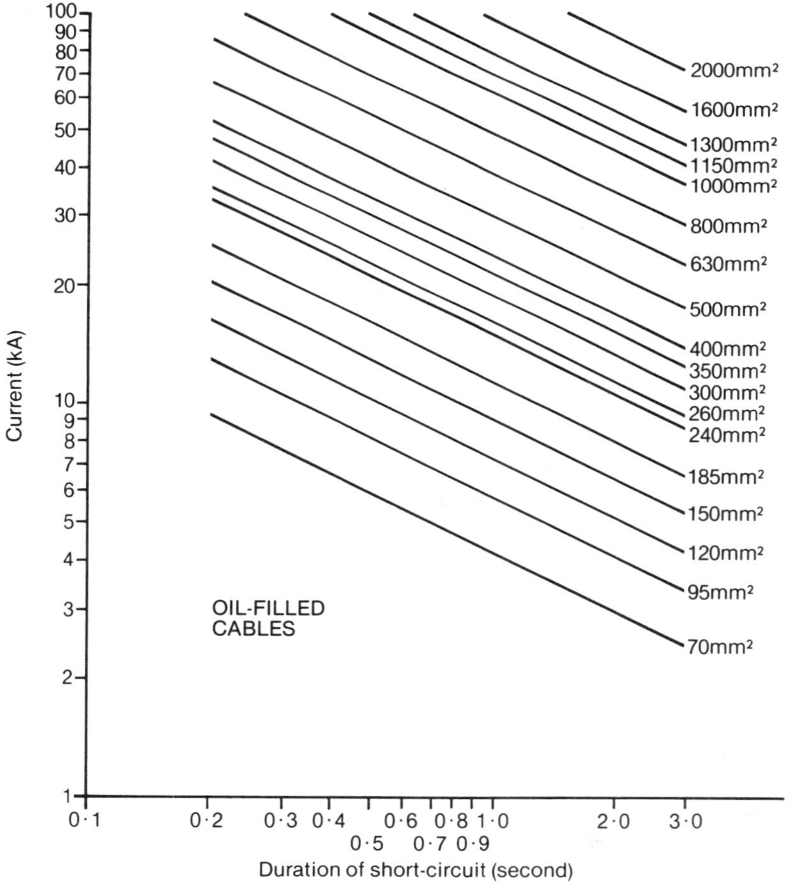

Fig. 9.8 Short-circuit ratings for single-core oil-filled cables with aluminium conductors (conditions as given under fig. 9.7)

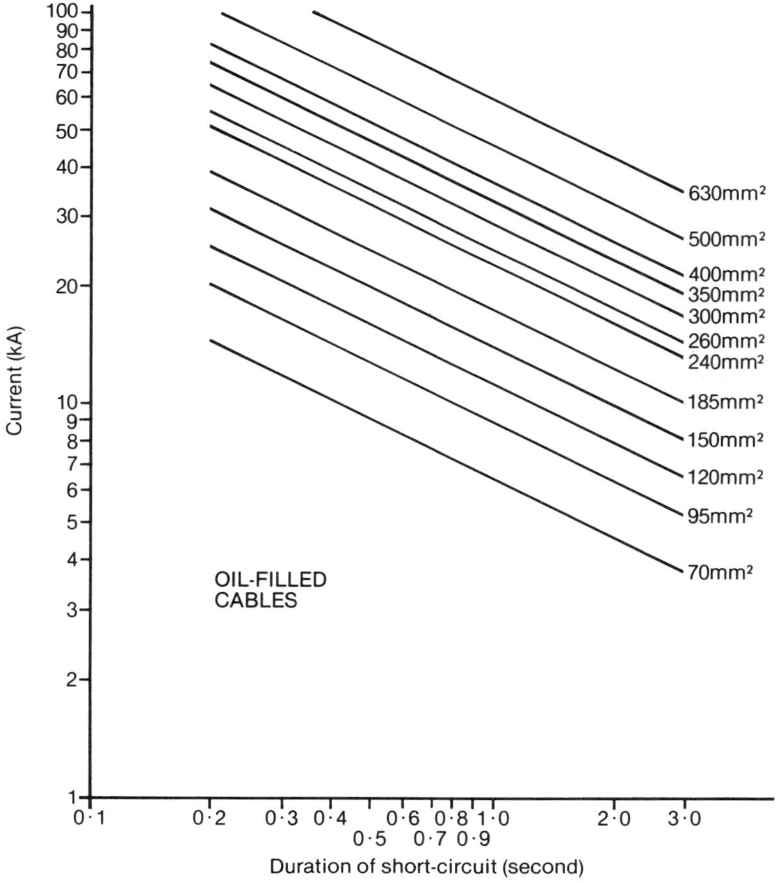

Fig. 9.9 Short-circuit ratings for 3-core oil-filled cables with copper conductors (conditions as given under fig. 9.7)

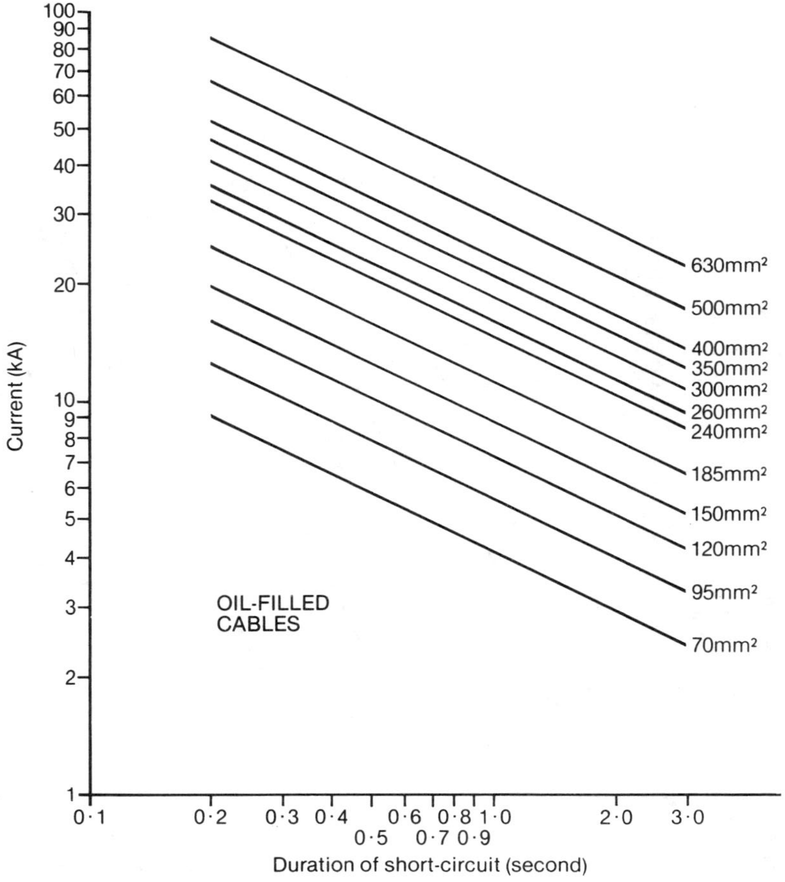

Fig. 9.10 Short-circuit ratings for 3-core oil-filled cables with aluminium conductors (conditions as given under fig. 9.7)

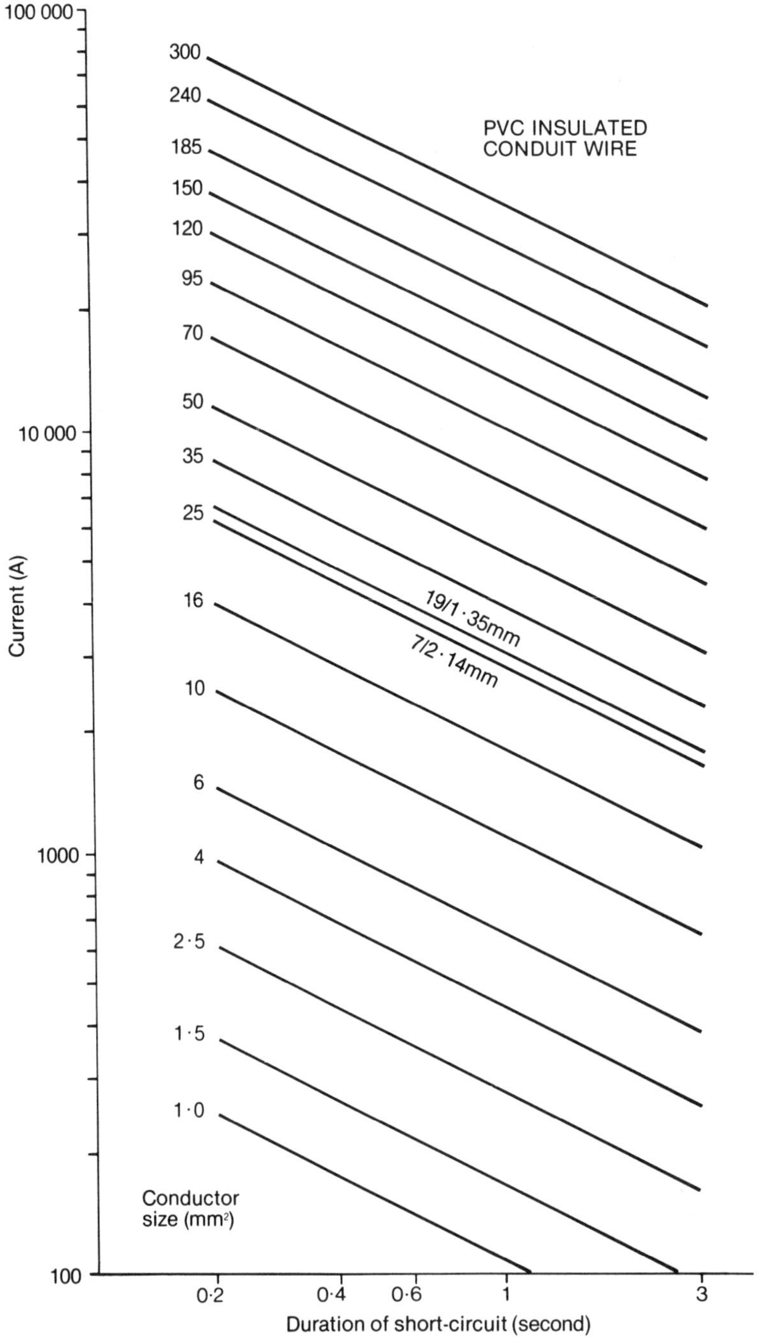

Fig. 9.11 Short-circuit ratings for PVC insulated conduit wires with copper conductors (70 °C at start of short circuit and final conductor temperature of 160 °C)

Table 9.4 Short-circuit ratings for wiring cables

Cable insulation	Conductor metal	Short-circuit current (A)
PVC	Copper	$115/103ST^{-1/2}$[a]
	Aluminium	$76/68ST^{-1/2}$[a]
65 °C rubber	Copper	$134ST^{-1/2}$
85 °C rubber	Aluminium	$89ST^{-1/2}$
Mineral	Copper	$135ST^{-1/2}$
	Aluminium	$87ST^{-1/2}$

[a] The lower value applies to conductors over 300 mm^2

ASYMMETRICAL FAULTS

The previous section was concerned with symmetrical 3-phase faults, with a short-circuit between the phase conductors. In the case of asymmetrical, i.e. earth, faults other factors have to be taken into account because the current is carried by the lead sheath and/or armour. In general, for small conductor sizes, the conductor temperature rise is still the limiting factor, but with the larger sizes a lower limit is imposed by lead sheath and armour considerations, as indicated in table 9.1. Lead sheaths are liable to be damaged if they are suddenly heated to temperatures above those shown

Table 9.5 Maximum allowable asymmetrical current to earth[a] (single-core PILS cables)

Conductor size (mm^2)	0.6/1 kV (kA)	1.9/3.3 kV (kA)	3.3/6.6 kV (kA)	6.35/11 kV (kA)	8.7/15 kV (kA)	12.7/22 kV (kA)	19/33 kV (kA)
50	1.4	1.6	1.7	1.9	2.3	2.9	3.8
70	1.6	1.8	1.9	2.3	2.5	3.1	4.0
95	1.9	2.0	2.3	2.5	2.9	3.6	4.6
120	2.2	2.4	2.5	2.9	3.2	3.8	4.8
150	2.5	2.6	3.0	3.1	3.6	4.3	5.3
185	2.9	3.0	3.2	3.6	3.9	4.6	5.8
240	3.3	3.4	3.8	4.0	4.6	5.3	6.3
300	3.9	4.0	4.2	4.7	4.9	5.7	6.8
400	4.7	4.7	4.9	5.5	5.7	6.6	7.7
500	5.6	5.6	5.7	6.1	6.8	7.6	8.8
630	6.6	6.6	6.8	7.2	7.9	8.8	10.1
800	7.7	7.7	7.9	8.3	9.1	10.1	11.4
1000	9.0	9.0	9.2	10.2	10.5	11.6	13.0
960[b]				9.8	10.6	11.7	13.2
1200[b]				11.8	12.2	13.4	14.9

[a] For 1 s rating
[b] Milliken type conductors (copper only)

Table 9.6 Maximum allowable asymmetrical fault currents to earth[a] (multicore PILS/SWA cable)

Conductor size (mm^2)	0.6/1 kV		1.9/3.3 kV 3-core (kA)	3.8/6.6 kV 3-core (kA)	6.35/11 kV		8.7/15 kV 3-core (screened) (kA)	12.7/22 kV 3-core (screened) (kA)	19/33 kV 3-core (screened) (kA)
	3-core (kA)	4-core (kA)			3-core (belted) (kA)	3-core (screened) (kA)			
4	3.1	3.4							
6	3.4	3.6							
10	3.8	4.9	5.0	6.4					
16	4.4	5.0	5.1	7.3	10.1	10.1			
25	5.2	6.1	6.0	8.7	11.3	11.3	12.8	17.9	
35	6.0	6.7	6.6	9.6	11.3	10.9	16.2	19.5	
50	6.8	8.9	8.5	10.3	14.3	12.0	16.4	20.6	26.9
70	8.7	10.3	9.9	11.6	15.7	15.4	17.8	21.3	27.5
95	10.1	12.0	11.3	15.0	17.5	17.1	20.1	23.2	33.5
120	11.4	15.4	14.4	16.5	18.6	18.7	21.3	24.9	35.7
150	15.3	17.9	16.0	17.9	20.2	20.2	22.9	26.7	37.0
185	17.1	20.1	17.5	19.8	22.1	22.1	24.9	33.2	39.5
240	19.4	23.6	19.8	22.6	25.0	24.6	32.2	36.8	43.0
300	21.8	26.3	22.6	25.0	31.6	31.6	35.1	39.9	46.3
400	25.0	34.5	29.8	32.6	35.6	35.7	39.3	44.4	51.0

[a] For 1 s rating

in the table and the armour temperature may be controlled by the performance of the extruded PVC in contact with it.

Maximum allowable asymmetrical fault currents for the more common distribution cable types are given in tables 9.5–9.10. Unless otherwise stated, the ratings apply to cables with stranded conductors. They are also for a fault duration of 1 s. For other periods the values should be divided by the square root of the time in seconds. In the case of lead sheathed wire armoured cable it is assumed that the current is shared between the lead sheath and the armour.

ELECTROMAGNETIC FORCES AND CABLE BURSTING

In multicore cables a short circuit produces electromagnetic forces which repel the cores from each other, and if they are not adequately bound together the cable will tend to burst. The effect is of importance with unarmoured paper insulated cables, as the insulation may be damaged in the process. For conductor sizes of 185 mm^2 and above and currents above about 30 kA, the damage which can be caused by bursting forces imposes limitations on the ratings deduced by the thermal basis used in table 9.3 and figs 9.1–9.6, i.e. there is a cut-off point irrespective of fault duration. For unarmoured 3-core belted paper cables with stranded conductors these limits are given in table 9.11.

Table 9.7 Maximum allowable asymmetrical fault currents to earth[a] (PVC insulated wire armoured cables with solid aluminium conductors)

Conductor size (mm^2)	Aluminium armour		Steel armour			
	0.6/1 kV single-core (kA)	1.9/3.3 kV single-core (kA)	0.6/1 kV			1.9/3.3 kV 3-core (kA)
			2-core (kA)	3-core (kA)	4-core (kA)	
16			1.6	1.8	2.7	3.3
25			2.4	2.7	3.2	3.5
35			2.6	3.1	3.5	3.8
50	2.8	3.2	4.0	3.5	5.0	5.1
70	3.2	3.6	4.4	5.0	5.5	5.7
95	3.6	5.2	4.8	5.7	6.5	6.2
120	5.2	5.6		6.1	8.9	8.4
150	5.7	5.9		8.4	9.7	9.1
185	6.2	6.4		9.5	10.8	9.7
240	7.0	7.0		10.6	12.1	10.6
300	7.6	7.6		11.7	13.4	11.7
380	10.9	10.9				
480	12.2	12.2				
600	12.9	12.9				
740	17.8	17.8				
960	20.2	20.2				
1200	22.1	22.1				

[a] For 1 s rating

Table 9.8 Maximum allowable asymmetrical fault currents to earth[a] (PVC insulated wire armoured cables with copper conductors)

Conductor size (mm^2)	Aluminium armour		Steel wire				
	0.6/1 kV single-core (kA)	1.9/3.3 kV single-core (kA)	0.6/1 kV				1.9/3.3 kV 3-core (kA)
			2-core (kA)	3-core (kA)	4-core (kA)	4-core (reduced neutral) (kA)	
1.5			0.7	0.7	0.7		
2.5			0.8	0.8	0.9		
4			0.9	1.0	1.5		
6			1.0	1.5	1.7		
10			1.8	1.9	2.1		
16			1.7	1.9	2.7		3.3
25			2.7	2.9	3.4	3.4	3.6
35			2.9	3.3	3.7	3.6	4.0
50	3.1	3.5	3.3	3.7	5.4	4.2	5.4
70	3.5	3.9	3.7	5.3	6.1	5.9	6.1
95	4.0	5.7	5.4	6.1	7.0	6.9	6.6
120	5.7	6.2	5.8	6.6	9.7	9.5	9.1
150	6.4	6.5	6.4	9.3	10.8	10.4	9.7
185	7.0	7.0	8.9	10.2	11.7	11.4	10.4
240	7.8	7.8	9.9	11.4	13.2	12.7	11.4
300	8.6	8.6	11.0	12.7	14.7	14.3[b] 14.7[c]	12.7
400	12.2	12.2	12.3	14.0	20.6	19.9	14.0
500	13.4	13.4					
630	14.6	14.6					
800	20.6	20.6					
1000	22.9	22.9					

[a] For 1 s rating
[b] 300/150 mm^2
[c] 300/185 mm^2

Armouring provides sufficient reinforcement to prevent damage due to these bursting forces. Screened paper insulated cables are similarly affected but it is seldom that such cables are used in the unarmoured condition.

Cables with polymeric insulation, either thermoplastic or thermoset, are more resistant to damage than paper cables but would have a short-circuit rating limitation due to bursting forces if they were unarmoured.

When installing single-core cables it is necessary to hold the cores together with adequate binding straps, or to use suitable cleats, to withstand bursting forces.[1] This is an aspect of particular importance for cables in generating stations.

Table 9.9 Maximum allowable asymmetrical fault currents to earth[a] (XLPE insulated wire armoured cables with solid aluminium conductors)

Conductor size (mm^2)	Aluminium armour		Steel armour			
	0.6/1 kV single-core (kA)	1.9/3.3 kV single-core (kA)	0.6/1 kV			1.9/3.3 kV 3-core (kA)
			2-core (kA)	3-core (kA)	4-core (kA)	
16			1.2	1.4	1.6	2.7
25			1.5	2.3	2.6	3.0
35			2.2	2.6	2.9	3.2
50	1.6	2.8	2.4	2.9	3.3	4.5
70	2.6	3.1	2.8	3.3	4.9	5.0
95	3.0	3.1	4.1	4.8	5.4	5.5
120	3.2	4.3		5.2	7.6	7.4
150	4.8	4.6		7.4	8.4	8.0
185	5.2	5.2		8.2	9.4	8.6
240	5.7	5.7		9.2	10.5	9.6
300	6.3	6.3		10.1	11.7	10.3

[a] For 1 s rating

THERMOMECHANICAL EFFECTS

The high temperature rise resulting from a short circuit produces expansion of the conductors which may cause problems due to longitudinal thrust of the conductors and bodily movement of the cable if it is not adequately supported. The possibility of excessive thrust is also important if the cable has a solid conductor.

Design of joints and terminations

The effect on joints is more critical with buried cables; i.e. because of the ground restraint on the cable surface the cores may tend to move longitudinally within the cable and into the accessory. The magnitude of this thrust can be very high, e.g. 50 N/mm^2 of conductor area, and is particularly important with large conductors.

If the filling material in the accessory is sufficiently soft to permit movement of the cores, the force may cause buckling and collapse within the accessory. Once this has occurred, a tension will develop as the conductors cool down and this can create further problems such as a stress on the ferrules sufficiently high for the conductors to pull out. This is the reason for the 160 °C temperature limit on soldered conductor connections.

Other factors arising are that (a) the design of fittings applied by mechanical and compression techniques must be adequate to cater for stability of electrical resistance at the temperature generated and (b) in the case of paper insulated cables the outer casing must be able to deal with the high fluid pressure caused by expansion of the

Table 9.10 Maximum allowable asymmetrical fault currents to earth[a] (XLPE insulated wire armoured cables with copper conductors)

Conductor size (mm^2)	Aluminium armour		Steel armour				
	0.6/1 kV single-core (kA)	1.9/3.3 kV single-core (kA)	0.6/1 kV				1.9/3.3 kV 3-core (kA)
			2-core (kA)	3-core (kA)	4-core (equal) (kA)	4-core (reduced neutral) (kA)	
16			1.7	1.7	1.9		3.1
25			1.7	2.4	2.7	2.7	3.1
35			2.4	2.7	3.1	3.0	3.3
50	1.8	2.7	2.6	3.0	3.5	3.3	4.6
70	2.7	3.1	3.1	3.5	5.1	5.0	5.1
95	3.1	3.3	4.4	5.0	5.7	5.6	5.7
120	3.3	4.8	4.9	5.5	8.0	6.3	7.8
150	4.8	5.1	5.4	7.8	9.0	8.6	8.4
185	5.4	5.7	7.4	8.6	9.9	9.7	9.0
240	6.0	6.0	8.4	9.7	11.3	10.9	9.9
300	6.4	6.8	9.2	10.5	12.4	11.8[b]	10.9
300	6.4	6.8	9.2	10.5	12.4	12.4[c]	10.9
400	9.1	9.1					
500	10.5	10.5					
630	11.8	11.8					

[a] For 1 s rating
[b] 300/150 mm^2
[c] 300/185 mm^2

cable impregnant and its possible flow into the accessory, with consequent softening of the joint filling compound.

Differences between copper and aluminium conductors

Although the coefficient of expansion of aluminium is somewhat higher than that of copper, the effect as far as stress is concerned is largely balanced by the lower elastic modulus of aluminium. Forces causing buckling are therefore of a similar order. On the other hand, in the temper used for solid conductors, aluminium is a softer metal and the yield under compressive forces during heating could result in higher tensile forces on cooling. When such conductors were first introduced it was considered that a lower permissible short-circuit temperature might be necessary but subsequent experience has not indicated need for special treatment.

When limitations are imposed by lead sheaths or electromagnetic forces, the type of conductor metal is irrelevant in theory but, in respect of bursting forces, aluminium is

Table 9.11 Limitation due to bursting of unarmoured belted multicore paper-insulated cables

Voltage (kV)	Aluminium conductor		Copper conductor	
	Size (mm^2)	Short-circuit rating (kA)	Size (mm^2)	Short-circuit rating (kA)
0.6/1	240	33	120	25
	300	35	150	27
	400	37	185	29
			240	33
			300	36
			400	38
1.9/3.3 and	240	33	185	33
3.8/6.6	300	35	240	35
	400	38	300	37
			400	38
6.35/11	240	39	185	36
	300	41	240	39
	400	43	300	41
			400	43

at some disadvantage compared with copper because of the physical size effect for equal rating.

Installation conditions

As mentioned above, the effects of longitudinal thrust are most important for cables which are buried in the ground. However, as discussed in chapter 27, it is also important that cables installed in air should have adequate support spacings and/or rigid cleating to prevent excessive generation of expansion and contraction in local spans, particularly associated with accessories.

In the case of cables with thermoplastic insulation and oversheaths, it is also important to prevent excessive local pressure on the cable which could cause deformation of the material. This could occur due to small bending radii, by unsuitable fixing arrangements at bends or by unsatisfactory clamping devices. Similar remarks apply to thermosetting insulation with large conductor sizes because of the high temperature of 250 °C which is quoted for XLPE and EPR.

GENERAL COMMENTS

It is usual to quote short-circuit ratings, as is done in the tables and figures, relation to the basic cable design and type of insulation. It must be stressed that, as outlined in the latter part of this chapter, such values are only applicable if the method of installation and the accessories are appropriate. These aspects may represent the weakest links and are often overlooked.

However, there may be some mitigating circumstances. In order to have a standardised basis for the publication of short-circuit ratings, it is assumed that the short circuit occurs whilst the cable is already at the maximum temperature for continuous operation. This is seldom the case. When it is important to design or choose a cable to secure a very high short-circuit rating and all other circumstances can be predicted fairly accurately, the tabulated figures may even be increased by an appropriate factor.

REFERENCES

(1) Foulsham, N., Metcalf, J. C. and Philbrick, S. E. (Oct. 1974) 'Proposals for installation practice of single-core cables'. *Proc. IEE* **121** (10).

Chapter 10

Technical Data Applicable to Cable Planning and Usage

Many of the cable characteristics which are mentioned and for which methods of calculation are given in chapter 2 also provide data required in the planning of installations and give information to cable users for controlling operation. The d.c. and a.c resistance of the conductors, the inductance and the inductive reactance calculated from it and the impedance, derived from the resistance and reactance, are data required by the designer of the installation and likely to be of interest to the user. This also applies to the capacitance, from which charging current can be calculated, and the power factor, from which, together with the charging current, the dielectric losses can be derived. The other losses, in conductor and metallic coverings, in addition to their effect on current ratings, are again of interest to designers and users on their own account.

Similarly the sustained current carrying capacity and short-circuit rating, dealt with in detail in chapters 8 and 9 respectively, constitute technical data applicable to installation planning and usage.

There is no need to dwell further on aspects fully covered in the chapters mentioned. This chapter is confined to a few additional aspects and to the application of the parameters of cables rated up to 600/1000 V for compliance with the fifteenth edition of the IEE Wiring Regulations published in March 1981 and the amendments published since then, which are likely to be incorporated in the sixteenth edition.

CHARGING CURRENT

The charging current is the capacitive current which flows when an a.c. voltage is applied to the cable as a result of the capacitance between the conductor(s) and earth and, for a multicore cable in which the individual cores are not screened, between conductors. The value can be derived from the equation

$$I_c = \omega C V \times 10^{-6} \text{ (A)} \tag{10.1}$$

where I_c = charging current (A/km)
ω = 2π times the frequency of the applied voltage
C = capacitance between the electrodes between which the voltage is applied (μF/km)
V = applied voltage (V)

In normal operation, C is the capacitance to neutral, V is the voltage to neutral, i.e. U_0, and the charging current is the current in each phase. The expression $\omega C U_0 \times 10^{-6}$ is then recognisable as part of equation (2.12) in chapter 2, where it is multiplied by U_0 and the power factor to give the dielectric loss.

In addition to its relevance to operating conditions, a knowledge of the prospective charging current is required in deciding the currents that have to be provided by test transformers. For cables which do not have individually screened cores, e.g. belted cables, the test voltages may be applied as single-phase voltages between each conductor and the others connected to the metal covering, and between the bunched conductors and the metal covering. The values of capacitance for estimating charging current are then the values given in chapter 2 appropriate to these forms of connection, instead of the equivalent star capacitance (capacitance to neutral) given the symbol C in chapter 2, applicable under 3-phase voltage conditions.

VOLTAGE DROP

When current flows in a cable conductor there is a voltage drop between the ends of the conductor which is the product of the current and the impedance. If the voltage drop were excessive, it could result in the voltage at the equipment being supplied being too low for proper operation. The voltage drop is of more consequence at the low end of the voltage range of supply voltages than it is at higher voltages, and generally it is not significant as a percentage of the supply voltage for cables rated above 1000 V unless very long route lengths are involved.

In the tables included in this publication and in the IEE Wiring Regulations, voltage drops for individual cables are given in the units millivolts per ampère per metre length of cable. They are derived from the following formulae:

for single-phase circuits $mV = 2Z$
for 3-phase circuits $mV = \sqrt{3}Z$

where mV = volt drop in millivolts per ampère per metre length of cable route
Z = impedance per conductor per kilometre of cable at maximum normal operating temperature (Ω)

In a single-phase circuit, two conductors (the phase and neutral conductors) contribute to the circuit impedance and this accounts for the number 2 in the equation. If the voltage drop is to be expressed as a percentage of the supply voltage, for a single-phase circuit it has to be related to the phase-to-neutral voltage U_0, i.e. 240 V when supply is from a 240/415 V system.

In a 3-phase circuit, the voltage drop in the cable is $\sqrt{3}$ times the value for one conductor. Expressed as a percentage of the supply voltage it has to be related to the phase-to-phase voltage U, i.e. 415 V for a 240/415 V system.

The IEE Wiring Regulations used to require that the drop in voltage from the origin of the installation to any point in the installation should not exceed 2.5% of the nominal voltage when the conductors are carrying the full load current, disregarding starting conditions. Since the issue of the Amendments dated May 1984 to the fifteenth edition, the 2.5% limit has been modified to a value appropriate to the safe functioning of the equipment in normal service, it being left to the designer to quantify this. However, for final circuits protected by an overcurrent protective device having a nominal current not exceeding 100 A, the requirement is deemed to be satisfied if the voltage drop does not exceed the old limit of 2.5%. It is therefore likely that for such circuits the limit of 2.5% will still apply more often than not in practice.

The reference to starting conditions relates especially to motors, which take a significantly higher current in starting than when running at operating speeds. It may be necessary to determine the size of cable on the basis of restricting the voltage drop at the starting current to a value which allows satisfactory starting, although this may be larger than required to give an acceptable voltage drop at running speeds.

To satisfy the 2.5% limit, if the cable is providing a single-phase 240 V supply, the voltage drop should not exceed 6 V and, if providing a 3-phase 415 V supply, the voltage drop should not exceed 10.4 V. Sometimes, in selecting the size of cable for a particular duty, the current rating will be considered first. After choosing a cable size to take account of the current to be carried and the rating and type of overload protective device, the voltage drop then has to be checked. To satisfy the 2.5% limit for a 240 V single-phase or 415 V 3-phase supply the following condition should be met:

$$mVIL \leq 6000 \text{ for the single-phase condition}$$

or

$$mVIL \leq 10\,400 \text{ for the 3-phase condition}$$

where I = the full load current to be carried (A)
L = cable length (m)

If the size of cable required on the basis of current rating does not fulfil the requirement for voltage drop, or if it is foreseen at the outset that voltage drop rather than current rating will be the critical factor, then, to select the cable making use of the values of mV given in the tables, the maximum acceptable value of mV can be calculated from the following relationship for a 3-phase cable:

$$mV \leq 10\,400/IL$$

For a single-phase cable, 6000 replaces the 10 400 in the expression for 3-phase cable. The smallest size of cable for which the value of mV in the tables satisfies this relationship is then the minimum size required on the basis of 2.5% maximum voltage drop.

For other limiting percentage voltage drops and/or for voltages other than 240/415 V the values of 6 V (6000 mV) and 10.4 V (10 400 mV) are adjusted proportionately.

Calculations on these simple lines are usually adequate. Strictly, however, the reduction in voltage at the terminals of the equipment being supplied will be less than the voltage drop in the cable calculated in this way unless the ratio of inductive reactance to resistance of the cable is the same as for the load, which will not normally apply. If the power factor of the cable in this sense (not to be confused with dielectric power factor) differs substantially from the power factor of the load and if voltage drop is critical in determining the required size of cable, a more precise calculation may be desirable.

In the June 1987 Amendments to Appendix 9 of the IEE Regulations information is provided to enable account to be taken of the phase angle of the load, denoted by the symbol ϕ. For cables with conductor cross-sectional areas of 25 mm^2 and above the volt drops in the tables, expressed as millivolts per ampère per metre of cable (mV/A m), are given in columns headed r, x and z. The z values are derived from the cable impedances and correspond to those represented by mV in the previous formulae. These values apply when no account is taken of phase angles. The r and x values are the resistive and reactive components respectively.

The regulations give the following formula for calculating the approximate voltage drop taking account of the phase angle of the load:

$$\text{mV/A m} = (\cos\phi)\,(\text{tabulated }(\text{mV/A m})_r) + (\sin\phi)\,(\text{tabulated }(\text{mV/A m})_x) \qquad (10.2)$$

In this book the voltage drop values given as such in the tables are $(\text{mV/A m})_z$ values, but resistances at maximum operating temperature and reactances are given under the heading 'electrical characteristics' for some types of cables for which use could appropriately be made of the above formula. These resistance and reactance values are for each conductor and, for 2-, 3- and 4-core cables, can be multiplied by 2 for single-phase or d.c. circuits and by $\sqrt{3}$ for 3-phase circuits to give the $(\text{mV/A m})_r$ and $(\text{mV/A m})_x$ values.

For cables with conductor cross-sectional areas of 16 mm^2 or less the resistive and reactive components of voltage drop are not given separately in the tables of appendix 9 of the Regulations. This is because resistance so predominates that the r and z values are virtually the same, the phase angle for the cable being close to zero. For these cables the voltage drops, taking account of the phase angle ϕ of the load, can be calculated approximately by multiplying the tabulated value of mV/A m by $\cos\phi$.

The following example demonstrates the difference that there could be between calculating the voltage drop from the impedance of the cable as an entity compared with the calculation which takes account of the resistive and reactive components and the phase angle of the load. If equipment having a 3-phase reactance of 1.5 Ω and a resistance of 0.75 Ω is to be supplied by a 3- or 4-core 70 mm^2 (copper) XLPE insulated cable, the impedance of the load is $(1.5^2+0.75^2)^{1/2}$, i.e. 1.676 Ω. The cosine of the phase angle of the load is 0.75/1.676, i.e. 0.447, and $\sin\phi$ is 1.5/1.676, i.e. 0.895. The a.c. resistance per kilometre of the cable conductor at maximum operating temperature is 0.342 Ω and the reactance is 0.075 Ω. These values can be obtained from table A14.18. The corresponding 3-phase $(\text{mV/A m})_r$ and $(\text{mV/A m})_x$ values, obtained by multiplying by $\sqrt{3}$, are 0.592 and 0.130 respectively. The value of $(\text{mV/A m})_z$ would be the vector sum of these, which is 0.606. The effective value of mV/A m taking account of the resistive and reactive components for the cable and the phase angle of the load is $0.592 \times 0.447 + 0.130 \times 0.895$, i.e. $0.265 + 0.116 = 0.381$. This is less than two-thirds of the z value of 0.606 which would be used if phase angles were not taken into account, and allows the use of a cable that is about 50% longer for a given voltage drop.

Another factor which can be taken into account when the voltage drop is critical is the effect of temperature on the conductor resistance. The tabulated values of voltage drop are based on impedance values in which the resistive component is that applying when the conductor is at the maximum permitted sustained temperature for the type of cable on which the current ratings are based. If the cable size is dictated by voltage drop instead of the thermal rating, the conductor temperature during operation will be less than the full rated value and the conductor resistance lower than allowed in the tabulated voltage drop. On the basis that the temperature rise of the conductor is approximately proportional to the square of the current, it is possible to estimate the reduced temperature rise at a current below the full rated current. This can be used to estimate the reduced conductor temperature and in turn, from the temperature coefficient of resistance of the conductor material, the reduced conductor resistance. Substitution of this value for the resistance at full rated temperature in the formula for impedance enables the reduced impedance and voltage drop to be calculated.

The IEE Regulations give a generalised formula for taking into account that the load is less than the full current rating. A factor C_t can be derived from the following:

$$C_t = \frac{230 + t_p - (C_a^2\, C_g^2 - I_b^2/I_t^2)\,(t_p - 30)}{230 + t_p} \tag{10.3}$$

where t_p = maximum permitted normal operating temperature (°C)
C_a = the rating factor for ambient temperature
C_g = the rating factor for grouping of cables
I_b = the current actually to be carried
I_t = the tabulated current rating for the cable

For convenience the formula is based on a temperature coefficient of resistance of 0.004 per degree Celsius at 20 °C for both copper and aluminium. This factor is for application to the resistive component of voltage drop only. For cables with conductor sizes up to 16 mm^2 this is effectively the total mV/A m value, but for cables with larger conductors it is the $(\text{mV/A m})_r$ value in formula (10.2).

Cable manufacturers will often be able to provide information on corrected voltage drop values when the current is less than the full current rating of the cable, the necessary calculations having been made on the lines indicated. If the size of cable required to limit the voltage drop is only one size above the size required on the basis of thermal rating, then the exercise is unlikely to yield a benefit. If, however, two or more steps in conductor size are involved, it may prove worthwhile to check whether the lower temperature affects the size of cable required. The effect is likely to be greater at the lower end of the range of sizes, where the impedance is predominantly resistance, than towards the upper end of the range where the reactance becomes a more significant component of the impedance.

The effect of temperature on voltage drop is of particular significance in comparing XLPE insulated cables with PVC insulated cables. From the tabulated values of volt drop it appears that XLPE cables are at a disadvantage in giving greater volt drops than PVC cables, but this is because the tabulated values are based on the assumption that full advantage is taken of the higher current ratings of the XLPE cables, with associated higher permissible operating temperature. For the same current as the same size of PVC cable, the voltage drop for the XLPE cable is virtually the same. If a 4-core armoured 70 mm^2 (copper) 600/1000 V XLPE insulated cable, with a current rating of 251 A in free air with no ambient temperature or grouping factors applicable, were used instead of the corresponding PVC insulated cable to carry 207 A, which is the current rating of the PVC cable under the same conditions, application of formula (10.3) would give

$$C_t = \frac{230 + 90 - (1 - 0.68)\,60}{230 + 90} = 0.94$$

(the figure 0.68 is 207^2 divided by 251^2). If the $(\text{mV/A m})_r$ value for the XLPE cable

(0.59) is multiplied by 0.94, it gives, to two significant figures, 0.55, which is the same as for the PVC cable. The $(\text{mV/A m})_x$ value for the XLPE cable is in fact a little lower than that for the PVC cable, 0.13 compared with 0.14, but this has little effect on the $(\text{mV/A m})_z$ value which, to two significant figures, is 0.57 for both cables.

POSITIVE, NEGATIVE AND ZERO SEQUENCE IMPEDANCE

The values of cable impedance mentioned so far, and listed in the tables, relate to normal operating conditions. Under fault conditions the general symmetry is disturbed and for the calculation of currents which will flow when a fault occurs the impedances of the equipment in the system applying to the normal symmetrical conditions may not be the relevant values. For the calculation of prospective fault currents, use is made of the resistance and reactance to positive, negative and zero phase currents.

In a fault occurring between all three phases in a 3-phase system or between phase and neutral in a single-phase supply the conditions are symmetrical and for the cable involved the normal values of a.c. resistance and reactance per conductor are the operative values. However, for a fault between two phases of a 3-phase system or a fault from phase to earth, asymmetrical conditions occur.

For a fault between phases the current is calculated from

$$I_f = \frac{U}{Z_1 + Z_2} \text{ (A)} \qquad (10.4)$$

where I_f = fault current (A)
U = voltage between phases (V)
Z_1 = positive phase sequence impedance (Ω)
Z_2 = negative phase sequence impedance (Ω)

For a fault between a phase and earth the current is calculated from

$$I_f = \frac{3U_0}{Z_1 + Z_2 + Z_0} \text{ (A)} \qquad (10.5)$$

where U_0 = phase-to-neutral voltage (V)
Z_0 = zero phase sequence impedance (Ω)

Thus the zero phase impedance, which takes into account the path back to the earthed neutral of the system, enters into the equation for an earth fault but not for a phase-to-phase fault.

The impedances here are the total impedances which will contribute to limiting the current at various points in the system in the event of faults at critical places. The cable impedance is only a part of the total. Other equipment and any impedances deliberately introduced to limit the fault current have to be included. The values for individual parts therefore have to be dealt with as resistances and reactances, or as impedances in the form $R + jX$, so that they can be added as vector quantities.

Here only the values for cables are considered. Usually planners and users will ask cable manufacturers to supply the figures and introduce them into their overall calculations for the system. The following methods of calculation are used by manufacturers.

Positive and negative sequence impedances

For cables, the positive and negative sequence impedances are the same and are the values derived for symmetrical conditions in chapter 2.

The resistance is the a.c. conductor resistance, taking account of skin and proximity effects. The values of a.c. resistance listed in the tables are for maximum normal operating conductor temperature. These are not the most appropriate values to use to calculate maximum fault current, as the fault might occur under lightly loaded conditions when the resistance is lower. The a.c. resistance at ambient temperature might therefore be required instead. On the other hand, the a.c. resistance at maximum normal operating temperature would be an appropriate value to use in determining what short-circuit capability is required of the cable, because the short-circuit ratings of cables are normally based on a limiting temperature rise from the maximum normal operating temperature (see chapter 9).

The reactance is the reactance per conductor calculated from the inductance, as described in chapter 2.

Zero sequence resistance

The zero sequence resistance of the conductors per phase is the a.c. resistance of one conductor without the increase for proximity effect described in chapter 2. The increase for skin effect is included. To this value is added the following as appropriate:

for 3-core cables: three times the resistance of the metallic covering
for single-core cables: the resistance of the metallic covering
for SL cables: the resistance of one metallic sheath in parallel with three times the resistance of the armour

The metallic covering for 3-core and single-core cables may be a metal sheath, armour or a copper wire and/or tape screen, whichever is the metallic layer which will carry earth fault current. If the cable has a metallic sheath and armour, the resistance of the metallic covering is the resistance of the two components in parallel.

Some 3-core cables may contain interstitial conductors or copper wire screens on each core to carry earth fault currents. In general, where there is such a component for each core, it is the resistance of one of them which is considered. When the earthing component is a collective one, i.e. a common covering for all three cores, its resistance is multiplied by three. Where both types of earth current carrying components are present, the example given for the SL cable (three sheaths but only one armour) is followed. In effect the calculation is equivalent to determining the resistance of all the earth paths in parallel and multiplying by three for the resistance per phase.

The resistances are calculated from the cross-sectional areas and resistivities of the metallic layers. For a sheath the cross-sectional area can be calculated from the diameter and thickness. For wires, the resistance of a single wire may be divided by the number of wires and a correction made for their lay length as applied. When wires are applied helically or in wave form, their individual lengths exceed the length of the cable by an amount depending upon the ratio of their lay length to their pitch diameter. For example armour wires applied with a lay of eight times their pitch diameter have a length approximately 7.4% greater than the length of the cable.

Zero sequence reactance

For single-core cables, the zero sequence reactance of the cable per phase can be calculated from the equation

$$X_0 = 2\pi f \times 10^{-3}\,[0.2 \log_e(D/d) + K]\ (\Omega/\text{km}) \qquad (10.6)$$

where X_0 = zero sequence reactance
f = frequency (Hz)
D = mean diameter of metallic covering (mm)
d = conductor diameter (mm)
K = a constant depending on the conductor construction as in chapter 2, equation (2.2)

The similarity between this and the combination of the equations for inductance and reactance in chapter 2 is evident. The value D, which amounts to twice the spacing from the conductor to the metallic covering, replaces the $2S$ where S is the spacing between conductors in normal operation.

For a frequency of 50 Hz the equation simplifies to

$$X_0 = 0.314[0.46 \log_{10}(D/d) + K]\ (\Omega/\text{km}) \qquad (10.7)$$

For a 3-core cable the equation is

$$X_0 = 0.434 \log_{10}(D/GMD)\ (\Omega/\text{km}) \qquad (10.8)$$

where GMD is the geometric mean diameter of the conductors in the laid-up cable. Conventionally, the value of GMD is taken as 0.75 of the diameter of the circle which circumscribes the conductors in the laid-up cores, assuming the conductors to be circular.

The equation for the 3-core cable is analogous with that for single-core cable, the value K now not being relevant and the 0.434 including multiplication by 3 for reactance per phase.

IEE WIRING REGULATIONS

The IEE Wiring Regulations relate to electrical installations at voltages up to 1000 V a.c. in and around buildings. They do not apply directly to the public supply system, to which statutory regulations apply, but to consumers' installations which, more often than not, take their energy from the public supply system.

The Regulations are not statutory in England and Wales but are generally accepted as providing the basis for a safe and reliable installation. The Electricity Boards would be unlikely to connect to the public supply system an installation which did not comply substantially with them.

The implications of the Regulations for the selection of cables arise from aspects which should be taken into account whether covered by the Regulations or not, e.g. voltage drop: the requirements in this respect have already been covered as being of general importance irrespective of the particular requirements of the Regulations. However, the Regulations give specific guidance on other aspects which are based on international consensus, as well as the advice drawn from wide ranging representation of the electrical engineering interests in the UK, and it is convenient to consider the impact on cables of the requirements of the relevant regulations as specifically stated.

The following sections relate to the fifteenth edition of the IEE Wiring Regulations published in March 1981 and amendments since then, up to and including those of June 1987. Other relevant publications are those by Jenkins[1] and Whitfield.[2]

Protection against overload current

Chapter 52 of the Regulations, dealing with selection of cables, conductors and wiring equipment, requires by Regulation 522-1 that the cable shall have a current carrying capacity adequate for the load to be carried and it refers to appendix 9, where the detailed information on current rating is given. However, it is Section 433 'Protection against overload current', which effectively decides the current rating required for the circuit cabling. There, in Regulation 433-2, it is required that the device protecting a circuit against overload should satisfy the following conditions:

(a) its nominal current or current setting I_n is not less than the design current I_b of the circuit
(b) its nominal current or current setting I_n does not exceed the lowest of the current carrying capacities I_z of any of the conductors of the circuit
(c) the current I_2 causing effective operation of the protective device does not exceed 1.45 times the lowest of the current carrying capacities I_z of any of the conductors of the circuit

These requirements may be expressed as follows:

$$I_b \leqslant I_n \leqslant I_z \qquad (10.9)$$

$$I_2 \leqslant 1.45 I_z \qquad (10.10)$$

Clearly from conditions (a) and (b), as abbreviated in the relationship (10.9) the required current rating of the cable is not determined directly by the circuit current but has to be not less than the nominal current of the fuse, or other overload protective device, which in turn has to be not less than the circuit current. The cable rating is determined directly by the overload protective device selected for the circuit and, as fuse ratings progress in discrete steps, the cable rating may be more than it would need to be if related directly to the circuit current.

Condition (c), abbreviated in the relationship (10.10), does not constitute an invitation to overload cables by up to 45% of their rated current, but is to safeguard against the worst consequences of overloads occurring through mistake or accident. The intention is that, if an overload of 45%, or preferably less, should occur, the protective device should operate, interrupting the current, within 'conventional time'. Conventional time varies with the device but is not more than 4 hours.

For a cable in air, a 45% overload persisting for several hours would cause a temperature rise of more than double the design value for sustained operation. While the degree of deformation of PVC due to softening in a single excursion to such a temperature is regarded as tolerable on the basis of tests, the chemical deterioration of most insulants, including PVC, is accelerated by increased temperature, and overloading, especially if repetitive, is bound to take a toll of cable life.

It has to be accepted that, if the devices providing overload protection are to pass their full rated currents for an indefinite period without interruption, there must be a reasonable margin between their rated currents and the currents causing them to interrupt the supply. The 1.45 factor is met by most of the standard types of device and also corresponds to an overload temperature close to the limit that can be tolerated for a relatively short time by PVC, which, because of its thermoplasticity, is perhaps the most vulnerable at high temperatures of the commonly used insulants.

Of the standard protective devices it is accepted in the Regulations that fuses to BS 88 or BS 1361, or circuit breakers to BS 3871: Part 1 or BS 4752: Part 1, if they comply with relationship (10.9), will automatically ensure compliance with (10.10). This may not be obvious from examination of the standards for the protective devices. For example in BS 88 the conventional fusing current is given as 1.6 times the rated current. However, account is taken of the difference in the conditions of the tests used to determine values in the standard and the practical conditions of use, in which, for example, the freedom to dissipate heat differs. These devices are therefore considered to operate in practice at not more than 1.45 times their nominal current or current settings, and compliance with the requirement that the nominal current of the device is not more than the current rating of the cable ensures also that the operating current of the device is not more than 1.45 times the current rating of the cable.

It is when rewirable fuses to BS 3036 are chosen as the means of protection that condition (c) takes effect. For these fuses the currents causing operation within 4 hours may be twice their rated currents. Therefore, to comply with the requirement that the operating current of the fuse should not exceed 1.45 times the current rating of the cable, the cable must have a higher rating than when use is made of the other standard types of protective device previously designated.

Referring back to the relationship (10.10) expressing condition (c) of Regulation 433-2, i.e. $I_2 \leqslant 1.45 I_z$, if $I_2 = 2I_n$ it follows that I_n should not be greater than $0.725 I_z$. Thus Regulation 433-2 states that where the device is a semi-enclosed fuse to BS 3036, compliance with condition (c) is afforded if its nominal current I_n does not exceed 0.725 times the current carrying capacity of the lowest rated conductor in the circuit protected.

The effect of this is, of course, that the current rating of the cable, with any correction factors for ambient temperature, grouping or other relevant conditions, must be not less than the fuse rating divided by 0.725, i.e. not less than 1.38 times the fuse rating. Therefore the use of a rewirable fuse imposes a penalty in size of cable required when this is determined by current rating. Of course, if the size of cable is determined by other considerations, such as voltage drop, there may be no such penalty.

These requirements are in line with international (IEC) rules, which are published in sections having the common reference number 364 and in which the relevant section on protection against overcurrent is IEC 364–4–43.

Protection against short-circuit current

Section 434 of the IEE Wiring Regulations ostensibly specifies requirements for the devices used to protect against short-circuit currents, but it may affect the choice of the cable to be used. The device has to be chosen to protect the cable used effectively, but conversely the cable has to be chosen so that it is effectively protected by the device used. As with Regulation 433 (overload protection) it is concerned with co-ordination between protective devices and conductors.

The basic requirement for protection against short circuit is that all currents caused by a short circuit at any point in the circuit shall be interrupted in a time not exceeding that which brings the cable conductors to the admissible limiting temperatures. The maximum time T for which the protective device should allow the short circuit to persist is derived from the following equation:

$$T = k^2S^2/I^2 \text{ (s)} \tag{10.11}$$

where S = cross-sectional area of conductor(s) (mm^2)
I = effective short-circuit current, r.m.s. if a.c. (A)
k = a value depending on the conductor metal and the cable insulant

In Regulation 434-6 values of k are given for cables with copper and aluminium conductors with each of the usual insulating materials. A value is also given for soldered joints in copper conductors.

The derivation of the formula is essentially as described in chapter 9 of this book, dealing with short-circuit ratings. The important difference between equation (10.11) and equation (9.1) in chapter 9 is that the value k in (10.11) differs from the value K in (9.1). In chapter 9, K is a function of the volumetric specific heat of the conductor metal, its resistivity and its temperature coefficient of resistance. In the IEE Wiring Regulations k embraces all these parameters but also includes the permitted temperature rise between the normal sustained conductor temperature and the short-circuit conductor temperature. The values of k in Regulation 434-6 are, in fact, equivalent to the figures by which $ST^{-1/2}$ are multiplied to give the short-circuit current shown in the last column of table 9.3 in chapter 9.

If the same device is used to protect against short-circuit as against overload current, in accordance with the requirements for protection against overload already given, it may generally be assumed to provide the required protection against short circuit and checking against the short-circuit requirements is not necessary. This is confirmed in Regulation 434-5. There is a note to this regulation, however, warning that for certain types of circuit breaker, especially non-current-limiting types, this assumption may not be valid for the whole range of short-cicuit currents. It is valid for the standard types of fuse. If the fuse rating is not greater than the cable rating and if the fuse will operate within 4 hours at 1.45 times the cable rating, then the current–operating time characteristics of fuses, and the relationship between sustained current carrying capacities and short-circuit capacities of cables, are such that cable short-circuit capacity will not be exceeded.

In order to serve as the short-circuit protection, the protective device must be placed at the supply end of the circuit so that it protects the whole of the circuit cabling, wherever the short circuit may occur, and it must have a breaking capacity adequate for the prospective short-circuit current which could occur at that point. The overload protective device, on the other hand, can be placed close to the load since an overload, defined as excess current occurring in an electrically sound circuit, can only arise from the load. A common example would be an overload device in a motor starter.

The device providing protection against short circuit may therefore be separate from the overload protection and may have a nominal current in excess of the sustained current rating of the cable. It is then necessary to check that the combination of cable and short circuit protection complies with Regulation 434-6. Constraints on the selection of the device for short-circuit protection may result in a magnitude and duration of short-circuit current that dictate the size of cable, instead of the sustained current, overload protection requirements or voltage drop. In this case the required conductor size can be calculated from the following transposed form of equation (10.11):

$$S = IT^{1/2}/k \ (\text{mm}^2) \tag{10.12}$$

The conductor size used should be the next higher standard size to the value calculated as S, unless S happens to be very close to a standard nominal cross-sectional area.

More conveniently, the required conductor size can be obtained from the data for standard cables given in chapter 9.

Where the short-circuit condition is critical, it is necessary to check that the protection is adequate for the minimum short-circuit current it has to protect against, and not only for the maximum current occurring due to a fault at the supply end of the circuit. The characteristics of protective devices are such that the heating effect of a relatively low short-circuit current in the time taken for the device to interrupt the current may be greater than the heating effect of a higher short-circuit current causing the device to operate in a shorter time.

The fifteenth edition of the IEE Wiring Regulations includes in appendix 8 graphs showing the maximum time to operation against current for the standard types of fuse and for miniature circuit breakers. These can be used to derive the value of T for the prospective short-circuit current for checking compliance with Regulation 434-6. The Commentary on the regulations includes the same graphs together with superimposed lines showing the maximum time for which short-circuit currents of varying magnitude may be allowed to persist for compliance with Regulation 434-6 when the cable is PVC insulated with copper conductors; these graphs are useful for a quick check when the cable is of this commonly used type.

From the graphs in the Commentary it is evident that for short-circuit protection by fuses to BS 88 and BS 1361, the minimum short-circuit current is the critical value as far as the heating of the conductors is affected, but table 10.1 based on the characteristics of a 100 A fuse to BS 88: Part 2, taken as a typical example, demonstrates the point. As the heating effect is proportional to I^2T, the lower fault

Table 10.1 Comparison of heating effects of short-circuit currents interrupted by a 100 A fuse to BS 88: Part 2

Short-circuit current (I) (A)	Maximum time for fuse to operate (T) (s)	I^2T (A^2 s)
550	4.5	136×10^4
700	1.5	74×10^4
850	0.7	51×10^4
1000	0.35	35×10^4

currents, with longer durations, are the more critical. The pattern is not quite the same for fuses to BS 3036 for which I^2T may be somewhat higher for small values of T than for some longer periods, but checking against the maximum and minimum prospective currents will cover the intermediate values.

In the Regulations a short circuit is defined as an overcurrent resulting from a fault between live conductors of differing potential. A fault to earth is not a short circuit as defined. Nevertheless it is necessary to check that the conductors will not overheat during a fault to earth. Because the earth fault current is likely to be less than the short-circuit current between conductors, it is likely to persist for longer and therefore cause greater heating, as illustrated in table 10.1.

Protection against indirect contact

In the measures for protection against electric shock detailed in chapter 41 of the Regulations, protection against shock by indirect contact refers to contact with exposed conductive parts made live by a fault, as distinct from direct contact with parts which are live in normal operation. An exposed conductive part is defined as a conductive part of equipment which can be touched and which is not a live part but which may become live under fault conditions.

When the method of protection against shock by indirect contact is by automatic disconnection of supply in the event of a fault to earth, the impedance of the protective conductor included in the cable or of the metal covering over the cable, e.g. metal sheath and/or armour, may be an important parameter.

As with other aspects, much of the terminology in the Regulations follows international documentation: a protective conductor is a conductor used to connect conducting parts (other than live parts) together and/or to earth. The circuit protective conductor is the conductor which generally follows the cable route connecting the exposed conductive parts of the equipment supplied back to the main earthing terminal of the installation.

The circuit protective conductor may be a conductor in the cable or other continuous metallic component of the cable. It may also be separate from the cable, e.g. a separate conductor, metallic conduit or trunking, but for present purposes it is protective conductors which are parts of cables that are considered.

The basic requirement contained in Regulation 413-3 is that during an earth fault the magnitude and duration of the voltages between simultaneously accessible exposed and extraneous conductive parts anywhere in the installation shall not cause danger.

In Regulation 413-4, the requirement of Regulation 413-3 is considered to be satisfied if

(a) for final circuits supplying socket outlets, the earth fault loop impedance at every socket outlet is such that disconnection occurs within 0.4 s
(b) for final circuits supplying only fixed equipment, the earth fault loop impedance at every point of utilisation is such that disconnection occurs within 5 s

The requirement for faster disconnection in circuits supplying socket outlets than in circuits supplying only fixed equipment takes account of the use of socket outlets for supplying equipment which may be held in the hand while in operation, when the risk is greater.

When the protection is afforded by an overcurrent protective device, the time for disconnection depends upon the current and the current–time characteristics of the device. Regulation 413-5 gives the maximum values of earth fault loop impedance which, at a voltage to earth U_0 of 240 V, will give currents sufficient to operate various types of fuse and miniature circuit breaker in 0.4 s (table 41A1) or in 5 s (table 41A2). The values are calculated by dividing 240 by the current giving operation in the appropriate time, as derived from the graphs in appendix 8 of the Regulations.

The earth fault loop impedance includes the impedance of the phase conductor and the protective conductor of the circuit and the impedance of the supply to the circuit. For larger installations the consumer may have his own supply transformer and the impedance of this and of any cabling and other equipment between it and the final circuit is within the control of the designer. For smaller installations, where the supply is taken direct from the public distribution system, the earth fault loop impedance includes a part external to the installation. This external impedance includes that of the supply authority's transformer and the phase and protective conductors of the cabling from there to the consumer's installation.

When the installation has been made, the earth fault loop impedance can be measured, but at the planning stage an estimate has to be made if protection against shock by indirect contact is to be by interruption of supply by an overcurrent device. When part of the impedance is in the supply authority's system, it is indicated in the Commentary on the Regulations that this impedance external to the installation will not normally exceed 0.35 Ω if the system is one with CNE conductor, as applies to most new parts of the public supply system, and will not normally exceed 0.8 Ω if the earthing is provided via the lead sheath of the older type of public supply cable. In particular cases, the supply authority may be able to give a more precise value and should be asked anyway, if only to confirm that the normal maximum will apply.

Occasionally the supply authority may not be able to supply an earth terminal with reliable connection back to the substation earth and in this event an earth electrode has to be supplied by the consumer and the earth fault loop impedance includes the resistance of this and the path through the ground to the supply earth. The installation and its source of supply then becomes a TT system instead of a TN system and circuits supplying socket outlets are required to be protected by residual current devices (current operated earth leakage circuit breakers) having a rated residual operating current not exceeding 30 mA. The designations, such as TN and TT, to describe types of system earthing are fully explained in appendix 3 of the Wiring Regulations.

In the Regulations, the measure for protection against indirect contact by automatic disconnection of supply is designated more fully as 'protection by earthed equipotential bonding and automatic disconnection of supply'. It is required that extraneous conductive parts should be connected by equipotential bonding conductors to the main earthing terminal of the installation. In the event of a fault to earth, the voltage between exposed conductive parts and simultaneously accessible extraneous conductive parts is therefore the voltage drop in the circuit protective conductor between the exposed conductive part and the main earthing terminal. This is the product of the earth fault current and the impedance of the circuit protective conductor.

In IEC 364-4-41, which is taken into account in the IEE Wiring Regulations, the corresponding measure of protection relates the magnitude of the voltage to maximum disconnecting time for circuits which may be used to supply equipment to be held in the hand. The IEE Wiring Regulations, while adopting the 0.4 s disconnection time as a condition satisfying Regulation 413-3, do not preclude other methods of complying with the regulation and refer in particular to an alternative method prescribed in appendix 7 of the Regulations which makes use of the IEC relationship between the magnitude of the voltage and the time for which it may be allowed to persist.

A critical condition in the IEC relationship between 'touch voltage' and maximum disconnecting time is 50 V for 5 s. It can be shown that, for most of the standard overcurrent protective devices, if the 50 V, 5 s condition is met, then all the shorter disconnection times required for higher voltages will also be met. This does not apply to semi-enclosed fuses (BS 3036) and from appendix C of the Commentary on the Regulations it is apparent that, for these, the critical condition is 240 V for 0.045 s; if this is satisfied the permissible longer times for lower voltages will also be satisfied.

In appendix 7 of the Regulations, impedances of protective conductors are tabulated for the various standard protective devices. These values ensure that the voltage drop in the protective conductor will not exceed 50 V when the disconnection time is 5 s and will not reach excessive voltages when the disconnection time is shorter. If the impedance of the protective conductor does not exceed the appropriate value in these tables, the total earth fault loop impedance may be up to the value for disconnection in 5 s, for circuits supplying socket outlets, instead of for disconnection in 0.4 s.

In some circumstances it may be convenient to make use of appendix 7, rather than try to arrange for disconnection within 0.4 s. The following figures extracted from the Regulations can be used as examples to demonstrate this when the protective device is a fuse to BS 1361:

Fuse rating (A)	5	15	20	30
Z_s for 0.4 s disconnection (Ω)	11.4	3.4	1.8	1.2
Z_s for 5 s disconnection (Ω)	17	5.3	2.9	2.0
Z_2 as in appendix 7 (Ω)	3.57	1.08	0.63	0.42

where Z_s = earth fault loop impedance
Z_2 = maximum impedance of protective conductor required by appendix 7 method

If the supply is from the 240/415 V public supply network the earth fault loop impedance Z_e external to the installation may, under adverse circumstances, be 0.8 Ω. Adjusting the previous figures to obtain the maximum impedances Z_c of the cable conductors to meet the two disconnection times gives the following:

Fuse rating (A)	5	15	20	30
Z_c for 0.4 s disconnection (Ω)	10.6	2.6	1.0	0.4
Z_c for 5 s disconnection (Ω)	16.2	4.5	2.1	1.2
Z_2 as in appendix 7	3.57	1.08	0.63	0.42

For circuits protected by 5 and 15 A fuses, it is not likely that advantage can be taken of the higher cable impedance for 5 s disconnection because of the associated limitation on the impedance of the protective conductor. The protective conductors in cables are not usually of lower impedances than the phase conductors and, if they are of the same impedances, they may be up to 5.3 Ω and 1.3 Ω respectively to give disconnection in 0.4 s, i.e. higher than they need to be to comply with appendix 7. For a circuit protected by a 20 A fuse, the difference is smaller, but with the 30 A fuse there is a clear benefit from the method of appendix 7. With the 30 A fuse the impedance of the protective conductor may be 0.42 Ω, provided that the total cable impedance, phase plus protective conductor, is not more than 1.2 Ω, whereas for disconnection in 0.4 s the impedance of the phase and protective conductors in series must not exceed 0.4 Ω, i.e. less than that of the protective conductor alone for compliance with appendix 7. In this instance the method of appendix 7 is the better proposition.

The cable in the circuit might be a 4 mm^2 flat twin and earth cable to BS 6004 in which the protective conductor is the 1.5 mm^2 earth continuity conductor. The resistance of the phase and earth conductors together, per metre of cable, is 0.0231 Ω. For these small sizes the resistance and impedance are practically the same and so this value can be taken as impedance. It is derived from appendix 17 (tables 17A and 17B) of the Regulations which takes account of the increase in temperature and consequently in resistance during the fault period. The maximum length to meet the 0.4 s disconnection time would be 0.4 divided by 0.0231 (0.4 Ω being the maximum value of Z_c to allow disconnection in 0.4 s), i.e. 17 m to the nearest metre. For disconnection in 5 s the length could be three times this (1.2 divided by 0.0231), but with the method of appendix 7 the limit in this case will be set by the resistance of the protective conductor. The 1.5 mm^2 protective conductor has a resistance per metre at 20°C of 0.0121 Ω, and multiplying this by 1.38 in accordance with table 17B in appendix 17 of the regulations, to take account of the temperature rise during the fault, gives 0.0167 Ω/m. The maximum cable length to comply with the value of Z_2 is therefore 0.42 divided by 0.0167, i.e. 25 m. The tabulated voltage drop for this cable is 0.011 V/m A so that, at a load of 30 A, the maximum length to meet the 2.5% (6 V) maximum, if this is applied, would be 18 m. This is only a little more than the 17 m to give disconnection in 0.4 s, but the actual current to be carried in normal operation may well be less than 30 A, the rating of the fuse. Given that the next lower standard fuse rating is 20 A, the load to be carried might be only 25 A, for example. The rating of the cable clipped direct or embedded in plaster is 36 A, and for an actual load of 25 A application of formula (10.3) gives a factor of 0.93 which can be applied to the voltage drop. Using this and 25 A instead of 30 A in calculating the cable length would allow 23 m to be used. The adoption of the method of appendix 7 of the Regulations therefore permits the cable to be used in the maximum length which meets voltage drop requirements, whereas disconnection in 0.4 s would set a lower limit. In general, resource to appendix 7 will be helpful when a large part of the earth fault loop impedance to give disconnection in 0.4 s is taken up by the external impedance.

In the example quoted above reference was made to the need to take account of the heating effect of the fault current on the resistances of the conductors. Appendix 17 of the Regulations gives guidance on this aspect for phase and protective conductors, and combinations thereof, for sizes up to and including 35 mm^2, for which inductance can be ignored. In that appendix table 17A gives resistance values at 20 °C, which are as quoted in BS 6360 and appendix A4 of this book for individual conductors. The values for combinations of phase and protective conductors are derived by simple addition. Table 17B in appendix 17 of the regulations gives the factors by which the values of resistance at 20 °C can be multiplied to give values applying during the period of the fault. The data are presented here in table 10.2. The multipliers are based on the simplification that the effective resistance during the fault period is that corresponding to a temperature halfway between the maximum normal operating temperature and the maximum permitted temperature which may be reached at the instant of interruption of the fault current, i.e. the maximum short-circuit temperature (see chapter 9). For PVC insulated cables of the smaller sizes, for example, the two temperatures are 70 and 160 °C and the mean of these is 115 °C. This is 95 °C above the 20 °C at which the standard resistances are quoted. Thus, using a temperature coefficient of resistance of 0.004 for both copper and aluminium conductors the multiplier for temperature during the fault is $1 + 95 \times 0.004$, which gives the tabulated figure of 1.38.

These multipliers apply to conductors which are within the cable. For protective conductors external to the cable lower values are appropriate because the starting temperature is the ambient temperature instead of the cable temperature. Strictly the multipliers are also only applicable to conductor sizes up to and including 35 mm^2. Table 10.2 is applicable to larger conductors in cables operating on direct current but for a.c. operation inductance and the skin effect may become significant for large sizes.

Table 10.2 Multipliers to apply to resistance at 20 °C to give resistance during fault

Insulation material	PVC (70 °C)	85 °C rubber	90 °C thermosetting (e.g. XLPE)
Multiplier	1.38	1.53	1.60

Of the various combinations of phase conductors and protective conductors that might be employed, a common practice in the UK for heavier loads is to use wire armoured PVC or XLPE insulated cables with the wire armour as the circuit protective conductor. These types of cable, with PVC insulation to BS 6346 or with XLPE insulation to BS 5467 and BS 6724, therefore merit particular consideration.

The contribution to earth loop impedance of these cables comprises the impedance of a phase conductor in series with the impedance of the armour, the path of the return fault current via the armour being approximately concentric with the phase conductor. Under these conditions the impedance of the conductor can be taken to be approximately its d.c. resistance at 20 °C multiplied by the appropriate factor in table 10.2, to take account of temperature. In theory, with a.c. operation the skin effect will slightly increase the resistance of the larger conductors, but in the cables with the larger conductors the resistance of the armour so far exceeds the resistance of the conductor that a small approximation in the latter is insignificant in the calculation of the total earth fault impedance.

Because the return current is concentric to the phase conductor, inductance is low, but experiments done by ERA Technology for cable makers have indicated that for steel wire armour, which is, of course, magnetic, an allowance for reactance should be made. The conclusion from the measurements is that 0.3 mΩ is an appropriate value for all sizes of steel wire armoured cable.

In the same experiments there was no discernible rise in the temperature of the armour when currents flowed at magnitudes and for times to give disconnection using fuses of ratings equal to or slightly less than the cable ratings. It was concluded that the armour resistance could be taken as the maximum applying during normal operation, i.e. 10 °C less than the maximum permissible conductor temperature in normal operation. The armour temperatures applying are therefore 60 °C for PVC insulated cables and 80 °C for XLPE insulated cables. On the basis of a temperature coefficient of resistance for steel at 20 °C of 0.0045, the multipliers to convert resistances at 20 °C, as quoted in the cable standards, to resistances at these temperatures are 1.18 for PVC insulated cables and 1.27 for XLPE insulated cables.

The contribution per metre of a steel wire armoured cable to earth fault loop impedance is then the sum of the resistances of phase conductor and armour in milliohms, each adjusted for temperature as above, added vectorially to 0.3, the armour reactance. For example, for an XLPE insulated cable with conductor resistance R_c milliohm per metre at 20 °C and steel wire armour resistance of R_A milliohm per metre at 20 °C, the contribution per metre of cable to the earth fault loop impedance would be

$$[(R_c \times 1.6 + R_A \times 1.27)^2 + 0.3^2]^{1/2} \text{ (m}\Omega)$$

Table 10.3 and 10.4 give calculated values for 2-, 3- and 4-core steel wire armoured PVC insulated 600/1000 V cables to BS 6346 and XLPE insulated 600/1000 V cables to BS 5467 and BS 6724, all with copper conductors. Comparing tables 10.3 and 10.4, it appears that the earth loop impedances for XLPE insulated cables are, size

Table 10.3 Contribution of steel wire armoured cables to earth fault loop impedances, 600/1000 V PVC insulated cables to BS 6346, copper conductors

Conductor size (mm^2)	Contribution by cable to earth fault loop impedance (mΩ/m)			
	2 core	3 core	4 core (all equal)	4 core including reduced neutral
1.5	29.3	28.7	27.9	–
2.5	21.0	20.6	19.6	–
4	15.2	14.6	11.8	–
6	12.3	9.68	9.09	–
10	7.13	6.90	6.54	–
16	5.72	5.37	4.19	–
25	4.08	3.85	3.49	3.49
35	3.57	3.22	2.98	2.98
50	3.03	2.79	2.09	2.56
70	2.63	2.04	1.81	1.81
95	1.83	1.71	1.45	1.48
120	1.65	1.54	1.09	1.11
150	1.50	1.09	0.98	1.01
185	1.10	0.99	0.89	0.90
240	0.97	0.87	0.78	0.80
300	0.88	0.78	0.70	0.73
400	0.78	0.71	0.55	0.56

Table 10.4 Contribution of steel wire armoured cables to earth fault loop impedances, 600/1000 V XLPE insulated cables to BS 5467 or BS 6724, copper conductors

Conductor size (mm^2)	Contribution by cable to earth fault loop impedance ($m\Omega/m$)			
	2 core	3 core	4 core (all equal)	4 core including reduced neutral
1.5	31.3	30.9	30.2	–
2.5	23.0	22.3	21.6	–
4	17.4	16.9	16.0	–
6	13.8	13.3	10.4	–
10	10.6	8.01	7.63	–
16	6.67	6.42	5.91	–
25	5.87	4.35	4.10	4.10
35	4.02	3.77	3.39	3.52
50	3.55	3.17	2.92	3.05
70	2.98	2.73	1.98	2.10
95	2.11	1.98	1.73	1.73
120	1.92	1.79	1.25	1.49
150	1.75	1.23	1.10	1.14
185	1.24	1.10	0.98	1.00
240	1.09	0.97	0.86	0.88
300	0.99	0.89	0.78	0.81
400	0.88	0.79	0.6	0.72

for size, significantly greater than those for PVC insulated cables. However, this is partly due to the assumption made in calculating the values that the full thermal ratings of the cables are utilised, both in normal operation and under fault conditions, i.e. that in normal operation the conductors of the PVC cables will be at 70 °C and those of the XLPE cables will be at 90 °C and under fault conditions the conductors will reach 160 °C in the PVC cables and 250 °C in the XLPE cables. If an XLPE cable is used for the same duty as the PVC cable of the same size and with the same overcurrent protection, its temperatures in normal operation and during an earth fault will be virtually the same as for the PVC cable. The multipliers for PVC insulated cables to take account of temperature during the fault can then be applied to the XLPE insulated cable. The earth fault loop impedance of the XLPE cable will generally still be higher at the same temperature because its dimensions and consequently the cross-sectional area of its armour are less, giving a higher armour resistance, but the difference will be smaller than the tables indicate.

For both types of cable the probability is that the temperatures during normal operation and on occurrence of a fault will be less than the maximum permitted values, on which the tabulated data are based. The current actually to be carried in normal operation must not exceed the rating of the overload protective device and the rating of the overload protective device must not exceed the rating of the cable. This makes it very likely that the current to be carried will be less than the cable rating and that the temperature at which the cable operates normally will be less than the permissible maximum on which the rating is based. If the cable is protected by a standard device that gives protection against overload as well as short circuit, i.e. with a rating not higher than the current rating of the cable, the current let through for a given time under fault conditions will fall short of that which would bring the conductors to their maximum permissible short-circuit temperature, as previously indicated in the section on protection against short-circuit current. The tabulated impedances may therefore be higher than apply in practice. They are useful to provide a check on earth loop impedance, but if, for a particular part of an installation, this is a critical factor in determining the size or length of cable which can be used, it may be possible to justify lower temperatures and associated multipliers for resistance by more accurate calculation of the temperatures applying to the circuit.

For example, a circuit to carry 120 A three phase might be protected by 125 A fuses to BS 88: Part 2. A suitable cable installed in free air with no rating factors to be applied for ambient temperature or grouping would be a 4-core 25 mm^2 (copper) armoured XLPE cable with a current rating of 131 A. Within reasonable limits of accuracy the temperature rise of the conductors is proportional to the square of the current, and since the temperature rise at 131 A is 60 °C the temperature rise at 120 A will be $60 \times 120^2/131^2$, i.e. 50.3 °C, giving a conductor temperature in normal operation of 80.3 °C. Under fault conditions the current which would operate the fuse within 5 s is slightly under 700 A. In formula (10.11) ($T=k^2S^2/I^2$) the value of k for a copper conductor XLPE insulated cable is 143, based on a maximum temperature rise of 160 °C (from 90 to 250 °C). With $T = 5$ and $S = 25$, the current giving this temperature rise is $143 \times 25/\sqrt{5}$, i.e. 1599 A. As the fuse will operate within 5 s at 700 A for the circuit being considered, the temperature rise will be $160 \times 700^2/1599^2$, i.e. 30.7 °C. For the circuit, then, the conductor temperature can be taken as 80.3 °C in normal operation and 111 °C at the end of the fault period, giving a mean temperature during the fault of, say, 95.7 °C. The armour temperature can be taken as 70.3 °C. Multipliers for resistances calculated for these temperatures during the fault are 1.303 for the conductor and 1.226 for the armour. The earth fault loop impedance calculated using these multipliers is 3.78 mΩ/m compared with the value of 4.10 mΩ/m shown in table 10.4 as applying when the temperatures are maximum permissible values.

For paper insulated lead sheathed cable, the lead sheath and the wire armour, if the cable is so armoured, can serve as the protective conductor. BS 6480 gives the resistances of these components for 600/1000 V cables. The resistance multipliers for calculation of earth loop impedances, based on maximum permissible temperatures, are 1.4 for conductors and 1.225 for armour, and it seems appropriate to allow 0.3 mΩ/m for armour reactance.

Cross-sectional area of protective conductors

The implications for circuit protective conductors of the requirement for interruption of supply in the event of an earth fault have already been considered, making reference to Section 413 of the Regulations. However, it is Section 543 which is actually headed 'Protective conductors'. Regulations 543-1 to 543-3 contain requirements for the cross-sectional area of protective conductors in general, and therefore for circuit protective conductors, which may be cables or parts of cables.

Regulation 543-1 requires, so far as it affects protective conductors which are a part of a cable or in an enclosure formed by a wiring system (e.g. single-core cables in conduit), that the cross-sectional area should either be calculated by a formula given in Regulation 543-2 or be in accordance with Regulation 543-3, which includes table 54F, relating the cross-sectional area of the protective conductor to that of the associated phase conductors.

After the earlier consideration of the requirements for protection against short circuit the formula in Regulation 543-2 should be familiar. The requirement is that the cross-sectional area shall be not less than is given by

$$S = (I^2T)^{1/2}/k \tag{10.13}$$

where S = cross-sectional area (mm^2)
I = the value (r.m.s. for a.c.) of fault current, for an earth fault of negligible impedance, which will flow through the associated protective device (A)
T = the operating time of the disconnecting device (s), corresponding to the fault current I (A)
k = a factor depending on the material of the protective conductor, the insulation and other parts, and the initial and final temperatures

The description of k is given above as it appears in Regulation 543-2. In fact k does not depend directly on both the insulation and other parts and the initial and final temperatures. The initial and final temperatures take account of the insulation and any other materials with which the conductor is in contact.

Values of k are given in the Regulation in tables 54B, 54C, 54D and 54E and are repeated here in Table 10.5. These values are derived by calculation on the lines described in chapter 9 of this book.

As an alternative to calculating the cross-sectional area of the protective conductor in accordance with Regulation 543-2, Regulation 543-3 allows that it may be selected, when it is of the same material as the phase conductor, in accordance with Table 10.6, which is copied from table 54F of the Regulations. Where the table requires the minimum cross-sectional area of the protective conductor to be one-half of that of the phase conductor and a precise half is not a standard size, the nearest standard cross-sectional area may be used. If the protective conductor is of a different material from the phase conductor, it is required that the protective conductor should have a conductance not less than the conductance resulting from application of the table.

The last requirement, relating to protective conductors which are of different metals from the phase conductors, is based on a simplification which, when the phase conductors are copper, results in the need to use larger cross-sectional areas of the metal of the protective conductor than is justified by equation (10.13). For a given current and time, the cross-sectional area required to meet the temperature limit is not related simply to the resistivity of the metal. It depends also on the volumetric specific heat of the metal, which in turn is a function of the density and the mass specific heat.

In Table 10.5 (a), the values of k for steel for the three sets of limiting temperatures are 52, 60 and 64, compared with 143, 166 and 176 for copper for the same sets of limiting temperature. The steel:copper ratio of these values is 1:2.75. Therefore, for a given current and time, the area of steel needs to be 2.75 times the area of copper

Table 10.5 Values of *k* for protective conductors

(a) Insulated conductors not incorporated in cables or bare conductors in contact with outside of cable covering

Material and conductor	Material of insulation or cable covering: PVC	85 °C rubber	90 °C thermoset
Copper	143	166	176
Aluminium	95	110	116
Steel	52	60	64
Assumed initial temperature (°C)	30	30	30
Final temperature (°C)	160	220	250

(b) Conductor as a core in the cable

Material of conductor	Insulation material: PVC	85 °C rubber	90 °C thermoset
Copper	115	134	143
Aluminium	76	89	94
Assumed initial temperature (°C)	70	85	90
Final temperature (°C)	160	220	250

(c) Conductor as a sheath or armour of a cable

Material of conductor	Insulation material: PVC	85 °C rubber	90 °C thermoset
Steel	44	51	54
Aluminium	81	93	98
Lead	22	26	27
Assumed initial temperature (°C)	60	75	80
Final temperature (°C)	160	220	250

(d) Bare conductors where there is no risk of damage to any neighbouring material by the temperatures indicated (assumed initial temperature 30 °C)

Material of conductor	Conditions[a]		
	Visible and in restricted areas [b]	Normal	Fire risk
Copper	228 (500 °C)	159 (200 °C)	138 (150 °C)
Aluminium	125 (300 °C)	105 (200 °C)	91 (150 °C)
Steel	82 (500 °C)	58 (200 °C)	50 (150 °C)

[a] The figures in parentheses are the limiting final temperatures
[b] The temperatures indicated are valid only where they do not impair the quality of connections

Table 10.6 Minimum cross-sectional area of protective conductor in relation to area of associated phase conductor

Cross-sectional area S of phase conductor (mm^2)	Minimum cross-sectional area (S_p) of the corresponding protective conductor (mm^2)
$S \leqslant 16$	S
$16 < S \leqslant 35$	16
$S > 35$	$0.5S$

to contain the temperature within the same limits. However, the resistivity of steel is about eight times the resistivity of copper, and therefore to meet the conductance requirement associated with Table 10.6 the area of a steel protective conductor would have to be about eight times the area of a copper protective conductor if the cable had copper conductors.

Similarly, between aluminium and steel the ratio of corresponding k values is about 1.83, whereas the ratio of their resistivities is 4.88. Further reference will be made to this aspect when considering the use of steel wire armour as protective conductor.

For non-sheathed single-core PVC insulated cables run in conduit or trunking, if a cable is used as a protective conductor it will be similar in construction to the phase and neutral conductor and the cross-sectional area can be chosen to comply with Table 10.6: no additional calculation is necessary.

For the flat twin and earth cable (2-core plus protective conductor), also to BS 6004, only the 1 mm^2 cable has a protective conductor of equal area to the phase conductor. The other sizes, all 16 mm^2 or less, do not comply with table 10.6 and calculation in accordance with Regulation 543-2 is required to check the adequacy of the protective conductors.

For these cables the temperature limit for the protective conductors may exercise control over the circuit arrangements. Tables 8A, 8B and 8C of appendix 8 of the Regulations give maximum earth fault loop impedances to give compliance with both the disconnecting times required by Regulation 413-4 and the thermal constraint on protective conductors, for copper protective conductors from 1 mm^2 up to 16 mm^2. Separate tables are given for application when fuses to BS 3036, BS 88 and BS 1361 provide the overcurrent protection and the tables are further subdivided according to whether the circuits feed socket outlets or fixed equipment. Many of the values of impedance given are the same as those in Regulation 413-5, governing the disconnecting time, and this implies that for these conditions the requirements of Regulation 413-4 are decisive. Some of the values, however, differ from those in Regulation 413-5, and where this occurs it indicates that the thermal restraints on protective conductors contained in Regulation 543-2 are decisive in setting the level of earth fault loop impedance. The levels are reduced compared with those for 5 s and 0.4 s disconnection in order to achieve shorter times and lower values of the product I^2T in equation (10.13).

Table 10.7 shows the fuses of the three types which would be used with each size of flat twin and earth cable when the fuse is to provide protection against overload as well as short-circuit current. Two values of earth fault loop impedance are included against each fuse rating. These are taken from tables 8A, 8B and 8C of the Regulations. The first value is for circuits feeding socket outlets and the second for circuits feeding fixed equipment (the latter is always the higher value). These values are the appropriate ones for the sizes of protective conductors in the cables.

Table 10.7 Maximum earth fault loop impedances for compliance with disconnecting times and temperature limits for protective conductors for flat twin and earth cables

Cable (mm^2)	Cable rating (A)	BS 3036 fuse		BS 88 fuse		BS 1361 fuse	
		Rating (A)	MEFLI (Ω)	Rating (A)	MEFLI (Ω)	Rating (A)	MEFLI (Ω)
1.5/1	20	15	2.7 5.6	20	1.8 2.2*	20	1.8 2.4*
2.5/1.5	28	20	1.8 4.0	25	1.5 2.0*	20	1.8 2.9*
4/1.5	36	20	1.8 4.0	32	1.1 1.4*	30	1.2 1.5*
6/2.5	46	30	1.1 2.8	40	0.8 1.1*	45	0.6 0.65*
10/4	64	45	0.6 1.6	63	(0.48 0.67*)	60	(0.35 0.37*)
16/6	85	60	(0.44 1.14)	80	(0.33 0.47*)	80	(0.24 0.27*)

* See text

The values marked by an asterisk are the impedances necessary in order to comply with the thermal restraint (Regulation 543-2) and those without an asterisk are necessary to give the required disconnection time (Regulation 413-4). In the first column of the table the cables are designated by two values, the first being the cross-sectional area of the phase conductors and the second the cross-sectional area of the protective conductor, e.g. 1.5/1 signifies phase conductors of 1.5 mm^2 and a protective conductor of 1 mm^2.

The table shows that when the disconnection time has to be 0.4 s the thermal constraint on the protective conductor does not influence the maximum earth fault loop impedance required provided that the rating of the fuse is selected to provide protection against both short-circuit and overload currents. This is not necessarily so if the fuse rating is higher and another device provides the overload protection, as reference to tables 8A–8C in the Regulations will show.

The values in parentheses are not included in the tables of the Regulations and have been calculated to complete the picture for the type of cable. When fuses to BS 3036 are used the thermal restraints do not influence the maximum impedances acceptable for 5 s disconnection, but the other fuses do place a restraint on the impedance except in one instance. The main reason for this difference is that the BS 3036 fuse has in general to be of a lower rating than the BS 88 and BS 1361 fuses for the same cable in order to provide overload protection (fuse rating ≤ 0.725 times cabling rating). Of course, the normal circuit currents using the BS 3036 fuses would have to be no greater than the fuse ratings, and so the full capacity of the cables would not be utilized. Lower rated fuses to BS 88 or BS 1361 could also be used with similarly reduced circuit currents.

The current ratings given for the cables are those for the usual conditions of installation, at 30 °C ambient temperature, as single cables, and without contact with thermal insulating materials. In other conditions the ratings might be reduced and lower rating fuses used accordingly. In that event the earth fault loop impedances both for the disconnection times and for compliance with Regulation 543-2 would change, as would their relationship to each other.

For the wire armoured cables to BS 6346, BS 5467 and BS 6724 the armour is more than adequate to meet the requirements of Regulation 543-2, provided that the fuse protecting against short-circuit current is chosen to give protection against overload current also, in accordance with Regulation 433-2.

Cross-sectional areas of armour for the 600/1000 V cables are given in the British Standards. In terms of conductance the areas of steel wire armour are insufficient to enable use to be made of Regulation 543-3, although, in terms of earth fault current carrying capacity, more than half of the sizes of 2-, 3- and 4-core cables with copper conductors and nearly all the sizes of 2-, 3- and 4-core cables with aluminium conductors have armour areas at least equating with the requirements for protective conductors in table 10.6. However, as has been said earlier, Regulation 543-3 requires equivalent conductances to table 10.6 areas, not equivalence of current carrying capacity, when the protective conductor is of a different metal from the phase conductor. It is in any case more appropriate to assess steel wire armoured cables against Regulation 543-2, which is more scientifically based than Regulation 543-3 and constitutes the fundamental requirement.

Tables 10.8 and 10.9 show how the required cross-sectional areas of steel wire armour to comply with Regulation 543-2 compare with the areas provided on the cables when fuses to BS 88: Part 2, with ratings not higher than the cable ratings, are used as overcurrent protection. Table 10.8 relates to 2-, 3- and 4-core XLPE cables to BS 5467 and BS 6724 and table 10.9 relates to 2-, 3- and 4-core PVC cables to BS 6346, all with copper conductors.

The required areas in these tables have been calculated from equation (10.13) using $k = 54$ for the XLPE insulated cables and $k = 44$ for the PVC insulated cables. They are the areas required to cater for 5 s disconnection time, when the product I^2T is higher than for short disconnection times. They are therefore the maximum areas required when the fuses are as stipulated. The current ratings of the cables are taken from appendix 9 of the Regulations and are the maximum values listed therein for the various methods of installation and an ambient temperature of 30 °C. The table is not intended for use to derive the current ratings of the cables, which are only given to show a step in the compilation of the data.

It is apparent that the actual areas of armour wires as used are all comfortably in excess of those required.

For cables with aluminium conductors the current ratings are lower and accordingly the fuse ratings and the currents to give disconnection in 5 s are lower. The result is that the required armour areas are substantially less than for cables with copper conductors. The actual areas of armour on cables with solid aluminium conductors are a little lower, because the cable diameters are a little less, than on cables with copper conductors, but the overall effect is that the actual areas exceed the required areas by a greater margin than for cables with copper conductors.

2-, 3- and 4-core cables with solid aluminium conductors and aluminium strip armour generally comply with Regulation 543-3. The main need is to ensure that connections are good and the armour is kept free from corrosion.

For paper insulated lead sheathed and wire armoured cables, in so far as they may

Table 10.8 Comparisons of steel wire armour areas required with areas actually provided when fuse is to BS 88 with rating no greater than the cable rating: 600/1000 V XLPE insulated cables with copper conductors.

Cable conductor area (mm^2)	Cable rating (A)	BS 88 fuse rating (A)	Current for 5 s disconnection (A)	Armour area		
				Required (mm^2)	Actual (mm^2)	
3- and 4-core cables					*3-core*	*4-core*
1.5	22	20	78	3.3	17	18
2.5	31	25	99	4.1	19	20
4	42	40	170	7.1	21	23
6	54	50	220	9.1	23	36
10	74	63	280	11.6	39	43
16	99	80	400	16.6	44	49
25	131	125	680	28	62	70
35	162	160	900	37	70	80
50	197	160	900	37	78	90
70	251	250	1500	62	90	131
95	304	250	1500	62	128	147
120	353	315	2100	87	141	206
150	406	400	2600	108	201	230
185	463	400	2600	108	220	255
240	546	500	3500	145	250	289
300	628	500	3500	145	269	319
2-core cables						
1.5	26	25	99	4.1	16	
2.5	37	32	130	5.4	17	
4	49	40	170	7.1	19	
6	63	63	280	11.6	22	
10	86	80	400	16.6	26	
16	115	100	540	22	41	
25	152	125	680	28	42	
35	188	160	900	37	62	
50	228	200	1200	50	68	
70	291	250	1500	62	80	
95	354	315	2100	87	113	
120	410	400	2600	108	125	
150	472	400	2600	108	138	
185	539	500	3500	145	191	
240	636	630	4300	178	215	
300	732	630	4300	178	235	

Table 10.9 Comparisons of steel armour areas required with areas actually provided when fuse is to BS 88 with rating no greater than the cable rating: 600/1000 V PVC insulated cables with copper conductors

Cable conductor area (mm^2)	Cable rating (A)	BS 88 fuse rating (A)	Current for 5 s disconnection (A)	Armour area		
				Required (mm^2)	Actual (mm^2)	
3- and 4-core cables					*3-core*	*4-core*
1.5	19	16	54	2.8	16	17
2.5	26	25	99	5.1	19	20
4	35	32	130	6.7	23	35
6	45	40	170	8.7	36	40
10	62	50	220	11.2	44	49
16	83	80	400	21	50	72
25	110	100	540	28	66	76
35	135	125	680	35	74	84
50	163	160	900	46	84	122
70	207	200	1200	61	119	138
95	251	250	1500	77	138	160
120	290	250	1500	77	150	220
150	332	315	2100	107	211	240
185	378	315	2100	107	230	265
240	445	400	2600	133	260	299
300	510	500	3500	178	289	333
400	590	500	3500	178	319	467
2-core cables						
1.5	22	20	98	4.0	15	
2.5	31	25	99	5.1	17	
4	41	40	170	8.7	21	
6	53	40	170	8.7	24	
10	72	63	280	14.3	41	
16	97	80	400	21	46	
25	128	125	680	35	60	
35	157	125	680	35	66	
50	190	160	900	46	74	
70	241	200	1200	61	84	
95	291	250	1500	77	122	
120	336	315	2100	107	131	
150	386	315	2100	107	144	
185	439	400	2600	133	201	
240	516	500	3500	178	225	
300	592	500	3500	178	250	
400	683	630	4300	219	279	

be used where the Regulations apply, the armour alone will provide a cross-sectional area of protective conductor similar to that for the XLPE and PVC cables and the extra capacity of the lead sheath helps to ensure that compliance with Regulation 543-2 presents no problems as long as the rating of the overcurrent protective device is not too far removed from the cable ratings.

When single-core cables are used, there will be at least two cable armours in parallel for a d.c. or single-phase circuit. For a 3-phase circuit there will be three or four cables with armours to serve as the protective conductor. The earlier statement that the armour of cables to BS 6346 and BS 5467 is adequate to meet Regulation 543-2 provided that the fuse provides overload protection as well as short-circuit protection was based on the area for the circuit being at least twice the area for a single cable.

Steel wire armour will only be used on single-core cables for d.c. circuits. With a.c. circuits the armour wires will generally be aluminium. Since the k values are higher for aluminium than for steel, this increases the fault current carrying capacity. This is largely due to the higher conductivity of aluminium, and for many of the single-core cables the two, three or four cable armours in parallel have a combined area sufficient to meet the requirements of Regulation 543-3, making calculation in accordance with Regulation 543-2 unnecessary. This applies to the following cables:

Cables to BS 6346 with copper conductors

2 cables in circuit:	sizes up to 185 mm^2 inclusive
3 cables in circuit:	sizes up to 500 mm^2 inclusive
4 cables in circuit:	sizes up to 1000 mm^2 inclusive

Cables to BS 6346 with solid aluminium conductors

2 cables in circuit:	sizes up to 740 mm^2 inclusive
3 or 4 cables in circuit:	all sizes (up to 1200 mm^2)

Cables to BS 5467 or BS 6724 with copper conductors

2 cables in circuit:	sizes up to 185 mm^3 inclusive
3 cables in circuit:	sizes up to 500 mm^2 inclusive
4 cables in circuit:	sizes up to 630 mm^2 inclusive

Cables to BS 5467 or BS 6724 with solid aluminium conductors

2, 3 or 4 cables in circuit: sizes up to 300 mm^2 inclusive (whole range).

If the fuse rating has to be higher than the cable rating, with separate protection against overload, for instance to avoid nuisance operation at starting current, then tables 10.8 and 10.9 do not apply and the fault current carrying capacity of the protective conductor may be inadequate to comply with Regulation 543-2. The check would have to be made on the lines of the tables taking account of the current for disconnection in the appropriate time. The only final control in the Regulations over the rating of the device used to give short-circuit protection is that it should comply with Regulation 434-6, which is concerned with protection of the phase and neutral conductors.

There is no assurance that a device selected on this basis would protect protective conductors complying with Regulation 543-3 from earth fault currents. It is recommended that when the short-circuit protective device has an appreciably higher rating than the cable, a check should be made with equation (10.13) for protection against earth fault current for both the protective conductor and, if necessary, the phase conductor.

In the Commentary on the Regulations, tables 3, 4, 5 and 6 give the required areas of protective conductor to comply with equation (10.13) according to the type and rating of device used for short-circuit protection, for various values of k. These would be very useful in any exercise such as illustrated in tables 10.8 and 10.9 but with different protection and/or cable. The answers derived from these tables may differ slightly from those in tables 10.8 and 10.9 for the same fuses and value of k because of differences in reading the graphs of fuse characteristics, which are plotted on logarithmic scales.

In Table 10.10 the exercise is carried a step further for 2-, 3- and 4-core wire armoured 600/000 V XLPE insulated cables with copper conductors. Here the minimum sizes of cable having cross-sectional areas of armour sufficient to comply with Regulation 543-2 are listed against each of the standard overcurrent protective devices mentioned in the Regulations. The current ratings of the cables in ampères are shown in parentheses for ready comparison with the ratings of the protective devices. The calculations are based on the I^2T values of the protective devices for 5 s disconnection. For shorter disconnection times the cable sizes providing the required areas would be no larger and in some instances might be smaller.

The table shows that the armour areas are generally adequate even when the rating of the protective device is a step above the cable rating and often adequate when the rating of the protective device is two or more steps above the cable rating.

For steel wire armoured PVC insulated cables the general situation is similar but, of course, not the same in detail.

Correlation of requirements

If any of the regulations exercised the ultimate control of the size of cable and its associated protective conductor and the maximum length in which it could be used, there would be no need for the others which are directed towards exercising similar controls. It is not possible to say, for example, that, if the voltage drop requirement is met, then the earth fault loop impedance is bound to be low enough to give disconnection of supply in the required time when a particular type of cable is used, or the other way about.

It has only been possible to say that, if the protective device gives protection against overload currents in accordance with Regulation 433-2, then, if it has the required breaking capacity and is suitably placed, it can be assumed to provide protection against short-circuit current, and even then an exception has to be noted for certain types of circuit breaker.

In an example quoted when considering protection against indirect contact by interruption of supply, it was noted that disconnection of supply within 0.4 s by a fuse to BS 1361 would limit the length to less than that required for 2.5% voltage drop when the impedance external to the installation was high, but if resource were made to appendix 7 to meet Regulation 413-3 it was the voltage drop and not the impedance of the protective conductor which set the limit on length.

Table 10.10 Minimum sizes of 600/1000 V XLPE insulated SWA cables with copper conductors to meet Regulation 543-2 for each rating of circuit protective device

Protective device designation	Required area of SWA (5 s disconnection) (mm^2)	Smallest cable providing required area of SWA		
		2-core (mm^2)	3-core (mm^2)	4-core (mm^2)
Fuses to BS 88: Part 2				
63A	11.6	1.5 (26)	1.5 (22)	1.5 (22)
80A	16.6	2.5 (37)	1.5 (22)	1.5 (22)
100A	22	6 (63)	6 (54)	4 (42)
125A	28	16 (115)	10 (74)	6 (54)
160A	37	16 (115)	10 (74)	10 (74)
200A	50	35 (118)	25 (131)	25 (131)
250A	62	35 (188)	25 (131)	25 (131)
315A	87	95 (354)	95 (304)	50 (197), 70 (251)
400A	108	95 (354)	95 (304)	70 (251)
500A	145	185 (539)	150 (406)	120 (353)
630A	182	185 (732)	150 (406)	120 (353), 150 (406)
800A	286	–	–	300 (628)
Fuses to BS 1361				
45A	9.9	1.5 (26)	1.5 (22)	1.5 (22)
60A	16.6	2.5 (37)	1.5 (22)	1.5 (22)
80A	21	6 (63)	4 (42)	4 (42)
100A	35	16 (115)	10 (74)	6 (54)
Fuses to BS 3036				
60A	8.7	1.5 (26)	1.5 (22)	1.5 (22)
100A	17.8	4 (49)	2.5 (31)	1.5 (22)
Miniature circuit breakers to BS 3871				
30A type 1	5.0	1.5 (26)	1.5 (22)	1.5 (22)
30A type 2	8.7	1.5 (26)	1.5 (22)	1.5 (22)
30A type 3	11.2	1.5 (26)	1.5 (22)	1.5 (22)
50A type 1	8.3	1.5 (26)	1.5 (22)	1.5 (22)
50A type 2	14.5	1.5 (26)	1.5 (22)	1.5 (22)
50A type 3	17.8	4 (49)	2.5 (31)	1.5 (22)

For protective devices smaller than those listed the smallest cable (1.5 mm^2) provides more than the required area of armour.

Where two pairs of figures appear in the column for 4-core cables the first pair apply to cables with all conductors of equal size and the second pair to cables with a reduced neutral conductor.

Table 10.7 indicated that, using fuses which provided overload protection, the earth fault loop impedances with flat twin and earth cables would be set by the disconnection requirement if this had to be effected in 0.4 s, but if the disconnection time could go to 5 s the limit on earth fault loop impedance would often be set by the thermal restraints for the protective conductor (Regulation 543-2). It would be possible to extend the exercise by deducing, for a given external earth fault loop impedance, what length of cable could be used without exceeding the remainder of the loop impedance. This could then be compared with the maximum length for compliance with voltage drop requirements. The exercise could be extended further to see how reference to appendix 7 affects the outcome when the external impedance takes up a large part of the total impedance for 0.4 s operation.

However, in the Commentary on the Regulations, which is recommended reading, chapter 12 is devoted to smaller installations, in which the smaller cables are used, and this deals thoroughly with the impact of the various regulations on the cables. It indicates that the voltage drop requirement is often the factor restricting the length of the circuit or, for a given length of circuit, determining the size of cable to be used. Of course, this is not invariably so and table 10.7 indicates that, if it is desired to use the flat twin and earth cable, the earth fault loop impedance may sometimes determine the size required, either to achieve the disconnecting time or to avoid overheating of the protective conductor on earth fault.

It may be useful to consider in a little more detail the larger cables, PVC or XLPE insulated with steel wire armour, used in larger industrial installations.

Tables 10.8 and 10.9 show that, if the fuse provides protection against overload current as well as short-circuit current, overheating of the protective conductor by earth fault current is not likely to be a problem. However, the armour as protective conductor cannot by any means be forgotten once compliance with Regulation 543-2 has been checked, because it contributes as a major component of the earth fault loop impedance, affecting the disconnection time. If disconnection is effected within 5 s with the fuses indicated in the tables, then Regulation 543-2 is met, but this is of no account unless the earth fault loop impedance permits disconnection in that time.

The current rating of the cable obviously sets a limit to the minimum size which can be used and, on the basis that the current carrying capacity is fully utilised, table 10.11 shows the maximum lengths of 600/1000 V copper conductor XLPE insulated wire armoured cables to comply with the requirements for earth fault loop impedance. The voltage drops for these lengths are then shown in the final column. For these cables the assumption is made that the supply will be provided by the consumer's own transformer. There is no provision to be made for external impedance, but, for the purpose of this illustration, 10% is subtracted from the maximum permissible earth fault loop impedance given in table 41A2 of the Regulations to allow for the possible effect of the transformer. The data are based on the use of fuses to BS 88 having a rating not higher than the cable rating and on disconnection in 5 s. The voltage drops are calculated from the mV/A m values given in appendix 9 of the Regulations assuming loads equal to the fuse ratings. The maximum lengths to satisfy the requirements for earth fault loop impedance are derived from table 10.4 herein.

For the smaller sizes (including those below 16 mm^2, not listed) it is likely that voltage drop will more often impose the limit on cable length than earth fault loop impedance. If the old 2.5% limit on voltage drop still applied it would control the lengths of all the 2-core cables listed and of the 3- and 4-core cables up to 50 mm^2.

For the larger sizes of 3- and 4-core cable the requirements for earth fault loop impedance appear to exercise the main control and this could also apply to some of the 2-core cables when voltage drops in excess of 2.5% are acceptable. When account is taken of differences in phase angles and that some of the cables would be carrying currents appreciably below their ratings (because of the steps in fuse ratings) and therefore be operating at lower temperatures than those assumed for the tabulated values, the voltage drop limitations might be further alleviated. The earth fault loop impedance could then prove to be the decisive restraint for many of the cables.

The figures in table 10.11 relate to the hypothetical arrangement, which is one to be considered, where a cable of one size runs over the whole distance from the supply to the point of utilisation. However, the larger cables will often carry a supply to a number of smaller cables which each supply a final circuit. There may be intermediate divisions of the current supplied by the large cable, so that there are several sizes of cable in series between the supply and the final circuit.

In these conditions, if each cable carries a current up to the rating of the fuse which protects it, the percentage voltage drops are additive and the total length of cable to meet the acceptable limit will lie between the lowest and highest values for the particular cables involved when they are used alone.

On the other hand, the total length of cable, as limited by earth fault loop impedance, can be substantially increased in these circumstances. The large cable at the supply end makes only a small contribution per unit length to the earth fault loop impedance required to ensure operation of the fuse protecting the smaller cable of the final circuit, and the total route length of cable can therefore be increased.

This can be illustrated simply by consideration of a 4-core 150 mm^2 XLPE insulated wire armoured cable supplying a number of circuits of which one comprises 4-core 25 mm^2 cable of the same type. Suppose, for convenience of calculation, that the 150 mm^2 cable is of the length which just meets requirements for earth fault loop impedance, i.e. 78.5 m. Suppose further that a voltage drop of 3.7% was acceptable for the equipment being supplied by the 25 mm^2 cable at a current of 125 A. This is the voltage drop shown in table 10.11 when 74.6 m of this cable is used alone between supply and point of utilisation and the 74.6 m is the maximum length, under these conditions, to satisfy the requirements for earth fault loop impedance. If the 25 mm^2 cable was taking its supply from the 150 mm^2 cable, the voltage drop in the 150 mm^2 cable (carrying 400 A) would be 2.3% and the length of the 25 mm^2 cable would be limited to that causing an additional voltage drop of 1.4%, i.e. $74.6 \times 1.4/3.7 = 28.2$ m.

The contribution of the 150 mm^2 cable to the earth fault loop impedance for the 25 mm^2 cable is 0.0864 Ω, which is a relatively small part of the 0.306 Ω required for the 25 mm^2 cable protected by 125 A fuses. It leaves 0.220 Ω for the 25 mm^2 subcircuit and this would allow 74.6 x 0.22/0.306 m, i.e. 53.6 m, of the 25 mm^2 cable to be used if no limit were imposed by voltage drop.

It can be concluded that either the earth fault loop impedance or the voltage drop requirement might limit the length of cable or the size required for a given route length, depending on particular circumstances. If a large cable supplies a number of circuits of smaller cables, the earth fault loop impedance is less likely to be the critical factor for the total route length.

Where the earth fault loop impedance is critical, an additional protective conductor separate from the cable can be used to reduce it, or supplementary bonding between exposed conductive parts and simultaneously accessible conductive parts in the same

Table 10.11 Maximum lengths of 600/1000 V copper conductor XLPE insulated SWA cables to meet earth fault loop impedance requirements for 5 s disconnection and voltage drops for these lengths

Cable size (mm^2)	Cable rating (A)	Fuse rating (A)	Maximum earth fault loop impedance (table 41A2) – 10% (Ω)	Maximum length (m)		Volt drop per metre (mV/A)	Volt drop for length (%)	
3- and 4-core				*3-core*	*4-core*		*3-core*	*4-core*
16	99	80	0.54	84.1	91.4	2.5	4.1	4.4
25	131	125	0.306	70.3	74.6	1.65	3.5	3.7
35	162	160	0.243	64.4	71.7	1.15	2.9	3.2
50	197	160	0.243	76.6	83.2	0.87	2.6	2.8
70	251	250	0.144	52.7	72.7	0.60	1.9	2.6
95	304	250	0.144	72.7	83.2	0.45	2.0	2.3
120	353	315	0.099	55.3	79.2	0.37	1.6	2.2
150	406	400	0.0864	70.2	78.5	0.30	2.0	2.3
185	463	400	0.0864	78.5	88.2	0.26	2.0	2.2
240	546	500	0.0585	60.3	68.0	0.21	1.5	1.7
300	628	500	0.0585	65.7	75.0	0.185	1.5	1.7
2-core								
16	115	100	0.405	60.7		2.9	7.3	
25	152	125	0.306	52.1		1.9	5.2	
35	188	160	0.243	60.4		1.35	5.4	
50	228	200	0.171	48.2		1.00	4.0	
70	291	250	0.144	48.3		0.69	3.5	
95	354	315	0.099	46.9		0.52	3.2	
120	410	400	0.0864	45.0		0.42	3.2	
150	472	400	0.0864	49.4		0.35	2.9	
185	539	500	0.0585	47.2		0.29	2.9	
240	636	630	0.0486	44.6		0.24	2.8	
300	732	630	0.0486	49.1		0.21	2.7	

equipotential zone can be employed. When the voltage drop is excessive at the necessary load current it can only be reduced by using a larger cable.

In the calculations in this section protection against short-circuit currents is provided by fuses having ratings no higher than the ratings of the cables they protect. If the fuses have higher ratings, the values calculated will be changed, although the basic methods will be valid. From table 10.10 it can be seen that the armour areas will often comply with the requirements relating to temperature rise on earth fault, even when the fuse rating is one or two or even more steps above that corresponding to the cable rating. However, the use of higher rated protective devices has a profound effect on the requirements for earth fault loop impedance. It is clear that, for the benefit of optimum utilization of cables, the protection should be as close as possible, consistent with the circuit current and other restraints on the selection of the devices. This is also consistent with optimum safety in minimising energy released under fault conditions.

REFERENCES

(1) Jenkins, B. D. (1981) *Commentary on the 15th Edition of the IEE Wiring Regulations*.
(2) Whitfield, J. F. (1981) *Guide to the 15th Edition of the IEE Wiring Regulations*.

PART 2

WIRING CABLES, FLEXIBLE CABLES, CABLES FOR GENERAL INDUSTRIAL USE AND FOR ELECTRONIC APPLICATIONS

Chapter 11

Cables for Fixed Installations

HISTORY AND DEVELOPMENT OF WIRING SYSTEM CABLES

In some of the earliest installations, which were in private houses, the current was carried by copper wires covered with cotton yarn, either lapped or braided, stapled to wooden boards which were subsequently varnished. By the time of the filament lamp, around 1880, multicore cables were available with wax impregnated cotton and silk insulation and lead sheaths.

Gutta percha and rubber were then being used for telegraph cables and in 1889 Hooper introduced a vulcanised rubber cable with insulation in three layers: (a) pure rubber next to the conductor, (b) a layer, often termed a 'separator layer', also unvulcanised and believed to contain a high proportion of zinc oxide which imparted a white or drab colour and (c) a final vulcanised layer with optimum physical properties. Sulphur and probably litharge were used as vulcanising agents – hence the black colour of the outer layer.

This construction was probably used to protect the copper conductor from reaction with sulphur but tinned copper conductors were later introduced for this purpose. The tinning also limited oxidation of copper wires exposed at terminals and facilitated soldering of the conductor for joints and terminations. Tinning was also advantageous to prevent interaction between copper and sulphur, reduce oxidation and minimise adhesion between the conductor and insulation to ease stripping of the insulation when making connections.

Rubber insulated cables were initially expensive and other types continued for many years, e.g. fibrous materials such as cotton or jute and later oil-impregnated paper. Woven cambric tapes coated with linseed oil variants found some use, particularly in North America. Power cable applications of the latter types continued for many decades.

The outer covering for rubber insulated cores was commonly a lapped woven cotton tape, waterproofed on one side by a coating of rubber compound, followed by a braid of cotton or jute impregnated with a preservative compound, usually wax based. In the early 1900s rubber outer sheaths were developed, based on the compounds then in use for cab tyres: hence the term cab tyre sheaths (CTS). As pneumatic tyres were developed this was changed to tough rubber sheath (TRS), the type of compound being very similar. One type of cable had rubber insulated cores laid side by side and enclosed in the TRS in a flat formation.

The need for concealment and protection of electric lighting wiring was recognised as desirable early in the history of domestic installations. Two basic systems developed, one on walls and building surfaces generally and the other buried in the plaster or otherwise in the decorative or structural parts of the building. One of the earlier versions of the former group consisted of wooden boards with grooves in which the insulated conductors were placed. A wooden cover or capping was then screwed on. In the second type of system, zinc conduit tubes were used into which were drawn the wiring cables. Later zinc was replaced by galvanised iron and then enamelled steel.

These two methods of installation determined the geometrical designs of modern wiring cables. The surface system led to the provision of flat cables with conductors laid side by side, the whole having an approximately rectangular cross-section. Early designs consisted of rubber insulated conductors enclosed in a lead sheath, followed by a similar arrangement in which the lead was replaced by a mechanically robust rubber compound, i.e. CTS or TRS.

In the buried or conduit system of wiring installations a number of individual insulated and protected conductors were drawn into the tubes as required. These were generally of the taped, braided and compounded type of finish, the wax compound on the braid acting as a lubricant during installation as well as serving its original preservative function.

Rubber eventually replaced all the types of insulation in the wiring systems. TRS and lead sheathed rubber insulated cables for surface wiring and the vulcanised rubber insulated taped, braided and compounded conduit cables were in general use until well after the Second World War.

Safety considerations required the bonding and earthing of exposed metal parts of domestic and public wiring systems at a very early stage. The forerunner of the present IEE Wiring Regulations was published in 1883. This required provision of conductors specifically for the purpose. Initially the lead sheath, when available, was considered to provide this function, but it was soon realised that separate low resistance earth circuits were necessary because of the difficulty of making reliable contact with such sheaths. The bonding of metallic sheaths and the provision of definite low resistance paths to a common earth at the supply source were also shown to be necessary, to avoid electrolytic corrosion due to stray currents. Consequently, wiring systems were developed in which various means of achieving these ends were featured. One of these consisted of a flat lead sheathed cable with rubber insulated cores which had a bare copper wire placed underneath the lead sheath and in contact with it throughout its length. It was introduced by the Callenders Cable and Construction Co. Ltd, in 1927. This basic design set the pattern for present day surface wiring cables.

Although different insulants and sheaths have been introduced, the emphasis on earthing as a safety feature has increased and hence also the need to provide an integral earth conductor. Consequently the most commonly used surface wiring cable in the UK has been the flat twin with earth (reference type 6242Y) as shown in fig. 11.1. CPC denotes circuit protective conductor, formerly known as earth continuity conductor (ECC).

The cable reference number as given above and used throughout part 2 of the book is based on a sequence originally introduced, some decades ago, by UK cablemakers. Although not to be found in any official standards, the system is still considered to be useful to manufacturers and users alike, and remains in general use.

The rubber insulated cable, with a variety of protective coverings, became the dominant type in wiring systems because of its flexibility and ease of handling. It

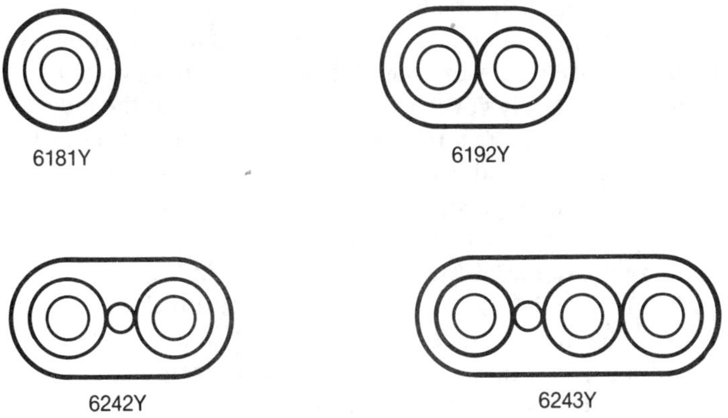

Fig. 11.1 Typical single-core and flat type wiring cables (6242Y and 6243Y with CPC)

remained virtually unchanged until the late 1930s. At that time a new thermoplastic material, plasticised poly(vinyl chloride) (PVC), began to be used in Germany and America for both the insulation and sheath of cables. The effect of the following war on world availability of rubber encouraged the use of this alternative material and within 20 years it had all but replaced rubber in wiring system cables.

Today PVC is still the most commonly used material. However, in recent years there has been considerable development of compounds with negligible halogen content and reduced smoke emission under fire conditions. Wiring system cables employing these new low smoke and fume materials are already being installed in public buildings and other areas where performance in fires is of special concern, and their use is increasing. A British Standard for the single-core non-sheathed conduit type is in preparation. This is distinct from BS 6724 for armoured and sheathed cables with low smoke and fume characteristics.

DESIGN OF MODERN WIRING SYSTEM CABLES

The two forms of cable have changed little over the years, i.e.

(a) insulated and sheathed: circular single-core and 2- or 3-core flat cables for surface wiring or direct burial in plaster
(b) insulated only: single-core for use in conduit, or bunched on trays, or in trunking

Voltage designation

The IEE Wiring Regulations recognise two voltage designations: extra low voltage and low voltage. The latter usually applies in buildings and is defined as 'exceeding extra low voltage but not exceeding 1000 V (1500 V d.c.) between conductors or 600 V (900 V d.c.) between conductors and earth'. Extra low voltage denotes voltages up to 50 V a.c. (120 V d.c.).

Historically, the voltage designations of wiring system cables, in the form U_0/U defined in chapter 2, have tended to relate to the relative thickness of insulations rather than the required electrical characteristics. To some extent the minimum thickness which can be applied reliably is a determining factor and over the years there has been significant reduction in dimensions as manufacturing techniques and materials have improved. However, the thicknesses of insulation (and sheaths) of wiring system cables are largely governed by consideration of the mechanical hazards encountered during both manufacture and installation. They cannot be determined on a strictly theoretical basis and are the result of practical experience. Whilst such cables are categorised by their mechanical duty, it is still important that they should not be used for applications above their rated voltage.

The system voltage in domestic and public buildings in the UK is rarely other than the standard 240/415 V. IEC 38 notes that voltages in excess of 240/415 V are intended exclusively for heavy industrial applications and large industrial premises.

The IEE definition given above aligns with the corresponding voltage category (Band II) recognised by both the IEC and CENELEC within the low voltage category. CENELEC Harmonisation Documents for wiring cables provide principally for two voltage classes: 300/500 V and 450/750 V.

In superimposing voltage classifications it is not surprising that apparent anomalies arise. However, it is necessary to match the voltage designation of a cable with that of the range of supply voltages for the intended application, if only as an easy means of eliminating unsuitable cables, e.g. telephone cables, from power distribution systems. It is also traditional to discriminate between different degrees of protection applied to the same conductor size by ascribing different voltage ratings. This introduces a further complicating consideration in that it implies a requirement for discrimination based on the risk of mechanical damage in service and the possible consequences of electrical failure, e.g. electric shock and fire.

When the subject of voltage ratings was considered in drawing up the European Economic Community (EEC) cable standards (CENELEC Harmonisation Documents), it was found that in Europe the highest voltage between the conductors in final power distribution circuits was 480 V. 500 V was therefore chosen as the standard. As most wiring cables operate on 3-phase four-wire systems or on single-phase systems derived therefrom, the corresponding voltage to earth is $500/\sqrt{3}$, which becomes 300 V when rounded up to the nearest 100 V – hence the above-mentioned 300/500 V designation as applied to the sheathed wiring system cables only.

The single-core types, with a single covering only and no separate sheath, are intended for use with further protection in the form of metal or plastic conduit, trunking or cable trays, where the risk of damage and contact is less. They are therefore given the higher voltage designation of 450/750 V. The 600/1000 V designation is given to such types when they are used for the internal wiring of switch and control equipment, the thickness of insulation being similar to that of the cores in armoured and sheathed cables.

Materials for wiring cables

Conductors

Conductors are now predominantly of copper as described in chapter 4, which also refers to the problems with aluminium in the commonly used types of wiring fittings and to the technically successful substitution of copper-clad aluminium.

Elastomeric wiring system cables and wires have tinned copper conductors. Tinning is less necessary now with synthetic rubber compounds than it was when natural rubber insulation was prevalent, but the tin layer has been retained as a safeguard against possible interaction between the copper and the insulation. It also aids removal of the insulation, as previously mentioned.

Insulation
The insulation of wiring cables until recently was almost exclusively PVC. However, as already noted, significant quantities of low smoke and fume (LSF) materials are now being employed. Other exceptions are that ethylene–propylene rubber (EPR) and silicone rubber (SR) are used for cables installed in very hot or very cold situations where the temperature is outside the range of PVC.

PVC insulation is usually of the general purpose type (type TI 1, chapter 3) compounded to have a higher tensile strength, better resistance to deformation and better electrical properties than the sheath.

The insulation for the single-core non-sheathed cable with low smoke and fume characteristics, e.g. as described by BICC as LSF (the description also used for cables to BS 6724), is a crosslinked material having physical and electrical properties comparable with those of PVC at normal ambient temperatures. Under fire conditions it shows reduced flame propagation and smoke emission and minimal acid gas emission. It has a maximum operating temperature of 90 °C and allows the cable to be installed at temperatures down to −10 °C.

Requirements for thermoset insulations are given later, with the descriptions of the cables.

Sheath or protective finish
The PVC compound (BS 6746, type 6) used for sheathing is specially formulated for the purpose and is somewhat different from that used in other applications, e.g. for the sheath of PVC insulated armoured power distribution cables (type TM 1). As it is not expected to contribute to the electrical performance of the cable, it can be more easily formulated to assist in its removal at terminations; an important point in installation economics.

A grey colour, with a matt surface finish, has become the standard for the sheath of wiring system cables, after experience with a number of other colours. It represents the best compromise between appearance, economy and technical performance. However, white sheathed cables are available where this is essential and black is usual for circular sheathed cables.

The protective finish applied over EPR insulation consists of a braid of textile yarn treated with a compound which renders the yarn moisture resistant and also behaves as a lubricant when the cable is drawn into conduit. Silicone rubber is usually protected by a braid of glass fibre yarn treated with an appropriate lacquer to prevent fraying.

Identification of cores by colours

While it has proved relatively easy to obtain agreement within Europe on common core colours for flexible cords, the extension into identification of fixed cables is still not fully resolved. Agreement to date covers the use of the bi-colour green/yellow for the insulated circuit protective conductor. The use of light blue for the neutral, which is the practice in the continental European countries, has also been accepted in principle for future standardisation. However, for the UK, blue for the neutral cannot be adopted without changing the UK phase colours, which include blue, with red and yellow for the other phases.

A satisfactory scheme for the phase colours has not yet been achieved, and lack of resolution within IEC and CENELEC has been a major obstacle to completion of universal wiring regulations and cable standards. A number of countries wish to use black for one or more of the phases, but because of the long-standing use in the UK of black to indicate the neutral core, there is reluctance, on safety grounds, to changing its use to a phase core, particularly in association with blue for the neutral, which would reverse the significance of the colours for the two cores between old and new cables.

Consideration is being given to other means of resolving the problem, such as having all phase cores brown, with numbers where necessary to identify the phases, but the final resolution is uncertain.

It will be noted that the Harmonised Cable Standards (BS 6004, CENELEC HD 21) preclude the use of the single colour yellow for the core identification of single core non-sheathed wires (type H07V). The fourteenth and fifteenth editions of the IEE Wiring Regulations stipulate the use of yellow to identify the second phase conductor in a 3-phase circuit. The yellow single-core (type 6491X) wire is hence not a harmonised type but is recognised as a UK National Standard only. For other individual cores it is advisable to consult the relevant cable standard or wiring regulations.

Standards and references

Details of standard cable types, reference numbers, voltage designations, British Standards and CENELEC Harmonisation Documents are shown in table 11.1.

Current CENELEC Harmonisation Documents are:

HD 21 (current issue HD 21 S2) – poly(vinyl chloride) insulated cables and flexible cords of rated voltage up to and including 450/750 V

HD 22 (current issue HD 22 S2) – rubber insulated cables and flexible cords of rated voltage up to and including 450/750 V

These documents embody the definitions that 'wiring cables' (German: Leitungen) are for nominal voltages up to 750 V. 'Mains cables' or 'power cables' (German: Kabel) are regarded as having rated voltages of 1000 V or above.

Differing installation practices and philosophies between the European countries, particularly with respect to the protective system, have made necessary the retention of certain national types of wiring system cable (e.g. flat sheathed cables in the UK and NYIF cables in Germany). These are designated National Types, which recognise national practices. As such they are subject to the national certification procedure (provided in the UK by BASEC) but cannot carry the CENELEC Common Marking ◁HAR▷ because they are not harmonised designs. Chapter 7 includes further explanation of CENELEC harmonisation, certification and the ◁HAR▷ mark.

Certain cables which are otherwise made in conformity with the Harmonisation Documents deviate in one or more details and cannot therefore have the ◁HAR▷ certification applied to them. An example is the PVC light non-flexible circular multicore cable to BS 6004 which has the UK national core colour identification.

Table 11.1 References and standards for wiring cables

Insulation	Cable type	Voltage (V)	Reference	CENELEC code	British Standard	CENELEC HD
PVC	Non-sheathed general purpose cable, single-core solid conductor	450/750	6491X	H07V-U	BS 6004	HD 21
PVC	Non-sheathed general purpose cable, single-core stranded conductors	450/750	6491X	H07V-R	BS 6004	HD 21
PVC	Non-sheathed single-core solid conductor for internal wiring	300/500		H05V-U	BS 6004	HD 21
PVC	Insulated and sheathed single-core solid and stranded conductor	300/500	6181Y		BS 6004	
PVC	Insulated and sheathed flat 2-core,	300/500	6192Y		BS 6004	
	solid and stranded conductors	300/500	6242Y[a]		BS 6004	
PVC	Insulated and sheathed flat 3-core	300/500	6193Y		BS 6004	
	solid and stranded conductors	300/500	6243Y[a]		BS 6004	
PVC	Insulated and sheathed 2-core circular	300/500		[b]	BS 6004	HD 21
	Insulated and sheathed 3-core circular	300/500		[b]	BS 6004	HD 21
	Insulated and sheathed 4-core circular	300/500		[b]	BS 6004	HD 21
	Insulated and sheathed 5-core circular	300/500		[b]	BS 6004	HD 21
EPR	60° rubber insulated OFR sheathed flat 2-core (festoon lighting)	300/500	6192P		BS 6007	
EPR	85° rubber insulated textile braided and compounded single-core	450/750	6101T		BS 6007	

[a] With CPC
[b] Harmonised designs, but not eligible for ◁HAR▷ marking because of non-standard core colours

A common shorthand code for designating the construction of cables has been formulated in CENELEC, as will be evident from the foregoing. The complete code is given in Harmonisation Document HD 361 (current issue HD 36152), 'System for cable designation'. CENELEC countries are obliged to use the code for designating harmonised cables in their national standards, but its use for other cables is optional. In the UK it has been adopted for harmonised cables only. Some parts of the code which are applicable to the simpler designs of wiring cables and flexible cords and cables are given in table 11.2, in which H signifies that the cable is a Harmonised Type. Examples are:

H07V-U: 450/750 V, PVC insulated solid wire conductor
H07RN-F: 450/750 V, rubber insulated PCP sheathed flexible conductor

Table 11.2 Designation of cable type

1st group: voltage designation	Following letters: covering materials and construction	Final letter: type of conductor
H03 ≡ 300/300 V	N ≡ PCP	-F ≡ flexible
H05 ≡ 300/500 V	R ≡ rubber	-R ≡ strand
H07 ≡ 450/750 V	T ≡ textile	-U ≡ solid wire
	V ≡ PVC	-K ≡ flexible for fixed installation

TYPES OF WIRING SYSTEM CABLES

PVC insulated and sheathed cables

In the UK these are 300/500 V to BS 6004. Details of sizes and technical data are given in appendix A6. Once installed they can be operated at temperatures from −30°C to +70°C. Precautions to be observed when installing cable at low temperatures are given in chapter 15.

Single-core cables
The single-core cables are normally supplied in a range of conductor sizes from 1 mm^2 to 35 mm^2. Single solid wires are used for conductor sizes of 1.0, 1.5 and 2.5 mm^2 and stranded conductors for the larger sizes. These conductor formations are also used in the flat cable designs described below, which they complement.

Flat cables
The flat form cable has proved to be very convenient for attaching to building surfaces, its small depth facilitating concealment. As described here, it is peculiar to UK practice, although somewhat similar cables are used in both Western Germany (NYIF cable, fig. 11.2) and the USA. It has won its position relative to competing types as a result of technical performance and economic advantage, both in use and in manufacture, together with its appropriateness to installation conditions and to UK safety practices.

It is available in two forms, i.e. with and without circuit protective conductor

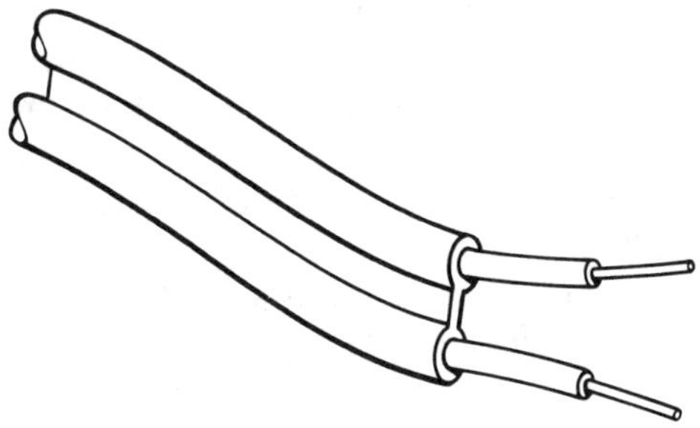

Fig. 11.2 German type of NYIF flat cable

(CPC). The CPC is not insulated and lies between two insulated conductors (see fig. 11.1). The size range for 2- and 3-core flat cables is from 1 to 16 mm^2.

Flat, 2- and 3-core cables with CPC have a single solid or stranded protective conductor, the size of which, relative to the area of the current carrying conductors, takes account of the IEE Wiring Regulations (section 543 of the fifteenth edition). With copper conductors there is a minimum cross-sectional area of 1.0 mm^2.

The thicknesses of insulation and sheath for the various sizes of cable have varied over the years. They have been influenced by a blend of practical experience and testing in relation to service requirements, improvement in manufacturing plant, advances in PVC compound technology and the application of quality assurance techniques to every aspect of cable making.

Circular multicore cables

A range of light PVC insulated and sheathed circular 2- to 5-core cables comes into this category, although they are not in common use in the UK. They may have solid wire conductors up to 10 mm^2 and stranded conductors above that. The total range is from 1.0 mm^2 to 35 mm^2. An additional extruded, soft unvulcanised inner covering (mastic) is used to fill the core interstices and to facilitate stripping. They find application on the continent in the larger installations particularly in damp situations, for prefabricated houses and in business, industrial and agricultural premises.

Although they are generally to an agreed Harmonisation Document, some sizes of the UK range included in BS 6004 are not included in the harmonised range. As colour coding for the core identification has not yet been agreed in CENELEC, this type of cable, whilst included in HD 21, is not regarded as fully harmonised and cannot carry the ◁HAR▷ mark.

60 °C rubber insulated and sheathed cable

This cable is designated 300/500 V and is to BS 6007. Although strictly not a cable for fixed installations, it is similar in design to the flat PVC insulated and sheathed cables described above. It has rubber insulation (60 °C insulation, BS 6899, type EI 1) and a tough polychloroprene (PCP) sheath (60 °C sheath, BS 6899, type EM 2) with stranded tinned copper conductors.

It is a direct descendant of the early wiring system cables and is retained solely for festoon lighting used as temporary circuits, for instance on building sites or for decorative purposes. The cable is designed to provide self-sealing connections with specially designed lamp holders, whose spike terminals penetrate the sheath and insulation to make contact with the conductor when they are clamped at intervals along the cable length.

Only one size, 2.5 mm^2, 2-core is available and further details are given in appendix A6, tables A6.7 and A6.8.

This cable is not a harmonised type and it is available only as a National Standard Type. The core colours are red and black and the sheath colour is black. The operating temperature range is from −30 °C to +60 °C.

PVC insulated non-sheathed single-core cable

This cable, of 450/750 V designation (reference 6491X), is covered by BS 6004 and HD 21. It is intended for use with additional mechanical protection as an inherent part of the wiring system, i.e. in conduit, ducts or trunking. It uses the same cores as those already described for flat sheathed cables but has a higher voltage rating, because when installed it is less subject to mechanical risks or hazards.

The conductor size range is considerably larger than for the flat cables as the conduit or trunking wiring system is much more widely used in large commercial and industrial installations. The standard range of conductor sizes is 1.5 mm^2 to 630 mm^2. In HD 21 the sizes from 1.5 to 16 mm^2 may be single solid wires, but stranded conductors provide additional flexibility and are available as an alternative. In the UK it is customary to use stranded conductors, although there is limited use of solid wires in sizes of 1.5 and 2.5 mm^2. Stranded conductors are used exclusively in sizes from 25 to 630 mm^2, ranging from 7-wire at the lower end to 127-wire at the upper limit.

Intended principally for the internal wiring of equipment such as switchgear, an extension of the conductor size range down to 0.5 mm^2 is available in three sizes of single solid wire, i.e. 1.0, 0.75 and 0.5 mm^2. The voltage designation for these three sizes is 300/500 V.

Sizes of 1.0 and 1.5 mm^2 are most commonly used for domestic lighting circuits; 2.5 and 4.0 mm^2 are used to supply socket outlets and the larger sizes are used on power circuits, e.g. lifts, pumps and on main feeds to distribution boards. The largest sizes of 500 and 630 mm^2 are used primarily in short runs at the mains intake positions between items of switchgear on large installations.

Details of dimensions, weights and technical data for cables with copper conductors are given in appendix A6, tables A6.1, A6.2 and A6.4.

These cables are available in a range of colours including green/yellow, yellow, red, black, white, blue, brown, grey. It should be noted that some colours are available only as National Types.

LSF single-core non-sheathed cable

This cable (reference 6491B) is rated 450/750 V and is used for fixed power, lighting services and earthing in industrial and other environments where its fire performance (reduced flame propagation, low smoke generation and minimal acid gas emission) can be beneficial. It is primarily intended for installation in conduit or trunking. A British Standard for this type of cable is in preparation.

The conductor size range is 1.5–35 mm^2, stranded conductors being used throughout. The LSF insulation is suitable for operation at continuous conductor temperatures up to 90 °C.

Dimensions are the same as for the single-core PVC cables (reference 6491X) described above, but LSF cables are somewhat lighter than the same sizes of PVC cables. Current ratings are the same at 30 °C ambient temperature, but the higher operating temperature allowable permits them to be used in ambient temperatures up to 50 °C without applying a temperature correction factor.

Crosslinked LSF compound is more flexible than PVC at low temperatures, thus allowing the installation of LSF cables at temperatures below 0 °C provided that the precautions given in chapter 15 are followed.

LSF cables can be supplied in a range of colours, including red, black, yellow, blue, green and green/yellow.

85 °C rubber insulated, single-core, textile braided and compounded

These cables are designated 450/750 V and are covered by BS 6007. They provide a range of cables for conduit installations where ambient temperatures exceed those appropriate to PVC insulation. The insulation is a heat-resistant elastomeric compound (85 °C insulation, BS 6899, type GP 1). Although the particular polymer is not specified in the relevant standard, that most commonly used is ethylene–propylene rubber in one of its forms, i.e. EPM or EPDM.

The conductor sizes range from 1.0 to 95 mm^2, the 1.0 mm^2 size having a single solid wire, the 1.5 and 2.5 mm^2 sizes solid or stranded conductors and the remainder stranded conductors with 7 or 19 wires, as appropriate.

Sometimes a separator tape, commonly of synthetic film such as polyethylene terephthalate (PETP), is applied over the conductor to facilitate removal of insulation at terminals. It is not common on the smaller sizes as it increases the diameter and is disadvantageous when a number of cables have to be drawn into conduit.

A further occasional feature, at the manufacturer's option, is a woven proofed tape applied over the insulation, mainly dictated by the method of manufacture. This may carry the mandatory printed legend indicating the nature of the insulation and its temperature category, namely Heat Resisting 85. Alternatively the legend may be printed on the surface of the insulation or on a narrow longitudinal tape inserted under the braid expressly for this purpose. Marking of this sort is advantageous in identifying the different types of rubber.

The overall mechanical protection of the insulation is provided by a braid of textile yarn treated with a preservative compound, usually based on a wax. The outer surface of this braid is coloured red or black to provide circuit identification. Further information is provided in appendix A6, tables A6.7 and A6.8.

The operating temperature range is −60 to +85 °C. These cables constitute a National Type.

CURRENT RATINGS FOR WIRING SYSTEM CABLES

Sustained ratings

Methods of deriving sustained current ratings and all the parameters associated with them are discussed in chapter 8. Ratings for individual types of cables are given in appendices A5–A11 and where appropriate these ratings are in accordance with the fifteenth edition of the IEE Wiring Regulations.

Short-circuit ratings

The method of deriving short-circuit ratings is given in chapter 9, and table 9.4 in that chapter includes data for calculating ratings for cables with the main types of insulation. A graphical presentation for PVC insulated conduit wires is included as fig. 9.11.

Short-time ratings

For current flows of shorter time than, say, 1 min, equilibrium conditions are not attained. Consequently for the recognised temperature rise of the conductor the current rating increases as the duration of current flow becomes less. These considerations are important in circuits such as those supplying motors where the starting current is considerably in excess of the full load current. Where frequent stopping and starting occurs, the cumulative effect of the starting current on the temperature rise of the cable needs to be taken into account.

Fig. 11.3 shows the short-time ratings for the smaller size of conduit wires to BS 6004, run singly in air, assuming an ambient temperature of 35 °C and a maximum

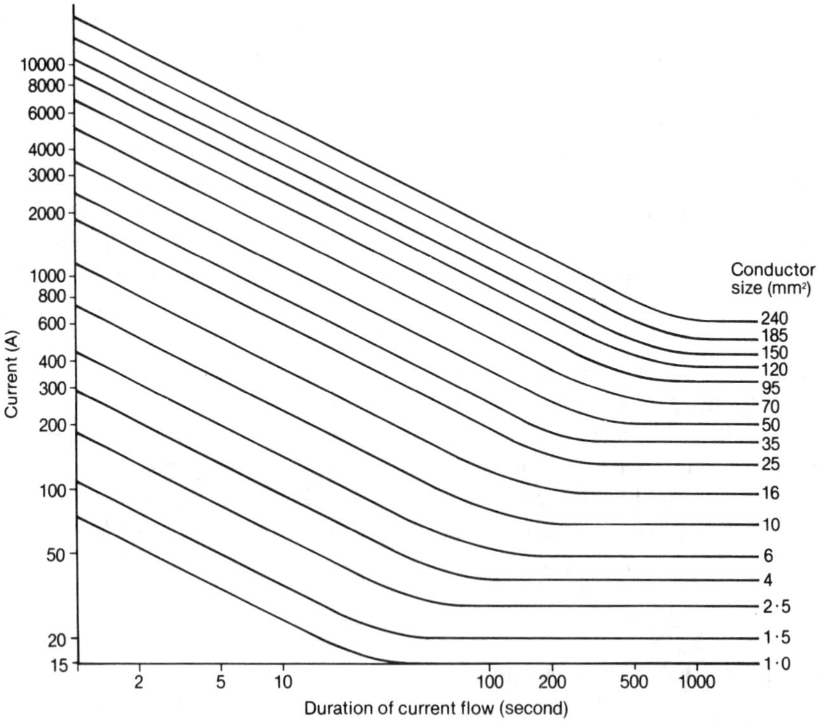

Fig. 11.3 Short-time current ratings of PVC insulated conduit cables with copper conductors, run singly in air at 35 °C ambient temperature

conductor temperature of 70 °C. The values are calculated on the basis that the conductor temperature starts at the ambient temperature, that the current flow ceases at the end of the defined period and that the conductor returns to ambient temperature before current flows again.

CABLES FOR GENERAL INDUSTRIAL USE

Industrial cables bridge the gap between wiring cables and the power distribution cables described in chapter 19. As discussed in chapter 21, cables with PVC insulation replaced the earlier paper insulated lead sheathed cables. The types now most commonly used are multicore cables with copper conductors insulated with PVC, EPR or XLPE, in sizes of 10 and 16 mm^2. Following the voltage designation previously discussed, they are usually classified as 300/500 V or 600/1000 V. As indicated by the conductor sizes, the applications include low power and control uses and supplies to small machines, e.g. in heating and ventilation systems. The use of armoured cables and trunking systems has replaced former conduit practice and increasing use is being made of unarmoured cables, particularly in continental Europe.

In terms of mechanical protection, the lower end of the range is similar to that represented by the circular PVC insulated, PVC sheathed 300/500 V, 2- to 5-core cables already described under the heading 'Wiring System Cables'.

PVC, armoured, power/control cables

In cases where significant risk of mechanical damage exists, it is usual to use the smaller sizes (up to about 16 mm^2) of 600/1000 V cables to BS 6346. This standard covers cables with galvanised steel wire armour, as described in chapters 19 and 21.

Up to 16 mm^2 the conductors are of copper, with circular solid wires for the smaller conductors and stranded construction for the larger sizes. Details are given in appendix A5, tables A5.1–A5.3.

Such cables are used for power supply or control in industrial and other environments, either outdoors, indoors or underground. Appropriate glands as specified in BS 6121 provide the proper termination for armour wires which is essential to provide adequate earthing of the armour and earth continuity.

Cables with thermoset insulation

PVC cables have been pre-eminent in power distribution and control systems in industrial environments. However, the thermoplasticity of PVC is a limitation which influences sustained current rating, overload and short-circuit rating of cables. This limitation is emphasised at high ambient temperatures. XLPE and EPR insulated cables, with the appropriate heat-resisting sheaths, offer advantages in that the conductors can be operated to a maximum temperature of 90 °C, with a maximum short-circuit temperature of 250 °C.

EPR insulated CSP sheathed cables, as originally used for shipwiring cables (BS 6883), are often used in applications such as steel manufacturing plants and rolling mills, where ambient temperatures can be high.

XLPE insulated armoured cables to BS 6724 with LSF bedding and sheath, which emit lower levels of smoke and corrosive products on exposure to fire, are becoming more widely used in industrial and other environments where their fire performance is an advantage, and can also be operated with sustained conductor temperatures up to 90 °C.

From the increased emphasis on co-ordination of overcurrent protection, short-circuit protection and cable ratings, these cables are likely to be of much more interest in the future in installations at normal ambient temperatures. They are the equivalent of PVC types in terms of ease of installation and jointing and of permissible bending radii. The larger cables of this type with XLPE insulation are described in chapter 22.

Cables for the oil and petrochemical industries

Because the PVC insulated, wire armoured, PVC oversheathed cable design, as used in general industry, has good ability to withstand a broad range of hostile environments, it is also the cable mainly used in oil and petrochemical plants.

An important difference, however, is that, as discussed in chapter 5, if such cables are buried in ground containing hydrocarbons, these materials may pass through the oversheath and into the centre of the cable and the hydrocarbons could be transmitted into fire risk areas. It is sometimes necessary, therefore, to incorporate a metallic sheath over the inner sheath. In the UK, a lead sheath is used with steel wire armour over it. In North America, an aluminium sheath with PVC oversheath and no armour is often preferred. Cables with XLPE or EPR insulation are also protected similarly.

Specifications for such cables are issued by individual oil companies and in the UK by the Engineering Equipment and Materials Users Association (EEMUA).

Cables with specially fire-resistant or fire-retardant constructions, either to keep important circuits in operation or to restrict the spread of fire, are of importance as also is the use of materials with low emission of acid gases and smoke in fires. This is discussed in chapter 6.

Cables for offshore oil installations generally follow the same pattern as for cables in ships and are described later in the chapter.

Cables for mining and quarrying

Fixed cables for mining and quarrying follow a similar pattern to that for general industrial distribution. For voltages up to 1.9/3.3 kV the most usual construction is with PVC insulation and steel wire armour. Some PVC insulated cable has been used for 3.8/6.6 kV and even a little for 6.35/11 kV, but currently British Coal specify EPR insulation for these voltages. Usually the armour is a single layer, but double wire armour is used for cables to be installed in mine shafts and is sometimes preferred for roadway cables.

There is also an overlap between what may be considered as 'wiring cables' and the power distribution cables covered in part 3 of this book. As cables of larger conductor size predominate, reference should be made to chapters 19 and 21 for more detailed discussion on cable types. Dimensions, weights and ratings are given in appendix A10 for cables in accordance with British Coal Specifications 295 and 656.

CABLES FOR RAILWAYS AND UNDERGROUND TRANSPORT

Trackside equipment and signalling

Before the electrification of parts of the UK railway system, the use of cables was predominantly for such applications as signalling, power operation of points and mechanical signals and signal lights etc. The cables were installed alongside the track on posts or in ducts. Initially the cable designs and materials represented an extension of domestic wiring practice with natural rubber insulation and sheaths.

Environmental factors such as water, mechanical hazards and fire subsequently encouraged the development of special compounds and the so-called 'oil based type rubbers' became used for insulation. These were vulcanised compounds with natural rubber, bitumen and vegetable or animal oil residues. They continued in use for railway cables long after similar use in general wiring cables because of their resistance to water penetration and mechanical damage. The introduction of PCP permitted a composite insulation consisting of a layer of natural rubber next to the conductor followed initially by two layers of PCP (RNN insulation, i.e. rubber/Neoprene/Neoprene (Du Pont registered trademark) and later by one layer of PCP (RN insulation). This had significant advantages in flame retardance and resistance to oil.

As PCP sheathing compounds are very tough, have outstanding weather and oil resistance and do not burn easily, the RN insulated type with PCP sheath became the standard for signalling, associated power circuits and the internal wiring of signal boxes. These cables continued to be widely used in the UK until the revision, in the mid-1980s of BR 872, 'Specification for railway signalling cables'. This retained many of the heavy duty PCP sheathed types but with RN insulation now replaced by EPR to BS 6899, type GP 1 (plus a maximum permittivity requirement). In addition to these, the new issue of BR 872 contains a range of halogen-free cables with reduced flame propagating properties, made up of non-sheathed single-core and sheathed single-core and multicore types, for wiring in signal boxes and other enclosed areas where fire performance is an important factor. With the increasing adoption by British Rail of the solid state interlock (SSI) signalling system, it can be expected that elastomeric types will eventually be replaced on longer routes by optical fibre data link cables, similar in design to British Telecom trunk telephone cables.

Signalling and communication cables associated with modern 25 kV overhead catenary systems have to be protected by electromagnetic screening because of the large, short duration power surges which are a feature of these systems. The use of copper and/or high permeability magnetic alloy tapes over the laid-up cores reduces the magnitude of induced voltages to tolerable levels.

Track feed cables

Power supply to the point of track feed follows fairly conventional public distribution practice and this also includes the supply to the 25 kV a.c. catenaries. In the case of low voltage live rail systems, heavy duty rubber cables are used for the connection to the live rail.

Early cables had moisture-resistant rubber for the insulation and heavy duty rubber sheaths. PCP was later used for sheathing. Present cable designs take advantage of the higher performance synthetic rubbers using EPR for insulation and CSP for sheaths.

Cables for locomotives and rolling stock

Conductors for cables for locomotives and rolling stock are of multistrand flexible construction because of the tortuous routes involved.

Single-core cables in ducts or conduit are normally used. For many years, EPR/CSP composite coverings on the conductor were dominant but, as in the case of more general wiring types, there has been an increasing demand for limited fire hazard (LFH) cables, often with negligible halogen content (ZH) materials, particularly for use below ground (e.g. in tunnels). Elastomeric cables may typically have a composite flame-retardant EPR/EVA covering. For the more complex wiring of electrical and electronic equipment, high performance 'thin wall' types will probably be employed, commonly insulated with one of the wide-ranging family of polyolefines. There has been a steady move towards materials with lower smoke emission and improved resistance to oils and fluids.

The need for improved communication with trains operating at the higher speeds has also encouraged the use of radio systems involving the use of radio frequency cables which are installed along the track and are designed to radiate and receive radio energy along their length. They are usually coaxial cables whose outer conductor is 'leaky'. This technique has been adopted to a limited extent in various national railway systems, particularly where lengthy tunnels prevent the use of conventional radio equipment, but its main application has been in metropolitan underground systems.

Mass transit underground railways

Avoidance of problems due to fire is particularly important in underground railway systems because of their effect in disrupting services and causing discomfort and panic among passengers, and possible loss of life or injury. The subject is discussed in chapter 6.

As a result, PVC insulated cables, which were widely employed until about ten years ago, both for power distribution and for signalling and information systems, have been virtually superseded by LFH types. Attempts to reduce flame propagation and the emission of toxic fumes and smoke to the lowest possible levels have been the subject of major development work in the cable industry. The requirements are generally embodied in performance specifications, which thus allow a variety of materials to be employed, and it is too early to predict which designs of cable will eventually prove most successful.

CABLES FOR SHIPS AND OFFSHORE OIL INSTALLATIONS

Standardisation of cables within the shipbuilding industry has been slow but, with the rapid growth in ships' electrical systems in the last few decades, there has been incentive to adopt high performance materials in efficient designs. The development of the offshore oil industry has extended this development with specialised requirements which, although they follow shipwiring practice, have also introduced new features.

Proliferation of cable types has been encouraged by the increasing complexity of electrical systems and the differing requirements of the classification authorities who register and insure ships throughout the world. The varying views of ship owners and builders, offshore operators and national specifying authorities have further inhibited standardisation. However, IEC Standard 92-3, 'Electrical installations in ships: cables (construction, testing and installations)', has been influential. It is now being completely revised and re-issued in separate parts to cover each aspect of ships' cables. Apart from the sections listed in chapter 7, new sections dealing with the general construction and test requirements for low voltage power cables and design details for 600/1000 V cables with extruded insulation have been agreed for publication, and a section for higher voltage power cables is in preparation. Within Europe most national shipwiring specifications adopt some, if not all, of the IEC 92-3 requirements. Such cables are also accepted by most classification authorities, including the American Bureau of Shipping (ABS), Bureau Veritas (BV), Det Norske Veritas (DNV), Germanische Lloyd's (GL), Lloyd's Register of Shipping (LRS) and the USSR Register of Shipping.

Materials

Conductors

Copper conductors are used universally, aluminium not having found application because of possible corrosion problems at joints and terminations. Due to the more tortuous installation routes, most cables have circular stranded conductors of more flexible construction than is used for equivalent cables on land, but some low voltage power distribution cables have shaped conductors in the range from 25 to 185 mm^2.

Insulation

EPR insulation, as specified in BS 6883, is widely used for its flexibility and good operating and short-circuit characteristics. Special formulations to BS 6899, type GP 2, are used for the higher voltage cables.

PVC is specified by a few shipyards, but it has a limitation because of a maximum conductor temperature of 60 °C in ships. XLPE is growing in popularity, but it results in a stiffer cable, which is unfavourable for bending and handling in the complex routes and confined spaces occurring in ship installations.

Sheaths

The choice of sheathing materials is varied and subject to local preference. Cables to the current issue of BS 6883 have CSP sheaths, which are classed as heat and oil resistant and flame retardant (to BS 6899, type RS 3), with an operating temperature range of −30 to 85 °C.

BS 6883 is undergoing a far-reaching revision, which is intended to provide for the requirements of offshore installations as well as ships. It is planned to include CSP sheaths with reduced acid emission (in fires) and with enhanced oil resistance, together with ZH sheaths. The latter can be formulated to give significantly lower smoke emission than CSP, but comparable ageing characteristics and oil resistance.

PCP is the preferred material in French and German yards, although it has an inferior ageing performance to that of CSP. The choice may be influenced by indigenous manufacture. In the Netherlands, Norway, Sweden and Finland, a combination of PCP inner sheath and PVC outer sheath is used.

A code which has found some recognition for the various constructions is as follows:

ME – EPR insulation
H – CSP sheath
PhB – phosphor bronze braid armour
SB – steel braid armour (galvanised)
V – PVC sheath

e.g. type MEH – EPR insulated, CSP sheathed only cable
type MEHSBV – EPR insulated, CSP inner sheathed, steel wire braided, PVC sheathed cable

Voltage designation

Installations in ships are self-contained and cover a wide range of functions. Generation is now commonly at 3.3 kV and in offshore installations there are also requirements for 6.6 kV, 11 kV and 13.8 kV cables. Standard voltages catered for in specifications include the following.

BS 6883

600/1000 V: power, control and distribution services
1.9/3.3 kV and 3.3/3.3 kV: power distribution in ships

The new issue of BS 6883 is expected to include unscreened cables up to 6.35/11 kV and screened cables up to 8.7/15 kV.

IEC 92-3

150/250 V and 440/750 V: power, lighting and control in ships and for fixed offshore oil installation services

IEC 502

1.8/3 kV, 3.6/6 kV, 6/10 kV and 8.7/15 kV: power distribution in ships and offshore oil installations

Construction

Cores are laid up in standard formations with up to 61 cores for the smallest sizes and 4 in the larger ones. Core identification is by the printing of numbers directly on the insulation surface or on woven proofed textile tapes lapped over the core, as preferred. Screened constructions, with a semiconducting layer over the insulation followed by copper tapes, are used at 6 and 11 kV. For difficult route conditions, a tinned copper wire braid may be used instead of copper tapes.

A sheath of CSP or other material, as discussed above, is applied over the laid-up cores, together with further protection as appropriate for the installation. A braided layer of galvanised steel or phosphor bronze wire is commonly applied over the inner sheath and is a necessary feature for cables where there is a danger of explosion, i.e. in tankers and offshore installations. For single-core cables, the wire for such a braid must be phosphor bronze, to minimize electromagnetic induction effects. The oversheath may be CSP (HOFR) or PVC (BS 6746, type 4).

Cables of 1.9/3.3 kV and 3.3/3.3 kV to BS 6883 have no screen or braid armour. It is assumed that they will be installed in protected routes. The volume resistivity of the sheaths of these cables must not be so low that there is risk of electric shock, due to capacitance effect, to anyone making contact with the exterior of the cable.

Details of dimensions, weights and current ratings are given in appendix A7. Those for cables to IEC 92-3 have been omitted from this edition of the book in view of the many changes now taking place (see above), especially to low voltage power cables, which will be standardised at 600/1000 V.

Publication of the new issue of BS 6883 is further away, and it has been considered best to retain the existing constructions in the appendices, but these also will be considerably affected by the impending revision. Apart from the changes to sheathing materials and voltage categories already noted, insulation thicknesses will be reduced to align more closely with those in IEC 502 (and the new IEC 92-3), using the more robust MEPR insulation (types GP4 or GP5 to BS 6899, according to operating voltage). There are also plans to include a very wide range of control and instrumentation cables.

Sustained current ratings

Ratings are generally more conservative than for land cables. They are tabulated in IEC 92 and in the UK in the IEE 'Regulations for the electrical and electronic equipment of ships' and 'Recommendations for the electrical and electronic equipment of mobile and fixed offshore installations'. They are based on an ambient temperature of 45 °C and a maximum conductor temperature of 60 °C for PVC insulation. This temperature is increased to 85 °C for EPR and XLPE at 1 kV and below. Above 1 kV the IEE Regulations reduce the temperature to 80 °C. Some classification authorities also have individual requirements which affect ratings.

Certain authorities governing offshore oil installations do not consider that the regulations for shipwiring cables need apply and consequently higher ratings may be used which exploit the full thermal capability of the cable materials. In such cases it is usual to base the ratings on an ambient temperature of 30 °C, and a maximum conductor temperature of 90 °C for EPR and XLPE or 70 °C for PVC, assuming that appropriate sheathing materials are used. An example is given in appendix A7, table A7.2. There have been suggestions in the UK that these higher ratings could apply equally well to cables in ships but, since many classification authorities still require ratings to be aligned with IEC 92, such a move might not meet with widespread acceptance until international agreement can be obtained.

Short-circuit ratings

Typical short-circuit ratings for EPR insulated ship cables operating at a conductor temperature of 90 °C are given in table 11.3. These are based on the conductor achieving a temperature of 250 °C.

Table 11.3 Maximum permissible short-circuit current for EPR insulated cables in ships

Conductor size (mm^2)	Current (r.m.s.) (kA)			
	1 s	0.5 s	0.2 s	0.1 s
1	0.15	0.22	0.34	0.48
1.5	0.22	0.31	0.49	0.70
2.5	0.35	0.49	0.79	1.12
4	0.57	0.80	1.27	1.80
6	0.85	1.20	1.90	2.7
10	1.45	2.0	3.2	4.5
16	2.3	3.2	5.1	7.2
25	3.6	5.1	8.1	11.4
35	5.0	7.1	11.2	15.8
50	6.8	9.6	15.1	21
70	9.8	13.6	22	31
95	13.6	19.2	30	43
120	17.1	24	38	54
150	21	30	47	67
185	26	37	59	
240	35	49		
300	44	62		
400	56			
500	70			
630	(91)			

In view of the large electromagnetic forces developed between the cores of multicore cables during short circuits (see chapter 9), it is recommended that armoured types should be used when the current is likely to exceed 20 kA. This applies also to single-core cables run in trefoil. At currents approaching 70 kA, there is at the moment no firm evidence about the ability of even armoured cables to stand up to the forces involved. Currents in excess of this value have been omitted from the table or placed in parentheses, although they could theoretically be carried by the cables on thermal considerations alone. Recent tests have shown that overheating of the conductor (due to the asymmetrical waveform of the current during the first few cycles of a short circuit) is not a serious problem for EPR cables at durations down to 0.1 s, and ratings for this duration have therefore been included.

Reactance and voltage drop

These factors are of particular significance for power cables in ships because of the likelihood of proximity to steelwork and the consequent inductive influence. Typical reactance values for certain dispositions of cables remote from steelwork are given in table 11.4. They are based on current BS 6883 insulation and sheath thicknesses and are likely to be somewhat higher for cables to the new issue. The method of calculation using these values is given in chapter 10.

Installation

Installation must be carried out in accordance with the appropriate regulations governing each application, as required by the classification authority. In the UK these are the IEE 'Regulations for the electrical and electronic equipment of ships' and the Rules of the Lloyd's Register of Shipping. IEC 92 'Electrical installations in ships' gives guidance which is accepted internationally.

Table 11.4 Reactance per conductor (EPR insulated cables) (mΩ/1000 m at 60 Hz)

Conductor size (mm^2)	2-core cable (single-phase) or 3- or 4-core cable (3-phase)	2 single-core cables touching (single phase) or 3 single-core cables touching in trefoil (3 phase)	
	Unarmoured or armoured	Unarmoured	Armoured
1.5	136	174	213
2.5	125	157	196
4	124	152	185
6	118	143	174
10	116	135	165
16	109	128	153
25	103	119	142
35	101	115	137
50	100	114	133
70	97	109	128
95	95	105	123
120	93	103	120
150	93	102	118
185	93	101	118
240	92	99	116
300	91	99	114
400		98	112
500		96	110
630		94	107

Precautions concerning the temperature of installation of cables are given in chapter 15. The adoption of minimum bending radii is an important feature to be taken into account and figures for guidance are given in table 11.5.

Cables required to maintain circuit integrity under fire conditions

The subject is covered in chapter 6 and special constructions applicable to cables for ships and offshore installations include the following.

Silicone rubber/glass insulation

This was the first successful design for elastomeric cable which could provide substantially increased integrity for circuits involved in fires. The cables were required

Table 11.5 Minimum installation bending radius

Cable	Bending radius (× cable outer diameter)
150/250 V, 440/750 V, 600/1000 V	
Up to 10 mm diameter	3
10–25 mm diameter	4
Over 25 mm diameter	6
Any armoured cable	6
Any cable with shaped conductors	8
1.9/3.3 kV and 3.3/3.3 kV	
Without armour or screen	6
1.9/3.3 kV to 6.35/11 kV	
Unarmoured	8
Armoured	12

to withstand the 3 hour fire resistance test which was later adopted internationally as IEC 331 (see chapter 6). A composite of silicone rubber and glass braid was applied to conductor sizes up to 16 mm^2, and silicone rubber coated glass fibre fabric tapes was applied to larger sizes. The cables were sheathed with CSP. The construction was widely adopted for essential power distribution and signalling circuits in naval ships, and was embodied in UK Ministry of Defence (Navy) Specification DGS 211 and US Navy Specification MIL-C-915. Similar types of cable, usually incorporating a phosphor bronze or galvanised steel wire braid armour, were used to a more limited extent in merchant ships and offshore installations, but there was a swing away from this construction when micaglass/EPR insulated types were introduced during the 1970s (see below).

Silicone/glass has continued to be the preferred insulation system for essential circuits in naval vessels, but the urgent need to eliminate cable materials which produce large quantities of corrosive gases and smoke in fires has brought about the development of the elastomeric sheath to MOD (N) Specification NES 518. It is based on non-halogenated polymer(s) and has outstanding resistance to many types of organic fluids; it has significantly lower smoke emission than CSP, but comparable ageing and flame-retarding characteristics. As already noted, ZH sheaths with many of the properties of NES 518 are to be available for cables to BS 6883, and can be expected to be in demand for other applications where exceptional performance under fire conditions is required.

Micaglass/EPR insulation

This design has a special ZH inner sheath, together with phosphor bronze or galvanised steel wire armour (helical or braid). Sheaths are available in either ZH material or CSP, the latter having reduced acid gas emission (limited to 5% when decomposed at 800 °C or 8% when decomposed at 1000 °C). Cable constructions are to the dimensional requirements of IEC 92-3 and are designed to withstand the IEC 331 fire resistance test at the increased temperature of 1000 °C.

Special designs
Special constructions complying with BS 6883 and IEC 502, as appropriate, are available, which in addition to withstanding a 1000 °C fire resistance test will also withstand other conditions which may occur during a fire, i.e. disturbance of the cable by vibration or falling debris, and application of water (by sprinkler or hose). For this test the IEC 331 gas flame is applied at 1000 °C for 5 min, during which an impact is applied at regular intervals to the cable. The fire source is then extinguished and the impact is continued for a further 5 min during which a high powered water jet is applied. The full working voltage between conductors and earth is maintained during the test.

Cables meeting these requirements are designed for operation at working voltages up to 1.9/3.3 kV. The cores have micaglass/EPR insulation, and are enclosed in a ZH inner sheath, heat and water barrier layers and a braid armour (phosphor bronze or galvanised steel). The overall sheath is of ZH material or the reduced-acid-emitting CSP described above.

FLOOR WARMING AND HEATING CABLES

As the purpose of these cables is not the supply of electricity but its conversion into heat, they are in the category of terminal equipment. Applications include under-floor heating, either as the main source of space heating or as background heating in domestic, public and industrial buildings, together with soil warming in horticulture and sports grounds. They are also used for road heating to prevent freezing and for pipe heating to maintain the temperature of pipes and containers in industry.

'Cold tails', consisting of standard insulated cables, are used to connect the heating cable to the mains supply.

Construction and materials

Heating cables are of single-core construction with conductors of resistive alloy, chosen to give an appropriate resistance per unit length and for resistance to corrosion and stress cracking.

Insulation is of crosslinked polyethylene (XLPE), specially compounded for heat and abrasion resistance, of radial thickness appropriate to the mechanical duty and voltage rating. Subsequent coverings, where used, are designed to provide integrated constructions to meet different degrees of mechanical hazard and the differing electrical protection and earth continuity requirements of the regulating authorities.

Where a PVC sheath is used, the PVC compound is of a heat-resisting grade (85 °C, BS 6746, type 4). Four constructions are available as indicated in appendix A6, table A6.8.

The resistance values are chosen to give particular heat emission per unit length of cable (W/m) at the commonly used nominal supply voltages of 220, 230, 240 and 380 V. Cables are supplied in standard manufacturing lengths to allow the maximum variety of installation requirements to be covered.

In many heating systems it is more convenient to design an installation to give the required heat output per unit area by using prefabricated heating cable units having a fixed standard total heat output at a particular supply voltage. These units have integral cold tails (supply leads) jointed at the factory, which are usually about 3 m in length. The length of the active part of the unit varies with the total wattage output and the supply voltage.

Performance characteristics

The heat output required is usually defined in terms of power input to unit area of the heated surface (W/m^2). This will depend on the temperature to be attained at the surface, the thermal characteristics of the ground or floor to be heated and the efficiency of any thermal insulation. With heated floors the presence and type of floor covering or carpet will also have an influence. The spacing of floor heating cables is determined by the required power input per unit area and the heat emission per unit length of cable (W/m).

For a given voltage, heating units have a predetermined heat output per total length to simplify selection and installation, and the cables have a range of conductor resistances. Information concerning the length required of a particular cable and the total power input to a given area to be heated is provided by the manufacturer in the form shown in fig. 11.4, which is a typical chart for 240 V supply.

Installation

In the UK the installation of heating cables is subject to the IEE Regulations, which

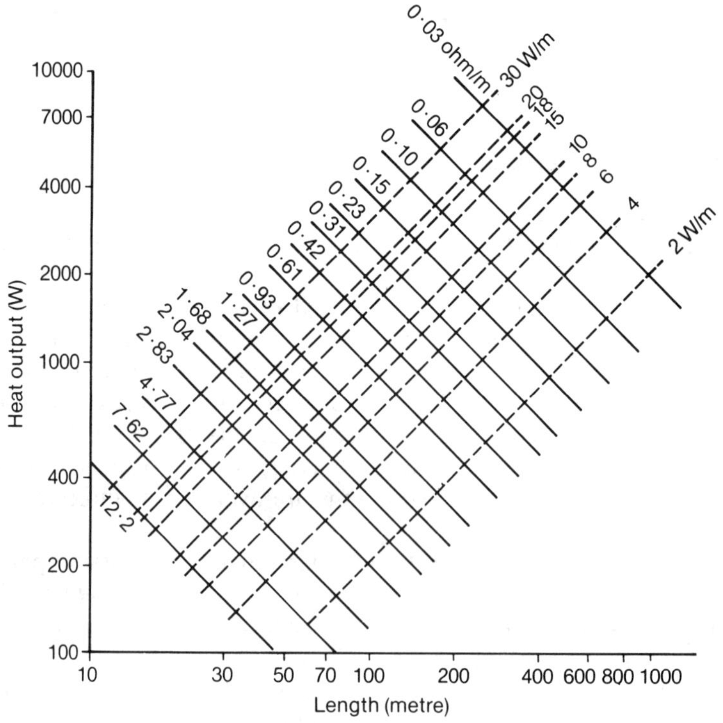

Fig. 11.4 Heat output at 240 V for XLPE insulated heating cable, types X, XB, XJ and XSBV

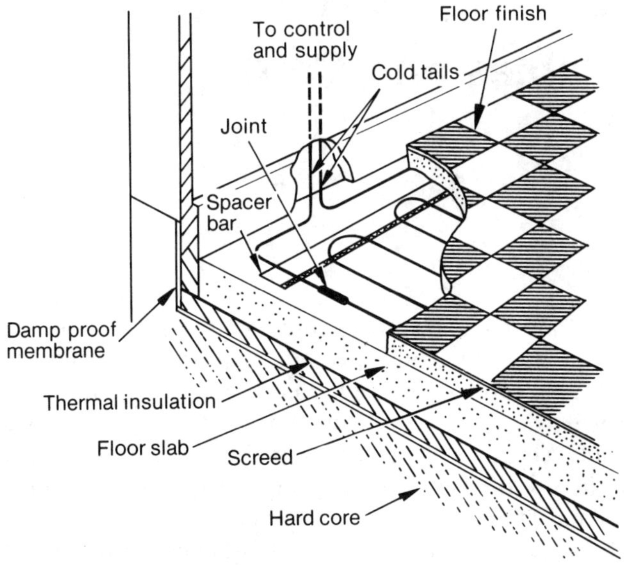

Fig. 11.5 Typical floor warming installation

invoke compliance with BS Code of Practice CP 1018, 'Electric floor warming systems for use with off-peak and similar supplies of electricity'. This gives, among other information, guidance on the temperatures of floors in floor warming systems. Other national authorities have corresponding requirements which vary significantly according to the particular applications common in that country and the practices with respect to protection. There are corresponding IEC recommendations. It should be noted, however, that consideration should be given to the installation environment (thickness of screed etc.) to ensure that the conductor temperature does not exceed 80 °C. Temperatures in excess of this will seriously reduce the life expectancy of the cable.

In a typical floor heating installation, the cables are embedded in a compact screed forming the upper part of a floor structure which incorporates a damp-proof membrane underneath. These cables should not be installed where permanently damp conditions exist or in constantly wet or frequently washed floors. Care must be taken to avoid mechanical damage to the cables during installation when laying floor screeds, during floor repairs and when driving or fixing metal nails, screws etc. for floor fittings. Cables and units should be fixed in position by spacer bars or other means to prevent cable movement or contact. Joints should be embedded in the floor screed along with the cable. A typical installation is shown in fig. 11.5.

In the event of damage occurring, faults can normally be located and repaired without disturbing a floor area greater than 200 mm × 200 mm. Advice on fault location and the specialist equipment used may be obtained from the cable manufacturer.

Chapter 12

Flexible Cables and Cords

Wherever a piece of moveable electrical equipment requires to be connected to the fixed wiring system in domestic, public, commercial or industrial premises, an appropriate flexible cable or cord is required. Because of the wide range of equipment using electric power, there is a corresponding wide range of flexible cables and, particularly, flexible cords. Flexible cords are for use with electrical appliances characterised by the use of relatively small amounts of power, while flexible cables are used for the connection of heavier equipment.

The variety of forms and protective finishes is indicative of the range of environmental factors in which electrical equipment is used. In the general wiring field they range from single insulated wires for the internal wiring of electrical appliances, including luminaires, to large multicore cables supplying heavy duty motors. Additionally there are many important special applications such as cables for cranes, hoists and lifts, cables for high temperature environments, for mining and quarrying, for electrical welding and for X-ray machines.

The operating temperature range for which there is an appropriate flexible cable is from −55 to 250 °C. The majority of general purpose flexible cables and cords are for systems below 1 kV and are designated 300/300 V, 300/500 V or 450/750 V. However, there are also specialised applications, notably power cables for mining and quarrying, with voltage designations of 600/1000 V, 660/1130 V, 1.9/3.3 kV and 3.8/6.6 kV.

In some cases of open cast mining operations, special designs of flexible power cables for 11 kV operation are supplied. Large flexible cables have been used for even higher voltages, but they are not entirely satisfactory as it is difficult to maintain effective dielectric stress control when the cable is subjected to repeated movement.

Standard designs of flexible cables for low power, high voltage applications, such as for the connections to X-ray tube electrodes, electron microscopes and electrostatic dust precipitator electrodes, are available for voltages up to 75 kV a.c. peak and 150 kV rectified d.c.

GENERAL PURPOSE CORDS AND CABLES

Standards

Flexible cords and cables were the first types of cable to be the subject of European harmonisation (CENELEC Harmonisation Documents HD 21 and HD 22). Much preliminary work had been done, however, in the preparation of IEC Standards, IEC 227 for PVC insulated flexible cables and cords and IEC 245 for rubber insulated flexible cables and cords, many of the requirements of which are embodied in HD 21 and HD 22.

In this work, agreement was reached on a colour code for core identification, an essential factor in complying with the safety aspect of the EEC LV Directive. The standard colours and sequences for 2-core cables and 3-, 4- and 5-core cables which include a protective conductor are as follows:

Cable	*Core colours*
2-core	Blue, brown
3-core	Green/yellow, blue, brown
4-core	Green/yellow, black, blue, brown
5-core	Green/yellow, black, blue, brown, black

The bi-colour green/yellow must be used only for the protective or earth core. The colour blue is normally reserved for identification of the neutral core. However, in circuits not having a neutral, blue may be used for other functions, provided that these are identified at the terminations. The colours brown or black are for identification of the live (phase) cores. Colours for single-core non-sheathed cords or cables include green/yellow and blue. Other colours not expressly forbidden by regulations may be used.

Colours expressly forbidden for flexible cords and cables complying with Harmonisation Documents, British Standards and the IEE Regulations are any bi-colour other than green/yellow, green alone and yellow alone.

In the UK the British Standards as given below were amended to align with HD 21 and HD 22.

BS 6500: Insulated flexible cords and cables
BS 6004: PVC insulated cables (non-armoured) for electric power and lighting
BS 6007: Rubber insulated cables for electric power and lighting

BS 6500 includes both PVC insulated and rubber insulated flexible cords. BS 6004 includes PVC insulated non-sheathed flexible single-core cables in sizes of 1.5 mm^2 and above in addition to the non-flexible cables referred to in chapter 11. BS 6007 includes 60 °C and 85 °C rubber insulated and sheathed flexible cables in single-core and 2-core to 5-core versions. Also included in BS 6500 are a number of National Standard Types, regarded as representing a particular requirement in the UK and elsewhere but not reflected in other European countries.

Table 12.1 provides a cross-reference between the CENELEC code designations and the conventional UK reference numbers for the main types of harmonised flexible cords. The fourth figure in the UK 'code' indicates the number of cores. For a further discussion on these reference codes, see chapter 11.

Materials

General purpose flexible cables and cords divide into two main groups, those insulated with PVC and those with thermoset (rubber) insulation. A further group for the upper end of the temperature range has silicone rubber or PTFE insulation.

Table 12.1 Designations for harmonised flexible cords

Voltage rating	CENELEC code	UK 'code'	Description of cord
PVC flexible cords			
300/300	H03VV-F	218(N)Y	Light cord, circular
300/300	H03VVH2-F	2192Y	Light cord, flat twin
300/500	H05V-K	2491X	Insulated only, single
300/500	H05VV-F	318(N)Y	Ordinary cord, circular
300/500	H05VVH2-F	3192Y	Ordinary cord, flat twin
Elastomeric flexible cords			
300/300	H03RT-F	204(N)	Insulated and braided
300/500	H05SJ-K	2771D	Insulated, glass braided, single
300/500	H05RR-F	318(N)	Insulated and sheathed
300/500	H05RN-F	318(N)P	Insulated and OFR sheathed
450/750	H07RN-F	398(N)P	Insulated and OFR sheathed

Insulation

The PVC insulated types generally have insulation compounds of type TI 1 or TI 2 to BS 6746 and HD 21, except that type 5 compound to BS 6746 is used in cables to BS 6141, 'Insulated cables and flexible cords for use in high temperature zones'. Type TI 1 is a general purpose insulation compound. Type TI 2 is a special flexible insulation compound which includes a transparent version. Both compounds have a maximum operating temperature of 70 °C. Type 5 is a hard grade of PVC with a maximum operating temperature of 85 °C.

Rubber insulated cords and cables have insulation compounds of types EI 1, GP 1 or EI 2 to BS 6899. Type EI 1 is a natural or synthetic thermoset insulation compound having a maximum operating temperature of 60 °C. Type GP 1 is a synthetic thermoset insulation compound having a maximum operating temperature of 85 °C. Type EI 2 is a silicone rubber insulation compound having a maximum operating temperature of 150 °C (180 °C where no restriction is imposed by the environment).

60 °C rubber insulation was originally based on natural rubber, but both 60 °C and 85 °C rubber insulations are now generally based on EPR.

PTFE insulation for BICC Intemp 250 (Registered trademark) is covered with a secondary insulating layer of glass/mica tape. The maximum operating temperature is 250 °C.

Conductors

Plain copper wires are almost always used for PVC insulated cores and tinned copper is used for rubber insulated types, but plain copper is now permissible for most elastomeric cables and cords to BS 6007 and BS 6500, provided that a separator is used. The high temperature cords and cables often have copper wires protected by nickel plating or may be of heat-resistant alloy in special cases.

Sheath and coverings

PVC for sheaths is specially compounded for flexibility and is normally type TM 2 to

BS 6746 and HD 21. However, a special grade is used for transparent sheaths. Other exceptions are type 4 to BS 6746 for heat-resisting cords and a special compound retaining its flexibility at low temperatures for BICC 'Polarflex' cords. The standard colours for the sheath are generally black or white. In special cases, provided that the quantity is sufficient to justify special manufacture, the clear bright colours possible with PVC may be used to advantage. Notable applications are the use of yellow (the standard colour for Polarflex) or orange to make cords supplying gardening power tools more visible and to reduce the risk of damage, and the use of pastel colours to match particular colour schemes on domestic appliances such as vacuum cleaners and food processors.

The variety of protective coverings for rubber insulated flexibles is influenced primarily by the environment. 60 °C rubber insulated cords have either a textile braid finish, a tough rubber (TRS) or a PCP sheath. Multicolour patterns are possible with a textile braid to provide an attractive appearance. Examples of those offered as standard are maroon, old gold, white, black with white tracers, blue/green/grey or red/green.

The sheath is provided in two standard versions, type EM 1 (ordinary duty) and type EM 2 (ordinary duty, oil resisting and flame retardant), both to BS 6899 and HD 22. EM 1 is usually based on natural rubber or a synthetic alternative, EM 2 on PCP. 85 °C rubber insulated cords have a sheath of ordinary duty heat-, oil- and flame-retardant rubber (HOFR) to BS 6899, type RS 3, which is usually based on CSP or CPE. The corresponding cables have a sheath of heavy duty heat-, oil- and flame-retardant compound (heavy duty HOFR) to BS 6899, type RS 4. As the provision of the necessary mechanical properties for natural rubber and PCP compounds depends largely on the incorporation of carbon black, especially with heavy duty versions, the sheath colour is black. HOFR compounds are less dependent on this type of reinforcement and are produced in white for cords in ordinary duty form. They can also be supplied in other colours for special applications.

The overall covering for silicone rubber cords and cables is a braid of glass fibre yarn treated with a heat-resistant varnish usually based on silicone resin. The outer covering for single-core PTFE insulated 'Intemp 250' cables consists of a glass braid with heat- and abrasion-resistant finish. For multicore types, single-core cables are laid together and then covered with a PTFE binding tape and a further glass braid with heat- and abrasion-resistant finish.

Construction and applications

The design and construction of flexible cords for particular applications is very important. The main factors to be considered are the degree of mechanical hazard, the amount of flexing, the balance between the size of the cord and the restraint it imparts on the appliance which it supplies, the environmental conditions, such as the presence of dampness or oils and solvents, and the operating temperature. Compromise has to be reached between flexibility and handling behaviour on the one hand and protection against mechanical damage on the other. Maximum flexibility and docile handling is achieved by building into the construction as much space and freedom of relative movement as is practical. Materials used to resist mechanical stresses are tough and resilient, and hence impose a corresponding influence on the amount of effort to bend, flex or otherwise move the cord.

The conductor construction involves the use of a larger number of smaller diameter wires relative to those of fixed cables. The maximum diameter of the wires used to obtain a given cross-sectional area of conductor is specified, thus defining the minimum number also. The wires are twisted together in a random bunch or bundle of wires. The number of twists per unit length is carefully chosen to permit reasonable bending and flexing of the conductor without damage, whilst avoiding stiffness. In the larger cables this bunched form of conductor better resists crush damage than the more regularly geometric, mechanically stable, rope stranded conductor which has some advantage in resistance to bending, flexing and twisting. In cases where compromise has to be struck between these factors, a number of bunched assemblies are stranded together in rope formation.

For very light duty applications on very small hand-held appliances such as electric shavers, the conventional forms of cord are not suitable, as a stage is reached in reducing the size of a cord where the smallest mechanically adequate conductor begins to dictate the flexibility. To meet this situation, a tinsel conductor is used, consisting of flattened wires of very small thickness wound round a supporting textile thread, a number of such threads being twisted together to give the required conductivity. This type of cord is available in parallel twin formation in one size only, maximum current rating 0.2 A.

Single-core and 2-core twisted cords are intended for the internal wiring of appliances, particularly luminaires (see below), and are used almost entirely with 85 °C or higher temperature forms of insulation. Mechanical stresses are minimal.

The lightest duty general purpose cord is the flat 2-core unsheathed type, which has the two conductors arranged parallel in one plane with a single covering of PVC. The cross-section of this covering is of 'figure-of-eight' (dumb-bell) or 'double D' form, thus providing a groove on each side between the insulated cores whereby they can easily be separated without damage for termination. It is designed for small light duty portable appliances and is subject to a Statutory Instrument: The Electrical Equipment (Safety) Regulations. The PVC sheathed version of the flat 2-core cord is also for light duty and achieves its flexibility by the use of a relatively thin sheath of a flexible PVC compound. This point demonstrates the conflict which can arise between desirable characteristics. PVC provides a cord which has a bright colourful easily cleaned smooth surface and is resistant to moisture. It has good appeal to users. However, as the thickness of sheath is increased to obtain better mechanical protection, the stiffness of the cord increases significantly, and this is particularly evident at lower ambient temperatures. The light duty cords, which also include in the standard range 2- and 3-core circular versions with twisted cores, have smaller thicknesses of insulation and sheath than the corresponding ordinary duty cords. They are appropriate for light portable appliances in domestic premises, kitchens, offices etc., where the risk of mechanical damage is small and there is a limited range of ambient temperature. Examples of their use are connections to table and standard lamps, office machines and radio and television sets. In appropriate cases, the heat-resisting (85 °C) version to BS 6141 can be employed, for instance when a power supply lead is required to operate in a high ambient temperature or is subject to heating by the appliance.

The importance of controlled freedom of relative movement of the components of flexible cords and cables is recognised in the specification requirement that the sheath must not adhere to the cores. This is of consequence both in flexing behaviour and in stripping the sheath when preparing connections, especially when automatic stripping machines are used. In some cases separate core interstice fillers, consisting of threads of textile fibres or extruded sections of plastic or unvulcanised rubber, are used. A tape or film separator may also be used over the laid-up cores to achieve these ends. PVC, with its lower resistance to cut propagation and lower stretch than rubber, is often preferred when automatic machine stripping is of concern.

Ordinary duty PVC cords have the same constructional features as the light duty cords, including flat forms. Because of the greater thickness of insulation and sheath, they are more robust and tend to be stiffer and less docile. This may not be of great consequence with appliances of limited movement, such as washing machines, refrigerators etc., particularly as these applications imply the possibility of a damp environment. Also, as they are designed for medium duty applications, the inference is that they will supply more heavy and powerful appliances than are appropriate to the light duty cords. Therefore their stiffness has less influence on the control of the appliance. Standard ordinary duty cords also include 4- and 5-core assemblies. Nevertheless, because of this stiffness, PVC flexible cables of size 4 mm^2 and above have not proved popular.

BS 6141 makes provision for 85 °C versions of the ordinary duty PVC cords, which can be substituted when cables are subject to higher operating temperatures than usual. For lower ambient temperatures, cables from the BICC Polarflex range (which are dimensionally the same as ordinary duty cords but remain flexible down to -20 °C) can be used for a variety of purposes on outdoor sites provided that they are adequately shielded from mechanical damage (see below).

Rubber insulated flexible cords and cables have, of course, a longer history than the PVC equivalents. The thickness of insulation and sheath which is practical with PVC is not so appropriate to rubber. However, rubber is considerably more flexible and resilient, a factor which becomes more evident as the size of the cable increases. The thermosets cover a wide temperature range and their properties are not as temperature dependent as those of PVC. For these reasons some of the constructions adopted historically to produce attractive light duty cords for normal indoor ambient conditions have persisted, against the competition from PVC. These consist of the use of textile yarn braids or a combination of rubber sheath/textile braid as the final covering. The degree of abrasion resistance afforded by this type of covering is dependent on the form and treatment of the yarn and the construction of the braid. Special performance test techniques have been developed, details of which are given in a later section.

In some circumstances, where considerable movement is involved, the degree of freedom of movement of the cores of a textile braided cord can be so high that it becomes disadvantageous in that the conductors can be bent round such a small radius that permanent uneven elongation of the conductors results and kinks are formed which lead rapidly to fatigue failure of the wires. The use of a rubber sheath controls this behaviour, but for domestic purposes the attractive appearance of the coloured textile braid would be lost if this was used alone. Consequently a long established combination of the two types of protection exists in a National Standard cord, the so-called UDF cord. In this design, a thin covering of rubber, much less than the normal rubber sheath thickness, is applied over the twisted cores with their interstice fillers. The textile braid is then applied so that it is partially embedded in the rubber layer. The combined coverings thus complement each other in controlling the natural bending radius of the cord whilst retaining the attractive appearance of the textile braid.

The upper end of the temperature range for which standard flexibles are available is covered by 300/500 V silicone rubber insulated and glass braided cables (up to 150 °C), used mainly for fixed wiring in appliances, and 600/1000 V Intemp 250 PTFE/micaglass insulated and glass braided cables (up to 250 °C), mainly for control and supply circuits in industrial environments.

A requirement of wiring regulations is that flexible cords or cables should be protected by a metallic screen or armour when they are exposed to risk of mechanical damage, or in situations where a particular hazard of electric shock exists, or in atmospheres where there is the risk of fire or explosion. Therefore versions of the standard PVC and rubber cords and cables are available with either a tinned copper wire braid, galvanised steel wire braid or a galvanised steel strip armour which is applied spirally and interlocked, e.g. BICC ARMAFLEX (registered trademark). Usually an additional outer sheath of the same material as the standard sheath of the cord is applied over the metallic protection. Where a visual check of the state of the metallic protection is needed, this outer sheath can be of transparent PVC. Cables with tinned copper wire braids are commonly used in workshops and on building sites. Galvanised steel wire armoured cables (braid or pliable wire armour) are also used on building construction sites. This type of cable, and the corrugated steel strip armoured cable, are used for the final connection to motors.

Tests

Identical test methods for the abrasion resistance and flexibility of rubber insulated flexible cords are contained in the relevant British and International Standards.

Abrasion resistance

Fig. 12.1 shows a diagrammatic representation of the test equipment. A sample of the cord is caused to rub against a similar sample of cord wound on a flanged mandrel. The test sample is maintained under tension by a weight fixed to one end and the other end is attached to a mechanical device which imparts movement of a defined distance and rate of travel. After 20 000 single movements, the insulation of the cord must not be exposed by more than a specified amount and the cord must maintain its electrical integrity.

Flexing test

The apparatus used is shown in fig. 12.2. The test is carried out on a sample energised with an a.c. voltage and mechanical loading. It must withstand 60 000 strokes without loss of electrical integrity. The electrical and mechanical loading and the form of the pulleys vary according to the type and size of the cord.

Full details of both tests are given in BS 6500, which also includes tests for the flexing and impact behaviour of cords with tinsel conductors.

Technical data

General details of the size ranges, dimensions, weights, volt drop and current ratings are given in appendix A8.

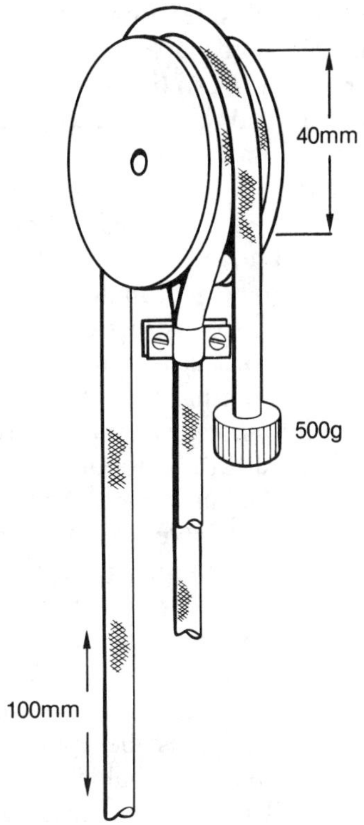

Fig. 12.1 Equipment for abrasion test on textile braided flexible cords

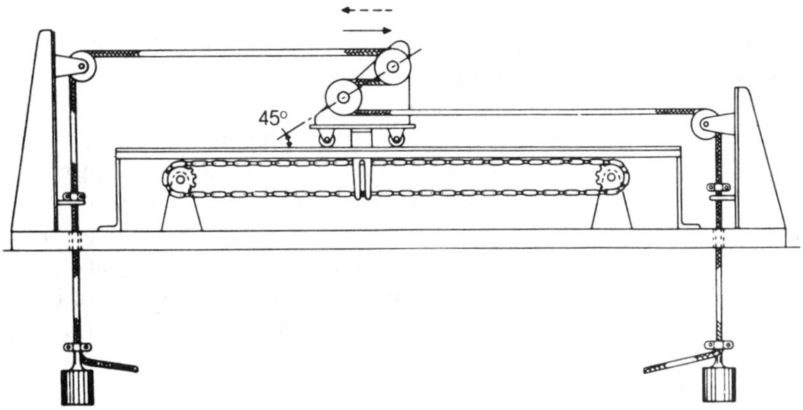

Fig. 12.2 Equipment for flexing test on flexible cords (Courtesy of British Standards Institution)

Current ratings

It will be noted that the rated currents for flexible cords given in appendix A8 are lower than those given for the corresponding size and type of fixed wiring cable. Although they are based on the same logic as the current ratings for other cables, they are influenced by subjective considerations, primarily human reaction to the surface temperature. As flexible cords are handled or touched by people, the concept of 'touch temperature' is of overriding importance. Empirically the current ratings for cords have been established in relation to PVC wiring cables protected by overcurrent devices which will not operate within 4 hours at 1.5 times the designed load current of the protected circuit, e.g. the rewireable fuse. From experience and measurement it has been established that, slightly modified, these result in cord surface temperatures, in air, that are acceptable to the majority of users.

Although the temperature designations of materials are retained in flexible cords, all cords have the same basic rating, for the reasons explained above. Temperature designation of the materials of a cord has significance in relation to rating when ambient temperatures higher than normal have to be taken into account. Consequently rating factors are given for ambient temperatures related to the temperature designations of the insulation and sheath materials.

In the case of general purpose flexible cables, the current ratings are derived in the same way as for comparable fixed cables and have no subjective element.

It should be noted that the current ratings given apply only to a single cord or cable in free air, not wound in coils or on a drum. The current ratings which apply in these circumstances are considerably less than those tabulated. The appropriate values vary with the number of coils and the design of the drum. This needs to be emphasised particularly in relation to the reeling drums supplied for use with extension cords for domestic purposes. In some cases the appropriate current rating may be less than half the current rating given in the tables.

The current rating for the parallel twin, PVC insulated, tinsel conductor cord is 0.2 A maximum.

CABLES FOR MINING AND QUARRYING

The difficult geological conditions and particularly the mechanically hostile environment at the coal face in UK mines probably represent the most demanding application for flexible cables in industry. Three main types of flexible cable are in use. One is an unarmoured cable for supplying power to coal cutting machines, often referred to as cutter cables or trailing cables. Another, with flexible steel wire armour or pliable wire armour (PWA), is for supplies to coal conveying and loading machines, remote control gear, coal face lighting and moveable transformers. Also under this heading come auxiliary multicore cables for control and monitoring of large mining machines. The third type is a relatively light unarmoured cable for hand-held shot hole drilling machines and similar equipment requiring a highly flexible yet robust supply cable. These systems are fed by the fixed cables described in chapter 11.

All these cables, or similar ones, find application in other types of mining or rough industrial situations worldwide. Versions of the PWA cables are used for supplies to machinery in open cast mines, quarries and other miscellaneous mines; also to cranes, dredgers, excavators, tunnelling machinery and supplies on civil engineering construction sites.

The relevant specifications are as follows.

BS 6708: Trailing cables for mining purposes

BS 6116: Elastomer insulated flexible trailing cables for quarries and miscellaneous mines
BCS 188: Flexible trailing cables for use with coal cutters and for similar purposes
BCS 504: Flexible trailing cables with galvanised steel pliable armouring
BCS 505: Flexible trailing cables for use with drills
BCS 653: Flexible multicore screened auxiliary cables with galvanised steel pliable armouring

The use of cables in UK mines is governed by regulations issued by Her Majesty's Inspectorate of Mines.

BS 6708 is currently being revised. The present issue already includes most of the cables in British Coal Specifications 188, 504 and 505. It is now planned to include those in BCS 653, and also all the types in BS 6116 (which will be withdrawn when the new issue of BS 6708 is published). It is hoped to include a number of types which have not previously been covered by any British Standard. These are 640/1100 V cables with screened cores in flat configuration; 3.8/6.6 kV armoured cables with three screened cores; and 3.8/6.6 kV and 6.35/11 kV unarmoured cables with screened cores.

Unarmoured cables for mining machinery

Historical

The first successful attempts to use electrical coal cutting machines took place in the period 1885–1890. Many devices were proposed to protect the supply cables and they all exhibited degrees of compromise between high flexibility and mechanical protection. They included single rubber insulated cores drawn into hose-pipes enclosed in a leather jacket formed by sewing the layers of a leather strip together, or wrapped in canvas and bound with rope. Eventually, multicore cables with cores twisted together and padded to a circular section with jute yarn and then jute braided were introduced. These were unsatisfactory in wet mines and around 1906 a non-hygroscopic sheath was developed. This consisted, initially, of vulcanised bitumen protected by bitumen impregnated tape, impregnated jute yarn and spirally applied tarred rope. In later versions the rope was replaced by a braid of whipcord, or in some cases leather strips or even metal chain armour. These forms of protection were superseded by the tough rubber sheath, sometimes reinforced by an embedded cord braid or layer of canvas. The introduction of PCP in the late 1930s brought a further step forward since it made practical a cable which was tough, flame retardant and water resistant. By the middle of this century PCP was the only sheathing material for flexible cables used in mines and quarries in the UK and most other industrialised countries. Heavy duty CSP has more recently been introduced for quarry cables included in BS 6116.

Materials

There had been little challenge to natural rubber as the insulation for these cables until the designs were metricated in 1970. However, the introduction of butyl rubber, EPR and CSP to cable making indicated that the cores of flexible mining cables could be improved in respect of current rating and resistance to mechanical damage, notably the effects of crushing. CSP was only used for a short period for insulation because electrical problems were experienced with the earth protection system, due to the high cable capacitance. EPR and composite EPR/CSP are now the only recognised insulants.

Construction

Because of the risk of accidental explosion and fire in coal mines, devices to minimise the contribution of flexible supply cables to such accidents are major design features. Equally important is the protection of operators against electric shock. Salient principles of electrical safety philosophy in UK mines are low impedance earthing of the neutral point and protective switchgear based on earth fault current, excess current and current unbalance sensing. Consequently, virtually all flexible cables have a separate earthing conductor, the only exception being type 11 (see below) in which the four core screens form the earth. Earthing conductors may or may not be insulated. All cables also have a metallic barrier or screen of defined conductance enclosing the cores. In the case of early cables this screen consisted initially of a braid formed of tinned copper wires, or in some cases a layer of seven-strand formations applied spirally. The advantage of the latter arrangement was that it enabled connections for earthing to be made more easily. The essence of these, as with all components, is maximum flexibility with maximum resistance to the mechanical stresses arising from constant movement, often in confined spaces over extremely rough ground. The spiral screen was found to be more prone to damage due to twisting than the braid and it was eventually eliminated.

Further development provided the composite braid screen in which the members are composed of tinned copper wires in one direction and of textile yarn in the other direction. This was originally cotton, but nylon fibre is now used because of its greater strength and stretch. In this context it will be noted that the collectively screened arrangement, i.e. all cores within a common braid, is not a recognised design because it does not provide protection against a phase to phase fault, a common result of crush damage. Additionally it was shown that the volume of combustible material within the screen was sufficient, under fault conditions, to disrupt the cable explosively and to provide a potential source of explosion or fire externally.

Some standard types of trailing cable are shown in fig. 12.3. These constructions comply with all the requirements described earlier for flexibility and provide more positive arrangements for maintaining geometric stability in view of the extreme conditions of bending, flexing and twisting to which they are submitted. The life of this type of cable is determined by its mechanical history and the amount of damage it sustains before it becomes irrepairable.

All these types are designed for 3-phase operation and consist of three individually screened power cores, an earthing conductor and a pilot conductor.

The cores are assembled in a geometrically symmetrical and mechanically stable arrangement and the maximum pitch or lay length of conductor wires, cores and screen wires is closely controlled. Except in the case of type 10, which is discussed below, the three power cores are placed with their screens in contact. In type 7, the earth conductor is not insulated and is placed centrally in contact with the power core screens. In type 14, the earth conductor is insulated to the same diameter as the power cores thus giving the most mechanically correct arrangement but making the

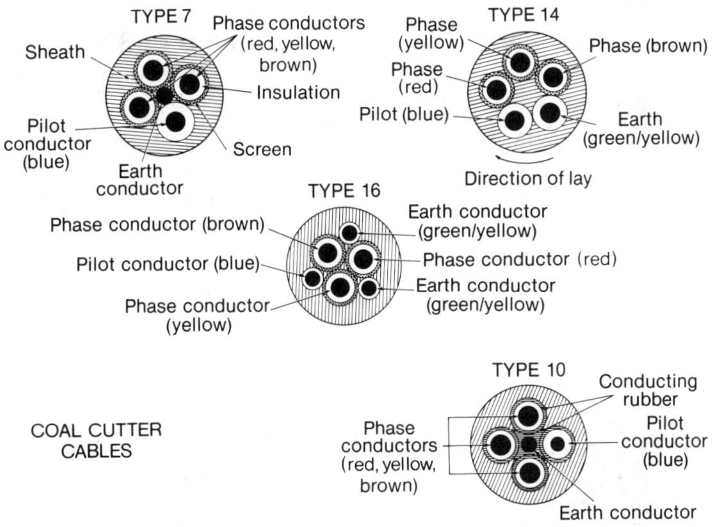

Fig. 12.3 Cross-sections of coal cutter cables with metallic and conducting rubber screens

cable larger than types 7 and 16. The earth conductor in type 16 is divided into two parts, each insulated and of the same size as the pilot core. This provides the smallest cable of the three patterns.

In recent years, several variants of type 7 have been introduced. Type 7M has a screened pilot core of the same conductor size as the power cores, which provides a more balanced construction for conditions in which the cable may be subject to an unusual degree of flexing or tension. In type 7S the pilot core is replaced by a unit made up of three cores, to give additional monitoring or control circuits to the machine being supplied by the cable. Type 11, which is made only in the 16 mm^2 size, has a screened pilot core but no separate earth conductor, and is designed to meet special service conditions in which a central conductor (as in the normal type 7) would be likely to break. In UK mines all coal face machines are remotely controlled and the pilot conductor is used to operate the remote control circuit. The core assembly is enclosed in a substantial sheath of black PCP compound complying with BS 6899, 60 °C heavy duty OFR sheath, type RS 2, with an additional tear resistance requirement (see BS 6708).

The core insulation complies with type FR 1, 85 °C insulation to BS 6899 or is an MEPR compound with special mechanical properties as specified by British Coal. Core identification is by a layer of tape applied over the insulation. Red, yellow and brown colour coding is used for the power cores, and blue for the pilot core or pilot unit, the three pilot cores in type 7S being coded black, white and blue.

As will be evident from the designs discussed above, considerable development has occurred in improving the safety, robustness, flexibility, size and weight of trailing cables. The diversity of conditions has dictated the degree to which the various designs are adopted. However, with the increasing emphasis on mechanisation, the elimination of the more difficult seams, and common ownership, considerable rationalisation of cables has taken place. One design change which offers considerable reduction in fault current, and elimination of the danger that fractured screen wires penetrate the core insulation, incorporates conducting thermoset material for the protective screens. A design of cable, type 10 to BCS Specification 188, is shown in fig. 12.3. Such cables have been in use under strictly controlled circumstances for a considerable number of years.

The main influence on the rate of adoption arises from a fundamental difference in the path of the earth fault current from that in metallic screened cables. For the conducting rubber screened cable fig. 12.4 illustrates that the path of the fault current is radial from the phase conductor to the earthing conductor. The conducting rubber elements are not required to carry current longitudinally, whereas in the metallic screened cable the screens are required to carry all, or a substantial part of, the fault current. The internal cable circuit is shown symbolically in fig. 12.4.

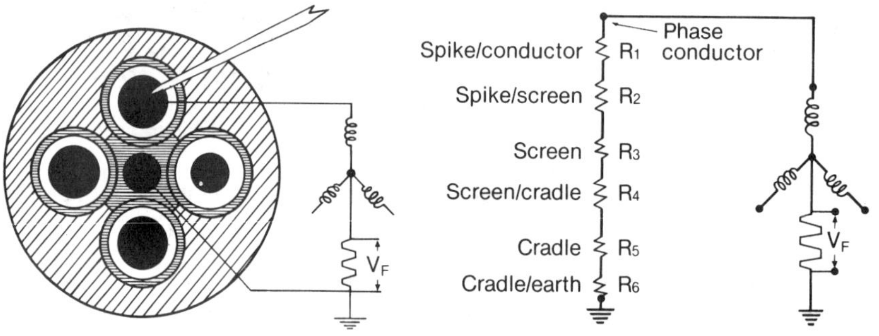

Fig. 12.4 Equivalent circuit diagram of fault current path for coal cutter cables with conducting rubber screen

With standard electromechanically operated protective switchgear, currents of the order of several amperes are required for operation. This is no problem for the low resistance circuits of the metallic screened cable. In the conducting rubber cable the resistance of the screen material (R_3 and R_5) is inherently higher, and the interface resistances (R_4 and R_6) are critical. All these resistances are subject to considerable variation due to mechanical deformation and relative movement. Fault currents, normally required to operate standard earth leakage protection, would add to these changes owing to heat generation, and consequently the conducting rubber cable is only suitable for use with voltage operated (electronic) protection devices. These require an impedance inserted between the neutral point of the supply transformer and earth, across which an operating voltage V_F due to a fault is developed. Since present UK mining regulations require the supply neutral to be solidly earthed, i.e. via minimum impedance, conducting rubber screened cables and their associated switchgear can only be used when dispensation is obtained from the mining inspectorate. A special test of the effectiveness of conducting rubber screens, based on the above concepts, is contained in BCS 188.

Technical data

Details of the cable range together with dimensions, weights and current ratings are given in appendix A10, tables A10.1–A10.3.

Voltage and current rating

The rated voltage for cutter cables is 640/1100 V. Current ratings are based on 25 °C ambient temperature and a maximum conductor temperature of 75 °C. Both continuous and intermittent ratings are provided, the latter based on the most severe operating cycle normally employed with coal cutting machines. The ratings are given in table A10.2, together with the cycle from which the intermittent ratings are calculated and the rating factors to be applied for higher ambient temperature.

As with other flexible cables the ratings do not apply if the cables are used on drums or in coils or where heat dissipation is otherwise reduced. Nor do they take account of volt drop. This can be calculated from the values of resistance and reactance in table 12.2. The values are for one power conductor.

Table 12.2 D.C. resistance and reactance of coal cutter cables

Nominal area of power conductor (mm^2)	Nominal d.c. resistance (mΩ per 100 m at full load current)	Nominal reactance (mΩ per 100 m at 50 Hz)				
		Types 7, 7S and 7M	Type 10	Type 11	Type 14	Type 16
16	150	10.9		10.9		
25	96	10.7	12.2		10.9	9.9
35	69	10.1	11.8		10.4	9.4
50	47	9.8	11.5		10.0	9.0
70	34	9.5	11.1		9.8	8.7
95	25	9.4	10.3		9.7	8.5
120	19	9.2				

Pliable wire armoured (PWA) cables

PWA cables are designed for situations in mines and quarries where the risk of mechanical damage is high but where limited, relatively infrequent, movement is involved. For instance in UK mines they are used as flexible extensions of the fixed power cables in roadways on the primary side of transformers supplying power to face machines. They are also used to connect the secondaries of the transformers to remote control switchgear. These transformers and switchgear are moved periodically as the coal face advances. Except in auxiliary cables to BCS 653 (see below), the materials and constructional features are the same as for cutter cables. 2-, 3- and 4-core assemblies are provided as standard for voltages up to 3.8/6.6 kV with screened cores and at 320/550 V and 1.9/3.3 kV with unscreened cores. 320/550 V auxiliary cables have up to 24 ETFE insulated screened cores and are intended for use on large mining machines (external to the machine), to provide interconnection between machine sections or between machine sections and associated auxiliary equipment.

Some designs are available for supplies to dredgers, draglines and excavators used in alluvial and open cast mining. The cores are normally unscreened except for voltages higher than 6.6 kV.

A summary of the PWA cables available for mining purposes is as follows:

(a) 320/550 V cables with unscreened cores (rubber insulated) and screened cores (ETFE insulated)
(b) 640/1100 V cables with screened cores for remote controlled circuits, coal face lighting, conveyors and loaders
(c) 1.9/3.3 kV cables with screened cores for roadway distribution, conveyors etc. and with unscreened cores for operating pumps etc.
(d) 3.8/6.6 kV cables with screened cores for use primarily as roadway extension services

BS 6708, BS 6116 and BCS 504 detail the standard designs recognised under UK Mining Regulations for use in mines and quarries. They are referred to by type numbers.

Types 62, 63, 64, 70, 71
These types are assumed to carry currents well below their thermal capacity and are standardised in one size only, normally 4 mm^2. The conductor size is decided primarily by mechanical considerations. With the exceptions of types 70 and 71, all have screened cores. Core insulation is MEPR/CSP to BS 6899, type FR 1, or special MEPR to BCS 504.

Types 201, 211, 321, 331, 631
These are for 3-phase distribution and are standardised within a range of sizes from 10 to 120 mm^2. Type 201 has three screened power cores only, type 321 has three unscreened power cores and an unscreened earth core, and the remaining types have screened power cores plus an unscreened earth core. Core insulation for types 201 and 211 is MEPR/CSP to BS 6899, type FR 1, or special MEPR. For types 321, 331 and 631 the insulation is of composite type FR 2 to BS 6899 or special MEPR as specified by British Coal.

Construction of above types to BS 6708 and BCS 504
In all types the cores are assembled (round a PCP or other thermoset centre when required) and covered with an inner sheath of PCP, type EM 2 to BS 6899, which provides a bedding for the armour.

The PWA consists essentially of a helical layer of seven-wire strands of galvanised steel wires applied with short lay. In the UK there is a statutory requirement that the armour of mining cables shall have a conductance of not less than 50% of the conductor within the cable having the highest conductance. To meet this requirement it is necessary, in some cases, to include some copper wires in the armour.

The outer sheath of these cables is PCP, heavy duty OFR to BS 6899, type RS2, with the tear resistance increased to 7.5 N/mm.

Construction of cables to BCS 653
Types 506, 512 and 518 have 6, 12 and 18 cores respectively, with conductors of area 1.34 mm^2 (19/0.3 mm wires). Type 524 has 24 cores, with conductors of area 0.93 mm^2 (19/0.25 mm wires). The cores are insulated with ETFE and then individu-

ally screened with copper wire braids. After assembly of the cores, the cables are completed in the same way as the elastomeric types described above.

Cables to BS 6116
Whereas the cables referred to above are intended for deep mines, including coal mines, those defined by BS 6116 are intended for quarries, open cast mines and other miscellaneous mines in which the 'Regulations for quarries and metalliferous mines' apply.

The standard type references and voltage designations are as follows:

type 20: 600/1000 V, 3-core, 2.5–150 mm^2, single-phase
type 21: 600/1000 V, 4-core, 2.5–150 mm^2, 3-phase
type 321: 1.9/3.3 kV, 4-core, 16–150 mm^2, 3-phase
type 621: 3.8/6.6 kV, 4-core, 16–150 mm^2, 3-phase

All the cables include an earthing conductor for the apparatus fed by the cables, as required by the above Regulations. The power cores do not have a metallic screen for fault protection. Type 621 has a semiconducting, stress control tape over the insulation. The PWA does not have copper wires included. All other details are the same as for PWA cables to BS 6708.

Technical data
Details of dimensions, weights and current ratings are given in appendix A10, tables A10.4–A10.7, A10.9 and A10.10.

Current ratings
The ratings quoted in the appendices do not apply to cables on drums or in coils. Under these conditions the ratings depend on the provision for heat dissipation. Also where cables are used outdoors, in direct sunlight, particularly in tropical zones, a factor must be applied.

Voltage drop
Values of d.c. resistance and reactance for use in calculating voltage drop are given in table 12.3

Unarmoured flexible cables – drill cables

Originally these cables were designed to supply hand-held shot hole drilling machines in mines. The growth of mechanical mining has resulted in a corresponding reduction in this application. However, they have come to be used in a number of other situations where a highly flexible yet robust supply cable is required.

BS 6708 and BCS 505 formerly covered the designs and requirements for unscreened and screened cables, but on grounds of safety the unscreened design has been withdrawn by British Coal. The present cables are

type 43: 5-core, conducting rubber screen
type 44: 5-core, composite copper/nylon braid screen

Table 12.3 D.C. resistance and reactance of PWA cables to BCS 504

Conductor area (mm^2)	Nominal d.c. resistance (mΩ per 100 m at full load current)	Nominal reactance (mΩ per 100 m at 50 Hz)				
		Types 62, 63	*Types 64, 70*	*Type 71*		
4	570	12.3	13.0	13.4		
		Type 201	*Type 211*	*Type 321*	*Type 331*	*Type 631*
10	235	12.0	12.9			
16	150	10.9	11.7			
25	96	10.4	11.2		12.4	
35	69	9.9	10.6	12.0	11.8	
50	47	9.6	10.4	11.4	11.2	12.7
70	34	9.2	10.0	10.9	10.7	12.0
95	25	9.0	9.9	10.5	10.4	
120	20	8.8	9.5	10.1	10.1	

Although shot hole drilling machines in UK mines operate at 125 V between phases, with the neutral point earthed so that the voltage to earth is limited to 72 V, the insulation thickness and protection on drill cables are such that they are rated at 600/1000 V and may be used at voltages up to this in installations other than coal mines and where the UK Mining Regulations do not apply. Generally, the construction and materials are the same as for the coal cutter cables but only one conductor size of 6 mm^2 is produced as standard.

To give better flexibility to the type 44 cable, a polyethylene terephthalate film tape is included over the braided core screen. It will be noted that, because of the extreme requirements for these cables, the geometry of the cross-section is symmetrical, with the conductors all in the same pitch circle. The shaped thermoset cradle centre ensures mechanical stability. As an aid to identification, a yellow longitudinal stripe is applied during manufacture to the sheath of the conducting rubber screened type 43 cable.

Technical data

The dimensions and weights of drill cables are given in appendix 10, table A10.8.

Current rating

The size of conductors for drill cables is selected primarily on mechanical considerations and when used in UK coal mines they operate at currents much less than their maximum thermal ratings. When used elsewhere the rating for 6 mm^2 types 43 and 44 is 46 A.

FLEXIBLE CABLES FOR OTHER INDUSTRIAL APPLICATIONS

Welding cables

Welding cables are used to connect the secondary, high current side of a welding transformer to the welding electrode holder and for the earthing or return lead. As electrical welding involves low voltage, high current conditions, the electrical demands on coverings are not onerous. Prior to the 1960s, when compounds based on natural rubber were the most common coverings for flexible cables, it was considered necessary to use two-layer coverings. The first layer was insulation compound (VR) to provide the electrical performance and the second layer a heavy duty sheath (TRS) to withstand the very rough mechanical conditions in service.

Because of the high current involved, conductor cross-sections tend to be large. With hand-held electrodes, minimum restraint on the operator is essential and flexibility is of paramount importance. These cables are predominantly of single-core construction and conductors consist of multiple bundles of small diameter wires. A paper or polyethylene terephthalate separator tape is applied over the conductor to prevent the coverings keying into the conductor and hence provide controlled relative movement with improved flexibility and mechanical life.

The introduction of the high performance synthetic rubbers in the 1960s enabled improved single- and dual-covering welding cables to be developed. The most successful have been EPR and CSP, used individually or in combination, the choice being dependent on conditions in the particular circumstances. The salient advantage common to both materials is heat resistance. Whereas natural rubber covered cables are limited to a maximum operating temperature of 60 °C, both EPR and CSP can be operated at 85 °C, with significant improvements in current ratings, ageing and weather resistance. In addition, CSP has resistance to oil and chemical contamination and is flame retardant. Compounds of both materials have more than adequate electrical properties together with combinations of other properties to meet the specific requirements for many situations.

Conductors have traditionally been of copper, but in recent years aluminium (sometimes alloyed with small amounts of other metals to give greater strength) has also been used on a considerable scale, though its popularity has varied to some extent with the fluctuations in world metal prices. Aluminium cables are lighter than copper and offer significant savings in weight when high welding currents are required, and on projects where the distances and complexity involved in welding current distribution call for large amounts of cable. As pointed out in chapter 3, extra care is required when fitting terminations to aluminium conductors.

As aluminium is more difficult to draw reliably to the same small sizes of wire that are common with copper, larger wire sizes are used in the conductors. Also aluminium conductors have a lower fatigue resistance and breakage can occur more frequently, particularly in the cable near to the electrode holder. This can be overcome by connecting a short piece of the appropriate copper conductor cable between the electrode holder and the end of the aluminium cable.

The relevant British Standard is BS 638, 'Arc welding power sources, equipment and accessories', Part 4, 'Specification for welding cables'. It includes coverings of single-layer type RS 5 or RS 3 (HOFR) 85 °C rubber to BS 6899 and a two-layer covering, type GP 1 and type RS 3 to BS 6899. The alternatives of plain or tinned copper wires or aluminium wires with each covering are recognised. The coverings are identified by colour as follows:

single-layer	RS 5:	light grey (suffix T)
single-layer	RS 3:	orange (suffix H)
two-layer	GP 1:	black (suffix TQ)
	RS 3:	orange

RS 5 and GP 1 are normally EPR compounds and RS 3 can be CSP or CPE.

Details of dimensions and weights are given in appendix 9, table A9.1.

Voltage designation

The cables discussed here are recognised for welding duty at voltages to earth not exceeding 100 V d.c. or a.c.

This limitation does not apply to the voltage produced by a superimposed high frequency supply or other similar low power device used for starting or stabilizing an arc. When required they may be used at voltages above 100 V but not exceeding 450 V. When used under the latter conditions adequate protection against damage to the coverings must be provided.

Current rating

The quoted ratings of welding cables, as given in appendix A9, table A9.3, are based on an ambient temperature of 25 °C and a maximum conductor temperature of 85 °C. They are assumed to be in free air with unrestricted natural ventilation.

For equivalent current rating, the aluminium cable has a larger conductor diameter and a correspondingly greater overall diameter, although it is appreciably lighter than the copper cable.

Early current ratings for welding cables were established by experience, based on hand welding practice where, in general, cables were energised for short periods and had long rest periods. The introduction of welding machines with appreciably longer periods of energisation necessitated a review of rating procedures. This was also needed because of the introduction of the higher performance materials. As a result, the concept of a 'duty cycle' was introduced which allows currents higher than the continuous rating to be used, dependent on the times for which the cable carries current in a given period. The period chosen is five minutes and the duty cycle is defined as

$$X = \frac{\text{time (min) of current flow}}{5} \times 100\%$$

The continuous ratings are now determined by means of the methods dealt with in chapter 8 and the ratings for any particular situation are related to them through the use of the duty cycle. Current ratings for representative duty cycles are given in appendix 9, table A9.3. For any other duty cycle the following formula can be used:

$$I_1 = I_c\,(100/X)^{1/2} \qquad (12.1)$$

where I_1 = rating for required duty cycle
I_c = continuous rating (100% duty cycle)
X = required duty cycle (%)

Resistance and voltage drop
Values for the range of both aluminium and copper conductor welding cables are given in appendix 9, table A9.2. When long lengths of cable are used between the welding set and the electrode, larger conductors than are indicated by thermal considerations must be used to avoid excessive voltage drop. These larger cables are more awkward to handle and may cause inconvenience to the operator. This can be avoided by reverting to the normal size of cable indicated by current rating at a point near to the electrode holder.

Flat flexible cables for mobile machines (cranes and hoists)

The electrical supplies to mobile industrial machinery are frequently provided by conventional circular-section cables as described previously. Where the path of the flexible cord or cable needs to be closely defined and controlled, or where space is limited, the geometry of the conventional cord or cable may be inadequate and a special solution would then be required. This can be achieved by restricting the flexing to one plane by arranging the cores side by side in one layer and enclosing them in a rectangular-section sheath. Thus the flexibility of the cable is improved in the required plane compared with a circular-section cable. Such cords and cables have a better space factor and are most appropriate where the supply cable is wound on a drum or reel as the machine is operated over a regular route. Examples are cranes and hoists where the cable is often suspended in festoons from a travelling hanger on a track.

Cores are insulated with EPR type GP 1 to BS 6899 and are the same as those in the corresponding circular flexible cords and cables. The sheath is HOFR type RS 3 to BS 6899. The maximum number of cores available as standard varies with conductor size. Cores are arranged parallel, in a single layer, and are divided into groups of two or three separated by webs of sheathing material to ensure transverse stability. Identification is by means of numbered cores. The range and dimensions of flat flexible cords and cables are given in appendix A8, table A8.23.

Current ratings
Because the rectangular section gives a greater area for heat loss, the ratings of flat-section cords and cables on a thermal basis are equal to or better than the corresponding circular versions. They are given for guidance in appendix A8, table A8.22. These values assume the cable to be in free air and straight, i.e. not coiled or reeled, and that a maximum of three cores are loaded. Requirements for individual installations vary widely and specific consideration has to be given to each application.

X-ray cables

As X-ray tubes have to be mobile, so that they can be placed in correct relationship to the object to be examined, they are generally housed separately from their power supply and control units. Connection to the power supply is by means of a cable or cables, which must be as small as possible and very flexible. Supplies to the tube consist of a low voltage a.c. heater supply and a high voltage d.c. cathode/anode supply, which can be up to 500 kV d.c., with a low current of the order of tens of milliamps. In some cases provision is made to connect the control voltage. X-ray cables are therefore an example of a flexible cable where electrical considerations are predominant.

For maximum flexibility, the features discussed under general purpose flexible cords are applicable. To keep the size of the cable as small as possible, the operating maximum electrical stress in the dielectric must be as high as can be tolerated safely. The insulation compound is specially formulated for the purpose. Dielectric loss angle and permittivity need to be kept low to reduce dielectric heating under a.c. conditions and high insulation resistance is important for d.c. operation. Many factors are common with the use of polymeric insulants for high voltage power cables discussed in chapter 25, e.g. freedom from partial discharges in voids and the importance of using clean materials free from inclusions of foreign particles. EPR has now replaced the traditional composite PCP/NR as the main insulation. To minimise the effects of corona discharge and to provide stress control, it is protected by an inner layer of conducting EPR and has a stress relief tape applied over it.

The construction is in the form of a concentric high voltage cable with the auxiliary cores at the centre, within the inner high voltage conductor. The auxiliary cores are insulated with one of the high performance thermoplastic materials such as ETFE or FEP to give the minimum core diameter with high electrical and mechanical integrity. The assembled cores are padded with an appropriate yarn filler and taped with PETP film to give a circular cross-section. A layer of small diameter tinned copper wires is then applied helically to form the high voltage conductor. The diameter attained is hence sufficient to reduce the level of electrical stress at the inner surface of the insulation.

The outer conductor takes the form of a braid of small diameter tinned copper wires. When required, it is covered with a PETP film tape to prevent the overall protection from keying into it and restricting flexibility.

Final protection depends on the duty and can be a CSP or PVC sheath, normally white or grey in colour, or a braid of white nylon yarn for maximum flexibility. X-ray cables are supplied with a protective tape, helically applied, to prevent soiling of the cable in handling; it may be removed after installation.

Electrical characteristics

The low voltage conductors are rated at 5 A for operation at 240 V a.c. r.m.s., but will withstand 5 kV d.c. with respect to the high voltage conductor. The operating voltages for the standard cables are given in appendix A9, table A9.4. In some cases a high voltage supply with an earthed centre point is adopted, thus allowing two cables to be used to handle a total voltage of twice that for one cable.

Range and dimensions

The range and dimensions of standard X-ray cables are included in appendix A9, table A9.4. The cables are used with special terminations designed to terminate the conductor in such a way as to avoid points of high electrical stress; the fitting of these terminations is a skilled operation.

Coil leads

BS 6195, 'Insulated flexible cables and cords for coil leads', defines a coil lead as 'an insulated flexible conductor connected directly and permanently to a coil winding or other component of electrical apparatus and usually connected to some form of terminal'. This description covers a surprising range of cords and cables which have to cater for widely varied environmental conditions. They provide connections to the electromagnetic coils of motors, generators, transformers, relays, circuit breakers, actuators etc.

Although simple in construction, they include a wide range of materials; BS 6195 deals with a comprehensive selection but it is by no means exhaustive. Insulation materials range from general purpose PVC through a selection of rubbers to PETP, glass fibres, polyimide film, ETFE, FEP and PTFE. Increasing use is also being made of irradiation crosslinked polymers for the lower voltage categories. BS 6195 only deals with the more commonly used types and schedules them by operating temperature range and insulation material as shown in table 12.4.

Conductors

The flexible conductors are either simply bunched or multi-bunched, depending on size, and are formed of plain copper (with PVC) or tinned copper wires for operation up to 150 °C or nickel plated copper above 150 °C.

The standard size range is from 0.22 to 400 mm^2. Sizes above 2.5 mm^2 with thermoset insulation are usually supplied with a PETP film under the insulation to facilitate stripping.

Table 12.4 Types of coil leads to BS 6195

Type	Insulation	Continuous operating temperature (°C)	
		Minimum	Maximum
1a	PVC, general purpose (type TI 2 to BS 6746)	−20	+70
1b	PVC heat resisting (type 4 to BS 6746)	−20	+85
3 and 4	Thermoset polymer and compound dependent on voltage category: CSP (type OR 1), EPR/CSP (type FR 1 and FR 2 to BS 6899)	−30	+90
5	Silicone rubber compound (type EI 2 to BS 6899)	−60	+150
7	PETP fabric tape/PETP braid, synthetic resin varnished	−50	+110
8a	Varnished glass fibre fabric/ glass fibre braid, treated with synthetic resin varnish	−50	+130
8b	Varnished glass fibre fabric/ glass fibre braid, treated with silicone resin varnish	−50	+180

Insulation
The choice of material is governed by the environmental conditions and the operational temperature. Coil leads are used in air, in inert gases and in oil, water or refrigerating liquids. Various conditions impose limitations, e.g. exposure to oil reduces the maximum operating temperature of thermosets and exposure in an enclosed static atmosphere limits the operating temperature of silicone rubber.

A common requirement in the manufacture of equipment is that the coil lead must withstand the temperatures and chemicals involved in potting, encapsulation or impregnation. The choice of insulation must take these into account by testing under actual conditions. BS 6195 recognises the situation but, as it is impractical to specify standardised conditions of test, the subject is left for collaboration between cable supplier and user.

Voltage designation
The classification (for which reference should be made to BS 6195) is unique to the UK and is based on the 1 min test voltage applied to the equipment. It covers a range of working voltages from 300 V to 11 kV. The higher voltage categories (E and F), with EPR/CSP insulation, have a semiconducting graphite coated fabric tape over the conductor for stress control and the size range is limited for the same reason.

Current rating
As the conditions for heat dissipation vary so widely in different designs of equipment, it is difficult to quote specific ratings. BS 4999, 'General requirements for rotating electrical machines', Part 71, 'Winding terminations', includes ratings for reasonably well vented machines.

Standards in Europe and North America
The coil leads used in Europe and North America are generally similar to those in the UK and are controlled by National Standards and associated Approval Schemes. The latter have considerable importance as the key to obtaining import licences for electrical equipment is often the use of approved components. Typical of bodies operating such schemes are the Underwriters Laboratories Inc. (UL) in the USA, the Canadian Standards Association (CSA) and Verband Deutscher Electrotechniker (VDE) in Germany.

Because of the different way of expressing the conditions applicable to operating temperature, the comparison between UK and North American Standards may often be misleading. For example, in North America heat-resisting grade PVC is given a 105 °C temperature designation. PVC can degrade if held for long periods at this temperature, and clearly such temperature designations are not intended to indicate continuous operational life, as is UK practice, where similar material would be rated at 85 °C.

In addition to silicone rubber and varnished PETP or glass fibre constructions for operation at continuous temperatures above 100 °C, use is made of EVA (110 °C), ETFE (150 °C), FEP and polyimide (200 °C) and PTFE (260 °C). Some of these materials are also used for lower temperatures because of their resistance to chemicals.

Chapter 13

Auxiliary Cables (Pilot and Telephone)

The term auxiliary refers to cables associated with power distribution and transmission systems used for control, protection, signalling and speech, and data transmission purposes. Such systems are mainly operated by the Electrical Supply Authorities but similar applications occur in many industrial systems.

STANDARDS

The total range of cable types used throughout the world is vast. It may be illustrated, however, by the cables for public supply systems in the UK, which are covered by the Electrical Supply Industry (ESI) Standard 09–6, 'Auxiliary multicore and multipair cables'. This standard includes three types of thermoplastic insulated cable:

(a) PVC insulated multicore cables
(b) polyethylene insulated multipair cables
(c) PVC insulated, light current, multipair control cables

It also defines the general operating conditions for the power systems with which the above cables are associated. Cables to ESI 09–6 are required to withstand induced voltages caused by surges on the adjacent power system. This is achieved by varying the insulation thicknesses and/or the design of armour, according to the design level of surge. Three levels of disturbing conditions are catered for, defined by the induced voltage which would be anticipated between conductor and earth on an unprotected circuit: not exceeding 5 kV, 5–15 kV, and above 15 kV.

The screening factor of the armour is designed to reduce the induced voltage on the conductors to that appropriate to the thickness of insulation. Three standard armour designs are used to cater for the majority of power system installations. However, instances may occur where, due to exceptional lengths of parallel routes and/or fault current levels, special designs are necessary. All the cables meet the requirements of BS 4066, Part 1, 'Tests on electric cables under fire conditions', but in some cases cables with reduced flame propagation characteristics are required (chapter 6).

For industrial applications the standard cables described for fixed installations in chapter 11 are generally used, e.g. PVC insulated wire armoured cables to BS 6346 and, for ships and oil installations, elastomeric insulated cables to IEC 92–3.

PVC INSULATED MULTICORE CABLES

These cables are virtually the same as the PVC insulated and sheathed SWA cables to BS 6346 described in chapter 11. Differences are that only one size, 2.5 mm^2, is used and, to provide better flexibility in terminal boxes, the conductor is of stranded form. The standard range of core numbers is more limited, namely 2, 3, 4, 7, 12, 19, 27 and 37 cores. Core identification is by means of black numbers on white insulation throughout. The use of plastic binder tapes over the laid-up cores is mandatory.

In some cases the galvanised steel wire armour is coated with a waterproof compound, commonly based on bitumen, to inhibit penetration of water along the armour wire interstices. Corresponding to transmission cable practice, when it is necessary to check the integrity of the oversheath by d.c. tests, a graphite coating can be applied to the surface of the oversheath.

PVC multicore cables to ESI 09–6 are used to connect substations and power stations for the remote operation of, for example, tap changers and for protection circuits associated with transformers, switchgear etc. The cable capacitance is often of importance to the circuit design and the nominal equivalent star capacitance is 440 nF/km.

The voltage designation is 600/1000 V and the cores will withstand an induced voltage up to 5 kV.

POLYETHYLENE INSULATED MULTIPAIR CABLES

Intended largely to provide circuits for speech and data transmission, as well as for feeder protection, these cables are essentially telecommunication cables.

Construction

The cores consist of a single plain copper wire 0.9 mm in diameter insulated with polyethylene (type 03 of BS 6234). There are two thicknesses of insulation which are dependent on the anticipated induced voltage, 0.5 mm for 5 kV and 0.8 mm for higher voltages. The cores are twisted into pairs which are then laid up in combinations of 4, 7, 19, 37 and 61.

All cables, except the 4-pair arrangement, have three of the pairs designated as being capable of operation as carrier frequency circuits. Pair and cabling lay lengths are chosen so as to minimise coincidence and hence crosstalk. Carrier pairs are placed in the innermost layer and are separated by audio pairs to minimise mutual coupling. Core and pair identification is by combination of two self-coloured cores, according to a specified colour scheme, following conventional telephone cable practice. The assembled pairs are contained by a plastic binder tape followed by an inner sheath of black polyethylene (type 03C of BS 6234) and then armour and a PVC outer sheath.

Armour

Three standards of armour are specified to provide differing screening factors corresponding to three levels of disturbing electromagnetic field intensity from adjacent power circuits. They are graded by induced voltage level as quoted previously.

For induced voltages up to 5 kV the armour consists of standard thickness galvanised steel wire SWA to BS 1442. For the range 5–15 kV the armour is similar but the wire is of heavier gauge. For voltage levels which would otherwise exceed

15 kV an improved screening factor is provided by the use of a single layer of aluminium wire armour. The wire is in condition H 68 to BS 2627.

Because of the susceptibility of aluminium to corrosion in the presence of moisture, coating of the aluminium wire armour with a waterproof compound is mandatory. When specified by the purchaser, the outer sheath of all cables can be graphite coated to enable d.c. electrical tests on sheath integrity to be carried out.

Filling between cores

To cater for wet situations where water ingress to the cable cores may be a hazard, with consequent disruption of transmission characteristics, the core interstices may be filled with an appropriate compound during laying-up. The compound is formulated to have low mobility in the operating temperature range of the cable and to be compatible with the insulation and sheath materials. Although also chosen to have minimum effect on the transmission characteristics, it does cause some modification relative to those of unfilled cables. Consequently different values of primary transmission characteristics are applicable in the test requirements. A water penetration test is also specified to check the effectiveness of the filling in preventing longitudinal transmission of water.

PVC INSULATED MULTIPAIR LIGHT CURRENT CONTROL CABLES

Although of similar construction to the polyethylene insulated cables in the previous section, these cables are not intended for telecommunication and therefore no transmission characteristic measurements are required. They are designed primarily for use where an independent two-wire circuit is needed for control, indication and alarm equipment associated with switchgear and similar power apparatus. For such circuits the working voltage does not normally exceed 150 V d.c. or 110 V a.c., with currents lower than the thermal rating of the conductor. The voltage designation is 100 V.

Most of the cable is installed indoors and it is not armoured. However, to cater for other situations an SWA version is provided which will withstand induced voltages up to 5 kV.

The standard conductor size is a single wire of 0.9 mm diameter. It is of tinned copper but, as a thermoset insulation is not used, the tinning test of BS 6360 is not required. However, as many of the terminations used have soldered connections, the conductors have to meet the solderability test of BS 2011: Part 2.

Pair numbers are standardised as 2, 5, 10, 15, 20, 25, 30, 40, 50, 75 and 100.

A hard grade general purpose PVC compound (type 2 of BS 6746) is used for the insulation and, in view of the electrical duty, a thickness of 0.3 mm is required, thus enabling cable dimensions to be achieved which are appropriate to the equipment with which the cables are used.

Two cores are twisted together to form pairs, except in the case of the two-pair cable which is laid up in quad formation. The twisted pairs are then laid up in layers to give the appropriate total number. Core and pair identification is by self-coloured insulation, two different colours identifying a pair in accordance with a specified colour scheme following conventional telephone cable practice. Plastic binder tapes are applied over the laid-up pairs.

The non-armoured cable is sheathed with a black general purpose PVC compound type TM 1 or type 6 in accordance with BS 6746. A rip-cord may be inserted longitudinally between the outer binder tape and the sheath to facilitate sheath removal.

In the case of the armoured cable, the inner sheath (bedding) is the same as the sheath on non-armoured cable. Over this is applied standard galvanised steel SWA, appropriate to the diameter of the cable, followed by a black PVC sheath (type TM 1 to BS 6746).

Chapter 14

Manufacture of General Wiring Cables

GENERAL FEATURES OF MANUFACTURING FACILITIES

The very wide range of applications and the consequent large variety of cable types, and the variety of materials used, create a complex situation for the provision of manufacturing facilities. Because of this the general wiring cable factory employs a larger number of processing techniques than other more specialised cable plants. The considerable size range, which includes cables from a few millimetres to a hundred or more millimetres in diameter, is a further complication because of the range of machine sizes which must be provided to carry out any particular operation.

Volume of production may also vary a good deal, so that manufacturing facilities must on the one hand be versatile and flexible enough to cater for short production runs and on the other hand be capable of dealing with large volume production. Often these requirements result in several types of plant existing in the same factory to carry out a particular process.

However, factories may vary considerably in their degree of specialisation. At one extreme is the purpose designed factory to achieve maximum economic advantage from rationalisation of cable types and materials, and optimum use of mechanical handling, with automatic control and virtually continuous output. At the other is the factory making cables for various applications, using many different materials and a wide range of plant, which enables it to react quickly to changes in pattern of demand. Commonly the manufacturing facilities within and between factories are grouped according to whether the cables produced have thermoset or thermoplastic coverings.

MANUFACTURING PROCESSES

As a consequence of the range and variety of general wiring cables, a large number of processes are used for their manufacture. These can be grouped as follows:

(a) conductor forming, i.e. wire drawing and annealing, wire coating (tinning and plating), bunching and stranding;
(b) insulating and sheathing, which consist mainly of the various techniques of extrusion appropriate to the characteristics of the material used, but also include tape and yarn wrapping and braiding, with associated impregnation and varnishing; with thermoset materials there is also, essentially, a vulcanising, i.e. crosslinking, operation;
(c) assembly, including laying-up of cores, taping, braiding and armouring.

Many of the cable manufacturing processes have common principles and are described in chapter 26. Emphasis is therefore placed here on those especially associated with general wiring cables.

Conductor forming

Conductors for general wiring cables are characterised by the high proportion of small diameter wires used. In wire drawing there is a predominance of fine wire machines using natural and synthetic diamond dies for the smaller sizes. Conventionally the smallest copper wires were drawn from rod in three stages, with separate furnace annealing at each stage. This batch annealing has now largely been replaced by continuous annealing, the wire being heated electrically through its inherent resistance, in tandem with the wire drawing machine.

Tin coating of copper wire is usually carried out in association with wire drawing, the tin being applied by hot dipping or electroplating. In modern high speed production units, which combine drawing and annealing in-line, on a virtually continuous basis, the tin may be applied on the input wire. In the case of nickel-coated conductors, used in cables for high temperatures, the nickel is usually electroplated on the final wire size, although it is sometimes applied by cladding in which a composite copper–nickel billet is drawn into wire.

The introduction of multihead wire drawing machinery has taken the conductor forming process a step further. Up to eight wires can be drawn and annealed simultaneously and grouped together on the take-up reel. To produce flexible conductors of the required construction, two or more groups of wires are bunched together by one of the processes described below. Much higher speeds are possible than when bunching a large number of individual wires. For seven-wire conductors the wire drawing and stranding can be carried out in tandem, again giving significant improvements in manufacturing efficiency.

The conductor assembly operations of bunching and stranding have the common principle of twisting, as used in rope making. The methods used are decided by the small size and large numbers of wires which make up flexible conductors. For the bunching and stranding operations, which are used to produce the majority of conductors for flexible cords and cables, four principal types of machine are used, the elements of which are as follows.

(a) The reels containing the single wires are held in fixed frames or 'creels', the wire being drawn through a fixed guide and a forming die and then passing via a rotating arm or 'bow' to the take-up reel, which rotates about its own axis. The action imparts two twists to the wire for each revolution of the bow. This is the high speed double twist machine. A modified version of this machine is used to manufacture the high quality formation-stranded conductors required for cores with low radial thicknesses of insulation.
(b) The reels are held in fixed frames or 'creels', the wire being drawn through a fixed guide and a forming die by a take-up reel which rotates about its own axis and also about the principal axis of the machine. This machine is the drum twisting buncher.
(c) The wire reels are carried on a rotating cradle, as in a stranding machine

(chapter 26). However, no attempt is made to lay the wires in a definite geometric pattern as in stranding, the wires being gathered in a bunch in the forming die.

(d) The reels containing the single wires are supported within a rotating cage. The reels remain stationary in space, the necessary twisting action being imparted by the cage, to which the wires are attached by guides. This is the tubular stranding machine.

There are variations of these machines, imparting differing degrees of twist to the individual wires. The types of machine in (a) and (d) give the higher production speeds but are usually limited to the small and medium conductor sizes. The larger flexible conductors can be made on the machines described in (b) and (c), or by further bunching processes using any of the bunching methods (multi-bunch conductors). Flexible conductors of the 'rope stranded' type (chapter 4) are made on stranding machines.

The above machines differ in scale, depending on the size and length of conductor to be produced. The considerable lengths of conductor necessary for high speed continuous covering operations have resulted in the development of improved process handling techniques. These include the 'spinning off' of wire from stationary reels, where wire is thrown over the flange of a reel by a rotating guide, the reel being placed with its axis parallel to the direction of wire travel. Alternatively the reel may be placed flange down and the wire 'spun off' vertically.

Insulating and sheathing

The historical methods of applying rubber insulation by building up layers of unvulcanised tapes, applied either longitudinally or by spiral wrapping, have largely disappeared. Rubbers and thermoplastics are now applied mainly by extrusion.

The fundamental components of an extrusion line for cable coverings are indicated in fig. 14.1 (see also chapter 26). Over the years, there has been some rationalisation of extruder design. Whereas early machines for use with thermoplastics were distinctly different from those for rubber, those now in use are similar for both types of material, with only minor differences in design and operation. The introduction of high temperature vulcanising techniques and high performance rubbers has contributed to this trend.

For small-scale jobbing work, the smaller and more versatile extruders tend to be used, though larger machines may be required for sheathing. Large extruders with

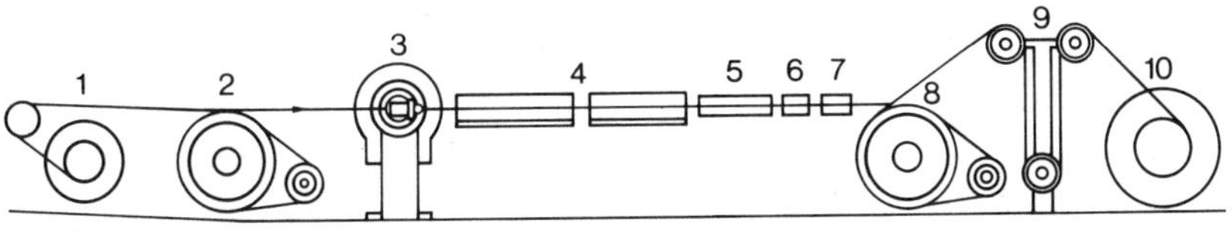

Fig. 14.1 Typical layout of cable extrusion line with (1) input drum, (2) capstan wheel, (3) extruder, (4) cooling trough, (5) spark tester, (6) diameter gauge, (7) eccentricity gauge, (8) capstan wheel, (9) tension controller, (10) output drum

high output are used for insulation on high speed lines for large volume production. Twin or triple extruders with a combined head are used for high voltage cores requiring the simultaneous application of screens with the insulation or for applying insulation and sheath on single-core cables such as welding cables.

Extrusion lines, particularly the high speed lines for thermoplastics such as PVC and PE, now have a high degree of instrumentation and automatic control, in respect of both the performance of the line units and the physical characteristics of the product. For example, eccentricity and diameter of insulation can be monitored continuously and electrical testing of the insulation, by application of high voltage, is also carried out in-line. Tension control is usually effected automatically, and on bulk production lines there is mechanical handling for input materials and processed wire and cable, together with provision for continuous running by changing input and output drums whilst the line is operating normally.

In principle, high temperature polymers are processed in the same way as described above. Silicone rubber is extruded similarly to other rubber compounds, although it can be applied in liquid form.[1]

Fluoropolymers such as FEP and ETFE are thermoplastic and (like polyethylene) have a well defined melting point. They are therefore melt extruded[2] similarly to PE. Because of their relatively high melting temperatures, special heat-resistant alloys are needed for some components of the extruder. PTFE is an exceptional case as it is not truly thermoplastic, owing to its very high molecular weight. Screw extrusion cannot be used because it results in shearing of the polymer particles. Instead, the powdered polymer is blended with a suitable liquid lubricant, formed into a billet, and then applied to the wire by a ram extruder. The lubricant is subsequently evaporated off in an oven, and the temperature of the cable is then raised to 400 °C, causing the polymer particles to coalesce. The process is analogous to the forming of powdered metals and ceramics by sintering. The sintering oven is usually placed in line with the extruder.

Curing (crosslinking)

In the chemical process of crosslinking, or vulcanisation as it has usually been termed with rubber, the modification of the polymer matrix in thermoset materials is initiated by heating the covering after extrusion. It may be at atmospheric or high pressure. Originally the treatment was a batch process, with the uncured cores or cables supported in trays containing powdered chalk or talc, or contained in tightly wrapped textile tapes or within a lead sheath and wound on a steel cylinder. The trays or cylinders were heated by pressurised steam in an autoclave. Subsequently the tapes or lead sheath were removed, if not required as a final component of the cable. This practice still survives for short length production of cables with certain rubber polymers, such as PCP and CSP. Compounds based on EPR may occasionally be processed in this way, but it is more efficient to use higher temperatures than are generally practical with steam autoclaves.

A commonly used high temperature method is that of continuous vulcanisation (CV) carried out by means of high pressure steam (14–20 bar) contained in a tube into which the extruded covering passes directly. Introduced in the 1940s in a horizontal arrangement (HCV), as an alternative to the steam autoclave method for the bulk production of small cores and cables, it has since been further developed for larger diameter cores and cables in a catenary arrangement (CCV), and for the largest products in a vertical form (VCV).[3] The coverings of general wiring cables are generally smaller in volume than, say, distribution and transmission cables and consequently higher extrusion speeds are possible, particularly when insulating.

As crosslinking by chemical means is time and temperature dependent, greater throughput from a CV line involves the use of higher temperatures or a longer steam pressure tube. Steam as a heating medium has a disadvantage in this context, as large increases in steam pressure are required to gain only modest increases in temperature.

Alternative heat transfer fluids have therefore come into use. Molten salt baths (LCM) at atmospheric pressure are now widely used for continuous curing of sheaths. Besides providing a convenient means of high temperature heating, they overcome other disadvantages of steam CV. The LCM system utilises a relatively deep bath of salt into which the cable is dipped, thus eliminating the restrictive CV tube which can cause damage when the cable makes contact with it. Also the cable is accessible as soon as it leaves the extruder, so that there is a considerable reduction in scrap at the beginning and end of each cable run compared with long CV lines.

However, because of operation at atmospheric pressure, porosity of the covering is a problem. Porosity is due to volatile substances, principally moisture, in the compound and is suppressed in the high pressure environment in a steam CV tube. By special formulation this porosity can be almost entirely eliminated in sheath compounds, and the salt bath technique has been found most useful for sheathing, especially for cables which could not be satisfactorily processed by steam CV, e.g. large multicore signalling cables. Insulation compounds cannot be processed in this way, however, as the special formulations render the electrical characteristics unsatisfactory.

More recently, the problems of porosity in the crosslinked material have been tackled by combining some of the features of LCM and high pressure steam CV. This approach uses what is called a 'pressurised liquid salt continuous vulcanisation system' (PLCV).[4,5] In this system molten salt is circulated through a vulcanising tube which is similar in arrangement to the steam HCV tube but much shorter. Because of the density of the molten salt, many cables are relatively buoyant and contact with the CV tube can be eliminated. This reduces the problems with the control of tension in the cable, which occur in all steam CV lines, so that a wider range of cables can be processed. The vulcanising tube is pressurised using air or an inert gas such as nitrogen, depending on whether oxidation of the compound is a hazard. The gas pressure system is independently controlled and is varied to suit the product. The pressure may be up to about 7 bar.

Other 'dry' vulcanising systems (see also chapter 26) have been used, e.g. nitrogen alone as both heat transfer and pressuring medium, with the addition of infrared heating.[6] Many polymers can be crosslinked without the use of chemicals and heat, by means of electron beam irradiation.[7] So far, because of cost, this method has found application mainly for specialised cables for the communication, electronic and aircraft industries.

Silicone rubber coverings are commonly cured in hot air continuous vulcanising tubes. To develop maximum performance they may be subject to a second (or post) cure in a hot air oven as a batch operation, to eliminate the volatile products of the crosslinking reaction.

The introduction of the Sioplas and Monosil processes (described in chapter 3) has seen a more general return to batch curing. As pointed out in chapter 25, the silane crosslinking technique allows greater flexibility and much improved running speeds at the extruder, with a useful reduction in scrap levels (compared with long steam pressure lines). Used initially for curing relatively low-filled compounds, its first major impact in the UK was on the production of XLPE. With improved control of moisture content in filling materials (vital in order to avoid premature crosslinking of compound in the extruder), the range of polymers which can be processed by this technique has increased considerably.

Assembly

The cable assembly operations are similar in principle to conductor stranding and bunching. The laying-up of cores and armouring of general wiring cables are carried out on similar machines to those described above and in chapter 26 for conductor forming.

Although there is a predominance of small diameter cores containing flexible conductors, there must be a sufficient range of machines to handle cores from 2–3 mm in diameter up to sizes overlapping those of distribution cables. The laying-up of cores for large volume products such as 2- and 3-core flexible cords is carried out on high speed machines similar to those used for bunching small conductors. However, cables with a large number of small cores are common, and the laying-up of these cores is very similar to armouring or large conductor stranding, where provision must be made to apply a large number of cores or wires in one pass. These machines usually have more than one cradle containing the cores or wires, the cradles being arranged in tandem. The laying-up machines are usually equipped with taping heads, so that binder tapes can be applied, as necessary, over each layer of cores.

The braiding process may be used for applying materials ranging from yarns of cotton, viscose, rayon, nylon, PETP and glass, through plain, tinned or nickel-plated wires to phosphor bronze and steel wire. Depending on the cable sizes the braiding machines may be set to operate in either a vertical or a horizontal arrangement.

The most versatile type of machine is that in which two sets of bobbins follow two concentric interwoven sinusoidal tracks in opposite directions so that the strands of yarn or wire are helically interwoven on the core or cable. A range of machine sizes of this type covers all the requirements of braid application for the whole spectrum of general wiring cables. However, for textile braiding of small cores and cables there is a higher speed type of machine in which the bobbins are carried in two rotating carriages on the same axis, one above the other. The strands of yarn are caused to interweave by means of stationary guides which deflect them sinusoidally as they are applied to the cable.

QUALITY ASSURANCE

Over the last two decades, formal quality assurance systems have become an integral part of general wiring cable manufacture. Final test and inspection functions have been combined with a specialised in-process inspection organisation, as previously operated for cables for defence applications, and expanded into a comprehensive system involving stage monitoring, statistical data analysis and auditing. The approval scheme operated by BASEC, which is described in chapter 7, is in most cases interlinked with the factory quality assurance organisation, and provides the link with the CENELEC certification scheme.

In modern factories, quality assurance has been extended into all aspects of production, from the examination of incoming materials and the servicing of supplier approval schemes to final inspection and maintenance of product approvals. The overall scheme is recorded and defined in a quality manual which forms the basis of the manufacturer's relationship with his customers. More information is given in chapter 7.

REFERENCES

(1) Fresleigh, R. M. and Kehrer, G. P. (Feb. 1980) 'Fabricating wire and cable with liquid silicone'. *Rubber World* **181** (5), 33–35.
(2) Edwards, I. C. (Mar.–Apr. 1978) 'Fluorinated copolymers – properties and applications in relation to PTFE'. *Plast. Rubber Inst.* **3** (3), 59–63.
(3) Blow, C. M. (1975) *Rubber Technology and Manufacture*. London: Newnes-Butterworths.
(4) Smart, G. (1978) 'PLCV – a progress report'. *48th Annual Convention of the Wire Association.*
(5) Smart, G. I. (Oct. 1977, May 1978) 'Continuous vulcanising systems using liquid salts under pressure'. *47th Annual Convention of the Wire Association, Boston, USA*; also in *Wire J.*
(6) Sequond, D. C. and Kailk, D. (Mar., Apr. 1979). 'Power cable vulcanisation without steam' *Elastomerics* **111** (3), 32–37; *Elastomers Plast.* **11**, 97–109.
(7) Brandt, E. S. and Berijka, A. J. (2 Nov. 1978) 'Electron beam crosslinking of wire and cable insulations'. *Rubber World* **179** (2), 49–51.

Chapter 15
Installation of General Wiring Cables

In most electrical systems a major consideration is the installation of the wiring. Well defined practices and conventions in relation to fundamental principles have formed the framework of national codes of practice, with adaptations to suit particular applications. As there are usually a number of engineering interpretations of any particular set of circumstances, it is perhaps not surprising that philosophies vary on some aspects of wiring installation in different countries. In particular, attitudes in other European countries on earthing, and consequently earth conductors and cables containing them, differ appreciably from those in the UK. Protection of circuits is another area where significant differences occur. For instance, the use of circuit breakers in domestic premises has been more widely adopted in France and Germany than in the UK. The use of domestic ring final subcircuits and their associated fused plugs is confined to the UK and certain Commonwealth countries.

NATIONAL AND INTERNATIONAL WIRING REGULATIONS

The legal status of wiring regulations has also differed worldwide, as has the attitude to inspection and approval of both installation and equipment, not least regarding cables. Many of the less industrially developed countries in the world had no wiring regulations or codes of practice but are now seeking to establish them. In the light of this and a greater interest in wider international markets by the electrical engineering industries, a realisation developed that common internationally accepted requirements were necessary. These requirements are defined in general terms and can be interpreted at a national level, the aim being to establish common levels of safety and to eliminate barriers to international trade.

IEC requirements

This realisation resulted in the setting up by the IEC of a committee to deal with recommendations for electrical installations in buildings. The work of this committee has produced an outline of requirements for electrical installations within which most of the detailed considerations are at a sufficiently advanced stage to influence national wiring regulations. It is contained in IEC 364, 'Electrical installations of buildings', which has the following framework:

Part 1: scope, object, fundamental principles
Part 2: definitions
Part 3: assessment of general characteristics

Part 4: protection for safety
Part 5: selection and erection of equipment
Part 6: inspection and testing
Part 7: requirements for specific installations

Chapter 52 of part 5, 'Cables, conductors and wiring materials' covers

(a) methods of installation
(b) general rules
(c) current carrying capacity
(d) cross-sectional area of neutral conductor
(e) voltage drop
(f) terminations and joints
(g) mechanical and external stresses
(h) corrosion
(i) electromechanical stresses
(j) fire barriers

Thus the factors to be considered in designing and carrying out an electrical wiring installation are defined. The treatment of each factor is essentially in general terms and the requirements for particular installations are expressed in terms of 'external influences'. A comprehensive framework of installation practice results, within which it is possible to consider the factors relating to wiring system cables. The level of engineering competence is taken to be that of a professional engineer responsible for the design of electrical installations. External influences include, for example, environmental conditions, types of installation and persons using the installation. It is therefore clear that the IEC requirements cannot be used directly as simple rules. In the UK the fifteenth edition of the IEE Wiring Regulations interprets these IEC requirements. In the case of developing countries it is anticipated that it will be some time before particular requirements for installations emerge and part 7 of IEC 364 caters for installations in special situations, such as bath/shower rooms, swimming pools, saunas, construction sites and agricultural and horticultural premises.

UK wiring regulations

Through membership of IEC, and in Europe through membership of the EEC and consequently CENELEC, there is a degree of commitment for participating countries to embody the IEC requirements into their national wiring regulations. Indeed there is an obligation for CENELEC members to follow CENELEC Harmonisation Documents, which are based on IEC Standards. Consequently the fifteenth edition of the IEE Wiring Regulations published in 1981 adopts the IEC format and concept of expression.

In the case of cables in particular, reference to the standards has been used to make the intent clear in specific cases and to avoid conflict with the fourteenth edition and cable standards. All designated cables are required to comply with the appropriate British Standard.

The format of the fifteenth edition is the same as that of IEC 364. The section dealing directly with cables is covered by chapter 52 in part 5, 'Cables, conductors and wiring materials'. It is subdivided into

521: selection of types of wiring system
522: operational conditions
523: environmental conditions
524: identification
525: prevention of mutual detrimental influences
526: accessibility
527: joints and terminations
528: fire barriers
529: supports, bends and space factors

Whereas previous editions of the IEE Wiring Regulations were aimed particularly towards domestic and commercial premises, both IEC 364 and the fifteenth edition of the IEE Wiring Regulations apply to any installation. There are, of course, parallel regulations for specific applications as, for example, IEC 92, 'Electrical installations in ships' together with the regulations for the various Classification (insurance) Authorities referred to in chapter 11.

In the case of UK installations it may also be necessary to take into consideration the regulations and the legal requirements relating to particular classes of electrical installations, as listed in appendix 2 of the fifteenth edition of the IEE Wiring Regulations. These cover such areas as factory installations and those on construction sites, cinematograph installations, installations in coal mines, quarries and metalliferous mines, and agricultural and horticultural installations.

The framework of IEC 364 and the fifteenth edition of the IEE Regulations forms a convenient and thorough list of the factors influencing the installation of cables. While no attempt is made to discuss this information in detail it is appropriate to make comments as below.

SELECTION OF TYPES OF CABLES AND CORDS

Appendix 10 of the fifteenth edition of the IEE Wiring Regulations contains a comprehensive list of the types of non-flexible and flexible cables and cords, with details of their intended use and any additional precautions where necessary. It considers the hazards of mechanical damage and corrosion, and points out that other limitations may be imposed by the relevant regulations, in particular those concerning maximum permissible operating temperature. Thus attention is drawn to an important point that the factors referred to above cannot, in practice, be taken in isolation. Appendix 10 does not claim to be exhaustive.

The IEE Regulations do not apply to flexible cords used as part of a portable appliance or luminaire. In connection with such applications the following publications contain further information and guidance.

(a) BS 3456: Safety of household and similar electrical appliances
(b) BS 4533: Electric luminaires (lighting fittings)
(c) Appendix A of the cable specifications BS 6004, BS 6007, BS 6231 and BS 6500, and appendix B of BS 6141
(d) The Electrical Equipment (Safety) Regulations 1975

(e) The Electrical Equipment (Safety) Regulations 1976 and the associated booklet
(f) 'Administrative Guidance on the Electrical Equipment (Safety) Regulations 1975 and the Electrical Equipment (Safety) (Amendment) Regulations 1976' (available from HM Stationery Office)

Armour

It is indicated in the regulations that flexible cables and cords may incorporate a flexible armour of galvanised steel or phosphor bronze, or a screen of tinned copper wire braid. Such armour becomes necessary in a number of situations to comply with the requirements for protection against risk of mechanical damage. Of the British Standards listed in the IEE Wiring Regulations, only BS 6500, 'Insulated flexible cords', expressly makes provision for the use of a screen of braided tinned copper wire and only BS 6116, 'Rubber insulated flexible trailing cables for quarries and miscellaneous mines', expressly makes provision for the use of galvanised steel pliable wire armour (PWA). Cables to BS 6007 can be supplied with suitable armour and reference should be made to the cable manufacturer for details. Cables to BS 6708, 'Trailing cables for mining purposes', referred to in chapter 12, also find applications in these circumstances. Flexible armour includes braids of galvanised steel wire or phosphor bronze wire as applied to the cables for shipwiring and offshore oil installation described in chapter 11. The use of phosphor bronze wire, either as PWA or braid, enables mechanical protection to be provided for single-core cables used in a.c. circuits. The use of such protection, with appropriate glands, becomes essential in flame-proof installations in environments where there would be a particular hazard of explosion.

Operating temperature

The tables of current ratings in the appendices include the limiting temperatures on which the current carrying capacities of the various types of cable are based. These are the maximum conductor operating temperatures and it should be appreciated that sheath temperatures can reach values only 10–15 °C lower. Where cables reach these temperatures it is necessary to consider the effect of such temperatures on materials which might come into contact with them, such as non-metallic conduit, trunking and ducting, and decorative finishes. The surface temperature of cables is also important where there is the possibility of contact with people or livestock. With humans the threshold of pain occurs at a temperature of about 70 °C but temperatures near this may cause some discomfort and involuntary reaction. This situation has been taken into account in determining the rating for flexible cords but special attention needs to be given to flexible cables insulated with silicone rubber or PTFE.

A common mistake with flexible cords and wiring system cables is to apply tabulated current ratings to extension cords which are coiled on reeling drums used in association with portable appliances or to cables which are retained on their despatch reels and used for temporary circuits. In the case of PVC cables, melting of the insulation or even the whole of the covering may occur in such circumstances.

Where cables are installed in roof spaces, or in cavities between floors and ceilings, they should be installed in such a way that they are not covered by thermal insulation material. A cable so covered can have its current carrying capacity reduced by up to 50%. This is particularly important in single-storey buildings where a major part of the wiring installation can be in the roof space. With certain forms of thermal insulation material, precautions are necessary to prevent interaction with PVC sheaths; otherwise loss of plasticiser, affecting the physical properties of the sheaths, can result.

Another important thermal effect may arise when cables with a lower limiting temperature are installed alongside fully loaded power circuits using cables with a higher limiting temperature. A particular example of this can occur in distribution systems where the thermoplastic telecommunication or control cables are installed adjacent to power circuits. In this and similar cases the lower temperature cables must be installed at such a distance that their limiting temperature is not exceeded.

In wiring regulations, heating cables are generally treated as energy-using equipment, and the requirements for cables do not normally apply. National requirements for heating cable installations vary considerably in different countries and for different applications. Some general comments are made in chapter 11 on the installation of floor heating systems and advice is available from the cablemaker. British Standard CP 1018, 'Electric floor-warming systems for use with off-peak and similar supplies of electricity' provides general guidance relating to the UK.

ENVIRONMENTAL CONDITIONS

Appendix 6 of the fifteenth edition of the IEE Wiring Regulations gives an explanation of a code for classification of external influences and lists three main categories:

A – environmental conditions
B – type of utilisation of premises
C – type of building construction

At present the IEC work is insufficiently complete to be used, but it is intended that particular installations will be described in terms of the relevant external influences, which will then determine the applicable requirements. The IEE fifteenth edition goes some way towards dealing with the types of environmental conditions identified in the IEC work as indicated below.

Temperature

The influence of ambient temperature on the current rating of cables is dealt with in chapter 8 and typical correction factors for different ambient temperatures are given in the relevant appendix for the particular type of cable.

There is a warning in the appendix to the IEE Wiring Regulations dealing with cable current ratings, which refers to the effect of exceeding the limiting temperatures used in calculating full thermal ratings. The need for this may readily be appreciated from the discussion in chapter 3 on the thermal degradation of insulating materials and effects on service life.

A common example of these effects occurs in lampholders where it is sometimes not realised that very high lamp cap temperatures can arise with filament lamps. As a result of conduction and convection of heat, the temperature of the cord in and adjacent to the lampholder can exceed what is tolerable for most general purpose insulants. This can result in a much reduced service life and often a short-circuit fault. The recommendation to use an appropriate heat-resisting flexible cord for pendant and batten lampholders and with tungsten filament lamps cannot be too strongly emphasised.

Although less emphasis is placed in wiring regulations on the lower end of the ambient temperature range, low temperatures can be important both during and after installation. Most insulating and sheathing materials stiffen to some extent as their temperature is progressively reduced. PVC shows this effect more markedly than do the rubbers or polyethylene. Once installed, PVC is quite satisfactory at temperatures down to −30 °C if protected from violent impact. However, the general duty compounds will shatter if bent violently, or particularly if struck hard at temperatures below freezing point. PVC compounds specially formulated for low temperatures show a marked improvement in this situation. Overvigorous stripping of the sheath of a flat wiring system cable after it has been stored overnight in frosty conditions has been known to shatter the core insulation. PVC insulated and/or sheathed cables which have been stored at temperatures below freezing point should be allowed to stand for at least 24 hours at a temperature above 10 °C before they are handled for installation. BICC LSF insulation and sheathing compounds are more flexible than PVC at low temperatures but, to avoid the risk of damage during handling, cable should be installed only when both the cable temperature and the ambient temperature have been above −10 °C for the previous 24 hours, or where special precautions have been taken to maintain the cable above this temperature. Most rubber cables also remain flexible at quite low temperatures. For example, EPR and silicone rubber insulated cables can withstand reasonable bending down to −40 °C and −50 °C respectively. PCP stiffens as the temperature is reduced below 0 °C but will not shatter from impact above −35 °C. It is advisable to allow PCP sheathed cables that have been subjected to low temperatures time to warm up before they are handled. CSP and CPE behave in a similar manner to PCP and the same precautions should be taken.

Presence of water

The IEC code covers eight classes of presence of water, from ‘negligible’ to ‘submersion’. All are of concern to some extent in connection with the use of cables, since even the ‘negligible’ category does not preclude the occasional presence of water vapour. It may not be generally realised that all organic materials are permeable to water to some extent, and as a result cables which are subjected to prolonged immersion in water will eventually reach the stage where water penetrates through the sheath and insulation to the conductor unless special precautions are taken, such as the incorporation of a metal sheath or other form of water barrier. Whether deterioration of performance occurs in the case of unprotected cables at low voltage depends on the type of insulation and the degree of contamination of the water. Polyethylene is less susceptible than PVC and thermoset materials.

Some circumstances amounting to continuous submersion are not always obvious. The surroundings of swimming pools, both indoors and out, the substrata of roads and paths, paved or concreted outdoor areas and the floors of domestic or industrialised buildings where large amounts of water are regularly used so that they can be almost permanently waterlogged, are all examples of locations where the failure of inappropriate cables has occurred. The need to limit the use of glass fibre insulated cables to only the 'negligible' category of location should be self-evident.

Corrosive or polluting substances

The risk of corrosion to cable components incorporating aluminium is specifically dealt with in the regulations. As far as cables are concerned, the most likely cause of contact with active substances arises from accidental spillage or the treatment of surfaces to which they are attached. Painting of cables is usually harmless. However, creosote and preservative liquids based on copper compounds should not be applied to surfaces to which cables are attached. It is almost impossible to prevent substantial contamination with these substances in liquid form, resulting in chemical deterioration of cable coverings. There is no objection to the installation of cables on surfaces pretreated with these substances and allowed to dry.

In some industrial environments hostile substances can be present as an inherent or incidental part of the process being served, such as in chemical and oil installations, electroplating etc. PVC, PCP and CSP sheaths all have excellent records in providing protection in these cases.

If present in quantity for an appreciable length of time, hydrocarbon fluids and organic solvents will cause embrittlement of PVC compounds by extracting plasticiser. Absorption of certain oils and solvents will cause softening and swelling of thermoset cable components. The permanence of the latter effect will depend on the volatility of the liquid and the degree of contamination. The softening and swelling caused by volatile solvents generally disappears once the liquid has evaporated and little permanent damage may result. The effect on cables of installation in ground containing petrol or other such hydrocarbons is discussed in chapter 5.

Mechanical stresses

The IEC classification recognises impact and vibration as two categories of mechanical stress, with a further unspecified class under consideration. Bending, flexing, twisting and abrasion are obvious further considerations where cables are concerned. Flexing and twisting relate especially to flexible cords and cables.

Avoidance of excessive strain at permanent bends in field installations is covered by specifying minimum installation radii. Values for specific types of cable are given in the appropriate chapters and are summarized in appendix A17.

During installation it is necessary to avoid excessive bending. Repeated bending can result in irreversible straining of the conductor wires, with resultant kinking. Cables with larger numbers of small cores are particularly vulnerable. Twisting, either during installation or in use, can result in similar damage. If the torsion is in the direction of lay of the cores, so tending to tighten the construction, the forces may be sufficient to kink the cable, even with large sizes, causing permanent damage. Twisting in the opposite direction may appear to give less obvious damage, but buckling of the conductors can occur, especially in large multicore cables. Armoured cables are subject to 'bird-caging' of the armour. Flexible PWA cables are particularly prone to early failure due to twisting arising from the cable being allowed to roll in use. Braid armour overcomes this problem.

During installation, twisting should always be avoided by allowing the despatch reel to rotate as the cable is pulled off. Turns of cable should not be allowed to escape over the drum or reel flange. If long lengths cannot be pulled directly into position they should be coiled down in figure-of-eight formation (chapter 27). This also applies to large flexible cables in service, including those with pliable armour.

Damage by fauna

In the UK the most likely form of damage under this heading is that due to gnawing by rats. It is apparent that rats will gnaw any material or object which crosses the line of a regular path or run. The only cable protection which can be relied upon is a hard metal covering in the form of conduit, sheath or armour. Cases of this type of damage were reported when lead sheathed wiring cables were used.

In countries where termites are common they are a recognised hazard to most organic materials including of course cable coverings. Further information is given in chapter 5.

Solar radiation

Exposure to direct solar radiation, even in the UK, has a pronounced accelerating effect on the degradation of organic cable sheaths. All sheaths for outdoor use should contain carbon black, which if well dispersed and of appropriate type provides the best protection against attack by ultraviolet light (photo-oxidation). CSP, PCP, PVC and polyethylene sheath compounds formulated with weather resistance in mind have probably the best performance.

The infrared radiation from the sun is absorbed by all bodies directly exposed, and their resultant temperature, relative to their surroundings, is dependent on ventilation and the colour and smoothness of their surface. Rough black bodies, which have the highest coefficient of absorption, can have their temperatures considerably increased by this effect. It is therefore necessary to make allowance for it when determining the ambient temperature for current rating purposes.

JOINTS AND TERMINATIONS

In domestic and similar wiring systems, the consideration of joints and terminations is almost entirely concerned with the selection of appropriate fittings with mechanical connectors. With the increasing use in the last decade of somewhat stiffer cables, and cores having a single solid wire conductor, the need has been recognised for adequate space within the fitting, and for due attention to be given to minimum bending radii to avoid localised pressure on the insulation.

Purpose-designed joints and terminations are required for industrial distribution systems for fixed installations, and these no longer demand the high degree of skill necessary in the past. Conductor joints and terminations can be made simply and readily with compression fittings, and soldering is seldom now required. The enclosure is usually a plastic mould filled with cold-pouring resin, as described for distribution cables in chapter 28.

Many terminations and connectors for large flexible cables, including mining and welding cables, now also rely on compression fittings. Joints in flexible conductors, unless effected by means of a plug and socket cable connector, are strongly deprecated, as any other form of conductor joint leads to a very rapid flexing failure due to the localisation of stress at the inevitable short stiff section of conductor.

Due to the very arduous mechanical duty of flexible trailing cables, techniques for their repair have developed into a specialised craft, especially in the mining industry. Advice and materials for this purpose are available from the cablemaker.

Chapter 16

Mineral Insulated Cables

The trade name 'Pyrotenax' aptly characterises the outstanding feature of mineral insulated cables as the ability to survive in fire. The beginning of mineral insulated (MI) cable can be traced back to the late nineteenth century when a Swiss engineer, Arnold François Borel, first proposed a cable constructed from inorganic materials completely enclosed in a metallic sheath, patenting this invention in 1896. His intention was to construct a cable that would operate at high temperatures, even in fire, and at the same time would be resistant to severe mechanical stresses. The idea then lay dormant until 1934, when a French company devised a commercially viable process and began to manufacture MI cable at Clichy under the trade name 'Pyrotenax'. In 1936 a British company, Pyrotenax Limited, was established to produce MI cable under licence.

Since those days MI cables have been adapted for such diverse applications as temperature measurement and heating, and copper sheathed MI cable has become established as a general wiring cable, particularly in hostile situations where its characteristics are especially sought after. Its compact dimensions and its freedom from the need for additional mechanical protection make it economically attractive for a wide range of domestic wiring applications and it is ideally suited for neat and unobtrusive wiring in churches and historic buildings.

CONSTRUCTION

The construction of a typical MI cable is illustrated in fig. 16.1. Current carrying conductors are embedded in highly compacted mineral insulation and the whole is encased in a metal sheath. Typically, the conductors and sheath are made of copper

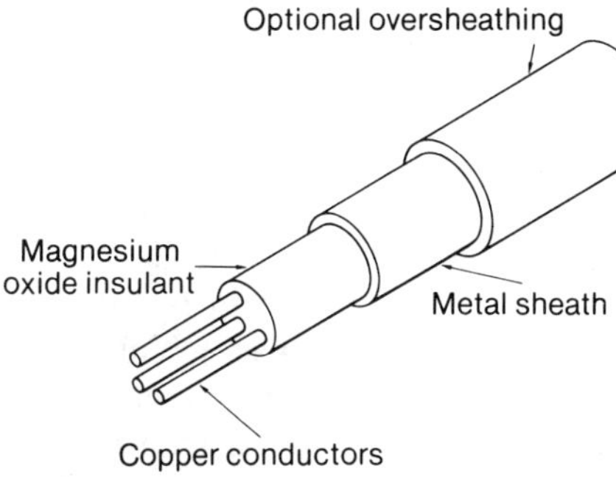

Fig. 16.1 Construction of a typical mineral insulated cable

and the insulation is magnesium oxide. On copper sheathed cables an extruded thermoplastics or other outer covering may be applied when required for corrosion protection, identification or aesthetic appeal.

Wiring cables are made in a number of conductor sizes, ranging from 1 mm^2 to 240 mm^2, and with a number of cores, ranging from 1 to 19. Usually, only single-core cables are made with conductors larger than 25 mm^2. Cables with 7, 12 and 19 cores usually have conductors of small cross-sectional area. The details relating to cable dimensions, weights and number and size of conductors are given in appendix A11.

Cables are designed and manufactured in accordance with the provisions of BS 6207 and also meet the requirements of the IEC and other standards.

CHARACTERISTICS

Performance at high temperatures

The non-organic materials used in the construction of MI cable give it characteristics significantly different from those of other electric cables. Of special note are its non-ageing properties and its performance at high temperatures. Copper MI cables can operate continuously at up to 250°C and for short periods of time at temperatures up to 1083 °C, the melting point of copper. This property enables them to continue operating in a fire, supplying power to essential services and, in many cases, afterwards to remain in working condition.

Mechanical deformation

The cable can withstand severe mechanical abuse such as bending, twisting and impact without appreciable deterioration of its electrical properties. Even when heavily deformed, as illustrated in fig. 16.2, it can maintain electrical integrity and continue to function. No additional protection is necessary when it is used under mechanically hazardous conditions, and this feature makes the cable economically attractive for many applications.

Corrosion

Copper sheathed cables are resistant to most organic chemicals and can operate indefinitely in most industrial environments. A green patina may form on the sheath after long exposure to atmosphere but this does not indicate harmful chemical attack. Copper will corrode in contact with ammonia or mineral acids and if the presence of either of these is suspected then bare copper sheathed cables should not be used. Adequate protection against this kind of attack can be provided by an outer covering made of a thermoplastic material, e.g. PVC or polyethylene, or, now being used increasingly, halogen-free polyolefin coverings containing additives such as alumina trihydrate, which do not readily propagate flames and have very low smoke and acid gas emission under fire conditions (see chapter 6). Alternatively, the metal sheath can be made of another material, such as cupro-nickel or stainless steel. It is worth noting that copper does not suffer significant corrosion when exposed to air

Fig. 16.2 A mineral insulated cable hammered flat and continuing to supply power to an electric lamp

bearing sea-water spray and therefore corrosion protection is not usually necessary when copper sheathed cables are used in offshore oil installations.

Resistance to radiation

With the exception of the optional plastic oversheath the constituent materials are practically unaffected by radiation and therefore MI cables can be used in high radiation environments with confidence that no deterioration with time will occur.

Current rating

Since magnesium oxide is a refractory material, the current carrying capacity of MI cables is not determined by the usual criterion of deterioration of the dielectric material with rising temperature but by a combination of the temperature characteristics of the surrounding materials with which cables are in contact and consideration of permissible volt drop. For their size, MI cables have a higher current rating than most other cable types.

In appendix A11, tables A11.1, and A11.2 give current ratings for the 500 V light duty range of cables. Tables A11.4 and A11.5 give similar data for the 750 V heavy duty range. Voltage drops are in Tables A11.6 and A11.7.

Resistance to voltage surges

The characteristics of a mineral insulation such as magnesium oxide, unlike those of organic insulation, do not alter with time and the initial dielectric strength is retained indefinitely. Consequently a smaller safety margin can be used as there is no deterioration to allow for.

In the initial stages of manufacture magnesia powder is compressed until it reaches a stable density beyond which no further compression occurs. In this state the powder density reaches about 75% of the density of magnesium oxide crystals, and there is very little air left in the spaces between the particles. However, the air which does remain may form continuous paths between the conductors or conductors and sheath. The mechanism of electrical breakdown is complex, being influenced by that of air and magnesium oxide crystals, and the dielectric strength of compacted magnesia is between that of a magnesium oxide crystal and that of air.

It follows that, when a breakdown occurs, the discharge path follows a path of ionised air but does not penetrate powder particles. When the discharge ceases, the air deionises and the insulation reverts to its normal state.

Low energy discharges through compacted magnesia powder do not damage the insulation and can be repeated indefinitely without any adverse effect. On the other hand high energy discharges can, and on occasion will, result in insulation breakdown leading to short circuit. A probable explanation of the observed effects is that a low energy discharge ionises the air but leaves the metal conductors unaffected, and, as energy increases, metal in increasing quantities is vaporised from the conductors and on cooling is deposited on magnesia particles. A sufficiently high energy discharge can vaporise enough metal to form a continuous path between conductors.

In summary, compacted magnesia insulation cannot be degraded by heat, by mechanical forces (other than excessive bending) or by being subjected to electrical stress, and thus will not be damaged by low energy voltage surges. If voltage surges are sufficiently energetic to vaporise conductor metal then, as a consequence, the insulation can also be affected.

MATERIALS

Insulation

A wide variety of mineral materials has been proposed, and occasionally used, as the dielectric in MI cable. These include aluminium oxide, beryllium oxide, calcium carbonate, fine clay, sand, and powdered glass, but long experience has shown magnesium oxide to be the most suitable. It is chemically and physically stable, has a high melting temperature, high electrical resistivity combined with high thermal conductivity, is non-toxic and is readily available in a sufficiently pure form.

Magnesia is derived from one of two raw materials, either magnesite (magnesium carbonate) mined in various parts of the world but notably Greece and India, or magnesium hydroxide precipitated from sea-water or subterranean brine by the addition of limestone or dolomite. The carbonate or the hydroxide is heated in kilns at temperatures between 900 and 1800 °C to produce magnesia powder whose properties will vary with the type and source of raw material and the calcination temperature. Low calcination temperatures yield soft, amorphous and cohesive powder, whereas higher temperatures produce harder, more crystalline powder with less affinity for water. The type of powder used will depend on the method of manufacture employed and the intended application of the cable.

All types of magnesia powder, even when compacted, have some affinity for water and therefore cables have always to incorporate appropriate terminations which provide a seal against the ingress of moisture.

The resistivity of any magnesium oxide at room temperature is very high but decreases with rising temperature. High temperature properties, particularly resistivity, depend greatly on the kind and amounts of impurities present and studies are continuing aimed at obtaining a better understanding of the effects of impurities. Fig. 16.3 shows the relationship between resistivity and temperature for several grades of magnesia.

Because magnesia is hygroscopic it is important to dry the powder thoroughly before it is introduced into the cables. Wide variations in high temperature performance may result from traces of moisture in the powder although very small amounts are unlikely to have a significant effect either on resistivity or dielectric strength.

Table 16.1 shows a typical composition of magnesia produced from mined magnesite.

Conductor material

The two conditions which have to be met by the conductor material are high conductivity, essential for the efficient transfer of electrical energy, and ductility which is necessary for satisfactory processing. Tough pitch high conductivity copper satisfies these requirements for most general wiring cables, although in some types of

Table 16.1 Typical composition of magnesia produced from mined magnesite

		%
Calcium oxide		2.5
Iron oxide		0.26
Silica		5.5
Boron	less than	0.001
Sulphur		0.075
Chlorides (NaCl)		0.002
Magnesium oxide		Remainder

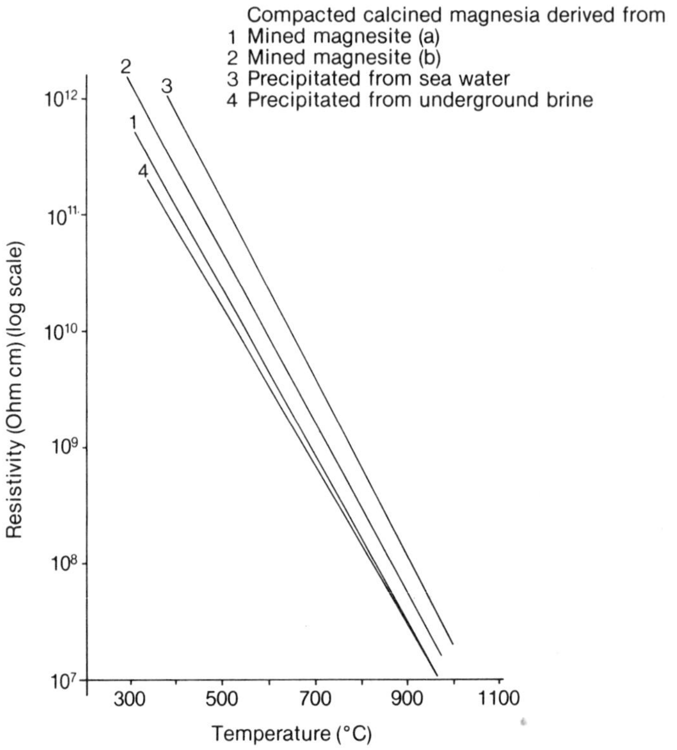

Fig. 16.3 Resistivity as a function of temperature for four grades of compressed magnesia powder used as cable insulants

cable it is necessary to employ oxygen-free h.c. copper. Aluminium has also been used in a commercially pure electrical grade; with a conductivity about two-thirds and a volume cost about one-third that of copper, it has an obvious economic potential.

Sheath material

The standard sheath material is phosphorus deoxidised copper with a conductivity of about 80% IACS. Other materials which may be used include mild steel and aluminium and, more recently, cupro-nickel and austenitic stainless steel which finds increasing application in aggressive environments.

MANUFACTURE

Several manufacturing methods have been evolved during the period of time spanning about 50 years. Until recently all methods were similar in that in all cases a relatively short, large diameter composite comprising an outer metal tube, conductor and a mineral filler was assembled initially and then compacted and elongated to finished size by repeated drawing through dies. Frequent interstage annealing was necessary in order to restore ductility to the composite cable. On reaching final diameter, the cable was fully annealed to impart maximum conductivity to the conductors and to make it pliable in order to improve handling during installation. In most cases the 'start tube' was about 10 m long and 50 mm in diameter.

Methods of continuous production of MI cables have now been developed.

Batch process

In the block filling method, illustrated in fig. 16.4, blocks of magnesia are first formed under high pressure to the required density and appropriate dimensions. The blocks are heated in a furnace to expel moisture present either in the free state or in chemical combination and then pushed into the tube with the holes for the conductor rods kept in registration, and the rods are inserted.

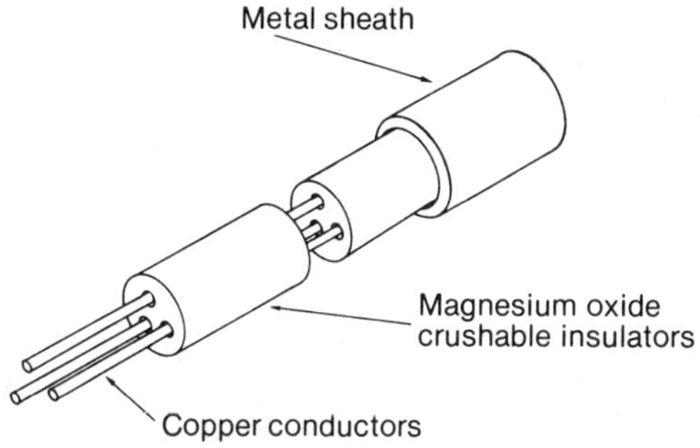

Fig. 16.4 Block filling process for mineral insulated cable manufacture

The composite 'start assembly' is processed by successive drawing and annealing to final size, during which operation the blocks are crushed and reduced to highly compacted powder.

A similar start assembly can be produced in less time by a ramming process. A start assembly is prepared consisting of a tube and conductors retained by a plug pressed into the bottom end of the tube. A ram with suitable apertures for the conductor rods is placed in the tube and magnesia in powder form is introduced into the space between the plug and the bottom of the ram, either along the annular space between the tube and the ram or through a tubular passage along the ram axis. The ram reciprocates relative to the tube assembly and the powder is compacted at each down stroke. The reciprocation is continued until the tube is completely filled with packed powder. It is necessary to achieve sufficient packing density to ensure that when the assembly is drawn through a die for the first time the conductor rods are held firmly in place and the required conductor geometry is maintained.

The composite assembly is processed to finished cable in the manner already described.

An alternative method is to fill tubes with powder and to compact by drawing through a die to avoid the need for ramming. A start assembly consisting of a tube and conductor rods is prepared, with the lower end of the tube reduced in diameter so that it can be passed through a die. Powder is introduced through a guide tube usually incorporating shroud tubes which enclose the conductors and maintain them in correct registration. Then the composite assembly is drawn progressively through a die, the cross-sectional area of the bore is reduced and the powder is compacted sufficiently to hold the conductor rods firmly in place for further processing.

Continuous process

For a long time now, cables of other types have been made by continuous process but, until recently, the manufacture of MI cables has remained essentially a batch process. The evident disadvantages of batch processing have been the cause of considerable effort expended on development aimed at making the process continuous.

Essentially the process developed by the manufacturers comprises several steps carried out consecutively. The process begins with metal strip of suitable dimensions which is continuously formed into a tube and seam welded. Conductor rods and powder are continuously introduced through a guide tube. At the lower end of the guide tube there is a die which precisely locates the rods in relation to the outer tube. The space below the die is filled with powder so that the rods are held in the correct position. Before the cable can be handled it must be reduced in cross-sectional area in order to compact the powder to a density sufficiently high to preclude any undesirable conductor movement relative to the outer tube. This can be done by rolling or drawing and both methods have been used.

It has been established that cable produced by this process has mechanical and electrical properties indistinguishable from those of cable produced by conventional processes.

SEALS

As mentioned above it is necessary to exclude atmospheric moisture from MI cables and seal development has perforce accompanied cable development. The earliest seals utilised a bituminous substance applied to a pot, which also did duty as a gland, screwed to the end of the cable sheath. This was superseded by a cold seal which relied on a castor oil based plastic compound contained in a screw-on pot. Similar types of seal are still used with various types of sealing media, including epoxy resins and putties, silicone oil based compounds and ceramics.

The design and manufacture of seals are carried out in accordance with the provisions of BS 6081.

Chapter 17

Cables for Electronics Applications

INTRODUCTION

The speedy and accurate transfer of information is an essential requirement of modern civilisation. The behaviour of the transmission medium is of basic importance, and must produce at its distant receiving end a change of some kind which will be correctly interpreted as meaning a definite event at the sending end. Communication systems which can use cables as the transmission medium include telephone, radio, television and data. Electronics cables find a wide range of applications in computers, automation, robotics, aerospace and data communications. Internal wiring within electronics equipment has been reduced with circuit board developments, but the increasing demand on information technology has required an increase in interconnecting cabling between individual equipments, with more sophisticated designs and transmission characteristics.

TRANSMISSION SYSTEMS

Baseband and broadband

In a baseband system, data from different users is combined in a common path in a digital stream. Thus the cable carries only one channel, which by time division multiplexing can accommodate many users. Baseband systems use cables ranging from complex coaxials to simple twisted pairs.

In a broadband system, data from different users are allocated different frequency channels and simultaneously share a common cable. A high bandwidth cable is therefore required, such as the coaxials developed for community antenna TV (CATV). Broadband systems can transmit both digital and analogue signals and can accommodate multiple video, audio and data channels.

Analogue and digital

Analogue systems use a controllable smoothly varying property of electricity to represent information, such as current or voltage amplitude or frequency. In digital systems information is manipulated in digital form as a stream of on–off or high–low pulses or binary digits (bits). Fig. 17.1 shows an analogue and a digital signal.

With the continual need to increase data communication capacity, digital transmission is appealing for short distance links because, with relatively low cost electronics, it can substantially increase the capacity of low cost cables. In analogue transmission, video and data are more demanding on the fidelity of transmission,

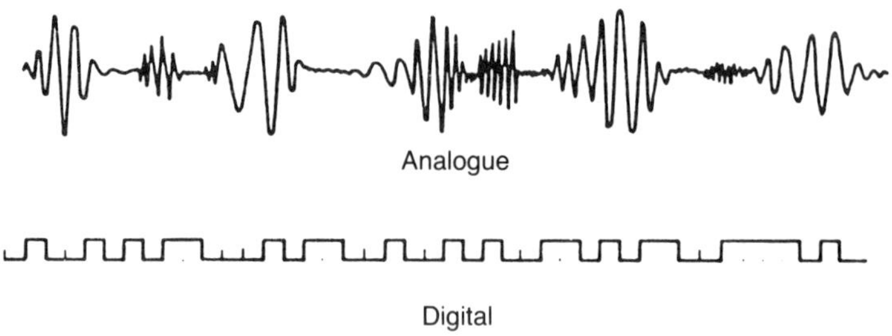

Fig. 17.1 Analogue and digital systems

and whenever the signal is amplified the noise is also amplified. With digital transmission, each repeater regenerates the pulses so that a pulse train can travel through a noisy medium being repeatedly reconstructed and remaining impervious to much of the noise-inducing sources.

Digital transmission, however, requires a greater frequency bandwidth than analogue, but because the signal is regenerated frequently it can operate at a lower signal-to-noise ratio. The main factors in favour of digital transmission are ease of system design, the potential to increase capacity by the use of digital repeaters at frequent intervals, decreasing costs of circuitry and, last but not least, the rapidly increasing need to transmit digital data on networks.

It should be noted that, for purposes of cable design, digital pulses can be treated as the sum of a series of harmonically related sine waves, with short rise time pulses being in effect wide band radio frequency signals.

Balanced and unbalanced

For balanced systems, twisted pair cables are used and the output of the line driver is balanced to earth so that, when one terminal is positive, the other is negative by the same amount. The receiver responds to the differential voltage between the lines and rejects any signal which changes the voltage on both lines. Provided that the conductors in the pair have identical transmission characteristics, the effects of outside interference are reduced.

For unbalanced systems, one conductor of the pair is connected to earth, and although twisted pair cables can be used, multiconductor and coaxial cables are favoured with less expensive components when interference is not a problem. Examples of balanced and unbalanced systems are shown in fig. 17.2.

Bandwidth and data speeds

Analogue transmission is generally divided into three bands. In telephony the voice band is defined as 300–3400 Hz, and frequency bands wider than voice bands are termed wide band. A communication channel with a bandwidth less than the voice band is narrow band.

Similarly, in digital communications transmission speeds are usually separated into three ranges: low speed (0–300 bits per second), medium speed (600–4800 bits per second) and high speed (above 9600 bits per second).

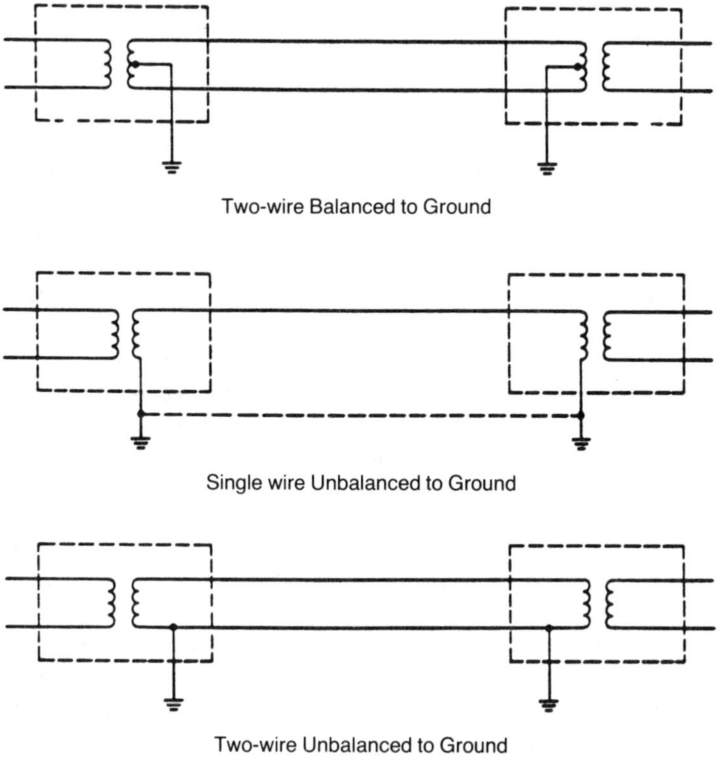

Fig. 17.2 Balanced and unbalanced systems

In radio engineering the bandwidth of a tuned amplifier is commonly defined as the width of the band of frequencies over which the power amplification does not drop to less than an assigned fraction of the power amplification at resonance. This fraction is usually one-half, corresponding to 3 dB loss in amplification. Transmission lines in general have an attenuation which is a function of frequency and can be constructed to have bands in the frequency spectrum where transmission is good, whilst attenuating other frequencies. In telephone carrier systems such lines or filters are used to separate the various channels.

In general, bandwidth is the frequency range between the lowest and highest frequencies that are passed through a transmission system with acceptable attenuation. For economic reasons, most data communications systems seek to maximise the amount of data that can be sent on a channel.

Serial and parallel transmission

Data are commonly transmitted by changes in current or voltage on a cable. Such transfers are called parallel if a group of bits move over several lines at the same time, or serial if the group of bits move one by one over a single line.

In parallel transmission each bit travels on its own line, and a clock signal on an additional line controls the receiver sampling. Parallel transmission is used over short distances because it is faster than serial which is preferred over long distances when multiple lines become costly.

Local area networks

Computing equipment represents a significant investment and must be used efficiently and effectively. The desire of users to connect computers, terminals, word processing and related equipment to allow discrete units to operate as part of an integrated information system has led to the development of networking.

Local area networks (LANs) are a means of providing universal data communication within a single premises with shared data transmission, storage and peripheral resources. Similarly metropolitan area networks (MANs) provide facilities for data communications between sites within a neighbourhood, for distances up to say 40 km, and wide area networks (WANs) describe the worldwide systems which provide national and international data telecommunications.

Three basic topologies are commonly used for LANs: star, bus and ring, as shown in fig. 17.3. From the user's point of view, they lead to differences in the amount of cable needed to provide a given number of access points, the ease of adding extra connections and the effect of failures. For interconnecting a scatter of points on a site, a bus will generally use the least cable, followed by a ring and then a star. It is generally easier to add connections to a bus than to a star, which may require an extra arm, or to a ring, which must be broken. A star network is least affected by failures of the devices or cables attached to it, but is likely to fail entirely if its central point, or 'hub', fails. A bus will fail if cut; but the whole network will generally not fail if one of the access points, or 'nodes', is faulty, because the node is merely a connection to the highway and can be designed to switch itself out in the event of a fault. Rings, however, are the least reliable because each node is an active repeater, and the failure of one node breaks the ring unless expensive redundancy is built into the system to overcome this.

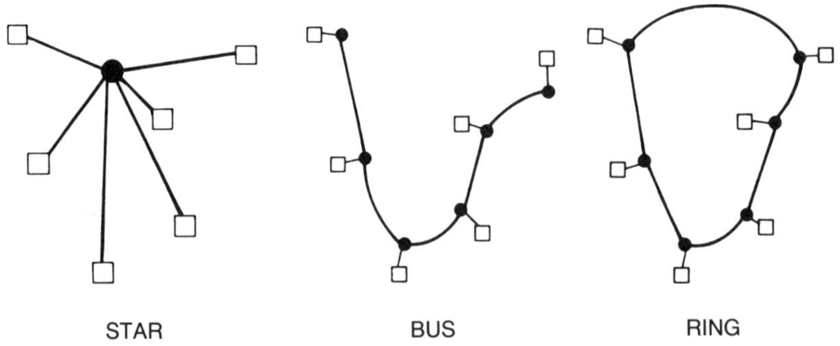

Fig. 17.3 Basic local area network topologies

LANs also differ in the type of cables that they use. They may be implemented in coaxial or twisted pair copper cable, or in fibre optics. With some types it is possible to intermix copper and fibre optic sections in the same network, to obtain the specific benefits of each where required. Fig. 17.4 shows typical LAN cables.

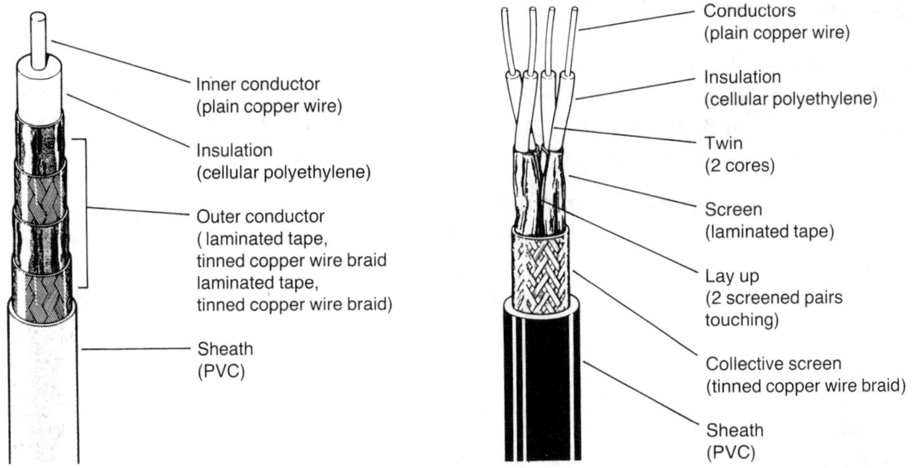

Fig. 17.4 Typical local area network cables showing large coaxial cable for bus systems (*left*) and ring system cable (*right*)

LANs vary considerably in their size capability, from a few tens of metres to several kilometres. They also differ in the number of devices that can be connected to them, from as few as ten up to several thousand. The rate at which they can transfer information varies widely, from 300 bits per second to 100 megabits per second or more.

DATA COMMUNICATIONS CABLES

Applications

The interfacing and connection of most data transmission equipment can be effected using either coaxial cables, screened or unscreened twisted pair cables or optical fibres.

For microcomputers, which use low speed data transmission over short distances, unscreened multicore or multipair cables can be used. For the interconnection of data processors, instruments and microcomputers, where signal interference is a consideration, cables are generally screened.

Minicomputers require medium speed data transmission and here interfaces using screened twisted pair cables are suitable. When signal speeds are fairly low a braid screen is sufficient but for higher speeds a foil screen or composite foil and braid screen is more suitable. A further refinement is to use individually screened pairs to minimise the effects of crosstalk, thus making possible the transmission of data over longer distances.

For mainframe computers where high speed data transmission is required, cables are specially designed to the performance of individual equipment.

Transmission characteristics

A transmission line is a network with four fundamental properties of resistance, inductance, capacitance and conductance. These are called the 'primary parameters', and they are defined by the cross-sectional geometry of the line and the materials used in the conductor and dielectric. They are denoted by

R = loop resistance (ohm) per unit length
L = inductance (henry) per unit length
C = capacitance (farad) per unit length
G = conductance (siemens) per unit length

and are related to the 'secondary parameters'

Z_0 = characteristic impedance
α = attenuation coefficient
β = phase coefficient

by the following relationships:

$$Z_0 = \left(\frac{R + j\omega L}{G + j\omega C}\right)^{1/2} \ (\Omega) \qquad (17.1)$$

and

$$\alpha + j\beta = [(R + j\omega L)\ (G + j\omega C)]^{1/2} \qquad (17.2)$$

where $\omega/2\pi = f$, the frequency in hertz, and the exression $\alpha + j\beta$ is often called the propagation constant.

Expanding and equating the real and imaginary parts of this equation gives

$$\alpha = \left\{\frac{[R^2 + \omega^2L^2)\ (G^2 + \omega^2C^2)]^{1/2} + RG - \omega^2LC}{2}\right\}^{1/2}$$
$$\text{(neper per unit length)} \qquad (17.3)$$

which determines the rate of change in amplitude with cable length and

$$\beta = \left\{\frac{[(R^2 + \omega^2L^2)\ (G^2 + \omega^2C^2)]^{1/2} - RG + \omega^2LC}{2}\right\}^{1/2}$$
$$\text{(radian per unit length)} \qquad (17.4)$$

which determines the rate of change of phase with cable length.

Primary parameters

Resistance

A wide variety of conductor materials is used in electronics cables. As well as copper in solid or stranded form, copper-covered aluminium and copper-covered steel are used, the latter for small conductors where strength is required. These may also be tinned or silver plated.

Skin and proximity effects must be taken into account when considering resistance. The ratio that the effective a.c. resistance has to the d.c. resistance of a conductor is called the resistance ratio, which increases with frequency, with the conductor material conductivity and with the size of the conductor.

In a cylindrical plain copper wire at 20 °C, when the frequency is sufficiently high, substantially all the current in the conductor is confined to a region very close to the surface, with a depth given by the relations $d = 0.66\sqrt{f}$ mm.

Inductance

Both self-inductance and mutual inductance are manifestations of the interaction of currents and fields. If the current in a circuit changes, the flux is altered and an electromotive force is induced. This effect is known as self-induction.

If part of the flux in a circuit is linked with a second circuit, there is said to be mutual inductance, and the circuits are inductively coupled. Mutual inductance is defined as the ratio of the flux linkages in the second circuit produced by current in the first to the current in the first circuit. It follows that skin and proximity effects which change the flux pattern will have an effect on inductance.

Capacitance and dielectric materials

A capacitor is formed whenever a dielectric separates two conductors between which a potential difference can exist. Capacitance is the ratio of the charge which can be stored in a capacitor to the potential applied to it. If the capacitance between given electrodes with a certain dielectric is compared with that between the same electrodes *in vacuo*, the ratio is a figure characteristic of the dielectric material and is known as the permittivity or dielectric constant.

A perfect capacitor, when discharged, gives up all the electrical energy that was supplied to it in charging. In practice some of the energy is dissipated, mainly as dielectric losses.

In electronics cables the materials used for the insulation or dielectric are therefore critical to the transmission performance. Most plastics are considered as electrical insulators, and when assessing their potential use in cables the dielectric constant and power factor are considered over the range of operating temperatures and frequencies. Suitable materials for high performance cable would have low dielectric constant and power factor over a wide range of temperature and frequency and these parameters should not be adversely affected by high humidity.

Molecules of a dielectric may be either polar or non-polar. In the case of polar molecules the dielectric constant under a.c. conditions is increased as a result of the rotation of the polar molecules under the influence of the applied voltage. The extent to which this polar action is effective however, depends, on the frequency and the temperature. The result is that polar dielectrics have a certain characteristic behaviour with respect to temperature and frequency. If the temperature is lowered sufficiently, polar rotations are prevented, causing the dielectric constant of the material to decrease. Similarly, if the frequency is made sufficiently high, the polar molecules are not able to follow the alternations of the applied field and the dielectric constant decreases. Hence the power factor of a polar dielectric becomes quite large for certain combinations of temperature and frequency. The variation in dielectric constant and power factor for a polar dielectric as a function of frequency for two temperatures is shown in fig. 17.5.

Non-polar molecules do not exhibit these changes in dielectric constant or peaks of power factor, and materials such as polyethylene are therefore used for higher

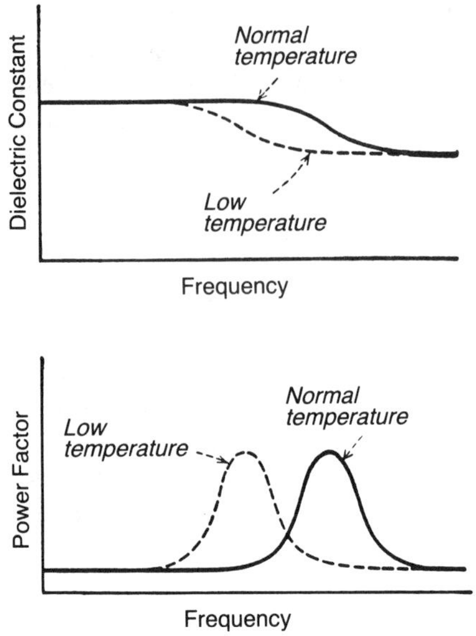

Fig. 17.5 Variation of dielectric constant and power factor of polar materials

Table 17.1 Electrical properties of insulating materials

Material	Dielectric constant		Power factor	
	50 Hz	1 MHz	50 Hz	1 MHz
Polyethylene	2.30	2.30	0.0003	0.003
Polypropylene	2.15	2.15	0.0008	0.0004
PVC	6.9	3.6	0.08	0.09
Nylon	4.0	3.4	0.014	0.04

performance cables. Typical values of dielectric constant and power factor for materials commonly used in electronics cables are shown in table 17.1.

The capacitance of a cable depends on the dimensions and configuration of the conductors and screen, if any, and the effective permittivity of the dielectric. Capacitance can therefore be varied by changing the conductor size, the insulation thickness or the permittivity of the insulation. In high frequency digital transmission, capacitance rounds or distorts the pulse shape as shown in Fig. 17.6(a), causing errors. With a low capacitance, cables can cope with faster rise times, increased bit rate capacity and longer transmission distances.

Conductance

When two parallel conductors have a potential difference between them, a certain amount of current will flow because of the finite resistance of the insulation. For an air dielectric the conductance is negligible, but when other dielectrics are used, as is

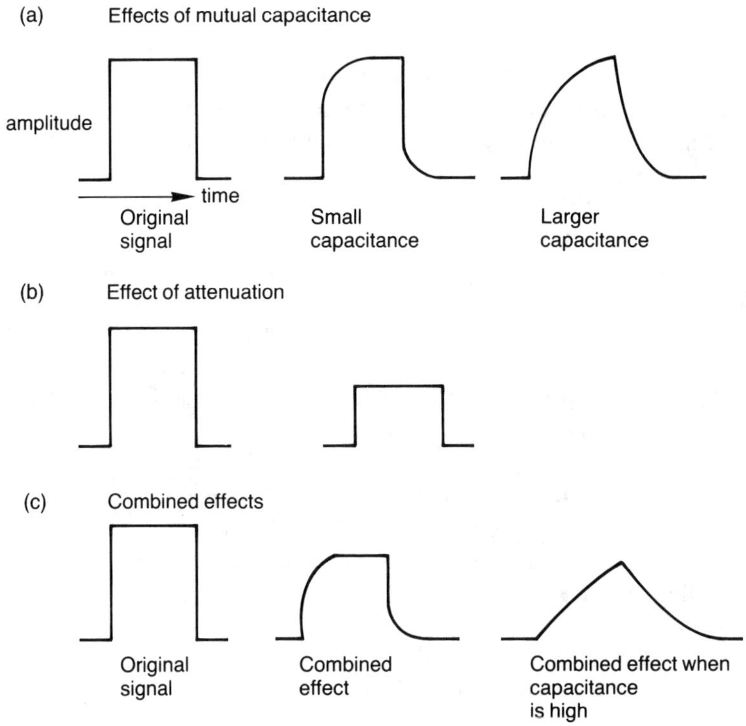

Fig. 17.6 Effects of capacitance and attenuation on digital signals

the case with cables, the conductance is determined by the power factor, capacitance and frequency according to the relationship

$$G = \omega C \tan \delta \tag{17.5}$$

Secondary parameters

Impedance

If a signal is fed into an infinitely long uniform line the ratio of voltage to current at any point along the line is constant and is called the 'characteristic impedance' of the line, usually denoted Z_0. If the line is now cut to a finite length and a load impedance equal to Z_0 is connected across the far end, it behaves as if it were still infinitely long. Power fed into the line will be absorbed by the load and none will be reflected back. The line is then correctly terminated or matched.

Not all the power which is fed into the line will reach the load at the far end. In practice power losses occur in the line itself, because of resistive dissipation in the conductors and dielectric losses in the insulation. For a correctly terminated cable, the ratio of output power to input power, in decibels, is the attenuation of the cable.

The condition in a terminated line can be represented by a wave travelling forward towards the load. If the load is not a correct termination to the line a certain proportion of the forward travelling signal will be reflected back towards the input. Similar reflections can occur from points along the cable which for some reasons may differ from the mean impedance. These reflections cause increased line losses, since both the forward and backward waves are attenuated and each contributes to the overall loss. So for minimum line power losses the amplitude of the reflected wave must be reduced to zero, in other words there must be no standing waves on the line. A standing wave results from the combination of reflected and forward waves travelling in opposite directions. Under conditions of zero standing wave the load is said to be matched to the line.

The ratio of the maximum to minimum values of voltage which occur at points half a wavelength apart on a mismatched line is called the voltage standing wave ratio (VSWR). On a lossless line the VSWR is constant throughout the length and is equal to the ratio of the load impedance Z_L to the characteristic impedance of the line Z_0.

Another term in common use is the voltage reflection coefficient, which is defined as

$$\text{reflection coefficient} = \frac{Z_0 - Z_L}{Z_0 + Z_L} \text{ or } \frac{\text{VSWR}-1}{\text{VSWR}+1} \tag{17.6}$$

This is often expressed as a percentage, and it follows that for an open or short-circuited line the reflection coefficient is 100%; it is zero for a correctly terminated line.

From the reflection coefficient follows another common expression, the return loss ratio, which is measured in decibels and is numerically given by

$$\text{loss ratio} = 20 \log_{10} \left(\frac{1}{\text{voltage reflection coefficient}}\right) \tag{17.7}$$

In a perfect cable the dimensions and effective permittivity on which the characteristic impedance depends will be constant throughout the length. Such an ideal cable cannot be achieved in practice because of manufacturing tolerances. For example a change in the diameter of the insulation will result in a corresponding alteration of characteristic impedance at that point. Whenever an impedance change occurs, a small reflection of the forward travelling signal results. If these impedance changes happen in a random manner the effects tend to cancel out, but the manufacture of insulated core involves rotating machinery, and there is always the possibility of dimensional changes recurring at regular intervals along the cable rather than at random. The term 'structural return loss' is used as a measure of the losses which arise from internal reflections within the cable, as distinct from return losses arising from mismatched terminations.

Impedance matching is important in data communications because, as well as reducing the energy reaching the receiver, depending on their location mismatches can add to or subtract from the desired signal level and give rise to data errors.

The relationship between the characteristic impedance and the primary parameters is

$$Z_0 = \left(\frac{R + j\omega L}{G + j\omega C}\right)^{1/2} \ (\Omega) \tag{17.8}$$

and for most cable insulations G is neglected in comparison with ωC.

At low frequencies ωL can be neglected in comparison with ωC and the relationship becomes

$$Z_0 = \left(\frac{R}{j\omega C}\right)^{1/2} \ (\Omega) \qquad (17.9)$$

At high frequencies R can be neglected in comparison with ωL, and if G can be neglected in comparison with ωC then

$$Z_0 = \left(\frac{L}{C}\right)^{1/2} \ (\Omega) \qquad (17.10)$$

Attenuation

The voltage amplitude of a signal decreases as it travels along a cable owing to the resistance of the conductor and dielectric losses, as shown in fig. 17.6(b). In the relationship between attenuation and the primary parameters, at low frequencies ωL is small compared with R and if G can be neglected in comparison with ωC then

$$\alpha = \left(\frac{\omega \, CR}{2}\right)^{1/2} \ \text{(neper/length)} \qquad (17.11)$$

whilst at high frequencies when R is small compared with ωL and G is small compared with ωC then

$$\alpha = \frac{R}{2Z_0} + \frac{GZ_0}{2} \ \text{(neper/length)} \qquad (17.12)$$

In this case $R/2Z_0$ represents the attenuation due to ohmic losses in the conductors, which varies as the square root of the frequency owing to the skin effect. The term $GZ_0/2$ is the attenuation due to the dielectric losses and is directly proportional to frequency.

The relative variation of these two causes of attenuation is of significance when high frequency cables are designed. The permittivity of the insulation should be kept as low as possible for low attenuation, and it should also be noted that the use of lower permittivity insulation in a cable of given impedance and overall size means that larger conductors are required to maintain the given impedance which in turn reduces the ohmic losses.

Since the rise time of digital signals can be related to high frequencies, they are attenuated more than the lower frequency components, resulting in rise time degradation and the rounding of pulse edges; this effect, combined with the effects of capacitance, is illustrated in fig. 17.6(c). Excessive attenuation can prevent the signal reaching the amplitude required by the receiver, resulting in data errors.

Phase coefficient

As with the other relationships with the primary parameters, phase coefficient can be simplified at low and high frequencies to

$$\beta = \left(\frac{\omega CR}{2}\right)^{1/2} \ \text{(radian/length)} \qquad (17.13)$$

at low frequencies and

$$\beta = (\omega LC)^{1/2} \text{ (radian/length)} \tag{17.14}$$

at high frequencies. Of more practical interest at high frequencies is a further relationship given by

$$v = \frac{\omega}{\beta} = \frac{1}{(LC)^{1/2}} \text{ (metre/s)} \tag{17.15}$$

where v is the velocity of propagation in the cable. In parallel data transmission a uniform velocity of propagation is important to ensure that bits arrive at their destination at the same time and skew errors are avoided.

The velocity ratio is the velocity of propagation in a cable compared with its free-space velocity; it is dependent on the square root of the insulation permittivity and so the lower the permittivity is the higher is the velocity of propagation. For polyethylene insulation the velocity ratio is about 0.66.

Cable insulation

PVC insulation is used for low speed applications but for high speeds materials such as polyethylene or polypropylene are used because of their better electrical characteristics. In addition to being used in solid form, they can be applied as a cellular material with a permittivity of about 1.45. One method of producing cellular polyethylene is by mixing a chemical additive with the raw material in the extruder. At the extrusion temperature this 'blowing agent' decomposes to produce small cells of nitrogen gas which give the cellular structure, and hence the required low permittivity. There is a tendency for residual blowing agent to give a slightly higher power factor than desirable but on balance the use of cellular material offers a good advantage. A second technique for producing cellular polyethylene is direct gas injection at extrusion, with the advantage that the reduced chemical residue results in lower dielectric losses.

Although cellular dielectrics can have low permittivities, they can be mechanically weak. A method used to strengthen them is to crosslink them by irradiation.

There are a number of other methods of fabricating low permittivity dielectrics for coaxial cables by using semi-airspaced constructions with solid polyethylene as the main insulating material. In one method, discs of polyethylene spaced at intervals give an effective permittivity of about 1.07. This type can be made to very close impedance limits and is used extensively for wide band carrier telephone and video trunk routes.

Another construction is the helical membrane type. A continuous tape of polyethylene is applied in the form of a helix along the inner conductor. This gives an effective permittivity of 1.1 which, as in the case of the disc spaced cable, is approaching the lowest practical limit.

A further type shown in fig. 17.7 uses a thread and tube construction in which a thread of polyethylene is lapped round the inner conductor and a close fitting polyethylene tube is extruded over this, giving a permittivity of about 1.3.

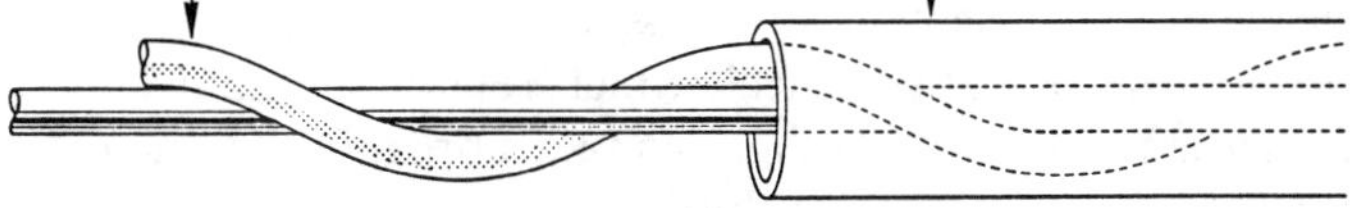

Fig. 17.7 Thread and tube dielectric construction

Screening

An important requirement for many electronic and data cables is adequate screening against various kinds of electromagnetic influences and the need to preserve the integrity of the signal from interference or noise either inside or outside the transmission line.

Many screen designs have been developed to combat the effects of interference. The ideal screen would be a homogeneous thick walled copper tube. Such screens are used on RF and CATV cables, sometimes corrugated to improve flexibility. Sometimes a lighter aluminium tube is used.

Another form of low loss outer conductor is a copper tape applied longitudinally to the insulated core with an overlap. Because current travels longitudinally, a gap or overlap parallel to the axis of a coaxial cable does not affect the attenuation. A typical construction has a copper tape which is corrugated to give better flexibility. It is regarded as a semi-flexible cable, suitable for fixed installations.

Another cheaper version uses a much thinner copper tape. This is not corrugated but has an additional copper wire braid. It is suitable for fixed installations but is not as mechanically robust as the corrugated thick tape construction.

Copper wire braids are used extensively on many types of electronics cables. They are applied with a machine in which two sets of bobbins called spindles or carriers rotate in opposite directions round the cable core with an interweaving chain motion. Each bobbin contains a number of separate wires, referred to as the number of ends. By varying the number of spindles and ends and the lay length of the braid different degrees of coverage can be obtained.

The theoretical understanding of the a.c. resistance of braids and the way in which current flows in them is based mainly on the results of experimental measurements. It is thought that at lower frequencies the current flows mainly along the individual braid wires. The fact that there are two sets of wires spiralling in opposite directions cancels out any inductive effect that would otherwise be present. At higher frequencies the currents tend to flow parallel to the cable axis, so that the contact resistance between crossing braid wires becomes important. This can have an effect on the stability of the attenuation of the cable with time since if the contact resistance increases then the attenuation at microwave frequencies will increase. It has been found that silver-plated braid wires with an appropriate braid design give better stability of contact resistance than plain copper.

Many data cables employ screens manufactured from very thin metallic foils backed with a polyester film to provide strength. Such laminated tapes are applied longitudinally or helically and have the advantage of resulting in only small increases in cable diameter. To optimise screening efficiency, a copper wire braid can be applied over the foil screen or double-sided laminates can be used.

The efficiencies of cable screens are described by the parameter 'coupling impedance' or 'surface transfer impedance', which relates the induced current flowing on one side of a screen to the longitudinal voltage appearing on the other side. For a homogenous tubular screen it is given by

$$Z_T = \frac{\rho}{2\pi t(ab)^{1/2}} F(u) \tag{17.16}$$

where

$$F(u) = \frac{u}{(\cosh u - \cos u)^{1/2}}$$

and

$$u^2 = \frac{2t^2 \mu\omega}{\rho} \tag{17.17}$$

where ρ = screen resistivity
t = screen thickness
$(ab)^{1/2}$ = screen geometric mean diameter
μ = screen permeability
$\omega = 2\pi f$

It follows that the lower the surface transfer impedance is, the better the screen is. For screens other than homogeneous tubes, the surface transfer impedance is usually measured using the triaxial arrangement shown in fig. 17.8.

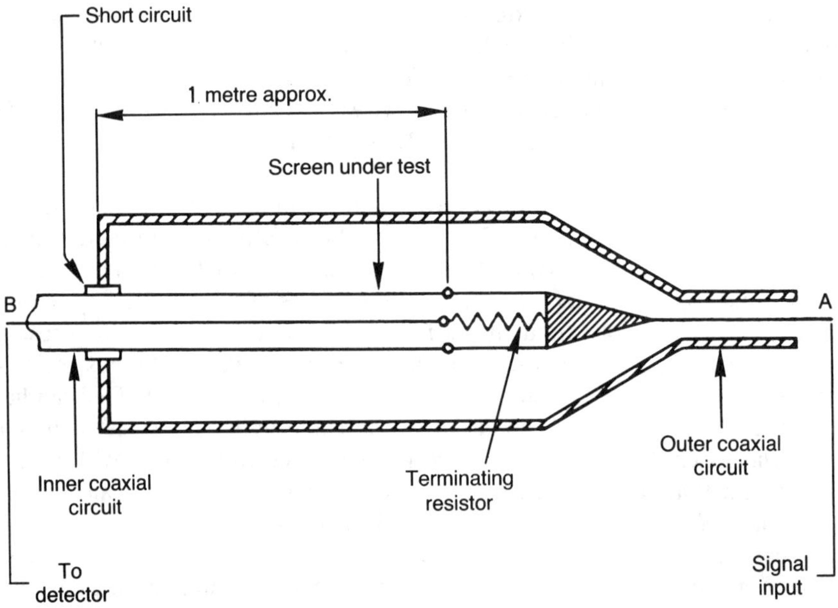

Fig. 17.8 Schematic diagram of triple coaxial apparatus

Surface transfer impedances are shown in fig. 17.9 for various screen constructions at frequencies up to 30 MHz. Curves A and B show the typical drooping characteristic of the better screens. Curve C shows the most popular type of screen, a single copper wire braid, which has a rising characteristic with a typical value of 200 mΩ/m at 30 MHz. To improve screening performance a second braid may be applied either directly in contact with the first (curve D) or with an intersheath (curve E).

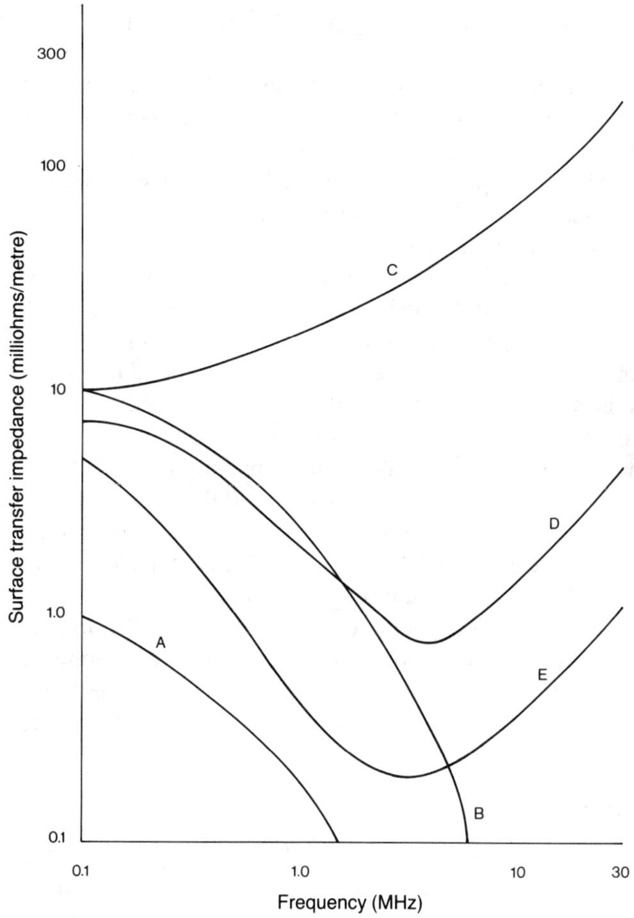

Fig. 17.9 Surface transfer impedances of various screens: curve A, seam welded copper tape 0.25 mm thick; curve B, overlapped corrugated copper tape 0.18 mm thick; curve C, single-wire braid; curve D, double-wire braids in contact; curve E, double-wire braids with intersheath

The ratio of the resistance of a wire braid to the resistance of an equivalent tubular conductor is called the braiding factor and is given by

$$K_B = \frac{K_L}{2K_F} + \frac{\pi K_L K_F}{4} \tag{17.18}$$

where $K_L = 1 + \pi^2 D^2/L^2$ the lay factor
$K_F = mndK_L^{1/2}/2\pi D$, the filling factor
D = mean diameter of braid
m = number of spindles
n = number of wires (ends) per spindle
d = braid wire diameter
L = braid lay length

The cover provided by a braid is $100K_F(2 - K_F)$%, and the braid angle is given by $\tan \phi = \pi D/L$.

Typical wire braid screens have a braid angle of about 40° and a cover of just over 90% which is equivalent to a filling factor of 0.7. Braids can be optimised for surface transfer impedance in terms of the numbers of spindles and ends, wire size and lay length, but generally a compromise is achieved between screening efficiency, manufacturing costs, flexibility and ease of termination.

Laminated foil tape screens provide 100% cover, and their screening efficiency is determined by the material and thickness of their metallic component. Improved efficiencies can be achieved by using double-sided foils in the form of a metal/polyester/metal sandwich, combinations of foils or combinations of foils and copper wire braids. Fig. 17.10 shows the surface transfer impedance for various screens incorporating foils. Curve A is for a small coaxial cable with a single tape containing aluminium foil 0.05 mm thick. Curve B is for a multipair cable, with individual pairs screened with a single tape with an aluminium thickness of 0.025 mm, and an overall screen comprising a double-sided foil, each side 0.01 mm aluminium, and a tinned copper wire braid. Curve C shows the surface transfer impedance of the large coaxial cable illustrated in fig. 17.4 (left) which has a tape/braid/tape/braid screen, the tapes being double-sided aluminium/polyester.

Another type of screen has been developed for applications in nuclear plant installations where very low limits are set on leakage from one control circuit to another. These 'super screened' cables have a mu-metal tape lapped between two braids and show surface transfer impedance values at 30 MHz as low as 1 μΩ/m.

COAXIAL CABLES

In general coaxial cables perform better than their pair counterparts at higher frequencies. For a given attenuation, the size and cost of a coaxial is less than that of a twin or pair cable of comparable performance. They do not display the instability of characteristic impedance, attenuation and electrical length typical of screened twins, but at lower frequencies the screening efficiency of a balanced twisted pair can be superior.

Design features

The basic coaxial cable design is an inner conductor surrounded by a dielectric and a concentric outer conductor.

The general theory concerning transmission characteristics applies to coaxial cables, but in addition consideration should be given to particular aspects of design related to the application and methods of manufacture.

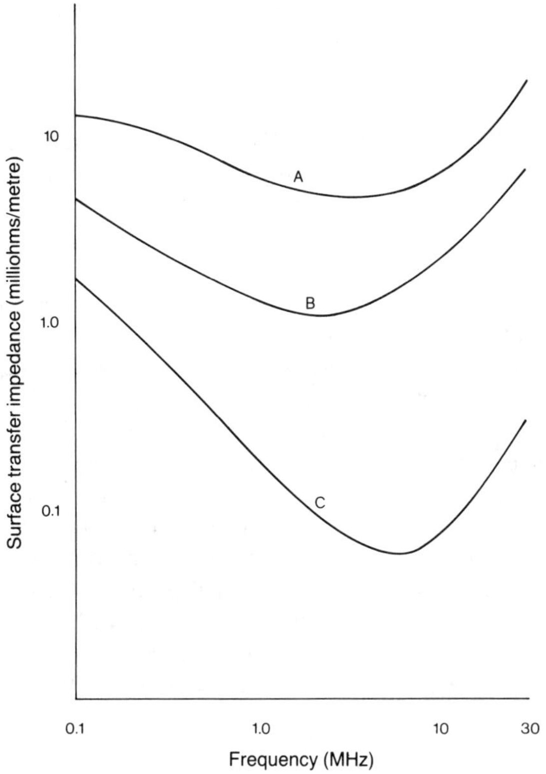

Fig. 17.10 Surface transfer impedance of cables with foil screens: curve A, single aluminium foil 0.05 mm thick; curve B, single- plus double-sided foil with copper braid; curve C, foil/braid/foil/braid

Inner conductor

The preferred form is solid plain annealed copper. For high frequency use, because of the skin effect copper-covered steel may be used, but at frequencies below 10 MHz some current will flow in the steel core. For larger cables, copper tubes or copper-covered aluminium are used.

Stranded conductors can increase the high frequency resistance by up to 25%, and the resistance of tinned copper wire is higher than that of plain copper wire at frequencies above 10 MHz.

Silver-plated conductors are used at very high frequencies because of their smoother surface finish as well as their good conductivity.

Dielectric

Insulation with low and stable permittivity and power factor is preferred. This can be solid polyethylene or cellular polyethylene or one of the various types of semi-airspaced dielectrics.

Outer conductor

The best form of outer conductor giving low attenuation and good screening is a solid copper tube. For flexible applications copper wire braids are used or combinations of thin tapes and copper wire braids.

Outer protection

For indoor and general applications, a PVC sheath may be applied overall. For more arduous environments or outdoor use a steel armour and further PVC sheath can be applied.

Low and high impedance coaxial cables

Some special cables have been made with a characteristic impedance as low as 14 Ω. Low impedance is obtained by the use of a relatively large inner conductor formed by a wire braid over a plastic core. The characteristics of the cable are very sensitive to small variations in conductor diameter.

High impedance cables can be made by increasing the inductance per unit length by the use of a helically wound inner conductor. The increase in inductance reduces the velocity ratio and such cables can be used as delay lines. By the use of a plastic core loaded with magnetic material as a former for winding the inner conductor, impedances as high as 4000 Ω can be achieved together with velocity ratios as low as 0.001. For this low velocity ratio it takes a signal 3.0μs to travel 1 m of cable. The delay and high impedance are obtained only at the price of high attenuation. At high frequencies the capacitance between adjacent turns of the helix resonates with the inductance at a cut-off frequency above which there is no transmission.

Radiating cables

There is an increasing demand for rapid communication services in the interests of efficiency, safety and convenience as witnessed by the expanding use of two-way mobile radio systems, radio paging and radio control. However, there are certain situations where conventional free-space radio transmission from aerials is not practical, e.g. in mines, tunnels, power stations, industrial areas and linear situations such as railways and motorways. The range of natural radio propagation in tunnels is very poor, only a few hundred metres at the most, so that communication with a distant receiver inside a tunnel is impossible using normal techniques. One way of overcoming this problem is to use a radiating cable or leaky-feeder technique in which the required radio signals radiate from a cable rather than from a conventional aerial.

The basic principle of this technique is shown in fig. 17.11. A two-way base radio station is connected to a long radiating cable transmission line which runs throughout the area where communication is required and transfers signals to and from the mobile stations through the radiation field from the cable. The special design of cable is sometimes called a leaky feeder because when it is fed with radio signals at one end it leaks small amounts of energy all along its length to be picked up by nearby mobile aerials.

The bifilar or unscreened twin cable is economic and radiates well, although the attenuation is very unstable. Even at the lower frequencies a large increase in attenuation occurs when the cable is laid on the floor or mounted close to walls. Experience in coal mines has shown that a serious increase in attenuation occurs when a layer of wet coal dust accumulates on the cable surface. However, with specially designed coaxial cables, good radiation and stable attenuation can be

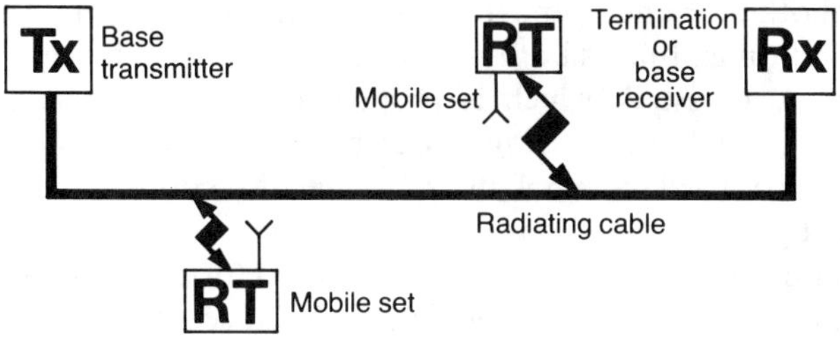

Fig. 17.11 Radiating coaxial cable system

achieved when the cable is wet or dirty or mounted on walls. In these cables the outer screen is a corrugated copper tape perforated with a series of holes, as shown in fig. 17.12, to provide and control the radiation.

Experimental work has shown that radiation from an apertured tape cable depends on the dielectric permittivity of the insulation, and the stability of attenuation under wet and dirty conditions depends on the surface transfer impedance.

A theoretical treatment of the field leakage through a row of holes in an apertured screen has shown that at 30 MHz the surface impedance can be calculated using the formula

$$Z_T = \frac{4nd^3}{D^2} \text{ (m}\Omega\text{/m)} \qquad (17.19)$$

where d = hole diameter (mm)
D = screen diameter (mm)
n = number of holes per metre

The optical coverage of apertured or braided screens is sometimes quoted as a characteristic. However, if the surface transfer impedance depends on nd^3/D^2 and the optical cover depends on nd^2/D, it can be seen that optical coverage is not a direct measure of screening efficiency.

A general purpose radiating coaxial will have a permittivity around 1.4 and a surface transfer impedance of 500 mΩ/m.

TWISTED PAIR CABLES

Crosstalk

Cables with twisted pairs are used where balanced signal transmission is required, together with low crosstalk. Crosstalk refers to interference on one channel caused

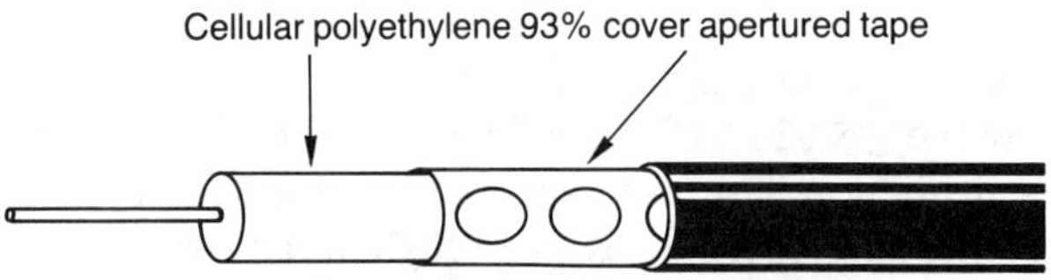

Fig. 17.12 Apertured tape screened radiating cable

by a signal in another channel and occurs between cable pairs carrying separate signals. This definition embraces both near end crosstalk and far end crosstalk. Near end crosstalk is the crosstalk which is propagated in a disturbed channel in the opposite direction to the current in the disturbing channel, and far end crosstalk is propagated in a disturbed channel in the same direction as the current in the disturbing channel.

Crosstalk is fundamentally the resultant of two factors, or couplings: capacitance unbalance and mutual inductance. Capacitance unbalance gives rise to electrostatically induced potential differences between the wires of the disturbed pair. This coupling is important at all frequencies. When the capacitance of one conductor against the sheath and all the other conductors is not the same as the capacitance of its mate (similarly measured) the pair is said to have a capacitance unbalance, which is measured by the difference between these two capacitances. When the capacitances are equal, the pair is said to be balanced. It is generally desirable to keep the capacitance values as low as economically practicable by using low permittivity insulations.

Mutual inductance gives rise to electromagnetically induced potentials along the wires of the disturbed pair. This coupling exerts little influence at audio frequencies but becomes increasingly important as the frequency increases.

Both couplings are due to departures from balance between the circuits concerned. In design and manufacture, attempts are made to ensure that the distances between the wires of one pair and the wires of another are equal, as well as the distances between each wire and earth. This is done by careful choice and control of materials, insulation thicknesses and twinning lays and tension, but unavoidably during manufacture small differences occur which result in residual values of the couplings.

For unscreened pair cables at audio frequencies

$$\text{crosstalk} = 20\log\left(\frac{8}{\omega\, k\, |Z|}\right)\ \text{(dB/length)} \tag{17.20}$$

where $\omega = 2\pi f$

k = capacitance unbalance between the two pairs for the relevant length (farad)

$|Z|$ = modulus of the characteristic impedance of the pairs at frequency f Hz

Since capacitance unbalance is an electrostatic coupling, it can be reduced by enclosing either or both of the interacting pairs in a screen. The screen need only be thin, and laminated foil screens are generally used.

At higher frequencies, mutual inductance becomes important and differential twinning lays in adjacent pairs are used to achieve the best results.

Design features

A variety of twisted pair designs is used, as shown in fig. 17.13. Conductors are generally in the range 18–24 AWG solid or stranded, and tinned for ease of termination. PVC insulations are used for short distances and low speed data, but for higher speeds and longer distances polyethylene and polypropylene in solid or cellular form are used. Individual pair screens to reduce crosstalk are generally laminated foils and incorporate a drain wire to achieve satisfactory electrical con-

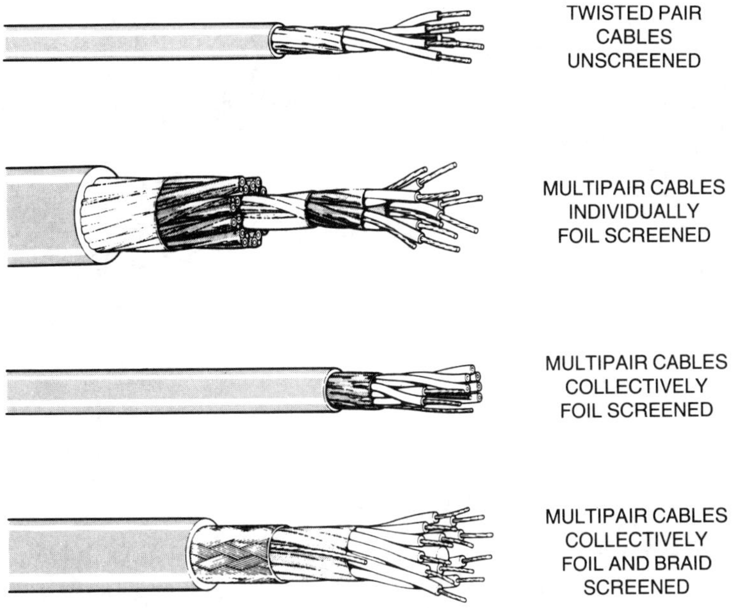

Fig. 17.13 Twisted pair cables

nections. Overall screens are used as protection from outside interference and can be laminated foils with or without an overall braid.

Overall sheaths are generally PVC formulated to suit the particular application, including high and low service temperatures, and to impart flame retardance.

PART 3

SUPPLY DISTRIBUTION SYSTEMS AND CABLES

Chapter 18

Supply Distribution Systems

In the UK the total generating capacity of the public electricity supply system at the beginning of 1988 was 63 868 MW and the maximum demand 55 241 MW. From 1948 to 1988 the total number of consumers in England and Wales rose from 10.80 to 21.91 million and the total length of the main circuits energised at voltages below 132 kV increased from about 266 000 km to 597 320 km. The latter figure is made up of 228 124 km of overhead line and 369 196 km of underground cable. From 1948 a vigorous programme of full rural electrification was pursued in which overhead lines were used for economic and practical reasons, but in urban and industrial areas the system has been developed using cables laid directly in the ground and connected to ground-mounted substations. Mains cables operating at voltages up to 11 kV are usually laid in public footpaths or service reservations alongside the carriageways, where space is allocated for each public service, but cables operating at higher voltages often have to be laid in the carriageway. Tablc 18.1 shows the lengths of underground and overhead main circuits in service at each voltage level in England and Wales in 1988.

Growth in the connection of new consumers and the rate of construction of new circuits reached a peak in the late 1960s. Typical data for the annual commissioning of new public mains in the 1980s are shown in table 18.2. Since 1980 attention has turned increasingly to refurbishment of the existing system and this is expected to become the major category of expenditure by the year 2000. Priority will have to be given to switchgear, transformers and overhead lines, but the underground cables now in service are still generally sound and are unlikely to need to be replaced for many years.

While there is a broad similarity among the European public electricity distribution systems, a much wider variation is found in the USA, but one feature common to most of the American utilities has been the use of ducted systems with manholes to accommodate cables in city centres. Another is the high proportion of overhead circuits in urban networks. Objections to the appearance of overhead lines, and mandatory requirements that in certain areas new supplies be provided by underground cable, have led to the development of a system known as Underground Residential Distribution (URD), which is discussed later in this chapter, and there is a commitment to the eventual undergrounding of existing overhead lines in urban areas.

PARAMETERS OF ELECTRICITY SUPPLY SYSTEMS

In the development of early electricity supply systems, many direct and alternating voltages, frequencies, phase numbers and connections were used to achieve the most

Table 18.1 Public mains in service in England and Wales in 1988

	66 kV	33 kV	22 kV	11 kV	6.6 kV	Low voltage
Overhead (km)	3299	22 058	5566	131 559	2002	63 504
Underground (km)	1135	13 193	2558	93 557	15 203	242 060

Table 18.2 Public mains commissioned and number of consumers in England and Wales in 2 year periods of the 1980s

Circuit voltage	66 kV	33 kV	22 kV	11 kV	6.6 kV	Low voltage	Number of consumers (million)
1981–82							
Overhead (km)	34	96	27	1399	47	197	20.66
Underground (km)	7	121	19	954	71	1932	
1983–84							
Overhead (km)	3	92	30	1131	9	211	21.05
Underground (km)	4	65	24	951	74	2295	
1985–86							
Overhead (km)	8	105	23	927	12	230	21.49
Underground (km)	9	47	15	1065	48	1349	
1987–88							
Overhead (km)	18	476	18	1135	26	315	21.91
Underground (km)	6	93	18	1255	43	2627	

economical use of capital, but the arrangements discussed below have become predominant in modern systems.

Frequencies and phase numbers

Symmetrical three-phase system

A symmetrical 3-phase a.c. system with an earthed neutral and a frequency of 50 Hz or 60 Hz is now used almost universally for main power distribution systems (fig. 18.1(a)), some of its advantages being the following.

(a) Alternating current may be generated without a commutator and transformed to higher or lower voltages by static transformers.
(b) A 3-phase winding makes efficient use of the armatures of cylindrical machines and of the cores of transformers.
(c) In a symmetrical 3-phase system the phases are mutually displaced by the same angle, 120°, and the magnitudes of the voltages between the phases are all equal, as are the magnitudes of the voltages between the phases and the neutral.
(d) A 3-phase supply will excite a magnetic field rotating in a definite direction which is easily reversed.

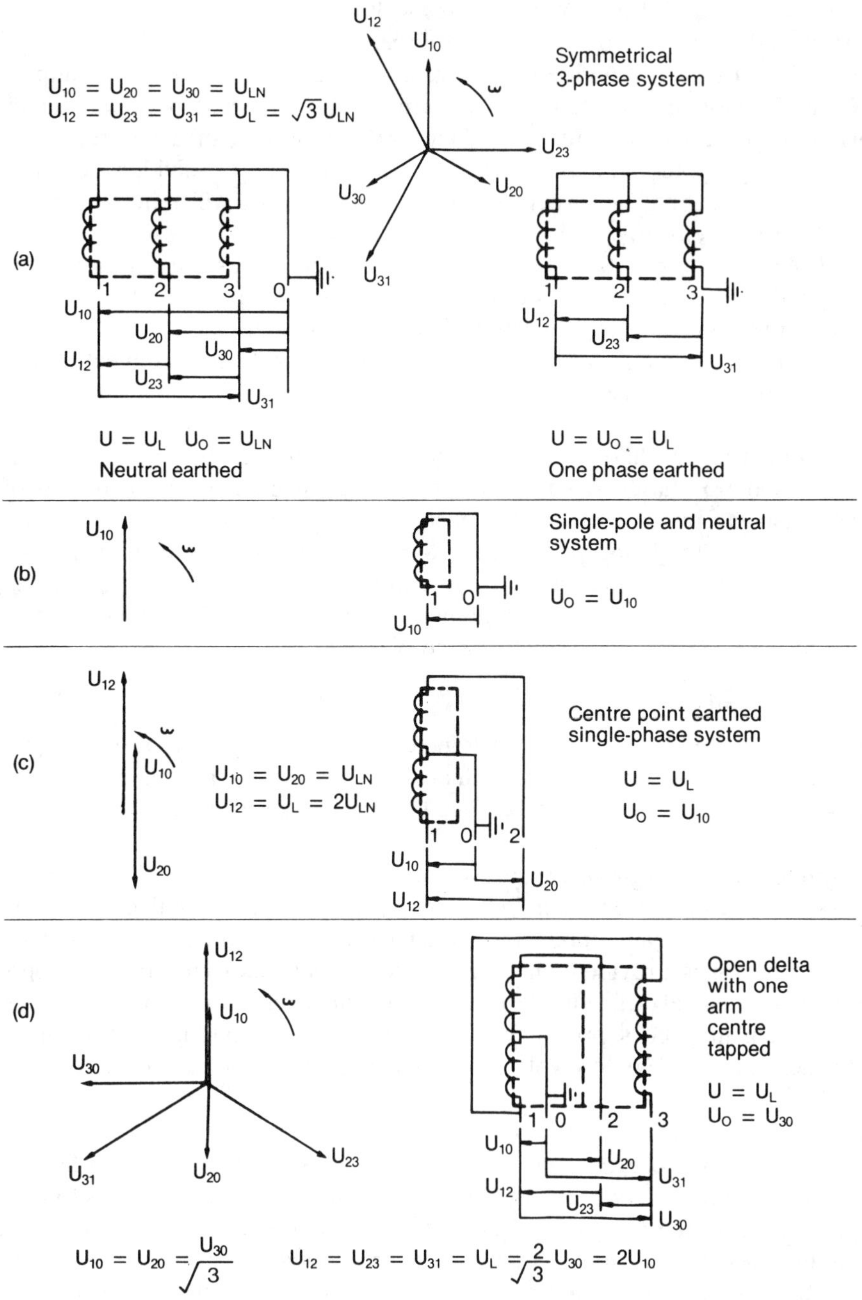

Fig. 18.1 Voltage relationships of some systems currently in use and diagrams showing the arrangements and connections of the secondary windings of the infeeding transformers. The heavy broken lines represent the magnetic cores

(e) The voltage applied to a symmetrical load that is normally connected in delta may be reduced by connecting it in star without the use of a neutral conductor.

(f) A frequency of 50 Hz or 60 Hz relates well to the normal speeds of mechanical drives and is high enough to prevent discernible flicker from electric lamps and low enough to avoid undue interference with telecommunications equipment.
(g) While 3-phase and single-phase loads may be connected between the phases without the use of a neutral conductor, the provision of a neutral conductor allows single-pole-and-neutral supplies to be given to individual loads and if these are distributed between the phases the currents will tend to cancel each other in the neutral.
(h) A 3-phase system with loads connected between phase and neutral may be supplied from a 3-phase system without a neutral conductor by the use of a transformer with a star-connected secondary winding.
(i) A single-phase system may be supplied from a transformer connected between two phases of a 3-phase system.

The symmetrical 3-phase system is used throughout the UK with a frequency of 50 Hz. In some 3-phase systems, one phase is connected to earth instead of the neutral, as shown in fig. 18.1(a). A 3-phase line then has only two live conductors, no neutral conductor being provided, but their potential to earth is higher than it would be if the neutral were earthed. Only one conductor of a single-phase tapping need be live but if no single-phase tappings are made between the two live phases a balance of loads on the phases will not be obtained.

Single-pole-and-neutral system
In the UK isolated low voltage single-pole-and-neutral systems (fig. 18.1(b)) are used where the total demand is less than 50 kV A and a small number of single-phase loads would be difficult to balance between three phases.

Centre-point-earthed single-phase system
Some systems have two live conductors carrying potentials relative to an earthed neutral that are in phase opposition to each other, as shown in fig. 18.1(c). If a neutral conductor is provided, the current from loads connected between opposite poles and the neutral will tend to cancel in the neutral, as in the 3-phase system. Such a system may be supplied from a centre tapped winding on a single-phase transformer. In the USA low voltage systems are commonly of this type.

'V' system with one arm centre tapped
The extension of the centre-point-earthed single-phase system shown in fig. 18.1(d) is sometimes used. It allows 3-phase and single-pole-and-neutral supplies to be given from a 4-wire distribution system. There is a low voltage winding utilising two limbs only of a 3-phase transformer. The windings on the two limbs are connected as two sides of a delta and one is centre tapped to provide the neutral. Single-pole-and-neutral supplies then have half the line to line voltage. A disadvantage is that the load is unevenly shared between the phases. In Tokyo low voltage supplies are given from this type of system.

Importance of the neutral conductor
In all the systems using a neutral conductor to give supply to single-phase loads, its

integrity is essential to prevent excessive voltages from being applied to the loads on the less heavily loaded phases.

Constraints on the choice of circuit voltage

For a given frequency and number of phases, it can be shown that the most economical circuit design occurs when the conductor related cost C_c of the circuit is equal to the capitalised cost C_i of the I^2R losses and the voltage related cost C_v of the circuit is equal to the sum of the other two costs, i.e. $C_v = 2C_c = 2C_i$. Conductor size and circuit voltage should therefore rise together as circuit power rating P rises, i.e. $C_v \propto C_i \propto \sqrt{P}$. In fact the high cost of transforming stations, and the need to standardise transformers, switchgear and cables, limits the number of voltage levels that can be used and normally a distribution system takes the form of three or four superimposed networks each operating at its own uniform voltage and fed by transformers connected to the network operating at the next higher voltage level, as shown in fig. 18.2. Typical examples of network voltages are given in table 18.3.

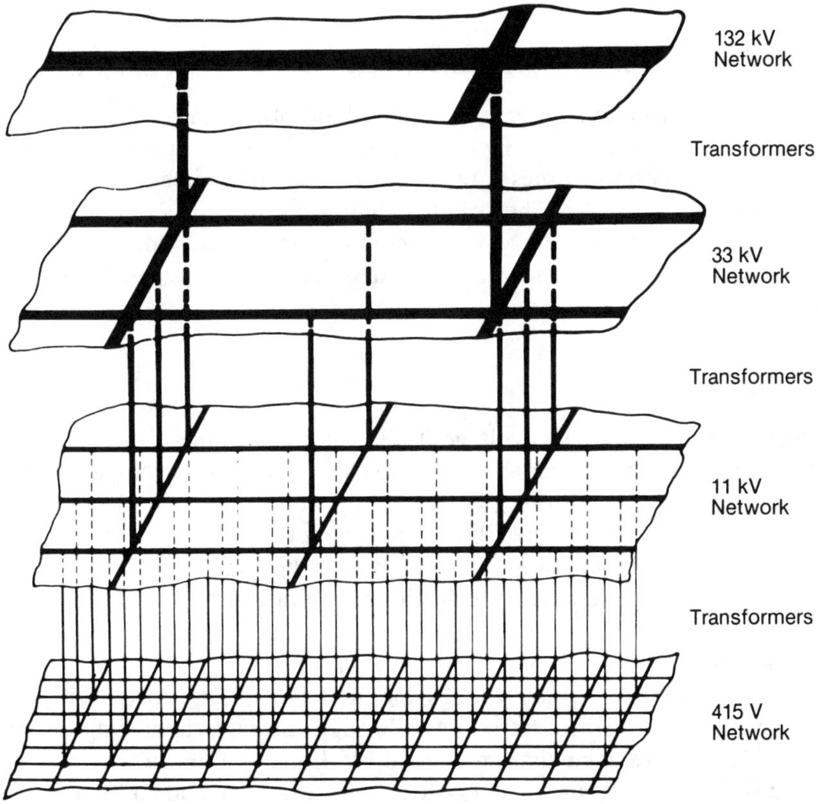

Fig. 18.2 Superimposed networks forming a distribution system

Table 18.3 Typical examples of network voltages

UK	Germany	USA
132/76.2 kV	110/63.5 kV	138/79.7 kV or 120/69.3 kV
33/19.1 kV	30/17.3 kV	46/26.5 kV or 40/23 kV or 24/13.9 kV or 22/12.7 kV
11/6.35 kV or 6.6/3.81 kV	20/11.5 kV or 10/5.77 kV or 6/3.46 kV	13.2/7.6 kV 4.8/2.8 kV
415/240 V	380/220 V	220/110 V

The second group of voltage levels is sometimes omitted, i.e. 33/19.1 kV etc.

CABLE NETWORKS

Constraints on the choice of conductor size

In underground distribution systems, the lower limit of the range of conductor size S that may be used at each voltage level is set by the short-circuit current I that could flow and the total operating times T of the protection and switchgear in the approximate relationship $S = kI\sqrt{T}$. The result is that a mat of cables in a small range of sizes is operating at each voltage level in most urban and industrial areas. The alternative policies followed in organising these cables into networks are outlined below.

Contiguous networks

The cables operating at each voltage level can be arranged into a contiguous network of distributing interconnectors connecting substations that feed in from a higher voltage as well as feeding loads directly or through transformers stepping down to a lower voltage network. This arrangement allows load normally supplied by a substation that is out of service, or has to be taken out of service, to be transferred to other substations through the interconnectors.

Parallel operation of transformers through the network

If the network and transformer ratings are matched to the load, the in-feeding transformers may be operated in parallel through the interconnecting distributors. This makes for a more even sharing of load by the in-feeding substations, reduced losses, reduced voltage regulation, smoother voltage control and continuity of supply on the loss, owing to a fault, of an in-feeding transformer. Fluctuating loads cause less disturbance to the supply voltage since the system impedance is reduced throughout the network while the short-circuit levels at the in-feeding substations are less than they would be if the same transformer capacity were concentrated at one substation.

Unit protection

Further, if unit protection is applied thoroughly to the higher voltage networks, as shown in fig. 18.3, there is greater freedom to interconnect and a fault on any high voltage cable will not normally interrupt supplies. Unit protection is not applicable to low voltage distributors, which are normally protected by fuses. Distribution systems developed on these principles invite the use of a single rating for transformers feeding into each network and a single circuit rating at each voltage level. Examples of contiguous networks are shown in figs 18.4, 18.5 and 18.6.

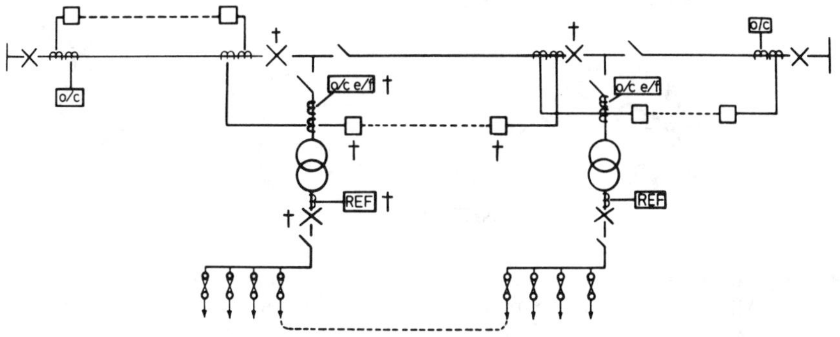

Fig. 18.3 A protection scheme used in an HV interconnected network. The automatic circuit breakers are arranged to form units that include one transformer and one section of cable linking two substations. Unit protection, having unlabelled relays in the diagram, covers the HV cables and switchgear and an overcurrent and earth fault relay covers the transformer and LV busbars. There is also restricted earth fault protection on the low voltage winding of the transformer. Each of the relays marked with a dagger trips all the circuit breakers marked with a dagger to isolate the unit. Any number of substations may be connected into the interconnector. Back-up overcurrent protection covers the whole interconnector

Radial networks

An alternative policy is to develop radial distribution networks supplied from relatively large substations where a security of supply appropriate to the load is provided, multiple feeders being used to supply a substation in which several transformers are installed (fig. 18.7). Several cable sizes appropriate to the prospective loads that they are likely to carry might be used at each voltage level within the limitations set by fault currents. This policy aims to provide system capacity at the lowest cost per kilovolt amp installed and to match each component to its prospective load.

Provision for load growth

Throughout most of the history of electricity supply there has been a vigorous growth in demand and the new systems that are installed should be able to cater for growing loads. It is important, nevertheless, that the initial investment should not be

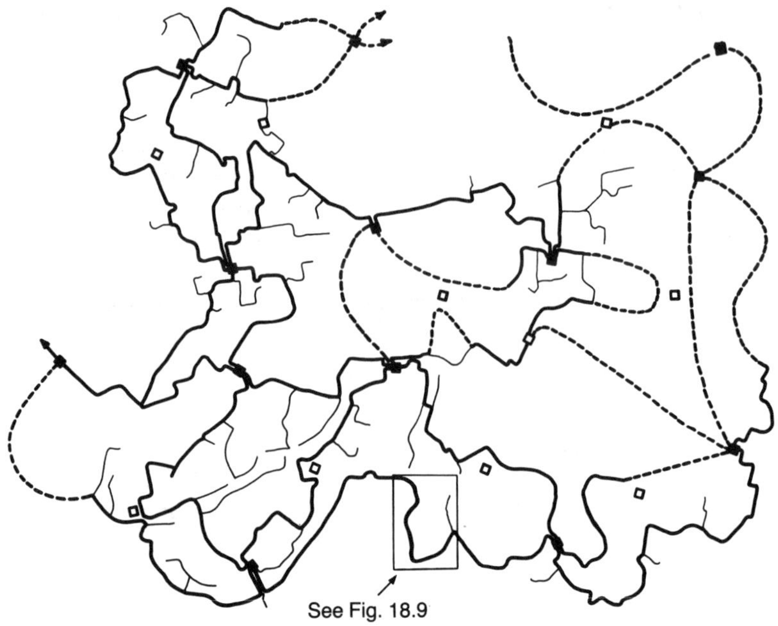

Fig. 18.4 A uniform LV network on a residential development that is in the process of construction. All the cables are 95 mm^2 waveform. The fine lines represent spurs off the interconnectors which are shown as heavy lines. The broken lines show further interconnectors that will be formed as the development extends. Sites acquired for reinforcement substations are shown by open squares

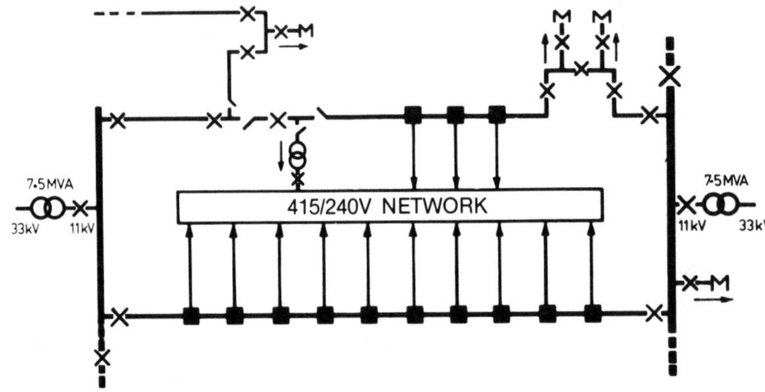

Fig. 18.5 Part of an HV interconnected network on an industrial estate. The cable and busbars extend as shown by the broken lines. Power flows out of the HV network are shown by arrows. M indicates commercial metering. One substation with an HV branch is shown in detail. The solid squares represent substations of the type detailed in fig. 18.3

greater than is necessary. Two main strategies have been applied to the solution of this problem in the UK.

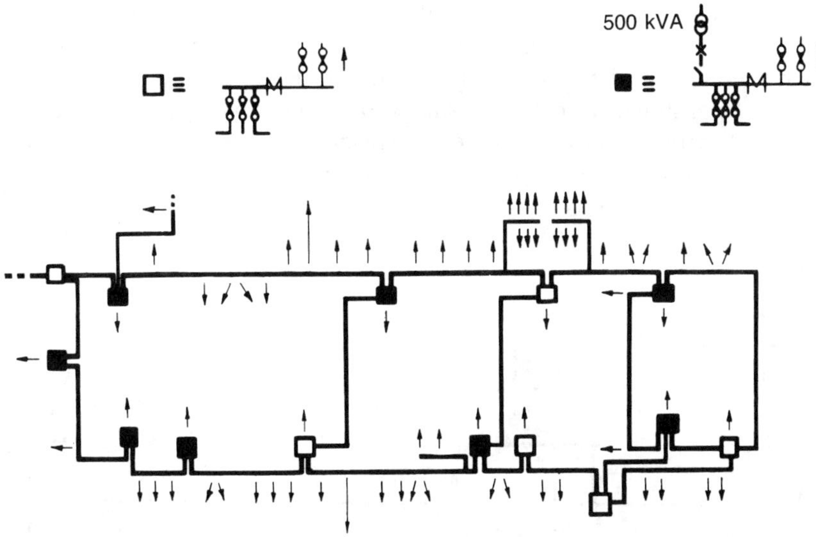

Fig. 18.6 Part of the LV network fed from the HV network shown in fig. 18.5. 185 mm^2 LV cables are used throughout the industrial estate. Points from which supplies are given are shown by arrows. Substations equipped with LV fuse boards only are shown by open squares. M represents busbar metering

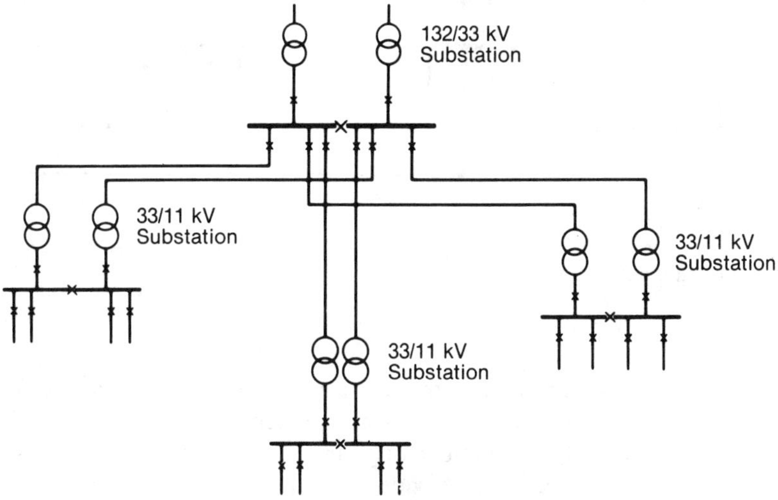

Fig. 18.7 Duplicate feeders and double transformer substations in a radial distribution network

Uniform network

One policy has been to lay down a uniform contiguous network at each voltage level with one main cable size throughout, matched to a standard transformer rating, the substations having the minimum dimensions to accommodate the transformer and its associated switchgear. The substations are spaced to provide for the estimated early load density and when the load rises above the rating of the network, which is matched to the transformers, the most heavily loaded interconnectors are relieved by being turned into further suitably sited standard substations, as shown in fig. 18.8. In this way the installed transformer and substation capacity are kept as small as possible, the distribution of transformers corresponds to the distribution of load and the capacity of the cable network is not based on a speculative assessment of load growth.

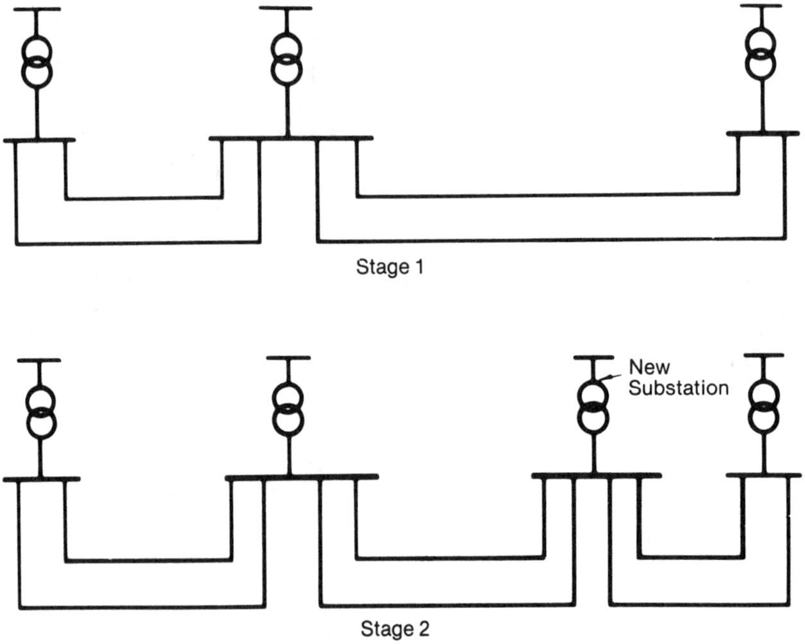

Fig. 18.8 Reinforcement of a uniform contiguous distribution network by the provision of an additional infeeding substation

Tapered network

The other strategy has been to construct a 'tapered' distribution network in which the cable size at each part of the network is matched to the load density that is expected to be reached after a number of years. Transformer capacity sufficient for the estimated early load density is provided initially and further capacity is installed in the same substation when the load requires it. Additional cables and switchgear may also be necessary. A tapered network does not lend itself so readily to parallel operation of transformers through the network, nor to reinforcement from additional substations.

SUPPLIES TO RESIDENTIAL DEVELOPMENTS

The choice of suitable locations for the substations is most important in the economic design of any distribution network. This applies whether the system comprises a uniform interconnected network with small standard substations or is a tapered network with fewer larger substations.

Design of uniform low voltage networks for residential developments

As only one cable size and one transformer rating are used, the main objectives in the design of a uniform residential network are that the substations and interconnecting distributors be evenly loaded, that the distributors provide adequate interconnection between adjacent substations, that the substations be suitably spaced for the early load density, that sites for additional substations sufficient for the predicted ultimate load density be provided in suitable locations and that the distributors be routed so that they may be turned in to the additional substations. Fig. 18.4 shows a uniform network on a residential development that is in the process of construction. All the cables are 95 mm^2 waveform type and the substations all have 500 kV A transformers.

Design of tapered low voltage networks for residential developments

In recent years extensive studies on the design of tapered underground distribution systems for new housing estates have shown the following.

(a) The ratings assigned to low voltage cables should be economic ratings in which the capitalised costs of the losses are taken into account. This requires some additional capital outlay to cover extra cable cost but some saving can be made in overall costs, which include jointing and electrical losses.
(b) A maximum of four cable sizes should be used as the benefits from the use of a larger number are small.

Residential service connections

In the UK supplies to private houses are given by single-phase services consisting of an earthed neutral conductor and a phase conductor carrying a potential to the neutral of 240 V. The service connections account for about half of the total capital cost of the network supplying a new housing estate and much thought has been given to means of simplifying the installations and reducing costs. An arrangement in which up to four single-phase concentric service cables are jointed directly to the 3-phase waveform main in one joint and connections are laid from houses serviced directly to adjacent houses is shown in fig. 18.9. In the interest of phase balance it is preferred that three service cables are connected at one joint and that not more than two houses are supplied by each service cable. This method has been found to be very successful.

Another option that has become more popular is to require the developer to lay a 50 mm diameter duct directly from each meter cupboard to the main. A service cable is threaded through the duct when the cupboard has been made secure and jointed directly to the main. Jointing costs may consequently be increased but cable installation costs and voltage drop are reduced.

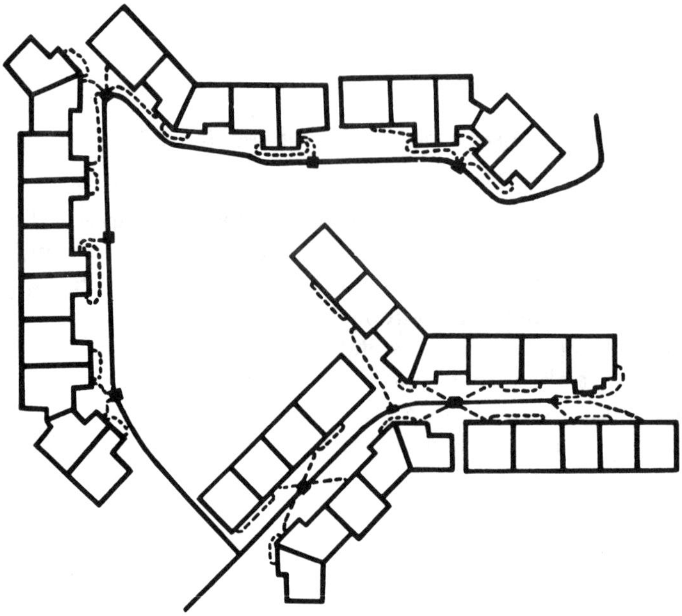

Fig. 18.9 A detail of fig. 18.4 showing service connections. 25 mm^2 single-phase waveform service cables are distributed evenly between the three phases of 95 mm^2 main

Underground residential distribution

Underground residential distribution (URD) is a system that was developed in the USA to take the place of the pole-mounted residential distribution systems that were used there until the 1960s. It consists of single-phase high voltage distributors supplying 50 kVA, 100 kVA and 150 kVA transformers which step down to low voltage. Each feeds between eight and 16 residential consumers by service cables radiating from the transformer or from multiservice pillars. In the USA the transformers are centre tapped and three conductors are taken to each house, giving supplies at 220 V between live conductors and 110 V between each live conductor and the earthed neutral.

In one arrangement studied in the UK, high voltage three-phase-and-neutral cables run from the primary substation in a ring through several distribution points where the three phases are split by switchgear that provides individual control for the incoming cables and individual control and fuse protection for the single-phase distribution cables. The distribution cables have a single live core with a concentric copper neutral conductor directly in contact with the ground. At each transformer the high and low voltage neutral/earth conductors are bonded together. The transformers are installed in small underground vaults. In each transformer there is a high voltage fuse. Cable connections to the high voltage side of the transformer are made by plug connectors which operate satisfactorily under water. The low voltage connections are made off at a sealed busbar.

In the USA high air-conditioning loads and lower housing densities favour this type of system especially in view of the lower value (110 V) of phase–neutral voltage.

In the UK it was estimated in 1970 that a URD system of this type, for a development with an average diversified demand of 6 kW per dwelling, could cost 26% less than a conventional low voltage distribution system. However, the saving would be reduced to 16% if account were taken of the cost of losses. As the cost of transformers increased with the increasing price of copper in the early 1970s no significant savings could be achieved.

COMMERCIAL AND INDUSTRIAL SUPPLIES

Loads at commercial and industrial premises range from a few hundred watts to hundreds of megawatts, and the voltage at which the supply is given is generally determined by the supply capacity required in comparison with the normal transformer ratings used at each voltage level. The range of supply capacities provided at each voltage level by one Electricity Board is given in table 18.4. Some of the arrangements by which the supplies are given are shown in figs 18.5 and 18.6.

Table 18.4 Typical ranges of supply capacities provided at each voltage level

Network voltage	Range of supply capacities normally provided	Normal ratings of transformers used
415/240 V	35–1000 kVA (100–1000 kVA)	11 kV/415 V, 500 kVA
11 kV	1–20 MVA (2–20 MVA)	33 kV/11 kV, 7.5 MVA
33 kV	Above 15 MVA (above 30 MVA)	132 kV/33 kV, 60 MVA

For supply capacities within the ranges shown in parentheses in table 18.4, accommodation for one or more transformers stepping down from the next higher voltage is normally required by the Electricity Board. An alternative supply is normally provided for loads greater than 1 MVA and wherever economically practicable for lower loads.

LOADS THAT CAUSE DISTURBANCE ON THE SYSTEM

National regulations set limits to the permissible variation of the voltage at a consumer's supply terminals, but disturbances to the supply voltage within those limits are often unacceptable to the consumer. In general a lower system impedance to any point from which a load is supplied reduces voltage fluctuations caused by that load. On the other hand a lower system impedance probably means that more transformer capacity is operating in parallel and supplying more customers from a more extensive network. This means that more customers will be affected by any disturbance, whether caused by loads or short-circuit faults, and disturbances will be reflected more strongly onto the higher voltage levels. There is therefore a trade-off.

Fluctuating load currents

Relatively small fluctuations in voltage, if repeated frequently, may have a quite unacceptable effect on incandescent lighting. A change in voltage of 1% once every second is very irritating. At ten times per second some people will notice even a variation of 0.25%. Such fluctuations in voltage are caused by reactive current surges drawn by motors, welding machines and arc furnaces, a major component of the voltage dips being generated in the reactive impedances of the transformers supplying the loads. Current surges can also cause protection systems to operate. If the surges cannot be reduced sufficiently, e.g. by the use of special motor starting equipment, it may be necessary to supply the offending load from a higher voltage network with a lower impedance and higher protection settings, the supply probably being metered at the higher voltage.

Another solution may be to increase the transformer capacity supplying the affected network, or, if the cable or line from the transformer is contributing greatly to the system impedance to the load, an additional cable may be provided to supply the fluctuating load alone. A subtler approach, which is often very effective, is to join two radial distributors from different transformers so forming an interconnector from which to supply the fluctuating load. This effectively reduces the impedance of the system to the load by increasing both the circuit capacity and the transformer capacity through which it is drawn. In any case, the voltage fluctuation at the 'point of common coupling', i.e. at the point on the system nearest to the disturbance generator from which both the disturbance generator and other consumers are supplied, is the condition to be controlled.

Harmonic currents

Harmonic currents generated by non-linear impedances, rectifiers, thyristor controls etc. can overload power factor correction capacitors and interfere with electronic equipment. Supply authorities set limits for the magnitudes of the harmonic currents that they will allow consumers to inject into the public distribution system and it may sometimes be necessary for the consumer to install resonant by-pass filters to absorb the harmonics generated by his equipment. Again the total solution may require the connection of the load into the system at the higher voltage.

Adjustment of network voltage

In general it is better to operate switchgear and cables at the highest voltage for which they are designed, so as to exploit their full short-circuit and load ratings. Short-circuit power levels on the HV network tend to rise as generation capacity and dynamic loads increase and the short-circuit ratings of switchgear may become inadequate, even if the capacity of the transformers feeding that part of the network is not changed. Even so, after an increase in network voltage, the capacity of the transformers feeding into the network can usually be increased by the ratio of the increase in voltage, and so the capacity of the whole network can be raised and the impedance of the system to the points of common coupling of fluctuating loads or harmonic generators reduced.

In the UK various voltages, ranging upward from 2 kV, have been used for HV distribution systems and some cables and switchgear have been installed which are only suitable for 6.6 kV or less. However, most of the high voltage cables now in use are suitable for 11 kV and so is most of the switchgear installed since 1948. The switchgear that is not insulated for 11 kV does not comply with modern standards for other reasons and will have to be replaced. There is therefore a strong case for the increase of lower HV network voltages to 11 kV.

Before applying the higher voltage it is usual to pressure test each circuit, unless there is a record that the appropriate test voltage has been previously applied. Sometimes old joints will fail on test and will have to be remade. Sometimes it is known that the type of joint used in a certain period was not suitable for 11 kV and those joints are remade before testing.

One of the obstacles to this course is the cost of changing transformers to operate at the new voltage, but there are compensating factors.

(a) Modern transformers have much lower iron losses; for example a typical 500 kVA transformer with a laminated core of grain-oriented cold-rolled steel has an iron loss of 0.7 kW compared with 1.7 kW for a similar transformer with a hot-rolled laminated steel core. The capitalised savings in the cost of losses resulting from the renewal of the transformer, added to the scrap value of the old transformer, help to pay for the new transformer.
(b) Newer transformers recovered owing to a change in system voltage can often be reused on a part of the network that is to remain at the lower voltage.

A change of voltage will be made much simpler if transformers purchased for use initially at the lower voltage are also suitable for use at the higher voltage. This facility can be provided for about 10% extra cost.

EARTHING

In the UK the 1937 Electricity Supply Regulations require that every distribution system should be connected to earth. The secondary windings of transformers stepping down to 6.6 kV or 11 kV are normally star connected and the star point is connected to earth. The connection may be solid, or if it is necessary to reduce the potential earth fault current an impedance may be inserted. Low voltage distribution systems must be solidly connected to earth to ensure that there is no rise in potential that would cause danger in the case of a fault connecting the high voltage system and the low voltage system. 3-phase transformers feeding low voltage distribution systems have star-connected secondary windings with solidly earthed neutrals, and one pole of the secondary winding of each single-phase transformer stepping down to low voltage is solidly earthed.

The 1937 Regulations allowed transformers to be operated in parallel through a low voltage network with an earth connection at each transformer provided that each transformer had a delta-connected winding, and relaxations of the regulations extended these provisions to high voltage networks. If the delta connection is applied to the secondary winding, an interconnected-star earthing choke may be used to provide the earth connection. Typical system earthing arrangements are shown in fig. 18.10. The 1988 Regulations do not specify the provision of a delta-connected winding but make the 'person concerned' responsible for limiting 'the occurrence and effects of circulating currents' between earthed neutrals.

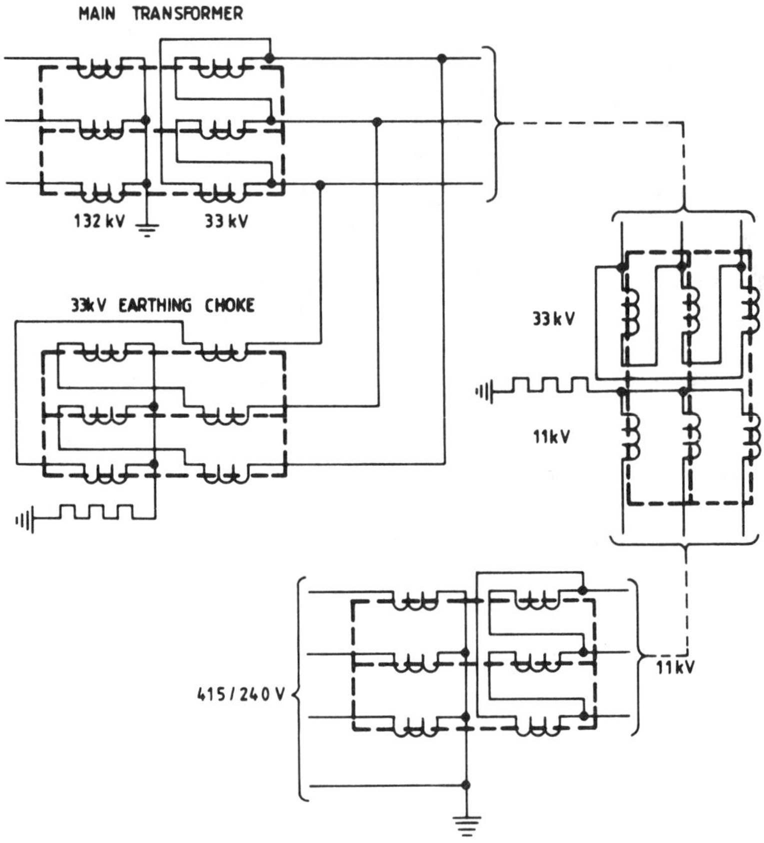

Fig. 18.10 Typical system earthing arrangements. An 11 kV earthing resistor is not always used

Protective multiple earthing

Where underground cables with contiguous metal sheaths bonded to the substation earthing systems were used in low voltage distribution networks, and earth terminals connected to the cable sheath were provided for the consumers' use, a low resistance connection between the system neutral and earth and low resistance return paths from the consumers' earthing systems to the transformer neutral were maintained. At the same time there was a problem on low voltage overhead line networks, where it was more difficult to make a low resistance connection between neutral and earth and consumers' earth fault currents had to return through the ground. One solution was to string an earth-continuity conductor on the overhead line, but it was found that if it was broken or a joint failed a long time could elapse before the fault was reported as supplies did not depend on it. This led to the idea that if the neutral conductor were used to provide a low resistance return path for earth fault currents its failure would be noticed quickly while, with suitable bonding and earth electrodes, dangerous potential differences on consumers' premises could be avoided.

In 1955 approvals were granted for additional connections to be made between neutral and earth, collectively referred to as protective multiple earthing (PME). Under these approvals PME was applied to many overhead low voltage distribution systems, although the imposed conditions made it difficult to apply to existing underground installations.

This experience led to relaxations and clarification of the original conditions and opened the way for the general application of PME to underground low voltage distribution networks and the use of CNE cables for extensions and alterations of existing networks.

SHORT-CIRCUIT CURRENTS

When a short circuit is closed on an inductive source, there is a transient d.c. surge which dies away within a few cycles. This is superimposed on the alternating fault current and so the first peak of current may be 1.7 times the peak value of the a.c. component of current alone. If synchronous or asynchronous rotating machines are connected to the network they will contribute to both the d.c. and a.c. components of the current during the initial surge, but only the a.c. components of the contributions from synchronous machines will persist after the initial surge, and these only at a reduced level. Therefore, if there is a preponderance of motor loads on the network, the ratio of the first current peak to the peak value of the steady state short-circuit current may be even greater than 1.7.

A transformer with a delta-connected primary winding and a star-connected secondary winding will make a greater contribution to the current in a nearby earth fault than it will to each phase current in a 3-phase fault, unless an earthing resistor is used as shown in fig. 18.10.

However, if transformers in separate substations are interconnected through a cable network, the contributions to fault currents made by remote transformers will be reduced by the impedances of the network and, because a cable network offers a higher impedance to earth fault currents than it does to currents flowing between phases, the maximum earth fault current on an interconnected network is often lower than the maximum 3-phase fault current even if earthing resistors are not used.

On high voltage urban networks there is not usually any difficulty in obtaining sufficient fault current to operate the appropriate protection, but on low voltage networks the system voltage and the ohmic impedances of the transformers and network are lower, so the impedance of cable local to the fault and the impedance of the fault itself are more effective in reducing the short-circuit current. Therefore, if low voltage cables, particularly small mains and service cables, are too long, the fault current will not be sufficient to operate the circuit protection at the substation.

PROTECTION

The main objective of power system protection is to maintain the stability and integrity of as much of the power system as possible by disconnecting faulty equipment that endangers the system. Therefore, it is necessary for the protection system not only to detect and disconnect the fault but also to be discriminative in isolating as little of the system as possible in the process.

The distribution system may be thought of as a number of units, each of which can be isolated by automatic circuit breakers. Unit protection compares the currents flowing at the ports of each unit, normally using pilot wires. It will discriminate to isolate only the faulty unit, independently of the level of short-circuit current, and without using time delays, although the protection zone cannot correspond exactly with the protected unit and there has to be either a blind spot or an overlap between the protection zones within the switchgear. In applying unit protection it is necessary, and desirable, so to arrange the automatic circuit breakers that the units are as small as possible, as in the arrangement shown in fig. 18.3.

In other classical protection systems, which may be used as a back-up to unit protection and to cover its blind spots, the basis for the detection of the fault is current level, while the bases for discrimination may be current level, graded time delays or system impedance between the protection relay and the fault. If there is a transformer in the circuit, an instantaneous overcurrent relay, discriminating purely on the basis of current level, may be used to protect the circuit as far as the primary winding of the transformer, but otherwise graded time delays are used to provide discrimination in both overcurrent and impedance protection schemes. This is significant because the size of cable required to carry a particular short-circuit current depends on the time for which the current is allowed to flow.

Allowing for the operating time of the circuit breaker, and for errors and overshoot in the relays, a differential time delay of about 0.4 s is necessary to ensure discrimination between circuit breakers. Within a high voltage distribution network there may be three overcurrent protection levels, one on the out-feeding transformers discriminating with the lower voltage protection, one on the circuit breakers that control the distributors at the in-feeding substations and an intermediate one. To obtain discrimination between these levels on a radial distributor the cables covered by the main distributor protection would therefore be required to carry the short-circuit current for about 1.5 s or longer at the higher voltages. A short circuit on an interconnector is fed from both ends and so the problems of discrimination and stress on cables are not as great.

The advent of digital techniques is making it possible to use criteria other than mere current level or impedance in detecting faults or discriminating in their isolation. For example 'source protection' sees faults not only on a cable distributor but also on the small transformers connected to it. It looks for sudden changes in the phase angles of the currents in the feeder at the source from which it is fed. It is very likely that a further development, 'differential source protection', will allow the same principle to be applied to a distributor fed from more than one source. It may also be possible to transmit digital signals directly over the power cable, so providing what is effectively unit protection without the use of pilot cables.

On LV distribution networks HRC fuses are used which, by their speed of operation, protect cables from damage due to high short-circuit currents. The greater problem is one of ensuring that sufficient short-circuit current will flow to operate the fuse. A 300 A fuse is unlikely to clear a fault that is fed by a 95 mm^2 aluminium cable longer than 800 m. This corresponds to the lengths of the interconnectors on a residential development with a housing density of 25 houses per hectare and a diversified demand of 1 kW per house, supplied from fully loaded 500 kVA substations. At higher load densities or lower transformer loadings, the interconnectors are shorter. The length of a spur cable that can be protected by the fuses at the ends of an interconnector depends on the position at which the spur is connected.

COMPUTER AIDS TO POWER SYSTEM ANALYSIS AND DESIGN

The electrical power system load flow was amongst the earliest of engineering problems to be tackled by digital computer, and it is now possible to perform large power flow, fault level and even transient stability calculations in a matter of seconds. Interactive computing allows a dialogue to take place between the engineer and the analysis program at a computer terminal, while a graphical display unit can present results in a clearly comprehensible form and also offer easy interaction via a 'light pen' or similar facility. These features are exploited in the Interactive Power System Analysis (IPSA) system, developed by the University of Manchester Institute of Science and Technology and Merseyside and North Wales Electricity Board. The engineer simply 'points' to the network diagram to indicate the next configuration to be studied, and results are displayed against the network diagram, or where appropriate as a graph.

Other interactive systems, for instance the ICL DINIS, are being developed to allow cable routes to be digitised graphically and used to calculate impedance and susceptance values that are then used in the system analysis.

For some years the Electricity Council in the UK has monitored the loads of selected samples of consumers, and the Electricity Council Research Centre, Capenhurst, has developed a computer program (DEBUT) which makes use of the typical daily load curve and variance of certain consumer types in finding the optimum tapering for a specified radial network.

Chapter 19

Distribution Cable Types, Design and Applications

The distinctions between distribution and transmission at the upper end of the voltage range of distribution cables and between distribution and wiring at the lower end are not very precise. In the framework of this chapter, however, it is convenient to regard distribution cables as power cables for fixed installation of rated voltages from 600/1000 V up to 19/33 kV. Cables of lower voltage rating, auxiliary cables and flexible cables are covered in part 2, and the types of cable for voltages above 33 kV are included in part 4.

VOLTAGE DESIGNATIONS AND EFFECTS ON CABLE DESIGN

Generally, distribution cables are given voltage designations, called the rated voltages, according to the nominal voltages of the systems in which they are intended to operate. For example, in Great Britain cable standards give details for 1.9/3.3 kV, 3.8/6.6 kV, 6.35/11 kV, 12.7/22 kV and 19/33 kV cables, these voltages corresponding with the more common system voltages in the country. Also included are 8.7/15 kV cables to provide a step between 11 kV and 22 kV, mainly for cables to be exported to other countries where 13.8 or 15 kV systems are common.

The 600/1000 V designation does not quite conform with the same pattern. Although there are systems of about 600/1000 V, the bulk of the 600/1000 V cable is used in 240/415 V systems in the UK and at similar voltages, e.g. 230/400 V and 220/380 V, in other countries. At this voltage level the cables are designated by the highest nominal system voltage for which they are suitable. Since the cable design is dictated to a considerable extent by the mechanical rigours associated with the various installation conditions for distribution cables, and not simply by the electrical duty, the same design is rationalised for all voltages up to the nominal 1000 V, which is the upper limit of the internationally adopted 'low voltage' band. Allowing the generally accepted 10% upward variation on the nominal voltage (see later), these cables are suitable for a maximum of 1100 V.

The full voltage designations are in the form U_0/U, where U_0 relates to voltage between the conductor(s) and earth and U to the voltage between conductors for which the cable is suitable. In the voltage designations, such as 6.35/11 kV and 19/33 kV, the ratio of $U_0{:}U$ is $1{:}\sqrt{3}$, appropriate under normal operating conditions for the usual 3-phase system with the neutral point directly earthed or earthed through a resistance or reactance. However, in some systems designed to enable continued operation with a fault to earth on one phase, by the use of arc suppression coils for instance, the voltage to earth on the two sound phases will rise under such conditions towards the phase-to-phase voltage. It is acceptable to use a cable rated as 6.35/11 kV in an 11 kV system, for example, in which immediate isolation of the affected section does not occur when there is a fault to earth, provided that the period of operation under the faulty condition is limited. Cable insulation will withstand a degree of electrical over-stressing for limited periods without undue effect on its overall performance.

In the 1984 edition of IEC Publication 183, 'Guide to the selection of high voltage cables', three categories of system, A, B and C, are defined. Category A systems are those where earth faults are cleared as rapidly as possible and anyway within 1 min. Category B systems are those which, under fault conditions, may be operated for a short time only with one phase earthed. This period, the standard says, should in general not exceed 1 hour, but a longer period can be tolerated as specified in the relevant cable standard. In fact both the relevant standards for 1–33 kV cables, IEC 502 for cables with extruded insulation and IEC 55 for paper insulated cables, do extend the period to 8 hours. Moreover both these cable standards, which are specifically mentioned as relevant standards by IEC 183, recommend cable of the same voltage ratings for category A and category B systems of the same nominal voltages. As far as it affects the selection of cables of appropriate voltage rating up to 33 kV, therefore, categories A and B might well be combined into a single category, as they were in the previous edition of IEC 183.

British Standards and most European practice follow IEC, with category B allowing for an earth fault to persist for 8 hours at maximum, this being regarded as a practical period in which to take action to repair a fault while keeping the system operational.

The 8 hour limit applies to a single occasion of operation with a fault to earth. In the UK there is the further stipulation that for classification as category B the expected total duration of earth faults in any year should not exceed 125 hours. This same limit of 125 hours per year applies in some other countries, Germany for example. It is not expected that the limit would be reached in practice, but repetitive over-stressing has a cumulative effect and in theory an 8 hour limit on a single incident could lead to an unrestricted total time of successive incidents.

Category C in IEC 183, and in British Standards, includes all systems not falling into categories A or B, which means systems where the voltage U_0 to earth may exceed $U/\sqrt{3}$ for periods in excess of the limits stipulated for category B. Cables for category C systems need more insulation to earth than those for category A and B systems of the same phase to phase voltage. The recommendation in the IEC cable standards and in British Standards for cables which have the whole of the insulation to earth applied to each conductor, i.e. cables with extruded insulation and all cables having a screen on each core, is to use for a category C system a cable of the next higher standard rated voltage than the cable for a category A or B system of the same phase to phase voltage. Thus for a category C 3.3 kV system a 3.6/6.6 kV cable would be used, for a category C 6.6 kV system a 6.35/11 kV cable would be used, for a category C 11 kV system an 8.7/15 kV cable would be used, and so on. This is clearly set out in the appendices to British Standards dealing with selection and operation of the cables.

For paper insulated cables of the belted type, there is no need to increase the thickness of insulation between conductors to cater for category C systems; only the thickness of the belt insulation needs to be increased. Designs are therefore provided for category C systems with the voltage designations 3.3/3.3 kV, 6.6/6.6 kV and 8.7/11 kV. The value of U_0 of 8.7 kV for the belted cable for the 11 kV category C system is chosen to provide consistency with the value of U_0 for the screened cables, which for the same system would be rated 8.7/15 kV. The 8.7/11 kV cable is not designed specifically for 8.7 kV between conductors and earth. In normal operation the voltage to earth will be below 8.7 kV (generally 6.35 kV) and under earth fault conditions it may exceed 8.7 kV. The 8.7/11 kV designation should be recognised simply as indicating cable for an 11 kV category C system.

In the same system of designation a belted cable for a 15 kV category C system would be rated 12.7/15 kV in the UK. Now that standards generally specify screened cables only for 15 kV, this does not arise, but some European countries have made 12/15 kV belted cables and no doubt quantities of these are still in use.

So far in this chapter, for simplicity, the designations of voltage rating of cables from 3.3 to 33 kV have been explained in terms of British values, corresponding with standard British system voltages. In other European countries the nominal system voltages are not quite the same, being in general 10% lower, i.e. 3.0, 6.0, 10, 20 and 30 kV instead of 3.3, 6.6, 11, 22 and 33 kV, and the rated nominal voltages of the cables differ in the same way. Since the tendency in IEC standards for cables is to refer to the continental voltages, doubts have arisen in the past about the applicability to cables of British voltage ratings, even to the extent of whether the insulation thicknesses given for the continental voltage ratings are applicable to British cables with voltage ratings 10% higher. This is now clarified in IEC 183, which includes a table of which the part relating to cables of rated voltages from 3 kV up to 33 kV is shown here as table 19.1.

Table 19.1 Relationship between U_0/U and U_m

Rated voltage of cables and accessories, U_0/U (kV)	Highest voltage for equipment, U_m (kV)
1.8/3 and 3/3; 1.9/3.3 and 3.3/3.3	3.6
3.6/6 and 6/6; 3.8/6.6 and 6.6/6.6	7.2
6/10 and 8.7/10; 6.35/11 and 8.7/11	12
8.7/15	17.5
12/20; 12.7/22	24
18/30; 19/33	36

The highest voltage for equipment is the maximum voltage, excluding transient voltages, for which equipment used for each nominal system voltage should be designed, and is usually represented by the symbol U_m. It is the highest voltage which can occur under normal operating conditions at any time and at any place in the system.

Cables of rated voltages to which a common value of U_m applies all have to be suitable for that maximum voltage. 10 kV and 11 kV cables, for example, should both be suitable for a maximum sustained voltage of 12 kV. Similarly the nominal voltage ratings of 3 and 3.3 kV, 6 and 6.6 kV, 20 and 22 kV and 30 and 33 kV are equivalent in their effect on cable design. Whatever is specified in IEC cable standards for 3, 6, 10, 20 and 30 kV cables applies equally to 3.3, 6.6, 11, 22 and 33 kV cables respectively.

U_m is a phase-to-phase voltage; it is the maximum voltage corresponding to the nominal voltage U. The nominal voltage U_0, between phases and earth, also of course has a corresponding maximum of value equal to U_0 multiplied in the ratio U_m:U, which amounts to 1.1 or 1.2.

In the IEC cable standards and in British Standards, where guidance on selection of cables according to the nominal voltage and category of system is given, it is now shown clearly that the same cable is recommended for the Continental nominal system voltages as for the British nominal system voltages 10% higher. For example in the IEC standards the 10 kV cable is specified for 11 kV (nominal) systems and in the British Standards the 11 kV cable is specified for 10 kV (nominal) systems.

In some countries, which include the UK, there is a preference that the voltage ratings of cables should be expressed internationally in terms of the maximum voltages for which the cables are suitable. This would be consistent with the practice for some other items of equipment, in addition to removing ambiguity. Indeed in some countries, Sweden for example, this is already done. In Sweden the voltage of a single core cable for a category A or B system is designated in the form $U_m/\sqrt{3}$, e.g. $12/\sqrt{3}$ kV (meaning 12 divided by $\sqrt{3}$).

Internationally there is no agreement to full adoption of a similar procedure at present, but the trend is in that direction and IEC standards for cables now give more prominence to U_m. The IEC moves in this direction are reflected in British Standards. Where not unwieldly, U_m is being included in the voltage designations of cables, giving a full designation in the form U_0/U (U_m). Thus in IEC standards we have cables described as 18/30 (U_m = 36) kV, for example, and in British Standards as 19/33 (U_m = 36) kV.

In North America the standard system voltages differ from those in Europe (see IEC Publication 38, 'IEC standard voltages'). In the USA standards published by IPCEA, NEMA and AEIC for XLPE insulated cables the steps of insulation thickness change at the voltage steps 600 V, 2 kV, 5 kV, 8 kV, 15 kV, 25 kV, 28 kV and 35 kV. These are not necessarily standard system voltages, but for a voltage between these steps the insulation thickness is the same as for the next higher voltage step.

The manner of catering for differences between systems of the same phase-to-phase voltage (U in IEC terminology) differs in the USA from the European method of categorisation. The cable standards refer to 100%, 133% and 173% insulation levels. The 100% level is suitable when the system provides for practically immediate isolation when a phase becomes earthed, the limit being set at 1 min. For longer periods up to 1 hour the 133% level is suitable. If a phase may remain earthed indefinitely, or presumably for more than 1 hour, the 173% level applies. In the XLPE cable standards mentioned insulation thicknesses are given for the 100% and 133% levels, but for the 173% level the cable manufacturer should be consulted.

APPLICATIONS OF CABLE TYPES FOR PUBLIC SUPPLY

22 kV and 33 kV cables

In the UK and other countries 33 kV cables are widely used for distribution in public supply systems. At this voltage the merits of the pressure-assisted types of cable, covered more fully in part 4, come into consideration. These include oil-filled cables and internal gas pressure cables, with either reinforced lead sheaths or aluminium sheaths. The choice between pressure cable, paper insulated solid type cable and from the 1970s XLPE or EPR insulated cables, depends upon technical and economic factors applying to the particular installation.

In the UK the 3-core paper insulated, screened, lead sheathed and steel wire armoured cable has had the greatest use for 33 kV, then the oil-filled cable, which in turn has been more used than gas pressure cable. The same types of cable have been supplied overseas for similar purposes. XLPE insulated cable has had increasing use during the 1980s as an alternative to paper insulated cable.

The use of 22 kV as a distribution voltage for public supply in the UK is confined to the northeast part of the country, where 22 kV cables take the place of the 33 kV cables used in other parts. 20 kV, however, is a widely used distribution voltage in other European countries, such as France and Germany. The traditional British type of 22 kV cable is the 3-core paper insulated, screened, lead sheathed and wire armoured type.

The SL type of cable, having a lead sheath on each core, is covered by BS 6480, the British Standard for paper insulated cables, for 33 and 22 kV, but its use in the UK has been very small compared with the type having the three cores under a common lead sheath. Being more expensive, the SL cable has generally been used in the UK only for installations where the advantage of three separately sheathed cores which can be split up for termination has been particularly convenient. This might apply for fairly short route lengths where an armoured 3-core cable was preferred to three single-core cables. The SL cable has had rather more use in continental Europe and in some of the Commonwealth countries. For cables with oil–rosin compounds the absence of filler spaces is of benefit in restricting compound drainage. Before MIND cables became established this was of more significance and even after the MIND cable, originating in the UK, had spread to Commonwealth countries, it still did not replace cable with oil–rosin impregnant throughout the whole of Europe, its use in Germany, for example, remaining exceptional.

Even in the 1950s a few isolated installations of cables insulated with thermoplastic polyethylene (PE) were made in the UK, but these were primarily to gain experience rather than for direct technical or economic benefit. In the UK the use of the paper insulated types of cable has predominated for 33 and 22 kV but XLPE insulated cable has gained ground in the 1980s.

In other parts of the world there has been a marked swing towards cables with crosslinked types of extruded insulation, especially XLPE. In countries where skilled labour for jointing and terminating of cables is scarce, there is more incentive to adopt cables with extruded insulation than there is in countries where there is a background of long experience with paper insulated metal sheathed cables. Skill and care are required with all the types of cable, but the extruded insulations are less susceptible to moisture pick-up and do not involve the plumbing of metallic sheaths. Moreover the crosslinked insulations can be operated at higher temperatures and this is of greater benefit in the Middle East, for instance, than in the cooler climates of northern Europe.

In North America, Japan and some European countries cables with extruded insulation, generally of the crosslinked types, have been adopted, largely to the exclusion of paper insulated cables. Amongst European countries this change was probably most rapid in Sweden. The economic and other factors influencing these changes vary between countries and the changes which occur in some countries do not occur at the same rate, if at all, in others.

During the 1970s, when the worldwide trend towards extruded insulations for increasingly higher voltages gathered momentum, there was no clear case for following this trend over the general range of voltages for cables for public supply in the UK. However, during that period the production facilities of British manufacturers became increasingly oriented towards export markets, and the cable produced for public supply systems in the UK, as a proportion of the total cable produced, progressively diminished, although remaining an important part. British manufacturers gained wide experience with cables having crosslinked extruded insulation and supplied large quantities overseas during the decade, mainly for voltages up to 15 kV, and at the end of that period had entered the field at 33 kV and even higher voltages.

Given the availability of the plant and manufacturing technique, for 33 kV the single-core XLPE insulated cable without armouring can compete with the conventional 3-core paper insulated lead sheathed and armoured cable. The 3-core lead sheathed paper insulated cable is normally armoured, since it depends for exclusion of water upon the lead sheath, which would be vulnerable to mechanical damage if unprotected. Armouring of the XLPE cable is less needed and, provided that the magnitude and duration of earth fault currents are kept reasonably low by the system arrangements, a relatively light copper wire screen will suffice as the surrounding earthed metal layer.

Around the turn of the decade several installations of 33 kV single-core XLPE insulated cables were made in the UK. The quantities of cable were relatively small, but marked the beginning of a trend which has progressed to larger scale use.

In the UK the 33 kV cable has been mainly single core, but some 3-core armoured cable has been used. Also 3-core armoured cable has been supplied, on a larger scale, to overseas customers.

While the crosslinked insulations have clear advantages in providing for higher operating temperature both for sustained and short-circuit conditions, the use of thermoplastic polyethylene (PE) has not been universally abandoned. In France, for example, Electricité de France have adopted a single-core 20 kV cable for which the specification provides for the use of PE as well as XLPE insulation.

11 kV and 15 kV cables

In the British public supply system 11 kV is the main distribution voltage between 240/415 V and 33 kV. 6.6 kV systems were once fairly common but have largely been converted to 11 kV. 15 kV is not a standard British system voltage but, taken to embrace 13.8 kV, is a common voltage in countries to which Britain exports cables.

The continental European 10 kV, as already indicated, is regarded as equivalent to the British 11 kV for cable design purposes. In North America 8 and 15 kV, while distinct steps for the determination of insulation thickness, call for generally similar types of cable.

For several decades up to about 1970 the type of cable used in the UK, Europe and the countries influenced by them, such as the Commonwealth countries of Australia, New Zealand and India, as well as countries supplied by them, was predominantly the 3-core paper insulated, lead sheathed, armoured and served cable. The corresponding single-core cable, generally not armoured, was used for the most part only for short interconnectors or tails, or for unusually high currents requiring large conductors. For 11 kV the 3-core belted cable was the more popular, but some supply authorities preferred the screened design. Some 15 kV belted cables were used overseas, but towards the end of the period the screened design was standardised for this voltage.

There were some variations from the normal form, particularly in cable finishes. For example in the London area wire armoured cables without serving were used for pulling into ducts. When extruded PVC oversheaths were introduced these were sometimes used instead of taped servings for cables to be installed in corrosive environments or to be installed partly indoors when a clean finish and/or one which would not readily propagate flames if affected by fire was required.

In the 1950s some aluminium sheathed cables had been made in the UK, using a technique of pulling the cable into an oversize pipe which was then died-down. At first these cables had the same protective servings as were customarily applied to lead sheathed cables, as the susceptibility of aluminium sheaths to corrosion when buried was not fully realised, and experience was not satisfactory (chapter 5). The inclusion of rubber and/or PVC tapes in the servings was not a complete solution because of their limited resistance to mechanical damage unless they were used in thicknesses which tended to offset the economic advantage of using an unarmoured aluminium sheath in place of lead.

After that experience the use of aluminium sheaths for 11 kV cables did not come into prominence again until early in the 1970s. In the meantime, presses which could be relied upon for the extrusion of aluminium sheaths had become established, and extruded plastic oversheaths, principally PVC, which provided better protection against corrosion were available and widely used. Aluminium sheaths were by then well established for pressure assisted cables and at the lower end of the voltage range the Consac cable, with aluminium sheath as combined neutral and earth conductor (chapter 23), was in regular supply.

A clear cost saving could be achieved by using an aluminium sheath with extruded PVC oversheath in place of the traditional lead sheath with wire armour and bituminised fibrous bedding and serving. When the aluminium sheathed 11 kV cable was introduced, therefore, it was fairly rapidly adopted by most of the Electricity Boards of the UK electricity supply industry. The conversion was not complete and in some areas the armoured lead sheathed cable remained in demand, but the aluminium sheathed cable has become the most used type for new 11 kV installations in the distribution system for public supply.

At first there was use of both cables with corrugated sheaths and cables with smooth sheaths. In due course, however, the consensus of users favoured the corrugated sheath, mainly because of the greater flexibility and lower thermo-mechanical forces at joints, these practical advantages for installation and use outweighing the less obvious advantages of the smooth sheath. The rationalised cable has become the belted corrugated aluminium sheathed cable in the three stranded aluminium conductor sizes of 95, 185 and 300 mm^2. The screened cable is used in the Midlands and the southeastern parts of the UK, however, and other conductor sizes are sometimes required.

The introduction of 10 kV paper insulated cables with extruded aluminium sheaths, generally similar to the British 11 kV cable, occurred somewhat earlier in Germany, but there the cost in comparison with the lead sheathed cable, usually armoured with steel tape, was apparently different and it did not replace the traditional cable to the same degree as in the UK.

It is of interest to note that in Italy 10 kV paper insulated lead (or lead alloy) sheathed cables with PVC oversheaths are used without armour. In the UK the general view is that the relatively soft lead sheath requires armouring, whereas with the harder aluminium armouring is not necessary.

In the world at large during the 1970s, the trend away from paper insulated cables towards the cables with crosslinked extruded insulations, already mentioned for 33 kV cables, was developing more rapidly for cables in the 10–15 kV range. As usual in the development of new insulating materials suitable for a range of voltages, their adoption occurred earlier and more rapidly at the lower end of the range and extended upwards gradually to the voltages where the demands made on them became more onerous.

Already in the USA PE, at first, and later XLPE insulated cables were in general use. In the USA there is a wide use of single-phase distribution at the 8–15 kV voltage levels. For this application a cable with a circular phase conductor and a concentric neutral conductor arranged around the screened insulation is an economic type for which extruded insulation is particularly attractive. Such cable is used with or without an extruded oversheath ('jacket' in US terminology).

In the developing countries comprising the export markets for cable manufacturers, although distribution at 10–15 kV is mostly 3-phase, the trend to crosslinked extruded insulation developed for the reasons already mentioned in connection with 33 kV cables, in addition to any desire on the part of the users to be fashionable in following the most modern practices. The aluminium sheathed paper insulated cable did not make much impact in these markets: the aluminium sheath required even more demanding jointing techniques than the traditional lead sheathed cables.

Thus in the UK, where there was not a great demand at home for 11 kV cables with extruded insulation for the public supply system, an increasing proportion of manufacturer's production of 10–15 kV cable during the 1970s was of this type, and this has continued in the 1980s.

In view of the general world trend and the effect that this would have on manufacturing plant, the cablemakers and the electricity supply industry in the UK gave consideration to preparing a provisional standard design of cable having extruded crosslinked insulation which in the long term could prove technically and economically viable. The design which first emerged from these joint deliberations was a 3-core cable having shaped solid aluminium conductors, extruded semiconducting conductor screen, XLPE or EPR insulation, extruded strippable semiconducting insulation screen, a semiconducting extruded unvulcanised compound based on synthetic rubber as a common covering over the laid-up cores, a concentric screen of copper wires in waveform, and a PVC oversheath. Limited quantities of this cable have been put into use, but it has not been adopted widely.

Later it was considered that a design based on three single cores, which would enable advantage to be taken of terminating techniques using pre-moulded stress control and insulating fittings, to which polymeric cables lend themselves, would have greater potential for economies and convenience in overall systems. A design is being investigated in which each core consists of stranded aluminium conductor, semiconducting conductor screen, XLPE insulation, extruded strippable semiconducting insulation screen, semiconducting water-swellable tape, aluminium/polymer laminate applied longitudinally with an overlap and a polyethylene oversheath. The polyethylene oversheath bonds to the polymer layer of the aluminium laminate during its extrusion and seals the overlap, so that the aluminium layer becomes the main barrier to water as well as being the outer earthed metal layer. The water-swellable tape, as the description implies, swells up in the presence of water; its function is to block the space between the core and the aluminium layer to inhibit passage of water along the cable in the event of local penetration. Three such cores are laid up together to form what is described as a 'triplex' cable. Generally, during laying-up, stranded copper conductors would be inserted in the centre interstice of the cores and/or the outer interstices. These are to provide additional earth fault current carrying capacity, as the aluminium layer on each core is only 0.2 mm thick and has limited current carrying capacity of its own. Further details of the 'triplex' cable are given in the paper entitled '11 kV polymeric insulated triplex cable' presented at the IEE Conference in November 1986.[1]

This design has similarities with the type of 20 kV cable used in France, which also makes use of an aluminium laminate on each core and is of the triplex form. In France the system is designed to limit earth fault currents to much lower levels than generally apply amongst the Area Boards of the electricity supply industry in the UK. Catering for earth fault currents under conditions of both a fault in the cable and a fault in another part of the system, giving rise to through-fault currents, is a particular problem affecting polymeric cables in the UK, where the levels tend to be high and are different between Boards.

While they may not come strictly within the category of distribution cables, the cables used in power stations certainly form part of the system for public supply. A considerable quantity of 11 kV cable is used in the cabling of UK power stations and for this application the type with extruded crosslinked insulation, XLPE or EPR, was standard until relatively recently, when much greater emphasis was placed on catering for the effects of fire (see later). Single-core cables are convenient for this purpose, much of which is interconnection, and with the extruded insulations 'dry' terminations (i.e. not compound filled) can be used in a compact form and can also be readily designed to enable easy disconnection and reconnection. The standardised design of cable has circular copper or aluminium conductor, more often aluminium, extruded semiconducting conductor screen, XLPE or EPR insulation, semiconducting insulation screen, copper tape, extruded PVC inner sheath, aluminium wire armour and PVC oversheath. This is a light cable compared with lead sheathed paper cable, which had been used previously, and allows some savings in the strength of supporting structures. The high short-circuit current capacity of cables with the crosslinked insulations, compared with cables having other insulants, is also a particular advantage in power stations. As the installations are for the most part in air, the water treeing phenomenon, while it cannot be disregarded, assumes less importance than for cables for burial in the ground.

A 3-core cable of the same basic type, having three similar copper taped cores laid-up together before application for the inner sheath and generally having galvanised steel instead of aluminium wire as the armour, has often been used for site supplies during the construction of power stations. A similar construction is also popular in overseas markets for general purposes.

The changes being introduced to power station cables to take account of all the effects when cables are involved in fires will not affect the general constructions, but the materials used in cables for new power stations, especially for beddings and oversheaths, will differ from those previously used in such cables. The type of PVC used for bedding and oversheathing of power station cables has been that described as 'reduced propagating'. This was necessary to meet stringent flame propagation tests on bunches of cables installed vertically in prescribed formations. The test was introduced when experience showed that the types of PVC compound more generally used on cables would spread fire under such conditions, which simulate situations met in power station installations. The requirements now specified for cables for new power stations, while including the demanding reduced flame propagation requirement, also embrace other aspects of performance in fires, such as low smoke emission and extremely low acid gas generation, which eliminate the use of PVC. Other performance requirements, relating, for example, to ageing and water permeation, go beyond those covered by previously conventional testing, and for pressurised water reactor nuclear power stations there are special additional requirements for cables for use in the containment areas. Cables employing special materials and combinations thereof have been under development and test in recent years to provide a range which has been described as the 'new generation of power station cables'. More information is given in the paper entitled 'Cables for new power stations' presented at the IEE Conference in November 1986.[2]

Cable with extruded insulation is also an appropriate type for the single-core interconnectors and tails in the substations of the public supply system. The quantity of cable is small compared with the buried 3-core distribution cable, but it justifies separate consideration and a change from paper insulated to XLPE insulated cable began in the UK in the late 1970s. The design differs from the original design for the CEGB power stations, mainly in that it is unarmoured. A copper wire screen is applied helically onto the extruded semiconducting insulation screen and this is covered with a PVC oversheath.

600/1000 V cables

The types of cable used for public supply are covered in chapter 23, which deals with CNE cables. Before these types became established, the commonly used cable was the 4-core paper insulated, lead sheathed and armoured type. The four conductors were the three phase conductors and the neutral, and the lead sheath provided the main earth path to the substation earth.

When the PVC insulated 600/1000 V cable with shaped conductors became an established type at the beginning of the 1960s, it was not adopted for buried installation in the public supply system in the UK mainly because, as a thermoplastic material, the PVC would be subject to softening and deformation at the overload temperatures which might arise. In some countries, such as Germany, where it is understood that closer protection of the 600/1000 V public supply cables against excess current is practised, PVC insulated cables are used. As mentioned in chapter 23, a PVC insulated and sheathed cable without metallic covering has become the most widely used type of cable there.

In the UK adoption of 600/1000 V cables with extruded insulation for the underground public supply system, apart from service cables (chapter 24), awaited the development of cables with the crosslinked types of insulation included in the 'Waveconal' cable. These types of insulation, of which XLPE is the most commonly used, are more tolerant of overloads than thermoplastic materials such as PVC.

In accordance with the normal approach of adopting new insulants first at the lower voltages, the Waveconal cable was the first type of distribution cable with XLPE insulation to be put to major use in the UK, early in the 1970s. Since then BS 5467, which covers 600/1000 V and 1.9/3.3 kV cables with XLPE or HEPR insulation (HEPR is a hard version of EPR), has been published. This cable was produced for some years before publication of the British Standard but was not used for the public supply system in this country, where the CNE types were preferred.

In France, cable of the same basic design as the Waveconal type is used and there is also a substantial use of Districable with XLPE insulation.

In Germany there was some usage of the Consac type of cable starting prior to its introduction in the UK, but it seems now to have lost its place to the 4-core PVC insulated cable without metal covering. There are indications that the latter may in turn be displaced, to some extent at least, by cable of similar construction but having XLPE insulation.

In the developing countries, which constitute an important part of the cable manufacturers' export market, the trend has been towards cable with extruded insulation, as at higher voltages, but beginning sooner. Armoured PVC insulated cables of the type covered by BS 6346 have been used even in climates where ambient temperatures are high, and in some countries this has continued, but largely these have given way to cables with XLPE insulation, such as specified in BS 5467. At the same time the 4-core paper insulated, lead sheathed and armoured cable had still not gone completely out of use by 1980, when quantities were still being supplied.

It should be noted that the statements made about the non-use of PVC cables on any significant scale for public supply do not apply to installations in power stations. The conditions of use of these cables are much more closely akin to those in industrial installations and, for voltages up to 3.3 kV, armoured PVC insulated cables to BS 6346 were the standard type in Great Britain for power stations, as in industry. For new power stations replacement of these by cables of the 'new generation' is projected, as previously explained for 11 kV cables.

CABLES FOR GENERAL INDUSTRIAL APPLICATIONS

For power supplies within the more general types of industrial plants the same types of cable have been used at the higher end of the voltage range as for the public supply system, but the relative usage of the various types is inclined to be more weighted towards those which are simpler for installation rather than the more sophisticated types. A factor influencing the choice is that generally the route lengths are shorter and this also places more emphasis on the ease of terminating the cables.

11–33 kV cables

At 33 kV the paper insulated, lead sheathed and armoured cable has predominated, although the pressure assisted systems have been used for some of the larger installations.

For 11 kV, the traditional paper insulated, lead sheathed and armoured cable has again had the major use. The larger part of this has been of belted construction, but the screened type has been favoured by some users. A factor which has influenced the choice of screened cable in some industries has been the wish to reduce the possibility of faults between phases and to try to confine faults to the phase to earth condition, with better control over the magnitude of fault current. The screened cable, particularly if a copper screen is used instead of the more normal and cheaper aluminium, improves the prospect of achieving this. The use of aluminium conductors, standardised for the public supply system in the UK for all 11 kV cables, is less general in the industrial sector because, while cables with aluminium conductors have intrinsically been more economical than those with copper conductors over a long period, effective terminations are more easily achieved with copper. There are two aspects to this, one being that effective connection to copper is more easily made by soldering or mechanical means, and the other being that a smaller size of copper conductor is required for the same current rating and this makes it easier to accommodate the cable in connecting chambers on equipment. Ease of termination again playing a part, the aluminium sheaths adopted for public supply cables have not been much used for industrial application.

On the other hand, cables with extruded insulation offer more advantages over paper insulated cables for industrial application than for the public supply system. When these types of cable came into general use, beginning at the lower end of the voltage range, the first insulants used were the thermoplastic materials, led by PVC. In some countries use was extended up the voltage range and in Germany, for example, there was some use of 10 kV PVC cables. The first issue of IEC 502, 'Extruded solid dielectric insulated power cables for rated voltages from 1 kV up to 30 kV', included requirements for PVC insulated cables up to 15 kV. In general for voltages of 6 kV and above the trend has been away from PVC to PE and, as they became available, the crosslinked materials XLPE and EPR. The preference for PE over PVC was influenced by its lower power factor and permittivity, which offered prospects for use at even higher voltages. Nevertheless, there was still some use of PVC for 10 kV cables in some countries at the beginning of the 1980s.

In the UK there has been little use of PVC for voltages above 3.3 kV except for mining cables, which are mentioned later. There was some use of PE for voltages of 11 kV and thereabouts for cables for special applications where its dielectric properties were particularly advantageous and there was some use of it for the 11 kV cables in power stations and for site supplies during construction of power stations prior to the adoption of crosslinked material. However, PE insulated cables did not become established in the UK for more general applications, and it was not until the 1970s, as the manufacturing facilities developed in the country for cables with the crosslinked insulants, that the interest in extruded insulations for 11 kV cables broadened. Now they are well established, mainly with XLPE insulation, although they have not completely replaced the paper insulated cables. The relevant British Standard is BS 6622, 'Cables with extruded crosslinked polyethylene or ethylene–propylene rubber insulation for rated voltages from 3800/6600 V up to 19 000/33 000 V'.

Cables for voltages up to 3.3 kV

At the low end of the voltage range (up to 3.3 kV), in contrast with the higher voltages, there was a rapid changeover from paper insulated to PVC insulated power cables for industrial use in the late 1950s and early 1960s. At the low operating electrical stresses the dielectric properties of PVC were quite adequate. There was no need for conductor or insulation screens, as were thought desirable for 11 kV, and shaped conductors could be used, once the extrusion technique had been developed, without regard to the stress-raising effect. No metal sheath was required and the simplicity of terminations was a major factor in promoting the swing, the cleanliness of the cable and its convenience for handling, associated with flexibility and lightness, also contributing. It was also 'flame retardant', as then defined by the current standard tests.

The thermal limitations of PVC, which inhibited its use for cables in the underground public supply system in the UK, are of much less account in industrial installations or in power stations. In these installations the current to be carried by each cable over a planned future period is known reasonably precisely and close protection against excess current is provided. The international standards giving rules governing electrical installations up to 1 kV in buildings (IEC 364) require that the overload protective device should operate within a limited time at a current not greater than 1.45 times the current rating of the cable, and this requirement is included in the IEE Wiring Regulations. This ensures that the conductor will be limited to a temperature not causing a high degree of deformation of thermoplastic insulation.

The type of cable generally used in the UK is the wire armoured construction specified in BS 6346. The laid-up PVC insulated cores have a common covering of PVC tape or extruded PVC layer which acts as a bedding for the wire armour, over which is applied an extruded PVC sheath. Single-core cables are included in the British Standard, but are generally used only for short interconnections or very large loads. More often the cables are 2-core for single-phase supply (phase and neutral conductors), 3-core or 4-core. For 3-phase supplies, the 600/1000 V cables are more often 4-core than 3-core, including the three phase conductors and the neutral to suit the more commonly used systems. The neutral conductor may be of the same cross-sectional area as the phase conductors or of approximately half the phase conductor area, depending upon the magnitude of the current that the neutral conductor may have to carry in the particular application. The wire armour serves as the protective conductor. Usually the armour has adequate conductance for this purpose, but occasionally an additional earthing conductor external to the cable may be run in parallel with it. Sometimes the conductance of the armour is increased by incorporating hard drawn copper wires in place of some of the steel wires.

Except for the smallest sizes of cable, the taped form of bedding for the wire armour provides a more economical cable than extruded bedding. This is partly because the tape bedding is thinner for the medium and large sizes of cable and partly because it can be applied in the same operation as laying-up the cores or armouring, whereas extrusion of the bedding is a separate operation. The tape bedding, which is adequate for most of the installation conditions in industry, has therefore been more often used than the extruded form. However, if the cable is to be used with a gland which is to seal onto the bedding, as for example when flameproof glands are used in a hazardous atmosphere, a cable with extruded bedding should be used. For cable to be buried in ground where waterlogging is envisaged an extruded bedding is also to be preferred. An extruded bedding is, in effect, an inner sheath protected by the armour and, although PVC insulation is not susceptible to moisture in the same way as paper, it does absorb water to a degree, with an effect on its electrical properties. The inner sheath is therefore worthwhile under onerous conditions.

BS 6346 includes cables with stranded copper conductors and with solid aluminium conductors. Cables with stranded aluminium conductors can be supplied, but the concept when the standard was prepared was that a user wishing to have the benefit of the lower cost of aluminium conductors would be best served by having the most economical form of these, the solid type. Also included in the standard are cables with aluminium conductors and aluminium flat strip armour. The multicore cables of the latter type have an armour conductance that is generally not less than half that of the conductors. In practice, however, the cable having the greatest use is that with copper conductors and galvanised steel wire armour.

In continental Europe there is more use of unarmoured 600/1000 V PVC insulated cable in industrial installations. Such cable often includes a protective conductor, making it, for 3-phase use, a 4-core or 5-core cable, according to whether it includes a neutral conductor. BS 6346 includes unarmoured cables, but when the standard was prepared this was intended to cater for overseas usage more than to meet demand in the UK.

Cables of the same general construction as the PVC cables but having instead crosslinked insulation, primarily XLPE, became available in the 1970s and BS 5467 for wire armoured cables with this type of insulation for voltages up to 3.3 kV was published in 1977. In a later revision unarmoured 600/1000 V cables have been added. These cables have the advantage over PVC insulated cables of higher current ratings and short-circuit capacities and are eminently suitable for the same types of installation. Advantage can be taken of the higher ratings when the current which the cable can carry is controlled by the thermal limitations of the insulation, but not where the conductor size is determined by consideration of voltage drop. Economy in conductor area through higher current density also has to be balanced against the extra losses entailed. During the 1970s and the early part of the 1980s there was no marked swing in the UK from PVC cables to XLPE cables for these uses but in the latter part of the 1980s, as more economic processes for making the XLPE cables, based on the silane method of crosslinking, were developed, there was a fairly rapid transition to XLPE insulated cable as the standard stock type. Its suitability for higher operating temperatures was a clear advantage, as long as it was not more costly, and even if it is not always possible to take advantage of its potential there was little to be lost in using it where the PVC insulated cable would otherwise have been employed.

Also, during the 1980s, sheathing materials were developed which evolve very much reduced amounts of smoke and acidic fumes than PVC when involved in fires. This development, as exploited, for example, in the LSF (low smoke and fumes) cable, led to BS 6724:1986, 'Armoured cables for electricity supply having thermosetting insulation with low emission of smoke and corrosive gases when affected by fire'. Although this British Standard provides for either XLPE or EPR to be used as the insulation, XLPE is more generally used. When burned, XLPE does not produce the dense black smoke and hydrochloric acid gas associated with PVC. While the bedding and oversheathing compounds are critical in the fire performance of the LSF type of cable, the insulation has to be compatible with the concept of low smoke and corrosive gas emission.

Cables with low smoke and fume characteristics were first developed in the UK for the London Underground railway system, where, of course, the avoidance of dense smoke and irritant gases in the event of a fire is a very important consideration. Once the materials and means of production of the cables had been developed their use spread for public buildings, hospitals, installations in tunnels, commercial premises and industrial environments. They have become an appreciable and growing proportion of the cable supplied in this voltage range and cables employing similar materials, but with constructional variations, are also used for higher voltages for installation where the performance in fires is of importance.

Cables used in coal mines

The cables used to carry power into mines towards the working face are regarded essentially as cables for fixed installation, as distinct from the flexible cables used near the coal face which undergo movement and flexing while carrying current. The roadway cables, laid along the underground tunnels, form the large component of the fixed cabling but the cables installed in the shafts are an essential part. The roadway cables may be moved on occasions but are fixed while carrying load.

Until the introduction of PVC insulated mains cables, the type of cable used in the UK was generally insulated with impregnated paper, lead sheathed and armoured with two layers of galvanised steel wires (double wire armour). A typical outer covering was tape and jute braid impregnated with a flame-retardant paint.

When PVC insulated mains cables became available there was a fairly rapid change to them for the mining application. A particular advantage of PVC over insulation consisting of layers of paper tape is its greater mechanical resilience. Failures occasionally occurred in paper cables as a result of internal damage resulting from impact or crushing by rock falls. Tests indicated that PVC insulation was more resistant to such damage.

At that time most of the roadway and shaft cables were rated 1.9/3.3 kV and the design of PVC insulated cable adopted and still used followed fairly closely the design for this voltage covered by the British Standard. The main differences are that the bedding for the armour, which is extruded, is increased to give additional mechanical protection to the cores, a hessian tape is applied over the extruded bedding, i.e. immediately under the armour, and the latter has bitumen compound applied to it between and over the wires. The hessian tape is primarily to act as a holder for the bitumen and the bitumen is regarded as a desirable extra protection against corrosion for the armour. Originally the cables were double wire armoured (DWA), but later some use of single wire armoured (SWA) cables developed. A PVC sheath is extruded over the armour.

At one stage solid sector shaped aluminium conductors were adopted for these 3-core 3.3 kV cables, but they were subsequently abandoned, with reversion to stranded conductors in the interest of greater flexibility. The desire for flexibility also accounted for the adoption of single wire armour as an alternative to double wire armour.

The regulations relating to installations in mines required that the armour on the paper insulated cables should have a conductance not less than 50% of the largest conductor in the cable. Depending on the cable size, this made it necessary to include a number of tinned hard drawn copper wires in the armour of some of the cables. When the PVC insulated cable was adopted, since it had no lead sheath to supplement the armour conductance, a 75% minimum armour conductance was specified for the DWA cables. For the SWA cables, used later, to avoid too high a proportion of the wires being of copper, a 60% level of conductance is specified.

When 6.6 kV came into use in some mines the use of PVC insulated cables was extended to this voltage. This has been the major use of PVC insulated cables at 6.6 kV in the UK. One design of 6.6 kV cable was the same as for 3.3 kV except for an increased thickness of insulation. A second design was similar but had in addition a copper tape applied on a semiconducting tape bedding around each core. The prime purpose of the copper tapes is to provide an earth return path around each phase to carry sufficient current to operate sensitive protection in the event of an earth fault on any phase. The design with the copper tape screens tended to become the standard.

In the 1970s, when a further increase in voltage to 11 kV was contemplated, a small amount of 11 kV PVC cable was supplied. This differed from the 6.6 kV cable in that the conductors were circular and conductors and insulation were fully screened in addition to having greater insulation thickness. However, the UK National Coal Board (now British Coal) later decided to adopt EPR insulation for 11 kV cables and to extend its use downwards to 6.6 kV. The elastomeric properties of EPR, with their benefits for flexibility and resistance to impact and crushing, played an important part in this decision. The designs of the EPR insulated 6.6 kV and 11 kV cables are basically similar to those of the PVC insulated cables, as described above, except for the insulating material.

British Coal have their own cable specifications. These have the numbers 295 for the PVC insulated cables and 656 for the EPR insulated cables.

In most countries there are special designs of cable for mining applications. Usually extruded insulations and armouring are features. In the USA, however, an unarmoured mining cable is used which has copper tapes on the screened cores and copper conductors for earth currents laid in the interstices between cores. It has a fairly heavy thermoplastic or rubber sheath. As the mining techniques, traditions and experience vary, differences in emphasis on the characteristics required of the cables are reflected in the designs employed in different countries.

Cables for oil refineries

In those areas in oil refineries where there may be spillage of oil and its products or chemicals used in the industry, the designs of cable used generally incorporate some modification from the normal standard designs. Solvents especially are able to penetrate through the materials used for extruded insulations and sheaths. While this does not have a serious effect on the properties of the materials themselves, it is clearly desirable to prevent inflammable liquid or vapour gaining access to the cable, passing along it, and emerging at terminations. For such situations the cables usually have a metal sheath, not required for extruded insulations in most other installations.

For cables with PVC, XLPE or other extruded insulations which have to meet these conditions, a number of oil companies specify that a lead or lead alloy sheath should be applied over the assembly of cores. Some specifications require an extruded inner PVC sheath under the lead sheath, but more often the lead sheath is applied directly over a binder holding the cores together. The cables are wire armoured and have a PVC oversheath. The bedding for the armour may be either PVC tapes or an extruded layer of PVC. For the conditions of use it is necessary that the covering over the lead should provide adequate protection against mechanical damage and corrosion.

Some users have adopted a thin aluminium sheath protected by an extruded oversheath instead of a lead sheath with armour. This reduces cost, but the construction appears more vulnerable to the effects of corrosion.

When paper insulated cables are used, they are metal sheathed anyway, but for lead sheathed wire armoured cable, which is the usual type, PVC beddings and oversheath are used.

BASIS OF CABLE DESIGN

Thickness of paper insulation

Table 19.2 shows the thicknesses of paper insulation specified in the international standard IEC 55–2.

For paper insulation the thicknesses are minimum values; the specification requires that, when measured by the method stipulated, the thickness should not be less than that shown in the table. The method of measurement in effect gives the average thickness of the layer around the core or around the cable, but with an insulation comprising layers of tape each of substantially uniform thickness there is no significant variation around the periphery.

As indicated by the notes to table 19.2, the thicknesses given in the tables for rated voltages 6/10 kV and above include allowances for semiconducting or metallised screening layers. Some of these screening layers are required and some are optional, the option of whether to include them being the manufacturer's. It is because some of the screening layers are optional that the insulation thicknesses are given in this way. If the manufacturer includes the screens, he may reduce the thickness of actual insulation by the applied screen thicknesses or by a certain allowed amount, whichever is smaller, the concept being that the improvement in electrical performance achieved by screening permits this reduction in the insulation. If the manufacturer uses a screen of thickness greater than the allowed value for either required or optional screens, then he may only reduce the insulation thickness by the allowed value. If the manufacturer does not apply the optional screens, then the full thickness given in the table has to be applied as insulation.

The following summarises this aspect.

6/10 kV single-core cables
Screening of conductor and over insulation are both optional. The allowance included in the thickness if either or both are used is up to 0.2 mm.

6/10 kV 3-core belted cables
Screening of conductor and over belt insulation are both optional. The allowances included in the thicknesses are as follows:

(a) if conductor screening only is used, up to 0.4 mm between conductors and up to 0.2 mm between conductors and sheath;
(b) if belt screening only is used, up to 0.2 mm between conductors and sheath;
(c) if both conductor and belt screening is used, up to 0.4 mm between conductors and between conductors and sheath.

6/10 kV 3-core screened cables
Conductor and core screening are both required. The allowance included in the thickness is up to 0.2 mm.

8.7/10 kV 3-core belted cables
Conductor screening is required, and screening over belt insulation is optional. The allowances included in the thicknesses are as follows:

(a) if conductor screening only is used, up to 0.4 mm between conductors and up to 0.2 mm between conductors and sheath;
(b) if both conductor and belt screening is used, up to 0.4 mm between conductors and between conductors and sheath.

8.7/15 kV, 12/20 kV and 18/30 kV single-core and three-core screened cables
Screening of conductor(s) and over insulation is required. The allowance included in the thickness is up to 0.3 mm.

In BS 6480 those screening layers which are optional in the IEC standard are specified as required layers. This simplifies the way in which insulation thicknesses can be presented and they are specified as thicknesses of insulation alone, not including screens, appropriate amounts to allow for the latter having been subtracted from the IEC values.

While there are some variations, the thicknesses of paper insulations specified in the national standards of the Western European countries are much in accord with the IEC standard. This is less a matter of the national standards being based on the IEC standard than of the IEC standard taking account of the experience and the national standards of the developed countries, which existed long before the international standardisation took place, with compromises to resolve differences.

Thickness of extruded insulation

Table 19.3 shows the thicknesses of extruded insulation specified in IEC 502.

For this type of insulation the thicknesses given are 'minimum average' values, i.e. the average of a number of measurements around the core is required to be not less than the value in the table. The thickness of an extruded insulation is likely to be less uniform than that of a laminar insulation and the smallest of the set of measurements around the core, often designated the 'minimum thickness at a point', is allowed to fall below the thickness given in the table by an amount not exceeding 10% plus 0.1 mm.

These thicknesses for extruded insulants, given in table 19.3, are all exclusive of screening. The 3.6/6 kV cables with PE or XLPE insulation are required to have semiconducting screens over the conductor and over the insulation, but the 3.6/6 kV

Table 19.2 Thicknesses of impregnated paper insulation

Conductor size (mm^2)	600/1000 V singlecore (mm)	600/1000 V multicore		1.8/3 kV singlecore (mm)
		Conductor/conductor (mm)	Conductor/sheath (mm)	
4	–	1.2	1.0	–
6	–	1.2	1.0	–
10	–	1.2	1.0	–
16	–	1.2	1.0	–
25	–	1.4	1.2	–
35	–	1.4	1.2	–
50	1.2	1.4	1.2	1.8
70	1.2	1.4	1.2	1.8
95	1.3	1.4	1.2	1.8
120	1.3	1.4	1.2	1.8
150	1.4	1.8	1.4	1.8
185	1.4	1.8	1.4	1.8
240	1.6	2.0	1.6	1.8
300	1.7	2.0	1.6	1.8
400	1.8	2.0	1.6	1.9
500	2.0	–	–	2.0
630	2.0	–	–	2.0
800	2.0	–	–	2.0
1000	2.0	–	–	2.0

Rated voltage (kV)	Number of cores	Range of conductors (mm^2)	Insulation thickness	
			Conductor/conductor (mm)	Conductor/sheath (mm)
1.8/3	3	16–400	2.4	1.8
3/3	3	16–400	2.4	2.1
3.6/6	1	50–1000	–	2.4
3.6/6	3	16–400	4.2	2.7
6/6	3	16–400	4.2	3.1
6/10	1	50–1000	–	3.0[a]
6/10	3 belted	16–400	5.8[a]	3.5[a]
6/10	3 screened	16–400	–	3.0[b]
8.7/10	3 belted	16–400	5.8[b]	4.3[b]
8.7/15	1	50–1000	–	3.9[b]
8.7/15	3 screened	25–400	–	3.9[b]
12/20	1	50–1000	–	5.0[b]
12/20	3 screened	25–400	–	5.0[b]
18/30	1	50	–	7.3[b]
		70–1000	–	7.0[b]
	3 screened	35	–	7.8[b]
		50	–	7.3[b]
		70–400	–	7.0[b]

[a] May include screening layers
[b] Includes screening layers

Table 19.3 Thicknesses of extruded insulations

Conductor size (mm^2)	Insulation thickness									
	600/1000 V			1.8/3 kV			3.6/6 kV			
	PVC (mm)	XLPE (mm)	EPR (mm)	PVC (mm)	XLPE (mm)	EPR (mm)	PVC (mm)	PE (mm)	XLPE (mm)	EPR (mm)
1.5 and 2.5	0.8	0.7	1.0							
4 and 6	1.0	0.7	1.0							
10	1.0	0.7	1.0	2.2	2.0	2.2	3.4	2.5	2.5	3.0
16	1.0	0.7	1.0	2.2	2.0	2.2	3.4	2.5	2.5	3.0
25	1.2	0.9	1.2	2.2	2.0	2.2	3.4	2.5	2.5	3.0
35	1.2	0.9	1.2	2.2	2.0	2.2	3.4	2.5	2.5	3.0
50	1.4	1.0	1.4	2.2	2.0	2.2	3.4	2.5	2.5	3.0
70	1.4	1.1	1.4	2.2	2.0	2.2	3.4	2.5	2.5	3.0
95	1.6	1.1	1.6	2.2	2.0	2.4	3.4	2.5	2.5	3.0
120	1.6	1.2	1.6	2.2	2.0	2.4	3.4	2.5	2.5	3.0
150	1.8	1.4	1.8	2.2	2.0	2.4	3.4	2.5	2.5	3.0
185	2.0	1.6	2.0	2.2	2.0	2.4	3.4	2.5	2.5	3.0
240	2.2	1.7	2.2	2.2	2.0	2.4	3.4	2.6	2.6	3.0
300	2.4	1.8	2.4	2.4	2.0	2.4	3.4	2.8	2.9	3.0
400	2.6	2.0	2.6	2.6	2.0	2.6	3.4	3.0	3.0	3.0
500	2.8	2.2	2.8	2.8	2.2	2.8	3.4	3.2	3.2	3.2
630	2.8	2.4	2.8	2.8	2.4	2.8	3.4	3.2	3.2	3.2
800	2.8	2.6	2.8	2.8	2.6	2.8	3.4	3.2	3.2	3.2
1000	3.0	2.8	3.0	3.0	2.8	3.0	3.4	3.2	3.2	3.2

Rated voltage (kV)	Range of conductors (mm^2)	Insulation thickness			
		PVC (mm)	PE (mm)	XLPE (mm)	EPR (mm)
6/10	16–1000	4.0	3.4	3.4	3.4
8.7/15	25–1000	5.2	4.5	4.5	4.5
12/20	35–1000	6.4	5.5	5.5	5.5
18/30	50–1000	–	8.0	8.0	8.0

PVC and EPR cables need not include such screens. Cables for 6/10 kV and above have semiconducting conductor and insulation screens for all the insulating materials.

Generally these thicknesses are adopted by the European countries. There is a partial exception in the UK where the thicknesses for the material known as HEPR for 600/1000 V and 1.9/3.3 kV cables are those specified in IEC 502 for XLPE instead of those for EPR. The test requirements relating to mechanical properties for HEPR differ, however, from those for EPR in the IEC standards.

It is understood that in Japan the insulation thicknesses specified in national standards for XLPE insulated cables are somewhat greater than the IEC values but for export purposes the IEC values are used.

In the USA, where the rated voltages differ from those taken as the standard values in IEC 502, the IEC insulation thicknesses are not applicable. However, table 19.4 compares the 100% levels for XLPE specified in the IPCEA/NEMA publication mentioned previously with IEC thicknesses, and it will be seen that there is not a very wide difference.

The insulation thicknesses specified in the USA for EPR for the voltage range 5–35 kV are the same as for XLPE. For these voltages both types of cable have conductor and insulation screening.

Table 19.4 Comparison of USA and IEC thicknesses of XLPE insulation

Rated voltage (V)	Insulation thickness USA (mm)	Insulation thickness IEC (mm)	Rated voltage (V)	Insulation thickness USA (mm)	Insulation thickness IEC (mm)
600	0.76–2.03		10000		3.4
1000		0.7–2.8	15000	4.44	4.5
2000	1.14–2.29		20000		5.5
3000		2.0–2.8	25000	6.6	
5000	2.29		28000	7.11	
6000		2.5–3.2	30000		8.0
8000	2.92		35000	8.76	

Dimensions of other component layers

Thicknesses of metallic sheaths and extruded non-metallic coverings and the dimensions of armour wires and tapes are generally derived from formulae or tables which relate the thickness to the diameter of the underlying cable. For some layers comprising lapped materials, such as tapes, the thickness may be the same for the whole range of diameters. Examples are fibrous beddings and servings for armoured paper insulated lead sheathed cables, which in IEC 55–2 and BS 6480 have specified approximate thicknesses of 1.5 and 2 mm respectively for the whole range of cable sizes. For other lapped layers there may be only two or three different thicknesses related to quite wide steps in diameter. For example, two thicknesses of steel tape, 0.5 or 0.8 mm, are sufficient for steel tape armouring for the range of cables in IEC 55–2 and BS 6480. Extruded layers, including metallic sheaths, generally have the most gradual increments in thickness corresponding with comparatively small steps in diameter. Wire armour is intermediate, with five different diameters for the same range of cable sizes as accommodated by the two thicknesses of steel tape.

IEC 502 (cables with extruded insulants) and IEC 55–2 (paper insulated lead sheathed cables) both include appendices which give the methods for calculating the thicknesses of the various coverings applied over the core or laid-up cores of the cable progressively up to the final oversheath. The diameters to which the thicknesses are related by formulae or tables are termed 'fictitious diameters', because they are calculated by a formalised method and do not represent the real diameters that any particular manufacturer is expected to achieve. Thus there are standard thicknesses required by the specification irrespective of variations in diameter between manufacturers, due, for example, to degree of compaction or methods of shaping conductors, or between batches produced by one manufacturer.

In IEC 55−2 the thicknesses are pre-calculated and presented in comprehensive tables for each standard voltage and number and size of conductors. In this document the inclusion of the method of calculation is therefore mainly a record, but it may be used by manufacturers to calculate values for cables generally in accordance with the standard but not of the standard sizes included in the detailed tables. In IEC 502 such pre-calculated dimensional tables are not included, the standard covering a wide range of possible constructions, but manufacturers follow the method to derive values for the particular construction they quote against individual enquiries.

The practice in British Standards is to give constructional tables with pre-calculated values of thicknesses and armour dimensions even for the cables with extruded insulants, and the calculation methods, which are basically similar to the IEC methods, are not included.

Metallic coverings

Metallic sheaths are essential for paper insulated cables to exclude water from the insulation. For the extruded insulations there is not such an obvious need for a surrounding metallic layer for the effective functioning of the cable. However, IEC 502 requires that such cables of rated voltages above 1 kV should have a metallic covering. Unless there is an earthed low resistivity layer around the cable the electric field will extend beyond the limits of the cable and, if the stress is high enough, which may be the case at voltages above 1 kV, this may cause sparking to earthed metal in contact with or close to the cable or may affect any person who comes into contact with it.

If the cable includes a metal layer surrounding the cores individually or collectively for another purpose, for example metal tapes as part of the core screening, an earthed concentric conductor, a metallic sheath or an armour, then this may serve also for the shielding function. Otherwise a shield, which usually consists of copper tape(s) or wires, is applied especially for this purpose.

Cables without any metallic covering are used and are suitable for voltages above 1 kV in particular situations. An example would be overhead insulated conductor which is out of reach and well spaced from earth. At ground level, cables without metallic coverings might be used within enclosures and spaced from earthed metal. In standards for cables for general purposes, however, the emphasis is on requirements which normally apply, leaving special designs to be dealt with on an individual basis, ensuring full understanding of any limitations on their use.

In addition to fulfilling this shielding function, and perhaps also being a water-impermeable sheath or an armour, the metallic covering is often used as the cable component to carry fault current to earth in the event of an earth fault on the system. For this purpose it needs to have sufficient conductance and thermal capacity to avoid it becoming overheated when carrying the prospective fault current for the time required to operate the overcurrent protective device. Steel tape armour is generally not suitable for this function. It is applied helically with a short lay and a gap between the turns and its resistance per unit length of cable is high compared with wire armour, which is applied with a comparatively long lay. Although there are two layers of steel tape, contact resistance between the layers is likely to be high when carrying heavy currents, especially if, as often applies, the tape surfaces are coated with a preservative compound.

For similar reasons copper wires are preferable to tapes as a shield when it is required to carry heavy earth fault currents.

In British practice standard types of cable with extruded insulation, when armoured, are armoured with wires rather than tapes. The size of the armour wire increases with increase in cable size and usually the wire armour will cope with the earth fault current. However, British manufacturers supply cables armoured with steel tape when this is required by overseas customers. Steel tape might be preferred, being of lower cost, when it is primarily to provide mechanical protection or serve as a shield and not to carry substantial fault current.

The use of wire armour in the UK has been generally more extensive than in most other countries. It was customary in the UK, when using lead sheathed cables in the public supply systems, to have steel tape armoured cables for low voltage and wire armoured cables for the higher voltages. Wire armour was regarded as the superior type appropriate for the more important cables and the different armouring was a convenient means of distinguishing between low and high voltage cables when carrying out excavation after the cables had been installed.

On lead sheathed cables the current carrying capability of the armour is of less importance than on cables not having a metallic sheath to fulfill this function. Wire armour, however, is advantageous in providing longitudinal strength to the cable as well as resistance to impact. The benefits of this are obvious for cables to be installed vertically or supported horizontally in cleats, or for cables to be pulled into ducts or laid elsewhere where pulling tensions are likely to be high. Even for buried cables, it can be an advantage if there is some ground movement after the cables have been laid. The steel wire used is galvanised and this generally preserves it well from corrosion. Steel tape armour is sometimes galvanised but more often has a coating of a bituminous compound.

In continental Europe steel tape is the most common form of armouring for lead sheathed cables over the range of distribution voltages, the tendency being to reserve wire armouring for installations where longitudinal strength is particularly required. Wire armour, when it is used, is often in the form of flat wires, whereas the standard in the UK is round wire. There is sometimes difficulty in inducing flat steel wires to lie flat on the cable when applied and often a steel tape is applied helically with an open lay on top of them to hold them in position. This tape is often called a 'counter helix'. Such a binder tape is sometimes used even on round wire armour, under a serving or oversheath, but the British experience indicates that this is unnecessary.

REFERENCES

(1) White, T. M., Gibbs, J. W., Phillips, R. B., Hyde, H. B., Philbrick, S. E. and Bungay, E. W. G. (1986) '11 kV polymeric insulated triplex cable'. *IEE Second*

Int. Conf. on Power Cables and Accessories 10 kV to 180 kV. IEE Conference Publication No. 270.
(2) Philbrick, S. E., Bungay, E. W. G., Barber, M. D. and Williamson, A. E. (1986) 'Cables for new power stations'. *IEE Second Int. Conf. on Power Cables and Accessories 10 kV to 180 kV*. IEE Conference Publication No. 270.

Chapter 20

Paper Insulated Cables

For distribution and transmission purposes impregnated paper insulated cables have had an impressive record of reliability since the turn of the century. Of course, this excludes the development phases in the 1920s and 1930s when the use of non-screened (belted) cable was attempted at 33–66 kV (chapter 2). Some indication of the reliability of paper cables may be obtained from the fact that the UK supply industry depreciates such distribution cables over a 40 year life.

Although the basic construction has changed little since impregnated paper was first introduced, there have been continuous improvements in materials and manufacturing techniques which have led over the years to high quality and reductions in dimensions. Probably the most significant change was the introduction of non-draining impregnants in the 1950s. This overcame the problem of migration of impregnant which left a relatively 'dry' dielectric.

Much information on the properties of all the materials used and of the impregnated paper dielectric has been included in chapter 3, which should be read in conjunction with the present chapter.

CONSTRUCTION

Paper cables in the 1–33 kV range are often referred to as 'solid type', by which is meant that they are not designed to operate with an internal or external pressure, as is necessary for higher voltages (chapter 32).

As will be seen from fig. 20.1 the insulation consists of helically applied paper tapes with a small gap between turns. The registration of tapes in relation to each other is important to avoid successive butt gaps in a radial direction as discussed in

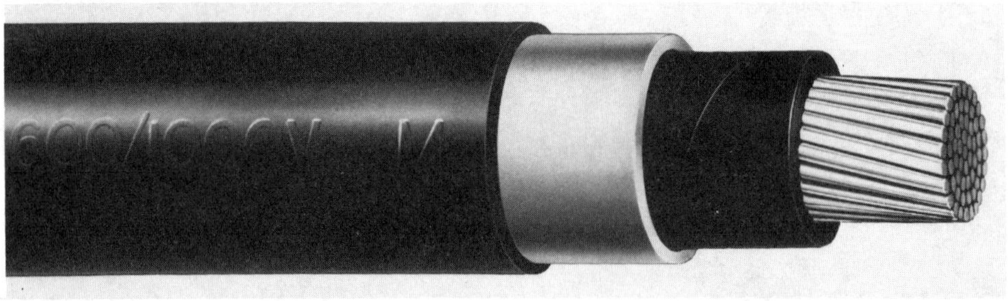

Fig. 20.1 Single-core, 300 mm^2, 600/1000 V, paper insulated lead sheathed cable with PVC oversheath

chapter 3. When cables are bent for drumming and laying the paper tapes have to slide over each other without undue creasing, wrinkling or tearing, and this is the reason for applying the tapes with a gap rather than an overlap. The gap width must be such that when the cable is bent to the smallest permissible radius it will not close completely and hence cause wrinkling of the paper. For bending reasons the mechanical design requirements are as important as electrical aspects in relation to insulation thickness, certainly for low voltage cables. These mechanical requirements cover such features as the angle and lapping tension during paper application, the width of the tape (generally 12–28 mm), the thickness of the paper (0.07–0.19 mm), the paper density and tensile strength.

The conductors in multicore cables are usually sector shape up to 11 kV and oval for 33 kV. Solid aluminium is used extensively at 1 kV. Stranded conductors are normally pre-spiralled (chapter 4) to reduce the possibility of damage to the insulation by twisting during the laying-up operation but this is not universal for the smaller sizes of 1 kV cable.

Belted construction

The cable design with a 'belt' of insulation over the laid-up cores (fig. 20.2) is the most economical in terms of total material cost. Such cables are nearly always used up to 6.6 kV and are the most common type at 11 kV.

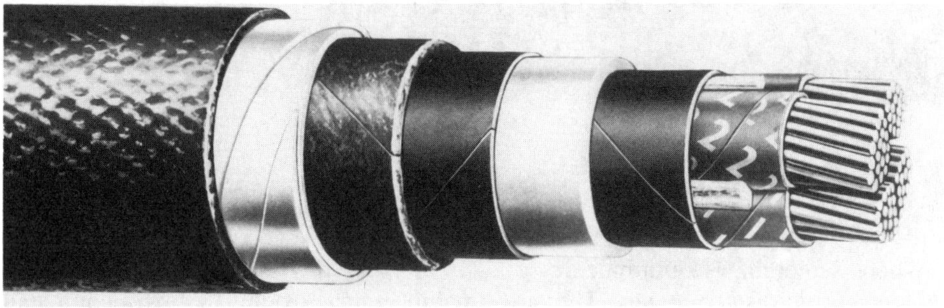

Fig. 20.2 4-core, 70 mm^2, 600/1000 V, paper insulated lead sheathed cable with STA and bituminous finish

The spaces between the cable cores under the belt are filled with jute or paper, but whereas the main insulation consists of paper tapes precisely applied, the filler insulation has to be softer and less dense so as to be compressed into the space available. It is hence weaker electrically and the stresses have to be limited to an acceptable level. For this reason belted cables are not generally used at voltages greater than 11 kV.

Although any discharge between the outside of the insulation and the metallic sheath may produce some discoloration of the impregnating compound, it has little effect on the life of the cable. However, when BS 6480 was revised in 1969 it was decided to specify the inclusion of a semiconducting carbon paper tape over the insulation for 6.35/kV belted cables. This subsequently became optional in IEC 55.

Screened construction

As explained in chapter 2, the electric strength of impregnated paper is weaker in the tangential direction than radially, and for the higher voltages it is necessary to ensure that the electrical field is radial. As operating voltages were raised with 3-core cables in the 1920s and early 1930s, this was the cause of extensive cable failures of belted cables. Hochstadter first pointed to the need for screening and the design is still sometimes referred to as H type. Screening consists of a thin metallic layer in contact with the metallic sheath (fig. 20.3). As it only carries a small charging current, the thickness is unimportant and all that is necessary is to have smooth contact with the insulation together with an ability to withstand cable bending without damage. A common form is a paper/aluminium foil laminate, pinholed to allow penetration of compound during impregnation (chapter 26), and applied with an overlap. The impregnation effect is not vital, however, and a thin copper or aluminium tape is often used because it is less susceptible to damage. Multicore cables usually require a binder over the laid-up cores and this is normally a copper woven fabric (CWF) tape. Fine copper wires are included in the fabric to provide electrical contact with the metallic sheath.

Fig. 20.3 3-core, 150 mm^2, 6.35/11 kV, screened PILS cable with PVC oversheath

Where screening is optional, i.e. at 11 kV, there has been long debate on the advantages and disadvantages. The latter mainly centre around the extra complexity and cost of providing screened joints. The advantage of the screened design is that the improved electrical quality permits operation to a higher temperature, and hence increased rating, but most users favour the belted design because of the simpler jointing.

The voltage limit above which it is deemed necessary to adopt insulation screening is also that at which it is prudent to include a screening layer over the conductor. This has the object of providing a smooth interface between the wires of a stranded conductor and the insulation, thus limiting discharge which may arise by increased electrical stresses due to small radius on the surface and because of possible voids. Conventional practice is to apply two semiconducting carbon-paper tapes over the conductors.

SL and SA screened cables

These are radial field type single-core metallic sheathed cables with the sheath acting as the insulation screen. SL and SA refer to sheathing with lead and aluminium respectively. In the case of the SL type the three corrosion protected cores are laid up together, and then armoured and finished with further corrosion protection (fig. 20.4). SA cables are laid up similarly with a PVC oversheath on each core and are not normally armoured.

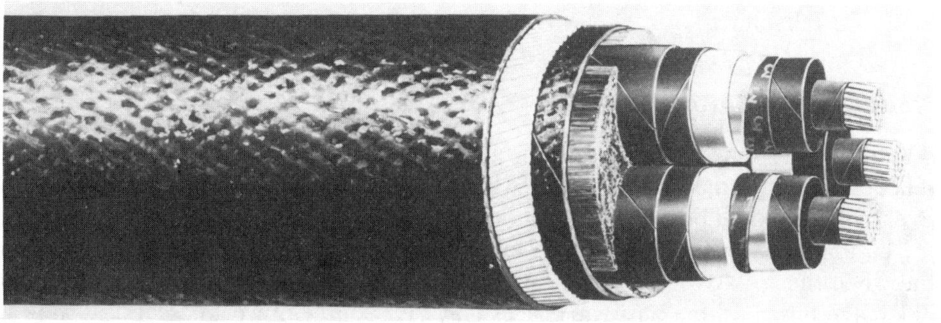

Fig. 20.4 3-core, 150 mm^2, 19/33 kV, SL cable

Although the amount of metal in the sheath is little changed compared with a cable having three cores within a single sheath, the greater diameter results in extra cost of bedding and armouring material and so increases the total cable cost. However, jointing and terminating is more convenient. Some users prefer to install three separate single-core cables rather than a multicore cable, but the multicore SL and SA designs provide some of the advantages of single-core cable and avoid the high magnetic losses which would occur with steel armour.

SL and SA cables are not commonly used in the UK but are extensively employed in continental Europe and in other countries following European practice. Possibly a factor which has been associated with individual preference relates to the draining of oil–rosin impregnant on hilly routes, as there is less compound under the sheath with the single-core construction. In the UK the problem was overcome by the use of non-draining (MIND) insulation.

METALLIC SHEATHS

The majority of paper insulated cables are sheathed with lead and the characteristics of lead sheaths have been discussed in chapter 3. In relation to cable design and specification the most important factor is the choice of unalloyed or alloyed lead according to the possibility of vibration during transport and after installation. Reference to the use of aluminium sheathed designs is made in a later section.

ARMOUR

The choice between steel tape (STA) and galvanised steel wire (GSW) armour for multicore cables is very much related to local practice. In general in the UK STA is adopted for 0.6/1 kV and GSW is favoured for higher voltages because of its better performance in resistance to mechanical damage and provision of improved longitudinal cable strength for handling purposes. In continental Europe and many other countries, however, steel tape armour, sometimes galvanised, tends to be used more extensively throughout the voltage range.

Aluminium sheaths are not armoured and are finished with an extruded layer of polymeric material, commonly PVC. Lead sheathed and armoured cables are now also often finished with extruded PVC but bituminous corrosion protection is also employed (chapter 5).

INSULATION CHARACTERISTICS

One of the most important features of impregnated paper is sensitivity to moisture – hence the need for metallic sheathing which increases jointing complexity. A moisture level of 0.1% would be average for modern cables but up to 1% is tolerable at 1 kV.

The impregnating compound has lower electric strength than impregnated paper and when the voltage is such that internal partial discharge can occur, i.e. mainly 6/10 kV and upwards, the butt-gap spaces may be a source of weakness unless they are well filled with impregnant (chapter 3). Discharge in the gaps is indicated by 'waxing' or 'cheesing' of the impregnant and ultimately may lead to breakdown. It is therefore important that for 10–30 kV cables the manufacturing technique and the viscosity versus temperature characteristics of the impregnant are such that the butt-gap spaces are well filled after cooling during manufacture and excessive migration does not occur at service operating temperatures. Nevertheless, it should still be noted that paper insulation has high resistance to such discharges in comparison with polymeric materials. Up to 3 kV, where discharge is not a problem, the cables may be drained of surplus compound before metal sheathing.

Insulation thickness

Reference to the electric strength of impregnated paper has been made in chapter 3 but it is not only this which defines insulation thickness. Particularly at the lower end of the voltage range mechanical requirements predominate and at the upper end allowance has to be made for the condition of the dielectric resulting from impregnant movement during load cycles to defined temperature. An indication of insulation thickness and operating stresses is shown in table 20.1 (see also chapter 19).

Even in the 6–15 kV range the electrical stress is not a primary factor and the operating stress of 2–4 MV/m is well below the capability of impregnated paper. However, because of the possibility of ionisation in voids it is necessary to ensure a high level of filling with impregnant.

The electrical stress becomes important at 33 kV and, partly to reduce stress at the conductor surface, oval conductors are usually used in preference to sector-shaped conductors. The use of oval conductors for multicore cables also improves the bending performance of cable with the thicker insulation. For the same reason, more insulation is required on very small conductor sizes, in contrast with the increase in insulation thickness with conductor size on lower voltage cables. At 66 kV, which is the limit for solid type paper cable, only single-core cables with circular conductors are used.

Table 20.1 Insulation thickness (minimum) and electrical stress (maximum) for paper insulated cables

Voltage (kV)	Conductor size (mm^2)	Belted design insulation thickness		Single-core and screened design	
		Between conductors (mm)	Conductor sheath (mm)	Insulation (mm)	Stress (MV/m)
0.6/1	50	1.4	1.2	1.2	0.24
	1000			2.0	0.13
1.9/3.3	50	2.4	1.8	1.8	1.3
	1000			2.0	1.0
3.8/6.6	50	4.2	2.7	2.4	2.0
	1000			2.4	1.7
6.35/11	50	5.6	3.4	2.8	2.9
	1000			2.8	2.4
8.7/15	50			3.6	3.3
	1000			3.6	2.6
12.7/22	50			4.9	3.8
	1000			4.9	2.8
19/33	50			7.3	4.4
	1000			6.8	3.2

MASS-IMPREGNATED NON-DRAINING (MIND) CABLES

Reference has been made in chapter 3 to the special impregnants used to prevent drainage of the compound when cables are installed vertically or on slopes. Such cables were pioneered by BICC in 1949, initially at 1 kV. Following extensive development work in collaboration with Dussek Bros Ltd, during the next two decades they subsequently became almost universally standardised in the UK over the whole voltage range.

When cables with oil–rosin impregnant are installed on routes having differences in level, the impregnant migrates towards the lower end and unless great care is taken in making joints and terminations there may be leakage of the compound. On steep gradients barrier joints may be necessary and there is also a danger of lead sheath expansion resulting in fracture. Even more important is the fact that the loss of compound reduces the electrical strength of the insulation at the higher end, and the creation of a vacuous condition may lead to ingress of moisture if terminations are not completely sealed. At voltages of 11 kV and above the loss of compound can cause a high level of discharge within the cable and experience has shown that this may be important even for quite modest vertical sections such as at pole terminations. Before the advent of MIND insulation it was necessary for cables on slopes either to be partially drained and to have considerably increased insulation thickness to reduce the stress or alternatively to be of the pre-impregnated paper type of non-draining construction. During the impregnation process of manufacture the MIND compound is very fluid and readily saturates the insulation. On cooling to ambient temperature the change of state to a soft solid form is accompanied by a slight contraction and with MIND insulation it is even more important than with oil–rosin to ensure that the cooling process is slow, with circulation of the compound through a cooling system to obtain temperature uniformity. This also prevents the formation of a skin of solid compound on the insulation surface which could act as a barrier to further compound entry. Even so, the volume impregnation factor is of the order of 93% in comparison with 96% for oil–rosin. Later MIND compounds have been better than the original ones with respect to coefficient of contraction.

The vital point is that in service the MIND compound will remain in position whereas oil–rosin compound may readily drain away and leave even more voids in the insulation. However, when cables are tested in the virgin condition, immediately following manufacture, MIND insulation shows more ionisation, i.e. difference in power factor between say one-half working voltage and twice working voltage. When BS 480 was amended in 1954 the limit for multicore 33 kV cables was raised from 0.0006 for oil–rosin to 0.006 for MIND to allow for this feature. Precise details have subsequently been further revised. Likewise the impulse strength of MIND cable is slightly below that of virgin oil–rosin cable. Nevertheless, it readily meets the British requirements of 194 kV at 33 kV and 95 kV at 11 kV, the latter being above the IEC requirement of 75 kV.

The fact that the initial ionisation is not of importance and that MIND cable provides excellent long-term performance can readily be shown by a stability test with the standard conditions of daily load cycles to a temperature 5 °C above the maximum permitted continuous limit and a voltage of 1.33 times the working level.

Periodical tests of the power factor at 1.5 and 2.0 times working voltage show that both oil–rosin and MIND cables reach a peak of power factor and are then stable. MIND cables reach this peak more quickly, generally after a few cycles, and the level may subsequently decrease. At working voltage, however, in contrast with oil–rosin insulation, MIND insulation shows little or no ionisation after a prolonged period of testing.

It has been argued in some countries that, under short-circuit conditions, MIND insulation could be inferior because the conductor temperature permitted is such that the compound may change to the liquid state. This has been difficult to establish experimentally and it is apparent that the temperature of the mass of cable is well below that of the conductor. MIND cables have shown a very satisfactory service performance for some 30 years. Any shortcomings in this and any other respects arising in non-draining cables made elsewhere have no doubt been due to lack of recognition of the expertise necessary in formulating satisfactory compounds and correct processing techniques.

ALUMINIUM SHEATHED PAPER INSULATED CABLES

In the early 1970s, when many users throughout the world were considering changing to HV polymeric insulated cables, British manufacturers were conscious that the service reliability of such cables appeared to be much lower than for paper cables and they drew attention to a further economy which could be obtained with paper cables whilst further development of polymeric insulation was proceeding. Substitution of an aluminium sheath for a lead sheath and armour provided a price saving of around

25%. Service trials were quickly arranged and by 1975 nearly all the UK Electricity Boards had changed to this construction for their 11 kV networks.

One problem in the early years related to the multiplicity of designs available, all adding to the cablemakers' stocks because lead sheathed cables would clearly not be superseded for many years. The aluminium sheath could be smooth, which was slightly cheaper, or corrugated (fig. 20.5) and, as with lead sheathed cables, some authorities favoured a belted and others a screened design. A review was carried out by the Board and in 1978 it was considered that the much better handling characteristics of the cable with corrugated sheath had a distinct advantage. It was decided to standardise the belted cable with corrugated sheath in conductor sizes of 95, 185 and 300 mm^2, though the Boards which had traditionally used screened cable remained with this type.

Fig. 20.5 3-core, 11 kV, belted PIAS cable with corrugated aluminium sheath

The service experience had shown that because the cable weight was reduced by 50% the smooth sheath designs up to 185 mm^2 were no more difficult to install than lead sheathed cable. Some problems could arise with larger sizes in duct installations owing to the stiffness of the cable. This extra rigidity was also detrimental in setting cable ends into equipment when space was limited in substations. The corrugated sheathed cable was particularly easy to install and had a distinct advantage over lead sheathed cable.

Another aspect of the increased rigidity of cable with smooth sheath concerns the possibility of mechanical stresses in joints, associated also with the high coefficient of expansion of aluminium. Within the joint there can also be 'bowing' of the cores in the joint sleeve after heating cycles. Whilst these problems can readily be overcome by the use of joints of the cast resin filled type, the increase in cost is not always considered to be justified. Those UK Electricity Boards which used smooth sheathed cables continued with standard bitumen filled joints on the basis that the cables were installed in open-ring circuits and very seldom reached full design load.

Manufacturing technique is particularly important for cables with corrugated sheaths because of the considerable increase in space between the insulation and the inside of the sheath. If this is completely filled with impregnating compound it is possible to generate very high internal pressures at operating temperature. It is consequently necessary to control the amount of compound between what is necessary to prevent ionisation within the insulation and that which produces a maximum pressure on heating. Another important factor is that, if the aluminium sheath should be damaged, water would enter the cable and all the cable affected would have to be replaced. There needs to be enough impregnating compound present to prevent water from penetrating along the cable. For internal pressure transmission cables, e.g. oil-filled cables, the corrugation ribs have a helical pattern (fig. 33.2) as this assists in the movement of oil along the cable. In the case of these solid type paper cables the annular corrugation design (fig. 20.5) has positive advantages. When a piece of sheath has to be removed for joints or terminations it is much easier to cut around one crest of a corrugation rib, and in the event of local penetration of the sheath the small clearance at the root of the corrugation, containing impregnating compound, is an obstacle to transmission of water along the cable.

The economic advantage of the aluminium sheathed design has undoubtedly been the main reason for the continued use of high voltage distribution paper cables in the UK, whereas XLPE insulation has proceeded to oust paper in many other countries. XLPE cables have not been competitive in price and their other attraction, that they do not require such highly skilled jointers, has had less impact because of the traditional skills available.

OPERATIONAL AND INSTALLATION PARAMETERS

Continuous operating temperature

Reference to conductor temperature limits as a basis for cable ratings is made in chapter 8. Table 20.2 summarises the requirements for paper cables.

The temperature of 80 °C for 1 kV cables is based on the physical and electrical degradation of the dielectric materials. At the higher voltages the limit is primarily associated with the imposition of conditions which will prevent increase in ionisation within the dielectric. Most distribution cables operate with cyclic loading, and hence with heating and cooling, predominantly on a daily basis. During heating there is expansion of the impregnant and for various reasons the compound may not flow back between the layers of paper; thus voids are created in which discharge may occur. Lead sheaths readily expand under pressure but do not contract when the pressure is reduced, thus reducing the likelihood of compound returning into the insulation. All these effects have a bearing on the maximum temperature which can be adopted. The temperature is lower for belted cables, due to the non-radial field, and reduces with increasing voltage because of the more serious effect of ionisation on cable life.

Table 20.2 Conductor temperature limits for paper cables

Voltage (kV)	Cable design	Maximum conductor temperature (°C)
0.6/1, 1.9/3.3, 3.8/6.6	Belted	80
6.35/11	Belted	65
6.35/11, 8.7/15	Screened	70
12.7/22, 19/33	Screened	65

Technically it has been proved feasible to develop satisfactory impregnating compounds and cable construction to permit a temperature of 85° C up to 33 kV but such cables have not been brought into commercial use.

Bending radii

Reference has been made to the need for materials and methods of manufacture to be chosen to mitigate against dielectric disturbance on bending. IEC 55, and hence most national standards, prescribe the minimum bending radii quoted in appendix A17.

The stiffness of impregnants changes with temperature to an extent which varies with composition and types of material used. If cables are to be installed in cold climates it is usual to prescribe a bending test to be carried out at an appropriate temperature, to ensure that there is no disruption of the insulation.

LIFE AND PERFORMANCE CHARACTERISTICS

The service performance of paper cables has been so good that it is accepted as the standard by which other types are judged. Apart from straightforward mechanical damage, one of the main causes of cable replacement is the entry of water and the travel of the water through a considerable length of cable. Electrical failures in the dielectric are rare up to 6 kV. At 11 kV and above they are more usually associated with the discharge and carbon tracking ('treeing') mechanism discussed in chapter 2.

An interesting type of breakdown was known for many years as 'pinhole type failure below terminations on 11 kV belted cable'. It was common in South Africa but also arose elsewhere. Although not necessarily associated with high altitudes the incidence was greater at heights of around 1000 m.

The failures invariably occurred in the vertical cable below terminations and at a distance of 1 to 15 m from the termination. There was intense pinhole type erosion of the dielectric papers, with no carbonisation but with green deposits both on the conductor and on adjacent insulating papers. After lengthy investigations it was established that the breakdown started from drainage of oil–rosin impregnant which allowed air to enter the cable through incomplete sealing of the wire interstices of the conductor in the termination. Discharge then occurred in the air-filled voids in the dielectric in the region of highest stress, i.e. where the conductors approach each other most closely and where the radii of the shaped conductors are smallest. The discharges resulted in the formation of oxides of nitrogen and ozone which attacked the paper to produce the pinholes and led to production of moisture. This combined with the oxides of nitrogen to form nitric acid which reacted with the copper to give the green copper nitrate.

The solution was to use hermetically sealed termination boxes. Also the use of non-draining cables mitigates against creation of voids and the suction of air into the cable.

TESTS

Testing procedure is discussed in chapter 28 and the following summary indicates the fundamental logic of the IEC test requirements.

Routine tests on completed cables

A 5 min a.c. test at a voltage of $2.5U_0 + 2$ kV for cables rated up to 3.6/6 kV, and $2.5U_0$ for cables for 6/10 kV and above, provides a very good indication of freedom from manufacturing defects. For the higher stressed cables, discharge activity becomes more important, though the actual level of permissible discharge is relatively high, certainly in comparison with polymeric cables. It is difficult to measure this level with adequate precision and hence, for cables of rated voltage U_0 of 8.7 kV and above, a dielectric power factor/voltage test is also specified. Limits are prescribed for maximum power factor and increase in power factor between specified voltages. These ensure that discharge is kept at an acceptable level.

Special and type tests

The ability of the cable to be bent without undue damage to the insulation is clearly an important requirement but, as it relates to the manufacturer's technique and reputation, it is not necessary to test every cable. Standard test conditions require bending to a radius much more severe than specified for installation followed by a voltage test. British practice in BS 6480 requires bending to a smaller radius than stipulated by IEC and also inspection of the insulation with limits to the amount of damage to individual paper tapes. Hence it allows for the use of smaller diameter despatch drums than often used elsewhere.

It needs to be established that no drainage occurs with non-draining cables and the test is carried out on a vertical sample heated to maximum specified conductor operating temperature. Compound exudation to a level of 2.5%–3.0% of the internal volume of the sheath is permitted to allow for the thermal expansion of the impregnant and the fact that slight separation of oil from the compound may occur under the test condition.

Type tests involve more stringent and elaborate procedures which are required only to establish the capability of a new manufacturer or at the development stage of a new design. They are only applicable to cables of U_0 8.7 kV and above. IEC 55–1 covers

(a) a power factor versus temperature test to 10 °C above rated temperature. The power factor limits are as follows: 20–60 °C, 0.0060; 70 °C 0.0130; 75 °C 0.0160; 80 °C, 0.0190; 85 °C, 0.0230.
(b) a dielectric security test with the application for 4 hours of a voltage of $4U_0$ for oil–rosin and $3U_0$ for non-draining insulation.
(c) another dielectric security test involving bending the sample and then sequential application of an impulse voltage and an a.c. voltage. The impulse voltages for U_0 voltages of 8.7, 12 and 18 kV are 95, 125 and 170 kV respectively.

British type test practice in BS 6480 for 19/33 kV cables requires sequential bending, loading cycles and impulse tests. The loading cycles involve daily heating to 70–75 °C. If there is no progressive increase in power factor the test may be terminated after 100 cycles but, if there is any doubt, 250 cycles are required. The impulse level is 194 kV.

The important requirements discussed for 11 kV belted corrugated aluminium sheathed cables are covered by type tests stipulated by the UK electricity supply industry involving (a) a minimum and a maximum internal pressure on heating to the conductor temperature limit and (b) a test for water penetration along the cable through a hole in the aluminium sheath.

Chapter 21

PVC Insulated Cables

PVC rapidly replaced rubber for wiring cables shortly after the end of the Second World War and was introduced in Europe for power cable insulation in the late 1950s, initially in significant commercial quantity in Germany. For corrosion protection, particularly with aluminium sheathed transmission cables, extruded PVC oversheaths became firmly established in the middle 1950s.

At that time, paper insulated cables were being used for industrial distribution and as fully impregnated non-draining paper had not then been completely accepted it was necessary to adopt some form of limitation of the amount of impregnating compound in the cable to minimise compound drainage problems. This caused either reduction in quality or increased insulation thickness. The use of PVC provided cables of excellent quality which were clean and much easier to handle. Being little affected by moisture they do not require a metal sheath and this also simplifies jointing and terminating. Consequently they quickly became adopted for industrial power applications.

A particular feature of the early development was associated with the fact that, whereas wiring cables have circular conductors, the conductors of power cables were sector shaped and the larger sizes pre-spiralled. Shaped-solid aluminium conductors had emerged as a strong competitor to copper at the same time. The use of shaped dies to extrude PVC to the profile of the conductor presented great concentricity problems which led to the 'float-down' or 'tubing-on' extrusion technique. This involves extruding the PVC as an oversize circular tube which is drawn to a snug fit on the conductor by a combination of vacuum and controlled conductor/extrusion speeds.

It can be said that PVC power cables truly became established in the UK by the IEE Symposium on Plastic Insulated Mains Cable Systems in November 1962 and the papers presented provide an interesting record.

APPLICATIONS

The fields of use fall into four distinct categories as discussed below. Especially as PVC from the outset had to compete with impregnated paper, the most important factor to be taken into account was the amount of softening at raised temperatures due to its thermoplastic nature. This can result in deformation of the insulation due, for example, to conductor thrust at bends. Paper cables will withstand fairly high short time overloads and consequently the fuse co-ordination does not need to be particularly refined. PVC cables need adequate protection against overload or alternatively a reduced rating has to be assigned to them. The situation in relation to the fourteenth and fifteenth editions of the IEE Wiring Regulations is discussed in chapter 10.

Industrial cables

Industrial usage covers distribution in and around factories at voltages up to 3.3 kV. Except possibly in North America, PVC cables have been almost universally used throughout the world since around 1960 and excess current protection does not present any serious problem. In the UK the conductors have been stranded copper or solid aluminium. In some other countries, stranded rather than solid aluminium has been preferred, but this has been due to some extent to economic factors relating to conductor manufacture rather than strict technical preference. Standard designs comprise single-core (stranded and solid sectoral) construction (fig. 21.1) and multicore constructions of 2, 3 and 4 cores (fig. 22.2) of equal shaped conductor sizes, i.e. without reduced neutral because this is uneconomic with solid aluminium (see appendix A13 for details).

Fig. 21.1 600/1000 V, single-core sectoral aluminium conductor, PVC insulated cable

Fig. 21.2 600/1000 V, 4-core copper conductor, PVC insulated SWA cable with extruded bedding

Public supply

Apart from house service cables, PVC has not been used for public supply in the UK because of the excess current protection problem. Normal distribution systems provide little or no protection for the cables, e.g. two Electricity Boards operate with a solid mesh and many others have a very coarse fuse at the substation at the end of a cable which may be tapered in cross-section along the route. This is not so in many other countries and there has been widespread use of PVC, even sometimes in tropical regions, when its use would be unexpected because of the undesirable effects of derating etc. However, PVC clearly has drawbacks for any public supply system and XLPE is taking over in this field.

Coal mining

Much power cable is used for fixed installation along roadways to take the supply from a main colliery shaft to the working face. Because the point of use is constantly changing, the individual cable lengths are fitted with couplers to enable the distribution system to be moved around as required. In the UK the standard voltages are 3.3 kV and 6.6 kV, with some requirement at 11 kV.

Paper cables were conventional until the 1960s but were then replaced by PVC primarily because of the better resilience of PVC in withstanding rock falls. UK requirements for 3.3 kV and 6.6 kV cables in the later 1970s have been at the rate of around 650 km/year. Similar use at 11 kV has largely been the only application of PVC at this voltage in the UK, but, as with other high voltage applications, XLPE and EPR are now also being used.

Initially the conductors were copper, but for economic reasons solid aluminium was introduced. After some years there was a further change to stranded aluminium because of flexibility problems in coiling the cables to take them down the mine shafts. Until the time that more attention was paid to flexibility (mid-1970s) it had been traditional for all such roadway distribution cables to be double wire armoured. This provided high earth conductance and a rugged construction. Subsequently both DWA and SWA designs have been used with earth conductances of 75% and 60% respectively. Shaft cables always have DWA and with single-point suspension the top section has quadruple armour. Fig. 21.3 shows a typical PVC insulated mining cable.

Fig. 21.3 3.8/6.6 kV, 3-core aluminium conductor, PVC insulated cable for roadway distribution in coal mines

High voltage cables

Reference to the use of PVC for HV cables is made in a later section.

DESIGN AND CONSTRUCTION

PVC cables may be unarmoured or armoured. If unarmoured they have an extruded PVC sheath over the single core or laid-up cores. If armoured the bedding may comprise plastic tapes or extruded PVC and an extruded PVC sheath is applied over the armour. Dimensions, weights, electrical characteristics and ratings of cables to BS 6346 are given in appendix A13.

Prior to the first issue of IEC 502 in 1975, there were some small differences between National Standards, but since then most have been amended to become almost identical.

Insulation

In the 1–3 kV range the insulation thickness required is somewhat arbitrary and is largely dependent on mechanical considerations, e.g. the physical loading which might be imposed on the cable. Such loading may result in some deformation of the insulation at raised temperatures, e.g. during manufacture or in emergency conditions in service operation. This is why there is more variation of thickness with conductor size than with voltage. At higher voltages electrical requirements predominate.

The general characteristics and properties of PVC insulation are discussed in chapter 3 and the special formulations for further reduction in flame propagation, together with reduced generation of toxic fumes and smoke, in chapter 6. For the normal run of cables BS 6346 stipulates a 'general purpose' compound from the types listed in BS 6746. However, BS 6346 caters only for cables up to 3.3 kV. For higher voltages the reduction in insulation resistance and increase in dielectric power factor at the top end of the operating temperature range become important to avoid instability (chapter 3). IEC 502 caters for this by stipulating PVC/A up to 3 kV and PVC/B for higher voltages. The essential requirement for PVC/B is that the product of the permittivity and the power factor must not exceed 0.75 between ambient temperature and 85 °C; also the power factor at 80 °C must not exceed the value at 60 °C.

A matter which causes some confusion is that three essential limits dictate the service operation of PVC insulation: (a) a sustained maximum temperature of 70 °C, which is determined by the thermal ageing characteristics of the material; (b) a temperature of the order of 120 °C which governs the maximum degree of deformation permissible in the time/temperature range required for the circuit protection to operate; and (c) a limit, which is now 150 °C but is likely to be increased to 160 °C, is used for the calculation of short-circuit ratings. The performance of the material can be assessed by tests on the material but overload and short-circuit limits have to be defined by tests on complete cables because they are at least partially dependent on the performance of the cable as a whole. Much work on these aspects has been carried out by ERA Technology Ltd.[1]

The confusion arises particularly with heat-resisting grades of PVC because, whilst they give some benefits in better resistance to ageing at temperatures above

70 °C, they may be little or no better in relation to deformation at these higher temperatures. BS 6746, 'PVC insulation and sheath of electric cables', and similar standards, quote heat-resisting compounds for a maximum conductor temperature of 85 °C. References may also be found to compounds for 100 °C or even 105 °C. The latter are generally not for power cables and relate to applications where the service at these temperatures is of relatively short duration and a limitation on cable life is recognised.

The essential point is that although heat-resisting compounds cannot be used to obtain higher sustained ratings, because of the circuit protection issue, they do have a value if cables have to be derated due to operation at higher ambient temperatures. If the ambient temperature is 25 °C the permissible temperature rise for standard PVC cable is 45 °C and this governs the sustained rating value. With an 85 °C compound the same temperature rise and rating can be obtained from an ambient temperature of 40 °C. The situation on circuit protection remains the same at 1.45 times the rated current.

Such heat-resisting compounds are, of course, significantly more expensive and when high temperature operation is important, ambient or otherwise, it is now usually more economic to use insulation of the thermoset type (e.g. XLPE or EPR) as this has a sustained conductor temperature limit of 90 °C.

Considerations relating to the flexibility of PVC also apply to cables required for installations at low temperatures, i.e. in countries with severe winters. It is not recommended to install normal PVC cables below 0 °C because standard PVC compounds become increasingly stiff and brittle at low temperatures. Special compounds with increased amounts of selected plasticisers can be formulated but here again it is now generally preferable on economic and technical grounds to use polyethylene or thermoset materials.

Core identification

The cores are normally identified by the colour of the insulation but there is no international standardisation. British practice is based on table 21.1, with red, yellow and blue indicating phase conductors and black the neutral.

Fillers and armour bedding

Fillers are required mainly with cables having circular cores so as to provide a reasonably circular profile. The armour bedding may comprise either (a) non-

Table 21.1 Core identification in PVC cables

Cable type	Colours
Single-core	Red or black
2-core	Red, black
3-core	Red, yellow, blue
4-core	Red, yellow, blue, black

hygroscopic tapes of around 0.8 mm thickness or (b) an extruded layer of suitable material (usually PVC) of thickness 1.0–2.0 mm according to cable diameter.

The extruded bedding provides a more robust construction and is normally preferred for cables buried in the ground. It is also essential if certain types of termination gland are used in flame-proof enclosures.

Armour

Standard specifications cater for a wide range of choice for armour, e.g. IEC 502 covers galvanised steel wire, plain or galvanised steel tape, plain or galvanised steel strip and aluminium strip. Comments on design considerations relevant to the different forms of armour used are given in chapter 19, and much depends on individual customer preferences or what had traditionally become accepted practice with paper cables. This has varied widely in different countries and established practices remain.

In the UK only two types of armour have been adopted and recognised by BS 6346 – galvanised steel wire and aluminium strip. Steel tape armour, as commonly used with paper cables, is more frequently used in continental Europe, and in some overseas countries it is sometimes galvanised when the users have a preference for preserving the armour in aggressive environments. With PVC cables there is a greater tendency to use galvanised tapes, thus avoiding the need to use bitumen. The armour can also act as an earth conductor, though steel tape is not very efficient in this respect. Steel strip armour is also widely used in continental Europe and the strip is normally galvanised.

The use of aluminium strip armour came early in the development of PVC cables and with the backing of the aluminium industry was associated with the introduction of solid aluminium conductors to produce an all-aluminium cable. The incentive at the time was also towards the use of the armour as a concentric neutral conductor. The strip type neutral never came to fruition, but for a time many users adopted aluminium strip armour, either because of the reduced cable price then prevailing or to obtain higher armour conductance in the earthing system. Also in the UK a view prevailed for a time that the IEE Wiring Regulations should be interpreted as requiring that in any cable the armour should have 50% of the conductance of a phase conductor – a situation which did not exist with many sizes of lead sheathed cable or PVC cables having galvanised steel armour. It was eventually established that such a requirement was not necessary. Nevertheless, there are occasions when the extra conductance of aluminium strip armour is beneficial and nowadays it is mainly only in such instances that it is used. The price advantage compared with galvanised steel wire has been lost, although it must be recognised that relative prices vary from time to time and from country to country.

Aluminium in strip or wire form also has an advantage for single-core cables because of the need to use non-magnetic material. A factor to be taken into account with aluminium armoured cables is that the termination glands should also be made from aluminium or be otherwise designed to be compatible.

A final point about the comparison between steel wire and aluminium strip armour is the resistance of the cable to impact blows. The aluminium strip is of much lower thickness and provides less resistance to damage.

Oversheath

IEC 502 allows for galvanised steel armour to be left bare and for cables to be oversheathed with PVC, polyethylene or other suitable material. Specific test requirements are quoted for PVC and polyethylene. Historically, crosslinked materials have been excluded because of the risk of deformation of the insulation at the vulcanising temperature.

BS 6346 excludes bare armoured cables and stipulates only a PVC oversheath of the same grade of material as the standard general purpose insulating compound. In practice bare armoured cables would only be suitable for clean dry indoor conditions and apart from the improved visual appearance the small extra cost for the oversheath is well worthwhile. It is believed that very little bare cable has been used throughout the world.

When PVC cables were first developed it was common practice to apply bitumen over the armour to obtain additional corrosion protection, i.e. following conventional paper cable practice. However, the bitumen extracted plasticiser from the PVC, so becoming a thin mobile liquid. Many industrial cables are installed with terminations below a vertical run of cable and the result was a nasty dripping of black liquid at the termination. The plasticiser migration can be avoided by having a separation layer of suitable tape between the bitumen and oversheath but such a layer is not easy to apply effectively and the value of the bitumen is doubtful. It was subsequently discarded for standard types of cable, although retained for special applications such as mining cables where the use of bitumen has been considered to be beneficial.

HIGH VOLTAGE PVC CABLES

IEC Specification 502 covers designs of PVC cables up to 20 kV but with a few exceptions the amount of cable used above 3.3 kV has been relatively small. These exceptions consist mainly of the mining cables discussed earlier and more general

Table 21.2 Comparative dielectric losses in cables

Voltage (kV)	Conductor size (mm^2)	Insulation	Dielectric loss (kWh/km year)
3.8/6.6	50	PVC	3109
	1000	PVC	11658
	50	XLPE	11
	1000	XLPE	30
	50	Paper	57
	1000	Paper	224
6.35/11	50	PVC	8955
	1000	PVC	29258
	50	XLPE	23
	1000	XLPE	78
	50	Paper	145
	1000	Paper	546

use in Germany. Chapter 25 deals with the subject of high voltage polymeric insulated cables and only the main significant features are outlined below.

In comparison with the alternative materials, such as impregnated paper and polyethylene, the electrical losses in PVC are high. Table 21.2 gives figures for some typical cables. Nevertheless, the dielectric loss is still only a small proportion of the total losses, the conductor loss being predominant.

However, as PVC is not competitive with XLPE the previous limited use has now almost ceased. A higher operating temperature can be sustained by XLPE, and hence higher ratings, and it is a more universal material in that it can be used up to much higher voltages.

Some interest in PVC has derived from the fact that it has much better resistance than PE or XLPE to partial discharge. Thus whilst PE and XLPE cables need to have conductor and dielectric screens above 3.3 kV, they are only required above 6.6 kV with PVC (and also with EPR). Furthermore, the permissible magnitude of discharge of $1.25U_0$ is 40 pC for PVC (also for EPR) but only 20 pC for PE and XLPE.

OPERATING CHARACTERISTICS

Ground containing hydrocarbons (oil refineries)

One of the few situations requiring special attention with PVC cables concerns installation in ground containing a significant quantity of petroleum hydrocarbon. This arises most often in oil refineries but it can happen in any place where such hydrocarbons are being handled. As discussed in chapter 5, PVC oversheaths are comparatively resistant to attack by petrol or similar hydrocarbons. All that happens from occasional spillages is that some plasticiser is leached out, with corresponding hardening, but if the cables are not subsequently subjected to severe bending this has little effect. The loss of plasticiser is not detrimental to the protective properties of the PVC.

However, whilst surrounded by hydrocarbons in this way, some of the hydrocarbon can diffuse through the PVC and will be present in any air spaces within the cable. It can then travel along the cable to leak out at joints or terminations and this could create a hazard. Consequently it is a common practice for PVC insulated cables in oil refineries to be lead sheathed. An alternative solution in some circumstances is to seal the cable and conductors at joints and terminations.

Operational life of PVC cables

As PVC insulation for power cables has only been in general use since the early 1960s it is perhaps still a little early to judge whether the ultimate life of PVC power cable will match that of paper insulated cables. There is no doubt that operating performance has been good and very few failures have occurred due to overheating. Problems due to softening at raised temperatures have already been referred to. A few failures have also occurred due to overheating resulting in thermal degradation. Some may have been due to inadequate attention to formulation to obtain the required stability but inevitably, if the standard PVC compound is heated for long periods much above its rated temperature, degradation is likely. The extent of degradation depends on temperature and time. The PVC becomes hard and brittle and darkens in colour and, due to the liberation of hydrochloric acid, copper conductors will be attacked with the production of green chlorides.

Loss of plasticiser due to heating in normal service or due to contact with other materials, such as bitumen in joint boxes, is rarely a problem. Some hardening of the PVC occurs but the electrical properties do not deteriorate. Providing the cables do not have to be moved subsequently, the loss of flexibility is not usually of importance.

Flame retardance

PVC cables in general, and the standard PVC compound as a material, are, to a degree, intrinsically flame retardant. However, under some conditions they may burn and it is even possible for flames to travel along the cable. Alternative compounds and construction are available when improved flame retardance is required, as described in chapter 6.

REFERENCE

(1) Parr, R. G. and Yap, J. S. (1965) 'Short-circuit ratings for PVC insulated cables'. ERA Report No. 5056.

Chapter 22

Thermoset Insulated Cables up to 3.3 kV

This chapter is essentially a supplement to the previous one, but covering cable with an alternative insulation material. The three thermoset materials admitted by most specifications are XLPE, EPR and butyl rubber, but the latter two are rarely adopted outside Italy and in this chapter the reference is essentially to XLPE. Requirements for EPR and butyl cables are identical to those for XLPE except, of course, that specific values for the insulation as a component are slightly different for the individual materials. Cable constructions are basically the same as those for cables with PVC insulation. The applications are also the same, but with some extension because in many countries, for reasons already stated, PVC cables have not found much favour for public supply systems. In general, XLPE insulated cables are a competitive alternative to PVC cables for industrial use and to paper insulated cables for public supply systems.

Cables up to 3.3 kV do not require conductor or insulation screens, whereas for 6.6 kV upwards the position is different in this respect. Cables for 6.6 kV and higher voltages are therefore more appropriately covered in chapter 25 on high voltage cables with thermoset insulation.

Cables with all three types of thermoset insulation are covered by IEC 502, but British Standard 5467 caters only for XLPE and EPR. Dimensions, weights, ratings and electrical characteristics of XLPE insulated cables are given in appendix A14.

COMPARISON BETWEEN THERMOSET INSULATED CABLES AND OTHER TYPES

Comparison with PVC cables

The important difference is the extra toughness of the insulation and, in particular, the ability to withstand much higher temperatures without deformation due to mechanical pressure. The better physical properties of XLPE enable the insulation thickness to be reduced and hence also the overall size of the cable. The continuous rating temperature is increased from 70 to 90 °C and the temperature for short-circuit ratings for the cable itself (as distinct from the whole system) from 160 to 250 °C. The large increase in continuous ratings indicated in appendix A14 implies that in many cases it will be possible to use a cable one size smaller, but in a majority of industrial applications this benefit cannot be achieved because the dictating factor is voltage drop rather than current rating. However, where derating factors have to be applied because of high ambient temperature, e.g. in tropical countries, the benefit is substantial.

Although XLPE cables have been available for many years, they have been slow in the UK in taking over from PVC power cables. This is largely because the crosslinking process affected manufacturing cost and their use tended to be restricted to applications where the current rating advantage could be fully exploited. With the reduction in cost obtained by developments in the silane process for crosslinking, the situation has now changed. It is to be expected that XLPE will gradually supersede PVC for power cable insulation.

PVC has a degree of flame retardance, though the extent depends on the test method taken as the criterion. XLPE burns readily and particularly important is the fact that drops of molten material fall away. Nevertheless, it is usually the characteristics of the complete cable which are more important than those of the insulation itself, as the bedding, armour and oversheath exert a strong influence on the behaviour of cable in a fire. XLPE has not suffered greatly, therefore, in comparison with PVC in this respect. For cables in the 1 kV range it is possible to compound XLPE with additives to introduce a modest degree of flame retardancy and such a material finds some application in the USA.

However, the additives generally contain halogens and give rise to similar fume and smoke problems as discussed in relation to PVC in chapter 6. When flame retardance is important, therefore, it is still necessary to establish all the factors relating to the test performance required to meet the service conditions and the ability of the complete cable design to meet the test conditions.

XLPE tends to be more stiff and rigid than PVC, but the difference in cable flexibility is fairly small and only marginally noticeable in cores of small conductor size.

Comparison with paper cables

Because paper cable ratings are based on 80 °C (up to 3.3 kV) the rating advantage of XLPE is less than with PVC but is still positive. The main advantage compared with paper cables is the availability of a cable without metallic sheath and the consequent advantages in laying and jointing, together with reduced bending radii. XLPE cables are much cleaner, more robust, lighter and easier to handle – important advantages in countries without traditional cable installation skills. Outside the UK they have therefore almost ousted paper cables in the voltage range under consideration. Even in the UK the waveform type of concentric neutral cable with XLPE insulation described in chapter 23 is used in larger quantities than the Consac cable with paper insulation.

CONSTRUCTION

As the concentric neutral design is covered in chapter 23, we are concerned here only with the conventional designs of armoured and unarmoured cables (figs 22.1 and 22.2) and, as already stated, the constructions are essentially the same as for PVC cables. The main design difference is that, because the insulation thickness is based more on mechanical considerations than on electrical requirements, the tougher nature of XLPE permits a considerable reduction in thickness (chapter 19). Details for individual cable sizes are included in appendix A14.

As with PVC cables, the bedding under armour may consist of either extruded PVC or two layers of PVC or other non-hygroscopic tapes. However, when PVC

Fig. 22.1 600/1000 V, single-core XLPE insulated cable with stranded conductor, taped bedding and aluminium wire armour

Fig. 22.2 600/1000 V, 4-core unarmoured cable with solid aluminium conductors

bedding and XLPE insulation are in direct contact with each other it is also necessary to ensure that no contamination occurs by migration of plasticiser from the PVC into the insulation. This may be done by suitable formulation of the PVC or by the inclusion of a separating layer of polyethylene terepthalate or polypropylene film.

The oversheath is normally of extruded PVC but BS 5467 and IEC 502 also allow for the use of an extruded layer of any suitable black synthetic material compatible with the operating temperature of the cable.

FUTURE PROSPECTS FOR CABLES UP TO 3 kV

XLPE is a material which has not only proved itself to be eminently suitable for this voltage range of 1–3 kV, but is also steadily finding acceptance for the whole field of power cables up to 132 kV and higher voltages. For the 1–3 kV range it is displacing the present main alternatives of PVC and impregnated paper and, although cable users are naturally slow to change from products which have given good service, this process is likely to continue.

Economics constitute a key factor. Another is that cablemakers maintain stocks of the most popular cables for industrial use and are naturally hesitant to hold too many alternative types. Therefore, when a trend based on sound technical and economic considerations is clear, it tends to dictate stocking policy, which in turn gives impetus to the trend. XLPE cable instead of PVC cable is becoming the predominant stock cable at 1–3 kV for industrial cables. EPR has largely replaced butyl rubber and has a few devotees, particularly where flexibility is important. It might carve a niche for some special applications, but XLPE is likely to dominate in the years immediately ahead.

OPERATIONAL CHARACTERISTICS

The notes below indicate any differences compared with the situation for cables with PVC insulation described in chapter 21.

Ground containing hydrocarbons

As the cables usually have a PVC oversheath, the situation is essentially the same as for cables with PVC insulation. Permeation of hydrocarbon through the oversheath into spaces between the armour wires and between the cores is usually more important than any subsequent effect of further permeation through the insulation into the conductor. Although XLPE has better resistance to hydrocarbons than PVC, this does not have great practical significance.

Ageing and operational life of the insulation

It has been explained that the limits of operational characteristics of PVC insulation are defined by the resistance to deformation at operating temperature, e.g. due to external mechanical pressure or conductor thrust at bends, and by the resistance to thermal degradation. XLPE is superior to PVC in both these respects. For material test purposes the ageing temperature for XLPE is 40 °C higher than for PVC.

Chapter 23
600/1000 V Cables with Combined Neutral and Earth for Public Supply

Combined neutral and earth (CNE) cables are used in the UK in systems having protective multiple earthing (PME), as discussed in chapter 18. The incentive for development of PME came from the need to retain good earthing and consumer protection when difficulties arose from the introduction of plastic water pipes. If the lead sheath of the paper insulated supply cable was not plumbed in joints it was not suitable for carrying fault currents through a sufficiently low impedance path back to the supply transformer. By using the neutral conductor of the supply cable for the purpose there was no need for a separate earth conductor in the cable and it soon became apparent that this could lead to considerable saving in the cost of distribution and house service cables operating at 240/415 V.

The reduction in cable diameter and hence materials cost is well illustrated in fig. 23.1 which shows a comparison between 600/1000 V 4-core PILS/STA cable with one form of CNE cable (Consac) of equal rating.

Initially PME systems had to be kept separate but when regulations were changed and it was appreciated that there were no problems in converting existing distributors to PME, or in mixing cable types within any single distributor, all new or replacement cable could be of the CNE type. Thus the supply authority did not need to maintain

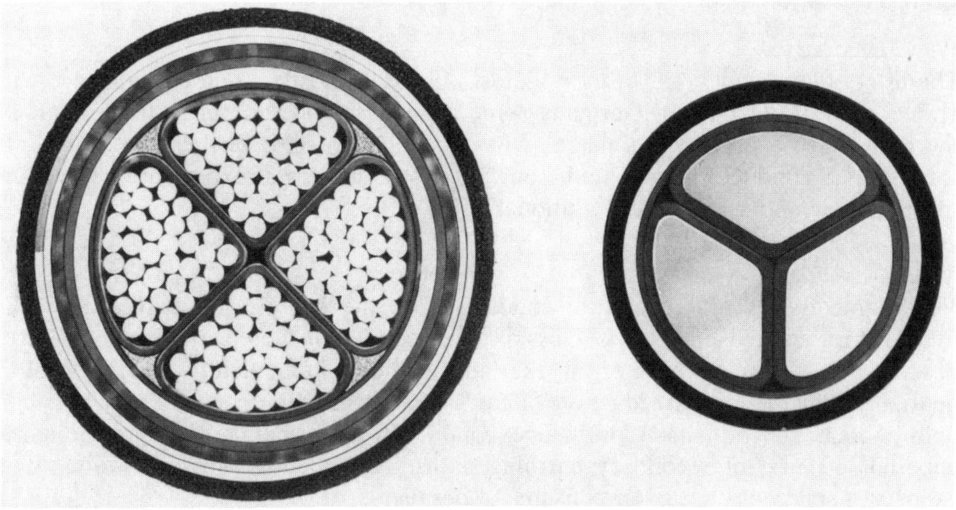

Fig. 23.1 Comparative diameters of 600/1000 V, 4-core PILS/STA and CNE cable of Consac type of equal rating

a stock of conventional cable with a separate earth conductor. This has largely been the situation in the UK since around 1970. The saving in cable cost was then of the order of 20% – 30% against PILS cable with aluminium conductors and the reduction in total installed cost about 10% – 15%. The annual savings over the whole of the UK were quoted in 1972 to exceed £2 million.

In other countries such as France and Germany, the basic network and regulations have been somewhat different, mainly because each consumer has to provide a separate earth. CNE cables were in use somewhat earlier than in the UK and there have been differences in the types of cable which have been favoured.

Although, certainly in the UK, the use of CNE cables has been associated with the use of PME, they can be used to advantage on any type of system. They need not be restricted to PME systems and this is the case in many countries of continental Europe.

The integrity of the neutral conductor is a feature to which reference is made later and another aspect is that the system should be so arranged that the neutral may never be disconnected. This also applies during operations to provide service joints and all the cable designs allow for joints to be made without severance of the neutral conductor.

TYPES OF CNE CABLE

Four basic designs have been used in Europe as a replacement for lead sheathed paper cables, namely Consac, Waveform, Districable and 4-core polymeric insulated cable without armour. Usually only two of these types have been predominant in any one country at the same time. In some cases a third design has emerged when one of those originally used has dropped out of favour.

General design details

Phase conductors

The use of aluminium conductors is almost universal, mostly stranded in France but always solid in the UK. In Germany some copper is still used and with aluminium there has been a progressive change from stranded to solid. In the UK the use of solid shaped conductors emanated from 5 years of successful experience by two of the Electricity Boards with conventional PILS cables.

Neutral conductors

The characteristics of the neutral conductor are the key design feature of CNE cables. If for any reason there is a loss of phase conductor there is the inconvenience of loss of supply to a consumer but the fault is known immediately. Corrosion of a neutral conductor means reduction of fault current carrying capacity and possible failure in its function as a protective conductor. This may not be immediately apparent because of secondary earthing paths. Nevertheless a rise in voltage of exposed metal could occur on consumers' premises.

Corrosion protection of the aluminium neutral conductor in CNE cables is a feature to which great attention has been paid in the design of individual cable types. The possibility of loss of conductance due to corrosion is also the reason why little attempt has been made to produce designs with a reduced size neutral conductor, although the Waveconal design has a 185 mm^2 neutral in the 240 and 300 mm^2 sizes.

Cable weight
The weight of aluminium CNE cables is about half that of PILS/STA cable with aluminium conductors. Consac cable is the lightest, with only 35%–40% of the weight of paper/lead cable. The low weight reduces the cost of cable laying because fewer workmen are needed.

Consac cable

First introduced in Germany with stranded phase conductors in the early 1960s, Consac retains the well-proven paper insulation but substitutes an aluminium sheath for lead and the sheath becomes a concentric neutral conductor (fig. 23.2). As with all the CNE cables there is a PVC oversheath for corrosion protection and with Consac a bitumen layer is applied between the aluminium and PVC to prevent passage of water along the interface in the event of damage to the oversheath. Consac was the first CNE cable to be used in the UK and it was adopted extensively in the late 1960s.

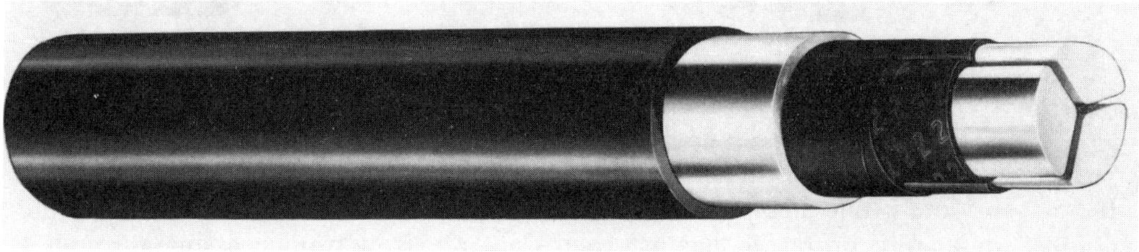

Fig. 23.2 Consac type of CNE cable

This application of aluminium for sheathing followed a decade of successful experience with high voltage pressure cables, e.g. of the oil-filled type. However, more care is taken in the installation of expensive transmission cables. They are also installed in deeper trenches and in sand. Hence with Consac there is a greater risk of damage to the oversheath and subsequent corrosion of the aluminium sheath in the early years of cable life.

A feature of Consac is that in the event of damage to the oversheath the corrosion mechanism on the aluminium sheath takes the form of pinholes. Water can then enter the insulation and will cause cable breakdown before there is sufficient general corrosion of the sheath to result in significant loss of conductance, i.e. unknown loss of the protective conductor is highly unlikely.

Steps are taken during manufacture to limit the clearance between the insulation and sheath and to control the amount of impregnant in this space so as to limit the longitudinal travel of moisture along the cable in the event of sheath damage.

Although Consac is available in sizes up to 300 mm^2 it tends to be rather stiff and difficult to handle at this size. In general, therefore, 185 mm^2 is the largest size used.

When first introduced, Consac had a disadvantage in comparison with other CNE cables because only soldering techniques were available for conductor joints and the joint casing was filled with bitumen. The advent of mechanical conductor joints and cast resin filling reduced this drawback considerably but the procedure for cutting the sheath to open a flap has undoubtedly been one important reason why some users have preferred to adopt an alternative design of cable.

Waveform type

This type of construction was first introduced in Germany with PVC insulation in the 1960s under the name 'Ceander'. The neutral conductor takes the form of a layer of aluminium or copper wires applied with constantly reversing lay as illustrated in the Waveconal cable shown in Fig. 23.3. This makes service jointing very easy, without any cutting of the neutral conductor, because when the oversheath is removed the wires may readily be pulled out to form two bunches for jointing purposes.

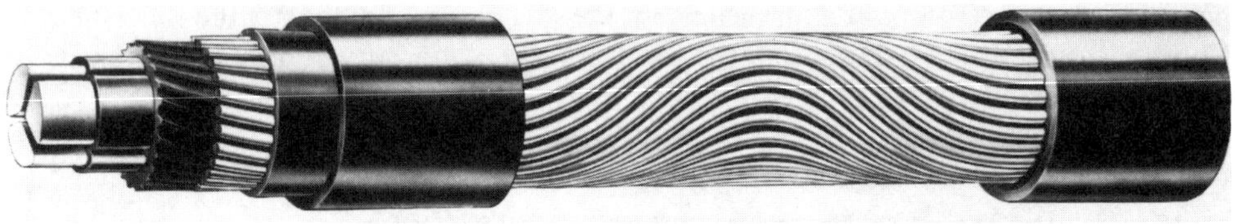

Fig. 23.3 Waveconal CNE cable with XLPE insulation

In Ceander cable in Germany, copper wires were used for the neutral conductor. It was considered that there was an undue risk in using aluminium because it could not be adequately protected against corrosion, and soil water passing through a damaged oversheath could easily travel along the cable. The design then became used in France with XLPE insulation as an alternative to PVC and with an aluminium wire neutral conductor. For additional corrosion protection of the aluminium, extruded layers of unvulcanised rubber were applied under and over the aluminium wire layer.

In the UK in the mid-1960s there were some trials with a cable similar to the French cable but with a copper wire neutral, under the name 'Wavecon'. However, for maximum economy the aluminium neutral version was soon preferred and widespread use began of 'Waveconal' cable. Compared with the French cable an important difference of the Waveconal design was that rather larger diameter aluminium wires were used so that they could be spaced apart. This allowed the two rubber layers to meet each other between the wires, so that in effect each wire is encapsulated in rubber. Much work was also carried out on the composition of the rubber type material so that it could be removed cleanly from the wires, had adequate resistance to deformation and good ageing properties. In the event of mechanical damage to the oversheath some wires may be exposed and can corrode, but water does not readily come into contact with neighbouring wires. In laboratory tests it has been shown that the voluminous corrosion products of aluminium may disturb the rubber to permit some further passage of water but the service performance of the cable has been satisfactory.

Because of fears of excessive corrosion of the aluminium neutral some supply Boards in the UK have adopted a Wavecon design with a copper wire neutral. This has an unvulcanised rubber bedding under the concentric neutral/earth wires, as with the Waveconal cable, but not necessarily a rubber layer over the wires.

In the UK the insulation has been XLPE from the outset and apart from service cables this was the first major departure from impregnated paper for public supply cables. Although the sustained ratings could be somewhat higher than for Consac, as they may be based on a conductor temperature of 90 °C instead of 80 °C, they are generally taken to be the same, voltage drop usually being a limiting factor.

Waveform has a slightly greater diameter and material content than Consac. A novel feature of manufacture is that in addition to the application of the neutral wires using a reversing lay head, two layers of rubber and the PVC oversheath are applied in the same operation.

Districable

Two UK supply Boards used Districable for a period of time but in general it has found little adoption outside France. Construction (fig. 23.4) is of 4-core design with solid aluminium conductors and XLPE insulation (formerly PVC) on the phase conductors. The neutral conductor, which is circular, has a thin lead covering for corrosion protection. A thin soft galvanised or tinned steel binder tape holds the laid-up cores together and there is a PVC oversheath. As the steel binder tape makes contact with the neutral/earth conductor there is an earthed metallic envelope, although the ability of the thin steel tape to convey fault currents to the CNE conductor may be somewhat limited.

Doubts have been expressed about the ability of the thin lead coating to serve as an adequate corrosion protection for the aluminium neutral conductor during installation and service, but the service performance has been satisfactory.

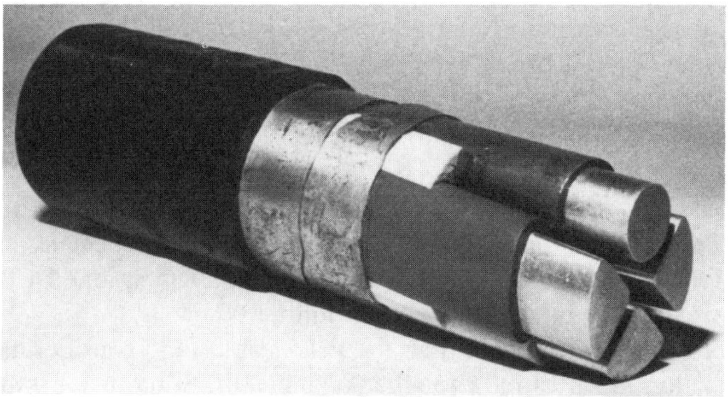

Fig. 23.4 Districable with solid aluminium conductors and XLPE insulation

4-core unarmoured cable

This design (fig. 23.5) reaches the maximum simplicity in distribution cable design as it merely consists of shaped conductors, generally solid aluminium, polymeric insu-

Fig. 23.5 600/1000 V, 4-core unarmoured cable with solid aluminium conductors and XLPE insulation

lation and a PVC oversheath. Originally introduced in Germany with PVC insulation it has now become the standard design in Germany for mains distribution and services. There has been some drift from PVC to XLPE insulation, however. It has been reported that up to 1979 some 300 000 km had been installed.

This unarmoured cable is used in some other European countries and elsewhere but not in the UK or France. Largely on grounds of safety, the authorities in the UK have not given permission to its use for direct burial and extra protection would not be economic. Possibly a desire, in the interest of standardisation, not to extend the multiplicity of cable designs brought into use over a short period of years has had some bearing on the decision. Another factor is that the Electricity Supply Regulations stipulate that cables in the high voltage range (specified as 650 V upwards) are required to have a metallic envelope. Although the cables concerned operate at 240/415 V, they are classified as 600/1000 V design.

However, the most important point concerns effects following third-party mechanical damage to cables and the fact that such damage, particularly from mechanised tools and excavators, has been occurring at an increasing rate during the last two decades. Any damage to the insulation on the neutral conductor could lead to the loss, by corrosion, of the protective conductor and damage to a phase conductor could cause currents to flow in other insulated buried metals.

Comparison of CNE cable designs

All the four types are very easy to handle for installation, especially in comparison with the former PILS armoured cables, but as already mentioned Consac has the disadvantage of stiffness in sizes above 185 mm^2.

They are, of course, less robust than the PILS cables and consideration was given to better protection, such as by a tougher oversheath. Some use has been made of high density polyethylene on Consac for this purpose, an additional modification necessary being a small change in jointing procedure to prevent retraction of the oversheath from the joint casing. However, the general opinion has been that, as a large proportion of cable damage is due to mechanised plant, extra expenditure on cable protection would not be economic.

In materials and manufacturing cost Consac is the most favourable design, even in comparison with the 4-core unarmoured cable. However, it is the total installed cost, including jointing, which is significant. The 4-core unarmoured cable is clearly the most attractive for jointing simplicity and Consac has a disadvantage because of the somewhat more difficult step in opening up the aluminium sheath. There is not a great difference between the overall costs for any of the designs and so once usage had become established for any particular one there has not been much incentive to make a change. Service experience with all of them has been satisfactory.

Knowing that the cables were less robust than former types and that faults due to third-party damage were increasing, consideration was given at an early stage to safety aspects when live cables were damaged by tools such as spikes and spades. One series of tests was carried out by the UK Electricity Council Research Laboratory (unpublished) and one by McAllister and Cox.[1] The results and conclusions were similar in each case.

The aspects investigated were related primarily to effects on personnel due to shock because of the tool becoming live and possible injury due to the flash and explosion. Little was known about the situation with existing cables, except that electrocution was very rare and that cases of severe burning had occasionally occurred.

Contrary to expectation, it was found that with PILS cables the reason that tools did not become live was not due to conductance of fault currents through the sheath and armour. Both the outer metal on the cable in contact with the tool and the end of the tool itself just burned away to leave the tool isolated. Thus cables with a metallic sheath, such as PILS and Consac, showed a greater severity of flash than Waveconal, Districable or 4-core unarmoured cable but there was less chance of the tool remaining live. It was concluded that greater incidence of severe accidents due to electrocution was unlikely and that overall there was little chance of increasing hazards by adoption of any of the CNE cable designs. A possibly important factor with 4-core unarmoured cable was that, because of the absence of any metal envelope, a workman would not be aware of striking a live cable, as there would not be any flash until the implement bridged between two cores. Because of the geometry there is therefore a somewhat greater chance of the more severe flash associated with a core to core rather than a core to earth fault.

Many different types of fault can be generated by sharp and blunt objects and the overall situation is quite complex. However, one aspect which did come out clearly was that synthetic insulation had some advantage over paper in that faults rarely developed to become of a sustained type which could damage a significant length of cable and/or lead to a 3-phase fault. Another facet was that the test result showed that there was no advantage in using a binder/cross flow tape around the neutral wires in Waveconal cable. Other tests had shown the undesirability of including this tape because it interfered with the corrosion protection capability of the rubber layer. In this context the limited value was also apparent of the thin steel binder tape in Districable to carry fault currents to the neutral earth conductor.

REFERENCE

(1) McAllister, D. and Cox, E.H. (1972) 'Behaviour of m.v. power distribution cables when subjected to external damage'. *Proc. IEE* **119** (4), 479–486.

Chapter 24
Service Distribution Cables

APPLICATIONS

As the name implies, the classification of service cable is associated primarily with the provision of an electricity supply from a distribution main, generally underground, to individual houses or other small consumers. The cables described here are designed for direct burial, as distinct from providing a service from an overhead line.

The type of cable is also suitable for any small-scale supply up to around 200 A single- or 3-phase with conductor sizes from 4 to 35 mm^2 in copper and from 6 to 50 mm^2 in aluminium. Apart from dwellings and shops with direct or looped services there are other wide-scale applications. The smaller sizes are used for street lighting and all the multiplicity of street furniture such as traffic lights and signs, and the larger sizes are very convenient for motorway lighting where the lighting needs to be controlled by wiring in specific circuits, i.e. as distinct from the majority of street lights which are now connected individually to a distribution main.

Paper insulated lead sheathed cables

Although virtually obsolete since the later 1960s a high proportion of existing houses in the UK are still supplied through a 2-core paper cable with steel tape armour and bituminous hessian serving. The terminations comprise a wiped connection to the lead sheath and usually a bitumen filled cable sealing chamber: altogether rather large and untidy compared with modern installation practice. Nevertheless, although the rubber insulated internal wiring of older houses will no doubt have been replaced, the main feed to the meter to pre-1960 vintage is still probably the original one and will be capable of continuing for a few more decades.

Split concentric cable design

When PVC insulation was developed for power cables in the later 1950s, the UK Electricity Boards carried out trials but came to the conclusion that problems might arise due to thermal deformation at high conductor temperatures which could not readily be prevented by the provision of better circuit protection. With service cables, however, the fuse at the point of supply provides good control, apart from mechanical damage to the cable itself, which is comparatively rare.

At this time it was still necessary to include a separate conductor in single-phase service cables, though on the larger sizes this earth conductor did not need to have the full conductance of a phase conductor. Hence the split concentric design shown in fig. 24.1 emerged and was fairly quickly adopted as standard. For the 16, 25 and

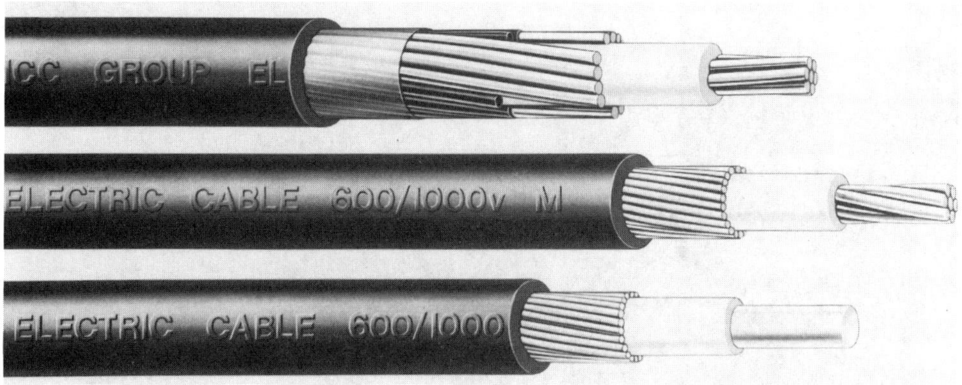

Fig. 24.1 PVC insulated 600/1000 V service cables: split concentric with copper phase conductor (*top*); CNE concentric with copper phase conductor (*middle*); CNE concentric with solid aluminium phase conductor (*bottom*)

35 mm^2 sizes the earth conductor is 16 mm^2 and for the larger sizes it is half the area of a phase conductor. A 3-phase design is very similar and has three laid-up insulated conductors in the centre instead of the single one shown.

In order to ensure that no corrosion of the neutral conductor occurs and to eliminate any possibility of faults in connections within the consumer's cut-out, the two conductors in the concentric layer, i.e. the neutral and the earth, each comprise copper rather than aluminium wires. The wires of the earth conductor are bare and are only separated from the lightly PVC covered wires forming the neutral conductor by a PVC string.

Within the building, the clean PVC sheath was much more attractive than the bituminised hessian finish of the paper cable and for the common 16 mm^2 size the overall diameter was reduced from 22.4 mm to 14.7 mm. Furthermore, the termination illustrated in fig. 24.2 is much neater and easier to make than the previous types necessary with a lead sheathed cable.

An armoured version of the single-phase cable is used for motorway lighting. Essentially the armoured design is the cable as already described with two additional layers applied over it, these being a layer of galvanised steel wires and an external PVC oversheath.

When the split concentric design was first introduced, aluminium had already replaced copper for the conductors of the main distribution cable and consideration was given to the use of aluminium for the service cable. For the small conductor sizes involved, the saving with aluminium has never been very great but designs with a circular solid aluminium phase conductor have always been available and some users have preferred them as an alternative to stranded copper. The connection in the cut-out is usually of the pinch screw type and there are not the same problems with a solid conductor as exist with a stranded conductor. Another reason that aluminium wires have not been used in the concentric earth and neutral layer is that, although mechanical damage to service cables was stated above to be rare, it does happen on occasions. Water may then enter the cable and with aluminium there would be a probability of serious corrosion of the important protective earth conductor.

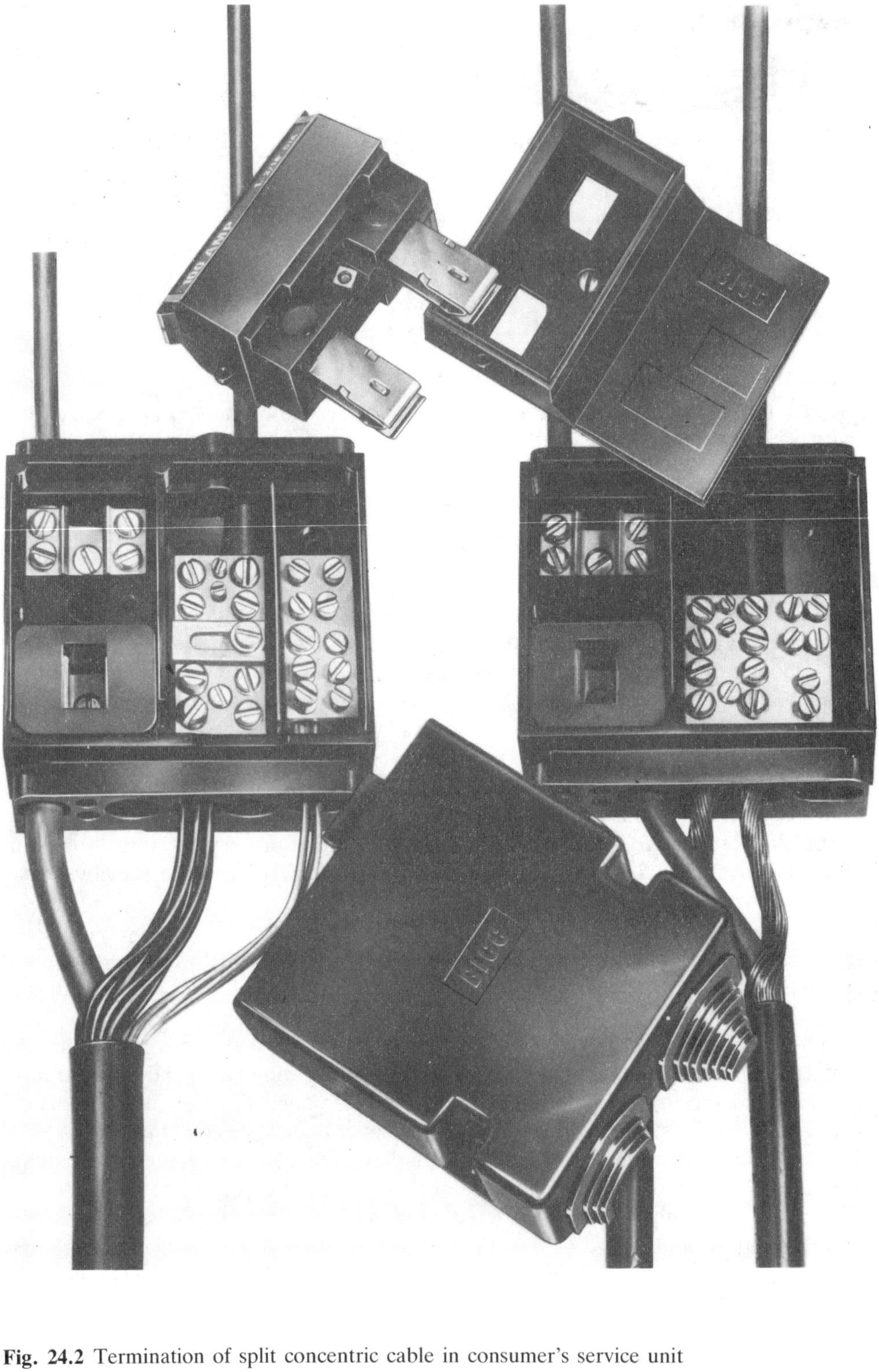

Fig. 24.2 Termination of split concentric cable in consumer's service unit

The provision of extra corrosion protection, as is done with Waveconal cable, would make the aluminium design uneconomic in comparison with copper.

Combined neutral and earth design

This design is often termed 'CNE concentric' or 'straight concentric' and is a simplification of the split concentric version for use when both the distributor and the consumer can operate with protective multiple earthing. One conductor may be eliminated and the concentric layer then consists of a simple layer of bare copper wires (fig. 24.1). For the copper 16 mm^2 size of around 100 A rating referred to above, the diameter is further reduced from 14.7 mm with the split concentric to 12.1 mm for the straight concentric cable. Both single- and 3-phase designs are available and these types now represent the bulk usage of service cable in the UK.

XLPE insulation

As PVC was the original insulating material for the concentric designs, its use has tended to continue. XLPE is the obvious alternative and has the advantage of being suitable for higher temperatures. The trend is towards replacement of PVC by XLPE, but the process is gradual. XLPE can also be used with a lower insulation thickness, but for some sizes of single-phase cable the diameter over the insulation is dictated by the space required to accommodate the concentric layer of wires.

UK standards

The single-phase split concentric cable with copper conductors and PVC insulation is covered by BS 4553. The 3-phase designs, the CNE type, cables with solid aluminium phase conductors and cables with XLPE insulation are included in an Electricity Supply Industry Standard ESI 09–7.

Waveconal service cable

There are some users of the Waveform distribution cable described in chapter 23 who have preferred to use small sizes of the same cable for service connections. However, this application is diminishing, largely on economic grounds. If such cable is used it is also important that the design of termination in the consumer's service unit is suitable to accommodate bunched aluminium wires.

Service cables outside UK

The split concentric and straight concentric designs of the type described are peculiar to the UK and are seldom used elsewhere. Practices vary widely from country to country and, in addition to the use of conventional 2-core and 3-core armoured and unarmoured cables, other prominent arrangements include the following.

USA

Underground cable services are less frequently adopted than in Europe and when used are generally associated with the URD system (chapter 18). A common practice is for 6–12 consumers to be fed from a small transformer in the high voltage (10–30 kV) network either directly from the transformer or through a distribution pillar using short lengths of secondary or service cable. The cabling needs to be of 3-wire type to meet the dual voltage supply requirement. The neutral is usually of reduced area. Solid aluminium is now the most popular choice of conductor and XLPE is common for the insulation, although copper conductors and polyethylene insulation are also used. Three single-core cables, merely comprising conductor and insulation, may be installed separately, frequently in a plastic duct, or more usually triplexed (laid-up) together with no outer sheath. There is no armour or earth conductor.

Germany

Changes from PILS cables to PME type systems involving both Consac and Waveform cables have been similar to those in the UK and are discussed in chapter 23. Practice has subsequently moved strongly towards the use of 4-core PVC or XLPE insulated distribution cable with a PVC oversheath but no armour. Services to consumers are of 3-phase type and a similar 4-core unarmoured cable is now widely used also for services.

France

The 3-phase services provided in France are as in Germany and 4-conductor service cable of combined-neutral-and-earth type is required. The normal design is now of 4-core construction having PVC or XLPE insulation on the phase conductors, a thin soft steel tape over the laid-up cores, in contact with the neutral conductor, and a PVC oversheath. With copper conductors the neutral conductor is left bare and with aluminium it has a lead sheath, i.e. the design is a small size of the Districable type described in chapter 23.

Chapter 25

Polymeric Insulated Distribution Cables for 6–30 kV

In the 1970s and 1980s, in the 6–30 kV cable range, there has been a swing worldwide away from paper insulation to the polymeric types. In the UK, in terms of usage the scale of the change has been smaller and its speed slower than in many other countries but, because much of the cable is made for export, the pattern of manufacture has moved substantially towards an increased proportion of cable with polymeric insulation.

Trends in the comparative costs of the cables themselves can be expected to have influenced the change, but another factor is that it has become increasingly difficult to secure, at reasonable cost, the skills required to joint and terminate the traditional paper cable. This is especially the case in the developing countries. Inevitably, the simpler concept and reduced level of expertise involved with the installation of polymeric cable has a significant influence on the swing away from paper cables.

Most of the installations in the 1970s and 1980s of large distribution networks in the Middle East, in the field of power cables, have predominantly used XLPE insulation. The improved current rating of polymerics at the higher ambient temperatures experienced in this part of the world must also be a further factor for preferring XLPE to paper.

Against this background, most industrialised nations have seen a reduction in demand for paper cables as the traditional markets have declined and there has been a growth in demand for polymerics from newer markets.

Synthetic polymeric materials were not new to power cables when the move towards them began to gather pace; polyethylene was used as an insulant as early as 1943. The high intrinsic electrical strength and low dielectric loss angle of polyethylene, together with its good resistance to chemicals, ease of processing and low cost, make it an ideal material for use in the manufacture of power cables. Its main disadvantage is the relatively low melting point of the material (105–115 °C), which means that the sustained current rating, overload and short-circuit temperatures are limited. By converting the thermoplastic polyethylene into a crosslinked thermoset, the melting point is greatly increased and the new material is well able to surpass the thermal capabilities of a paper insulated cable. The crosslinking can be achieved either by radiation or by chemical means and for the manufacture of power cables the latter is by far the most economic. For the manufacture of cables with a voltage exceeding 6 kV the additives are best kept to a minimum. In the case of the thermoplastic insulant only an antioxidant is added to the polyethylene and for crosslinked material the only further additives are those chemicals which are essential to achieve the carbon to carbon bonds.

Ethylene–propylene rubber (EPR) consists of approximately equivalent quantities of ethylene and propylene and it is often referred to as a copolymer. It was first used as an insulant during the early 1960s and is always used in its crosslinked form, which is achieved by a similar chemical means as with polyethylene. The main difference between XLPE and EPR is the greater flexibility of the rubbery material and this has advantages in some arduous installations.

FIELD OF USE

Initially the thermoplastic polyethylene was the most popular. Many kilometres of cable have been installed in Germany, France and the USA. Mostly the low density polyethylene (LDPE) has been used but there is also some experience in the USA with high density polyethylene (HDPE) as an insulant. HDPE has superior electrical properties to LDPE but it is more rigid. HDPE is more crystalline than LDPE and thus capable of operating at a higher temperature. It has been assigned a sustained rating of 80 °C, in comparison with 70 °C for LDPE. Its crystallinity at 70 °C is 75% whereas the figures for LDPE and XLPE are 40% and 30% respectively. Its saturation moisture content is approximately a fifth of that of low density materials. Nevertheless, its greater stiffness has mitigated against its wider acceptance.

Generally the use of EPR has been confined to those applications where its property of greater flexibility can be used to advantage, but in Italy and Spain EPR has been used widely throughout the voltage range. Although 132 kV cables have been manufactured with EPR, the higher loss angle and poorer thermal resistivity make it a poor competitor against XLPE at higher voltages. While EPR has excellent resistance to ozone and electrical discharges and the material was for this reason preferred to PE during the 1960s, changes in manufacturing techniques have led to a reduction in discontinuities and size of voids within cables to such an extent that advantage can no longer be taken of this positive characteristic. EPR is also more expensive than XLPE and it seems likely that applications for it will be confined to voltages of less than 30 kV, especially where flexibility of the core is an important factor, e.g. in the mining industry and in power stations.

Crosslinked polyethylene has become the most favoured insulant. Germany, Japan, the USA and Scandinavian countries have installed vast quantities of such cables.

SERVICE EXPERIENCE WITH POLYETHYLENE (PE AND XLPE)

In France the thermoplastic polyethylene has been preferred and the first 63 kV cable was installed in 1965. At the end of the 1970s there was in excess of 300 km operating at this voltage and a failure rate of less than 0.7 faults/100 km per year has been reported.[1] The move from paper to XLPE insulated cable in the 6–30 kV range, i.e. 20 kV in France, occurred around 1978, after experimentation with various materials and designs.[2] Once approved, the change to XLPE was fast: 900 km in 1978, 3500 km in 1979 and approximately 4000 km annually thereafter. By the end of 1985, the total length in operation was nearly 30 000 km, with a failure rate from internal causes of only 0.17 faults/100 km per year.

The German service history goes back to 1961, and at the end of 1983 there were nearly 8000 km of PE cable and over 16 000 km of XLPE cable installed in the voltage range 10–30 kV. The incidence of failures in Germany is 0.3 and 0.05 faults/100 km per year for PE and XLPE respectively.

XLPE has been installed in Japan since 1965 and today all cables up to 69 kV are made with this material. The Scandinavian countries swung to XLPE in the early 1970s and have installed many kilometres of cable in the voltage range 12–170 kV. In both these countries the services experience has been very good.

The American experience has been well documented and publicised in the surveys conducted by Thue.[3] A later survey[4] reported that 60 000 km of PE cable and 116 000 km of XLPE cable had been installed in the USA by the end of 1983. The service experience in the USA, which includes early designs, is unsatisfactory compared with that in Europe, the failure rate being five to six times that in Germany.

Inevitably, everyone can derive benefit from mistakes made by others. The Americans are to be congratulated on their bold and rapid swing to the extruded dielectric. Unfortunately, the sudden change did not provide sufficient time to understand fully the limitations of these otherwise excellent materials. The susceptibility of both PE and XLPE to premature failure arising from electrical discharge and water trees was overlooked. Early American designs utilized a semiconducting tape screen applied helically over the conductor. This was subsequently found to be a potential source of water trees and has since been superseded by an extruded layer of semiconducting material. Also insufficient care was taken in avoiding contamination of the insulant during both the compounding and the extrusion processes. Finally, many American engineers may rue the decision not to apply an oversheath over the cable. More often than not, the cable was laid in wet ground with the concentric copper wires, applied directly over the core screen, thus being exposed to the elements.

The tremendous technical effort which has been devoted to investigating and understanding the phenomenon of premature failures has not necessarily produced a clear reason or satisfactory explanation for the cause, but both producer and user have derived considerable advantages from this work.

The operating experience with 11 kV polymeric cable amongst Area Electricity Boards in the UK has mainly been limited to one Board.[5] Both XLPE and EPR insulated cables were purchased, and by the middle of 1986 over 150 km of 3-core and 30 km of single-core XLPE cable and about 50 km of 3-core EPR cable had been installed. A number of faults have occurred during nearly 8 years of operation, but only one early fault in an EPR cable has not been explained. All other faults were attributed to third party damage. Laboratory examination of specially excavated cables indicated that the EPR cables suffered less reduction in electrical strength due to water trees than the XLPE cables, giving improved life expectancy in wet conditions. However, there are many formulations of EPR compounds and difficulties in ensuring that the compounds used consistently have the water-resisting properties.

BREAKDOWN PHENOMENA

Breakdown mechanism

The electrical breakdown in polyethylene as a result of discharge is well understood and much work has been conducted on this subject.[6–8] It was shown that the failure occurs because of discharge activity, the intensity of which erodes fine channels in the polyethylene. The erosion can take three forms: melting, chemical decomposition and the production of microcracks in the polyethylene. In the case of chemical attack, the decomposition products of polyethylene are conducting and, with certain voids, can lead to a diminution of any subsequent discharges. This has the effect of increasing the life of the dielectric but only appears to occur in unvented voids or channels.

Experiments with fine needles inserted into polyethylene have shown that the tree growth is far more rapid when using a vented needle, i.e. a needle with a hole through its length vented to atmosphere, than an unvented one. In the case of the unvented sample, the discharges arising from the tip of the needle will erode the polyethylene and decomposition products, H_2 and CO_2, will be released which will increase the pressure in the channel. Paschen's law states that the breakdown strength of a gas is a function of the product of gas pressure and distance between electrodes. Hence as the pressure increases in a channel, the voltage required to cause the gas to discharge increases, and the discharges are suppressed. If the pressurised gas is given sufficient time it will diffuse through the polyethylene, reducing the pressure in the channel and thus the voltage required to cause further discharges. It is for this reason that accelerated tests on plastics containing unvented voids or channels are not useful. It is far more likely that such a model will have a reduced life at very low frequencies. Thus in this case high frequency retards the growth of trees whilst low frequency accelerates their growth.

The contrary is true for a vented tree. As the pressure in such a channel or void is constant the energy from successive electrical discharges is the same and in the frequency band of 50–1200 Hz it is now well established that the lifetime of a dielectric is inversely proportional to frequency.

The breakdown strength of a material is affected by both temperature and mechanical strain. Schultz[9] studied the relationship between electric strength and temperature for thin films of polyethylene. Fig. 25.1 shows this characteristic.

It is also well known that, if cables are tested with the core bent, the incidence of electrical failures on the outside of the loop, i.e. in the dielectric which is in tension, far exceeds the incidence in areas subjected to compression. McMahon and Perkins[10] found that residual mechanical strains in polyethylene lead to the production of microcracks under the action of electrical discharges and thus accelerate failure. All electrical trees are readily visible in polyethylene and fig. 25.2 shows an impulse failure on a sample of 6.35/11 kV XLPE cable.

The thermal breakdown mechanism, generally associated with paper and PVC insulated cables, may well account for some failures in low dielectric loss materials where the presence of contaminants, introduced during compounding and processing, can lead to small localised areas having a high loss. It is not possible to detect their presence as any measurement of loss angle records the predominant low figure for the dielectric, thus swamping the very small number of localised high loss sites.

Breakdown strength

The intrinsic breakdown strength of thin films of polyethylene is up to 500 kV/mm, whilst the a.c. breakdown strength of a cable is nearer a tenth of this figure. For an 11 kV cable, the r.m.s. breakdown stress at the conductor is typically 50 kV/mm and the maximum peak strength at the same position under an impulse test is 100 kVp/mm. The d.c. strength for polyethylene is nearly 20% higher than this figure at room

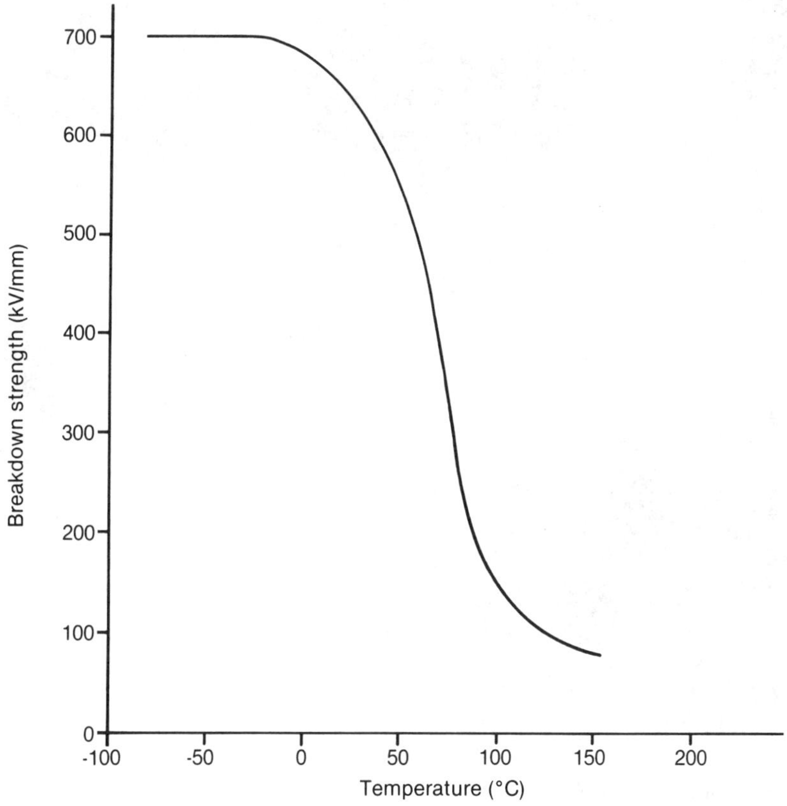

Fig. 25.1 Breakdown strength of thin films of polyethylene as a function of temperature (by permission of Academic Press)

temperature and 120 kV/mm is typical. The figures for EPR are somewhat lower at 40 kV/mm for a.c., 80 kVp/mm for impulse and 95 kV/mm under d.c. voltage.

The level of breakdown is a function of the rate of application of voltage. As an example, the figure for a cable where the voltage rise is rapid can be twice that for the same cable where a step rise is used. Unfortunately, there has not been any testing standardisation in this respect, but a starting voltage of 15 kV/mm followed by a rise of 1 kV/mm seems to be gaining favour.

Care must be exercised in the conditioning of samples exposed to such tests. For example, the breakdown strength of a freshly extruded cable will be approximately 20% greater than that of the same cable left unenergised for a year. The reason is that in many of the extrusion processes the voids are not at atmospheric pressure. In those processes using pressure during the crosslinking stage, the voids will initially be pressurised at up to 14 bar, whilst direct extrusion processes into a cold water trough at atmospheric pressure can result in the formation of contraction voids which will contain a gas at less than atmospheric pressure. As was discussed earlier, the breakdown strength of a gas is proportional to the product of pressure and size in accord with Paschen's law. Therefore in carrying out any electrical evaluation of

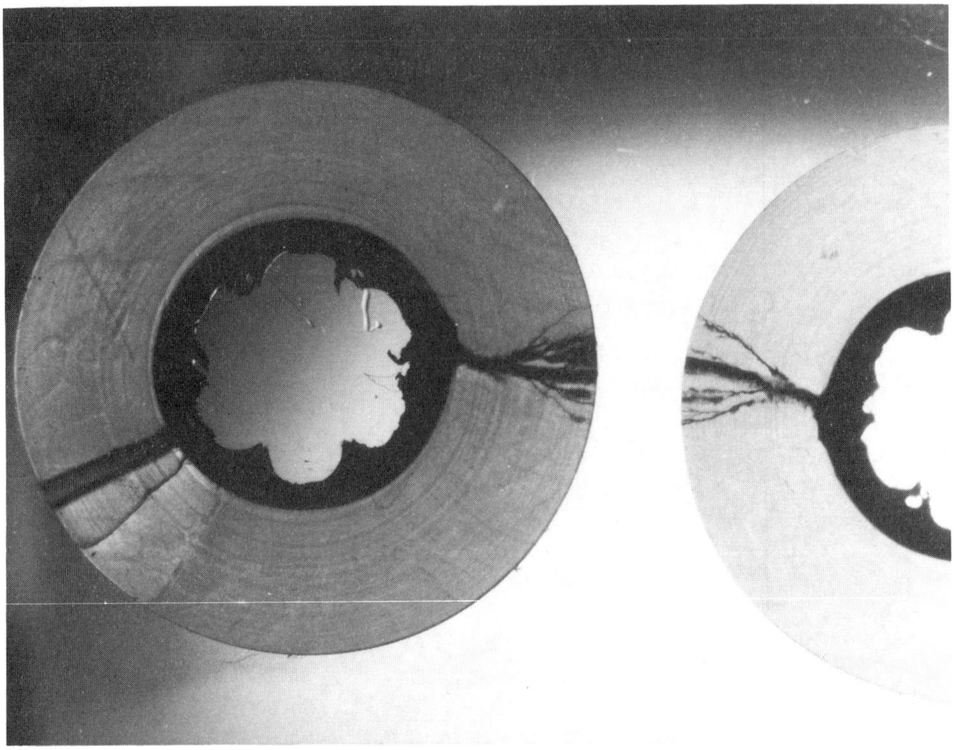

Fig. 25.2 Electrical impulse failure of sample of 6.35/11 kV XLPE cable

materials manufactured by different processes, it is essential to ensure that the samples are conditioned by a heat cycle.

As well as the effect of the history of the sample on its breakdown strength, the volume of dielectric under test is also a factor. In Schultz[9] reference is made to Leonardo da Vinci's conclusion that the tensile strength of wire decreased as the length of wire tested increased. Obviously, failures were occurring at the sites of flaws and the greater the length of wire tested, the greater are the chances that they will include imperfections. The same is true of plastics. Artbauer and Griac[11] found that, in the case of polyethylene, the breakdown stress was inversely proportional to the area of material under test to the power 0.15.

Again, because the probability of having similar flaws in samples of equal length is remote, it is necessary to evaluate approximately 20 specimens in order to establish a meaningful breakdown level for a polymeric cable. It has become fashionable to use the Weibull distribution, which is a mathematical representation to cover reliability. Its first application in the field of engineering was associated with the quality control of ball bearings during the early 1920s.

The most commonly used equation defines the probability of failure P as

$$P = 1 - \exp\left[- \left(\frac{E}{E_0}\right)^b \left(\frac{t}{t_0}\right)^a \left(\frac{Lr^2}{L_0 r_0^2}\right)\right] \qquad (25.1)$$

where E_0 = value of the stress corresponding to the breakdown probability of

63.2% of a voltage applied for time t_0 to a sample having length L_0 and radius r_0 over the conductor screen, i.e. derived on a model cable

E = conductor stress
t = time of application
L = length of cable under examination
r = radius of conductor under examination
a = characteristic constant of the dielectric (sometimes referred to as the time equivalent)
b = stress exponent (a characteristic constant of the dielectric)

It follows that to compare two cables

$$\frac{E}{E_0} = \left(\frac{L_0}{L}\frac{r_0^2}{r}\right)^{1/b} \tag{25.2}$$

The relationship between life and stress is given by

$$E^n t = \text{constant} \tag{25.3}$$

Therefore from the Weibull equation

$$\left(\frac{E}{E_0}\right)^b \left(\frac{t}{t_0}\right)^a = \text{constant}$$

$$\left(\frac{E}{E_0}\right)^n \frac{t}{t_0} = \left(\frac{E}{E_0}\right)^{b/a} \frac{t}{t_0}$$

where $n = b/a$. n is often referred to as the life exponent. Typically for polyethylene n is between 9 and 20, b between 10 and 20 and a between 0.5 and 2. The value of b is indicative of the amount of scatter of the breakdown figures. The higher the value of b the better and the more consistent is the polymer and the process.

Weibull plots are extremely useful laboratory tools which enable judgements to be made with regard to the selection of polymers and also comparison of products made by different processes. However, use of the n, b and a values obtained from short lengths of cable tested in a laboratory to derive the incidence of failure and the life span in service is not recommended. Inevitably, the failure mechanism at high voltage is completely different from the failure mechanism which occurs at the much lower stress in service and therefore the two cannot be compared.

WATER TREES

The growth of tree-like features in PE insulated power cables was widely reported in the early 1970s. It has since been the subject of much discussion with regard to mechanism of growth and effect on long-term cable performance.[12] Water trees have been classified by descriptive words such as bow tie, broccoli, delta, dendrite, fan, plume and streamer. They develop from voids, contaminants and defects which occur on either the conductor or the outer semiconducting screen. Many of the premature failures which have occurred in the USA have been ascribed to the existence of water trees emanating from the edges and irregular protrusions of semiconducting taped screens which were applied to many of the early cables.

The phenomenon is not confined to high stress. Many trees have been found in cables operating at stress levels of less than 1 kV/mm. Whilst most of the photographs shown in technical literature cover water trees in polyethylene they are not peculiar to this material and are present in EPR, EVA, polypropylene and PVC. However, they are far more difficult to study in these opaque materials.

Water trees grow in the direction of the electrical field and emanate from imperfections which have the effect of increasing the electrical stress at local sites. The branches of water trees are very narrow, of the order of 0.05 μm, and are not visible if the water is allowed to dry out of the specimen. Staining techniques are used and retention of the tree structure can then be maintained indefinitely. As an example, 0.1 g of rhodamine dye in a litre of water provides excellent definition of the trees in polyethylene if the samples are boiled in the solution for 15 min.

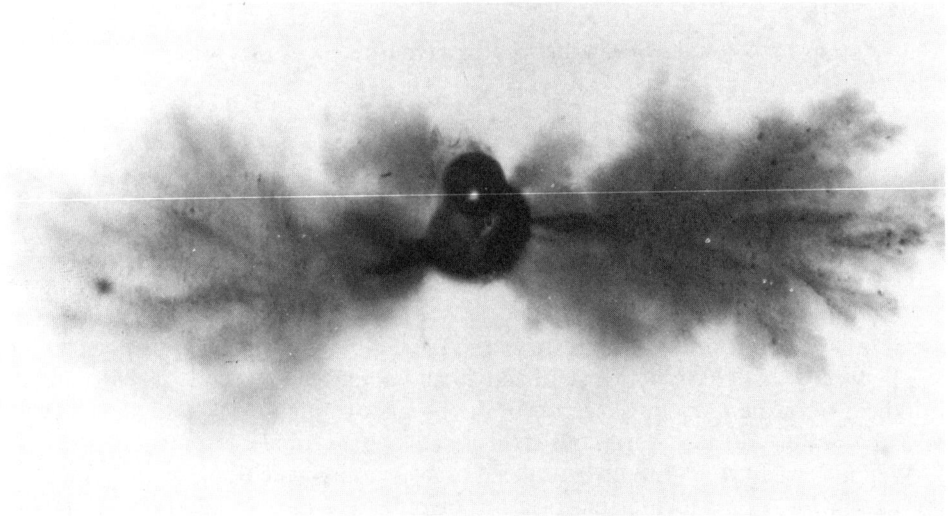

Fig. 25.3 Bow-tie water tree emanating from a contaminant in an XLPE insulated cable

The growth of a vented water tree with its source at a conducting screen is generally far more rapid than that of one emanating from within the dielectric. In nearly all cases the latter appear as bow-tie type and fig. 25.3 shows a typical example. The trees are generated from contaminants or voids existing within the dielectric and propagate in one or two directions towards the semiconducting screens.

The fact that water trees have a deleterious influence on the electrical properties is now well established but the mechanism is not fully understood. Fig. 25.4 depicts the reduction in breakdown strength of samples aged in water over a period of time; ageing in air results in only small decreases in strength. Fig. 25.5 is a photograph of an electrical tree which developed within a water tree.

Water trees increase in length with time, frequency and increasing voltage. However, in the case of frequency the acceleration factor is less than would be expected. As an example, samples energised at 500 Hz and 50 Hz show an acceleration factor of only 2 at the higher frequency and not the commonly accepted figure of 10. There does not appear to be any agreement on the influence of temperature, but it

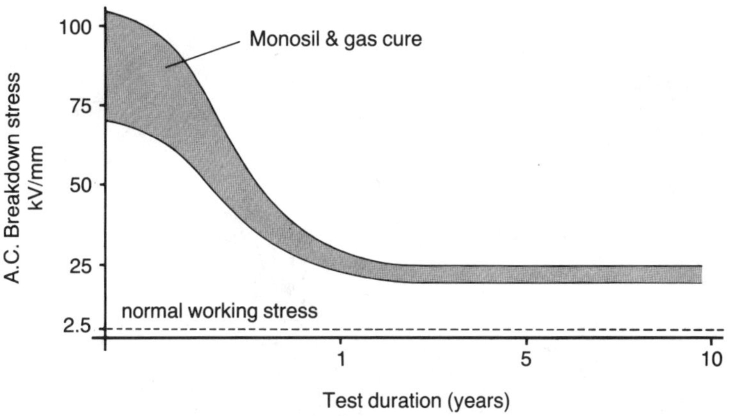

Fig. 25.4 Reduction in a.c. breakdown strength of XLPE cable aged in water at working voltage

seems reasonable that the less crystalline, more mobile, properties which prevail at 90 °C are more conducive to the growth of trees.

Water trees appear to be more profuse in highly strained dielectrics, and the same phenomenon seems to exist as in electrical trees where on bent samples of cable there is an excess of trees in the dielectric which is in tension and a paucity in the area which is in compression.

Initially it was assumed that the microstructure of the polyethylene was critical and that a dielectric cured in steam, having more voids, was more prone to form water trees than a material cured in a dry inert atmosphere. This has not been borne out in practice and there appear to be as many, if not more, trees in dry cured materials. Fig. 25.6 compares the density of the trees in two such materials.

It has been observed that the d.c. strength of cables is greatly affected when water trees are present. As an example, the d.c. breakdown strength of an 11 kV XLPE cable after manufacture may be about 380 kV, but after developing water trees as a result of being in service for 8 years the d.c. strength in certain environments can fall to less than 20 kV. In Japan, if a leakage current of greater than 0.3 μA exists on a cable subjected to a d.c. voltage equivalent to the a.c. rated voltage, the cable is considered to be suspect. As well as this change in d.c. strength, there is an increase in the dielectric loss angle. It is believed that the dielectric loss tan δ in the vicinity of a water tree can be as high as 1.0. This would account for the fact that the loss angle increases for the whole cable when only a small part of the total volume is affected by water trees. Again in Japan, cables with a tan δ exceedingly 0.05 are considered to be suspect.

The phenomenon of water treeing is still not fully understood and a number of mechanisms have been postulated and discussed in terms of chemical, electrical, electrostatic, thermal and mechanical effects. It is possible that several mechanisms are involved, the importance of each depending on the conditions and materials used.[7,8,12] Polymer morphology, internal mechanical stress, material purity (insulation and screens), the ionic concentration of the water, ion penetration and polymer oxidation are among the factors considered important in the propagation of water

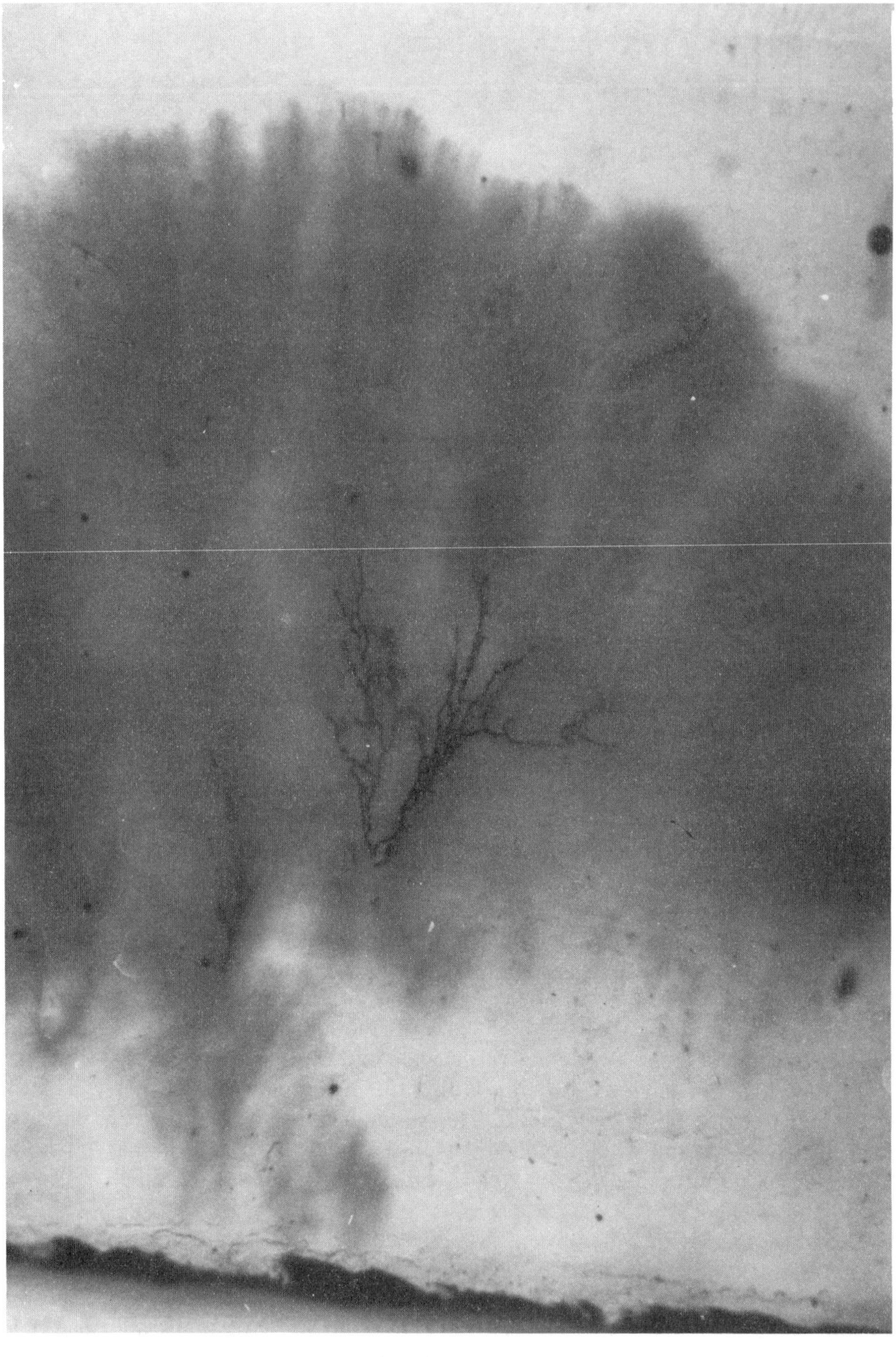

Fig. 25.5 Electrical tree forming within a water tree

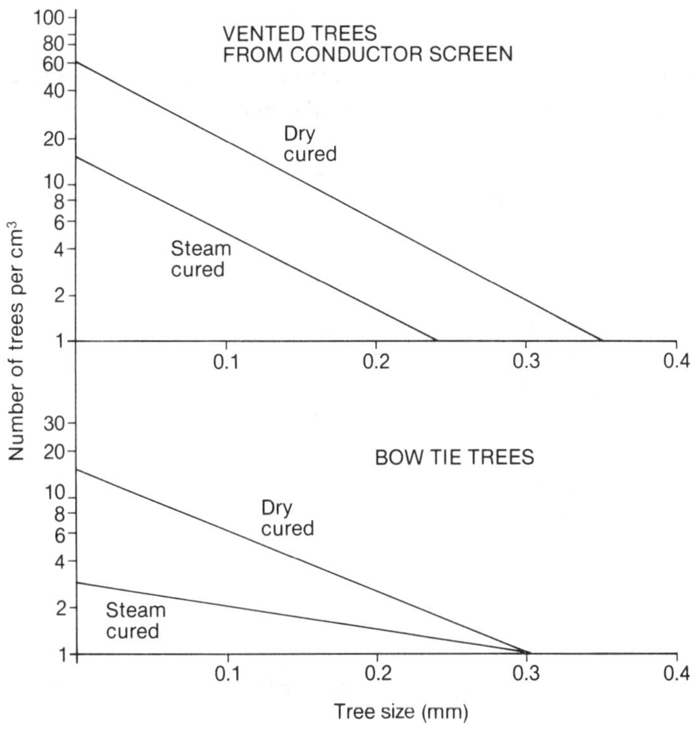

Fig. 25.6 Tree densities in steam and dry cured XLPE 6.35/11 kV cable after ageing in water at three times working voltage for 120 days

trees. As a possible example, the failure may be accounted for by dielectrophoresis, i.e. the motion of water in an electric field could serve to answer the reason why water diffuses into a cable against a thermal gradient. The water contained in a void vaporises or expands, thus increasing the pressure in the void and so generating fine cracks. The formation of oxygen during this process may accelerate the oxidation of the polyethylene, which would account for the increase in loss angle. The final electrical breakdown could then be a thermal runaway. Further references to published work on explanations of treeing phenomena are included in the Bibliography.

Two approaches have been used in the inhibition of water treeing: cable construction aimed at restricting water ingress to the insulation, and chemical additives, as will be mentioned again later.

DISCHARGE MEASUREMENT

Following a study of the failure mechanism occurring within polyethylene as a result of discharges, Mason[6] advocated the use of a non-destructive test at or near working voltage, in place of the conventional high voltage withstand test normally conducted on cable during routine testing. The discharge test at this time was recommended to be carried out at working voltage plus 20%, to cater for any switching surges which are likely to occur on a circuit. As discharge detection equipment has been improved (chapter 29) the discharge levels have been reduced, and more recently there has been a trend to move away from the non-destructive test and to carry out measurements at 2.5 or even 3 times working voltage.

Yasui and Yamada[13] have presented formulae for establishing the energies prevailing within voids subject to electrical breakdown, e.g.

$$r = \left[\frac{q(r_2 - r_1)(1 + 2\epsilon)r \log_e(r_2/r_1)}{24\pi\epsilon_0\epsilon^2 Vk}\right]^{1/3} \tag{25.4}$$

where q = charge transfer
$\epsilon_0 = 8.85 \times 10^{12}$ (F/m)
ϵ = relative permittivity of dielectric
V = voltage across cable
k = factor between 0.1 and 0.8 to cater for the surface area of the void involved in discharge
r = radius at position of void (mm)
r_1 = radius of inner screen (mm)
r_2 = radius of outer screen (mm)

The electrical stress existing within a void is equal to the stress in the insulant near the void multiplied by the ratio of the permittivity of the insulant to that of the gas within the void. A void contained within polyethylene operates at 2.3 times the stress in the dielectric surrounding the void. Figs 25.7 and 25.8 demonstrate the

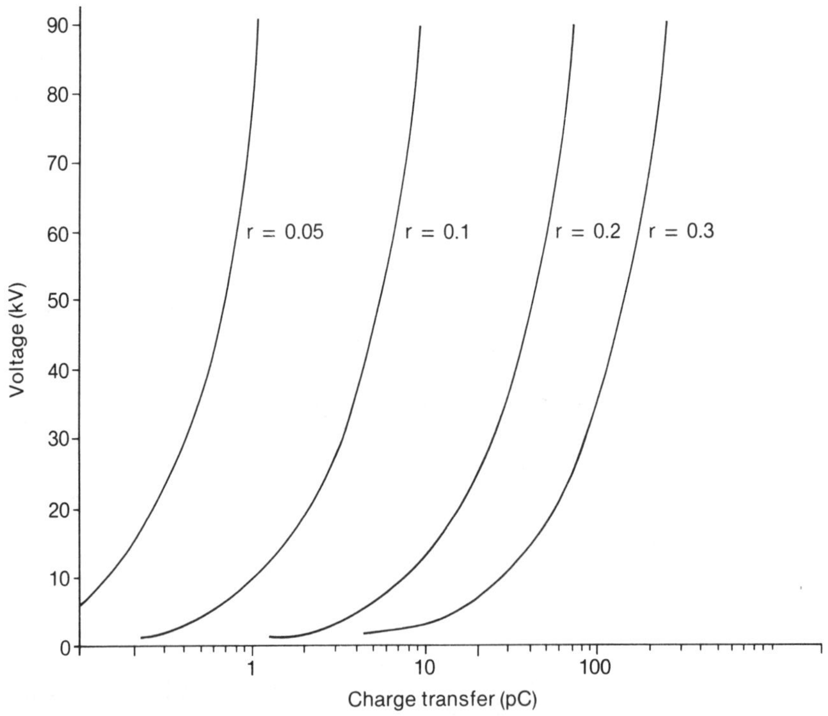

Fig. 25.7 Relationship between voltage, radius of void and discharge for 185 mm² 6.35/11 kV XLPE cable

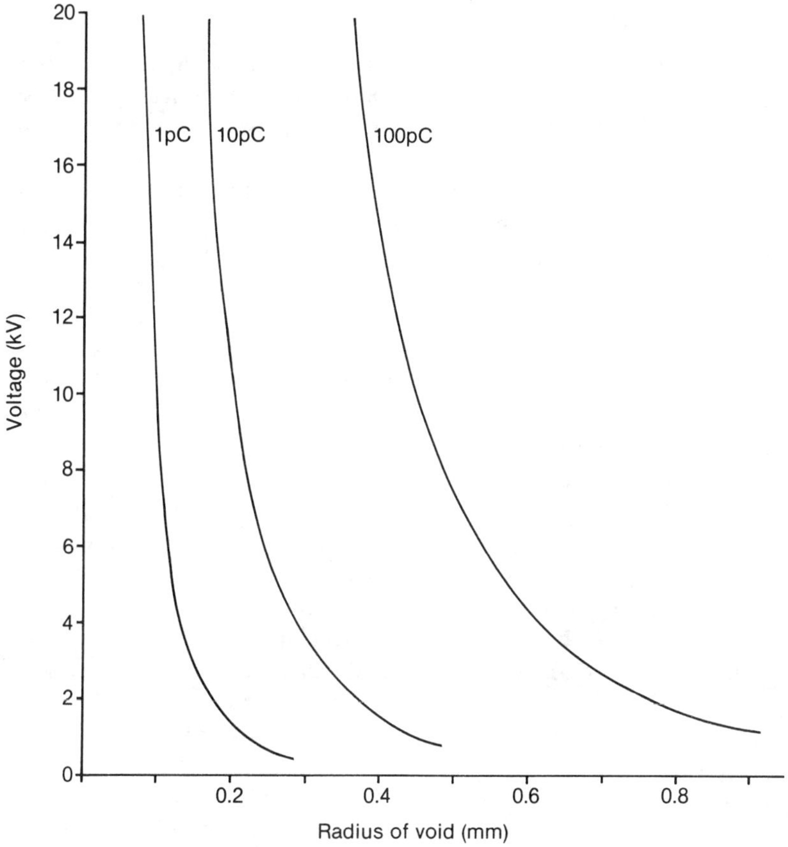

Fig. 25.8 Relationship between discharge energy, voltage and void size in a 185 mm^2 6.35/11 kV XLPE cable

significance of a void at atmospheric pressure for a condition of $k = 0.5$ for an 11 kV cable.

From fig. 25.7 it can be seen that increasing the level of applied voltage from 8 kV to 15 kV only causes a twofold increase in discharge. Similarly, reducing the size of the void from a diameter of 0.5 mm to 0.2 mm results in a reduction of the discharge magnitude from 10 pC down to 1 pC at a voltage of 8 kV.

The quantity of energy in picocoulombs (pC) represents 10^{-12} coulombs and this level of energy is extremely small. As new equipment becomes available which rejects the nuisance noise level, there is likely to be pressure to reduce the acceptable values of discharge magnitude. The urge to do so is not well founded. It is not based on any adverse service experience arising from discharge failures, neither is there any experimental evidence to suggest the deleterious nature of discharges of below 20 pC. Whilst the manufacturer of cable may be able to live with a small reduction in levels, as the processes and materials become more sophisticated the installer who joints and terminates the cable may well find it impossible to meet the requirements if they are applied to an installed network.

DESIGN OF POLYMERIC INSULATED CABLES

The conductors of all single-core polymeric cables are circular with stranded wires of either aluminium or copper. For 3-core cables, the conductors are also usually circular, but in the voltage range 3.6/6 kV to 12/20 kV solid sector shaped aluminium offers a lower cost product and has had some use.

Above certain voltages, as a means of containing the electrical field within the insulation, semiconducting screens are applied over the conductor and insulation. By this means it is possible to eliminate any electrical discharges arising from air gaps adjacent to the insulation. The coefficient of expansion of polyethylene and EPR is approximately ten times greater than that of either aluminium or copper, and when the conductor is at its maximum operating temperature of 90 °C a sufficiently large gap is formed between the insulation and the surface of the conductor to enable electrical discharges to occur. This discharge site and any others which are formed around a conductor when the cable is bent can be eliminated by applying a semiconducting layer over the conductor. Similarly, any discharges arising from air gaps between laid-up cores can be nullified by the use of a screen over the insulation.

During the early 1960s semiconducting tapes were applied over the conductor but these have since been superseded by an extruded layer. This has the advantage of providing both a smoother finish and, as it fills the interstices between the wires, a circular envelope around the conductor. By reducing the concentration of flux lines around the individual wires, the electrical stress around the conductor is reduced by between 10% and 15%. The semiconducting layer is compatible with, and bonds to, the insulation and a nominal thickness of 0.7 mm is typical.

When cables are manufactured with PE or XLPE insulation the semiconducting screens are required for voltages of 3.6/6 kV and above, whereas with EPR, because of its greater resistance to electrical discharges, screens only become essential at 6/10 kV.

The insulation thicknesses for the three insulants PE, XLPE and EPR are identical at each voltage level above 3.6/6 kV. At this voltage EPR is thicker. The radial thicknesses and electrical stresses are given in table 25.1.

Table 25.1 Insulation thicknesses and stress for polymeric cables

Rated voltage (kV)	Insulation thickness (mm)			Electrical stress (kV/mm) 185 mm^2 conductor	
	PE	XLPE	EPR	Maximum	Minimum
3.6/6[a]	2.5	2.5	3.0	1.63	1.28
6/10	3.4	3.4	3.4	2.07	1.52
8.7/15	4.5	4.5	4.5	2.38	1.60
12/20	5.5	5.5	5.5	2.79	1.74
18/30	8.0	8.0	8.0	3.12	1.67

[a] These figures are true for conductors up to 185 mm^2. Above this size the thickness increases. Chapter 19 provides more details

The outer semiconducting screen can comprise either an extruded layer or a semiconducting varnish applied to the insulation, followed by a semiconducting fabric tape. The extruded screen can be a compatible material which bonds itself to the insulation or a compound, such as an ethylene–(vinyl acetate) (EVA), which is strippable from the insulation. As the name implies, the bonded screen can only be removed with the aid of a cutting tool, whilst the strippable screen can be peeled away from the insulation.

In order for the strippable screen to have sufficient tear strength during removal from the insulation, it is necessary for the nominal thickness to be approximately 1 mm, but it may be thinner for harder materials. There are no such constraints with the bonded screen and, because semiconducting materials are very expensive, thicknesses are kept to a minimum, 0.5 mm being a typical figure.

Single-core cables are generally completed by the application of copper wires to provide an earthed envelope with a cross-sectional area of 16, 25 or 35 mm^2 dependent on the phase to earth fault level existing on the network. The cable is finished with an extruded oversheath. For networks with a very much higher fault level, or where the use of the copper screen is considered to be too flimsy, a copper tape is applied over the semiconducting layer, followed by an extruded bedding, then a helical application of aluminium armour wires and finally an extruded oversheath.

For 3-core constructions, the application of a copper tape around each screened core is more common. By the use of polypropylene strings or a PVC filler, to fill the gaps between the laid-up cores, the cable is formed into a circular shape over which is extruded a PVC bedding. The cable (fig. 25.9) is completed by the use of either steel wire or steel tape armour and an extruded oversheath. This construction with

Fig. 25.9 Construction of 3-core 8.7/15 kV XLPE insulated steel wire armoured cable

circular conductors leads to an expensive cable, and a similar design incorporating shaped solid aluminium conductors may in some cases offer a cheaper alternative.

In the UK, the ESI and the cablemakers agreed in 1976 to produce a standard for an 11 kV polymeric cable. This specified a 3-core cable having three shaped solid aluminium conductors insulated with XLPE and screened with a strippable semiconducting layer. A bedding of a soft semiconducting compound, extruded over the three cores, enables wave wound copper wire to be held firmly in position. A PVC sheath completes the cable (fig. 25.10). The advantages of the rubber layer are that, in the event of the sheath being penetrated, the volume of water which can travel through the cable is greatly reduced. Further the risk of the sheath being penetrated when the cable is struck by an implement is reduced because of the cushioning effect of the rubber layer. Finally, and most important, the phase to earth short-circuit performance is improved by virtue of the wires being kept in position when the cable is faulted by a metallic object, and because the air spaces are limited the intensity of

Fig. 25.10 Construction of 3-core 6/10 kV XLPE insulated cable with solid aluminium conductors

the flash is reduced. The Area Board service experience described earlier on 3-core cable related to cable substantially of this design.

However, this design has not been widely adopted and in 1983 it was agreed to review the situation and, taking into account the international scene, a 'triplex' cable design was proposed.[14] It consists of three single-core XLPE insulated cables with extruded screens, each having a longitudinally applied overlapped thin aluminium/ polymer laminate bonded to a polyethylene oversheath to inhibit water penetration. A semiconducting tape, swellable in contact with water, is applied over the strippable insulation screen to restrict longitudinal penetration of water in the event of damage to the outer layers. A number of aspects of the design are being assessed.

There are also variants of the single-core design and at 12/20 kV a construction similar in some respects to the triplex design has been developed in France. The dielectric screen is extruded over the insulation with a surface finish in the form of longitudinal grooves in the semiconducting material. These are filled with a powder immediately over which is laid a thin plastic coated aluminium foil which adheres to the outer oversheath. If water penetrates through the sheath, the powder swells, thus preventing the longitudinal travel of water along the cable.

At 18/30 kV, in the UK, a layer of semiconducting rubber is extruded directly over the dielectric screen of single-core cables. Copper wires are bedded into the rubber and a polyethylene sheath is applied overall (fig. 25.11).[15,16] A number of design options are being considered, particularly bearing on jointing and installation.

Fig. 25.11 Construction of single-core 18/30 kV XLPE insulated cable

CHOICE OF MATERIAL FOR INSULATION

Of the three materials under consideration, polyethylene is a thermoplastic whilst the other two, crosslinked polyethylene and ethylene–propylene rubber, are thermoset materials.

The excellent properties of PE are undisputed and the experience in France on an appreciable number of underground cables amply demonstrates this point. However, since PE is a thermoplastic, it is only suitable for use on those networks where the sustained rating and short-circuit limit is not exceeded. The material is not capable of withstanding one significant overload in its lifetime. Because its sustained temperature rating is 70 °C, the use of PE will generally be confined to those areas of the world where lower, rather than higher, ambient temperatures prevail.

On the other hand the two thermoset materials XLPE and EPR operate continuously at 90 °C and are capable of withstanding overloads and short-circuit temperatures of 250 °C. For these reasons their popularity has increased.

There are three main reasons for preferring XLPE to EPR as a dielectric for the vast majority of power cables, the minority use being confined to applications which can take advantage of the greater flexibility of EPR. The first reason is the ease of monitoring the quality of both the incoming compound and the finished cable. Unlike the permanently opaque EPR, XLPE is transparent in thin film at room temperature and, whilst translucent in thicker sections, becomes transparent at about 120 °C. Second, the fear of contaminating a dielectric is real and the fewer ingredients that have to be added to the polymer the better. In the case of XLPE only a few additives are used, whereas in EPR many more are added which may in themselves carry the damaging contaminants. An interesting development is the elimination of the separate compounding process for the preparation of the XLPE compound. Extruders are now available which enable a liquid component to be added, dispersed and mixed into the polyethylene during the extrusion process, thus eliminating the separate mixing cycle. As well as reducing costs, this step will further reduce the risk of contaminating the compound. Thirdly, and most important, the volume cost of XLPE is substantially lower than that of EPR.

Although it has been suggested that some EPR compounds are more resistant to water treeing than XLPE,[5,15] allowing designs where water may gain access to the insulation, i.e. 'wet designs', it is clearly necessary to have information on these EPR compositions and proof of their satisfactory long-term performance under wet conditions. This is also applicable to 'tree-retardant' XLPE compounds that are becoming available and being used overseas. When water treeing is seen as a hazard to long service life, XLPE appears to require some protection against moisture, but service experience of well made cables with extruded screens has been good for up to 20 years. Simpler designs, without water barriers but having more expensive insulating materials, have to be compared with the more elaborate 'dry designs' possibly required with the less expensive XLPE insulation.

Overall it seems likely that the increasingly greater use of XLPE, compared with PE and EPR, will continue.

MANUFACTURING PROCESSES USED TO PRODUCE CURED MATERIAL

For the manufacture of power cables the chemical process is adopted to effect the change from a thermoplastic to a thermoset material. Until fairly recently, continuous catenary vulcanisation (CCV) was the most popular. However, following the discovery of an alternative chemical reaction by Dow Corning[17] designated Sioplas, simpler processes have gained in popularity.

In the CCV process, the pre-compounded polyethylene, containing antioxidant and peroxide, is extruded onto a conductor at a temperature below the decomposition temperature of peroxide (130–140 °C). The insulated conductor immediately enters a heated vulcanisation zone, located within a tube of typically 250 mm diameter and 50 m length, which is in the form of a catenary. The now cured material is cooled in water, or an inert gas, in a continuation of the tube which can extend its length by a further 50–80 m. When the insulation first enters the tube it is still thermoplastic, and if at elevated temperature it touches the wall of the tube, deformation will occur – hence the need for a tube in the shape of a catenary. Obviously, a tube held in a vertical position meets these requirements and such equipment is referred to as a vertical continuous vulcanisation (VCV) line. The cost of installing a VCV far exceeds that for a CCV, hence the preponderance of the latter.

The heat required to raise the temperature of the insulation in the curing zone of the tube can be obtained from steam, high temperature nitrogen, radiant heaters fixed on the outside of the tube or by the injection of heated salts or oils into the tube. The heat provided to the insulation in one of these ways causes the peroxide (e.g. 2.5% dicumyl peroxide in polyethylene) to decompose, generating volatiles such as acetophenone, methane, water vapour, methylstyrene and ethane. In order to keep the voids which are formed by these gases within the insulation down to an acceptable size, the tube is pressurised to about 10–15 bar. As a direct result of the decomposition of peroxide, approximately 10^2 microvoids are formed in the insulation per cubic millimetre and they are between 0.001 and 0.01 mm in diameter. The insulation has to remain in the heated zone sufficiently long for all the peroxide to decompose and generally the temperature of the conductor has to be raised to 180 °C to produce curing of the insulation adjacent to its surface. Therefore throughput speed is reduced both by increase of conductor size and by thicker insulation.

Traditionally, steam was used to provide both the heat and the pressure in the tube, the steam vapour imparting its heat by diffusing into the insulant and condensing. This gives rise to the production of more voids in the insulation, approximately 10^3 per cubic millimetre in the size range 0.001–0.01 mm. Thus steam cured insulation contains 10^5 microvoids/mm^3, and whilst at first sight the figure is somewhat alarming, the voids represent less than 0.1% of the dielectric.

With the interest in higher voltage cables, the dry cure processes have been looked upon as producing a better dielectric. Long die cure, radiant heat under nitrogen or silicone oil and salt cure are all variants, and no voids other than those formed during the decomposition of the peroxide are produced.

The Sioplas and Monosil[18] processes, which have been used since the mid-1970s, were exciting developments, providing greater flexibility and economy to the producer. Both these processes are a chemical means of effecting the crosslinking. In the Sioplas process an extrusion/compounding operation is required in which 10% of the amount of peroxide used in the CCV process is decomposed and silane is grafted onto a carbon atom. This material, which is still a thermoplastic, is then extruded onto a conductor. In the Monosil process there is no separate pre-compounding/grafting operation as all materials are fed into the insulation extruder. In both cases the curing is effected in a water or steam vessel as a separate process. The crosslinking is achieved through a siloxane bond, which is similar to that obtained when curing silicone rubbers. As these processes eliminate the long pressure vessel, the lines are cheaper to install and maintain and the production rates are much faster. The simpler technique also allows greater flexibility and the production of less scrap during the starting up and closing down of the lines.

Fig. 25.12 compares the number of microvoids in XLPE produced by three different processes. Fig. 25.13 shows the impact of these microvoids on the electrical strength of the dielectrics produced by steam, radiant heat under nitrogen and Monosil curing processes. Generally there is nearly a 20% increase in the a.c. ramp

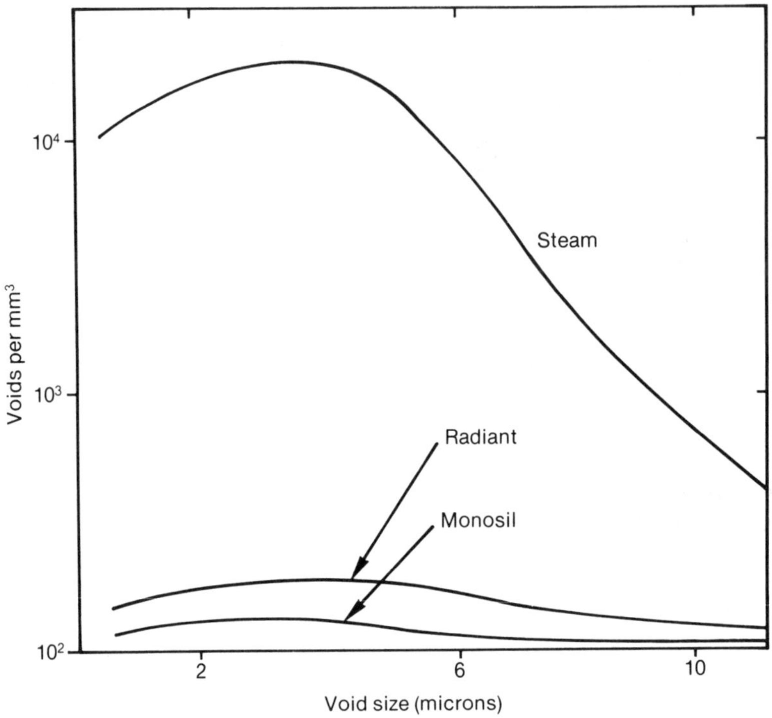

Fig. 25.12 Void count in XLPE by high resolution image analysis

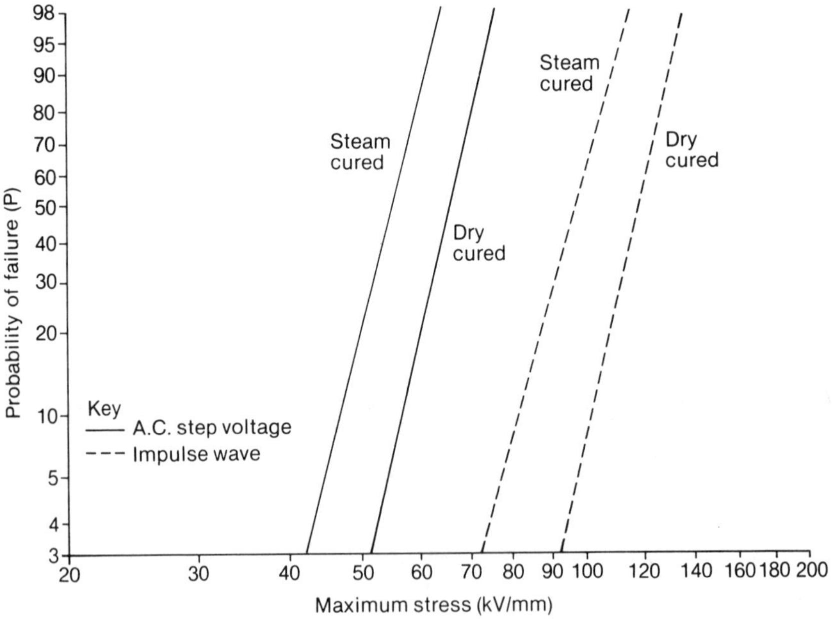

Fig. 25.13 A.C. and impulse breakdown strengths of steam and dry cured XLPE 6.35/11 kV cable

and impulse characteristics of dielectric made by the newer manufacturing techniques.

Unfortunately it has sometimes been assumed that the water introduced during the processing of steam cured polyethylene is responsible for the production of water trees which lead to the subsequent failure of the material. This is not the case, as shown by the life of steam cured cable: freshly extruded steam cured XLPE has a water content of 5000 ppm, but after standing for one week the water content reduces to 2000 ppm and one month after manufacture it is down to 1000 ppm.

Compared with these concentrations of water, dry cured materials will contain approximately 200 ppm and Monosil or Sioplas produced cables, after curing in water or steam, will hold about 250 ppm. Fig. 25.14 shows how temperature dictates the water content of polyethylene which is immersed in water or steam.

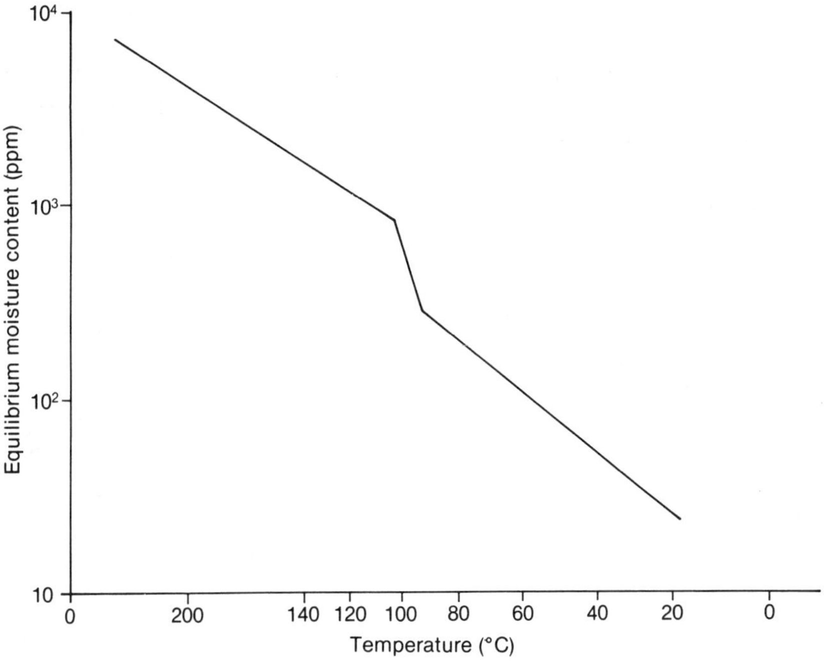

Fig. 25.14 Equilibrium moisture content of XLPE (100% relative humidity)

FUTURE PROSPECTS

Throughout the whole voltage range of distribution cables, the swing away from the traditional paper insulated types to polymeric insulated designs with advantages in ease of installation has been very significant. The lower capital cost and higher productivity processes associated with XLPE are likely to ensure a continued demand for these cables.

Provided that the lessons have been learned from the adverse service experience of some of the early cables, that care is exercised at the design stage and that high standards of cleanliness are maintained during the processing of the dielectric, it will be possible to derive the advantages and benefits of polymeric insulants, and to secure a long reliable life for such cables. Much research, development and application work, however, remains to be done.

REFERENCES

(1) Deschamps, L., Michel, R., Lepers, J., Jocteur, R., Midoz, J., Favrie, E. and Terramosi, G. (1980) 'Results of tests and experience in service in France with high voltage cables with synthetic insulation'. Paris: CIGRE Paper No. 21–06.
(2) Pinet, A. and Ferran, J. (1986) 'Operating experience with the 20 kV XLPE cable used on the French network'. *IEE Second Int. Conf. on Power Cables and Accessories 10 kV to 180 kV*. IEE Conference Publication No. 270, pp. 37–40.
(3) Thue, W. A. (1977) 'Field performance of polyethylene and crosslinked polyethylene cables'. IEEE Eng. Soc. Insulated Conductors Committee.
(4) Mashikian, M. S. (1986) 'Extruded medium voltage cable materials and practices in the U.S.A., Europe and Japan'. *Conf. Rec. 1986 IEEE Int. Symp. on Electrical Insulation*, pp. 13–22.
(5) Howard, R. S., Jenkins, T. and Brook, R. T. (1986) 'Operating experience with 11 kV polymeric cable systems in one U.K. Area Board'. *IEE Second Int. Conf. on Power Cables and Accessories 10 kV to 180 kV*. IEE Conference Publication No. 270, pp. 31–36.
(6) Mason, J. H. (1953) 'Breakdown of insulation by discharges'. *Proc. IEE, Part 1* **100**, 149–158.
(7) Ku, C. C. and Liepins, R. (1987) 'Electrical properties of polymers'. Munich: Hanser.
(8) Bartnikas, R. and Eichhorn, R. M. (1983) *Engineering Dielectrics*, Vol. IIA. ASTM 57P783. Philadelphia.
(9) Schultz, J. M. (ed.) (1977) *Treatise on Materials Science and Technology*, Vol. 10B, *Properties of Solid Polymeric Materials*. London: Academic Press.
(10) McMahon, E. J. and Perkins, J. R. (1963) 'Surface and volume phenomena in dielectric breakdown to polyethylene'. *IEEE Trans.* **PAS-82**, 1128–1135.
(11) Artbauer, J. and Griac, J. (1970) 'Some factors preventing the attainment of intrinsic electrical strength in polymer insulations'. *IEEE Trans.* **EI-5**, 104–112.
(12) Shaw, M. T. and Shaw, S. H. (1984) 'Water treeing in solid dielectrics'. *IEEE Trans.* **EI-19** (5), 419–452.
(13) Yasui, T. and Yamada, Y. (1967) 'Theoretical analysis and experiments on the internal discharge in a spherical void'. *Sumitomo Tech. Rev.* (10), 60–72.
(14) White, T. M. *et al.* (1986) '11 kV polymeric insulated triplex cable'. *IEE Second Int. Conf. on Power Cables and Accessories 10 kV to 180 kV*. IEE Conference Publication No. 270, pp. 41–45.
(15) Naybour, R. D. and Papadopulos, M. S. (1988) 'Water trees in polymeric insulated cables'. *Distribution Developments*, 30–37.
(16) Hyde, H. B., Le Poidevin, G. J. and Philbrick, S. E. (1986) 'The development of a single core polymeric cable for 33 kV distribution systems. *IEE Second Int. Conf. on Power Cables and Accessories 10 kV to 180 kV*. IEE Conference Publication No. 270, pp. 46–50.
(17) British Patent 1 286 460 (Dow Corning 1972).
(18) Swarbrick, P. (28 Jan. 1977) 'Developments in the manufacture of XLPE cables'. *Electr. Rev.* **200** (4), 23–25.

Chapter 26

Manufacture of Distribution Cables

The essential stages of manufacture are shown in fig. 26.1. Although the despatch length of cable is commonly 250 m for convenience in handling and installation, it is more economic to produce in lengths of the order of 2000 m and then to cut as required. Holding the long lengths in a stockyard (fig. 26.2) enables deliveries of standard items to be made from stocks, the higher capital cost being offset by reduced manufacturing cost and better service.

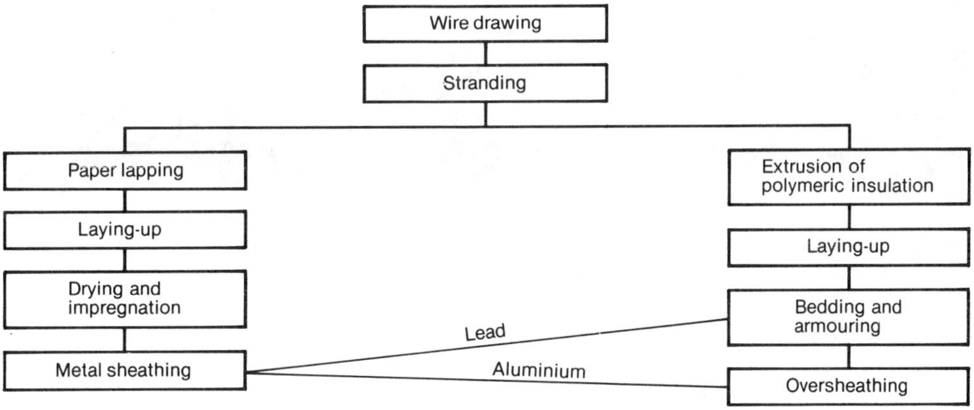

Fig. 26.1 Main processes in the manufacture of paper and polymeric insulated cables

One of the largest items in processing cost is the time to load the individual process plant with part-manufactured cable and materials and it is common for machines to operate for only 25–50% of the total time that they are available. Production in long lengths is helpful but the main factor is the time and labour cost for loading. New factories have benefited from being able to schedule a completely new layout with maximum benefit from arranging material handling at minimum cost. Apart from optimum siting of raw material stores this includes, in many cases, automatic delivery to machines and sometimes the actual loading into the machine. When the BICC factory at Wrexham was opened in 1970 the number of employees, for equal output, was almost halved.

To some extent this improvement was due to the use of machines with higher rate of output but examples of better material handling include such items as a conveyor system for automatic storage of conductor wire on bobbins and automatic loading into stranding machines, and automatic conveyor feed of lead ingots into extruder melting pots.

Fig. 26.2 Stockyard at BICC Wrexham factory with finished cable stock and drums awaiting despatch

WIRE DRAWING

For the wire sizes required for distribution cables, i.e. 1.43–3.29 mm, copper wire is drawn through a continuous series of dies from annealed rod of around 8.0 mm diameter. The number of dies normally required is 6–13, according to wire size, and they are copiously lubricated by a stream of suitable compound. In modern plant, speeds up to 1200 m/min are obtained and the finished wire is continuously annealed by electrical heating in a steam atmosphere. During the winding onto steel spools the change to a fresh reel is achieved without stopping the machine.

Reference has been made to the automatic conveyance of the reel to the stranding machines and fig. 26.3 shows the system with storage lanes for particular wire sizes. With this system much larger and heavier bobbins of wire can be handled, normally 500 mm in diameter and 220 kg in weight.

Aluminium is drawn similarly from 9.5 mm rod which is in an as-extruded condition, equivalent to an annealed temper. For the reasons given in chapter 3 the drawn wire is not annealed and is in a broad $\frac{3}{4}$H temper.

SOLID ALUMINIUM CONDUCTORS

Except for the smallest sizes, solid aluminium conductors are produced by hot extrusion from billets of aluminium. The extrusion may be by an aluminium fabricator,

Fig. 26.3 Stranding machines for conductors, with conveyor system for storage and delivery of bobbins of conductor wire

in which case a conventional straight-through extrusion press is used, or by the cablemaker himself using an aluminium sheathing press. The purity is normally 99.7% minimum but with the Schloemann sheathing press a higher temperature is possible and 99.5% minimum purity may be used. With this press it has also been found possible to use as-cast rather than machined billets, i.e. it is not necessary to remove the outer skin by machining. Generally two conductors are extruded together. The hot extrusion practice provides conductors in a soft temper, which although generally advantageous is undesirable for very small sizes because of possible stretching. These sizes are produced by drawing. (See also chapter 3.)

STRANDING

Conventional stranding practice was based around a layer of six wires laid over one wire and then succeeding layers, with lay reversal on each layer, giving a total number of wires increasing as 7, 19, 37, 61, 91, 127, 169. However, for conductors of shaped cross-section and for compacted circular conductors, which have now largely replaced the uncompacted type for distribution cables, these are not always the ideal numbers of wires. For example, six wires in the centre of a 2-core or 3-core shape of conductor conform better to the cross-section to be formed than six wires around one, and in a compacted circular conductor the compacting of the inner layers sometimes produced too small a diameter to accommodate six additional wires in the next layer. The basic practice of separate layers with reversed lays is still the most common construction although unidirectional stranding is sometimes used.

Fig. 26.3 shows typical stranding machines, each carriage having sufficient bobbins for one layer. The bobbins in the carriage may be 'fixed' or floating, the latter often being referred to as 'sun and planet' arrangement. Compacting tools or dies are normally installed for each layer. Shaping and pre-spiralling for multicore conductors is carried out at the same time. (See also chapter 4.)

A more recent technique, which permits higher output for small conductors up to 19 wires, is to dispense with a revolving carriage and feed the wires directly, as a 'bunch', into a shaping head.

PAPER LAPPING

Insulating paper is delivered in rolls of approximately 100 kg weight and 700 mm width. These are accurately slit into pads of appropriate width and diameter for use on lapping machines as illustrated in fig. 26.4. The angle of lapping, lay length, paper width and gap are all interrelated and dependent on the ratio of the speeds of head rotation and linear travel of the conductor.

Fig. 26.4 Paper lapping machine for 11 kV cables

The pads are mounted on a carriage which usually accommodates eight or more papers and individual carriages are able to rotate in either direction. Reversal of carriage rotation and hence direction of lay every eight or so papers is the most common practice for high voltage cables. It provides a more stable construction both during the lapping operation and in subsequent cable handling but, of course, has some penalty in that at each change there are butt gaps of double depth. A mechanism is provided for tension control for each paper and for the machine to be stopped if a paper should break.

The important factors of lapping in relation to the quality of the insulation are discussed in chapter 3, e.g. tension, gap width and registration of tapes in successive layers.

DRYING AND IMPREGNATION FOR PAPER INSULATION

Air and moisture have to be removed separately by heat and vacuum, both from the impregnant and the paper insulation plus fillers. The degasification of the impregnant is accomplished in a tall tank with the compound falling as droplets or flowing over plates to form a large surface area. The cable, either on steel drums or wound into trays, is placed in tanks which may be up to 4 m in diameter. The tops have special seals and the surfaces are heated by either steam or high pressure water. In modern plant the cable conductors are also heated by passage of direct current, to reduce the time for the whole mass to build up to temperature and to obtain better temperature distribution. Monitoring of the conductor resistance provides an accurate record of the cable temperature. A temperature of 125 °C is maintained during the drying process.

During the heating process the tank is evacuated to a level of the order of 13 N/m^2 and nowadays the whole process is controlled automatically on a basis of temperature, time and pressure. Adequate dryness may be checked by a pressure drop test, i.e. shutting in the tank and measuring the pressure rise in a given time period.

The impregnating compound, also heated to 125 °C and under vacuum, is then drawn slowly into the tank and the pressure is raised to 200 kN/m^2. After an appropriate impregnating period the tank is allowed to cool very slowly, and as discussed in chapter 20 it is important, particularly for MIND cables, for the impregnant to be circulated through a heat exchanger to obtain uniform cooling throughout the mass of cable insulation.

For low voltage cables, where complete filling of the insulation with impregnant is not essential, the compound may be pumped out of the tank whilst still hot and the cable left for surplus compound to be drained off. For high voltage cables, however, uniformity of cooling under compound to a temperature below the set-point of the compound is important, and this is most easily accomplished when the cable is in trays rather than on drums. Trays filled with compound to above cable level may be lifted out of the tanks to allow the final cooling to ambient temperature to proceed on the shop floor. Drums have to be removed at a temperature close to the set-point of the compound to avoid a large amount of compound adhering to the drum.

The total drying and impregnation process may take from 10 to 60 hours according to the plant, the amount of cable in the tank and the cable voltage.

EXTRUSION OF THERMOPLASTIC MATERIALS

All thermoplastic materials are applied by an extrusion process and PVC may be taken as a particular example. Pellets of the material are fed into the hopper of the extruder. They may be fully compounded, including colour, or the colour may be added at the same time by a metered second feed of coloured master batch. The hopper feeds by gravity into a long heated barrel through which an Archimedean screw revolves. As the PVC is forced along the barrel the additional frictional heat generated causes it to soften and in the compression process air is forced out backwards. An extrusion head containing male and female dies is located at the end of the barrel and may be at an angle of 45°–90° to it. Uniform flow of the softened material throughout the whole circumferential aperture between the dies is most important to obtain a concentric tube and freedom from overheating, which could lead to local decomposition within the extrudate.

To obtain the required degree of compression, the volume of material between the screw and barrel must be decreased towards the extrusion head, and screw designs to this end vary considerably. Fig. 26.5 illustrates the essential principles with the separate zones along the screw. Different materials require a varying ratio of barrel length to diameter, and 15–20 is a typical range for PVC. The depth of flights and amounts of compression also need to be adjusted to suit the material, as do the heating and cooling systems.

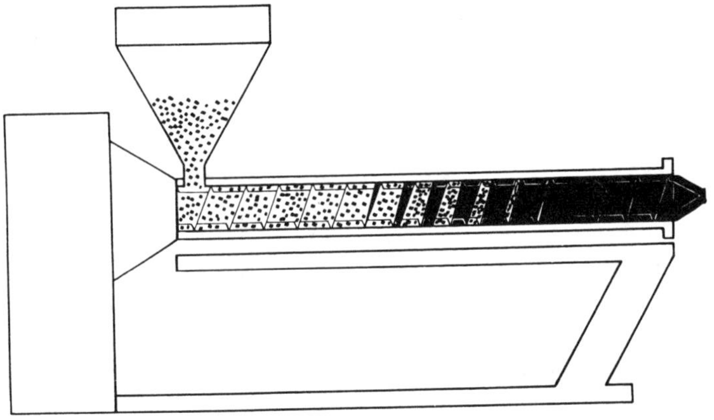

Fig. 26.5 Passage of thermoplastic material along an extrusion screw (Courtesy of Maillefer SA, Ecublens-Lausanne)

Maintenance of optimum temperature for the particular compound being extruded is vital and when the required temperature is reached the barrel heating may need to be reduced or even forced cooling applied. For PVC, a barrel temperature of 150–180 °C and a die temperature of 180 °C would be typical.

For thermoplastic extrusion, the dies are usually designed with concentric circular tips, i.e. to extrude a tube. If the surface to be coated is non-circular, e.g. a shaped conductor, an oversize tube is reduced in size by a combination of vacuum and controlled line speed to form a perfect fit over the surface – often called a 'float-

Fig. 26.6 Extrusion of PVC oversheath by the 'float down' technique

down' or 'tubing-on' technique. This procedure also overcomes any problems in extruding over pre-spiralled conductors. Fig. 26.6 shows how the extrudate diameter is reduced for a PVC oversheath applied over a smooth surface. The technique is equally applicable to the provision of a close fitting oversheath on a corrugated aluminium sheath.

EXTRUSION AND CURING OF THERMOSETTING MATERIALS

At the time of extrusion, thermosetting materials are still thermoplastic and the only basic difference in technique is that they have subsequently to be cured (vulcanised). Originally this was a separate process but nowadays, except for the silane process discussed later, this operation is almost always carried out in line and known as continuous vulcanising (CV). For distribution cables the materials involved are XLPE and EPR. More use is made of XLPE and more procedures are available, but most of the basic principles apply also to EPR. Curing processes which have been used commercially for XLPE include

(a) continuous catenary vulcanisation (CCV) with heat transfer from either steam or a high temperature compatible fluid or from thermal radiation
(b) vertical catenary vulcanisation (VCV) which is similar but with a vertical tube
(c) irradiation by high energy electron beams
(d) MDCV: heat transfer by use of a very long land die in the extruder
(e) PLCV: liquid curing medium vulcanisation with heat transfer from a molten mixture of chemical salts under pressure.
(f) the silane chemical crosslinking process

A universal requirement for high voltage cables is that the insulating materials must be extremely clean initially, and during handling provision must be made to exclude any entrapment of dust or contaminants. This requires feeding arrangements from storage containers into the extruders without exposure to the atmosphere.

Many of the curing processes used for power cable insulation, e.g. (a) (b) (c) and (e) above, require the thermal decomposition of peroxides which are either precompounded into the polymer or added directly at the extruder. The temperature required is above 140 °C and the rate of cure is temperature dependent. It is important, however, that the curing should not begin during extrusion and hence the extrusion temperature should not exceed 140 °C. The curing temperature after extrusion may be up to 300–350 °C (somewhat less for elastomers) and to prevent void formation due to decomposition products from the peroxides a pressure above about 7 bar (0.7 MN/m^2) is required.

Vertical and catenary tubes with steam curing

Initially these processes were developed for the curing of natural rubber with sulphur and involved the passage of the cable through a long tube filled with steam at high pressure. The vertical tube has an advantage in that there is no undue sag of thick-walled soft extrudate as it leaves the die. However, as very long tubes of the order of 150 m became desirable for economic reasons, it became impractical on cost grounds to erect towers of this height. The catenary shape (fig. 26.7) is necessary to match the natural sag of the cable core as it leaves the extruder die at the top end of the tube, and so avoid any scraping along the tube wall. Various tension and other devices are employed to maintain the core centrally in the tube.

When extrusion is commenced, the upper end of the tube is coupled solidly to the extrusion head and high pressure steam is admitted to the tube at a temperature of the order of 210 °C. The lower part of the tube is filled with water, to cool the extrudate under pressure and so that it can be handled normally for drumming on leaving the tube. Approximately half the total length may be used for the cooling process but the proportion varies with technique and the thickness of the extruded layer.

Much attention to detail is necessary to prevent unnecessary wastage by the presence of inadequately cured material on starting and stopping extrusion and the process is clearly not suitable for producing short lengths of cable. Once set up it is preferable to extrude for days rather than hours and this, of course, necessitates very long continuous lengths of conductor of one size to be supplied to the extruder. Separate drums of conductor are used and welded together at the input end. An

Fig. 26.7 Catenary tube in CCV line

accumulator arrangement allows maintenance of steady conductor feed during the welding process.

Because the steam pressure is in the region of 20 bar (2 MN/m^2) the extrudate is pressed firmly against the conductor. This presents no problem with solid or heavily compacted stranded conductors having a relatively smooth surface, but if this is not the case a tape has to be applied longitudinally around the conductor to prevent passage between the wires.

For high voltage cables 'dry curing', as described later, is more often used for XLPE insulation than steam curing but, whichever technique is employed, at least three extruders are required for the insulation and two semiconducting screens. These may feed into a single extrusion head (often referred to as 'triple head') or the conductor screen may be applied from a separate head situated behind a dual head from which the insulation and outer screen are applied. Another variation is to employ two dual heads, the conductor screen and a thin layer of insulation being applied from one, followed by the bulk of the insulation and the outer insulation from the second. One purpose of the thin layer of insulation applied in the same head as the conductor screen is to protect the latter, which preferably should be kept as smooth as possible, from any slight abrasion which might occur on entry to the second head. The surface of the insulation from this first head becomes integrated with the main part of the insulation from the second head. This technique provides for the use, if desired, of a different insulating material for the thin layer next to the conductor screen, e.g. an XLPE of higher permittivity than the main insulation, which has the effect of reducing the electrical stress at the surface of the conductor screen. The use of such a facility is more relevant to cables for transmission voltages than to those for distribution voltages, but the same plant is usually employed for a range of voltages.

The output is an important factor in CV extrusion and is mainly related to the degree of cure which can be obtained in the length of heated tube available. Optimum productivity is derived from computer programs based on conductor size, volume of extrudate, temperature and length of tube etc.

Vertical and catenary tubes with dry curing

Differences between insulation produced by steam curing and by dry curing are mentioned in chapter 26 and for high voltage cables there is a preference for dry curing. In VCV and CCV lines dry curing is usually carried out by thermal radiation from the tube in a pressurised atmosphere of inert gas, usually nitrogen.

The pressure does not need to be as high as with steam as the temperature is independent of pressure and pressurising is mainly to prevent formation of voids from the peroxide decomposition products. The nitrogen in the curing section is not circulated, but is bled away at a low rate to prevent accumulation of gases produced by the curing reaction. The temperature, and hence output, is increased as the surface of the cable can be heated to 300 °C. To deal with such higher temperatures the tube may be heated up to 450 °C and needs to be fabricated from stainless steel or other suitable metal.

The heating of the tube may be by attachment of electrical elements to the outside of the tube or by d.c. heating of the tube itself. Good temperature control is essential and the core has to be maintained in the centre of the tube to maintain uniform curing. Cooling of the cable may be obtained by water in the lower part of the tube or by nitrogen circulated through external heat exchangers. Plant often provides for either cooling method to be used, depending upon what is preferred for the particular core being processed. Because of the high curing temperature, and hence a soft extrudate, it is important in a CCV line that the 'touch-down' point in the tube should not be reached until adequate cooling has taken place.

High temperature compatible liquids, such as silicones or polyalkylene glycol, may also be used for both curing and cooling.

Irradiation methods

High energy electron beams generated by linear accelerators of Van de Graaff type have been used for curing since the 1960s. In this process no peroxide is necessary and heating is not required. However, the process has mainly been applicable only to small cables, such as equipment wires, and to produce heat shrinkable materials for jointing purposes. For thicker wall insulation it has not proved to be economic.

Long land die process (MDCV)

Mitsubishi Dainichi continuous vulcanisation (MDCV) is named after the companies which developed the process in the early 1970s, again with the objective of obtaining curing in the absence of steam. The equipment is horizontal and very compact, the essence being to extend the die of the extruder to form a heated tube several metres long, to maintain the pressure and prevent void formation. Fast curing is achieved by the use of high temperature and on emergence the cooling is also carried out in a horizontal tube.

Liquid curing baths (PLCV)

Pressurised liquid continuous vulcanising (PLCV) is a technique based on the long established heated salt bath process (LCM) for vulcanising rubber cables. The salts consist of a eutectic mixture of potassium nitrate (53%), sodium nitrite (40%) and sodium nitrate (7%) and the temperature is up to 300 °C. Because of the buoyancy effects of the molten salts, an inclined tube can be used and the catenary form is not always necessary: this is dependent on cable weight.

Silane chemical linking (Sioplas and Monosil)

Methods of manufacture were fundamental to the discussion of the materials in chapter 3 and have already been outlined. The important characteristic is, of course, that no special curing plant, other than steam or hot water tanks, has to be installed and the extruders are of the conventional type used for thermoplastics.

LAYING-UP

To lay cores together, either very large diameter machines are necessary so that bobbins of core can be rotated around a common axis, or the cores can be run off horizontally from their drums into a die and then proceed onto a take-up drum which revolves on its own axis (drum-twister machine). The latter (fig. 26.8) is now commonly used because of higher output. Belt insulation for paper cables, or taped bedding for polymeric cables, is conveniently applied in the same operation.

LEAD SHEATHING

The discontinuous type extrusion presses with vertical rams and containers which have to be filled with liquid lead have now largely given way to continuous extrusion machines of the Hansson type. These operate somewhat on the lines of a plastic extruder except that the screw is vertical and is fed at its bottom end from a tank of liquid lead. The extrusion temperature is about 300 °C and the sheaths are sprayed with water on leaving the dies.

ALUMINIUM SHEATHING

Aluminium sheaths are formed by direct extrusion over the insulation, and as the temperature is around 500 °C special methods of cooling have to be adopted at the point where the sheath meets the insulation. Two types of press are used, both being supplied with heated billets of aluminium.

Fig. 26.8 Drum-twister laying-up machine

Fig. 26.9 Hydraulik continuous aluminium sheathing press

In the Hydraulik press (fig. 26.9) the sheathing is continuous because a subsidiary ram under the die box maintains extrusion pressure when the main ram is withdrawn for the insertion of a new billet. The Schloemann press (fig. 26.10) is of the horizontally opposed twin-ram type and has an ingenious automatic ratchet spanner arrangement so that the dies move apart when pressure is released. This prevents nipping of the metal at stop-marks, a feature which causes bad bending properties in conventional aluminium tube presses.

Fig. 26.10 Schloemann aluminium sheathing press

For the Schloemann press it is possible to use as-cast billets but surface machining is necessary for the Hydraulik press.

For the corrugated form of sheath an oversize tube is extruded over the cores and a corrugating head is placed between the extruder and the take-up drum.

ARMOURING

Steel tape armour is applied by a conventional taping process to which reference is made in chapter 5, beddings and servings of the bituminous type being applied during the armouring operation.

The conventional method for the application of steel wire armour is for wire on bobbins to be mounted on a large carriage which rotates around a central mandrel

Fig. 26.11 Drum-twister design of power cable armouring machine

through which the cable is drawn, by a large capstan wheel, at an appropriate speed to obtain the appropriate length of lay. Larger cables may require more than 70 wires, so that very large and heavy machines are necessary. For this reason more modern armouring machine design follows a practice originally developed for the high speed production of small wiring cables and based on the 'drum-twister' technique.

The armouring wires are drawn from stationary packs to form a ring of wires around the cable and the final drum containing the armoured cable revolves to derive the required lay of the wires. Fig. 26.11 illustrates a typical arrangement, the stationary packs being at the far end and the haulage mechanism of 'caterpillar' type in the middle of the machine. Such machines can handle copper wires down to 0.067 mm in diameter and steel wires up to 2.5 mm in diameter. The equipment shown is designed for cables having extruded beddings and oversheaths, i.e. there is no provision for the textile and bitumen bedding and serving applications common on conventional armouring machines. Nevertheless, taping heads for plastic or metal binder or separator layers can be seen on the machine.

Chapter 27

Installation of Distribution Cables

The majority of public supply distribution cables are buried directly in the ground, possibly with short duct sections, and this chapter deals mainly with such installations. In some areas such as in North America, however, there is a difference in that complete installation in ducts is generally preferred. This has the advantage in busy city areas that there is less disturbance to traffic and cable replacement is easier. Installation above ground is common for industrial sites and for cables associated with railways, the cables being supported on hangers or laid on fabricated steelwork or trays.

Distribution cables are usually supplied on wooden drums. The handling of the drum and suitable support at the optimum position is an important part of the installation operation.

Drum lengths of distribution cables are commonly of 250–500 m. Considerably longer lengths can often be installed satisfactorily but require much more care during running off. The inner end moves backwards and slack turns developing within the drum may result in kinking of the cable. The greater attention necessary and the possibility of damage may outweigh the cost of an extra joint.

For most types of installation the important stages may conveniently be divided into initial site inspection, trial holes, trenching, cable laying, reinstatement and final fixing.

SITE INSPECTION AND TRIAL HOLES

During the visit to site, decisions will be made on such matters as the method of installation, the special equipment required, e.g. pulling winches and any mechanised plant for digging, any duct positions for road crossings etc., and the general items of equipment necessary, including road signs and illumination.

It is then often necessary to dig trial holes to establish the trench route in detail. The trial holes will indicate the position of other services so that smooth bends can be provided to reduce the pulling loads when long lengths of cable are being installed. The trial holes also provide information on the nature of the ground for excavating and timbering purposes and on whether there is any chemical activity which would necessitate a special anticorrosion finish for the cable. Any unusual soil characteristic which might affect the thermal resistivity, and hence cable rating, would also be noted. Reference is made later to special precautions necessary if possible ground subsidence is suspected.

DRUM HANDLING

Cable drum trailers

Very often drums of cable have to be transported from a central depot to an installation site and it is when short lengths of cable are required that trailers are particularly valuable, i.e. instead of cutting and re-drumming in the depot, the whole drum length may be taken to site by a single crew vehicle and then returned.

Fig. 27.1 shows suitable equipment which makes the loading very simple by use of a manually operated hydraulic pump on the trailer. On site the drum is left in the cradle. On completion of pulling the cable end is capped and the drum is made secure and then returned to the depot. In the case of open routes, where the trench is free from obstruction, it is possible to pay off the cable from the towed trailer directly into the trench.

Fig. 27.1 Cable drum trailer (Courtesy of S.E.B. International Ltd)

General handling

If no hoisting equipment is available for the unloading of lorries, drums should never be simply dropped onto the ground. Apart from causing damage to the drum, the cable may also be damaged. Use of ramp boards, together with a winch or a coil of rope around the drum, is essential.

The drum should be mounted at the most convenient position for cable pulling and for manual installation. This is normally at the start of a reasonably straight section, preferably near the commencement of trenchwork.

It is important that any rolling of the drum to this position should be in accordance with the arrow on the drum wing as loose turns will develop, by unwinding, if the opposite direction is used. The distance of rolling should be kept to a minimum.

Drums are normally mounted so that the cable is pulled from the top of the drum and for very heavy cables it may be necessary to use a ramp to support the cable during passage into the trench. When cables have significant stiffness, e.g. those with non-corrugated aluminium sheaths, it may be preferable to pull from the bottom to reduce the tendency for the cable to come off with a wavy or spiral profile. As the cable is paid off, the drum rotates counter to the arrow which is intended to indicate the direction for rolling the drum into position.

Another factor which may affect the drum position is the presence of any services or obstructions at the trench entry, which could cause abrasion damage to the cable.

For mounting the drum a pair of screw jacks is adequate for relatively light drums but fabricated A-frames containing hydraulic jacks are necessary for heavier drums.

EXCAVATION

As most underground distribution cables are installed in the footpaths of built-up urban areas, the scope for mechanised excavation is very limited, because of the presence of other services such as telephone cables, gas and water pipes and surface water drains. For the URD type cables in the USA, installed in areas of low density housing, the situation is somewhat different and mechanised equipment has been gaining in popularity. As well as for straightforward trenching, special machines have been brought into use for digging, laying and backfilling in one operation, and also for cable laying without digging, by the use of a mole type plough.

Depth of laying

The standard depth of burial in the UK is 500 mm at 0.6/1 kV and 800 mm from 3.3 to 33 kV. As indicated in table 8.4 of chapter 8 there are some variations in depths throughout the world but they are not very substantial.

Timbering

As the excavation depth for most distribution cable installations is less than 1 m, there is seldom any need for full close boarded timbering. However, skeleton timbering may frequently be necessary to prevent deterioration of trench sides due to traffic vibration and to protect building foundations, street lamps etc. At a depth of 1 m the use of close timbering is dependent on ground conditions and for safety it is essential at depths below 1.3 m.

However, the key factor is overall safety for personnel and property. Safeguards may be necessary for a shallow trench next to an old building to avoid danger from possible collapse of walls etc.

Vertical timbers are usually 225 mm × 38 mm, horizontal poling boards 225 mm × 75 mm and struts 100 mm × 100 mm. Proprietary stretchers may be used instead of timber struts.

Excavated material

The material excavated from a trench can cause unnecessary nuisance and damage and requires care in handling. Interference with traffic must be avoided and hedges, ditches and drains must be protected. In street works the free flow of surface water is important.

Excavated surface materials (including base foundations in roadways) should be stacked separately from subsoils so that correct compaction and reinstatement can be achieved when backfilling. All excavated material must be cleared from the edge of the trench so that rolling back into the trench does not occur. This could represent a hazard both to operatives and to cable, particularly if any sharp edged stone is present. The bottom of the trench should be free from stone and, if necessary, riddled earth or sand should be used.

PIPES AND DUCTS

Vitrified clay single and multiway ducts in lengths of 1.0 m and 1.25 m are still the most popular because of their ease of handling and installation. In many installations multiway duct nests will be assembled utilising single pipes, thereby enabling the designer to optimise on cable spacing and route configuration.

The ducts should generally be in accordance with BS 65 and BS 540, with an internal ceramic or salt glazing. The single ducts are normally of the push fit plastic sleeve type although standard spigot and socket pipes (as in multiway ducts) of correct internal finish, which are properly laid, are satisfactory.

The absence of a collar on the push fit ducts enables multiway ducts to be constructed more easily from single pipes. For single-duct installations PVC has advantages in that longer lengths, with a degree of potential flexibility, can be utilised.

All pipes and ducts should be installed and jointed in accordance with manufacturer's specifications. They should be surrounded by 150 mm thickness of 4:2:1 concrete and layers of reinforcing mesh may be required on multiduct installations. To ensure correct alignment, a mandrel of slightly smaller diameter than the duct bore should be drawn through after laying. The duct mouth must be sealed to prevent ingress of soil. Prior to sealing long lengths of duct, a non-corrodible draw line should be left in for future use. Short lengths of duct can be 'threaded' using drain rods or wheel prior to cable installation.

After cable installation it may be necessary to fill the annular space between the cable and duct with a grout so as to improve heat transfer (see chapter 37).

Thrust boring, headings and tunnels

These constructions have to be considered by the installation engineer as an alternative to 'open-cut' duct installations. They are of particular advantage for road crossings where the normal depth of laying is precluded by existing services and/or the road or railway traffic flow cannot be restricted. Techniques are of a specialised nature beyond the scope of this chapter.

PREPARATION FOR CABLE LAYING

Cable stockings

A pulling rope has to be attached to the leading end of the cable, and a cable stocking is normally used for this purpose. Fig. 27.2 shows types with single and double thimbles. The latter are normally preferred because there is less damage to the cap on the cable end if the pulling load is high.

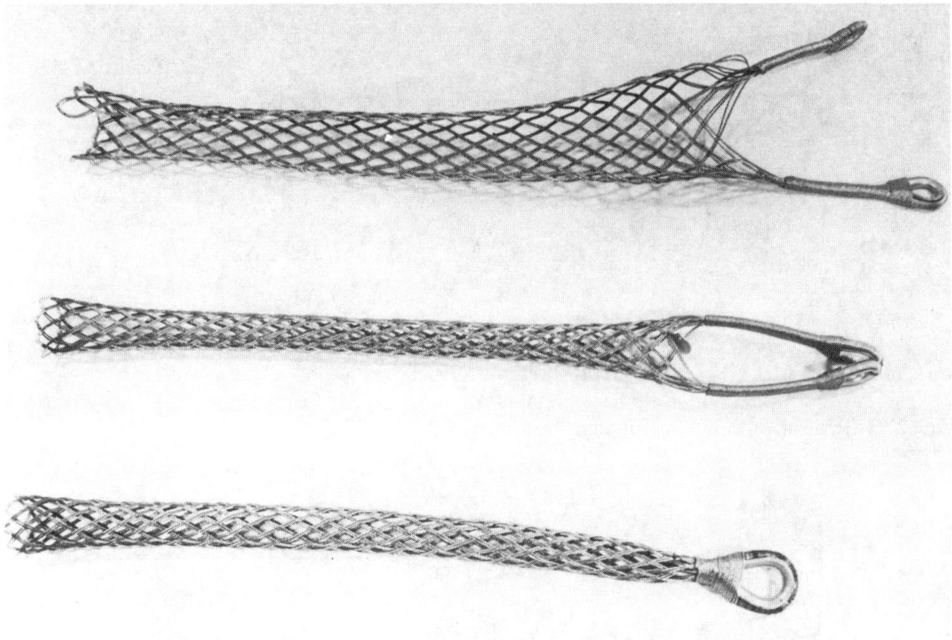

Fig. 27.2 Cable stockings with single and double thimbles (Courtesy of S.E.B. International Ltd)

Pulling eyes

With a stocking, the load is initially taken by the external cable components and is transferred by frictional forces to the conductors. If the load is high it may cause stretching of the outer layers and to avoid this a pulling eye may be plumbed to the armour, sheath and conductors to ensure distribution of the load across the whole section.

Many designs of pulling eye are available for different types of cable. Some are tubular with the conductors being sweated inside the tube and the metal sheath plumbed to the outside. Fig. 27.3 shows a pulling eye which can be adapted for most cable designs.

Fig. 27.4 shows an arrangement used by the UK Electricity Boards for aluminium sheathed cables. It is not a pulling eye in the strict sense, as it is only a means of anchoring the conductors and sheath in the cable end, and a stocking is necessary.

Fig. 27.3 Typical pulling eye for distribution cables

Fig. 27.4 Cable end with conductors anchored to aluminium sheath by the insertion of three pins (Courtesy of Southern Electricity Board)

Three holes are drilled through the cable with 60° phasing and threaded pins are screwed into tubes placed in the holes. When using this method it is important, immediately after laying, to cut off the cable end and re-seal the cable with a new cap.

Power winches

Power winches fall into two categories:

(a) compact lightweight designs utilising either a small petrol or compressed air engine as the power unit. Fig. 27.5 shows a typical example which is suitable up to 2 tonnes safe working load with speeds of 5–8 m/min.
(b) medium weight designs suitable for 2–4 tonnes, the larger sizes having a diesel power unit. Instead of relying on a direct pull these larger units utilise a pair of 'bull wheels' for wire bond haulage as illustrated in fig. 27.6.

With winch pulling, it is important to take steps to keep the pulling load to a minimum. The drum position should be chosen so that the longest length of straight trench is at the pulling end with any severe bends as close as possible to the drum.

Fig. 27.5 Lightweight winch with direct pull on spool containing the pulling bond (Courtesy of Thompson Winches Ltd)

Fig. 27.6 Diesel driven winch for safe working load of 4 tonnes. Transmission is through a gear box coupled to a pair of 'bull wheels' (Courtesy of Thompson Winches Ltd)

Pulling tension in a wire bond can be reduced by passing the bond through a snatch block where the trench changes direction (fig. 27.7). The pull is stopped just before the cable reaches the snatch block so that the bond can be removed from it. This arrangement also prevents the bond from causing damage by scoring the skid plates on the inside of the bend.

An alternative procedure for pulling by winch is the continuous bond method. Instead of attaching the bond to the leading end of the cable, the cable is lashed to the bond at about 1 m intervals. This method is mainly required for heavy cables and is seldom needed for distribution cables. It is described in chapter 39.

Preparation of the trench

Preparation comprises the installation, as necessary, of skid plates, rollers etc., and paying out the winch rope if using power assistance. Typical rollers and dual purpose rollers are shown in fig. 27.8. Cable rollers are necessary to prevent the cable from touching the ground and should be spaced a maximum of 2 m apart for normal size cable. With heavy cables this spacing may need to be reduced to 1.2 m. Correct positioning is important to keep the friction load component to a minimum.

Ducts should be clean and smooth and fitted with bell mouths at entry, and also at exit if followed by a bend.

The pulling tension is determined by a summation of the weights of cable up to a

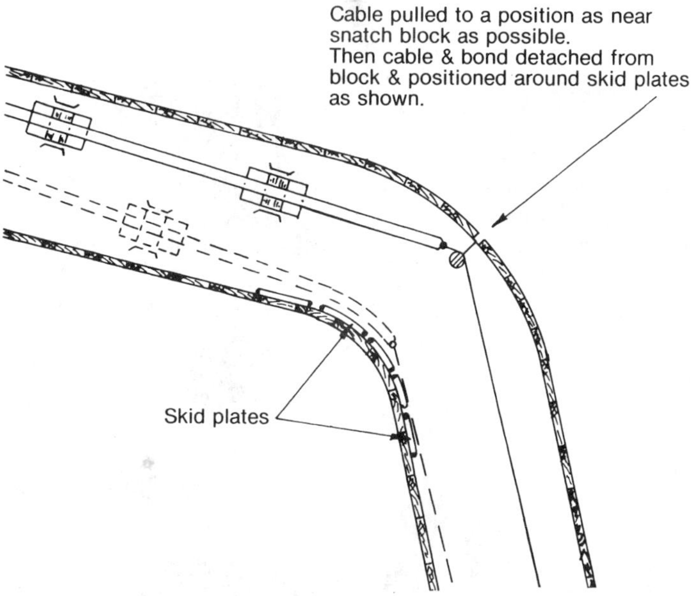

Fig. 27.7 Snatch block arrangement to reduce pulling tension on a bend

point of friction multiplied by the coefficient of friction at that point. Conditions vary widely according to cable type, cable finish and bend in a route, but a general average for the coefficient of friction is around 0.25. Under difficult conditions in ducts it may increase to 1.0, and in such situations graphite lubricants should be applied at duct entries to reduce the friction.

CABLE PULLING

The cable should preferably be drawn to its final position in a continuous manner. During stops, it will settle between rollers and may cause high strain on men and machines during re-starting. Whether the pull is manual or with a winch, it is necessary for one man to be stationed at the drum with a plank wedged against the wing so that over-running of the drum is prevented if pulling stops. Otherwise many loose turns can easily develop on the drum.

Heavy lead sheathed paper cables in long lengths may need very large gangs of men if winch pulling is not used. However, because of the large reduction in cable weight, only four to five men are needed for a 200 m length of 11 kV cable with corrugated aluminium sheath for an average route. Polymeric cables having no metallic sheath are even easier to install.

When pulling by a winch it is advantageous for the cable end to be taken by hand as far as possible before attaching the winch rope. This allows the leading cable rollers, skid plates etc. to take the load and settle under well controlled conditions. The winch operator must carefully observe the dynamometer to prevent overloading. On long pulls, good communication is essential, preferably by radio.

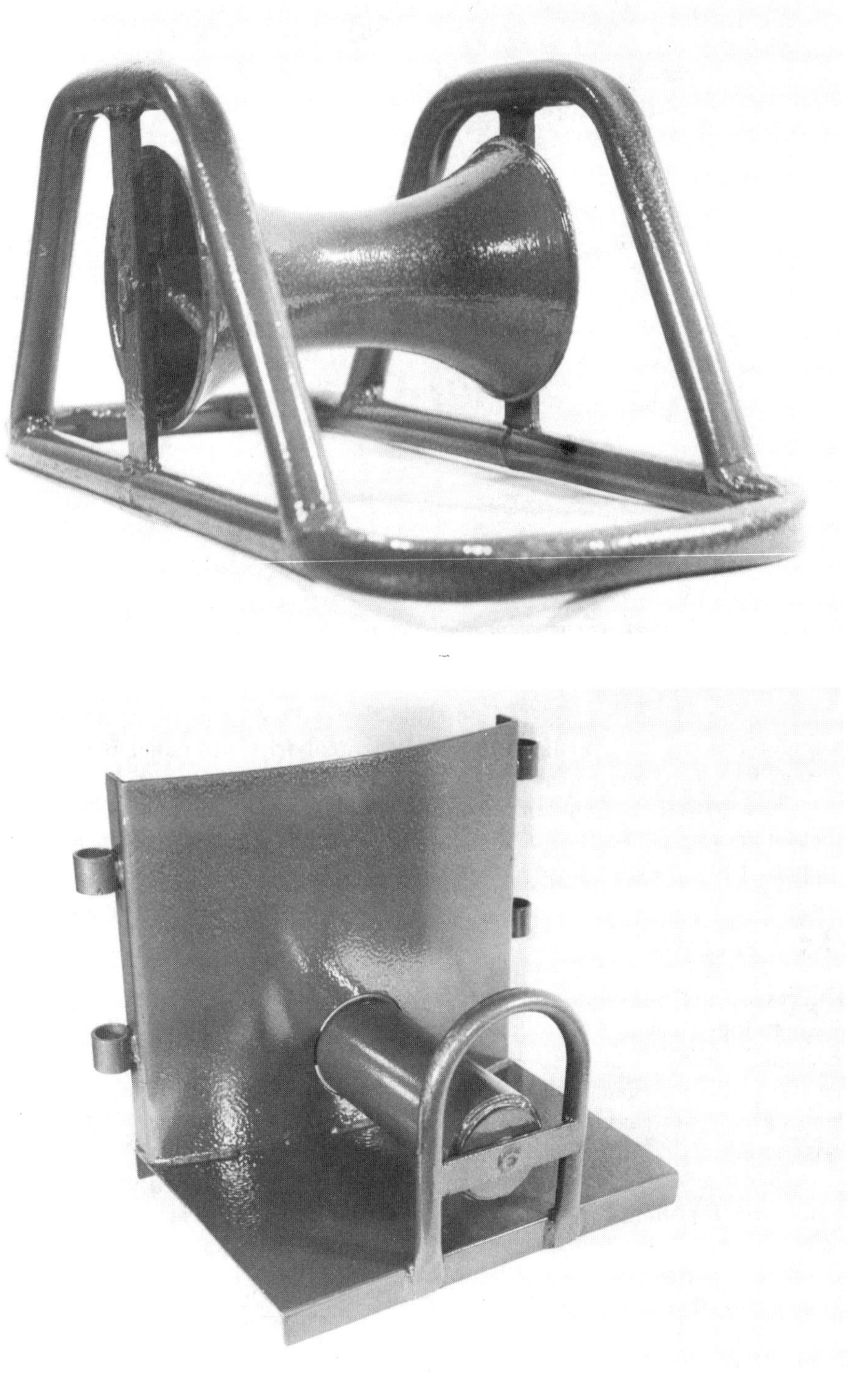

Fig. 27.8 Typical cable rollers, normal and dual purpose, i.e. combined with skid plate (Courtesy of S.E.B. International Ltd)

Final placing

Prior to disconnecting the pulling rope, the cable is laid-off, i.e. starting at one end it is carefully lifted from the rollers and deposited on the bottom of the trench. About 10 m of cable should be lifted at one time, any slack being carried forward. This exercise is fairly simple if only one cable is being installed but needs careful control if the rollers are to be re-used for further cables in the trench. The cables cannot be positioned until the last one has been pulled.

The end position of a cable may require double handling because it is not possible to draw cable straight into a substation or other building. In this case the cable is overpulled and then manhandled around to the duct entry and fed into the required position. At all times the loops should be kept as large as possible so that the bending radius is always above the minimum permitted. Similarly, at the drum position, the necessary length of cable may be unwound from the drum and laid out, if necessary in a figure eight if space is limited (see below), prior to cutting to length and placing in position. Immediately after cutting, the cable must be suitably sealed to prevent ingress of moisture. In this respect it is also important to examine the pulling end seal to ensure that it has not been damaged during laying.

Flaking cables

Cables have to be flaked, i.e. a substantial amount laid on the ground, when for some reason the drum cannot be mounted at a favourable position near the joint or termination. Cables of voltages higher than 11 kV must not be flaked. It is most frequently done on long lengths of auxiliary or pilot cables in order to obviate a joint in the middle of the length or, where the cables are laid in the ground, to enable the trench to be backfilled when only half the drum length has been laid. Where drums of pilot cable are twice the length of the accompanying feeder cable, it is common practice to position the pilot cable drum at the mid-position and pull the cable in the first half of the section, which can then be backfilled.

The remaining cable must then be flaked out in the shape of a figure eight in order to avoid twisting when it is carried forward into the trench or route ahead. The size of the figure eight will depend on the amount of space available and the length of cable to be absorbed, but in no circumstances may the diameter of each half of the eight be less than twice the minimum permissible bending radius r of the cable. The distances between the outer layer of cable on the drum and the nearest point of the figure eight must exceed $3r$.

For a drum mounted at the side of a trench or joint bay, the process of flaking is shown in fig. 27.9. It should be noted that in forming the second layer of the figure eight the cable coming up from the trench passes under that coming off the drum to form the half of the eight farthest from the drum as shown at E. Care must be taken to ensure that at no point in the flaking process is the cable bent anywhere at less than the minimum permissible bending radius, especially when turning the cable at the top nearest the drum. When flaking has been completed the inner end of the cable on the drum becomes the leading end for laying.

At the commencement of unflaking it is important that the new leading end of the cable is so directed that the cable does not incur a twist or kink as it comes off the top layer. Note particularly that if the end of the cable points towards the drum it

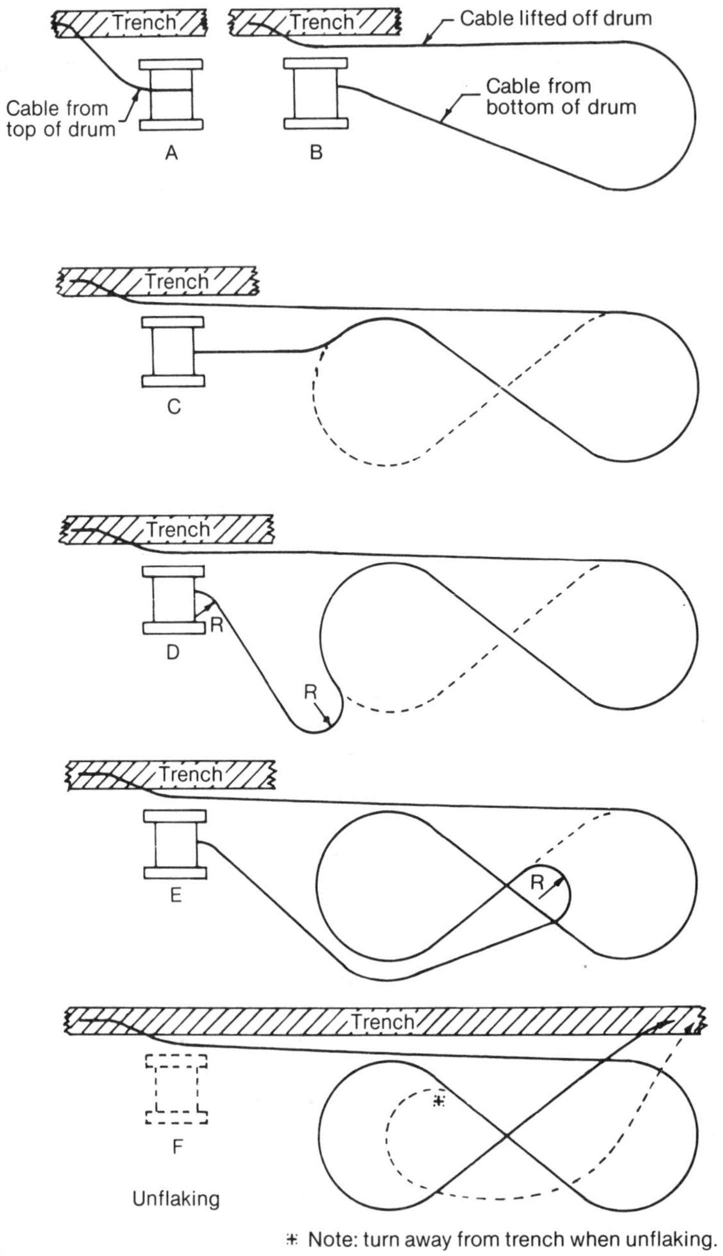

Fig. 27.9 Procedure for flaking cables by the figure eight method

must be reversed by turning away from the trench as at F. Care must also be exercised to prevent infringement of the minimum bending radius as layers of cable come off the figure eight during installation.

BACKFILLING AND REINSTATEMENT

Prior to backfilling, it is necessary to carry out a visual inspection and some items which require to be checked are as follows.

(a) The cables have a proper bedding.
(b) The spacing is correct if there is more than one cable in the trench.
(c) Cables at duct mouths are suitably protected with bushes of the correct size so that no damage is caused and vermin will not enter.
(d) Pulling equipment is removed. In the case of skid plates etc., this may need to be combined with backfilling to prevent collapse of the trench wall.
(e) The cable is free from obvious damage caused by installation. A very high proportion (possibly 90%) of cable failures in service is due to such damage. With cables having no armour, e.g. Consac, it may be necessary to ease the cable above the bedding sand in order to inspect the underside with a mirror. In such cases it is advisable to make a first inspection whilst the cable is still on rollers.

Backfilling

The cables should first be surrounded and covered with appropriate bedding material, using sand or riddled soil as necessary, to give a compacted cover of 50 mm thickness over the cable. Any required earthenware or concrete cover tiles or plastic marker sheet may then be placed centrally over the cable.

The first layer of backfill should be placed manually and compacted by hand punning until a thickness of 150 mm over the cover tile is reached. This acts as a cushion and subsequent material may be placed and compacted with mechanical equipment. Wet clay and wet sand should not be returned to the trench but otherwise the material should be added in the reverse order from excavation. Consolidation should be achieved by compaction in layers of 150 mm thickness.

Normally a temporary surface is left for a short time and this should comprise the original material, though tarmacadam will be needed for roadways. Further inspection will be necessary for settlement and corrective action to prevent accidents before final reinstatement. The use of special backfills for optimum current rating and action to be taken to obtain immediate permanent reinstatement are discussed in chapters 37 and 39.

GENERAL ASPECTS

Bending radii

Cables should never be bent to a small radius. The prescribed minimum should be considered to be the exception rather than the rule and the actual bending radius the largest which circumstances will permit. This eases the task of installation and reduces the possibility of damaging the cable.

It is particularly important to maintain a generous bending radius when cables are to be pulled by a power winch, so as to keep within maximum permissible tension and to prevent the cable being flattened around bends or in ducts. In the immediate vicinity of joints and terminations where the cable can be set in position after the pulling operation is complete, the radius becomes less critical.

The minimum bending radii required by UK specifications for the various types of cable are given in appendix A17. These radii are also generally representative of requirements throughout the world for similar types of cables.

Cold weather precautions

A cable must not be laid or otherwise bent when it is at such a low temperature that damage might be caused to the insulation or serving. With normal paper insulated cables and any cables having a standard PVC oversheath, cable laying should take place only when both cable and ambient temperature have been at or above 0 °C for the previous 24 hours, or when special steps have been taken to heat the cable to above this temperature.

If there is reason to suspect that the cable is below 0 °C, its temperature must be measured by inserting a standard glass bulb thermometer (−10 °C to +10 °C) between the turns of cable. For this purpose two to three battens should be removed from the drum at 45° and 135° positions. If the cable is below the temperature limit and the drum cannot be taken into a heated building, laying must be deferred until its temperature has been raised by the following method:

(a) Roll or turn the drum until the gaps made in the lagging occupy 135° and 225° positions.
(b) Place lighted paraffin operated danger lamps (not hurricane lamps) in a row on the ground beneath the gaps. The number of lamps will depend on the weight of cable, the ambient temperature, and the time available for heating. As a general guide, the lamps should be placed 100–150 mm apart, and the heating period should be at least 24 hours.
(c) Cover the drum to the ground with tarpaulin sheeting fitted close to the drum, but draped at a safe distance from the lamps. A little ventilation between the sheeting and the ground may be found to be necessary, but any large gaps allowing cold air to enter will seriously slow down the heating.
(d) After a heating period of 24 hours a couple of battens should be removed at 45° and 315° positions and the temperature of the cable measured.
(e) To allow for inequalities, and for cooling during laying, the temperatures reached should not be less than 5 °C.

Once a cable has become really cold, it will require many hours of continuous heating to bring it up to the required temperature. It is essential that heat is applied for sufficient time to warm the whole of the cable and not merely the outside layer. Drums to be heated should be placed as close as possible to the pulling positions so that the minimum time elapses after heating is stopped until installation takes place.

When pulling a cable which is only a little above the temperature limit, the region of bending must be watched for any cracking, and on detection of such effect the speed of pulling must be reduced until it ceases. If cracking of a minor nature occurs, the protective finish must be repaired.

As the heating of cables involves a fire risk, it is very important that the heating arrangements are kept under supervision and that a frequent check is made to ensure that the lamps are burning properly.

Cable laying in subsidence areas

In areas subject to subsidence, principally due to mining installations, care must be taken to prevent damage due to uncontrolled movement of the cable. Slight subsidence problems can normally be accommodated by laying the cable with a horizontal wave formation. The cable under this condition is held by the backfill and only minor movement can be achieved. More major movement of the cable can be accommodated utilising wave boxes which keep the cable in a less restrained vertical plane (fig. 27.10). Information regarding subsidence must be made available to cable design engineers at the earliest opportunity in order that wave boxes, if required, can be incorporated in the system.

Repairs to PVC or polyethylene oversheaths

It is very important that any damage to the oversheath observed after installation should be repaired before backfilling is commenced. If the cable has an aluminium sheath it is also essential to make a careful inspection for damage.

Strict attention to detail is necessary in making such repairs and only the approved materials specified should be used. Only a brief outline is given below and full instructions should be obtained from the cable manufacturer. Some of the methods quoted are only suitable for use after installation has been completed, when the cable will not be subjected to significant movement in service.

Superficial damage
The local area of damage is rubbed down with carborundum strip to the depth of the damage and chamfers of 25 mm length are formed at the edges. After cleaning with a suitable solvent, PVC self-adhesive tape of 25 mm width is applied under tension with 50% overlap. The taping is continued up the chamfer until the top is reached. Then another four layers are applied over a length extending 75 mm beyond the chamfer.

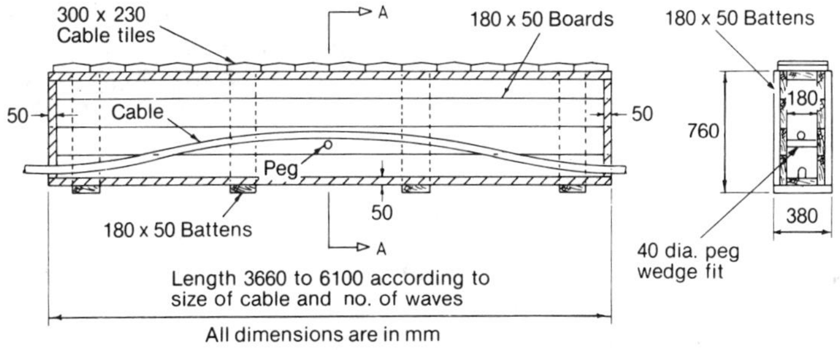

Fig. 27.10 Wave box for use in laying cable in areas subject to mining subsidence

Holes or slits in PVC oversheaths

The edges of the hole or slit are chamfered for a distance of 30 mm and the area around this is abraded over a length of 20 mm. The area is then cleaned with a suitable solvent and, if bitumen is present under the oversheath, care must be taken to remove it from the prepared surface. A patch is then applied to fill the area using an approved grade of special putty. This is followed by an overlapped layer of 50 mm wide PIB self-amalgamating tape extending 50 mm from the patch and three overlapped layers of PVC self-adhesive tape extending 100 mm from the edge of the PIB tape. In the case of slits, further strengthening by the addition of an epoxy resin bandage should be made if the cable is likely to be moved. Details are given later.

Removal of a complete ring of oversheath

After removal of the damaged ring a chamfer is formed, unless the cable has a corrugated aluminium sheath. In the latter case the edges are left square. The surface is then thoroughly cleaned with solvent, taking care to remove the graphite layer, if present. Four overlapped layers of 50 mm wide PIB self-amalgamating tape are then applied at high tension over a length extending to 50 mm beyond the original cut. PVC self-adhesive tape is then applied at one-third overlap to build up to a level corresponding to the original oversheath diameter. For corrugated aluminium sheathed cables the length should be up to the oversheath cut and for other cables up to the end of the chamfer.

Five layers of PVC self-adhesive tape are then applied, each one extending 5 mm further along the cable. The repair is completed with a resin poultice reinforcement consisting of six layers of ribbon gauze or bandage impregnated and painted with an approved grade of freshly mixed epoxy resin. This requires about 12 hours to cure.

PULLING LOADS

Cable stocking over normal cable end

For the majority of installations a cable stocking is applied over the end of the cable as cut and capped, i.e. it grips the outside of the cable and the pulling load may not be fully transmitted to the conductors. For paper insulated cables with lead or aluminium sheaths, unarmoured or steel tape armoured, the maximum pulling load tends to be dictated by the way the metal sheath is pulled forward over the insulation. This could cause damage to the insulation over 1–3 m at the leading end. In the USA the following formula has been suggested for lead sheathed cables without wire armour:

$$T = 3.33t(D-t) \text{ (kgf)} \tag{27.1}$$

where T = pulling load (kgf)
D = diameter over lead sheath (mm)
t = lead sheath thickness (mm)

Rather higher loads are possible if the cable has wire armour, whether the cable is pulled with a stocking over the armour or, as is sometimes done, the armour is extended over the end of the cable to form an attachment for the pulling rope, i.e.

a direct pull on the armour. Whatever method of attachment is used, the limiting load is then governed by the rotation on the end of the cable caused by untwisting of the armour.

Winch pulling with a prepared cable end

When cables are pulled by a power winch, more attention has to be given to the maximum pulling load that is permissible. For such installation a pulling eye attached to the conductors is necessary and traditionally it has been fairly standard practice to relate the maximum permissible load to the strength of the conductors, e.g. 6 kgf (58.8 N) per square millimetre of total conductor area for copper and 3 kgf (29.4 N) for aluminium. These figures are based on the ultimate tensile strength of the materials with a safety factor of about 2.5. Similar figures may be obtained by taking the 0.1% proof stress and a lower safety factor. It is desirable to specify a maximum load of 2000 kgf as such a load would indicate some unnecessary obstruction.

However, derivation of a maximum load in this way ignores some important factors, in particular the effect of side pressure in passing over skid plates or against duct surfaces at bends in the route. Excessive pressure can cause flattening and damage to the cable insulation or other components.

Muhleman[1] gives a detailed analysis of all the effects which govern pulling loads for duct installations but the approach is by mathematical treatment rather than practical observations.

It is extremely difficult and expensive to carry out effective trials on cables with different constructions and using a typical site installation with a range of tensions up to levels that cause damage. However, a comprehensive series of tests was undertaken in the UK in 1975–76 by the Southern Electricity Board in collaboration with the Electric Cable Manufacturers Confederation. The types of cable investigated included 11 kV paper insulated with smooth and corrugated aluminium sheath, Consac and Waveconal CNE cables. The route included two 120° or 90° bends and a duct section. By connecting the two ends of the cable with a wire rope in which a Tirfor winch was included, it was possible to vary the tension over a wide range. After each pull, samples of cable used were examined visually and also subjected to impulse test. In a separate series of tests, samples of cable were subjected to static pulling loads to investigate effects such as sheath extensibility.

The work highlighted a number of important points.

(a) Vertical rollers should not be used at bends because they cannot be set up with sufficient accuracy to prevent an individual roller from standing proud of the others.
(b) Skid plates combined with horizontal rollers (fig. 27.8) appeared to provide the optimum arrangement and, if high pulling loads are involved, careful setting is necessary to obtain a smooth curve.
(c) Skid plates easily become scored by the pulling hawser and good maintenance is required to prevent damage to PVC oversheaths.
(d) When aluminium sheathed cables were pulled with a stocking applied over a normal cable end, i.e. with a plumbed end cap, it was confirmed, as already mentioned, that one limit to maximum pulling tension was the amount of sheath extension which could be tolerated. By pinning the sheath and conductors

together, as described earlier, much higher tensions could be withstood. Ultimately the amount of flattening due to side pressure was found to be the limiting factor, although in the case of cables with smooth sheath the limit was at a level below that at which it is necessary to anchor the sheath to the conductor.

From this work, recommended maximum tensions for 11 kV PIAS cables were as shown in table 27.1.

Table 27.1 Maximum pulling load for 11 kV PIAS cables

Conductor size (mm^2)	Smooth sheath (kN)	Corrugated sheath	
		Without sheath anchor (kN)	With sheath anchor (kN)
95	5.9	4.0	6.9
150	7.9	5.4	9.8
185	9.8	6.4	11.8
240	13.7	7.9	14.7
300	19.6	9.8	19.6

At high ambient temperatures above 20 °C, there may be a tendency, particularly for cables with smooth metal sheaths, for the PVC oversheath under the stocking to stretch beyond underlying components. If the cable has a metal sheath it may be necessary to remove the PVC oversheath and apply the stocking directly over the metal sheath.

Consac and Waveconal cables

Consac cable is so light that winch pulling is seldom required and even then the loads are low. It is not necessary to anchor the conductors and sheath. Therefore, when pulling with a stocking over the cable end, the limit is imposed by stretching of the aluminium sheath. A reasonable maximum is that which corresponds to 90% of the 0.1% proof stress of annealed aluminium. This can be taken as 30 N/mm^2 of sheath cross-sectional area. The above tests showed that there was no undue deformation by side pressure at this level.

In the case of Waveconal cables, the limit is imposed by deformation of the rubber layer for the corrosion protection of the concentric neutral conductor. Tentative maximum pulling loads vary from 3.0 kN for 70 mm^2 cable up to 7.0 kN for 185 mm^2 and above.

SUPPORTS FOR CABLES ERECTED IN AIR

Support spacings for lead sheathed cables

Most distribution cables in air are suspended from open J-hangers or cleats and only a small proportion are installed on trays. Whatever method is used, it is necessary to pay attention to the effect of expansion and contraction, particularly if there are regular operating cycles to maximum load and the cables are lead sheathed. Fracture of lead sheaths due to local bending and fatigue has happened frequently, e.g. in generating stations on the cables connecting the generators to transformers, when the cable supports have been too close together. Expansion causes a thrust in the cable which can result in bodily movement of the cable across or through the support until slack cable builds up at some convenient position, such as a bend in the route. A short span of cable then has to accommodate the expansion and contraction of a long section length and the repeated flexing can lead to failure.

Holttum[2] was probably the first to publish a detailed investigation and draw attention to the benefits from using much longer spacings between supports than had been traditional. He provided a somewhat complicated formula to determine optimum spacing and recommended that in each span between supports the cable should be installed with a sag of 2% of the spacing. The object was that each span should be able to cater for its own expansion and contraction by variation of the sag, with no possibility of movement across the point of support. Such movement cannot be prevented adequately by clamps or cleats.

Prior to Holttum's work, a common conventional spacing was about 750 mm and for lead sheathed paper insulated cables he advocated that it should be increased to around 2–3 m according to cable size and weight. For a long time his theory was a little unpopular because it is much more difficult to obtain satisfactory visual appearance with long spacings and somewhat more care is required to obtain uniform sagging during installation. However, it became accepted that it was quite impractical with short spacings to cleat cables sufficiently rigidly to prevent bodily movement through supports and that longer spacings were undoubtedly beneficial. In addition to preventing the movement of cable across supports it it also necessary to provide positive restrictions by adequate cleating in sections containing joints and at bends or changes of level.

Subsequent to Holttum's original investigations, a simplified formula has become used more generally:

$$L^3 - \frac{Kd^2tL}{W} = \frac{V(9ne^4 + 11ma^4) \times 10^6}{W} \tag{27.2}$$

where L = distance between support centres (mm)
K = a constant depending on sheath material
d = lead sheath diameter (mm)
t = lead sheath thickness (mm)
W = weight of cable (kg/km)
V = a constant dependent on number of cores and cable type
n = number of conductor wires
e = diameter of each conductor wire (mm)
m = number of armour wires
a = diameter of each armour wire (mm)

The constants for PILS cables are given below.

K		*V*	
Unalloyed lead	0.60×10^4	Solid type, single-core	4.1
Alloy B	1.6×10^4	Solid type, 3-core and SL	0.34
Alloy $\frac{1}{2}$C	0.91×10^4	Oil-filled, single-core	0.46
Alloy E	0.85×10^4	Oil-filled, 3-core	0.38

Whereas Holttum recommended that the spacings from the formula should be minima, it is now taken that they should be maxima with a general average being 30% lower. Values are normally between about 1.5 and 2.5 m according to conductor size.

When cables are installed on trays or flat surfaces, so that it is not possible to obtain 2% sag between points of support, it is often necessary to adopt a similar principle but to arrange for horizontal instead of vertical movement. This situation arises most commonly with large conductor size cables, which are hence of single-core type and often installed in trefoil cleats. A convenient arrangement with such cleats is to form the cable into a uniform wave shape with the deflections in opposite directions on each side of the cleat. The cleats are installed in such a way that they can pivot about their axis. The cables are supported by further trefoil cleats halfway between the pivoting cleats and the latter cleats are on a suitable base to allow for horizontal movement. (See also chapter 37.) A similar principle is required if the cables are installed in flat formation.

Support spacing for cables without lead sheaths

As polymeric insulated cables such as PVC cables to BS 6346 and XLPE cables to BS 5467 do not have lead sheaths, there is not the same problem of possible cable failure but similar cable movement may occur and it is still desirable to arrange for 2% sag to be provided between supports. Bodily movement of cable due to thrust is more likely to occur if the cable has solid aluminium conductors and much wider spacings are necessary. Table 27.2 shows suitable spacings for cables in buildings, where compliance with the IEE Wiring Regulations is required. Actually these Regulations only cover cables with copper conductors up to 40 mm^2. If such compliance is not necessary the values given for copper conductor cables above 15 mm diameter may be increased by 50%.

Other considerations

Cable cleats provide a satisfactory means of supporting cables and wherever possible their use should be considered in preference to hangers, which if used should have adequate bearing surface free from sharp edges.

Multicore power cables installed in groups in air should have spacing all round for the dissipation of heat and even so some cables may need to be derated by 10%. Exact details vary with the number of cables and the method of installation. Full

Table 27.2 Support spacings for polymeric insulated cables

Overall cable diameter (mm)	Solid aluminium conductor		Stranded copper conductor	
	Horizontal spacing (mm)	Vertical spacing (mm)	Horizontal spacing (mm)	Vertical spacing (mm)
Below 15			350	450
15 to 20	1200	550	400	550
20 to 40	2000	600	450	600
40 to 60	3000	900	700	900
Over 60	4000	1300	1100	1300

details are given in ERA Reports 74–27 and 74–28 which respectively deal with the heat emission from cables in air and cables on perforated trays. Where, depending upon conductor size, 75 mm to 150 mm spacings can be arranged between fully loaded cables, no derating should be necessary provided there is free ventilation around each.

When power cables are double or treble tiered they should be cleated so as to provide free ventilation between layers, but with long cable lengths where voltage regulation governs the cable size the cables may not be fully loaded and mutual heating is accordingly alleviated.

As control cables can be accommodated in the spaces between power cables, careful planning of the configuration of the cables should result in an economic layout.

Provided the trays are of the perforated type and permit the circulation of free air, multicore power cables may be installed on trays in single-layer formation without cleats. Control cables can be bunched and uncleated when installed on trays.

Single-core cables are normally installed in trefoil formation, each trefoil cleat containing three different phases, and spaced as mentioned above.

In order to restrain the forces set up between phases under heavy short-circuit conditions it is sometimes necessary to bind the three phases together with specially designed binders positioned between the supporting cleats.

Another method of installing single-core cables on horizontal runs is on expanded metal trays with binders as mentioned above, but without attachment to trays. Where cables change horizontal or vertical direction they should be cleated to prevent an accumulation of expansion at the bends, the expansion being taken up along the straight sections.

REFERENCES

(1) Muhleman, C. E. (1976) 'Cable pulling'. *IEEE Conf. Rec. Pulp and Paper Industry Tech. Conf. Boston, USA*.

(2) Holttum, W. (1975) 'The installation of metal sheathed cables on spaced supports'. *Proc. IEE, Part A* **102**, 729–742.

Chapter 28
Joints and Terminations for Distribution Cables

Joints and terminations are a fundamental part of a power cable distribution system, and are expected to perform all the functions expected of the cable on which they are installed. The basic components are similar in each case, in that both must have conductor connections which are suitable for the full rating of the cables and sufficient insulation between phases and phase to earth to match the required performance of the cable. In addition, both must include some method of stress control when screened cables are involved, and they require some form of overall protection. There is a variety of different ways of providing these components, each with advantages and disadvantages. There is no universal joint or termination, and the type of product to be used must be selected according to the technical, economic and physical constraints of the particular installation.

Joint design must cater for both simple straight-through joints, where two identical cables are being joined, and also branch joints, which may be either T formation or breeches (Y) joints. At low voltage, in addition to straight-through and branch joints, service joints for one or more cables are required. In all cases the joint must be capable of accepting both copper and aluminium conductors in a large range of sizes, possibly with different sizes of conductor being connected within the joint. Transition joints for connecting cables of different designs or insulating material are also necessary.

Joint design on low voltage joints must take into account the practice in the UK on 600/1000 V cables of making off service joints with the main distribution cable live. This practice is extended to straight and branch joints where the cable to be connected to the system is open circuit, when large electric arcs will not be drawn when conductor contact is made. Various safety precautions are used when live jointing is carried out. These include the use of a rubber mat for the jointer to stand on, the use of special insulated tools, and also blankets and shrouds to cover the connectors or ferrules on phases not actually being worked upon.

The fitting of joints and terminations used to be a highly skilled art requiring much expertise in soldering and plumbing, together with precise application of insulation, mostly in tape form. Lack of availability of such an elite force with the necessary expertise used to create many problems and led to an excessive number of service failures in countries where the highly developed skills had not been acquired. From the mid-1960s, many new concepts have evolved which have reduced the time to make joints and terminations and, above all, have made it possible for highly reliable products to be obtained by relatively unskilled personnel.

DESIGN PRINCIPLES

Terminations

The basic requirement of a termination is that it must safely separate the phases in a cable to enable the conductors to be connected to whatever equipment is specified. This is obviously very simple in a 600/1000 V cable, but becomes more difficult as the cable voltage increases.

The separation of the phases in a termination must be such that the medium between phases, which may be air or some type of filling compound, will not break down under the normal service a.c., switching surge or impulse voltages. In addition, there must be no failure between phase and earth, either through the filling medium or by tracking along the interface between the filling medium and the cable insulation surface. The British Standard clearances for 'in air' and compound filled terminations are given in table 28.1.

Table 28.1 British Standard clearances in terminations

Rated voltage[a] (kV)	Insulating medium	Clearance between phases (mm)	Clearance between phase and earth (mm)
1.1	Compound or air	20	20
3.6	Compound	20	20
3.6	Air	90	65
12	Compound	45	32
24	Compound or oil	100	75
36	Compound or oil	125	100

[a] Maximum voltage for equipment: see chapter 19.

Where screened cables are being terminated, further difficulties are encountered. The dielectric screen must be removed from each core for a distance sufficient to prevent tracking failures along the core surface. The point at which the screen is terminated then becomes a high stress point and some method of overcoming this problem must be included in the termination design. Fig. 28.1 shows a schematic diagram of the electric field created at a screen termination.

Many types of termination are enclosed within earthed metal containers or boxes. However, some outdoor terminations are not protected in this way and therefore the cable cores must be protected from atmospheric conditions and from different types of pollution. The cable must also be sealed to prevent entry of unwanted substances, particularly moisture, into the cable.

Outdoor terminations must also be designed to overcome the phenomenon known as surface tracking. The outer protected surface of the cores will have a voltage gradient along its length. Water and other pollutants on the surface of the termination will reduce the surface resistance, allowing leakage currents to flow. The leakage currents quickly dry out areas or rings round the termination, forming dry bands. These dry bands are then forced to withstand almost all the potential gradient across the termination surface. Arcs across these dry bands then erode the termination insulation or more commonly attack the insulator surface, leaving carbonaceous

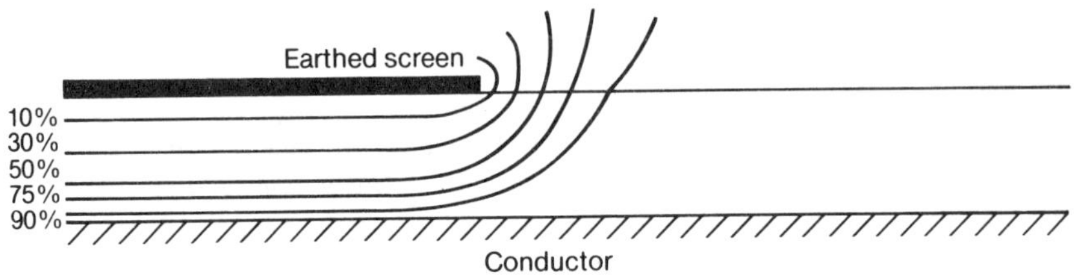

Fig. 28.1 Potential field at a screen termination

tracks which eventually lead to failure. The traditional approach to overcoming this problem is the use of porcelain insulators over each phase, each with a sufficient number of sheds to afford the termination a safe protected creepage distance. However, developments in recent years have now produced other solutions to this problem.

Joints

The various aspects to be considered in joint design are similar to those in terminations, but in a slightly different form.

The conductors of the cables to be jointed must be connected by a method which ensures electrical and mechanical integrity. The insulation between phases and between phase and earth must then be reinstated to satisfy the same design criteria as in the cable. This means that there must be no failure of the reinstated insulation, or failures along the interface between cable and joint insulations, under conditions which the cable is required to withstand. In joints on screened cables, some form of stress control is necessary to ease the electrical stresses caused by the change in dimensions between cable and joint. The insulated cores must then be bound together to prevent buckling of the cores when exposed to the thermomechanical forces generated in the cable when the cable expands on load.

Many joints, like cables, are required by specification to include overall earthed metallic envelopes as a safety precaution. The joint should also be capable of carrying through fault currents and therefore some designs may require an additional connection, or cross bond, to augment the current carrying capacity of the metallic envelope.

Finally the joint design must include some form of overall protection from mechanical damage and from the ingress of unwanted substances such as moisture.

Stress control in HV polymeric cable joints and terminations

PE and XLPE insulated cables of voltages above 1.9/3.3 kV are required to have screens applied over the dielectric on each core, and this applies to all polymeric cables for voltages above 3.8/6.6 kV. Satisfactory stress relief at the screen termination is an essential step in achieving an acceptable method of jointing and terminating such cables.

Requirement for stress control

By reference to the schematic diagram of the electrical stress in the region of the termination of a cable dielectric screen (fig. 28.1), it will be seen that not only is there an increase in stress within the dielectric in that region, but also there is a potential gradient along the interface between the dielectric and the surrounding space. The stress in the dielectric at the screen termination will be well above the design stress of the cable and premature failure can occur at this point. In addition, if the medium surrounding the termination is air, or if there is an air gap between the dielectric and the filling compound, then the stress in this area may be sufficient for the air to discharge even at working voltage. Polymeric materials are not as resistant to discharges as paper insulation and discharges in the termination region will erode the dielectric, eventually leading to failure. Thus in designing terminations for HV polymeric cables, it is necessary to be aware of both these problems and to include some form of stress control.

Stress cones

The traditional method of stress relief is the use of a stress cone. The stress cone is a means of controlling the capacitance in the area of the screen termination, thereby reducing the stress in the dielectric until, at the actual termination of the screen, the dielectric stress is at tolerable levels. The stress cone is continued beyond to the screen termination so as to reduce the potential gradient at the surface of the dielectric to a level where discharges will not occur. A schematic diagram of a stress cone is given in fig. 28.2(A).

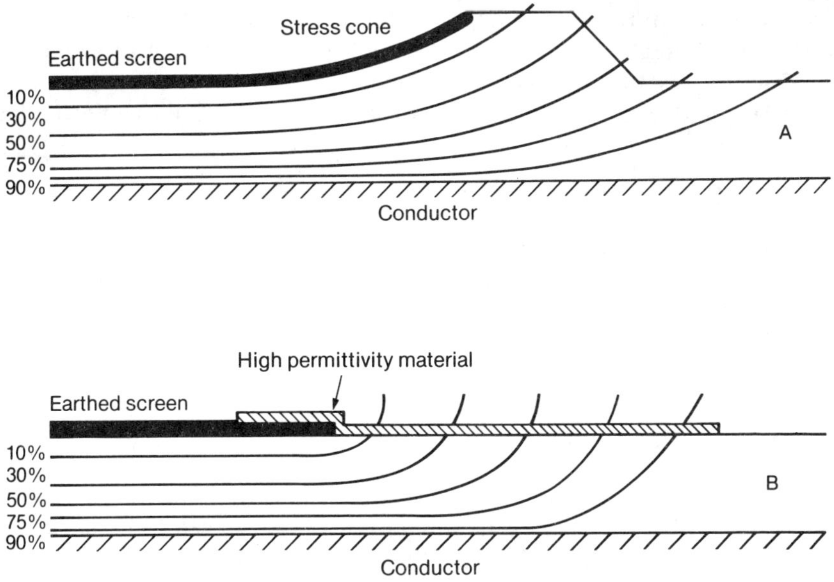

Fig. 28.2 Potential field at a cable termination using (A) a stress cone and (B) a high permittivity stress control layer

High permittivity materials

Materials with relative permittivities significantly higher than the dielectric can provide excellent stress control at terminations.

When materials of dissimilar permittivities are subjected to a potential gradient across their combined thickness, then the material with the lowest permittivity will be subjected to the highest stress. It is this physical phenomenon which enables stress control to be achieved by high permittivity materials. The effective action of a high permittivity material round the dielectric screen termination is to try to maintain the radial potential gradient in the cable dielectric behind the screen termination. Fig. 28.2(B) shows that the equipotential lines emerge only gradually from the dielectric, thus producing a smoother potential gradient at the dielectric surface.

Resistive coatings
Stress control can be achieved by the application of a resistive layer to the insulation surface at the screen termination. Ideally the layer will pass a small current and will therefore set up a linear voltage gradient along its length. However, the resistivity of the material has to be within quite a narrow band for the termination to work successfully. If the resistivity is too low, then the material will simply act as an extension of the dielectric screen and a high stress region will be created at the end of the resistive layer. If the resistivity is too high, then the material will have no appreciable effect and the screen termination will remain a high stress region.

Non-linear materials
Materials with non-linear current versus voltage characteristics are used successfully to provide stress control in polymeric cable terminations. When applied to the cable, the material works in a similar manner to the resistive termination, allowing small currents to flow through the cable dielectric and then along the layer to the earthed screen. However, as the current in the layer increases, so the resistance of the material drops, and a smooth linear voltage gradient is achieved along the layer.

CONDUCTOR CONNECTIONS

Several methods of connecting lugs or ferrules to conductors are available. They differ in the method of application and the amount of skill required, and also in the electrical and mechanical integrity achieved. Performance characteristics are stipulated in BS 4579, 'Performance of mechanical and compression joints in electric cable and wire connectors'.

Soldered lugs and ferrules

The most common type of soldered ferrule used on distribution cables is the weak-back ferrule, so called because of its design (fig. 28.3). It can be opened to allow positioning over the ends of conductors. The individual wires in stranded conductors are first tinned using an appropriate flux according to the conductor metal and then the ferrule is placed round the aligned conductors. Special care in the tinning operation is required with aluminium conductors. The ferrule is then filled with solder by basting from a hot metal pot. The ferrule is wiped and rubbed down when solid to give a smooth outer surface as illustrated. Grade M solder is normally used for copper conductors and Alca P for stranded aluminium.

In the case of solid aluminium conductors a more simple and reliable tinning technique is the use of an abrasion solder (predominantly tin with about 10% zinc).

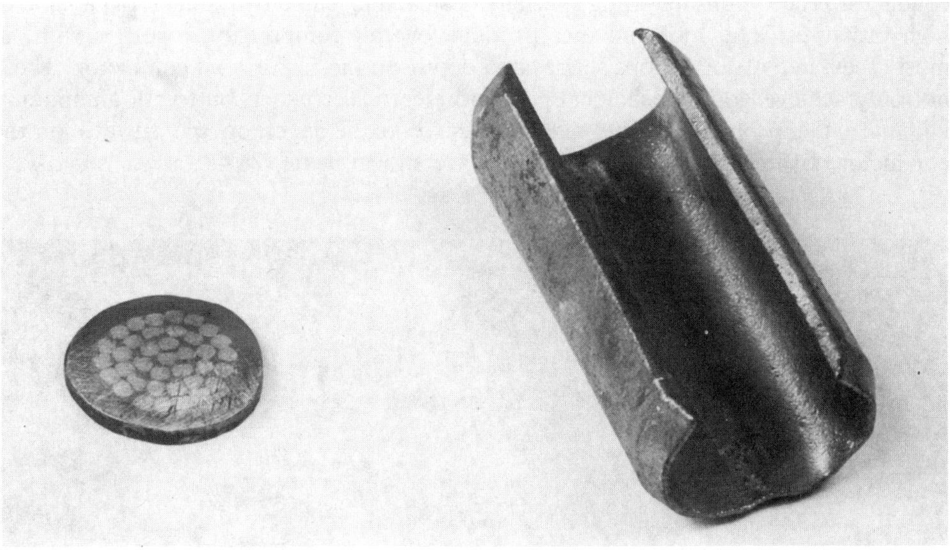

Fig. 28.3 Weak-back ferrule

The ferrule may then be filled with H grade solder.

Solid ferrules, which are tubes with filling holes rather than the weak-back split design, are applied by a similar method. They are generally reserved for 33 kV cables.

The fitting of soldered lugs is a very similar operation to that for ferrules, consisting of tinning the conductor and then filling the lug with solder by pouring in hot metal at the end.

The fitting of soldered lugs and ferrules is a highly skilful operation, which relies on the jointer's expertise to produce a solid ferrule in which there are no cavities or badly tinned conductor wires. A ferrule which is not soldered correctly will result in a high resistance joint which may well result in joint or termination failure. However, when made off in a satisfactory manner, soldered lugs and ferrules give a very acceptable method of conductor connection and have been in service for many decades.

On cables used at higher operating and short-circuit temperatures, soldered ferrules and lugs are not considered as acceptable as other connectors. On XLPE cables, for example, the high short-circuit temperature of 250 °C, together with the associated mechanical forces, creates a danger of the conductor pulling out of the ferrule. Soldered connectors impose a limit of 160 °C for short-circuit temperature (chapter 9).

Compression ferrules and lugs

This type of connector consists basically of a tube of metal which is compressed by large mechanical forces onto the conductor to produce good electrical contact and also good mechanical grip of the conductor. The compression of the ferrule onto the conductor is accomplished using specially designed dies in a hydraulic tool capable of high pressures. The tool and dies produce overall compression together with, in most cases, indents of various shapes and depths in the ferrule and conductor. These not only achieve good mechanical grip and electrical contact, but, with aluminium, eliminate the problem of the highly resistive oxide layer on the surface of the conductor. Examples of compressed lugs are shown in fig. 28.4.

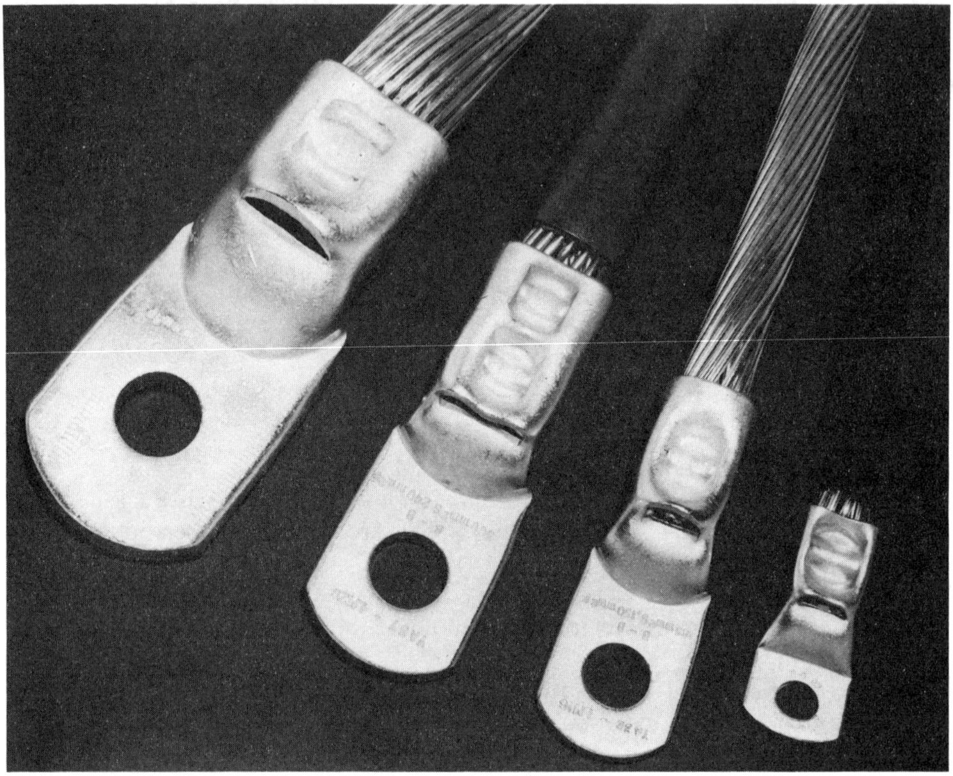

Fig. 28.4 Typical compression lugs

Compression connectors provide satisfactory reproducible results without the skill required to accomplish a soldered connection. They are particularly beneficial with aluminium conductors because of the extra care and attention necessary in soldering, in comparison with copper. The skill is designed into the tool and provided that the correct ferrules and dies are chosen the compression is always constant so that there is little chance of operator error. The use of soldered ferrules and lugs is therefore dwindling rapidly.

Mechanical connectors

Mechanical connectors are now an accepted component of many designs of 600/1000 V joint. A large number of designs are available, some of which are insulation piercing for cables with solid aluminium conductors, which simplifies procedure and reduces the problems when jointing live conductors. Examples of this type of connector are shown in fig. 28.5. All are designed round the principle of clamping the conductors using some form of screw arrangement. The part of the connector in which the conductors are clamped contains sharp serrations which bite into the conductor surface, assisting the mechanical and electrical contact. Generally some means is provided of achieving the correct torque on the screws, either by special tools or by shear headed screws.

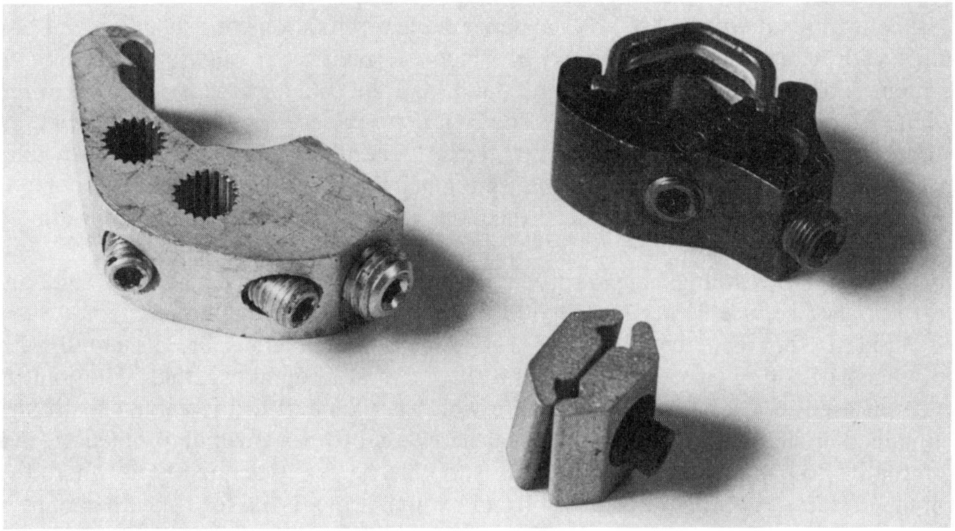

Fig. 28.5 Examples of mechanical connectors

As with compression connectors, mechanical connectors can be installed by unskilled personnel. However, they do not require the expensive tooling associated with compression connectors. They were originally introduced for service cable connections in joints, where current transfer was relatively small. They are now becoming accepted as connections in straight joints on the largest sizes of multicore 600/1000 V cable. The use of mechanical connectors is being extended into heat shrink and 11 kV applications by changing the outer edges of the connectors to reduce mechanical and electrical stresses.

Welding

Conductor welding is a technique normally associated with transmission cables and joints (chapter 38), but on occasion it is used on lower voltage cables. The main advantages of welding are that a conductor joint with excellent electrical and mechanical properties is achieved with no increase in diameter. This would be particularly important in submarine cables for example. The operation requires a highly skilled jointer and expensive ancillary equipment, which normally excludes this type of operation from distribution cable joints except where reliability is absolutely essential.

CONVENTIONAL DESIGNS FOR PAPER INSULATED CABLES

In this section the more traditional methods of jointing and terminating paper insulated cables are described. They are still the preferred techniques for most of the paper cables used in the UK because the jointing skills required are readily available and the material costs of these types of accessory are lower than for the more recently developed systems.

Joints and terminations for cables up to 1.9/3.3 kV

The conventional type of low voltage paper cable termination consists of a metal box filled with a bituminous compound in which the phases are separated. The cable armour is terminated in some form of gland, and the cable sheath is plumbed to the wiping gland at the entry to the box. The conductor connections, which are generally soldered, may be made within the box, or the termination may simply be a dividing box with insulated or uninsulated tails emerging. Designs for outdoor use may be of the inverted type, to afford some protection to the insulators or tails from atmospheric conditions.

Joints for low voltage paper insulated cables are generally based on soldered ferrules. For service joints the service cable conductor can simply be bound and soldered to the main conductor. The conductor connections are insulated with impregnated cotton or paper tapes, and the cores are bound together. The joint is then encased in a lead or copper sleeve which is plumbed to the cable sheath and contained in an outer cast iron or earthenware box for overall protection. An alternative to this plumbed type of joint is the mechanically bonded type, where the plumbed sleeve is omitted and a cast iron box with armour and lead sheath clamps is used. In both cases a bituminous compound is used as the filling medium in the plumbed sleeve and the outer box.

Joints and terminations for cables above 1.9/3.3 kV

In the traditional approach indoor terminations above 1.9/3.3 kV either can be in a form similar to the divider box for 600/1000 V cables described earlier or can be within an enclosed box on switchgear or a transformer, which then includes the equipment bushings. For belted cables, the terminations are very similar to those already described, but with increased clearances and tracking distances to cater for the higher voltages. The lead sheath may be belled, or flared, at its end to ease the high electrical stress in that region. For screened cables, some form of stress control must be used at the dielectric screen termination on each core. This can be achieved by suitable termination with carbon paper or with a few turns of lead rope at 11 kV, but stress cones are used at higher voltages. These are formed by applying impregnated crêpe paper tapes to each core to form a cone of specified dimensions and then extending the dielectric screen part way up the cone using lead rope.

Outdoor terminations for 3-core paper insulated cables in this voltage range can be described as divider boxes which are fitted with porcelain insulators rather than insulated tails. The porcelains are designed with a sufficient number and shape of sheds to eliminate the possibility of flashover or tracking failures. Single-core cables are terminated outdoors within porcelain insulators.

Joint design at voltages above 1.9/3.3 kV is of necessity more complex than for joints for low voltage cables because of the increased electrical stress in the cables and therefore joints. Although the number of different types is reduced, because the range only comprises straight and branch joints, there are a greater number of designs in use, which vary depending on the type of cable and the form of joint insulation employed.

All the traditional designs are based on the use of soldered ferrules. However, the joint insulation may be formed from impregnated cotton or crêpe paper tapes, from paper rolls, or from impregnated tapes together with insulating tubes. For belted cables up to 11 kV, lead or copper sleeves are then plumbed to the cables and filled with bitumen, as is the outer protection box.

For 11 kV screened cables, both screened and unscreened joints are available. For unscreened joints the dielectric screen of each core in each cable is terminated before the joint insulation using lead rope or possibly a small stress cone. For screened joints, the cable screens are carried over the joint insulation on each individual core. In either case the joint is completed with a lead or copper sleeve and an outer protection box, both filled with a bituminous compound.

These joints have been used successfully on lead sheathed cables for many years in the UK and in recent years have also been used on aluminium sheathed cables. It has now been recognised that, when operating at full rated temperature, the thermomechanical forces generated by aluminium sheathed cables may be sufficient to distort and buckle lead sleeved joints, which are therefore generally unsuitable for aluminium sheathed cables. Nevertheless, the UK Electricity Boards still use conventional joints for such cables because they are operated below full rated current.

Joints for 33 kV paper insulated cables are generally of the screened type and a range of designs has been approved nationally in the UK between the Electricity Boards and cable manufacturers. Fig. 28.6 shows typical arrangements.

For single-core straight joints, the conductor ferrule is fitted by soldering and is of solid type with tapered end. Impregnated crêpe paper tapes are used for the insulation. These have some elasticity to allow slightly changing contours to be negotiated successfully. The tape is built up to form a stress control taper adjacent to the core screen terminations and a copper tinsel stocking provides screen continuity over the insulation. A copper sleeve is plumbed to the metallic cable sheath at each end and is filled with semi-fluid oil–rosin compound. This compound ensures that no voids occur in the applied insulation and prevention of compound migration down the cable is achieved by means of sealing sleeves at the sheath terminations.

The joints for 3-core cables are similar, but armour clamps and tie rods are provided as shown in fig. 28.6. The joints are then contained in bitumen filled outer protection boxes, usually now made from glass fibre. Porcelain sealing ends and other types of terminations are available.

Typical examples of the dimensions of the straight joints shown in fig. 28.6 are given in table 28.2.

MODERN ACCESSORY DESIGNS

Resin filled joints and terminations

Resin filled joints are now the most common form of joint on 600/1000 V polymeric cable. Modern designs were brought into regular use in the 1960s along with the

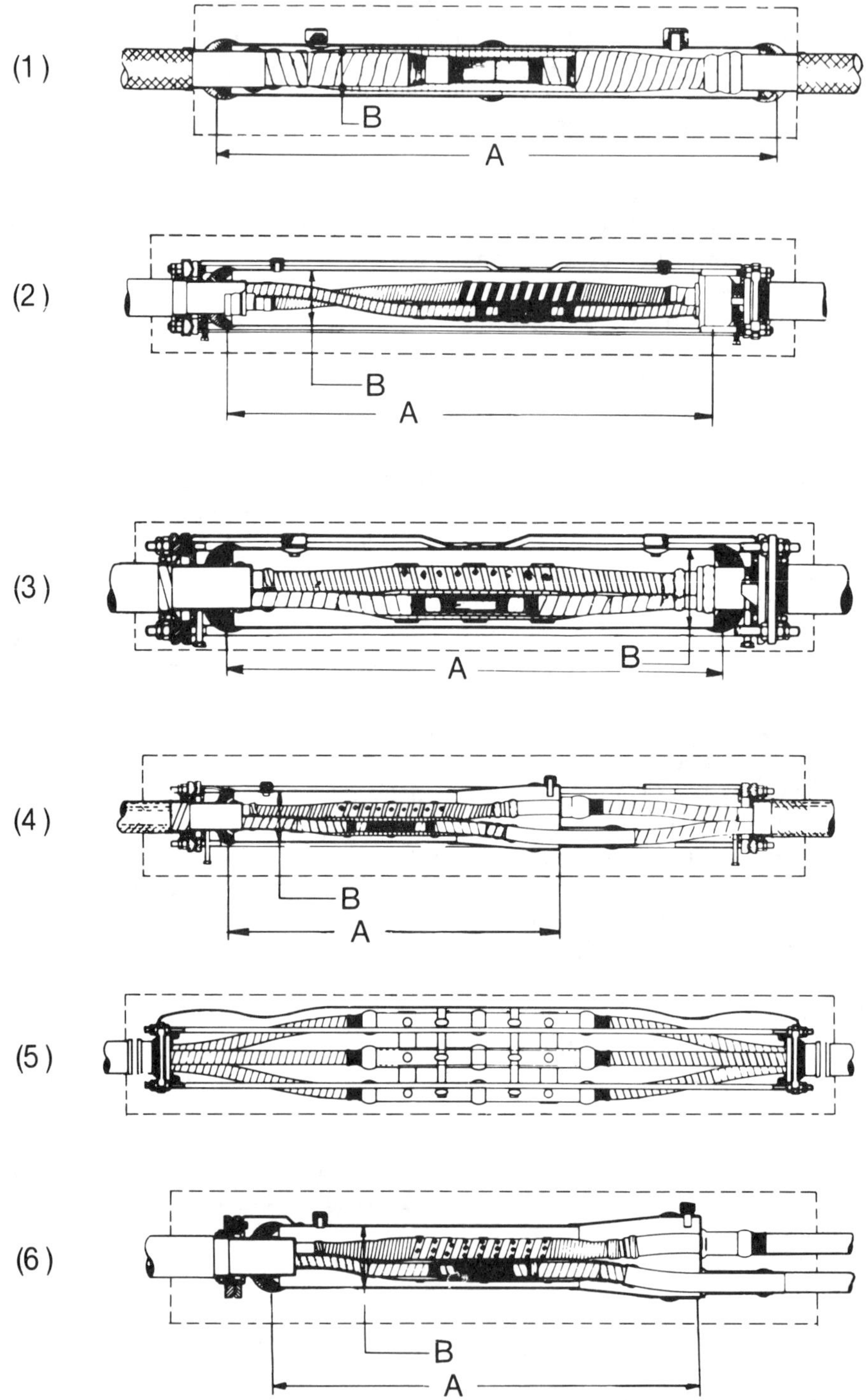

Fig. 28.6 Typical straight joints for 33 kV solid type paper insulated cables: (1) single-core; (2) 3-core with crossed cores; (3) 3-core; (4) 3-core to 3-core HSL cable; (5) 3-core HSL cable; (6) 3-core to three single cores

Table 28.2 Dimensions of copper sleeves in 33 kV joints

Core	Fig. 28.6 ref. no.	Conductor size (mm^2)	Copper sleeve A (mm)	Copper sleeve B (mm)
Single	1	400	815	67
		630	840	73
3-core	2	185	1250	120
		400	1360	150
3-core	3	185	950	120
		400	1050	150
3c to 3c HSL	4	400	1070	150
3c HSL	5	400	813	67
3c to 3 single cores	6	400	1070	150

introduction of CNE cables; mechanical conductor connectors were introduced at the same time. Since the initial use on Waveconal and Consac CNE cables, resin joints are now available on all types of low voltage power cables and their use has been extended in pilot and telephone cables and into high voltage joints and terminations.

The resin is a solid setting medium which provides mechanical protection for the joint and, by adhering to the various components within the joint, provides waterproof encapsulation. The resin also provides the electrical insulation between phases and phase to earth.

Although several resin systems have been investigated, only two are now in popular use. These are the acrylic and polyurethane systems. Both are supplied in packs of two or more components which are mixed just prior to pouring into the joint shell. The resin then cures or 'sets' into the hard encapsulation medium in approximately 30 min at normal ambient temperatures. The shelf life of the resins at present in use is at least 2 years in normal storage conditions. Special arrangements can be made for storage at high ambient temperatures.

Both resin systems are equally successful as a low voltage joint medium but acrylic resins have advantages during mixing. Acrylic resins are generally easier to mix and, unlike polyurethane resins, are unaffected by moisture during curing. Some polyurethane resins can cause skin irritation and inhalation of the fumes given off during curing should be avoided. Acrylic resins have no health hazards but are generally more expensive than polyurethane systems.

As stated earlier, resin joints are now available for all forms of low voltage distribution and service cable jointing and are suitable for all cable insulations at present in use. The joint design differs slightly depending on the joint manufacturer and the cable being jointed but all types have distinct advantages over the more conventional practices. The elimination of plumbed lead sleeves combined with the substitution of soldered ferrules by either compression or mechanical connectors have considerably simplified the technique, and a reliable joint can be produced consistently without the necessity for highly skilled personnel.

A typical resin joint for Waveconal CNE cable is shown in Fig. 28.7 which

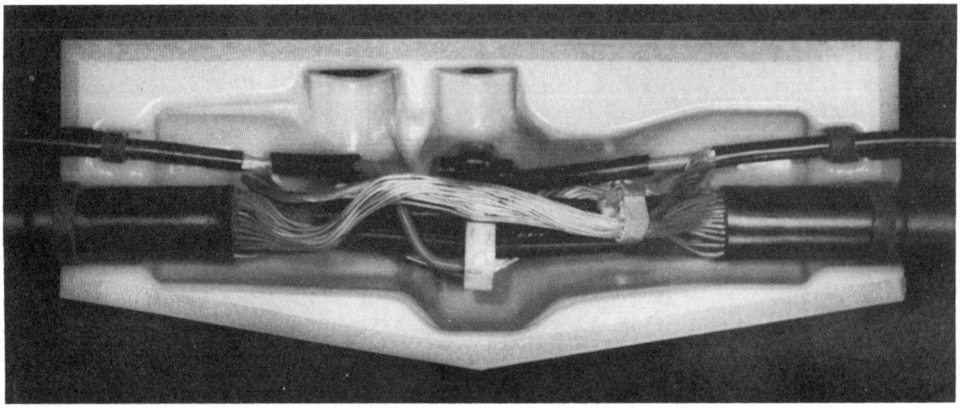

Fig. 28.7 Double-service cast resin joint in Waveconal cable

illustrates a service branch joint. Mechanical connectors are used on both the neutral/earth conductors and the phase conductors, the latter by means of an insulation piercing connector. The vacuum formed plastic shell acts as a mould for the resin, which is mixed and poured into the shell to complete the joint.

The use of resin systems on paper insulated cables has been extended to 22 kV for both joints and terminations where the resin provides the primary insulation between phases and phase to earth. Terminations use the same principle of a box filled with resin, which seals the crutch of the cable, and joints have a metal screen to comply with safety legislation. Stress control on screened paper insulated cables is effected by antimonial lead wire applied at the screen termination.

Resin is again used as the primary insulation on polymeric cables up to 22 kV. Stress control in these designs is provided by high permittivity tapes applied over the screen termination and extending over the conductor connector, providing stress control at this position, which becomes necessary at 22 kV and when the connector diameter exceeds that of the cable core.

For 33 kV polymeric cable designs, the resin continues to provide protection against mechanical damage and moisture ingress but insulation is provided by self-amalgamating tapes, typically polyisobutylene or EPR based. The insulating layer is parallel in the centre of the joint and tapers down to the screen terminations. A semiconducting layer is then provided by self-amalgamating tapes, producing stress relief by means of a stress cone (see Fig. 28.2(A)). Metallic screening is reinstated with a knitted copper tape.

Heat shrinkable accessories

One of the most beneficial developments in jointing, and particularly terminating, has been the emergence of shrinkable polymeric materials, of which the heat shrinkable type is by far the most common.

The heat shrinkable property is gained by first extruding or moulding the polymeric materials into the required shape or form and then crosslinking them by irradiation or by some chemical means. The components are then warmed and stretched by a predetermined amount and allowed to cool in this extended state. Because of the crosslinking process, the material has a type of 'memory', and when heated again it will relax into the shape in which it was crosslinked.

Heat shrinkable materials are particularly suitable for some components of terminations, e.g. tubes and udders, which under the action of heat shrink down and conform exactly to the contours of the cable and the splayed cores. Various mastics and adhesives are sometimes used to ensure watertight seals. Low voltage terminations, for example, for Consac cable, consist of an udder or glove which is applied over the cable crutch and, together with a special mastic type compound, forms a watertight seal onto the cable sheath. The individual cable cores are then protected from moisture by applying heat shrinkable tubes from the udder onto the lugs fitted to each conductor.

For outdoor and for higher voltage terminations, the sealing sleeves and udders are made from a non-tracking weather-resistant compound. Heat shrinkable sheds, made from the same material, are used to prevent tracking and flashover. At 11 kV and above, some form of stress relief is necessary, and this is achieved using a specially developed stress control tube applied at the screen termination on each core. For paper insulated belted cables at 11 kV, the udder is made from a semiconducting compound and this continues the earth envelope part way up each individual core, effectively 'converting' the cable to the screened design. The cable can then be terminated in a similar way to screened cables.

The main advantage of heat shrinkable terminations on paper cables is the elimination of compound filled divider boxes, making terminating a simpler, quicker and cleaner operation. When used in conjunction with compression conductor fittings, the jointing skill required, even for high voltage terminations, is reduced considerably. An example of an indoor heat shrinkable termination is shown in fig. 28.8.

Heat shrinkable terminations have now gained wide acceptance on paper insulated low voltage cables in the UK and at 11 kV outdoor heat shrinkable terminations are becoming more popular. However, termination boxes on equipment are still mainly designed for compound filling and therefore have reduced clearances. Heat shrinkable terminations which include specially moulded boots to insulate the phase conductor connections are available for these situations, but because there is no price incentive to move to heat shrinkable termination, and because skilled jointers are available, compound filled boxes are still prevalent in the UK.

Shrinkable terminations are available for polymeric cables in a very similar form to those for paper insulated cables. The stress control tubes used at the cable dielectric screen termination provide stress relief by virtue of the resistivity and permittivity of the material, which are carefully controlled during manufacture. Some manufacturers use tapes rather than heat shrinkable tubes to provide stress relief. The terminations are completed by the application of shrinkable non-track tubes and udders and, for higher voltages or outdoor situations, the application of a number of sheds. Terminations of this type are available for all voltages up to 33 kV and each kit will cover a range of conductor sizes.

Heat shrinkable joints consist of insulating tubes which are applied over each conductor connector. The joint also contains armour clamps and an overall protective sleeve. Various components are coated with sealant or adhesives where necessary to prevent the ingress of moisture.

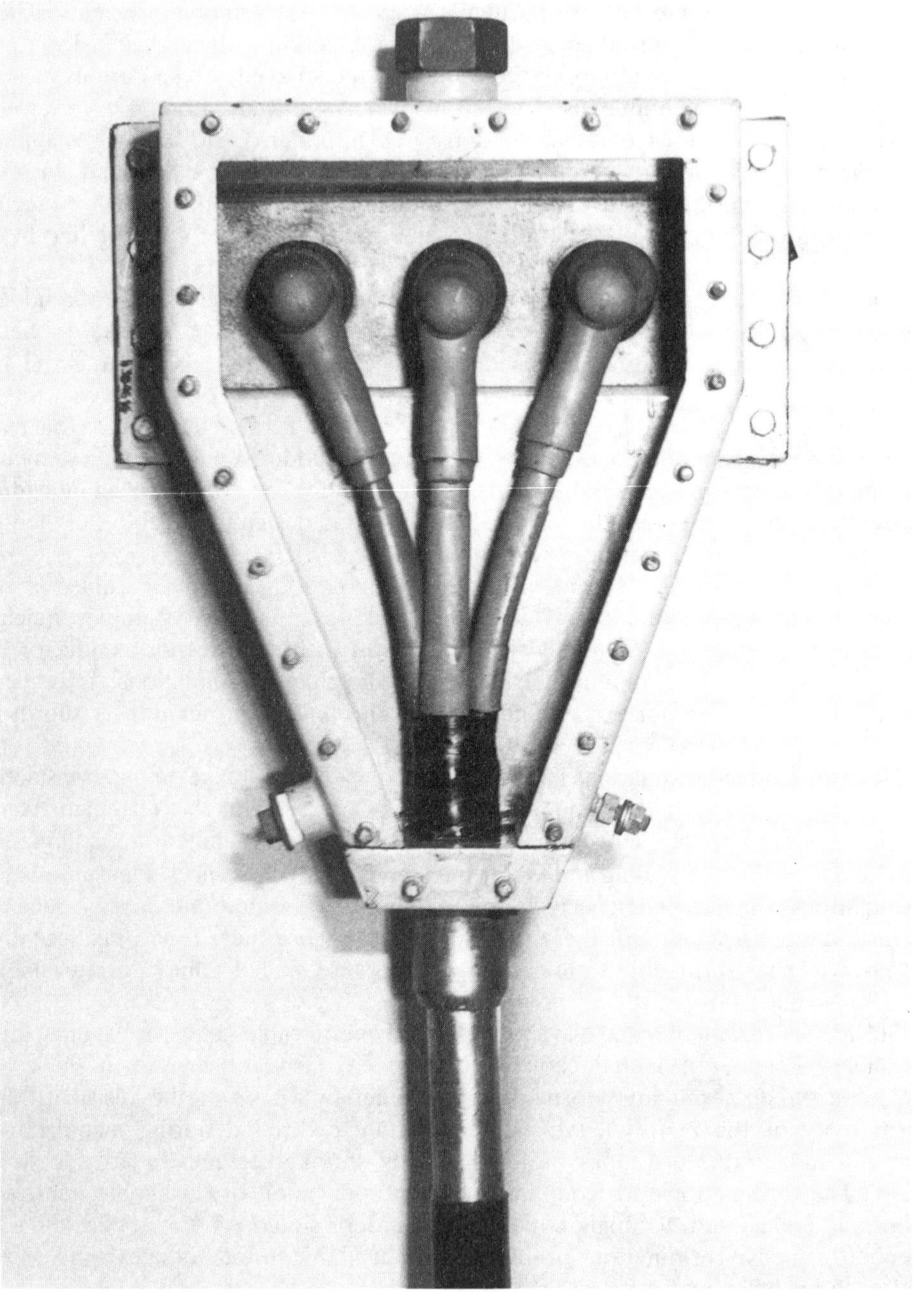

Fig. 28.8 Heat-shrink termination for 11 kV cable to transformer (Courtesy of Raychem Ltd)

Heat shrinkable joints for high voltage cables consist of a combination of stress control, insulating and screening sleeves, together with some mastic and adhesive materials to form watertight seals and to fill any voids within the joint. These joints are suitable for single- and 3-core cables, again with shaped or circular conductors.

For 33 kV joints, several insulation layers had to be applied over the stress control layer, followed by a semiconducting screening layer, metallic shielding and an outer protective sleeve. The latest designs utilise a co-extruded sleeve comprising an insulating rubber inner layer and semiconducting heat shrinkable outer layer. This reduces the number of layers to be applied and the fact that only the outer layer is heat shrinkable allows for more rapid insulation.

Latest developments include simpler 11 kV terminations which consist of the weather- and tracking-resistant tubing coated with a mastic, which not only provides a moisture seal but also provides stress control by virtue of its permittivity and resistivity. These have been combined with rubber elbow moulding to provide an alternative to the more widely used screened elbow connector described in the next section.

Pre-moulded joints and terminations

For the termination of HV polymeric cable stress cones built up using self-amalgamating tapes have been almost totally replaced by pre-moulded cones. These cones are designed to form an interference fit with the cable and are shown in fig. 28.9.

On cables with taped core screens, a semiconducting adapter is used to connect the semiconducting component of the cone and the latter is earthed through an earthing eye. Pre-moulded products have the advantage of being factory made and tested and can be installed very quickly. Although they will accommodate small variations in cable dimensions, it is preferable to be aware of the exact cable size when ordering terminations.

Indoor in air terminations consist of the stress cone and the conductor connectors. For outdoor use, pre-moulded sheds are used which interlock with each other and with a cap sealing onto the conductor connector (fig. 28.9).

Elbow connectors are a specific form of termination used to provide the connection to standardised transformer and switchgear bushings and have been extensively used on polymeric cables at 11 and 33 kV. A typical example is shown in fig. 28.10. A pre-moulded cable reducer forms an interference fit on the cable. This in turn fits into the elbow housing, which provides insulation, stress control at the conductor connector and a semiconducting outer skin to enclose the whole termination within an earthed envelope.

The conductor connector is compressed onto the cable conductor and fitted to the bushing by either a pin and socket or a bolted connection. The latter can be used to provide multiple cable connectors to the same bushing by means of connecting plugs, and other designs are suitable for connecting and disconnecting when the system is energised.

Unscreened elbow connectors are also available and there are two basic types. The first merely provides a connection to the bushing as an off-going terminal, which requires bolting to an already terminated cable and, if necessary, insulating by means of hand applied tape or heat shrink. The other type incorporates the cable

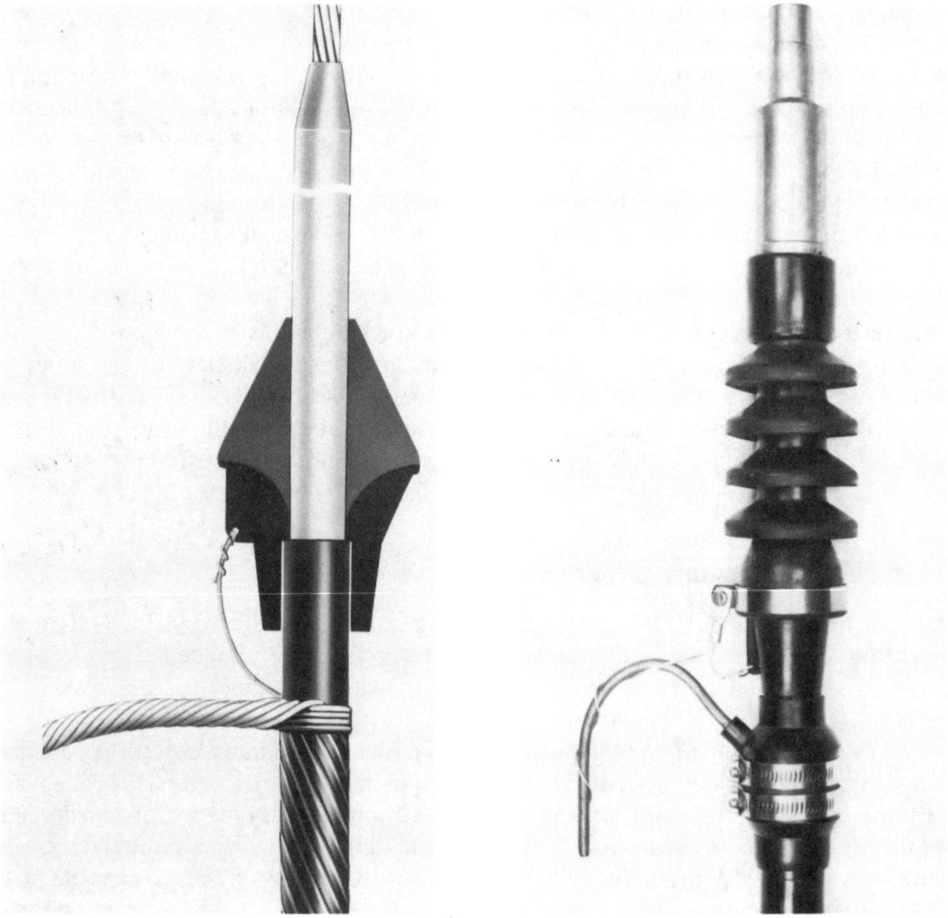

Fig. 28.9 Terminations of 11 kV polymeric insulated cable using pre-moulded push-on stress cone: indoor (*left*) and outdoor (*right*) (Courtesy of Amerace Ltd)

termination within the connector either using heat shrinkable components as described in the previous section or using an interference fit cable reducer as used in screened elbow connectors. Screened straight joints are also available using the same principles as described for screened connectors above: fig. 28.11 shows a 33 kV straight joint which uses a compression conductor connector and a split housing having semiconducting inner and outer layers with an insulating centre forming an interference fit with cable reducers.

An earthed metallic envelope is provided by a metal stocking which is protected against moisture ingress by means of a mastic lined heat shrinkable tube.

Stretched elastomer products

For high voltage joints and terminations an alternative method of applying the insulating layer to polymeric cable joints and terminations is to utilise an elastomer that is mechanically deformed to enable installation. Two variations on this theme

Fig. 28.10 Pre-moulded elbow connector for HV polymeric cable

are available. In the first the component is stretched and held in that form by a plastic support core. To install this the component is positioned and the plastic core removed, allowing the component to return to its original shape. Components available are cable end caps, tubes, crutch seals and skirted tubes incorporating rain sheds, enabling terminations, cable repairs and conductor connector insulation applications.

In the second variation a car type foot pump is employed to expand a rubber sleeve, enabling it to be readily applied to the cable. This tubing is available as a high permittivity form to facilitate stress control and in a non-tracking weather-resistant version for the outer layer. Other components such as rain sheds, crutch seals and covers for the conductor connector are slid into position after lubrication with silicone grease.

For jointing applications an insulating tube is used which has a semiconducting outer surface, and stresses at the connector position are controlled by using a high permittivity mastic. As with heat shrinkable and pre-moulded joints, metallic screen

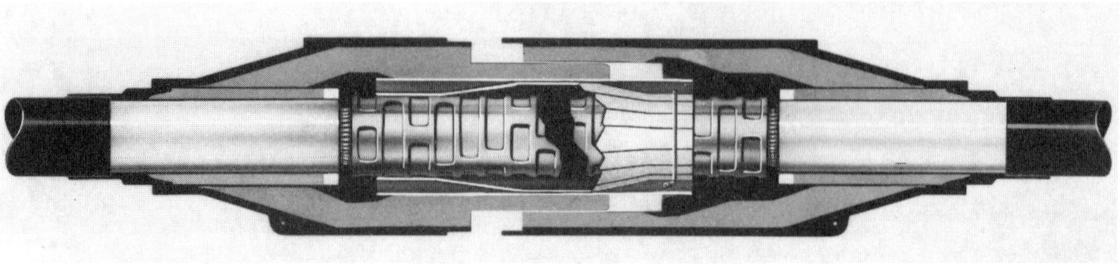

Fig. 28.11 33 kV pre-moulded straight joint for polymeric insulated cable (Courtesy of Amerace Ltd)

continuity is maintained using tinned copper braid. At present these designs are available for 11 and 22 kV cables.

TRANSITION JOINTING

Joints between polymeric and paper insulated cables require designs that prevent the impregnating compound in the paper cable from coming into contact with the polymeric cable insulation, which would cause swelling and loss of mechanical properties. The extruded semiconducting layers in polymeric cables need to be similarly protected, as contact with paper cable impregnant significantly increases their resistivity, impairing their ability to function.

The conductor connectors in transition joints are of the soldered type or have a central barrier in the case of compression ferrules. In either case this prevents movement of the impregnant along the conductor, between the wires, from one side of the joint to the other.

Two basic design approaches exist for transition joints. One is the 'wet' approach where a barrier layer is applied on the polymeric cable before the cable is incorporated into a conventional impregnated tape and resin insulated design as shown in fig. 28.6. In the other, 'dry', variant a barrier is applied in the paper insulated cable and then an essentially polymeric cable design is used. This is generally becoming accepted as the preferred method.

Various barriers have been successfully employed in resin and tape insulated joints e.g. varnished terylene, silicone rubber and PTFE. Heat shrinkable and stretched elastomer designs use the type of compounds formulated to provide good resistance to impregnating compounds.

Resin insulated and stretched elastomer transition joints are available for 11 and 22 kV systems; taped and heat shrinkable joints extend to 33 kV operation.

Chapter 29

Testing of Distribution Cables

The chief emphasis in testing centres around two aspects: (a) that any new design of cable will perform satisfactorily for a reasonable life-time and (b) that cables as manufactured meet specification requirements for quality. The reasons for some tests are obvious, e.g. conductor resistance and minimum thickness of important components, and these parameters can readily be specified and measured. The power factor of high voltage cables is important because of the economic cost of losses. However, testing to determine incipient faults has often had to be developed by experience over a long period, e.g. application of excessive voltage may itself create more incipient faults than it detects.

The main IEC and British Standards concerned with testing are given in chapter 7, and it will be seen that they are comprehensive. In referring to them it should also be noted that the tests to be carried out on each type of cable are included in the basic cable standards. For some tests complete detail is given in the cable standard, but for many cross-reference is made, as appropriate, to the separate standards for tests, often for details of the methods of testing and sometimes also for the requirements to be met. Although national requirements still differ in some respects, there is a general move towards adoption of the IEC standards, especially for polymeric cables. Nevertheless, as the IEC basis represents a consensus of opinion and is slow to evolve, it is often the case that national requirements are more severe for some specific details. Some reference to differences is made below, but on the whole the outline quoted is related to the IEC basis as given in IEC 55–1 for paper cables and IEC 502 for polymeric cables.

Most national and IEC standards cater for tests in four categories:

(a) 'routine tests' by the manufacturer on every finished length of cable (or, for spark testing, during manufacture) to ensure compliance with construction requirements and demonstrate the integrity of the cable.

(b) 'special tests' or 'sample tests' which are not practicable on every complete length of cable. They are made on samples of cable to represent production batches and provide a periodic check on manufacturing consistency. The term 'special test' is used in IEC standards, but the same tests are described as sample tests in British Standards, where they are divided into 'regular sample tests' and 'special sample tests' according to how frequently they are to be carried out.

(c) 'type tests' to be carried out during the development of a new grade of insulation or cable design to establish performance characteristics. They are not repeated unless changes are made which could alter these characteristics.

(d) site tests after installation.

Tests on materials taken from the cables may be included in the type tests but in addition there are standards for the materials themselves, as purchased or produced by the manufacturer, and also standards for methods of tests on materials. Reference to the important areas of materials testing has been made in chapter 3 and this chapter is mainly confined to tests on cables.

COMMENTS ON INDIVIDUAL TESTS FOR CABLES

Dimensions

Great care is necessary to obtain accurate and reproducible results and reference should be made to the appropriate specification for details of the technique and equipment necessary, e.g. ordinary or special micrometer, diameter tape, or microscope.

Insulation resistance and capacitance

Numerical results, for insulation resistance and capacitance, in terms of low or high values give little guidance on the quality of paper cables because they are predominantly related to the types of material used and the processing conditions. Although no figures are included in cable specifications, tests are usually carried out by cable manufacturers on individual cable lengths because they give a good indication of consistency of manufacture.

Similar remarks apply to polymeric cables but there are type test requirements for the insulation resistance of low voltage cables at working temperature in IEC 502, and BS 6346 includes routine tests at ambient temperature.

High voltage tests

For paper insulated cables, application of a high voltage provides probably the most searching test for any defects and it is also useful for cables with polymeric insulation, though with this insulation the measurement of partial discharge at a little above working voltage is possibly more significant. When testing at a cable factory it is convenient to use a.c. but for testing complete installations on site the use of d.c. is more practicable. Most specifications, e.g. IEC 55–1 and 502, permit the use of d.c. for factory tests at a level of 2.4 times the a.c. voltage.

The choice of voltage level always poses a problem because (a) if too high it could cause incipient damage which might affect subsequent service life and (b) breakdown under high voltage is time dependent. For example paper cables will withstand around ten times working voltage for short periods but the breakdown level falls to about 65% in 50–100 hours. By the end of this time the level has fallen to an asymptotic value and it used to be common practice to carry out a number of voltage versus time to breakdown (VTB) tests at various voltage levels to determine the 100 hours value. However, whilst such tests provide useful technical data for development purposes, the results have little relevance for assessment of service life. This is because the expansion and contraction of the impregnant during load cycles has an important effect, particularly in the case of non-pressurised cables in the 10–30 kV range.

Dielectric power factor (dielectric loss angle)

Although the power factor is quite low for paper cables and is even lower for PE and XLPE insulated cables, it does represent some loss in the energy distributed. Limits are therefore prescribed in the routine tests for paper cables of 8.7/15 kV and above, and also in type tests for PE and XLPE cables for 3.6/6 kV and above, and PVC or EPR cables of 6/10 kV and above. Power factor generally increases with voltage and although it also rises fairly sharply towards maximum operating temperature the minimum is usually around the middle of the operating temperature range. Limits are specified over a range of conditions in each case. In paper cables the check of increase with voltage is largely a test of the quality of impregnation as such increase indicates ionisation in voids.

As discussed in chapter 20, special formulations of PVC are required for high voltage cables because with standard grades the power factor may rise sharply between a mid-range temperature and operating temperature. This is covered by specification of a maximum value at 85 °C for the product of permittivity and power factor together with a requirement that the power factor at 80 °C must not exceed the value at 60 °C.

Impulse voltage tests

Switching operations or lightning may cause high transient or surge voltages to appear occasionally on cable systems and the ability to accommodate them has become a normal part of type test procedures. The test is performed on cable heated to maximum conductor temperature (tolerance −0, +5 °C) and after application of ten positive and ten negative impulses at the withstand level the same sample is subjected to a high voltage test. Some specifications require only three positive and negative impulses. In order to ensure that the sample tested is in a condition similar to cable in service, the testing is carried out on a sample which has had cycles of bending. Impulse testing is restricted to paper cables of 8.7/15 kV and above and polymeric cables of 3.6/6 kV and above. The IEC withstand voltage requirements are as follows.

Rated voltages (U_0/U)	kV	3.6/6	6/10	8.7/15	12/20	18/30
Impulse voltages	kV	60	75	95	125	170

Bending test

The ability of cables to bend during drumming and installation operations, without undue distortion or damage to any of the components, is an important requirement for any cable. Features of particular significance are damage to the insulation of paper cables and disturbance of the screen on all types of cable.

The test is carried out with a sufficient length of cable to produce a complete turn around a drum and normally comprises three complete reversed bending cycles at a radius which is more severe than the smallest permissible bending radius during installation. The radii are given in appendix A17. An exception is that only two cycles are required for smooth aluminium sheathed cables, a circumstance arising from the amount of sheath buckling which may occur with cables having a smooth sheath and which could affect the interpretation of the results.

After bending, the sample is submitted to a high voltage test and polymeric cables above specific voltages are also tested for partial discharge. There is a requirement for visual examination of the lead sheath, armour and protective finish of paper cables. British practice in BS 6480 also requires a visual examination of the insulation, with limits for disturbance and damage to individual papers. However, IEC specifications cater for any damage to the insulation and screens on all types of cables to be assessed by passing the electrical high voltage and, when appropriate, the partial discharge test.

For paper cables the bending test is a separate test in the category of special tests (special sample test in BS 6480). For polymeric cables, however, it is part of the type test sequence in which various tests are carried out on the same cable sample.

The general national and international specifications cater for testing at normal ambient temperature (10–25 °C) but special attention may need to be given to the insulation and protective finishes for cables to be installed in geographical regions having very low temperatures. This is covered by user requirements.

Drainage from paper insulation

The test applies to non-draining cables only and the IEC special test procedure is based on a 300 mm sample open at both ends. After heating in an oven for 8 hours to maximum conductor operating temperature, the amount of compound drainage must not exceed 1.5% of the interior volume of the metal sheath. British practice in BS 6480, where the test is a special sample test, and also the IEC type test require a longer sample of 900 mm, sealed at both ends, but with sufficient space at the lower end to collect drained compound. The heating period is 7 days. The test requirement is 3.0% maximum up to and including 3.8/6.6 kV and 2.5% for higher voltage cables. In this test the temperature condition is more severe than that arising in service because the heating is from the outside of the cable.

Tests under fire conditions

The test specified in IEC Publication 332: Part 1 and BS 4066: Part 1, which relate to flame propagation on a single vertical cable, may be required on cables having appropriate types of oversheath, i.e. PVC and suitable elastomeric compounds. This form of test has been used for many years, with some variations in the details over that period.

Now, however, IEC 332: Part 3 and BS 4066: Part 3 recognise that flame propagation in cable installations depends upon the amount of cable in the location and the disposition of the cables with respect to each other, as well as on the properties of the component materials. These specifications include three categories of test conditions, with variation of the density of non-metallic cable components as one of the differences in the test conditions between the three categories.

A test to measure the amount of hydrochloric acid gas evolved during combustion of component materials has also been standardised in IEC Publication 754: Part 1 and BS 6425: Part 1. BS 6724 also includes a test for smoke emission, which is on the lines of a test under consideration for international standardisation. These tests and the test specified in BS 4066: Part 3 are not applicable to the general range of standard cables but only to those specially designed to meet them. BS 6724 is the only British Standard which calls for them at present, and there are no international standards for distribution cables having the requisite properties.

These tests may be invoked in users' specifications for cables outside the scope of BS 6724, for particular applications, but then the total cable design and the choice of materials for each component have to be specially considered. London Underground Ltd, for example, specifies a smoke emission test and did so for a number of years before a similar test was specified in BS 6724.

The background and some details of the tests are covered in chapter 6.

MEASUREMENT OF PARTIAL DISCHARGE

Partial discharges in a cable are caused by the breakdown of the gas contained within voids in the insulation. The voids may be either dielectric bounded or at the interface between dielectric and conducting screens. The voltage at which the breakdown first occurs is known as the discharge inception voltage. The stress in the void is directly proportional to the relative permittivity of the insulation and, because the breakdown strength of a gas is much less than for solid insulation, the void can break down, causing discharges at voltages much lower than the operating stress of the cable.

For many years the quality of paper insulated cables has been assessed by measurement of the dielectric loss angle against increasing voltage. This is possible because of the even distribution of the losses due to the lapped construction of the paper dielectric. However, in extruded dielectric the random distribution and sizes of voids no longer allows characterisation of discharge by measurement of dielectric losses.

Most national and international specifications now require measurement of partial discharge and define the maximum level of discharge acceptable at particular test voltages.

Basic test circuits

The breakdown of a void within a dielectric can be likened to the charging and discharging of a capacitor. As the test voltage rises, a level is reached when the void discharges to a lower voltage. The voltage magnitude across the void then increases until it reaches the discharge inception voltage and discharges once again. The loss of charge caused by the discharge in the void results in a voltage pulse with a very fast rise time superimposed on the high voltage supply. The basis of all discharge detection circuits is to separate the voltage pulse, which may only be microvolts, from the test supply of kilovolts.

Three standard measuring circuits are shown in fig. 29.1. In each circuit Cb represents a discharge free blocking capacitor, Cx the test sample and Z the detecting impedance. The test circuit A is the most widely used and has the advantage that if a breakdown occurs in the cable under test no damage occurs to the detection equipment. Following a discharge in the test cable Cx, a pulse with a fast rise time is produced in the circuit containing Cx, Cb and Z. The voltage developed across Z is fed into a discharge detector amplifier.

Method C is a bridge circuit which can be used with two samples of similar capacitance. No discharge-free blocking capacitance is required and when well bal-

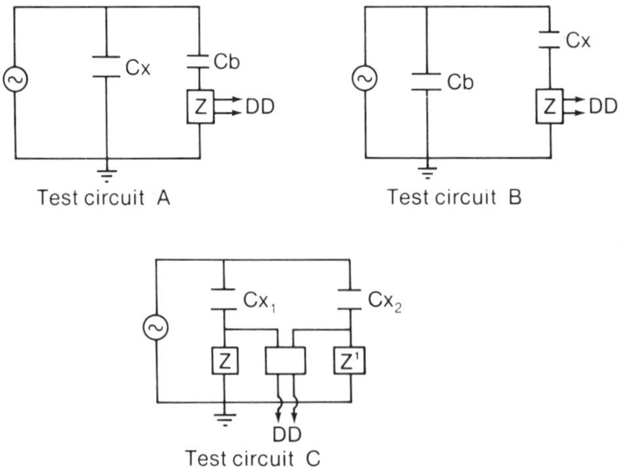

Fig. 29.1 Three circuits for partial discharge measurements

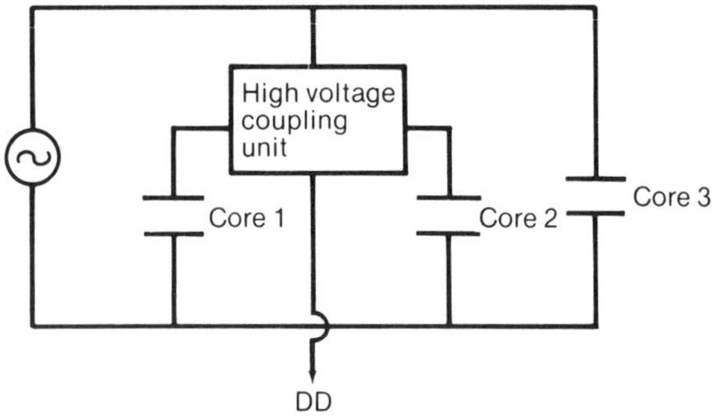

Fig. 29.2 Refined circuit for discharge measurement, with input unit at test potential

anced the circuit offers good rejection of external noise. A further refinement of this type of circuit has been developed in which the input units are at the test potential (fig. 29.2). This makes it possible to test any two cores of a 3-core cable with both screens at earth potential, giving extra rejection of external interference.

Detection impedances
The detection impedance Z may consist of pure resistance or an inductance which may be tuned to a particular detection frequency. This is the system used in the range of detectors developed by the Electrical Research Association, particularly in models 3–5. Various input units are available to match the capacitance of the cable under test.

Calibration of detectors

The magnitude of any given discharge can be determined by direct comparison with a known size of calibration pulse which is produced by injecting a step wave in series with a known capacitance. This is usually done before the test voltage is applied and the size of pulse for a particular picocoulomb level is noted. With this method the amplifier gain controls should not be altered until the test is completed. A more accurate method of direct calibration is to use a discharge-free high voltage capacitor to inject the calibration pulse permanently across the test sample during the test.

Indirect methods are widely used where the calibration pulse is injected across the measuring impedance Z. During the discharge test the calibration signal is varied until the magnitude corresponds to the discharge appearing from the test sample. A direct calibrator may be used after completion of the test to check the actual value.

Discharge measurement technique

Detectors

Most commercially available discharge detectors consist of an amplifier, a CRT display, a direct or indirect calibrator and sometimes a picocoulomb meter. The amplifier determines the response of the detector to discharge pulses in a cable and generally falls into two categories, narrow band and medium to wide band. The simplest indentification between the two types is by the output response to an input signal. A narrow band detector has a fully symmetrical response A, whilst a medium or wide band detector has an asymmetrical response of the alpha type (fig. 29.3).

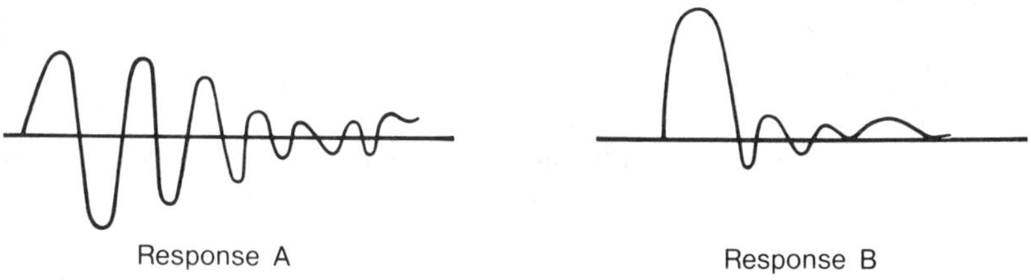

Fig. 29.3 Discharge detector response: A, symmetrical; B, asymmetrical

Generally, in cable testing, narrow band amplifiers can only be used in conjunction with cables terminated in their characteristic impedance, to prevent reflections. Medium or wide detectors with an alpha response can be used without resistors provided that the negative peak does not exceed specified limits, usually 15%.

Disturbance due to external interference

It is desirable to measure the smallest possible discharges in a cable in order to establish the existence of voids that are small in size. However, the smallest partial discharge level which can be detected is determined by the sensitivity of the detector. Under normal factory or site conditions, this sensitivity may be restricted by background noise, which is usually due to electrical interference originating outside the discharge detector and the measuring circuit. It often shows up similarly to discharge in voids, and can be up to tens of picocoulombs in size. Such electrical interference tends to create a great amount of difficulty in discharge measurement.

Interference control techniques

The commonly used interference control techniques are as follows.

(a) Good installation: proper layout of the test circuit is required to avoid unnecessary earth loops and sharp edges. Earth loops can be avoided by correct grounding techniques, i.e. all of the grounds which affect the measuring circuit are returned to one solid single earth point.
(b) Use of a high voltage filter: this is basically a low pass filter in the high voltage lead. It is purposely designed to give a high rejection ratio to suppress external interference coming from the main supply. It also presents a low impedance to the supply and a high impedance to the discharge pulses.
(c) Use of screened enclosure: a properly designed screened enclosure (Faraday cage) is widely used to suppress interference caused by electromagnetic and electrostatic radiation. Its disadvantages are the high cost and space constraints which are imposed by the enclosure.
(d) Use of balanced circuit: this is valuable in that noise originating in the power source or noise common to both test samples will be rejected. In order to achieve a high rejection ratio, the two samples must be almost identical in capacitance and similar in physical dimensions and length.

Superposition of discharge pulses

When testing a long length of cable, in excess of 100 m, there is a possible measurement error due to the addition or subtraction of discharge pulses. This is known as superposition.

Following a discharge, two equal pulses are propagated in opposite directions towards the cable ends. The pulse travelling towards the far end, if open circuited, is reflected and then travels in the same direction as the other pulse towards the detector, but with a time delay. If the time delay between the two pulses is less than the resolution of the detector (defined by the smallest time interval between two equal pulses which can just be seen separated) superposition of pulses can take place. Depending on the response characteristics of the discharge detector, superposition of the direct and reflected pulses may result in an increase in the amplitude of the response or may even cause complete cancellation of the response.

Elimination of superposition

Pulse superposition errors can be eliminated by terminating the cable with a resistor of equal value to the characteristic impedance of the cable. More recently, detectors have been developed to eliminate superposition problems by switching out the input to the detector for a short time after receiving the first discharge signal. The reflected pulse, following some time behind, is thus rejected from the measuring circuit. After a suitable period the circuit is reopened to allow further discharge signals to the detector.

Attenuation of discharge pulses

Pulses travelling down long lengths of cable are attenuated both in amplitude and charge, thus causing distortion and lengthening of the pulses. Partial discharge detectors which have been designed to give high resolution may not cope with the long, low amplitude pulses and give rise to measurement errors. Measurement techniques have to be adopted, therefore, to compensate for attenuation problems.

Attenuation factors

The attenuation factor α is defined as the ratio of the magnitude of a signal, injected at the near end of the cable to give a specified response on the detector, to the magnitude of the signal required to be injected at the far end of the cable to give the same response on the detector. If a partial discharge measurement is made first from one end of the cable, giving a response q_1 for a particular discharge, and then from the other end of the cable, giving a response q_2 for the same discharge, the true discharge magnitude Q is given as

$$Q = \alpha(q_1 q_2)^{1/2}$$

However, attenuation factors are only correct when the cable is terminated in its characteristic impedance. Measurements from the far end of an open-circuit cable may show no apparent attenuation, yet further into the cable as much as 8 dB attenuation may occur (fig. 29.4).

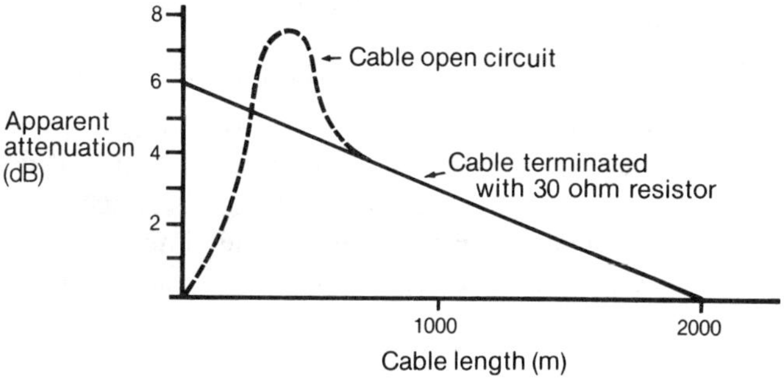

Fig. 29.4 Importance of terminating cables correctly for deriving attenuation factors

Continuous scanning methods

At one time it was a common practice to monitor the partial discharge level of high voltage polymeric cables at the time of the extrusion of the insulation by passing the core through detection equipment before drumming it. In this apparatus tubular electrodes are contained in a non-metallic tube of 6–20 m length, according to cable voltage, with the high voltage electrode in the centre and earthed electrodes near the ends. The tube is filled with a liquid of low conductivity, usually deionised water.

The technique has the advantage that the quality of the core is known immediately and any remedial action necessary, e.g. to extrusion conditions, can be taken quickly. However, for a variety of reasons, continuous scanning has largely been replaced by the separate block test method in which complete core or cable lengths are tested on drums. These reasons include the following.

(a) The most usual scanning procedure, as given above, is not suitable for use with screened cores because of overheating of the screen by the current which it carries. It is therefore necessary to use a more elaborate and complicated electrode system pioneered by Kreuger. The core is passed through a series of wheels, two of which are at high voltage and others are earthed, so that the drop in voltage is along the screen instead of into the deionised water. For safety purposes the whole of the cable-handling equipment, including the drum stand, has to be insulated from earth and a large enclosure is involved. More polymeric cables now have extruded screens and so, if scanning is required, there is a greater need for the more sophisticated test equipment.

(b) Scanning techniques were originally developed for polyethylene insulation and with the pressure curing methods for thermosetting insulation there is less tendency for large voids to be present. Improved manufacturing techniques, together with the need for clean insulation, have also considerably reduced the risk of faults due to high discharge level.

(c) When the dielectric screen is of the tape and varnish type the majority of partial discharge faults occur at the interface, and so a second test on the finished cable is still necessary after application of the screen.

(d) When the scanning procedure was first used the block testing method was not fully reliable. Subsequent developments overcame the initial problems and it is now the better technique.

Location of discharge site

An advantage of the scanning method is that the position of discharge is known immediately and can be marked on the core. After block testing it is necessary to carry out other tests for location. On application of high voltage, discharge pulses travel from voids in two directions. By measuring the time delay between direct receipt and receipt after reflection from the far end of the cable, the position can be derived (chapter 30).

Further developments in discharge measurement

Two developments are of importance. One is to provide discrimination between pulses originating in the test sample and those originating elsewhere; the other is aimed entirely at eliminating random background noise.

Pulse discrimination system

In this procedure a pulse discrimination system eliminates external interference from discharge measurements undertaken in a noisy environment. Using the circuit shown in fig. 29.5, the polarity of a current pulse in the test sample is compared with that in a parallel coupling capacitor. If there is an output when the two pulses have opposite polarity, it indicates a discharge in the test sample. A discrimination control module is provided to allow the operator to distinguish the discharges from either internal or external sources and from the sample or the coupling capacitor. This system can be used with transformers that are not discharge free, and any corona generated externally will be rejected.

Signal averaging system

This system employs the standard discharge detection circuits shown in fig. 29.1. A radio interference receiver or conventional discharge detector is used to provide an input to a discharge processor, which mainly consists of a signal averaging device and a display oscilloscope. Signal averaging is a method of signal analysis used to recover repetitive discharge signals buried in random noise.

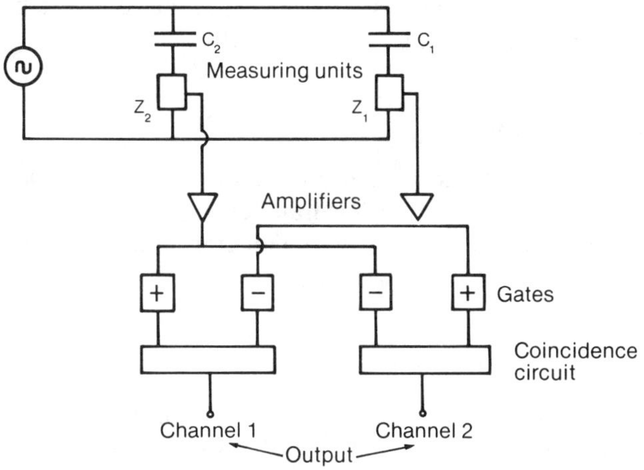

Fig. 29.5 Discharge measurement circuit for pulse discrimination system

The signal from the detector is fed to the discharge processor. It is then processed by the signal averager. The averaging system used operates by sampling the incoming signal digitally at a number of points of the applied 50 Hz waveform. The signal level at each point is stored, and after sampling over a number of selected cycles the average value of the signal at each point is determined. The noise is random and is averaged to zero. The output of the discharge processor then represents a probability of discharge at each sampling point.

When used in conjunction with the ratio interference receiver, the system is particularly useful for measurements on installed cables. The receiver is used principally to tune to a detection frequency with a high signal to noise ratio favourable to site conditions.

The system can provide excellent sensitivity, detecting down to very low discharge magnitudes, but calibration of the actual levels of discharge is difficult. However, the equipment provides an excellent method of determining whether discharges are present.

Future trends

With the advance in microelectronics technology, there will no doubt be further developments in computing techniques of signal processing, to store and analyse the incoming signal and to provide greater information such as the position of site of discharge, the true magnitude of the discharge and possibly the nature of the discharge.

ROUTINE TESTS ON CABLES

Tests during manufacture

Although useful to the manufacturer for quality control purposes, tests during processing are not significant to the user. An exception is that because of the size and weight of distribution cables it is not practicable for any tests on complete cables to be carried out with the cable immersed in water. High voltage a.c. spark tests are therefore made on polymeric insulation and sheaths.

Conductor resistance test

The resistance of every conductor is measured and corrected to a standard length at 20 °C. The main sources of error are inaccurate length and the sensitivity to temperature. Finished cables cool slowly and the conductors tend to be at above ambient temperature.

High voltage test

The test requires a 5 min application of an a.c. voltage of $2.5U_0 + 2$ kV for cables rated up to 3.6/6 kV and $2.5U_0$ for cables of 6/10 kV and above. For multicore non-screened cables the voltage is applied between conductors and also between any conductor and sheath. Cables with individually screened cores are tested from conductor to sheath only.

Power factor test for high voltage paper cables

This test applies only to screened cables of U_0 8.7 kV and above. The power factor is measured at 0.5, 1.25 and 2.0 times U_0. The value at $0.5U_0$ must not exceed 0.006 and the differences between the values measured at $0.5U_0$ and $1.25U_0$ and between the values at $1.25U_0$ and $2U_0$ are required not to exceed the limits given in table 29.1. British practice in BS 6480 requires the test only for 19/33 kV cables and the limits are half of the IEC values (IEC 55–1) given above.

Table 29.1 Maximum increase in power factor between test voltages for paper cables

Test voltage	Mass impregnated		Non-draining	
	U = 15 kV or below	U above 15 kV	U = 15 kV or below	U above 15 kV
$(0.5-1.25)U_0$	0.0010	0.0008	0.0050	0.0040
$(1.25-2.0)U_0$	0.0025	0.0016	0.0100	0.0080

Partial discharge test for high voltage polymeric cables

The test is required by IEC 502 for cables insulated with butyl rubber, PE or XLPE of rated voltage above 1.8/3 kV and with EPR or PVC of rated voltage above 3.6/6 kV. The magnitude of discharge at 1.5 times U_0 must not exceed 20 pC for butyl, EPR, PE or XLPE and 40 pC for PVC.

There are wide variations in national requirements for this test, together with a progresive tendency towards higher test voltages and lower permissible amounts of discharge. BS 6622 specifies 10 pC as a maximum at $1.5U_0$ for XLPE and EPR insulated cables in the voltage range from 3.8/6.6 kV to 19/33 kV. In this standard the 3.8/6.6 kV EPR cables are of screened design whereas in IEC 502 screening is not mandatory for 3.6/6 kV EPR cables.

SPECIAL TESTS ON PAPER CABLES

These cover the tests given below in accordance with details already quoted:

Measurements of dimensions, primarily the thicknesses of insulation, lead sheath, non-metallic sheaths and armour

Bending test, followed by a voltage test and sample examination

Drainage test, for cable with non-draining insulation

In BS 6480 most of the measurements of dimensions are regular sample tests and the bending and drainage tests are special sample tests.

SPECIAL TESTS ON POLYMERIC CABLES

Conductor examination, for compliance with IEC 228

Measurement of dimensions, including insulation, metallic and non-metallic sheaths and armour; also overall diameter, if specified

High voltage test, only applicable to cables of rated voltages above 3.6/6 kV and requires a voltage of $3U_0$ for 4 hours

Hot set test for EPR and XLPE insulation: conditions are prescribed for a test to check that the material has been properly cured to give the required thermal properties

In British Standards the conductor examination, most of the dimensional checks and the hot set test are regular sample tests, while the 4 hour voltage test is a special sample test. BS 6622 (6.6–33 kV cables) also provides for measurement of the resistivity of extruded semiconducting screens and the cold strippability of extruded semiconducting insulation screens, when this is required, as special sample tests.

TYPE TESTS FOR PAPER CABLES

It is with paper cables that the history of use at the higher voltages is the longest and the large user requirements show the greatest variations. British Standards are more demanding than IEC 55-1 which is summarised below.

Power factor/temperature test
The test applies to cables of U_0 8.7 kV and above and measurements are taken up to 10 °C above rated operating temperature. The limits are as follows: 20–60 °C, 0.006; 70 °C, 0.013; 75 °C, 0.016; 80 °C, 0.019; 85 °C, 0.023.

Dielectric security tests

The tests apply only to screened cables of 8.7 kV and above and are in two parts.

High voltage a.c. test
This test covers a period of 4 hours with 4 U_0 for mass-impregnated cables and $3U_0$ for non-draining cables.

Bending/impulse a.c. test
Reference has already been made to general conditions applying to the bending and impulse tests. The impulse test is carried out at maximum permissible operating temperature with a voltage of 95, 125 or 170 kV for cables with U_0 equal to respectively 8.7, 12 and 18 kV. The subsequent a.c. voltage application is at the same voltage as for the routine test.

Other tests

These comprise a drainage test as previously detailed together with non-electrical tests on non-metallic oversheaths.

British requirements

The most important difference in BS 6480 is that, although type tests are restricted to 19/33 kV cables, there is an onerous requirement for a lengthy loading cycle test requiring a minimum of 30 m of cable. A vertical rise of 2 m to the terminations is necessary and non-draining cables must have a vertical loop at least 6 m high. The installation has to undergo at least 100 cycles at 25.4 kV (1.33 times rated voltage) to a temperature of 70–75 °C. Each cycle comprises 6 hours heating and 18 hours cooling and not more than five cycles may be carried out in seven days. Hot and cold power factors at 25.4 kV are measured and if graphical plotting shows stability the test may be terminated after 100 cycles; otherwise it is continued up to 250 cycles.

TYPE TESTS FOR POLYMERIC CABLES

Type tests for polymeric cables are still in process of evolution and reference should be made to chapter 25 for an indication of the way in which knowledge of fundamental requirements is leading to a better understanding of the way that testing should be undertaken. Although the characteristics of IEC 502, as given below, are generally accepted internationally, there are many other additional specific tests which are favoured by different countries.

Electrical tests

Applicability
Tests are required for cables insulated with butyl, PE or XLPE of rated voltage above 1.8/3 kV and PVC or EPR of rated voltage above 3.6/6 kV.

Test sequence
In general the tests are required successively on the same sample, of 10–15 m length between accessories, with a sequence of

(a) partial discharge test
(b) bending test followed by repeat of (a)
(c) power factor/voltage test
(d) power factor/temperature test
(e) three heat cycles to a conductor temperature 10 °C above maximum rated temperature for the insulation; the heating is for 2 hours with 4 hours cooling
(f) partial discharge test
(g) impulse test at 5 °C above maximum rated temperature for the insulation
(h) 15 min a.c. test at the routine test voltage
(i) a 4 hour a.c. test at $3U_0$

Electrical test for low voltage cables
For cables rated at lower voltages than stipulated above the sequential testing is limited to

(a) insulation resistance at room temperature
(b) insulation resistance at operating temperature
(c) a 4 hour a.c. test at $3U_0$

Non-electrical tests

A wide variety of tests is stipulated in IEC 502 covering such fields as

(a) measurement of dimensions
(b) mechanical properties of the insulation material before and after ageing
(c) ageing tests on complete cable samples to test compatibility between materials
(d) specific tests for the insulation material
(e) test for behaviour of PVC at low temperatures

There are also trends towards additional tests to limit the amount of contamination in the insulation and for measurement of void content.

TESTS ON CABLES WITH SPECIAL PERFORMANCE IN FIRES

Cables designed to avoid some of the effects produced by the more standard cables when they are involved in fires are subject to the same tests as apply to standard cables of the same voltage rating with the same insulation, including tests on components in so far as these are the same as in more conventional cables. However, different requirements apply to the components that differ from those of conventional cables and the cables are subject to additional tests related specifically to the performance in fires.

In part 2 reference is made to requirements related to fire performance applying to cables for applications such as ships installations, railway systems and offshore installations but, within the scope of part 3, the British Standard for cables specially designed for fire performance is BS 6724, which is for wire armoured cables of rated voltages up to 1.9/3.3 kV with low emission of smoke and corrosive gases when affected by fire.

The fire-related tests specified in BS 6724 are as follows.

Corrosive and acid gas emission

This test, in accordance with BS 6425: Part 1, is made separately on samples of insulation, bedding for armour, any fillers and binders and the oversheath. The test measures the amount of hydrochloric acid gas (HCl) generated when a sample of given mass is burnt under specified conditions. The requirement of BS 6724 is that the HCl generated should not exceed 0.5% of the mass of the sample for each component.

Fire test on single cable

This is the test to BS 4066: Part 1 made on a sample of cable 600 mm long clamped vertically. One or two Bunsen or propane gas burners are used to ignite the sample (two burners for cables exceeding 50 mm in diameter), the time of application of the flames depending upon the mass per unit length of the cable. When the burners are removed the flames should extinguish before reaching within 50 mm of the top clamp, which amounts to 425 mm from the position where the flames impinge on the cable.

IEC 502 and British Standards for cables with extruded insulations provide for this test to be made, as a type test, on cables with PVC coverings if it is desired to claim compliance as a feature of the design. Generally PVC oversheathed cables will meet the test, but they would not meet the combination of fire tests specified in BS 6724.

Fire test on multiple cables

This test is to BS 4066: Part 3. It is made on a set of cables, each 3.5 m long, installed vertically, touching or spaced according to their size, and approaches much more closely a test on a full-scale installation than the test to Part 1 of the standard. The fire source is a multiple jet propane gas burner with controlled fuel and air input and a special test rig is required. BS 6724 requires the test category to be that involving a volume per metre of non-metallic cable materials of 1.5 litres. The requirement is that, after the cables have been exposed to the burner for a specified period, after which the fire source is stopped, the flames should not propagate up the cables to a distance greater than 2.5 m above the burner.

Smoke emission test

Samples of cable are arranged over a fire source consisting of a tray of alcohol, which is set alight in a test chamber which has come to be known as a 'three metre cube' because of its dimensions. A specified light source and a photocell at opposite sides of the chamber are used to make measurements from which the light absorbance of the smoke generated is calculated.

BS 6724 includes an appendix which describes how, by performing these tests as type tests on cables of selected sizes, type approval for the range of sizes can be obtained.

SITE TESTS AFTER INSTALLATION

The IEC Standards require a d.c. test at a voltage based on 70% of that permissible for factory tests, i.e.

(a) paper cables up to 3.6/6 kV, 5 min at $4.2U_0 + 3.36$ kV
(b) paper cables of 6/10 kV and above, 5 min at $4.2U_0$ kV
(c) polymeric cables, 15 min at $4U_0$ kV

In some countries doubts have arisen about the effects of d.c. voltage on polymeric cables and IEC 502 allows alternative a.c. testing, if agreed between the parties concerned, consisting of

either the system voltage U applied between conductors and screens for 5 min
or the normal voltage U_0 applied between conductors and screens for 24 hours

BS 6622 does not provide for this alternative for new installations, but does recommend that for installations which have been in use the manufacturers should be consulted for test conditions to take account of the particular circumstances.

Chapter 30

Fault Incidence and Location for Distribution Cables

No matter how carefully a cable is designed and manufactured it is exposed to many hazards once it leaves the controlled environment of the factory and is installed as part of an underground electricity distribution system. Table 30.1 shows the total number of underground system faults recorded in the UK during the period 1975–80, together with the average length of cable in commission during the same period.

Although 132 kV is now considered to be a distribution, or subtransmission, voltage, the types of cable, methods of installation and fault characteristics are similar to those of transmission cables and 132 kV is therefore covered in chapter 43. Serving fault location and leak location which are often required on transmission cables are also included in chapter 43.

Table 30.2 shows an analysis of the major causes of failure of underground distribution systems from which it can be seen that 'accidental contact' and 'ageing' are the main known categories.

Table 30.1 Distribution cable statistics, 1975–80

Voltage	Average length in service	Number of underground faults		
		Cable	Joints	Others
20–66 kV	19000 km	2011	342	377
6–11 kV	118000 km	23252	3752	5656
240/415 V	245000 km	–	–	231030[a]

[a] Includes cables and joints

Table 30.2 Major causes of failure of underground distribution systems

Cause	Percentage of total number of faults		
	20–66 kV	6–11 kV	240–415 V
Accidental contact	28.3	46.8	45.5
Ageing/wear	27.3	20.0	9.8
Faulty installation	7.1	6.9	3.2
Lightning	2.5	3.7	0.0
Subsidence	2.9	1.9	0.9
Others	31.9	20.7	40.6

'Accidental contact' often occurs during excavation operations on, or adjacent to, the route of a cable and frequently results in only minor damage so that some considerable time may elapse before the insulation deteriorates to the extent that the circuit protection operates. Whilst most cable faults arise from failure of the insulation, due either to ingress of moisture or loss of dielectric impregnant, faults in joints and terminations may be caused by overheating, subsidence and thermomechanical movement. Other causes of failure include lightning and switching surges, corrosion, vibration and internal ionisation.

The characteristics and methods of location of faults on all high voltage systems are similar and they are therefore considered together, but faults on 240/415 V systems present completely different problems and their characteristics and methods of location are covered separately. Irrespective of the voltage level, efficient fault location demands a systematic approach if time and cost are to be kept to a minimum and table 30.3 lists the four main stages required. Depending on the type of cable, the fault characteristics and the available test equipment, greater or lesser importance may be attached to one stage rather than another.

Table 30.3 Four stages of systematic fault location

Stage	Operation
(a) Diagnose	Confirm existence of fault to determine whether stage (b) is required before stage (c)
(b) Precondition	Change fault characteristic (if necessary) to suit equipment available for stage (c)
(c) Prelocate	Test(s) from cable terminals to obtain approximate fault location
(d) Pinpoint	Test(s) in locality indicated by stage (c) (usually from above ground) to confirm precise location of fault

FAULT CHARACTERISTICS

Faults can be divided into series or shunt types. Series faults occur where the continuity of one or more of the metallic elements of a cable, either conductors or sheath, is impaired. Usually series faults only become apparent when continuity has been lost completely on at least one conductor to cause an open-circuit fault.

Shunt faults occur where the insulation of one or more conductors is damaged. Although shunt faults on belted cables may involve more than one phase, the most common type of fault is the single phase to earth fault. On screened cables all shunt faults are earth faults. Combined shunt and series faults can also occur. Both shunt and series faults can be represented by the equivalent circuit of fig. 30.1 which shows the fault resistance R_f in parallel with a spark gap S/G and a capacitance C_f. The values of all the elements in the equivalent circuit can vary widely and are completely independent of each other. The breakdown voltage V_b, of the spark gap is determined by the separation of the two metallic boundaries of the fault which may be bridged by carbonised insulation in a typical shunt fault or air spaced in an open-circuit series fault. The value of the fault resistance is directly related to the degree of carbonisation of the dielectric and the value of the capacitance varies with the amount of moisture present. Table 30.4 lists the five main types of cable fault. Since

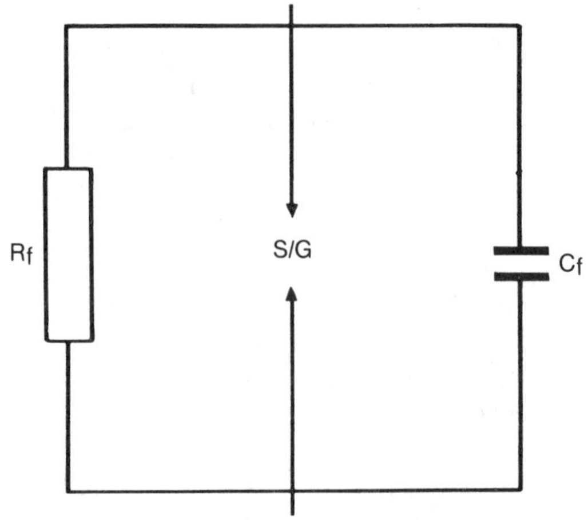

Fig. 30.1 Equivalent circuit of a cable fault

Table 30.4 Definition of fault types

Fault type	Resistance	Spark gap
Series	$\rightarrow \infty$	Breakdown under impulse or d.c.
Low resistance	$< 10Z_0$	Breakdown under impulse if R_f is not too low
High resistance	$> 10Z_0$	Breakdown under impulse
Flashing	$\rightarrow \infty$	Breakdown under impulse or d.c.
Intermittent	∞	Breakdown under prolonged d.c.

most modern methods of prelocation are based on travelling wave principles, rather than the previously used bridge methods, the dividing line between low and high resistance faults is taken as a resistance equal to ten times the surge impedance of the cable under test.

The surge impedance of single-phase and screened cables can be determined using equation (30.1) and the surge impedance of one phase of a 3-phase belted cable, with the other two phases floating, is determined from equation (30.2). The surge impedance of triple extruded XLPE cables with semiconducting screens is given by equation (30.3).

Single-phase or screened cable:

$$Z_0 = \frac{60}{\sqrt{\epsilon}} \log_e\left(\frac{d_c + 2t_c}{d_c}\right) \ (\Omega) \tag{30.1}$$

Three-phase cable:

$$Z_0 = \frac{68}{\sqrt{\epsilon}} \log_e\left(\frac{d_c + 3t_c + t_b}{d_c}\right) \ (\Omega) \tag{30.2}$$

Triple extruded XLPE:

$$Z_0 = \frac{60}{\sqrt{\epsilon}}\left(\log_e\left\{\frac{d_c + 2(t_i + t_c + t_o)}{d_c}\log_e\left[\frac{d_o + 2(t_i + t_c)}{d_c + 2t_i}\right]\right\}\right)^{1/2} \qquad (30.3)$$

where d_c = diameter of core conductor (mm)
t_c = thickness of core insulation (mm)
t_b = thickness of belt insulation (mm)
t_i = thickness of inner screen (mm)
t_o = thickness of outer screen (mm)
ϵ = relative permittivity of insulation

DIAGNOSIS

Usually the first indication of the possible existence of a fault is given by the automatic operation of the circuit protection. Occasionally protection may maloperate and it is therefore advisable to confirm the existence of the fault by applying an insulation test using a voltage test set or a Megger. If the insulation indicates a 'healthy' result the cable continuity should be checked before attempting to re-energise the cable. If the insulation tests shows 'faulty' cable, the value of the fault resistance should be measured with a low voltage instrument such as an AVO, and not a Megger.

The presence of moisture at the fault point can often be detected by reversing the connections to the AVO and checking whether the fault resistance appears to have altered. If moisture is present a difference will be measured in the apparent fault resistance due to the existence of an electrolytic cell within the fault. Continuity should also be measured using a low voltage instrument such as an AVO or, as is now common practice, using a pulse-echo fault locator to 'look' for the far end of the cable. One attraction of the pulse-echo instrument is that it is not necessary to apply a shorting link at the far end, although confirmation that the echo is coming from the far end, and not from an open circuit, is advisable. The main advantage of using a pulse-echo instrument to check continuity is that breaks in the cable sheath, e.g. a cracked joint plumb, can be detected as easily as breaks in the cable cores.

PRECONDITIONING

Depending on the type of equipment available for fault prelocation it may be necessary to attempt to alter the fault characteristics from, say, a high resistance to a low resistance, or from an unstable flashing condition to a stable resistive fault. The fault characteristic can be changed by passing current through the fault to carbonise the insulation, by re-energising the cable or by leaving the cable dead for sufficient time to allow moisture to penetrate. Of these alternatives the first is clearly the most attractive and purpose-built equipments are available, generally known as fault burners.

A fault burner must be able to produce sufficient voltage to initiate breakdown of a high resistance fault but must then be able to supply increasing amounts of current as the fault resistance falls. Table 30.5 lists the various outputs available on a typical fault burner, shown in fig. 30.2. Whilst reasonably successful on paper insulated

Fig. 30.2 Biccotest T108 15 kV fault-burner

Table 30.5 Output level of fault burner

Maximum output voltage	Maximum output current
15.0 kV d.c.	0.4 A
10.0 kV d.c.	0.8 A
5.0 kV d.c.	1.5 A
1.0 kV d.c.	7.5 A
240 V a.c.	15.0 A
100 V a.c.	60.0 A

cables, except for flashing and intermittent faults, fault burning has not proved so effective on cables with polymeric insulation, particularly XLPE.

PRELOCATING

For many years the Murray loop test and other bridge methods[1] were the mainstay of fault prelocation. Although they have now largely been replaced by methods based on travelling wave principles, no text on fault location would be complete without at least a brief mention of them.

The basic Murray loop, shown in fig. 30.3, when balanced gives the distance to the fault as

$$D = \frac{Q}{P + Q} 2L \tag{30.4}$$

where D = distance to fault (m)
L = length of cable (m)
P = fixed arm of bridge
Q = variable arm of bridge

Provided that the power pack is capable of passing a reasonable current through the fault resistance, and the resistance of all the external connections is kept low, the Murray loop will give very accurate results. If the fault resistance is high, and cannot be reduced by fault burning, it is possible to invert the bridge, i.e. interchange the position of the galvanometer and the power pack to increase sensitivity. However, this method of connection is more prone to interference from stray and induced voltages. A compact inverted bridge is shown in fig. 30.4.

Where a cable route is composed of a number of different cable conductor sizes or materials it is necessary to calculate the 'equivalent length' before using any bridge technique. The equivalent length of conductor 1 of cross-section S_1 with material of resistivity ρ_1 in terms of conductor 2 of cross-section S_2 with material of resistivity ρ_2 is given by

$$\frac{\text{equivalent length, core 1}}{\text{actual length, core 1}} = \frac{S_2\rho_1}{S_1\rho_2} \tag{30.5}$$

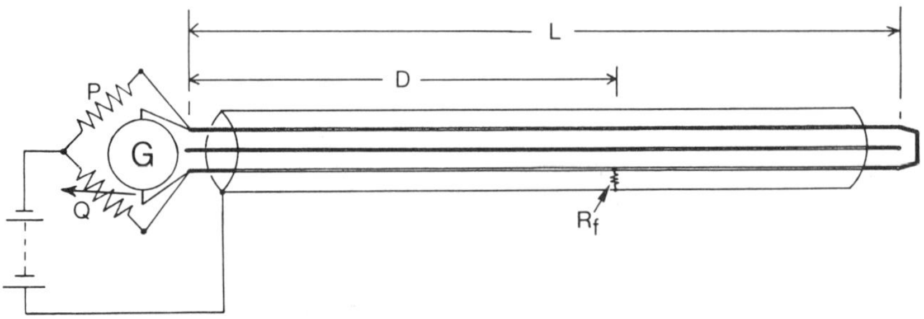

Fig. 30.3 Murray loop test

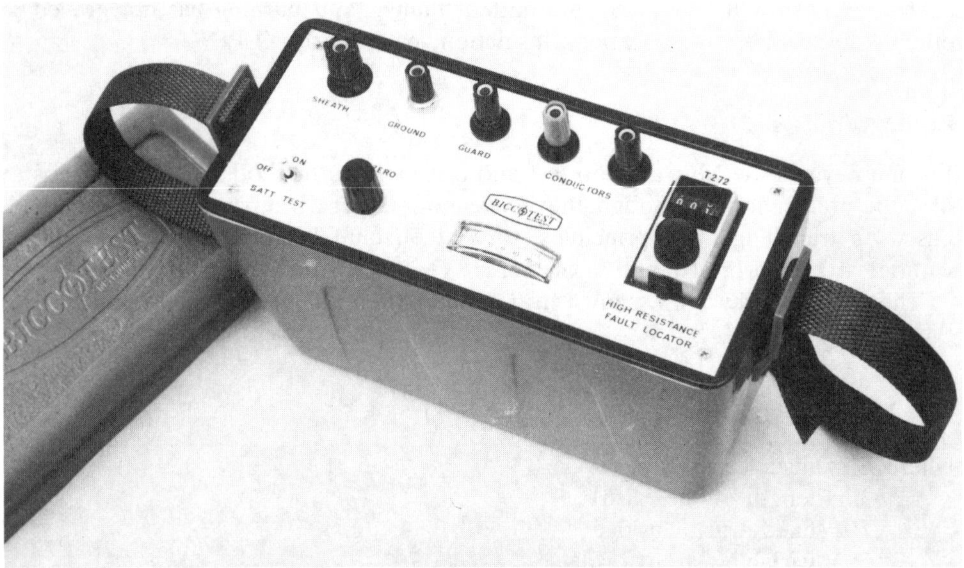

Fig. 30.4 Biccotest T272 high resistance fault locator (inverted bridge)

Care must be taken in converting the 'equivalent' distance to the fault, given by equation (30.5) when the bridge is balanced, into an actual distance if any cable other than the 'reference' type is present between the test end and the fault.

The travelling wave methods of fault location avoid the problems of equivalent length calculations on cable routes of mixed cross-section provided that the cable dielectric is the same throughout the route. The simplest of the travelling wave techniques is the pulse-echo method, illustrated in fig. 30.5. The time interval T (μs) for the low voltage pulse to travel from the pulse generator to the fault and back again can be used to determine the distance to the fault by equation (30.6) if the cable dielectric, or its relative permittivity, is known:

$$D = T\frac{v}{2} \text{ (m)} \tag{30.6}$$

where D = distance to fault
$v = 300/\sqrt{\epsilon}$ = velocity of propagation (m/μs)
ϵ = relative permittivity of cable dielectric

Using the symbols given in equations (30.2) and (30.3) the velocity of propagation for triple extruded XLPE cable is given by

$$v = \frac{300}{\sqrt{\epsilon}} \left\{ \frac{\log_e \left[\dfrac{d_c + 2(t_i + t_c + t_o)}{d_c} \right]}{\log_e \left[\dfrac{d_c + 2(t_i + t_c)}{d_c + 2t_i} \right]} \right\}^{1/2} \text{(m/μs)} \qquad (30.7)$$

The pulse-echo method depends for its success on recognising the reflection, or 'echo', from the fault amongst the other reflections caused by non-fault mismatches along the cable route, e.g. joints. The amplitude of the reflection is determined by the relative value of R_f and the cable surge impedance Z_0, and this is plotted in fig. 30.6 for both series and shunt faults. From fig. 30.6 it can be seen that the dividing line between low and high resistance shunt faults ($R_f\ Z_0 = 10$) represents reflections of greater and less than 5% respectively. With power cable surge impedances lying typically between 10 and 100 Ω the $10Z_0$ limit means that most cable faults cannot be prelocated without first being preconditioned. By comparison, most conductor faults, which are complete open circuits, at least at low levels of applied voltage, produce 100% reflections, thus making them readily identifiable. If a shunt fault has a significant fault capacitance it will give a negative going reflection similar to that produced by a low resistance fault.

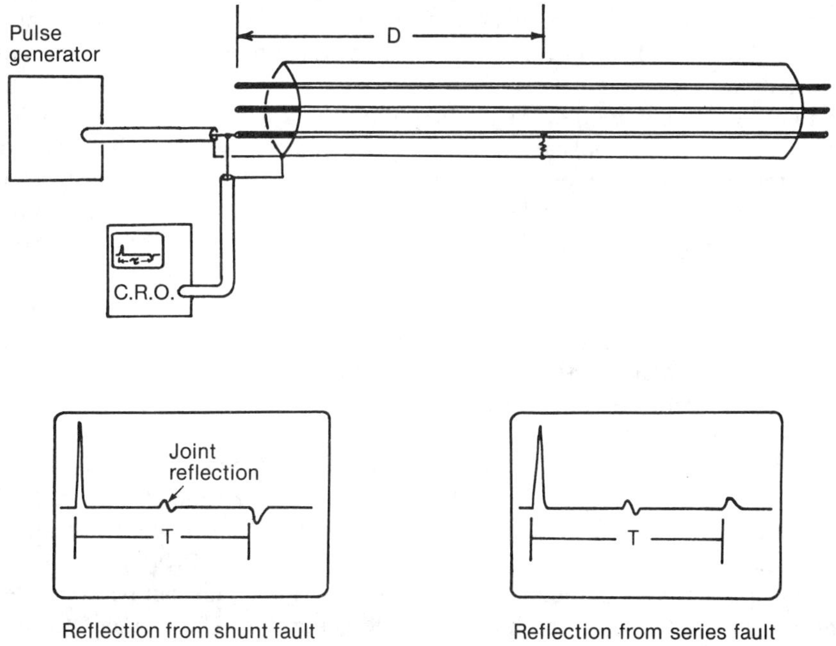

Fig. 30.5 Principle of pulse-echo method, and examples of typical waveforms

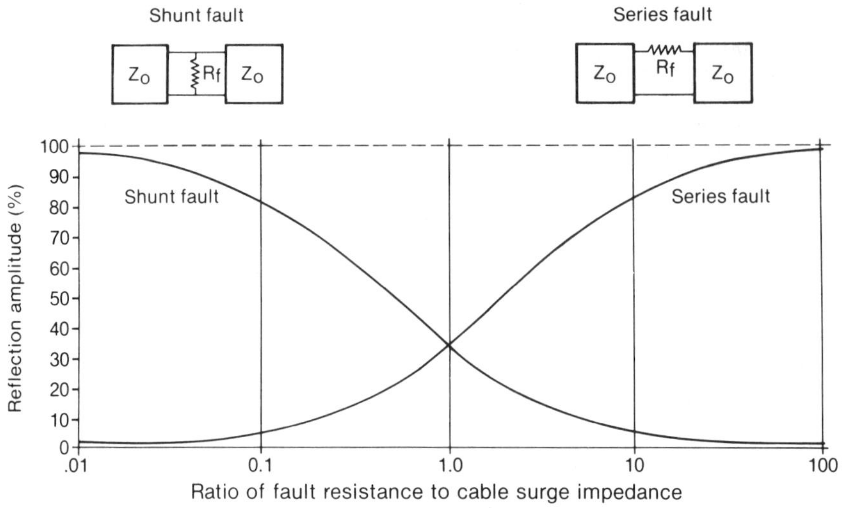

Fig. 30.6 Variation of reflection amplitude with fault resistance

Some improvement in detection sensitivity can be obtained by comparing the waveform obtained on the faulty phase with that obtained on a healthy phase, the two waveforms being superimposed on the CRT screen. Modern pulse-echo sets, such as the unit shown in fig. 30.7, include core comparison switching as well as an arrangement for displaying only the difference between two waveforms. Incorporating a digital readout of the distance to the fault and operating from its own internal batteries, the unit in fig. 30.7 is both convenient and accurate. However, if a high resistance or flashing fault cannot be preconditioned, low voltage pulse-echo techniques must be abandoned in favour of a high voltage method such as the impulse current method.[2]

The impulse current method (fig. 30.8) represents a comprehensive cable fault location system which avoids the need to precondition by using the high voltage surge generator, normally required for pinpointing, to provide a signal from which the fault position can be prelocated. When the surge generator is fired into a cable having a typical high resistance fault, the voltage wave travels along the cable and passes some way beyond the fault before the 'spark gap' breaks down. Breakdown never occurs immediately the voltage wave arrives at a fault due to a phenomenon known as 'ionisation delay'. However, when breakdown does occur two new travelling waves are launched into the lengths of cable on either side of the fault and these propagate to the cable terminals where, depending on the impedance of any connected equipment, they are reflected back towards the fault. Once flashover has occurred at the fault the ionised gas forms a low impedance path between the two 'spark gap electrodes' and hence any returning waves are reflected from the fault. The transients appearing at the cable terminals are therefore functions of the length of cable between that terminal and the fault. Both current and voltage transients are created but the simplest to detect is the current transient. This can be done by using a linear coupler in the return path of the surge generator. The distance to the fault can be determined from the time interval T (μs) between successive reflections of the breakdown pulse using equation (30.6).

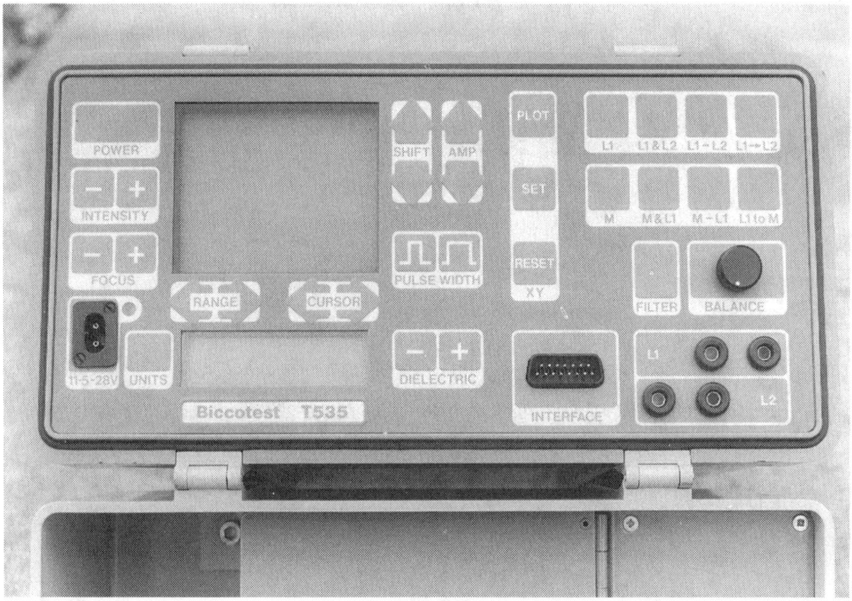

Fig. 30.7 Biccotest T535 pulse-echo cable fault locator

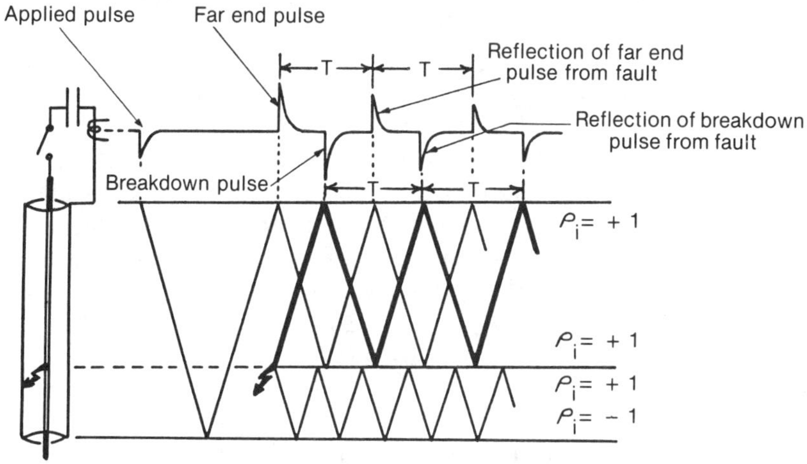

Fig. 30.8 Lattice diagram showing generation of current transient on a high resistance fault

The impulse current method can be used to locate all types of cable fault by appropriate interpretation of the transient waveforms. Since the waveforms are of very short duration it is essential to use some form of real-time recording. In the impulse current equipment, shown in fig. 30.9, the waveforms are first stored in a digital memory which is then repetitively scanned so that a reconstituted analogue waveform appears as a steady trace on the CRT. The instrument has a pair of vertical line cursors which can be positioned as required on the waveform. The

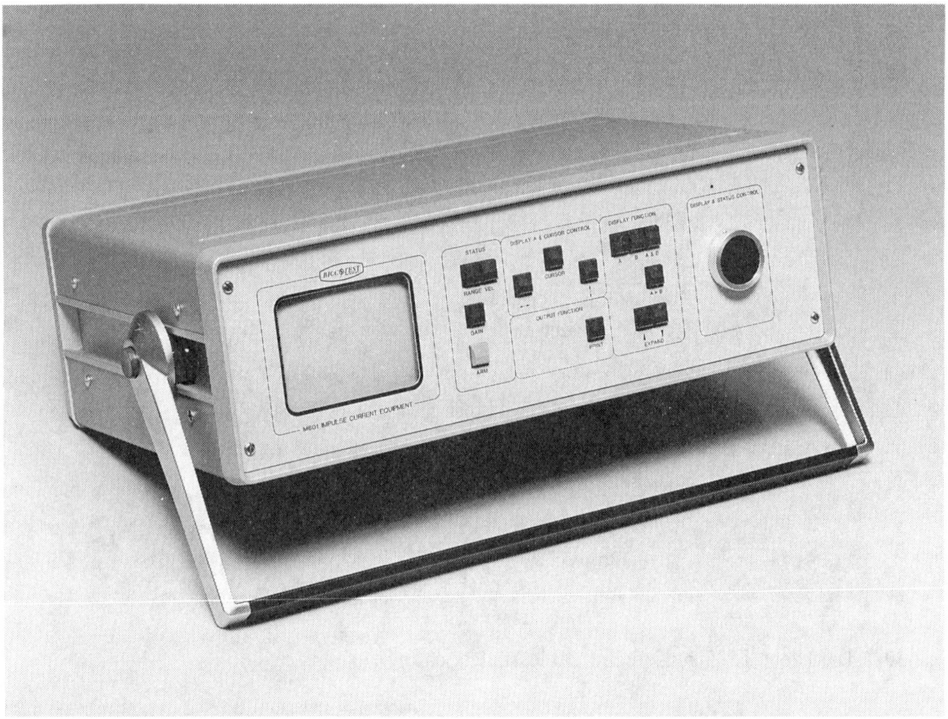

Fig. 30.9 Biccotest M601 impulse current equipment

distance will then be calculated and displayed in metres on the screen. The impulse current equipment can be used to prelocate flashing and intermittent faults by using a d.c. voltage test set to bring about flashover at the fault (chapter 43). It also incorporates a low voltage pulse generator so that it can be used as a conventional pulse-echo set if no surge generator is available, provided that the fault characteristics are suitable.

PINPOINTING

Pinpointing is essential on direct buried cables if the location and repair of a fault is to be accomplished with a single excavation. By far the most common method of pinpointing is to detect the acoustic signal produced at the fault by the application of a surge generator to the cable. The surge generator shown in fig. 30.10 incorporates a 'constant stored energy' feature whereby the capacitor bank is reconnected as the voltage range is varied so that it operates at maximum efficiency (table 30.6).

In some cases the acoustic signal can be detected above ground without any special equipment but in general it is an advantage to use a ground microphone and amplifier to pick up the mechanical shock wave. In addition to the acoustic channel, the unit shown in fig. 30.11 incorporates a magnetic detection system which responds to the current surges flowing in the cable being impulsed. The meter on the magnetic channel allows the user to ensure that the surge generator is operating and that the

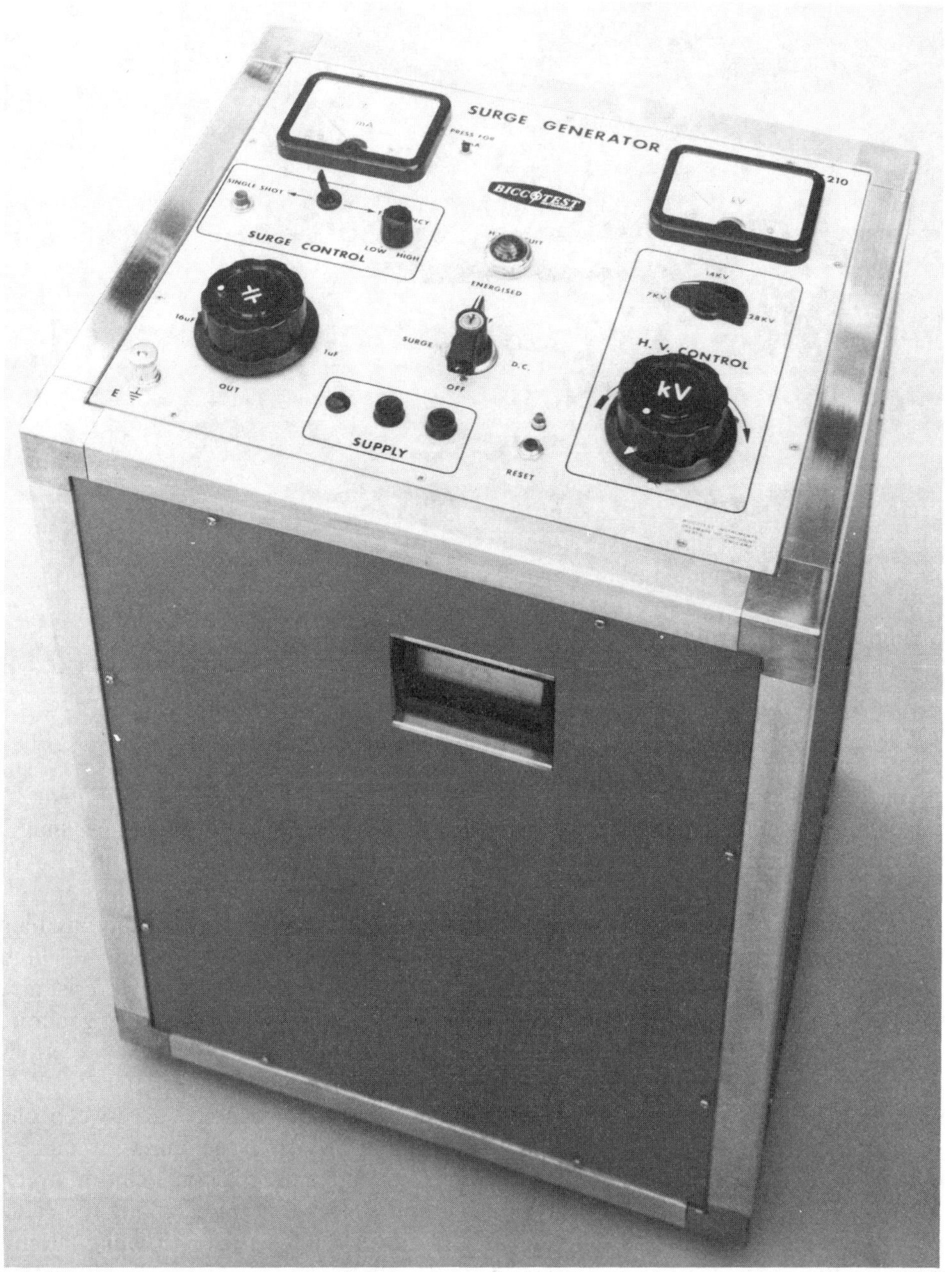

Fig. 30.10 Biccotest T210 30 kV surge generator

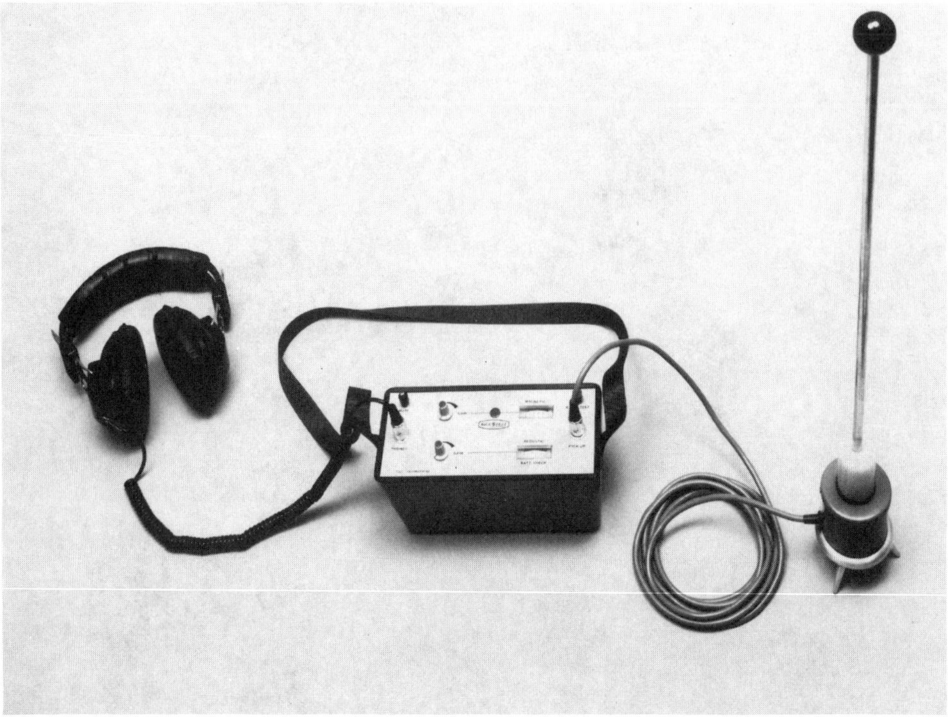

Fig. 30.11 Biccotest T202 acoustic detector with magnetic pick-up

microphone is positioned directly over the cable as well as providing a simple method of confirming that any acoustic signals are coincident with the application of the impulse to the cable.

The importance of the pinpointing stage cannot be over-emphasised and anything which might jeopardise the generation of the acoustic signal, e.g. prolonged fault burning, should be avoided. Once a fault develops into a very low resistance 'welded' condition it will short out the spark gap, making it impossible to generate an acoustic signal. In such cases it may then be necessary to make several excavations before the precise location of the fault can be identified.

If a fault occurs, or is created, where a low resistance path exists between one conductor and another, it is possible to pinpoint it using the audio frequency induction or BIMEC method. The audio frequency generator is connected between the two faulty cores and the signal radiated from the cable is traced along the cable route. As indicated in fig. 30.12, the signal induced in the search coil will exhibit a characteristic rise and fall, due to the lay of the cable cores, between the generator and the fault. Beyond the fault the signal will either disappear completely or, more probably will fall off very gradually without any further lay effect. The lay effect is the only positive means of identifying that the signal is emanating from the faulty cable and is not caused by re-radiation from other adjacent buried metallic services. Given suitable conditions, the BIMEC method of pinpointing can be used without prelocating the fault and without any record of the cable type, length or route.

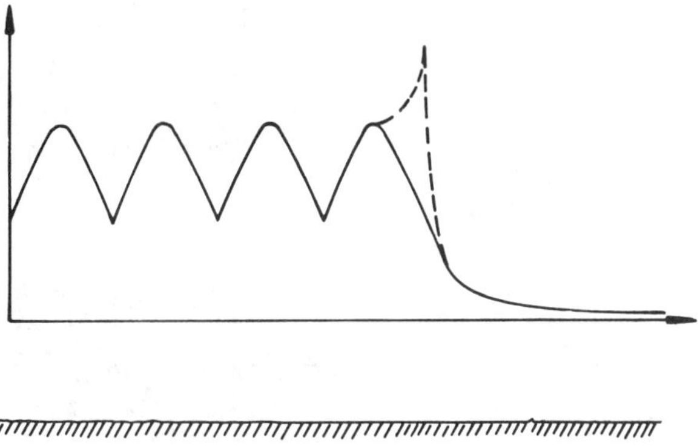

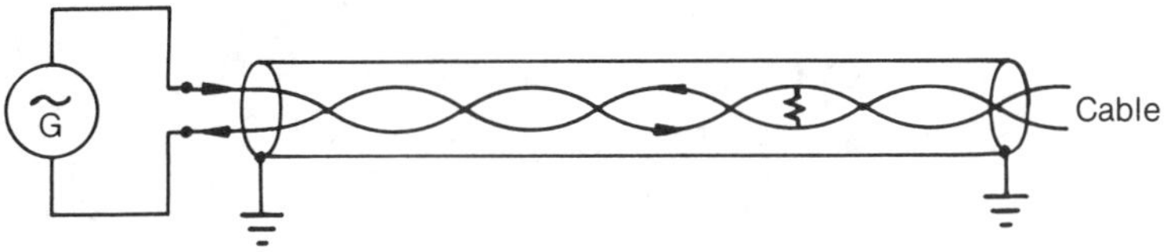

Fig. 30.12 BIMEC method for pinpointing core to core faults

Table 30.6 Voltage capacitance combinations for 'constant stored energy'

Voltage range	Capacitance	Stored energy
28 kV	1 μF	392 joules
14 kV	4 μF	392 joules
7 kV	16 μF	392 joules

CABLE TRACING

It is not uncommon for the precise route of a cable to be inadequately, or worse, incorrectly recorded. If there is any doubt as to the precise route and length of a faulty cable it is advisable to carry out a route tracing exercise before beginning the pinpointing stage. Route tracing can be performed in two ways. The first and preferable method is to use conductive connection onto two cores of the cable, as illustrated in fig. 30.12, but with a shorting link between the same two cores at the opposite end of the cable. With this connection it is possible to trace the cable route unambiguously as the characteristic lay effect will be observed. If it is not practicable to use the core to core conductive mode the signal may be applied by connecting the generator conductively between the cable sheath and a remote earth, or by using the inductive mode.

In the inductive mode, the signal is induced into the cable by feeding the generator either into an aerial which can be placed adjacent to the cable, e.g. above the cable

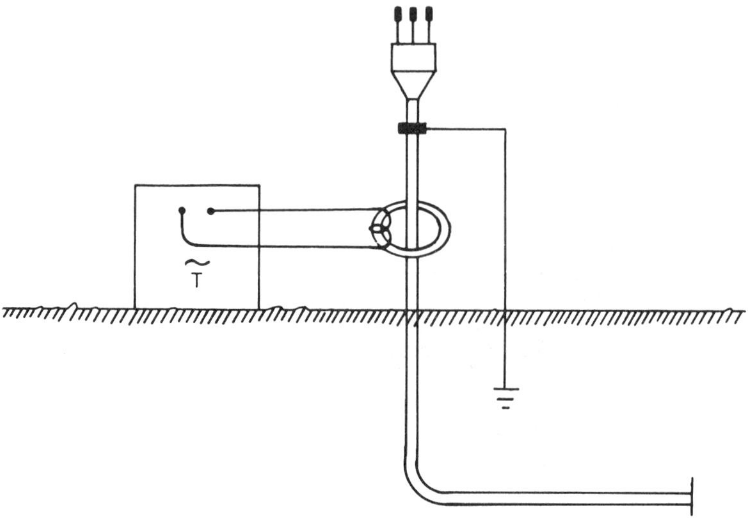

Fig. 30.13 Inductive method for locating cables and pipes

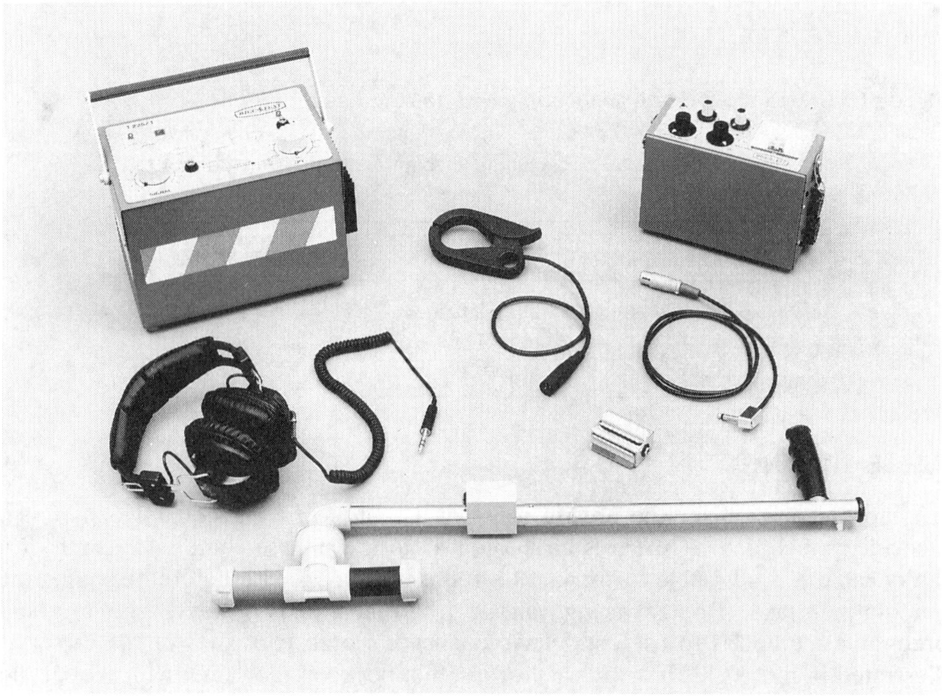

Fig. 30.14 Biccotest T225 cable and pipe tracing equipment

at a known point along its route, or into a special clip-on transformer which can be clamped around the cable, as indicated in fig. 30.13. Unlike the core to core conductive connection, neither the sheath to sheath conductive mode nor the inductive

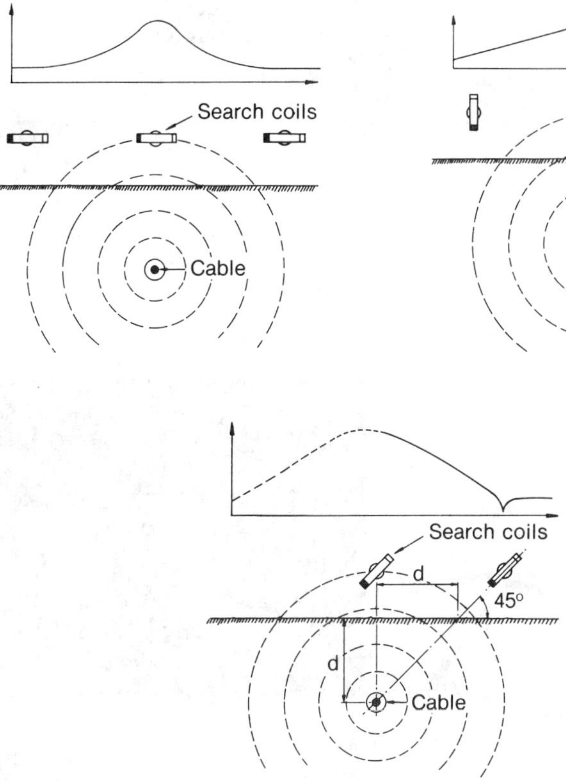

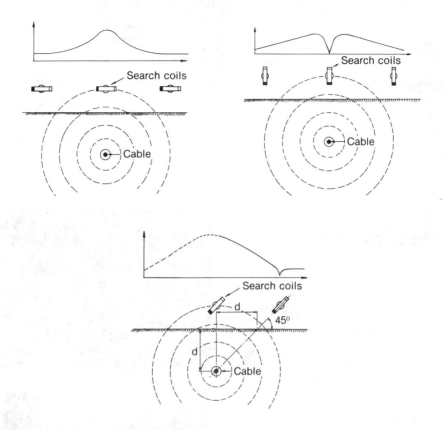

Fig. 30.15 Determination of position and depth of a buried cable

mode produce the characteristic lay effect and care must be taken to ensure that the wrong (i.e. a re-radiated) signal is not mistaken for the required signal. Fig. 30.14 shows a comprehensive kit which can be used not only to trace both cables and pipes but also to determine their buried depth by varying the orientation of the search coil.

Fig. 30.15 shows the response of the search coil when oriented horizontally, vertically, and at 45° and moved at right angles to the route of the cable. It should be noted that the sharp null obtained directly over the cable when the coil is vertical provides a far more accurate indication of the cable position than is obtained when searching for the much 'flatter' maximum produced by a horizontal coil. The horizontal orientation, however, does allow the cable direction to be determined, since a sharp null will again be obtained if the coil is rotated until its axis is parallel to the line of the cable.

FAULT LOCATION SYSTEMS

From the foregoing sections it will be realised that it is necessary to have a selection of equipment in order to be able to carry out a fault location exercise from diagnosis to pinpointing. Such a system might consist, for example, of a pulse-echo set, a fault

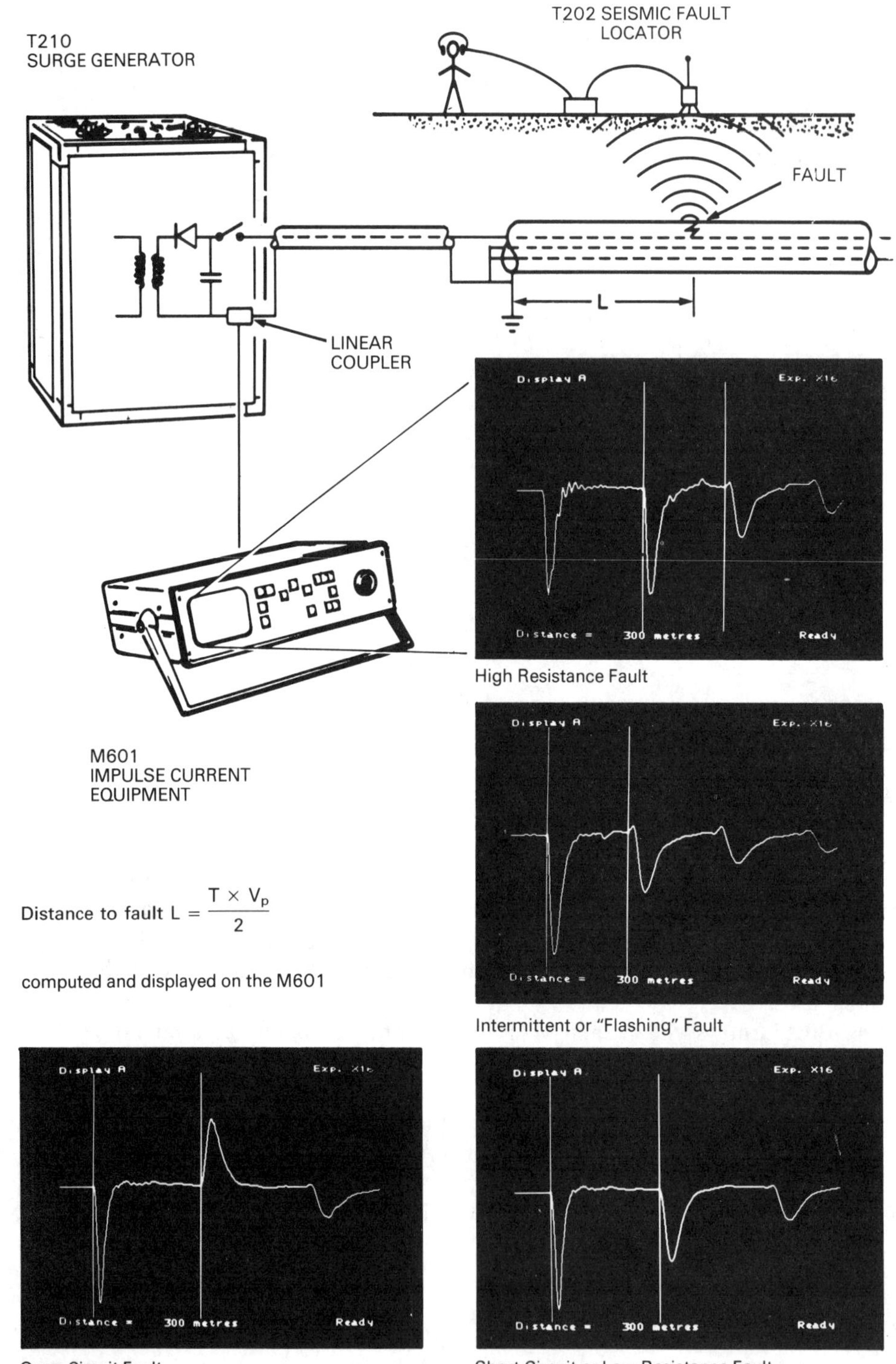

Fig. 30.16 Biccotest 'Compact 28' impulse current system

burner, a surge generator, an acoustic detector and a cable tracer. An alternative system might be the 'package', illustrated in fig. 30.16, based on the impulse current equipment which offers both greater portability and the capability of locating a wider variety of fault types as shown in the example waveforms.

Many electricity authorities now prefer to install cable fault location equipment in purpose-built test vans, so that a greater range and, possibly, more powerful versions of equipment can be provided. Test vans are usually designed for use in both fault location and voltage testing and provide greater comfort and convenience for the operator than is possible with portable equipment. On arrival at the test site the van is energised either from a local low voltage supply or from its own engine-driven generator, and high voltage leads are connected to the three phases of the cable to be tested. Once the necessary earthing conditions have been established (these being automatically monitored by equipment in the van) and the safety interlocks completed, all testing can be carried out from within the van. Fig. 30.17 shows a test van

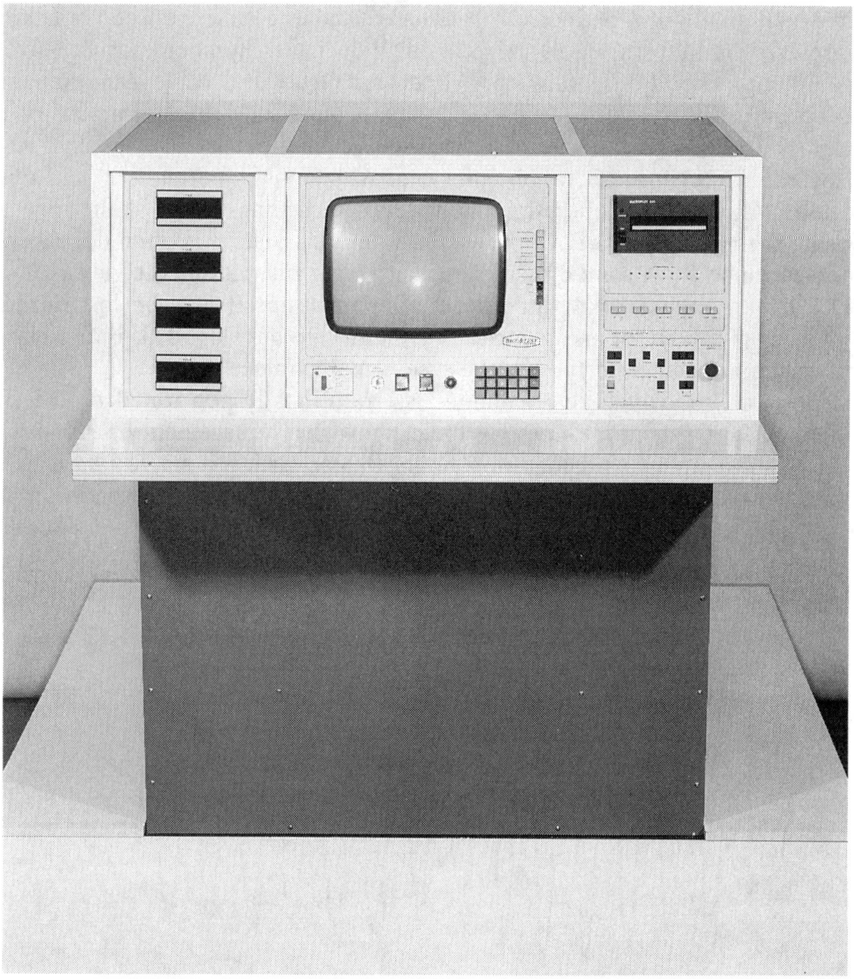

Fig. 30.17 Biccotest 'System M' for installation in test vans

module which has been designed for simple installation into a medium-sized van. The module incorporates a 28 kV, 1600 J surge generator, an 80 kV test set, an impulse current equipment set, high voltage switching and a comprehensive control and monitoring system.

CABLE FAULTS ON LOW VOLTAGE SYSTEMS (240/415 V)

The classification of faults on low voltage cables is generally based on their behaviour when re-energised at normal working voltage since it is usually impossible to isolate the cable from the consumers' installations during testing. Most faults on low voltage cables occur as a result of mechanical failure of the metallic sheath, which allows moisture to penetrate into the insulation and thereby initiate 'transitory' faults. A transitory fault does not cause the circuit fuse to operate as it lasts for only a fraction of a cycle and the fault current is limited by the impedance of the fault arc.

Successive transitory breakdowns extend the damaged region around the fault so that the rate of ingress of moisture increases and the time between breakdowns decreases. Eventually the fault current flows during a number of successive half cycles and the circuit fuse may then operate. Often the cable can then be re-energised immediately with a replacement fuse which may remain intact for some considerable time. The fault is then classified as 'non-persistent'. Finally, possibly after several further fuse operations, the fault will become 'permanent' and replacement fuses will appear to operate immediately. Recordings taken at the time of re-energising permanent faults have shown that the fault current is often non-sinusoidal and non-continuous, as can be seen from the typical substation voltage waveform of fig. 30.18. It is possible that sufficient conductor material may be lost during the development of a fault for an open-circuit condition to develop. This is also classified as a permanent fault, even though the fuse remains intact.

Diagnosis of low voltage cable faults was traditionally performed by the simple expedient of attempting to re-energise the cable with a replacement fuse. Fuses were also used in attempts to precondition faults by converting a single phase to earth fault into the more readily locatable phase to phase or open-circuit condition. If the preconditioning exercise was unsuccessful, fuses were again used in the 'cut and try' method of pre-locating, i.e. sectionalising the fault. Finally fuses were also used to generate an acoustic signal at the fault point for pinpointing purposes. For safety and

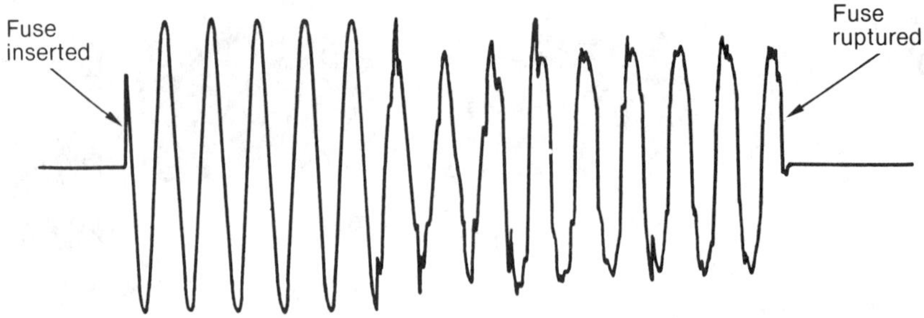

Fig. 30.18 Typical substation voltage waveform during the re-energisation of a low voltage cable fault

economic reasons some sort of MCCB re-energising device tends to have superseded the fuse in the fault location process.

An instrument for the pre-location of low voltage faults is shown in fig. 30.19. The instrument consists of a recording and display unit, a signal injector and trigger unit and a clip-on CT. The equipment is connected to a live cable as shown in fig. 30.20; the inductance in the re-energising device is to prevent the high frequency pulses from the signal injector from getting into the busbars and other connected cables. The signal injector sends a train of low voltage pulses into the cable. The recording unit has 16 high speed memories which store the waveforms resulting from the injected pulses; each successive waveform is stored in a new memory until all 16 memories are full. The memory selector then resets to zero and each memory is updated in turn. This process continues until the CT senses the passage of fault current; a trigger signal then allows a further eight pulses to be recorded before the selector is disabled. The memories now contain waveforms from before and during the fault and any two of these waveforms can be displayed simultaneously. The instrument also has a low speed memory which records the 50 Hz voltage waveform (fig. 30.20(c)). By displaying the contents of a high speed memory from the A portion of this waveform together with one from the B portion, a display like 30.20(b) is obtained. This shows clearly the divergence due to the fault and, by measuring the time T as indicated, the distance to the fault can be calculated. Provided that the fault maintains its arcing characteristic, it may then be pinpointed using the re-energising device in conjunction with the seismophone.

An interface is included in the instrument which allows the transfer of waveforms onto a standard cassette tape. This means that if the fault is non-persistent a waveform can be stored and at a later date fed back into the instrument for comparison.

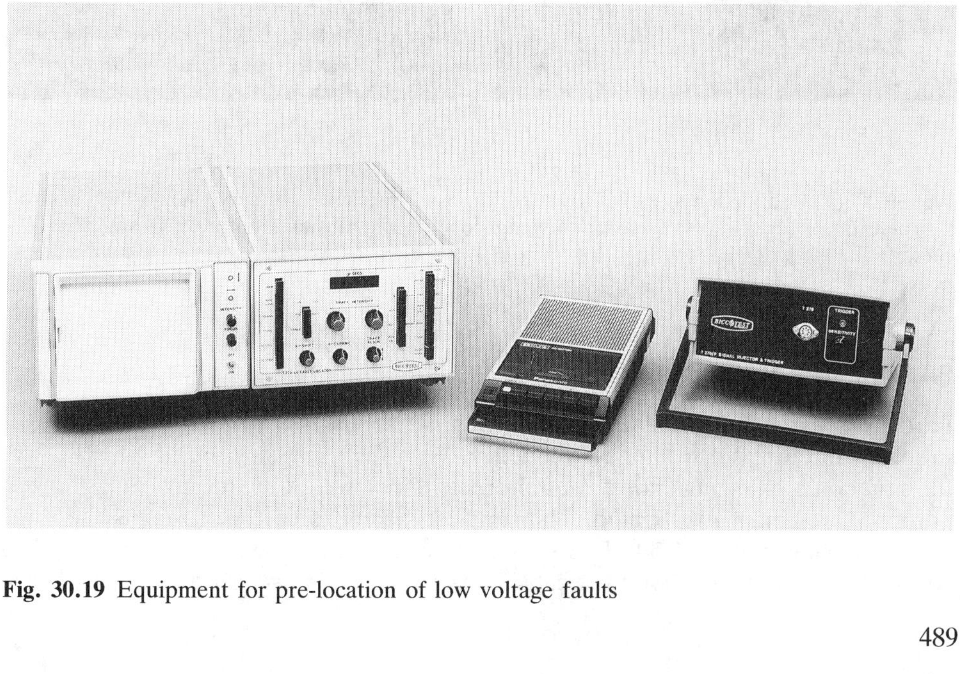

Fig. 30.19 Equipment for pre-location of low voltage faults

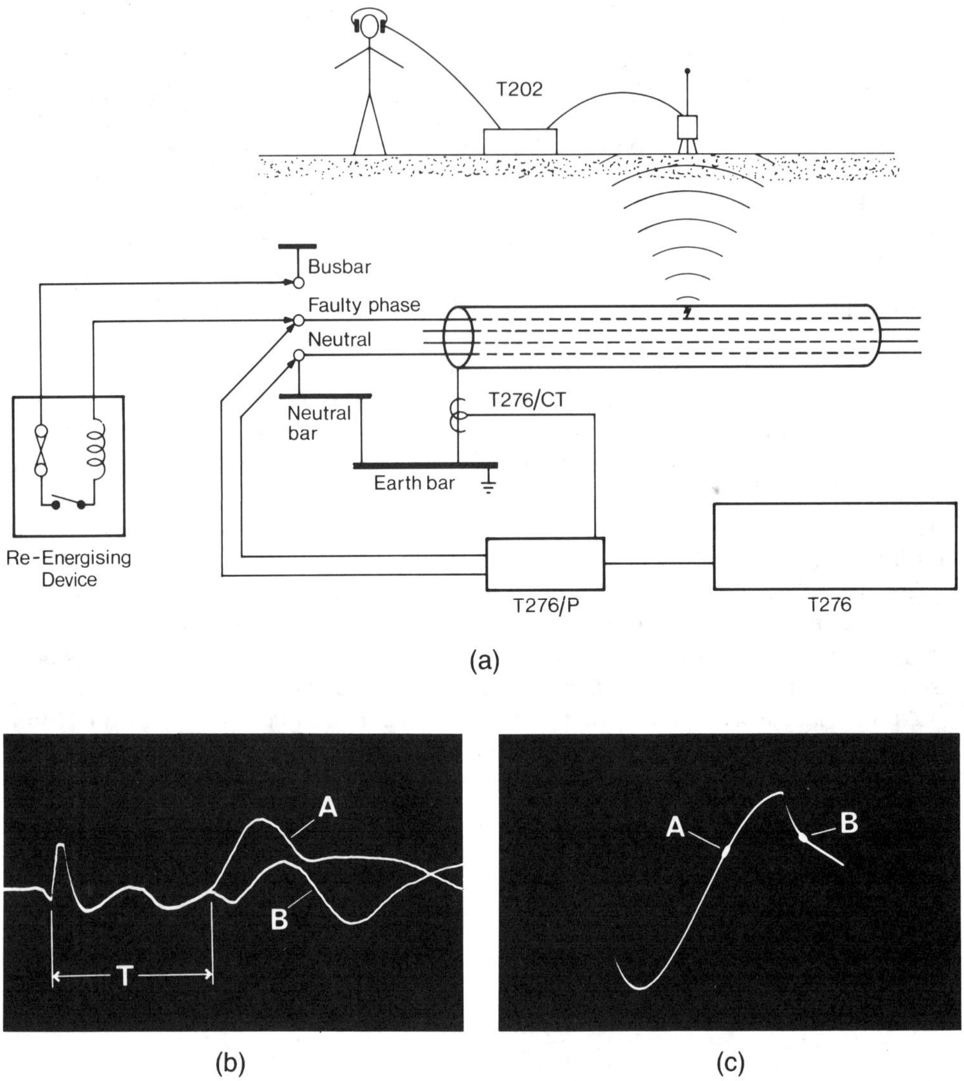

Fig. 30.20 (a) Connection to cable; (b) superimposed traces before (curve A) and after (curve B) cable fault; (c) 50 Hz waveform showing position of transients before (A) and after (B) cable fault

PARTIAL DISCHARGE LOCATION

Partial discharge testing of installed cables is not yet widely used because of the problems of energising at power frequency. With the increasing use of XLPE cables the situation is changing and various alternative methods of energising cables for test purposes are being investigated. The simplest system to emerge so far is the ramp generator shown in fig. 30.21. The series resistor R_s is selected to give a time constant, in combination with the cable capacitance, of between 1 and 10 in order to

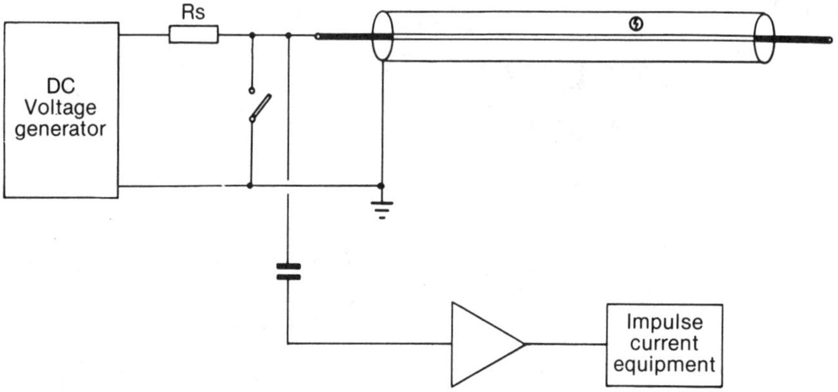

Fig. 30.21 Ramp generator circuit for partial discharge testing on installed cables

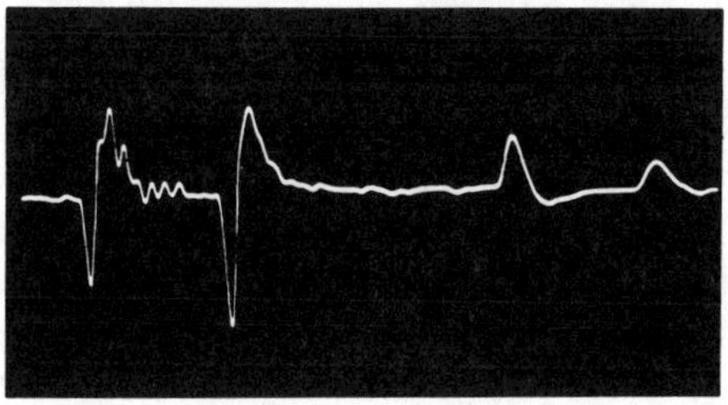

Fig. 30.22 Typical partial discharge transient

ensure that the stress distribution in the dielectric is similar to that occurring at power frequency.

Any partial discharges which occur during the application of the ramp voltage will create 'micro-transients' similar to those of the impulse current method which can be recorded, after amplification, with an impulse current equipment. Fig. 30.22 shows an example of a partial discharge transient which is formed by the two pulses which are launched into the lengths of cable on either side of the discharge site. Since the partial discharge site does not represent an impedance discontinuity to the two pulses, they can propagate freely along the whole of the cable length, reflecting totally from the open-circuit end and from R_s. The location of the site is determined by measuring the time interval T (μs) between the first and second pulses, which gives the distance of the site from the open-circuit end using equation (30.6).

REFERENCES

(1) Gooding, H. T. (1966) 'Cable fault location on power systems'. *Proc. IEE* **13** (1), 111–119.

(2) Gale, P. F. (1975) 'Cable fault location by impulse current method'. *Proc. IEE* **122** (4), 403–408.

Chapter 31

Future Development Prospects for Distribution Cables

For distribution cables in the range of rated voltages from 1 kV up to 33 kV extruded polymeric insulants have been replacing the traditional impregnated paper generally throughout the world. The capital investment and floor space required for the production of polymeric cables is less than that for paper insulated metal sheathed cables and the productivity per man is higher. Cablemakers in most industrialised countries have invested in facilities to produce polymeric cables, and this tends to establish the pattern for the future.

Thermoplastic PVC was the first of the polymeric insulants to gain widespread adoption in power cables and PVC cables became the established type at 1 kV and 3.3 kV for industrial applications. Later, for 11–33 kV cables, XLPE became the most favoured insulant in replacing paper. More recently XLPE has been replacing PVC at 1 kV and 3.3 kV.

In the UK, replacement of paper insulation by crosslinked polymers has been slower than in most other countries, particularly for cables used by the Area Boards of the electricity supply industry. At 11 kV the paper insulated aluminium sheathed cable is still the type most generally used in the public supply system. At 33 kV paper insulated cable remains the most used type, although there has been a significant increase in the proportion of XLPE cable in recent years. There is therefore scope for further movement in this area.

For the sheathing of polymeric cables PVC has had the greatest use, but for a number of years there has been increasing concern over the effects of cables that are involved in fires and this has led to a growing interest in, and use of, sheathing materials designed to alleviate these effects. Developments in this area will continue.

CABLES FOR INDUSTRIAL USE

At the lower end of the voltage range the convenience and satisfactory service of PVC cables in industrial installation resulted in their continued use for many years after the alternatives with crosslinked insulations became available. The better thermal properties of the crosslinked materials compared with thermoplastic PVC, allowing higher current ratings, were not decisive, as very often in low voltage installations the conductor size is selected on the basis of voltage drop rather than current carrying capacity alone. As long as cost considerations favoured PVC on a size-for-size basis, XLPE cables were generally only used when clear advantage could be taken of their properties. However, more recently developments in the crosslinking process, especially exploitation of the silane methods, have enabled XLPE insulated cables to be marketed competitively with PVC insulated cables. The potential benefits of XLPE, even if not always fully exploitable, have led to a swing to it from PVC and the more ready availability of XLPE cables from stock, arising from this, has accelerated the change. The process is not complete, but can be expected to advance.

Those industrial organisations using cables of higher voltages, such as 11 kV, have generally adopted the polymeric type for new projects. The 3-core cables have usually had circular conductors in the past, these being established as the norm when they were much more compatible with the method of manufacture than shaped pre-spiralled conductors. Some of the more modern methods of manufacture are more readily applicable to shaped conductors, which give some saving in the overall material usage in the cables, and XLPE insulated 11 kV cables with pre-spiralled shaped conductors have been supplied. Up to 11 kV there could be more frequent use of shaped conductors in the future, although circular conductors may often be preferred where they suit particular terminating techniques to which polymeric cables lend themselves.

For their roadway cables in mines, British Coal have been using PVC insulated cables for 1 kV and 3.3 kV and EPR insulated cables for 6.6 kV and 11 kV. The 6.6 kV EPR cables have shaped conductors (except for the small sizes) and the 11 kV cables have circular conductors. The general move to XLPE from PVC at 1 kV and 3 kV and the economy possible from adopting XLPE at 6.6 kV and 11 kV may influence future decisions on the types of cable.

CABLES IN FIRES

One of the factors affecting the move from PVC to XLPE insulation for 1 kV and 3.3 kV cables for industrial applications has been the use already of XLPE for cables to BS 6724, which is for cables that, when burnt, do not evolve dense smoke or hydrochloric acid gas, as does PVC. The materials used for the oversheaths and beddings play a major part in giving these cables the properties required, but PVC is also unsuitable as insulation, whereas XLPE and EPR produce relatively little smoke when burning and are of halogen-free compositions. Cables of the type covered by BS 6724, which for convenience are often described as LSF (low smoke and fumes), have had increasing use during the 1980s.

These cables have applications wherever they are installed in significant quantity and may be affected by fire and the products of their combustion can gain access to enclosed spaces where people may be congregated. Evacuation of public buildings, hospitals, underground tunnels and so on may be hindered by panic caused by obscured vision and severely irritant fumes, to aggravate the implicit physical dangers of a fire. Such considerations apply to many different situations coming within the broad description of 'industrial installations'. Another concern is the corrosion of metallic components of sensitive equipment by acid gas. There is therefore considerable scope for increased use of cables with LSF properties.

In the early development of these cables, in order to achieve the desired properties in a fire, there had to be some sacrifice of other sheathing properties such as degree of resistance to water permeation and mechanical strength. Thus BS 6724 states that the cables are intended primarily for installation in air and that where they are to be laid in any other environment reference should be made to the manufacturer. While the performance in fires is particularly relevant to cable installed in air, the cable route may often be mainly in air but include some parts underground or in damp situations. A restriction on the parts of the route for which the cable is suitable is then very inconvenient. Improvement has already been made in water resistance and this and further developments are likely to lead to more widespread use of this type of cable in place of the PVC sheathed type.

In the public supply sector, the CEGB attach great importance to the behaviour in fires of the cables used in power stations, which include 1 kV and 11 kV cables of the distribution types. At an earlier stage, emphasis was placed on minimising the propagation of flames along cables installed in bunches and special reduced propagating (RP) PVC compounds were developed. Now, for new power stations, requirements on other aspects of performance in fires, such as the generation of smoke and acid gases, are added to the demanding requirements on flame propagation and prohibit the use of PVC, which was once a major component of 1 kV and 11 kV power station cables as insulation and/or sheathing. For the cables for new power stations there are also demanding requirements on aspects not directly related to fires, such as water resistance and ageing. For cables to be installed in the containment areas of pressurised water reactor nuclear stations there are additional extra-demanding tests.

The combination of requirements specified by the CEGB go well beyond those of BS 6724 for cables intended for more general industrial use. Indeed, to meet the requirements for power stations, dual sheaths, i.e. sheaths having two layers of different compositions, one over the other, are projected. However, it seems likely that developments in materials and designs for the two purposes will impinge upon each other.

BS 6724 is for armoured cables of rated voltages up to 3.3 kV. A similar performance in fires is often required, however, for cables of higher voltages. The 11 kV cables for the CEGB have been mentioned, but other large cable users include London Underground Ltd, who have cables up to 22 kV in their tunnels. Cables of voltages above 3.3 kV are also required for the Cross Channel Tunnel. Cables for such higher voltages designed to limit smoke and acid gas emission if they are affected by fire are being supplied to London Underground, and further development of designs can be expected.

PUBLIC SUPPLY CABLES

At the low end of the voltage range of cables for the public supply system the paper insulated Consac cable still has significant use for new 3-phase 600/1000 V installations, although a majority of the Area Boards use the XLPE insulated Waveconal cable. However, the signs are now that more of the Boards who have been using Consac cable will change to Waveconal or Wavecon, the latter having a copper neutral/earth conductor instead of aluminium.

As previously indicated, at 11 kV the paper insulated cable with corrugated aluminium sheath is still used by most of the Boards but the move towards polymeric cables has been faster in recent years at 33 kV. In chapter 19 reference is made to the work aimed at evolving an optimum design of 11 kV polymeric cable for Area Board purposes, which would provide for economic systems and be generally accepted with confidence; this work will go on. The increased use of 33 kV XLPE cable is a trend which is likely to continue.

PART 4

TRANSMISSION SYSTEMS AND CABLES

Chapter 32
Basic Concepts and the Evolution of Pressurised Cable Types

PARTIAL DISCHARGE PROBLEMS WITH PAPER INSULATION

The use of the screened cable construction, first conceived in 1914, led to satisfactory cable designs for operation at 33 kV and to a limited extent at 66 kV. However, many failures occurred at 66 kV and higher voltages and were found to be caused by discharges in minute vacuous voids. Such voids are formed in the butt-gap spaces by expansion of the impregnating compound on heating, followed by insufficient contraction on cooling to fill the insulation completely. The voids contain low pressure gas extracted from the impregnant and are electrically weak. Partial discharges occur with sufficient energy for carbonisation of the paper to take place and this leads to the presence of carbon trees and ultimate electrical breakdown. The electrical stress in the insulation at which this breakdown phenomenon operates, i.e. in the region of 5 MV/m, also determines an upper limit of voltage of around 66 kV for such cables. There are no manufacturing problems in producing single-core 66 kV cables having an appropriate design stress, but 3-core cables are generally too large for normal manufacture. Discharge at lower stresses, in the range 2–4 MV/m, will cause some polymerisation of the impregnants with the formation of waxes (commonly called 'cheesing') but have little effect on the serviceability of the cable.

Emmanueli in the early 1920s was the first to find a solution to the problem. The oil-filled cable which he pioneered has continued ever since to be the most widely used design for very high voltages.

In the oil-filled cable, void formation is eliminated by maintaining the impregnant inside a metal sheath at a positive pressure, which for this purpose need not be very high. An alternative arrangement is to maintain the insulation under a high gas pressure. If the sheath over the insulation is reasonably flexible the gas pressure can be applied externally. In other designs the metal sheath is made sufficiently strong to withstand a high internal pressure and the gas is admitted into direct contact with the insulation.

TYPES OF PRESSURISED PAPER INSULATED CABLE

Over the years a large variety of cables with pressurised insulation have been developed and put into service. Two designs, both oil-filled, one at low pressure and one at high pressure, now account for the vast majority of new installations throughout the world. However, others using gas pressures still find some application and it is convenient to divide designs into groups, as shown in table 32.1. Each group may in turn be split into self-contained designs with lead or aluminium sheath and designs in which the cable is pulled into a pre-installed steel pipe, the pipe being subsequently filled with the pressurising medium of oil or gas.

Table 32.1 Pressure cable types and voltage ranges in commercial service

Fully oil-impregnated		Gas within insulation	
Design	Existing voltage range (kV)	Design	Existing voltage range (kV)
Lead or aluminium sheath			
Low pressure OF	30–525	Internal gas pressure	30–275
Mollerhoj flat cable	30–132		
Steel pipe			
High pressure OF	30–500	Internal gas pressure	30–132
External gas pressure with diaphragm sheath	30–275		

By the inclusion of operating voltages in table 32.1 it will be seen that oil-filled cables are suitable up to the highest voltage at present in service (525 kV); they also have some potential for use at 750 kV or even 1000 kV. Gas-pressurised cables, however, are limited to 132 or 275 kV according to design and this is associated with somewhat inferior electrical breakdown strength. On the whole they are not economically competitive with oil-filled cables but for some specialised circumstances they may be favoured because of advantages in terms of greater simplicity with the associated equipment and accessories or where steep gradients are involved.

Oil-filled cables

There can be some confusion about the interpretation of the generic description of an oil-filled (OF) cable and, in particular, the coupling of the term 'low pressure' with it. In general, when no other description is given, OF cable is taken to mean a self-contained cable which operates at a maximum static sustained pressure of 5.25 bar with transient pressures up to 8 bar. This is the conventional cable which has very wide usage and is discussed in chapter 33.

However, two other designs of cable which may be termed 'low pressure' have found applications in specific countries, although the use has now generally been discontinued.

Unreinforced sheath LP OF cable

In the USA there has been use of a cable which operates at a pressure which is sufficiently low to be withstood by a specially alloyed lead sheath having no reinforcement. The pressure has therefore to be kept below 1 bar, which limits its application to fairly flat routes.

Mollerhoj cable

Fig. 32.1 shows a type of cable which has been used in Denmark at voltages up to 132 kV. It is a truly self-contained cable because after the installation has been completed the ends are sealed and there are no feed tanks. The cores are laid side

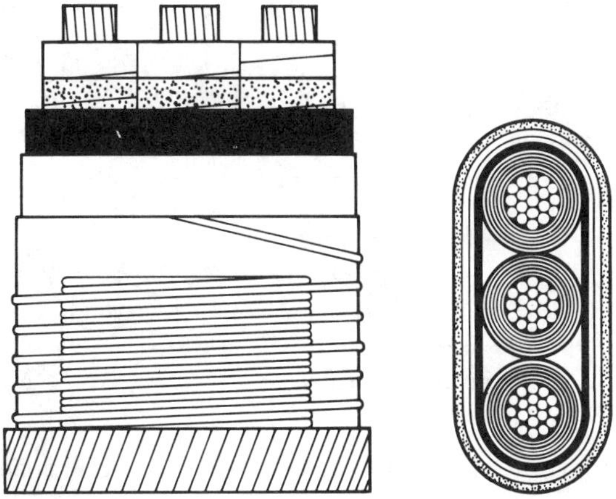

Fig. 32.1 33 kV Mollerhoj type OF cable

by side in flat formation under a lead sheath. By providing a longitudinally applied corrugated tape along each flat face of the lead sheath and binding them with helical wires and brass tapes, an elastic diaphragm is created which responds to changes in internal pressure on heating and cooling. The design has been used for submarine transmission to offshore islands but it has found little application outside Denmark. One of the reasons for this is that it is necessary to limit the temperature rise to prevent excessive fatigue of the lead sheath.

TRANSMISSION SYSTEM GROWTH

In most cases, transmission cables are used where sections of overhead line circuits have to be placed underground and so the requirements have been dictated by the needs of the overhead transmission grid system. When pressure cables first became established in the 1930s, the voltage range was from 33 to 132 kV and conductor sizes up to 200 mm^2 were adequate for a rating which did not exceed 110 MVA at 132 kV. In 1938, when bulk power transmission first commenced in the UK, the CEGB generating capacity was 8500 MW, and some idea of the change after the Second World War may be obtained from the figure of 12 841 MW in 1949–50 and 62 564 MW in 1973–74, with a maximum demand which subsequently continued at around 50 000 MW. A transmission voltage of 275 kV, with a winter circuit rating of 760 MVA, was required in the late 1950s and 10 years later the voltage had risen to 400 kV with a rating of 2600 MVA. To meet the requirements during the period, the cable designs were constantly being pushed towards their limits so as to match a single circuit of cable with a similar overhead line circuit. Conductor sizes increased to 2500 mm^2 in the 1970s. As the maximum cable diameter consistent with manufacturing and laying practicability was reached, it became necessary to obtain higher rating by more efficient removal of the heat generated in the cables by control of the properties of the trench backfill material and/or introduction of specific cooling techniques to prevent overheating of the cables.

In 1980 the amount of main transmission line and cable in service in the UK was 14 659 circuit km compared with 7660 circuit km in 1948 (see also table 32.2).

Table 32.2 Circuit length of national grid system transmission in 1987 in England and Wales (km)

Voltage	Overhead lines	Underground cables	Total
Below 132 kV	41	45	86
132 kV	422	152	574
275 kV	3619	446	4065
400 kV	9553	293[a]	9846

[a] Includes 162 circuit km d.c. cable at ± 280 kV

Although the proportion of underground cable in the UK is small, it is still large in comparison with most other countries. In spite of constant endeavours to improve the price ratio between underground cables and overhead lines very little change has occurred and it remains between about 10:1 and 23:1 according to voltage and installation circumstances.

IMPROVEMENT OF DIELECTRIC BY PRESSURISING

For the reasons explained earlier, relating to partial discharges associated with heat cycles, the conventional maximum operating temperature for 33 kV solid type paper cables is 65 °C. For many years pressurised cables were designed for continuous operation at 85 °C and more recently this has been increased to 90 °C in the case of modern oil-filled cables. The important effect of this difference on current carrying capacity is shown in fig. 32.2, which illustrates the situation for lead sheathed cables under British conditions. Part of the improvement is due to lower insulation thickness and hence better thermal conductance, but there is an improvement in dielectric strength as indicated in table 32.3 and fig. 32.3.

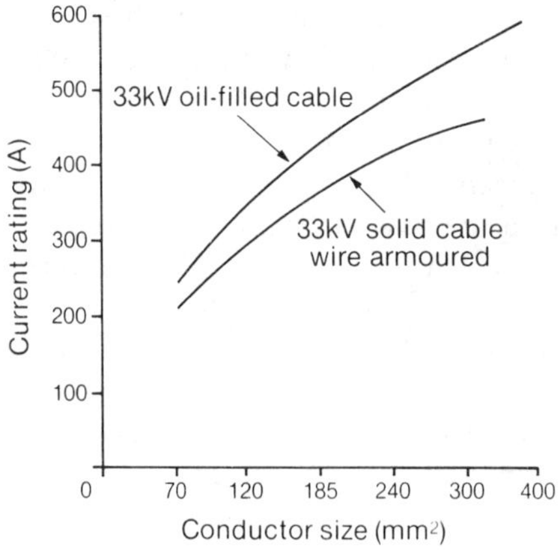

Fig. 32.2 Comparison of current carrying capacity of 3-core lead sheathed SC OF and solid type paper cables

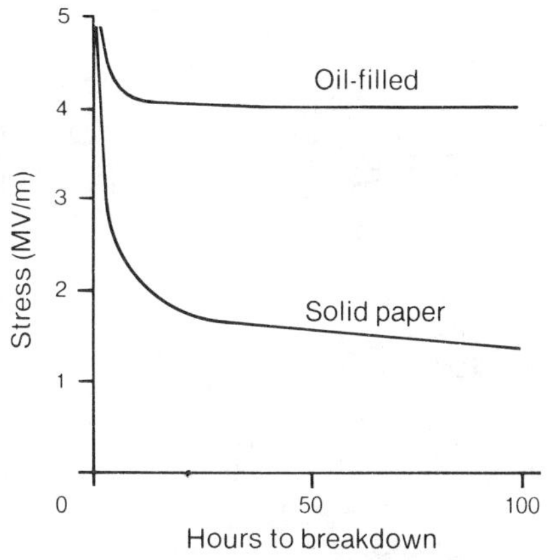

Fig. 32.3 Breakdown strength of SC OF and solid type paper cables

Table 32.3 Comparative dielectric performance of SC OF and solid cables

Parameter	OF cable (MV/m)	33 kV solid cable (MV/m)
Short time strength	50	50
Maximum long time strength	70	12–15
Design stress	7–17	5 max

DESIGN STRESS AND PERFORMANCE DATA

One of the paramount features of design stress for transmission cables relates to impulse voltage requirements to deal with transients caused by lightning and switching operations. In the case of OF cables, typical maximum stresses are about 100 MV/m for impulse and 40 MV/m for a.c., a ratio of about 2.5:1. Table 32.4 and fig. 32.4 show that the service requirement ratio varies between 10.1 and 6.1 according to voltage. Consequently cables must be designed on an impulse breakdown stress basis and this provides a large safety margin for a.c. performance. The reverse would lead to failure by impulse breakdown. The last column in the table illustrates that, owing to the lowering of the impulse-to-a.c. ratio as voltage increases, the design stress can be increased with voltage. The figures quoted are representative values and there may be some variation. In general, 33 kV pressurised cables have a minimum insulation thickness of 3.3 mm, which is based more specifically on what is required on mechanical considerations such as the effects of bending. Because the surface profile of Milliken conductors is not as uniform as that of other types, the insulation design stress is somewhat lower.

During the 1950s, when requirements for higher voltage cables steadily increased up to 400 kV, much attention was devoted to design considerations to achieve the higher impulse level necessary. It was appreciated that better impulse strength could be obtained by using thinner papers, higher cellulose density paper and paper with

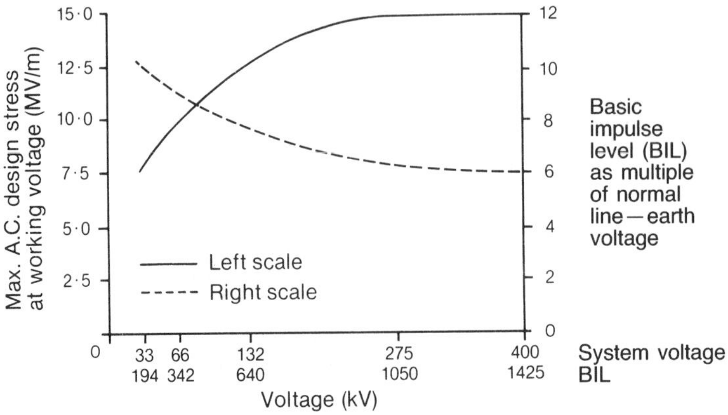

Fig. 32.4 Design stress for SC OF cables and relationship with basic impulse level of the system

Table 32.4 Comparison of impulse requirement and working voltage

System voltage (kV)	Working voltage (r.m.s.) (kV)	Impulse test requirement (kVp)	Impulse-to-a.c. ratio	Maximum OF cable design stress (MV/m)
33	19	194	10.2	7.5
66	38	342	9.0	10
132	76	640	8.4	12
275	160	1050	6.6	15
400	230	1425	6.2	15

greater air impermeability. However, with the steadily increasing thickness of insulation the bending properties of the insulation were also becoming much more critical, and ideal designs for good impulse strength were often opposed to what was required for bending. Also paper tapes of increased density and rigidity, whilst sliding more readily against the interlayer frictional forces without creasing and buckling, also tended to increase the dielectric loss angle and permittivity.

Solutions were found involving optimum choice of paper specification, grading of paper thickness throughout the insulation and precision control of lapping techniques, particularly concerning application tension. Coupled with this work was a need for larger conductor sizes and improved flexibility of conductors to overcome damage to the insulation by the higher forces necessary to bend the conductors.

Subsequently, more attention was devoted to dielectric loss angle, capacitance and improvement of current carrying capacity. Dielectric loss angle becomes more important with increasing voltage. In the case of solid type cables it also increases with cable operating temperature and may rise sharply with voltage due to the onset of partial discharge in voids. Pressurised cables generally have lower power factor and with oil-filled cables there is little increase with temperature and voltage.

The dielectric loss angle results in a transmission power loss which appears as heat and the dielectric loss D may be expressed as

$$D = U_0^2 \pi f C \tan \delta \; 10^{-3} \text{ (kW/km)} \qquad (32.1)$$

where U_0 = voltage to earth (kV)
f = power frequency (Hz)
C = electrostatic capacitance (μF/km)
$\tan \delta$ = dielectric loss angle

The heat generation has an effect on the current carrying capacity if a maximum cable temperature has not to be exceeded. At 33 kV the effect is very small but, as the power losses are proportional to the square of the voltage, the situation is very different at 400 kV and the reduction in rating could be as much as 25%. Reduction of dielectric loss angle has been obtained by such means as the use of deionised water during paper-making (chapter 3).

It will also be seen that, in addition to keeping the dielectric loss angle to a minimum for the highest voltages, the capacitance should be as low as possible. To achieve this by increasing the dielectric thickness is not practical and reduction of the permittivity of the paper by adoption of lower apparent density would also reduce the impulse strength of the cable. Development work involving the use of special paper/plastic laminates and/or plastic films for this purpose is discussed in chapter 44.

ALTERNATIVE DIELECTRICS TO IMPREGNATED PAPER

Improvements to the conventional construction of oil-filled cables to obtain higher current carrying capacity are discussed in chapter 37 and, as mentioned above, further work on reduced capacitance is described in chapter 44. An alternative approach, on which much work is proceeding, is to consider dielectrics comprising a solid extrusion of a thermoplastic or thermosetting material of intrinsically low power factor. Materials like polyethylene and crosslinked polyethylene have good potential properties and are attractive because of increased simplification by elimination of the equipment which it is necessary to install for a pressurised system. Chapter 36 deals with the current situation.

CHOICE OF CABLE DESIGNS AVAILABLE

It is difficult to give a clear summary because choice tends to be influenced by traditional user practice and by national preferences but some of the issues are determined by the cable voltage.

33–66 kV

The choice is between solid type impregnated paper, thermosetting insulation (mainly XLPE), gas-filled and oil-filled. The gas-filled cable tends to be used only where it has specialised advantages (chapter 34), and whilst the use of thermosetting insulation has been growing rapidly, so that within a few years it may predominate, it has not yet reached a stage of universal acceptance. The use of solid type cable above 45 kV is mainly for maintenance of existing systems of this type.

The current carrying capacity of solid paper cables is lower than for the other types but in some cases capitalisation of losses may detract from the advantage of using the smaller conductor size possible with other types. Solid type paper cables are also less attractive for use in countries where the ambient temperature is high, because of the effect of derating factors.

In comparing pressure cable with non-pressurised cable there are two important factors. One is the effect of route length because for short routes the cost of the ancillary equipment for pressure cables may be a relatively high proportion of total cost. The second is whether the extra skill and expertise necessary for installing and maintaining the system is readily available. Largely for this reason the use of pressure cable is diminishing at 33 kV.

132 kV and above

Thermosetting insulation is still at a relatively early development stage and above 275 kV the choice is effectively only between self-contained OF cable and high pressure pipe-type OF cable. The latter is mainly confined to North America and whilst having some advantages (chapter 35) tends to be less economically competitive.

In the range 132–275 kV the self-contained OF cable usually also has a cost advantage because of the higher design stress and as the voltage increases this outweighs the cost of the more expensive pressurising system. On the the other hand, where there are manufacturing and transient pressure considerations, as for long length submarine cables, the use of OF cables may not be practicable. In some cases the reduced jointing and installation skill applicable to gas cables and the greater local availability of nitrogen gas than cable oil may be attractive features.

Chapter 33

Self-contained Oil-filled Cables

The oil-filled cable is the most widely used type of transmission cable throughout the world and for a long time in the UK has been the only design used for new installations at 275 kV and 400 kV (fig. 33.1). First introduced in the early 1920s, development has been continuous ever since, to meet progressive demands for increases in voltage and current carrying capacity. This is still so today with a capability to meet future requirements for 750 kV and 1100 kV cables, together with further up-rating of 400 kV overhead lines. The highest voltage cables in service are the 525 kV cables which were first installed in the early 1970s at the Grand Coulee Dam.

CABLE DESIGN FEATURES

Construction

The standard design consists essentially of copper or aluminium conductors, paper insulation and an aluminium or reinforced lead sheath designed to withstand a sustained internal pressure up to 5.25 bar, with transient pressures up to 8 bar. In general, higher pressures might enable economies to be obtained in oil feeding arrangements but would usually be insufficient to justify the associated increase in the cost of cable and accessories. However, in special cases, such as cables installed on routes which have steep changes in elevation, it can be economic to design up to a maximum pressure of approximately 30 bar.

The basic concept is one of full impregnation of the whole of the insulation at all times by a low viscosity oil under pressure. As temperature rises, the surplus oil due to expansion is forced out of the cable into storage tanks and reverse flow takes place on cooling. The cable is filled with oil at the time of impregnation and sheathing and is subsequently kept in this condition throughout its life. It is despatched to site with an oil tank attached to take care of change of oil volume with ambient temperature. Even during the jointing operations of cable installation, an oil pressure and oil flow is maintained. The only exception to this is for cables which are installed vertically, e.g. cables for hydroelectric generating schemes. At Cruachan in Scotland the generators and transformers are in a cavern at the base of a mountain with 275 kV cables feeding an overhead line termination at a height of 352 m. To avoid the need for numerous stop-joints in such applications, the cable sheath has to be reinforced to withstand the hydrostatic pressure, in the above case 30 bar, and the cable needs to be partially drained under vacuum to control the flow during jointing at the lower end. Careful re-impregnation is then necessary before making the upper sealing end.

Fig. 33.1 275 kV OF cable with 200 mm^2 Milliken conductor and corrugated aluminium sheath

Ducts to provide channels for oil flow have to be incorporated in the cable design and are indicated in fig. 33.2, which also shows typical cable constructions.

For single-core cables an oil duct is normally included in the centre of the conductor, although for the short cable lengths which are used as terminations for 3-core cables the oil channel may be on the outside of the insulation and created by longitudinal ribs formed on the inside of a lead sheath at the time of sheath extrusion.

For 3-core cables having fillers between the cores, the oil duct is formed by the use of an open helix of steel or aluminium strip incorporated into the filler. When fillers are not necessary, i.e. with corrugated aluminium sheaths, the empty space between the cores produces a low impedance to flow without the necessity for a specific duct (fig. 33.3). Such constructions are known as ductless shaped oil (DSO) or ductless circular oil (DCO) according to the conductor shape.

The normal size range comprises single-core cables with conductors from 120 to 2500 mm^2 and 3-core cable from 120 to 630 mm^2, although at 33 kV the range extends downwards to 70 mm^2. Above about 150 kV, only single-core cables are available. This is because of a limit on overall diameter of about 150 mm associated with the maximum size of cable and cable drum which can conveniently be handled for installation.

Compared with distribution cables the use of aluminium for conductors was held back by problems associated with jointing, but following the introduction of the simple metal–inert gas (MIG) welding technique, the proportion of aluminium conductors has grown during periods when the price comparison has been favourable. For very heavy currents, of course, use of aluminium more readily causes increase in cable diameter toward the manufacturing limit. Conductor construction is similar for both metals but with the segmental form a small number of larger segments may be used with aluminium.

Except for the Milliken construction (fig. 33.1), the former general practice to

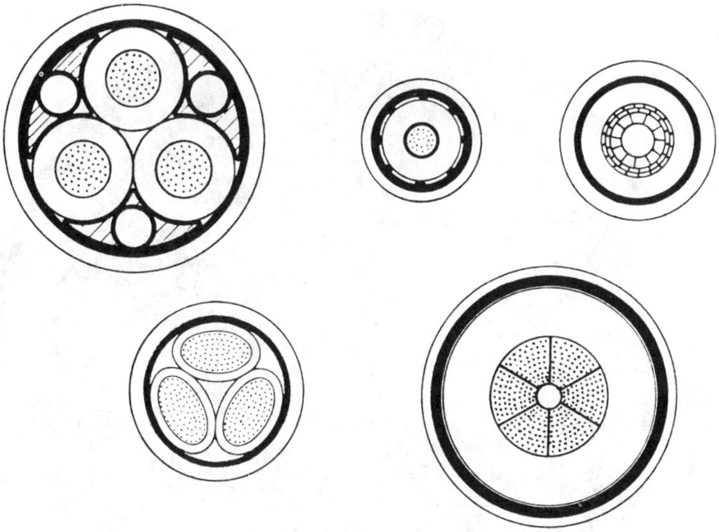

Fig. 33.2 Cross-section of typical self-contained oil-filled cables

Fig. 33.3 33 kV ductless OF cable with oval conductors

strand circular wires around an open steel spiral duct to form a hollow centre in single-core conductors now only applies for sizes of 150 mm^2 and below. Instead, a self-supporting ring is formed from segmental wires and this may form the basis for additional layers of circular wires, flat strips or segments applied with alternating direction of lay. Shaped segments provide better space occupancy than can be obtained by compacting circular wires and also better flexibility. Very great control of the segment dimensions and precision in placing them together in the stranding machine are both vital (fig. 33.4).

Two important factors arise with very large conductors for single-core cables,

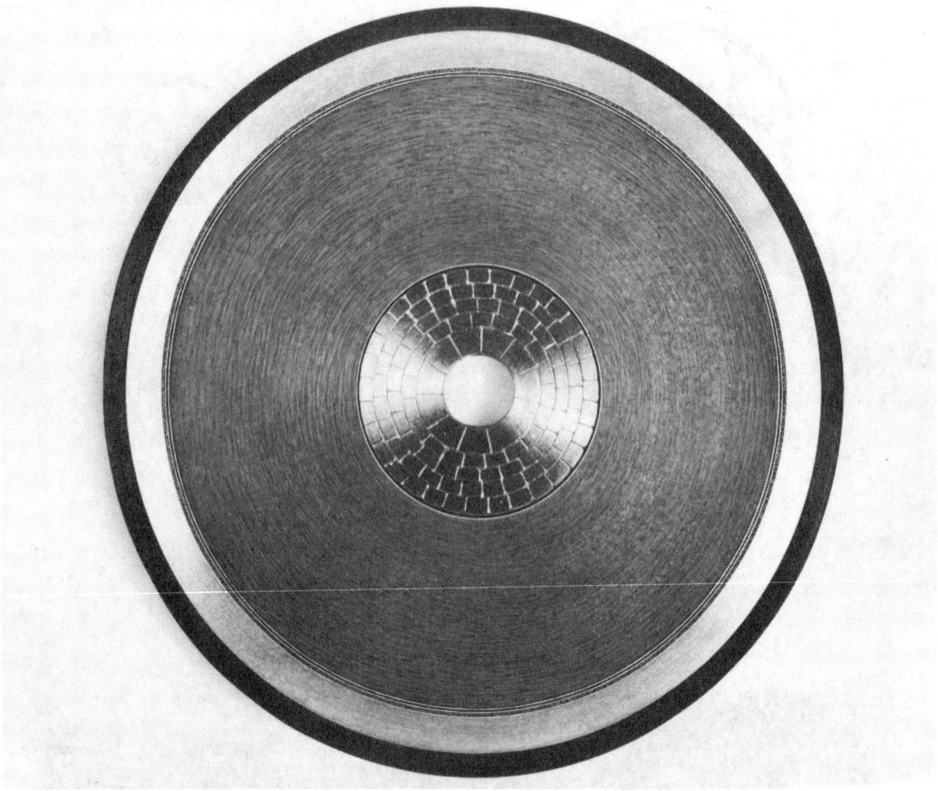

Fig. 33.4 525 kV OF cable with segmental wire conductors

namely mechanical thrust on heating and skin plus proximity effects. The former is discussed in chapter 40 but it may be noted here that aluminium produces less thrust than copper. Reference to skin and proximity effects and the use of Milliken conductors to reduce losses has been made in chapters 2 and 4. Usually the self-supporting duct construction is used up to about 1000 mm^2 but in certain cases it may be economic to extend this size if a larger internal duct is used. For larger sizes, Milliken conductors are generally adopted. They consist of six stranded cores usually laid around a 12 mm duct. Three cores are wrapped with plain paper and the alternate cores with carbon paper. The total number of wires may exceed 500.

The shape of 3-core cable conductors is normally oval at 33 kV and circular for higher voltages. They are stranded from round wires and compacted to provide a smooth surface or stranded from shaped or flat wires. Although solid aluminium conductors have been used extensively for 1 kV paper cable they are unsuitable for the higher voltages, except possibly for the smaller conductor sizes, because of disturbance of the lapped insulation on bending.

Conductor screens

Lapped tape screens are used to give the conductor a smooth surface and so avoid electrical stress concentrations on individual wires. A possible exception exists at

33 kV, where the stresses are low. Two main constructions are: (a) plain carbon papers and (b) metallised plain paper or coated carbon paper. Carbon paper is paper in which carbon is included during manufacture in sufficient quantity and of suitable type to make it electrically conducting. If a plain carbon paper conductor screen is used in a cable, it is found that the dielectric loss angle of the insulation increases with applied voltage owing to the influence of the electrical field on the surface of the carbon paper. As this occurs at the conductor surface the resultant effect on the dielectric loss angle of the cable decreases as the insulation thickness increases, i.e. as cable voltage increases. This effect of carbon paper is not as harmful as may at first be thought because it has been found that, with the constant application of voltage, the effect reduces with time and ultimately becomes negligible. Nevertheless, during the initial routine cable electrical testing it is possible that it may mask other imperfections and some cable manufacturers use screen constructions which eliminate or reduce it. This can be achieved by coating the carbon paper with metal foil or alternatively with paper of high air impermeability. The latter construction is carried out at the time of paper manufacture by producing 2-ply paper, one ply being carbon paper and the other insulating paper. Conductor screening by metallised paper also, of course, eliminates the effect.

The effect of screen construction on dielectric loss angle versus voltage characteristics is recognised in test specifications by allowing different values for the two constructions described.

Insulation

The importance of butt-gap width and depth have already been mentioned in relation to solid type paper cables. The subject is of still greater significance at transmission cable voltages because of effects on a.c. and impulse breakdown strength. Moreover, with the greater thickness of insulation, it is essential to take steps to prevent disturbance during bending. In addition to optimum selection of paper specification in terms of purity, density, impermeability and surface finish for satisfactory coefficient of friction, factors which have to be taken into account during design and manufacture include choice and control of paper width and thickness, lapping tensions and precision of application. Moreover to minimise the change in interlayer pressures due to changes in paper dimensions as a result of drying and impregnation, the moisture content of paper for cables for higher voltage is reduced before application and the lapping is carried out in a controlled humidity atmosphere (fig. 33.5). In the machine illustrated, precision of paper tensioning is obtained by electrical servo control which also maintains uniformity of tension when head rotation starts and stops.

Requirements for the optimum mechanical and electrical condition of the insulation are interrelated and often in opposition, so that compromise is necessary, e.g. thick papers favour mechanical stability but thin papers give the best electrical strength. In general, in the region of the highest electrical stress adjacent to the conductor, thicknesses of 75 μm are used, and at the outside variation from 125 to 200 μm is possible.

In most cases the design stress of OF cables is determined by the lightning voltage specified for the system rather than the 50 Hz design. The effect of a lightning strike on the cable is represented by impulse testing (chapter 42), the impulse strength of

Fig. 33.5 Paper lapping machine in a conditioned atmosphere

the insulation being affected by the constitution of the paper, the thickness of paper and the uniformity of the conductor. In the latter aspect it has been found that cables with Milliken conductors have a somewhat lower impulse strength than cables having conductors with normal stranding. Table 33.1 shows the design stresses used in the UK. It will be seen that, as the operating voltage increases, so does the design stress, because the specified impulse requirements become relatively less onerous.

Effects of paper purity and hence electrical losses are more important in relation to current carrying capacity and are discussed in chapter 35.

Table 33.1 Effect of impulse level on design stress

Operating voltage (kV)	Lightning impulse level[a] (kVp)	Ratio of impulse to operating voltage	Maximum design stress (50 Hz)	
			Non-Milliken (MV/m)	Milliken (MV/m)
33	194	10.2	[b]	[b]
66	342	9.0	10	9
132	640	8.4	12	10
275	1050	6.6	15	13
400	1425	6.2	15	15

[a] Voltage to earth
[b] Insulation thickness at 33 kV is determined by mechanical requirements

Insulation screen

All cables have a screen over the insulation to constrain the electric field to the lapped insulation. The screen must be sufficiently permeable to gases and oil to permit drying and impregnation of the cable and usually consists of carbon paper, metallised paper or metal tapes, singly or in combination.

Impregnants

Until the early 1960s, low viscosity mineral oil had always been used, the only change from the initial inception being some reduction in viscosity to enable the lengths of individual oil sections to be increased. When synthetic alkylates of dodecylbenzene type became available from other applications in the chemical industry, a progressive change was made to them because it was found that they were less subject to minor changes in quality, this being of particular importance during the turbulent conditions experienced by the oil industry in the 1970s. They are also technically superior at higher temperatures and the higher stresses being reached in service.

One of the important characteristics required from the impregnant is to absorb hydrogen and moisture which, although not formed under normal operating conditions, can be generated, for example, by debris introduced during jointing operations. Alkylates can absorb much more hydrogen and this ability increases rather than decreases with temperature.

Drying and impregnation

As with other types of paper insulated cables, OF cables are vacuum dried. It is necessary to achieve very low levels of moisture content to ensure that the lowest dielectric loss angles are obtained.

Several methods are used for impregnation. For many years the standard practice was to remove the cable from the drying tank, apply the lead sheath, place the cable in a steam heated vessel, evacuate the cable from both ends and then finally to vacuum impregnate the cable. Limitations to this process were that the insulation picked up some moisture during sheathing and that, as manufacturing lengths increased, the time for subsequent evacuation became very long. Whilst improvements are possible to reduce moisture regain, two alternative procedures have been developed, namely mass impregnation and vacuum sheathing. In the former the cable is impregnated with oil in the drying vessel. To ensure that no oil is lost from the cable during lead or aluminium sheathing the vessel is connected directly to the sheathing extruder and the cable is sheathed whilst still surrounded by oil. For this process (fig. 33.6) special drying vessels are required which can be situated directly behind the sheathing extruder and connected by suitable pipework. Techniques had to be developed to keep the cable under oil pressure throughout processing.

Similar techniques and equipment are needed for vacuum sheathing. At the end of the drying process the vessel is connected to the sheathing extruder and the

Fig. 33.6 Stainless steel drum being removed from stainless steel mass-impregnation tank

sheathing is carried out under vacuum. A separate process is then required for filling with oil. The main advantage of this process is that only the oil required to fill the cable is used, whereas a large quantity is in circulation for the mass impregnation process and special attention has to be given to drum and tank cleaning.

Lead sheaths

Originally all OF cables had lead sheaths but now a significant proportion are sheathed with aluminium for economic reasons. Exceptions are for submarine cables and for some installations where the higher electrical losses with aluminium exert an overall influence because spacing has to be limited. Nevertheless, lead has served well, provided that the cablemaker has recognised its limitations. In spite of the reinforcement which is necessary, hoop stresses may still arise in the sheath and a high quality with freedom from extrusion defects is paramount. The use of a continuous screw press or a ram press with Glover tray attachment is necessary to secure this quality.

Another important factor is that under the very low creep stresses which may arise due to the internal pressure, some types of lead alloy may fail by cracking after very small extensions. This limits the choice of alloy and the metallurgical structure associated with the type of extrusion press has also to be taken into account. Ram press sheaths are liable to recrystallation and grain growth during heating in the tank method of impregnation and small alloying additions are necessary to take care of this. UK manufacturers have basically used ½C alloy (0.2% tin, 0.075% cadmium) throughout the period.

Aluminium sheaths

Aluminium sheaths have many advantages because of reduced weight and cost and the possibility of dispensing with sheath reinforcement. Moreover by using a corrugated seamless aluminium (CSA) sheath, the thickness is reduced by around 50% compared with a smooth sheath and the cable flexibility is as good as or better than with a lead sheath. The extra resistance to crushing and flattening provided by such sheaths also means that fillers may be omitted between the cores of many 3-core cables, so that the interstitial space can serve as the oil duct. Finally, aluminium has vastly better fatigue strength for installations where vibration or slow high stress bending movement may be involved, e.g. in manholes.

The first OF cables introduced in 1952 with aluminium sheath had a smooth sheath, but after the corrugated version became available in 1959 it soon became standard. Smooth sheaths will withstand higher pressures but for the vast majority of installations the much thinner corrugated sheath is entirely adequate. If necessary the thickness may also be increased to cater for high static pressures resulting from steep gradients or vertical installation. In contrast with the corrugation for solid type paper cables, in which the ribs are of discrete type, i.e. transverse to the cable axis, OF cable sheaths are usually helically corrugated. The pitch varies from approximately 40% of the sheath internal diameter for small cables to about 25% for larger cables. Rib heights are within a range of 4% – 7% of the internal diameter and 3-core cables have somewhat deeper ribs than single-core cables because the permissible bending radii are smaller.

Reinforcement for lead sheaths

Although steel tapes may be used to reinforce the lead sheaths of 3-core cables it is now more usual to use copper alloy or stainless steel tapes for all cables. The tape is normally applied as a single layer and the thickness varies from 100 to 190 μm according to the cable diameter.

Armour

The only OF cables which require armour are those for submarine installations and these are discussed in chapter 45.

Anticorrosion protection

Extruded sheaths of PVC and medium or high density polyethyelene are used and details are as given in chapter 5.

HYDRAULIC DESIGN

An important consideration in the design of self-contained oil-filled cables is to ensure that under any operating conditions the pressure in the cable system is maintained between permitted values. The maximum is usually taken as 5.25 bar for sustained pressures and 8 bar for transient pressure. The minimum design value is generally 0.2 bar. As the pressure in the cable will change depending on elevations, it is necessary to carry out a survey of the cable route to determine its profile. To simplify the analysis of the pressures, it is normal to express the internal pressure in terms of metres of oil (1 m of oil at 15 °C corresponds to approximately 0.085 bar). Fig. 33.7 shows the variation of internal oil pressure along a route under static temperature conditions.

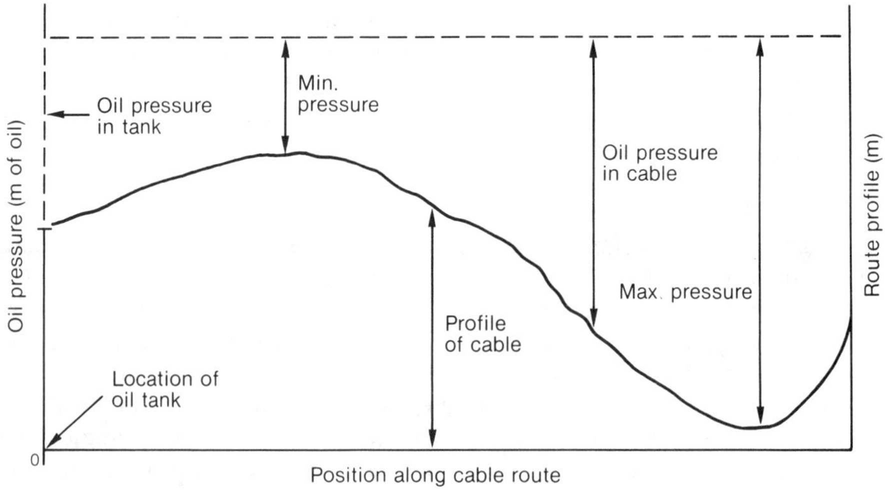

Fig. 33.7 Internal pressure variation along route of self-contained OF cable under static conditions

If the current in the conductor of the cable is increased, the temperature of the cable will rise and the increased temperature of the oil in the cable will result in thermal expansion of the oil. Therefore oil will flow from the insulation into the duct and then into the oil tanks. The flow will create a hydraulic pressure drop along the duct, and it is necessary to calculate this pressure in order to ensure that the specified maximum transient pressure of the cable is not exceeded.

For a unit length of cable δx situated at a distance x from the oil tank and assuming that the average temperature of the cable is rising at the rate of $\mathrm{d}\theta/\mathrm{d}t$, then the rate of oil expulsion is

$$V\,\delta x\,\alpha(\mathrm{d}\theta/\mathrm{d}t)$$

where V = oil volume of the cable (l/m)
α = coefficient of expansion of the oil

The quantity of oil flowing through the sample of cable situated at x in a route length of L metres is

$$V(L-x)\alpha(\mathrm{d}\theta/\mathrm{d}t)$$

The pressure drop δP along the duct of the section of cable δx in length is

$$\delta P = V(L-x)\alpha(\mathrm{d}\theta/\mathrm{d}t)b\delta x \tag{33.1}$$

where b is the hydraulic impedance of the duct per metre. Integrating from $x = 0$ to $x = L$ the pressure drop P along the complete length of cable is given by

$$P = V\alpha(\mathrm{d}\theta/\mathrm{d}t)b\,L^2/2 \tag{33.2}$$

It will be noted that the pressure drop is proportional to the square of the cable length, the oil volume per unit length and the rate of temperature rise. The latter depends on the increase in current loading but will be a maximum when full load is applied suddenly.

It can be shown that for a duct with a circular cross-section

$$b = 25.5\eta/r^4 \tag{33.3}$$

where η = viscosity of the oil (centipoise)
r = internal radius of the duct (mm)

The above assumes streamline flow. It will be seen that the transient pressure can be reduced by increasing the duct diameter and by reducing the viscosity of the impregnant. Except for special installations, the diameter of the central duct of single-core cables is standardised at approximately 12 mm.

In a similar manner to the transient heating pressure, a transient cooling pressure will arise when the temperature of the cable reduces. In this case the oil flows from the oil tank into the cable system.

These transient pressures will be superimposed on the static pressures and this is illustrated in fig. 33.8. It will be noted that the cooling transient pressure starts from a higher pressure at the tank position. This is because, during the heating period, oil has passed into the tank and hence has increased the oil pressure (see the following section).

The transient pressures only occur during changes in temperature of the system. The above analysis is a simplification of the hydraulic conditions as it does not allow

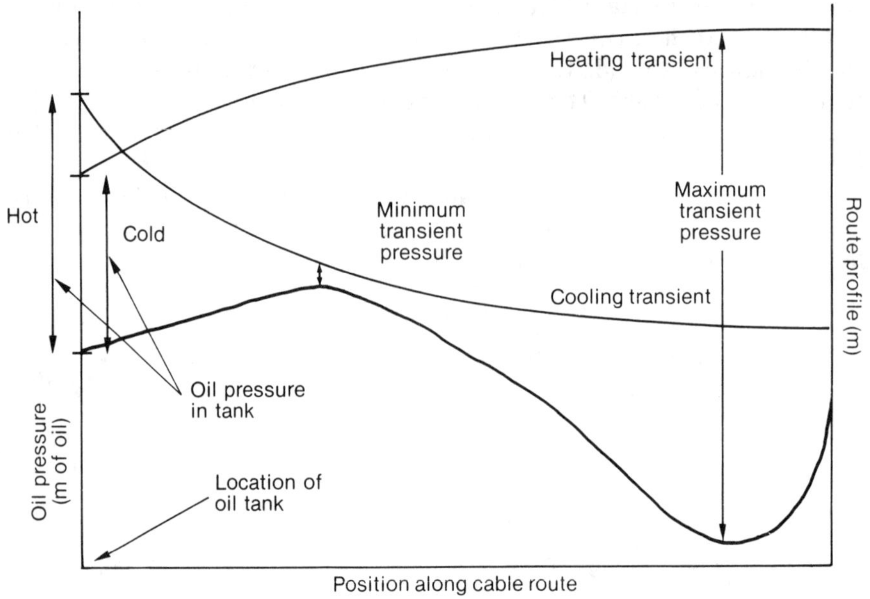

Fig. 33.8 Internal pressure variation along route of self-contained OF cable under transient conditions

for such factors as oil compressibility, the temperature gradient through the cable insulation, the variation of viscosity with temperature etc. In general the maximum heating transient will occur shortly after switching full load onto a cold cable, while the maximum cooling transient will occur shortly after switching off full load.

The analysis of static and transient pressures is an important part of self-contained oil-filled design. In practice the oil tanks are connected to a cable system at terminations or stop joints. In the case of 3-core cables, connection can also be made at straight joints as with these cables the oil ducts are situated in the interstices between cores. Fig. 33.9 illustrates the main principles in a diagrammatic form.

The feed tanks are available in a number of sizes from 88 to 300 litres to suit the volume of oil in the pressure section. The tanks may be installed above or below ground; in the latter case they are enclosed in a concrete shell.

Fig. 33.10 shows typical tanks for buried applications. In all cases the construction is cylindrical and inside the cylinder there are sealed flat capsules with flexible walls as shown in fig. 33.11.

The capsules contain gas which may be at atmospheric or higher pressure according to the duty for which the particular tank is required. The space within the tank not occupied by the capsules is filled with degasified oil and the actual oil content of the tank is typically between 30% and 50% of the nominal capacity.

The tanks may have to be installed at a site which is at a low level relative to the route profile and if the capsules had initially been sealed at atmospheric pressure they would be significantly compressed under no-load conditions. This would be wasteful of tank capacity and is avoided by pre-pressurisation of the capsules, in such cases, to a level which may be up to 3 bar. The characteristics of oil pressure for various degrees of pre-pressurisation are shown in fig. 33.12.

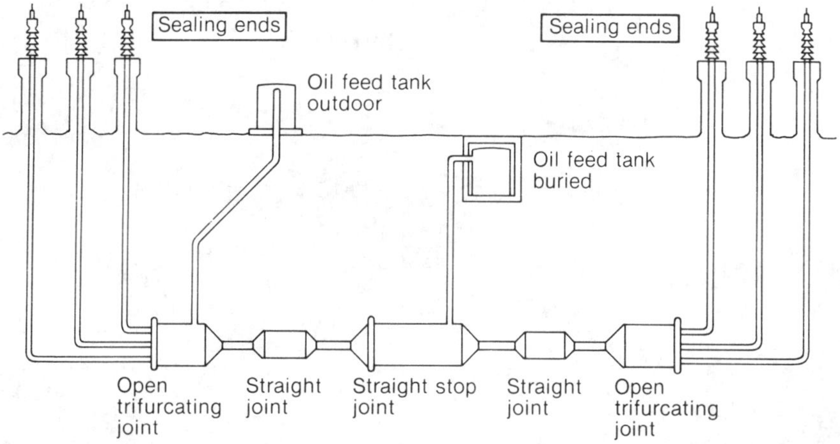

Fig. 33.9 Diagrammatic layout of a typical 3-core cable system

Fig. 33.10 Buried pressure tanks in concrete casings

Particularly when the route is undulating, the installation may need to be split into a number of separate oil sections and this is done by the use of stop joints, e.g. the inclusion of an epoxy resin barrier section in the centre of straight joints to

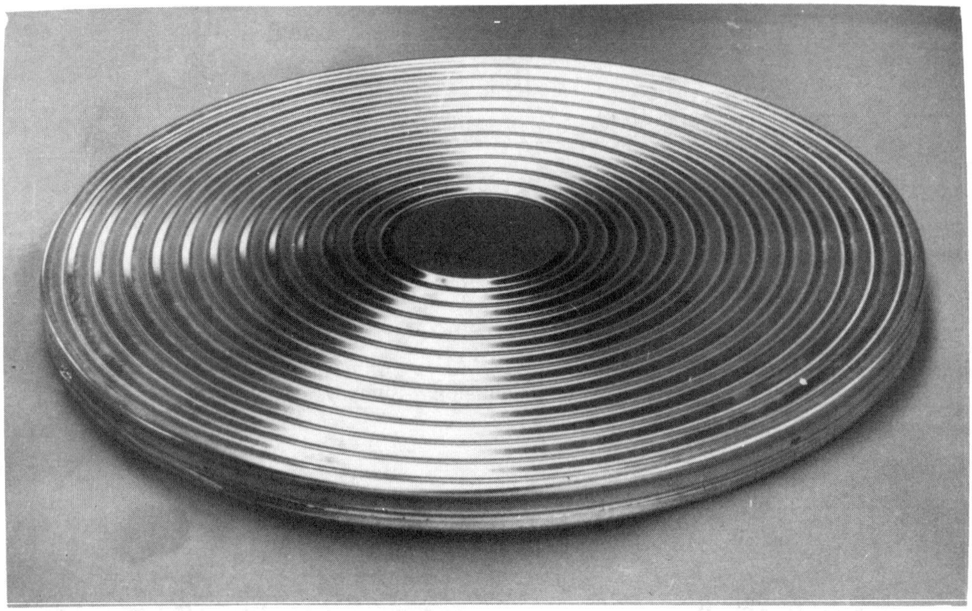

Fig. 33.11 Capsule as used inside pressure tanks

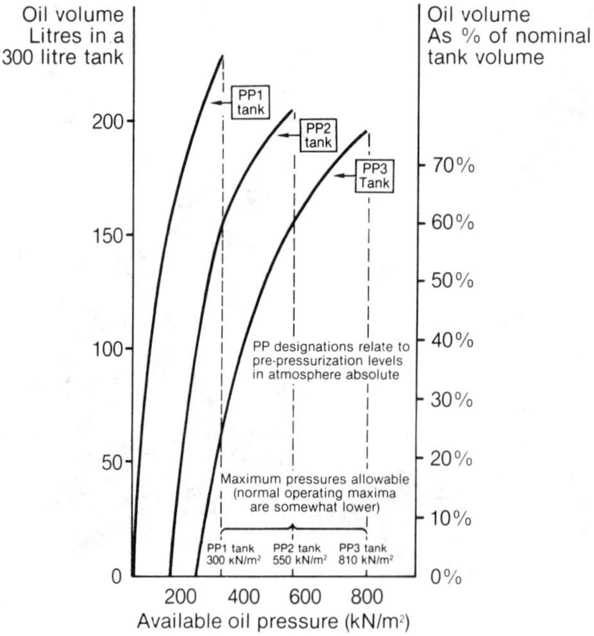

Fig. 33.12 Characteristics of pressure tanks at 15 °C

prevent any oil flow across the joint. The maximum economic difference in head is about 30 m to 40 m. Individual sections vary very considerably in length according to circumstances and may extend up to 3 km or more in special case. Fig. 33.13 gives an indication of what is an average case.

Whilst preparation of a preliminary hydraulic scheme which would be quite satisfactory is quite a quick and straightforward matter, the choice of the most economic solution at the planning stage is usually quite complex. It is advantageous not only to concentrate the tankage in large units at the smallest number of locations, but also to use a minimum of the more expensive straight stop joints. Such factors have also to be taken into account in calculating cable lengths between feed positions, to ensure that no excessively high static pressure, or low transient pressure, will arise at positions remote from the feed points.

Reliability of such a system is extremely high and very little maintenance is involved. Each hydraulic section is normally fitted with a pressure gauge having a low pressure alarm contact which is connected via a supervisory system to a suitable control centre. If the cause of loss of pressure is not obvious from examination of the pipework, methods of location have to be followed. These usually include freezing

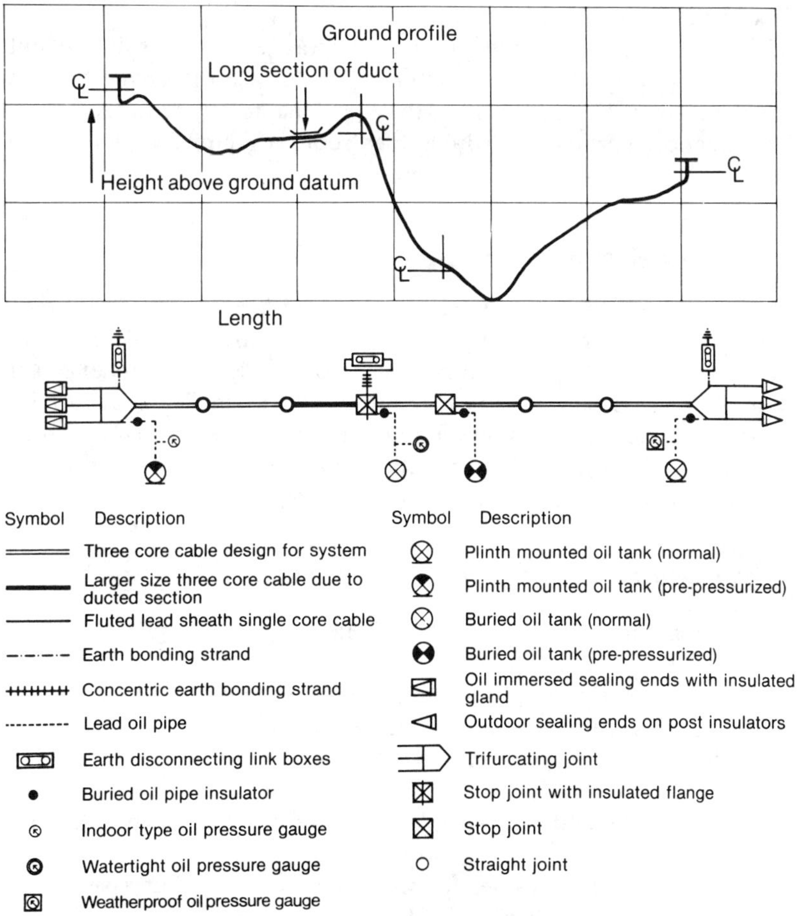

Fig. 33.13 Typical line diagram of a self-contained OF system

by the use of nitrogen gas and observation of pressure on each side of the frozen section to ascertain the side containing the leak. Most leaks are usually at very low rates and there is sufficient oil in the tanks for the system to be kept on load for a period until it is convenient to carry out a repair.

SYSTEM DESIGN

As outlined in fig. 33.13, a complete installation will consist of terminations to overhead lines or switchgear or transformers, plus usually straight and/or straight stop joints. The terminations are always made on single-core cables and with 3-core cables it is necessary to use trifurcating joints for connection to single-core 'tails'.

Use of single or 3-core cables

Up to about 150 kV, 3-core cables are manufactured as standard. Upwards from about 200 kV, size limitations dictate that only single-core cables are practicable. Between these voltages special consideration may be given to the manufacture of 3-core cable of smaller conductor sizes.

In general, a 3-core installation provides a more economic solution unless the route length is very short, say up to 200 m, in which case the saving by eliminating trifurcating joints may be significant. However, the rating required may exert a substantial influence, particularly with cables requiring large conductor sizes, and each scheme needs to be evaluated in detail.

Cables for railway electrification

In the UK and several other countries, railway electrification now uses an overhead catenary at 25 kV a.c., single-phase. A somewhat unusual OF cable is used as a supply cable, unusual because a two-conductor design is required, one being near earth potential. The construction is concentric with a small amount of insulation over the outer conductor. By using aluminium conductors the lightweight cable is particularly suitable for track-side installation and long spans of the order of 4.5 m may be adopted between cable support posts.

GENERAL TECHNICAL AND PERFORMANCE DATA

Appendix A16 contains information on the following:

Technical data: dimensions, weights, charging current, a.c. resistance and reactance for 33–400 kV cables with lead and corrugated aluminium sheaths (tables A16.2–A16.8); d.c. resistances are given in appendix A4 (table A4.1)

Power ratings: for single- and 3-core cables laid direct and in air (figs A16.1–A16.8)

Electric losses: representative values for small and large conductor size cables from 33 to 400 kV with lead and aluminium sheaths (fig. A16.9)

Chapter 34

Gas Pressure Cables

There are two basic types of paper insulated gas pressure cables, one type employing gas within the dielectric to suppress ionisation, and other type applying gas pressure external to a diaphragm sheath to maintain the dielectric under compression under all service conditions. Cables which employ a gas pressure external to the diaphragm sheath are known as gas compression cables.

This chapter does not deal with SF_6 insulated cables (which are not paper insulated), these being dealt with in chapter 44.

INTERNAL GAS PRESSURE CABLES

In this type of cable the insulation is saturated with nitrogen gas under a nominal pressure of 14 bar, which suppresses discharges which may otherwise have occurred in any cavities within the insulation. Two methods of manufacture are used, i.e.

(a) mass impregnation of the dried paper insulation with a viscous impregnant
(b) the application of paper tapes pre-impregnated with a petroleum jelly type of compound

The early designs of mass-impregnated cable were known as the impregnated pressure (IP) cable and the first commercial installation was carried out in 1940.[1] This type of cable was extensively used in the UK for operating voltages up to and including 132 kV during the 1940s and 1950s, first with a reinforced lead sheath and later with a smooth aluminium sheath.

Problems were encountered as a result of gas absorption by the impregnating compound, which caused frothing when the cable was being degassed, sometimes causing a blockage in the gas pipes or in the annulus below the metal sheath. After this occurred it was often difficult to re-pressurise the cable following repairs or diversions, the re-gassing process sometimes lasting many days before the cable could be recommissioned. Because of these problems and the improvements made in the self-contained oil-filled cable, commercial applications ceased at the end of the early 1960s. The design has continued to be used in North America as a pipe type cable[2] in which migration of impregnating compound does not cause a significant increase in the impedance to gas flow because of the large amount of free space between the cable cores and the pipe.

Another variety of this type of cable, used in North America, is the low pressure gas-filled cable.[3] This is a self-contained cable which operates under a nitrogen gas pressure of 0.6–1 bar. The cable has an unreinforced sheath. After impregnation the cable is drained of surplus compound to avoid the problems associated with

Fig. 34.1 3-core 33 kV gas-filled cable

compound migration described earlier. Because of the low gas pressure, the maximum design stress of this type of cable is only slightly higher than that of solid type paper insulated cables.

The basic principles of the gas-filled (GF) cable[4,5] are that the conductor is insulated with pre-impregnated paper tapes which are processed to ensure that the butt gaps in the insulation are devoid of impregnant and that, prior to entering service, the dielectric is charged with nitrogen to a nominal pressure of 14 bar to suppress ionisation. Hence the gas is an integral component of the composite dielectric.

Substantial lengths of single- and 3-core gas-filled cables are in use in the voltage range 33–138 kV and a limited amount of single-core 275 kV cable has been installed. The main attraction of this type of cable system is the relative simplicity of the ancillary equipment and jointing procedures.

Conventional stranded copper or aluminium conductors are normally used, but in some cases involving long routes of single-core cable, hollow-core conductors are used. All conductors are screened with metallised or carbon loaded paper tapes.

The insulating paper used for gas-filled cables is dried and impregnated in sheet form prior to slitting into tape widths. This process involves passing the paper over two rollers heated to about 200 °C, which reduces the moisture content from about 8% to less than 0.15%, thence into a vacuum vessel, which degasifies the paper, and finally through a tank filled with a paraffinic jelly, which impregnates the paper. Before winding the dried and impregnated paper into roll form it passes over two knives heated to 90 °C to scrape off all impregnating compound adhering to both surfaces of the paper. The large rolls of paper are slit into narrow tapes immediately prior to the start of the core insulating process.

The application of the pre-impregnated paper tapes follows standard dry paper lapping techniques, but as the core does not need to be dried and impregnated after the insulating process, the papers are dimensionally stable and the original lapping tensions are retained in the finished cable. The core therefore has good bending characteristics. The use of pre-impregnated paper tapes ensures that the butt gaps in the helically applied tapes are free of compound, thus providing a path for gas to permeate the dielectric when the cable is charged with nitrogen following the installation of the cable.

In 3-core lead sheathed gas-filled cables, impregnated and drained jute strings are laid into the interstices to allow gas to penetrate along the cable length. Aluminium sheathed gas-filled 3-core cables may be supplied without ducts or fillers in the interstices.

When gas-filled cables are provided with a lead alloy pressure retaining sheath, the application of metallic reinforcing tapes external to the sheath is necessary to enable it to withstand the internal gas pressure. In the earlier cables these tapes were protected from corrosion by a second lead sheath. Soon after gas-filled cables were first introduced, improved rubber and thermoplastic anticorrosion sheaths were developed and these replaced the lead anticorrosion sheath on subsequent cables. At a later date gas-filled cables were introduced with smooth aluminium sheaths which, unlike the lead sheathed cables, did not require additional reinforcement against the internal gas pressure and these are now generally favoured. The thickness of the aluminium sheath is dictated by the bending requirements of the cable. Both lead and aluminium sheaths are applied with a small annular clearance over the core(s) to provide a gas channel from end to end of each cable length. Modern cables are protected from corrosion by an extruded oversheath of high density polyethylene or PVC.

After installation, the gas pressure is maintained by a cubicle located at one end of the feeder, or, in the case of long cable routes, by a cubicle at each end of the route. The cubicle contains two or three cylinders of nitrogen connected into a manifold, the gas being fed into the cable at the base plate of the sealing end or into the trifurcating joint of 3-core cables. The gas feed is controlled by a two-stage regulator and the pressure is monitored by pressure gauges which are equipped with electrical contacts to signal an alarm at a remote substation should the gas pressure fall below 12 bar. In an emergency the cable can be kept in service for a limited time provided that the pressure does not fall below 9 bar.

The gas-filled dielectric has a low relative permittivity (typically 3.2) but the dielectric loss angle is nearly twice that of an equivalent oil-filled cable because of the higher moisture content of the papers. Fig. 34.2 shows the effect of the thickness of the paper (and therefore the depth of the butt gaps) on the ionisation inception stress when under 14 bar nitrogen pressure at ambient temperature.

The thickness of insulation applied to 33 kV gas-filled cables is 3.3 mm, this being dictated by mechanical considerations.

The minimum lightning impulse withstand stress of gas-filled cables is about 85 MV/m at the maximum permissible conductor temperature of 85 °C and the lowest permissible gas pressure. It is this parameter which determines the thickness of insulation required for the higher voltage cables. Taking impulse withstand requirements into account, it is usual to design 66 and 132 kV gas-filled cables to produce a maximum stress at the conductor surface of 8.5–10 MV/m at normal working voltage. When operating at the normal gas pressure, the gas suppresses all discharge activity within the dielectric at all voltages up to about 1.75 times the working voltage.

The cable is substantially non-draining at the maximum conductor temperature and may therefore be laid on severe gradients without adverse effect.

The service record of gas-filled cables has been satisfactory since they were first

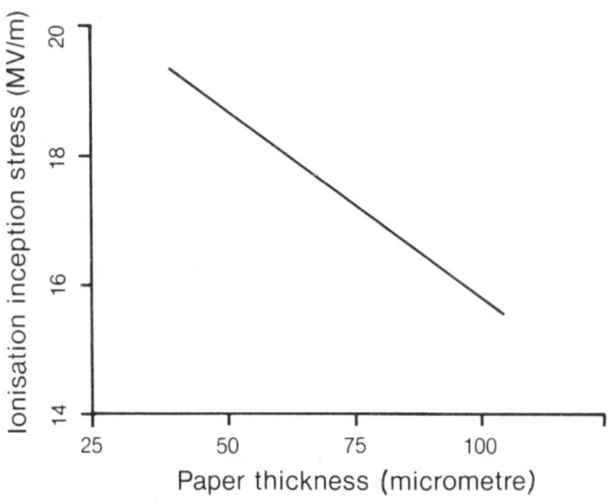

Fig. 34.2 Effect of paper thickness on ionisation inception stress at a gas pressure of 14 bar

introduced in 1937 and there is still a significant demand for this type of cable. The relatively simple terminal equipment required, the ease of jointing and the ready availability of bottled nitrogen in most parts of the world are attractive features, particularly where specialised supertension cable jointers are not available at short notice to repair a damaged cable. Often a damaged cable can be left in service by maintaining a gas feed until repairs can be under taken during a planned outage. Owing to the lower permissible electrical design stress and thicker metal sheaths, gas-filled cables are invariably more expensive than equivalent oil-filled cables. However, when such factors as the absence of stop joints and simplified jointing techniques are taken into consideration, the total gas-filled cable system may prove cheaper than an equivalent oil-filled cable system.

EXTERNAL GAS PRESSURE CABLES

The gas compression cable[6] is designed to facilitate the use of high electrical stresses by maintaining the dielectric in the fully impregnated state under all service conditions by the application of gas pressure external to a diaphragm sheath to prevent void formation within the dielectric. It was first introduced as a self-contained cable, the gas pressure being applied between a diaphragm lead sheath applied directly over the core and an outer reinforced gas retaining lead sheath. In recent years, gas compression cables have been more widely used in pipe type cable systems, three individual or laid-up sheathed cores being pulled into a pre-laid steel pipe which is then charged with nitrogen to a pressure of about 14 bar.

Oval shaped stranded conductors are used for all gas compression cables. The conductor is usually screened with carbon loaded paper tapes and insulated with paper tapes and the core is screened with metallised paper or non-ferrous metal tapes. The insulated core is dried and impregnated in a conventional cable vessel, the impregnant being a viscous compound. Copper or fabric tapes are applied over the diaphragm sheath to reinforce it against the internal pressure created by thermal expansion of the compound and by pressure due to compound migration if the cable is laid on a gradient. For pipe type systems three such cores may be laid up and armour wires applied over an appropriate armour bedding. For self-contained cable three such laid-up cores are sheathed with a reinforced lead sheath or aluminium pressure retaining sheath, served with an anticorrosion sheath.

The original design of gas compression cable was excessively heavy as both diaphragm and pressure retaining sheaths were of lead alloy. In later designs, the use of polyethylene diaphragm sheaths in both self-contained and pipe type cables introduced other problems. As polyethylene is slightly permeable, gas slowly penetrates the diaphragm sheath and goes into solution in the impregnant. When depressurising the cable the gas in the dielectric creates a residual pressure which gives rise to frothing of the impregnant.

Because the self-contained gas compression cable requires both a diaphragm and a pressure-resistant sheath it is generally uncompetitive with other types of pressure-assisted cables. The gas compression cable is therefore now in rather limited use.

The maximum design stresses used in the UK were as follows: for 66 kV cables, 8.5 MV/m; for 132 kV cables, 12 MV/m and for 275 kV cables, 15 MV/m. The maximum conductor size was 800 mm^2.

REFERENCES

(1) Brazier, L. G., Hollingsworth, D. T. and Williams, A. L. (1953) 'An assessment of the impregnated-pressure cable'. *Proc. IEE, Part 2* **100** (78).

(2) Association of Edison Illuminating Companies (AEIC) (Oct. 1982) 'Specifications for impregnated paper-insulated cable, high pressure pipe-type'. New York: AEIC C52–82.

(3) Association of Edison Illuminating Companies (AEIC) 'Specifications for impregnated-paper-insulated, lead covered cable, low pressure gas-filled type'.

(4) Beaver, C. J. and Davey, E. L. (1944) 'The high pressure gas-filled cable'. *J. IEE, Part 2* **91**.

(5) Thornton, E. P. G. and Booth, D. H. (1959) 'The design and performance of the gas-filled cable system'. *Proc. IEE, Part A* **106** (27).

(6) Sutton, C.T.W. (1952) 'The compression cable'. Paris: CIGRE Paper No. 202.

Chapter 35

High Pressure Oil-filled Pipe Cables

GENERAL DESCRIPTION

High pressure oil-filled (HP OF) pipe type cables are used mainly in North America and the USSR. This type of cable was pioneered in the USA and was known in its early days as 'Oilostatic' cable. Fig. 35.1 illustrates a typical HP OF cable. The three insulated conductors are drawn into a steel pipe which is subsequently filled with oil and maintained under a high pressure. Except at terminations, all cables are of 3-core construction, no oil ducts being required within the conductors or between cores.

The route has to be carefully chosen to keep bends to a large radius to prevent any damage to the cores, during pulling-in, arising from side pressure against the pipe wall. Joint bays may be spaced at longer intervals than for self-contained cables.

Fig. 35.1 230 kV HP OF pipe type cable

The basic principle of the HP OF cable is the same as that of the self-contained oil-filled (SC OF) cable, i.e. the insulation is kept fully impregnated at all times. To reduce drainage of oil from the insulation during transit from the factory to site, the cable is impregnated with an impregnant which has a much higher viscosity than that used for the SC OF cable, being similar in viscosity to the impregnants used for solid type cables. To ensure that full impregnation of the insulation is maintained during cooling cycles, it is necessary to use high oil pressures, the nominal pressure of present day systems being approximately 14 bar.

HP OF cables are at present in operation at voltages up to 550 kV (USSR),[1] but the amount at the maximum voltage is very limited and the highest voltage at which significant quantities of cable have been installed is 345 kV (New York USA).[2]

Conductors

Both aluminium and copper conductors are used up to a maximum conductor size of approximately 1250 mm^2. Larger sizes are generally not economic because the closeness of the cores in the pipe gives rise to a high proximity loss in the conductor (chapter 8). For the same reason, the change to the Milliken conductor construction is usually made at a lower conductor size than for SC OF cables. Normally the Milliken conductor is constructed from four stranded segments although conductors consisting of five segments have been used for experimental cables.

Insulation

The requirements for the insulating papers and lapping are generally similar to those already described for SC OF cables. However, in the case of HP OF cables there is an additional requirement for a very firm insulation to minimise deformation due to the side pressures which occur during installation, as previously mentioned.

The impregnant used for the cores would typically have a viscosity of about 3000 centistokes at 20 °C and for the higher voltage cables is usually of the synthetic type.

An important requirement is that the cable cores are transported to the installation site without significant moisture pick-up. In the early days this was achieved by applying a temporary lead sheath on each core and this was stripped off as the cores were pulled into the steel pipe. This technique has been replaced by the application of a taped moisture barrier around the individual cores and the despatch of the cores in an atmosphere of a dried gas on sealed drums. The barrier is applied to the impregnated core and usually consists of several layers of metal and plastic tapes. To produce a low coefficient of friction between cores and pipe and hence minimise pulling tensions, a D-shaped wire, usually of bronze, is applied helically with a short lay over each core with the rounded surface outwards.

The permittivity, dielectric loss angle and thermal resistivity of the dielectric are essentially the same as for SC OF cables. The higher operating pressure gives an advantage in a.c. strength and the somewhat higher viscosity of the impregnant at maximum operating temperature gives a slightly higher impulse strength. In practice, however, HP OF cables tend to be designed to slightly lower maximum stresses than SC OF cables to allow for the higher mechanical stresses imposed during installation.

STEEL PIPE AND INSTALLATION

The pipes are made of carbon steel complying with appropriate national standards for thickness and testing requirements. The size is chosen to permit adequate clearance between the three cores and the pipe. It is important to avoid an internal diameter of the pipe of about three times the diameter of the individual cores as it is possible for the cores to align across a diameter and jam during the pulling-in operation. A requirement of great importance is a need to have the internal surface smooth and clean so that on final filling with oil no serious contamination is introduced. Hence in manufacture the pipe must be cleaned and in some cases the internal surface is coated with a resin which is compatible with the pipe filling oil. Corrosion protection follows general pipe line practice and usually consists of an asphaltic mastic applied to a thickness of about 12 mm. This is supplemented by the application of cathodic protection to the pipes on completion of the installation. The principles of cathodic protection are similar to those adopted for other steel pipe applications. However, the cathodic protection system must be capable of handling the high currents flowing to ground under fault conditions. This is achieved by using devices such as cadmium–nickel batteries or polarisation cells which have a high impedance to d.c. but a very low impedance to a.c.

Compared with the installation of self-contained cables, a major advantage in heavily congested city areas is that only a short stretch of roadway needs to be opened up a time. Installation practice for the pipe is similar to general procedures for oil and gas pipelines in that sections are joined together before being lowered into the trench. A difference is that simple butt welding between pipes cannot be adopted because of the need for a smooth internal surface with no step or projections which might cause damage to the cores during pulling-in. The pipe ends may be flared or a bell and spigot type of joint may be used. The individual welds are tested as the pipe laying proceeds and then the whole length between jointing manholes is checked with dry nitrogen gas at high pressure.

Before cable installation proceeds, any moisture is removed by evacuation of the pipe. For the pulling-in operation the ends of the three cores are connected together and they are pulled into the pipe in one unit with close monitoring of the pulling tension. Depending on the ratio of core to pipe diameter, the cores may be in triangular or cradle formation.

When the laying, jointing and terminating have been completed, the pipes have to be filled with oil. This is carried out by evacuating the pipe to a low vacuum level and then filling with degasified oil. Because of the large quantity of oil contained in the pipe system, the unit used to degasify the oil must have a large output. The oil used to fill the pipe has a lower viscosity than that used to impregnate the insulation, a value of 160 centistokes at 20 °C being typical. This viscosity, associated with the large cross-sectional area of the pipe, results in low longitudinal transient pressures and these can usually be ignored in HP OF cable system design.

After the oil filling operation the system is connected to an oil reservoir and a pumping module is installed, either at one end or both ends according to the length. The purpose of the module is to maintain the required oil pressure in the system at all times. During a period of increasing cable temperatures, an oil pressure relief valve vents excess oil from the cable system into the oil reservoir. When the temperature of the cable system falls, a pressure switch set at a pressure below that of the relief valve comes into operation to activate the pumps to maintain the required pressure in the cable system. The oil reservoir is of sufficient volume to accommodate oil expansion from the cable system plus an additional amount to cater for oil leaks. The reservoir has either a blanket of dry gas or is operated under vacuum to prevent deterioration or contamination of the oil.

SYSTEM DETAILS

In the USA, large underground manholes are prepared at the positions where the cores are pulled into the pipes and these subsequently serve as positions for jointing. They are usually of very large construction produced from precast concrete sections and are of sufficient size for jointers to work comfortably, $5.5 \times 2 \times 2$ m being fairly typical. Although manholes are somewhat costly, the distance apart of jointing positions is usually longer than for self-contained cables.

Jointing practice is generally similar to that with other paper insulated cables, compression ferrules being used to joint the conductors and crêpe paper for the insulation. The three joints are accommodated in a single steel sleeve which bridges the main pipes. An important difference from self-contained oil-filled cables is that, because of the higher strength of the steel pipe, no stop joints are required to limit internal pressure due to differences in route profile.

Termination is achieved by an accessory which connects the main pipes to three smaller pipes. These three separate pipes need to be of non-magnetic material, e.g. stainless steel, to prevent magnetic hysteresis losses. The porcelains used to terminate the single cables have to be designed to cater for the higher internal pressure.

The pumping equipment includes duplicated pumps, automatic switching of pumps, low pressure alarms etc. and is connected through an appropriate monitoring system to a control centre.

CURRENT CARRYING CAPACITY

The current carrying capacity of HP OF cable is slightly inferior to that of 3-core self-contained oil-filled cables and significantly lower than that of single-core SC OF cable. The latter aspect is illustrated in fig. 35.2. The lower current rating compared with single-core self-contained cable arises primarily from two reasons:

(a) The proximity of the cores in the pipe causes the HP OF cable to have a higher a.c. conductor resistance and a higher thermal resistance to ground. In the case of SC OF cables both these effects can be reduced by increasing the spacings between the single-core cables.
(b) There are hysteresis losses in the steel pipe.

As with other types of cable, the ratings of the HP OF cable can be increased by forced cooling. The most widely used form of cooling is forced movement of oil along the pipe. In the case of a single feeder, an oil return pipe is laid alongside the cable and the oil is circulated along the cable and through the oil return pipe and a heat exchanger before being pumped back into the cable. In the case of a double feeder, an oil return pipe can be eliminated by using the second cable for the return oil.

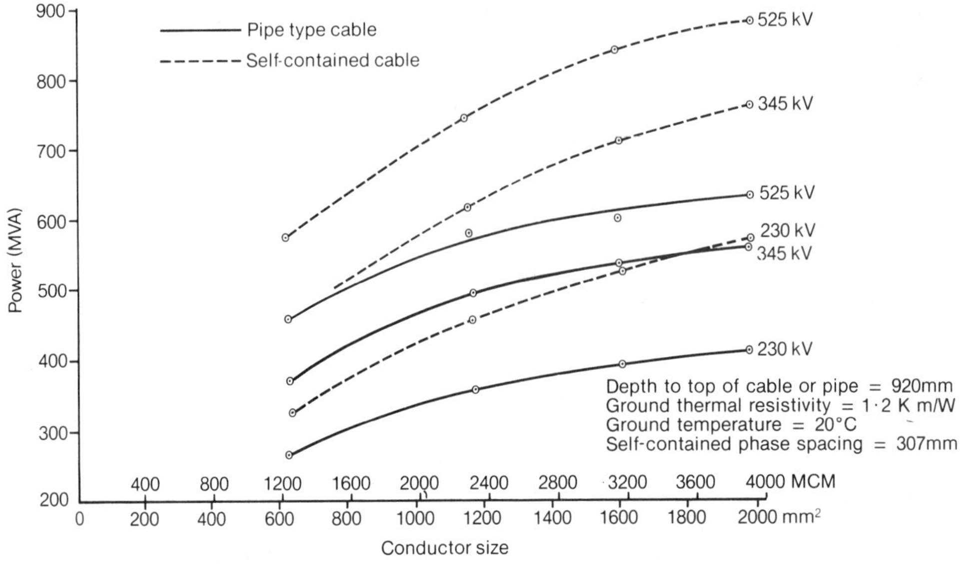

Fig. 35.2 Comparative ratings of HP OF and single-core self-contained oil-filled cables

Although not strictly forced cooling, oil oscillation has been used to overcome localised thermal limitations.

APPLICATIONS

On strictly economic grounds, it is usually difficult to justify the use of HP OF cable systems in place of directly buried SC OF systems for the majority of applications. However, there are certain situations when customers prefer this type of cable. These arise as follows.

(a) In certain countries it is standard practice to install all self-contained power cables in duct banks. This is to permit easy removal in case replacement is necessary. The rating of self-contained cables in ducts is lower than when directly buried due to the air space between the cables and duct. The HP OF cable is considered to be a cable in a duct and therefore the cost comparison with the self-contained cables in this case is more favourable. A further point is that self-contained cables in ducts require special manholes (chapter 39) which can affect the comparison.
(b) When installing HP OF cables it is not necessary to excavate the complete cable trench between joint bays at the same time. This has considerable advantages when a cable circuit is required to pass through a crowded city centre. The principle also applies, of course, to self-contained cable installed in ducts, but the economic effect is less favourable.
(c) Some utilities consider that the steel pipe provides greater protection against dig-ins than a self-contained cable system protected with concrete cover tiles.
(d) When installing HP OF cable it is possible to lay a spare pipe so that a second feeder can be installed at a later date without excavating a trench.

In recent years some problems have been experienced with HP OF systems arising from movement of the cores due to the effects of thermal expansion and gravity on inclined installations. In certain installations, when there is change of elevation, it has been found that there is progressive movement of the cores towards the bottom of the installation. This can result in localised bending of the cores or disturbance at joints. Attempts have been made to overcome the problem by stretching the cores after installation to take up slack but it is probably best to avoid the use of HP OF cable on such routes. Somewhat similar difficulties have been experienced due to thermomechanical movement of the cores, particularly adjacent to joints. Most of the problems have been associated with 345 kV cables where localised flexing of the cable has caused the gaps between papers to increase, with resultant soft spots.[3] The phenomenon is described in chapter 39. To overcome the problem the joints and adjacent cable are now reinforced to prevent the thermal expansion movement from being localised.

REFERENCES

(1) Gleizer, S. E., Goldobin, D. A., Kadomskaja, K. P., Khanukov, M. G., Obraztsov, Y. V. and Peshkov, I. B. (1982) 'Insulation development of oil-filled cables for heavy load transmission'. Paris: CIGRE Paper No. 21–08.
(2) Association of Edison Illuminating Companies (AEIC) (Oct. 1982) 'Specifications for impregnated paper-insulated cable, high pressure pipe-type' (4th edn). New York: AEIC C52–82.
(3) McIllveen, E. E., Waldron, R. C., Bankoske, J. W., Matthews, H. G. and Dietrich, F. M. (1978) 'Mechanical effects of load cycling on pipe type cable'. *IEEE Trans.* **PAS-97** (3).

Chapter 36

HV Polymeric Insulated Cables for Transmission Voltages

In the countries to which UK manufacturers export cables, nearly all the 66 kV cable and about half the 132 kV cable for new installations is of the polymeric type, with XLPE as the usual insulant. In the UK, where there is long experience with the pressure-assisted cable systems, there has been less incentive to use polymeric cables in the 66–132 kV range, but some substantial installations have been made and the polymeric cable is regarded as an alternative to the pressure-assisted types for use when the circumstances of the particular installation favour it.

The operating electrical stresses for polymeric insulation are lower than for OF cables and the insulation thicknesses are therefore greater. This leads to the use of a greater volume of material in the cable. One advantage is that there is no need for the auxiliary equipment required for pressure-assisted cable systems or for the same arrangements for system maintenance. This probably weighs heavily overseas and can also be important in the UK, especially for short route lengths. Dispensing with oil may also be a factor in situations where the effects of fire have to be considered, or may influence users who have had troubles with oil leaks on old cable systems.

INSULATING MATERIALS

Thermoplastic (linear) polyethylene (PE) and crosslinked polyethylene (XLPE) have been the most commonly used polymeric insulants for 66–132 kV cables, while ethylene–propylene rubber (EPR) has had limited use. The low dielectric losses of polyethylene, both PE and XLPE, make it an attractive proposition at high voltages. The importance of dielectric losses in high voltage cables is discussed in chapter 44. With a dielectric loss angle less than 0.001 and relative permittivity typically 2.3, polyethylene has a distinct advantage over impregnated paper in this respect. The same does not apply to EPR. Dielectric losses become increasingly important with increase in voltage and are even more significant at voltages above 132 kV. Having high intrinsic electrical strength as well, polyethylene is therefore generally favoured for the range of high voltage applications.

XLPE has the major advantage over PE that it enables the cables to be operated at higher temperatures. 90 °C is the maximum sustained operating temperature for XLPE, compared with 70 °C for PE. This has a significant effect on the relative current ratings. In France, some use has been made of high density polyethylene, with a maximum sustained temperature of 80 °C allocated; this reduces the difference from XLPE without achieving equality.

XLPE insulated cables are therefore used in most countries. In some countries where there has been substantial experience with PE, however, its use has continued, presumably because confidence in it has developed. The manufacturing process for

PE is simpler, without the complications of crosslinking. In France, for example, it was reported[1] in 1980 that 30 km of 90 kV and 65 km of 225 kV PE insulated cables were installed, some of which had been operational for nearly 10 years then, and the incidence of faults had been very small. As recorded in chapter 44, in 1986 there were said to be some 690 km of 225 kV PE cable in service and short lengths of 400 kV cable had been commissioned. PE has therefore not given way completely to XLPE, but use of the latter is growing more rapidly.

DESIGN OF HV POLYMERIC CABLES

All the higher voltage cables have circular conductors and only single-core constructions are adopted. The conductors are formed from compacted stranded wires and both aluminium and copper are used. As discussed in chapter 25, extruded semiconducting screens are used to sandwich the insulation. However, at these voltages a strippable screen is considered inferior to the bonded screen and the latter has been used exclusively. Conductor screens are generally about 0.8 mm thick, whilst the outer screen is a little thinner and thicknesses between 0.5 and 0.8 mm are fairly typical.

Unlike the situation up to 30 kV, there are no constructional standards available which dictate the thickness of insulation required at the various voltages. Nevertheless, there does appear to be a reasonable correlation between the various thicknesses used in most countries and table 36.1 shows typical figures. There are some departures from these, usually in a downward direction, but they give an approximate indication of practice.

Table 36.1 Relationships between cable voltage and insulation thicknesses

Voltage (kV)	Insulation thickness (mm)	Maximum stress at conductor (kV/mm)
33	8.0	2.7–3.2
66	12.0	4.0–5.0
110	18.0	5.0–6.5
132	20.0	5.5–7.0
225	24	8.0–10
275	29	8.5–10

A considerable number of HV polymeric insulated cables installed prior to the 1980s relied on the application of helically applied copper wires to act as the earth envelope. These wires were protected by either a PVC or a polyethylene extruded oversheath. However, because of the phenomenon of water treeing and the prospect that the onset and growth of water trees are likely to be accelerated by high electrical stress levels, it seems wiser to adopt an extruded metallic sheath to prevent the ingress of moisture to the insulant. At the same time, this sheath can also serve as the essential earth return path around the HV cable. Many other designs have incorporated the use of a lead sheath extruded either directly over the outer semiconducting extruded screen or over a further protective conducting tape.

Extruded metallic sheaths are protected by either a PVC or polyethylene oversheath. As with paper insulated cables, in order to monitor the condition of the cable both after installation and during its service life, a graphite layer is applied over the outer plastic sheath to enable d.c. voltage to be applied between this layer and the inner metallic envelope. Fig. 36.1 shows the design of a 66 kV XLPE insulated cable with an extruded lead sheath protected by a PVC oversheath.

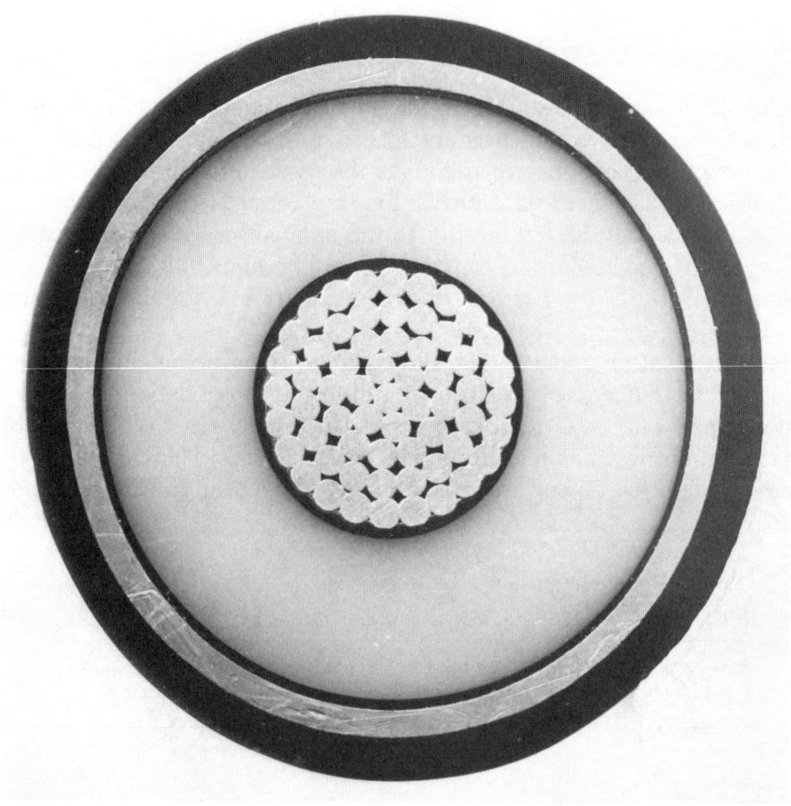

Fig. 36.1 66 kV XLPE insulated cable with lead sheath and PVC oversheath

A corrugated aluminium sheath is an alternative to the lead sheath. Substantial amounts of 66 kV XLPE cable with corrugated aluminium sheath, some with polyethylene oversheath and a smaller proportion with PVC oversheath, have been supplied to and installed in Singapore for example.

MANUFACTURING PROCESS

Linear PE is applied in a horizontal line. While there are now more complex horizontal lines for XLPE, the methods with which there is most experience suitable for crosslinked insulation of the thickness for cables above 33 kV employ either a vertical line or a catenary line. In chapter 25 the benefits associated with manufacture of XLPE by dry processes are discussed and these are preferred for the higher voltages. They can comprise any of the following: radiant heat under a pressurised inert nitrogen atmosphere, circulating pressurised heated nitrogen, circulating heated pressurised silicone oil or pressurised molten eutectic salts.

The insulant which emerges from any of these lines will have a moisture content of 250 ppm or less, dependent on the facilities adopted to cool the insulant as it leaves the vulcanisation zone.

For 66 and 132 kV cables, catenary lines have been favoured because the ratio of their output to capital cost is considerably higher than for a vertical line. The arrangement of the extruder is simpler with the vertical line and triple extrusion heads were first developed for this configuration. A triple head for a catenary line was not developed until later and the practice was to set the extruder applying the semiconducting screen to the conductor on its own at a distance of 2–3 m from the dual head connected to the extruders supplying the insulation and outer core screen. If the insulated conductor moves upwards or downwards as it moves through the catenary tube, the smooth layer of semiconducting material over the conductor can be scraped by the dies of the dual head. Minor imperfections in this layer have an adverse influence on the impulse characteristics of the cable.

Later, catenary lines for high voltage cables were installed with four extruders, in a dual/dual mode. The conductor screen and approximately 1 mm of insulation are applied simultaneously through the first dual head, followed by the application of the main wall thickness of insulation and the outer semiconducting layer at a second dual head, about 2–3 m down line from the first extruders. Any scuffing which occurs at the second head is immediately healed as the second layer of insulation welds to the under layer.

This configuration is also ideal for the application of an emission shield, if in the future the advantage of such a layer is amply demonstrated. The emission shield consists of a thin layer of extruded high permittivity material. It has the property of reducing the effect of any high stress area arising from imperfections on the surface of the conductor screen. As yet there is no universal acceptance of the advantage of such a layer.

The subject of contamination and its influence on the electrical properties is discussed in chapter 25. For HV polymerics to be satisfactory in service, scrupulous cleanliness is essential during both the compounding of the polymer and the manufacture of the cables. Manufacturers are imposing high standards of hygiene on suppliers of the polymer and in the transfer of the material to the extruder. Extruders are now available which enable the peroxide and antioxidant to be added to the polymer at the same time as the extrudate is applied to the conductor. This modern plant eliminates the need to precompound the additives into the polyethylene as a separate process. It also reduces the risk of contaminating the insulant and provides a lower cost material.

As a result of the decomposition of peroxide in the vulcanising zone, small microvoids are formed in the insulant which contain gases pressurised to approximately the same level as that pertaining inside the tube. Generally a figure of 10 bar is typical. The gases diffuse out through the insulant with time, thereby reducing the pressure within the void. If the insulant is exposed to high temperature too soon after being cured, there is a danger that the void size will increase within the now softened material. For this reason many manufacturers post-treat the cured cable prior to the application of an extruded metallic sheath. The core is left in a 'hot box' at a temperature of about 50 °C for up to 30 hours and by this means it is possible to accelerate the rate of diffusion of the volatiles out of the insulant.

The method of application of a lead or aluminium sheath is identical to the long established processes discussed in chapter 26.

CABLES FOR 275 kV AND ABOVE

The potential of polyethylene as an insulant for high voltage cables, especially on account of its low dielectric losses, and of XLPE particularly, with its permissible operating temperature of 90 °C, has already been mentioned.

A length of 275 kV XLPE insulated cable was installed in Japan as long ago as 1979[2] and since then more installations have been made of 275 kV cable produced there, although the total amount is limited. As recorded in chapter 44, short lengths of 400 kV XLPE cable have also been installed.

Other countries are developing XLPE cables for voltages around 275 kV and in Sweden, for example, a limited quantity has been produced. Experimental lengths have been made in the UK.

Cables rated at 275 kV and above are generally required to transmit large amounts of power; currents, as well as voltages, are high. Generally, therefore, the conductors are large and of the Milliken type. The cables are much heavier and larger than the normal range of cables for voltages up to 132 kV. The plant required to produce them is different in scale and in other respects, with perhaps a vertical extrusion and crosslinking line, which is the most expensive of the options in capital cost, offering the best prospects for consistent concentricity of thick insulation on heavy cable.

Whatever method of insulating is adopted, the capital costs for a manufacturer entering this field on a commercial basis would be high and a reasonably assured market would be needed for the cable that the plant was designed to produce and for other cables for which it was also suitable.

As discussed in chapter 44, there are other types of cable under consideration for high voltages and in the UK the XLPE cable for 275 kV and above can be regarded as being included in the scope of future developments.

REFERENCES

(1) Deschamps, L., Michel, R., Lepers, J., Jocteur, R., Midoz, J., Favrie, E. and Terramosi, G. (1980) 'Results of tests and experience in service in France with high voltage cables with synthetic insulation.' Paris: CIGRE Paper No. 21–06.

(2) Shinoda, S., Hikino, K. and Marumo, M. (1980) '275 kV XLPE insulated aluminium sheathed power cables for Okuyahagz No. 2 power station.' *IEEE Trans.* **SM–80**, 549–6.

Chapter 37

Techniques for Increasing Current Carrying Capacity

Because of the high cost of supertension cables compared with overhead lines the proportion of underground cables in the UK transmission circuits is less than 10% of the overhead lines.[1] Hence transmission voltages and power ratings are selected to give the most economic overhead rather than underground transmission system and cable ratings are normally dictated by the current rating of the overhead line to which they are connected.

In 1969 the overhead line ratings in the UK were substantially increased, following a reappraisal of the previously assumed limiting environmental conditions, but without departing from the traditional value of a maximum conductor operating temperature of 50 °C. Since that time the operating temperature has also been increased to 65 or 75 °C, according to the construction. The resulting overhead line ratings for 275 and 400 kV lines are shown in table 37.1.

It is through trying to meet these ratings (where possible with one cable per phase) that many developments in cable design, system design and installation practices have been made.

Table 37.1 Transmission capability of 275 and 400 kV UK overhead lines

		Rating (MVA) at three operating temperatures		
		50 °C	65 °C	75 °C
275 kV, 2 × 400 mm^2 conductors	Cold weather	905	971	1038
	Normal weather	730	854	953
	Hot weather	585	757	869
400 kV, 2 × 400 mm^2 conductors	Cold weather	1320	1412	1510
	Normal weather	1065	1242	1386
	Hot weather	850	1102	1264
400 kV, 4 × 400 mm^2 conductors	Cold weather	2640	2824	3021
	Normal weather	2130	2483	2771
	Hot weather	1700	2203	2527

Cold weather: ambient temperature < 5 °C
Normal weather: ambient temperature 5–18 °C
Hot weather: ambient temperature > 18 °C

The three most important aspects which have enabled cable systems today to meet the wide range of rating requirements at voltages from 132 to 525 kV have been (a) the use of special backfills, (b) attention to sheath bonding on single-core cables and (c) artificial cooling of the cable by the use of external water pipes or internal oil circulation.

SPECIAL BACKFILLS

Background

It was customary in the UK, up to the early 1960s, to assume a constant value for the soil thermal resistivity along the whole length of the cable route, and to calculate the conductor size required to carry the load continuously without exceeding the maximum design conductor temperature. Experience had shown that for most installations an assumed value of thermal resistivity of 1.2 K m/W had resulted in perfectly reliable cable systems. However, in July 1962 there were two successive failures of 132 kV transmission cables in the London area. Both circuits had been operating at or near full load almost continuously during the summer and the backfill in the region adjacent to the hot cables had dried out. The consequent increase in soil thermal resistivity and resultant overheating of the cables led to thermal runaway conditions and cable failure.

Because of these failures, considerable work was carried out to develop backfills for the cable surround which have a low value of thermal resistivity under fully dried conditions. These backfills are now grouped into two classes as follows.

Selected sands

These are sands obtained from approved selected sources so that the *in situ* thermal resistivity in the dried out state is not greater than 2.7 K m/W.

The category of selected sand has been arrived at from consideration of the availability in the UK of naturally occurring sands with good cohesion properties and of the general relationship between thermal resistivity and density of such sands in the dry state. The sand needs to be of a coarse type with a mixture of particle sizes.

Stabilised backfills

Stabilised backfills are composite materials specially selected so that the *in situ* thermal resistivity in the dried out state is not greater than 1.2 K m/W.

At present two main types of stabilised backfill are used: cement-bound sand which consists of selected sand mixed with cement in the proportions 14:1, and a sand–gravel mixture consisting of a 1:1 mixture of selected sand and gravel. The latter should have a particle size not less than 10 mm, preferably rounded particles and not more than 50% crushed material.

UK practice

Where required by rating and installation conditions, allowance for migration of moisture is today made by assuming that the thermal resistivity of all materials surrounding the cable within the 50 °C isotherm will have a value corresponding with a dry condition.[2] However, the cost of stabilised backfills is approximately three times that of selected sands, and therefore special backfills are only used where they can be justified economically. In practice, therefore for 132 kV and below, stabilised backfills are not normally used unless heavy loading is envisaged during summer conditions. At 132 kV the cable bedding is generally a selected sand and below 132 kV traditional locally available sands and riddled soil are usually used for backfilling. For 275 kV and higher voltage cables, where the dielectric losses tend to maintain elevated temperatures during periods of low load, stabilised backfills are now the normally accepted materials for the cable surround.

The typical improvement in rating of a 132 kV circuit, which results from the use of special backfills, can be seen in fig. 37.1. This shows the comparison between placing selected sand and stabilised backfills within the 50 °C isotherm, in an indigenous soil having a normal thermal resistivity of 1.2 K m/W and dried out thermal resistivity of 3.5 K m/W. It will be seen that in this case the use of selected sand results in an increase in rating of approximately 3%, and the use of stabilised backfill in an increase in rating of between approximately 15% and 20%, depending on conductor size. The method of calculating these ratings is based on that given by Cox and Coates.[3]

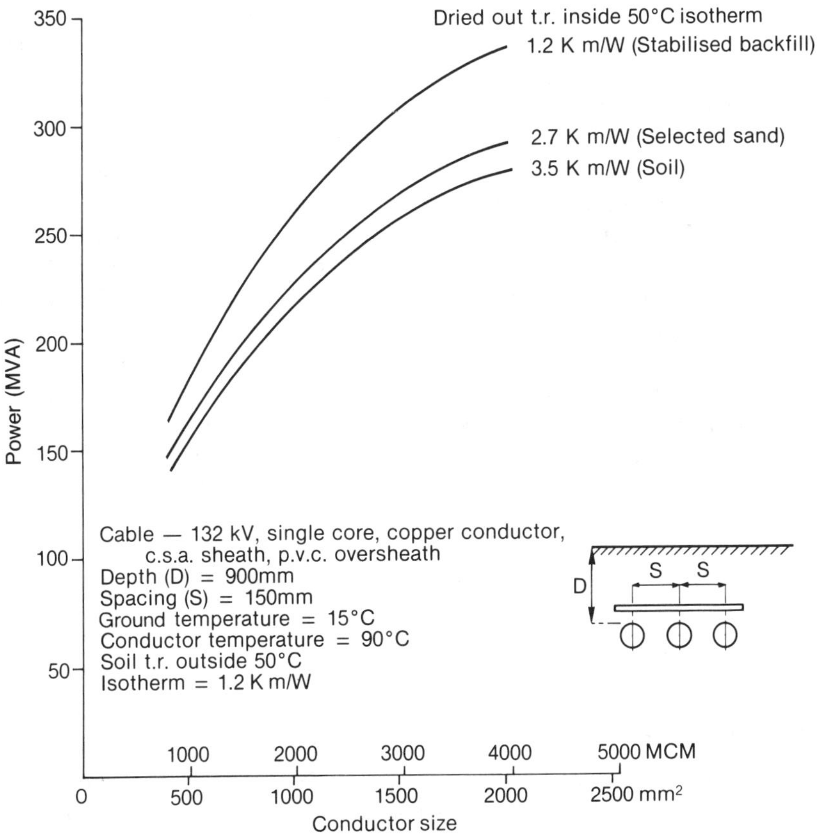

Fig. 37.1 Effect of dried-out thermal resistivity (t.r.) on the power rating of laid-direct 132 kV cable installation

Extension of UK practices overseas

Around the world a wide variation in soil thermal resistivities may be encountered from about 0.6 to 3.5 K m/W. The value for any particular installation has to be based on local measurements, and the calculation of current ratings normally assumes that this thermal resistivity remains constant. For instance, in Hong Kong the accepted value for rating calculations is 0.9 K m/W, which has been determined from a considerable amount of work by the local supply authority. However, for their first 400 kV installation it was considered that the effects of soil moisture migration should be allowed for. Thermal resistivity measurements along the route showed that the ground where the trench would be dug had a thermal resistivity of no greater than 0.7 K m/W and measurements of fully dried soil samples showed these to have thermal resistivities as low as 1.2 K m/W. The rating was therefore based on the soil within the 50 °C isotherm being fully dried out but with a general ground thermal resistivity outside this region not greater than 0.7 K m/W. Thus, in this case, the soil is being used for direct backfilling of a 400 kV circuit.

Reduction of ground thermal resistivity

Where high resistivity soils are encountered, such as in areas of the Middle East, replacing the cable surround with low thermal resistivity material can enable the required rating to be met with a reduced conductor or trench size, resulting in an overall cost saving. The lower thermal resistivity material placed in the trench and the thermal resistivity of the ground will give an 'effective' thermal resistivity value between the two. It is not possible, however, to calculate the thermal resistance of the elements in a multiple thermal resistance backfill arrangement by means of a simple mathematical formula. A number of computerised methods of solution are possible; one developed by Winders[4] enables the effective ground thermal resistivity to be deduced. This value can then be used to calculate the thermal resistances by the method given in IEC 287.[5]

A typical example of the effect of placing lower thermal resistivity material in the trench is shown in fig. 37.2 where, for the 132 kV cable configuration shown, the effective thermal resistivity of the middle cable to ground is given for the cables buried in soil of thermal resistivity 3.5 K m/W and with the trench progressively filled with material of 1.2 K m/W. Also shown in fig. 37.2 is the improvement in rating which results from the reduction in the effective ground thermal resistivity. It will be seen that in this case the effect of placing lower thermal resistivity materials in the trench is to increase the power rating from approximately 125 MV A to a maximum of 170 MV A (approximately 36% increase) depending on the amount of lower thermal resistivity material used.

Bentonite filled ducts

The air space between a cable and the inner surface of a duct has relatively poor heat transmission properties and this results in a reduced rating for cables installed within ducts compared with laid-direct systems.

Today this thermal problem has been eliminated on relatively short duct runs (less than about 70 m) by replacing the air with a mixture of bentonite, cement, sand and

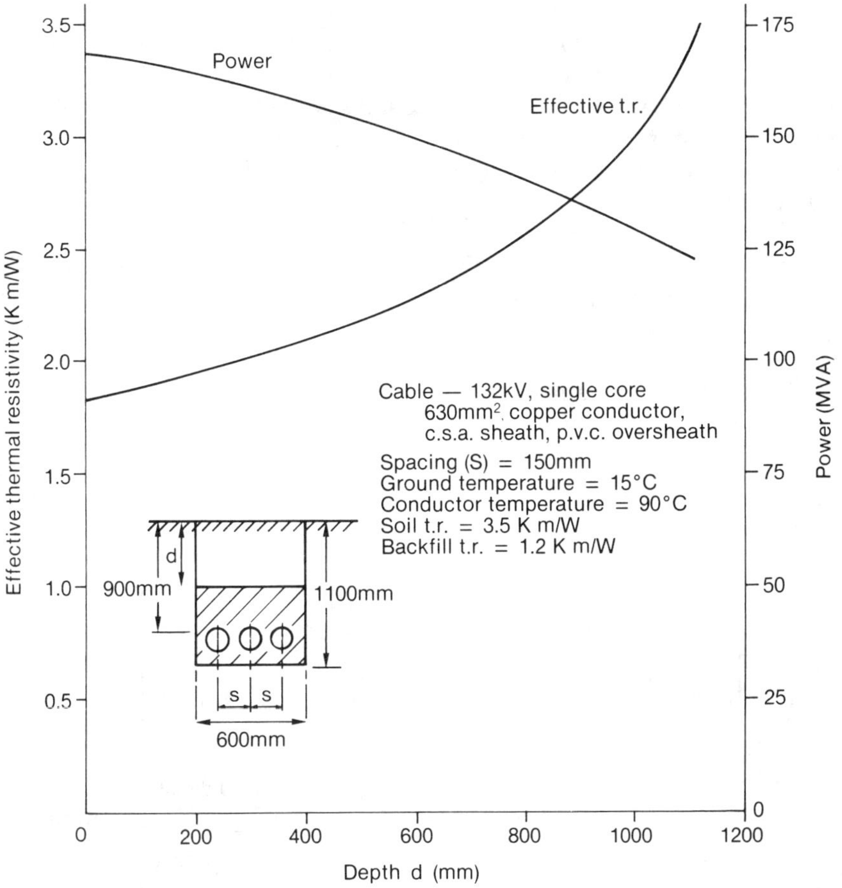

Fig. 37.2 Variation of effective ground thermal resistivity and power rating with depth of special backfill

water. This mixture can be pumped into the duct using standard pressure grouting techniques. When sealed within the duct it remains a gel which can be flushed out using water jets.

The grout is sufficiently stiff to provide a constraint against thermomechanical movement of the cable and it was for this reason that it was first adopted.

The ducts must be effectively sealed to prevent loss of the filling medium and also to preserve its moisture content under service conditions. Provided that the moisture is retained, the thermal resistivity of the bentonite grout will be less than 1.2 K m/W. The use of bentonite results in an increase in rating of approximately 10%.

Troughs

The availability of stabilised backfills has encouraged the adoption of an alternative method of installing cables in filled surface troughs. Considerable savings in excavation costs are possible and troughs have been used extensively in the UK for cable routes alongside railways, canals, in switchyards and in rural situations. The shallow troughs are formed from concrete with thick reinforced concrete lids to afford mechanical protection. The filling can consist of cement-bound sand or a sand–gravel mix.

Thermally, a trough system can be regarded as a shallow laid-direct system. However, conventional current rating procedures are not directly applicable, because the trough lid is not isothermal due to the close proximity of the cables. The rating is also much more influenced by changes in climatic conditions than a deeply buried cable. Experimental work has shown that these effects are best allowed for by adopting a higher effective ground temperature.

For a trough system with an effective ground temperature of 40 °C and a thermal resistivity of 1.2 K m/W, the resulting ratings are very similar to those of the laid-direct system as shown in fig. 37.3. However, if a lower effective ground temperature of 10 °C can be assumed (such as occurs during winter) the trough installation generally gives an improved rating compared with a laid-direct system.

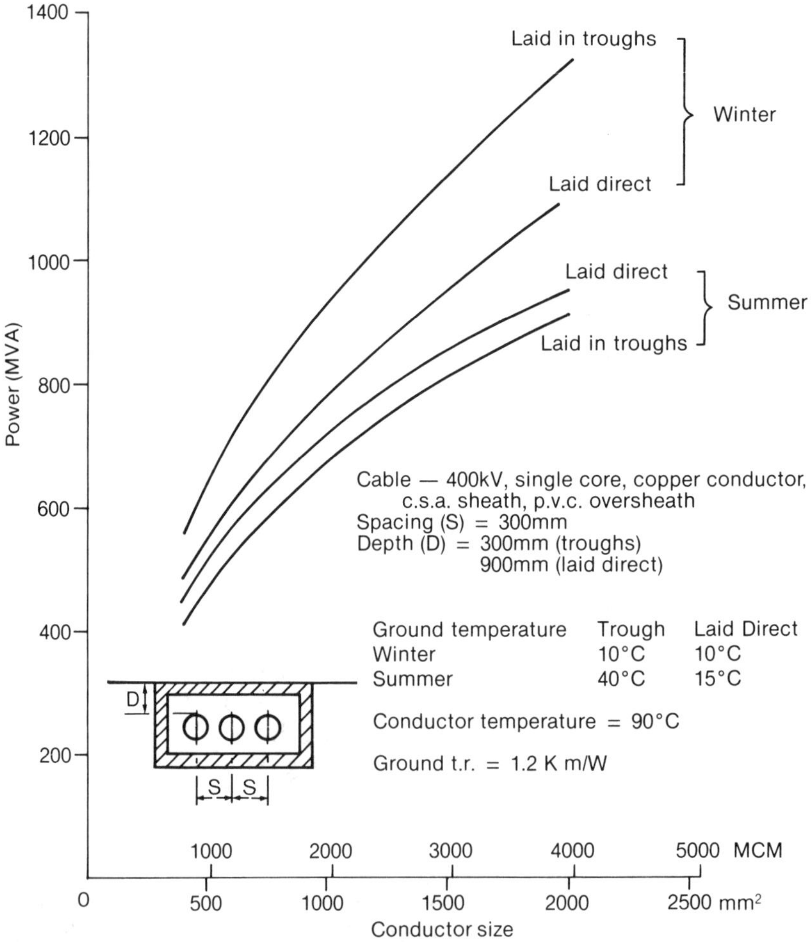

Fig. 37.3 Power ratings for cables installed in troughs

SPECIALLY BONDED CABLE SYSTEMS

Distribution voltage cables are normally installed with solidly bonded sheaths and, in order to minimise the sheath circulating currents on single-core cables produced by the magnetic flux linking the conductors and sheaths, they are nearly always laid in close touching trefoil formation. However, trefoil formation is poor for heat dissipation, as the three cables have a considerable heating effect upon one another. This is generally not a limitation for cable systems at 33 kV but with larger conductor sizes and higher voltages alternative 'specially bonded' systems[6] are more economic. At 275 and 400 kV they often provide the only practical means of meeting the required ratings with natural cooling.

Special bonding involves earthing the single-core cable sheaths at one point only and insulating all other points of the sheath from earth, so that the circulating sheath losses are eliminated and the phase cables can be spaced apart to reduce their mutual heating effect without increasing sheath losses.

When the sheaths are solidly bonded at both terminations, the circulating currents balance the induced voltages so that the whole of the sheath (assuming zero earth impedance) is at ground potential. If one termination only is grounded, the sheaths are subjected to a standing voltage of zero at the ground connection and maximum at the point furthest from this connection. This voltage is proportional to the conductor current and in fig. 37.4 the manner in which the sheath voltage is influenced by cable spacing is shown. To protect the sheath insulation against transient voltages arising from lightning or switching transients it is therefore necessary to fit sheath voltage limiters (SVLs) at all joint and sealing end positions where the sheath is insulated from earth.

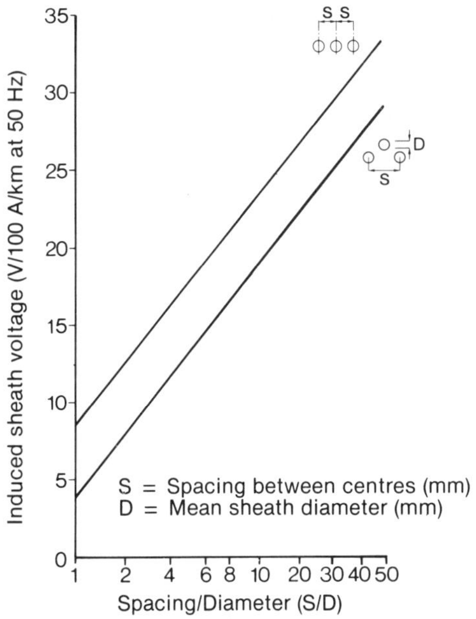

Fig. 37.4 Variation of induced sheath voltage with axial spacing

Three basic variations of specially bonded systems are commonly used: end-point bonding, mid-point bonding and cross-bonding.

End-point bonded system

In this system the sheaths at one termination are earthed and at the other termination are insulated from ground and fitted with SVLs as shown in fig. 37.5. It is necessary to provide a separate earth continuity conductor for fault currents which would normally return via the cable sheaths. In the UK the standing voltage at the sealing end is usually limited to 65 V, and protection from contact with the exposed metalwork at the terminations is provided by resin bonded glass fibre shrouds. The standing voltage is proportional to the cable length and therefore the voltage limitation imposes a limitation on the length of the cable that may be bonded in this manner (about 500 m).

Mid-point bonded system

Bonding of the mid-point is used where the route length is too long to employ an

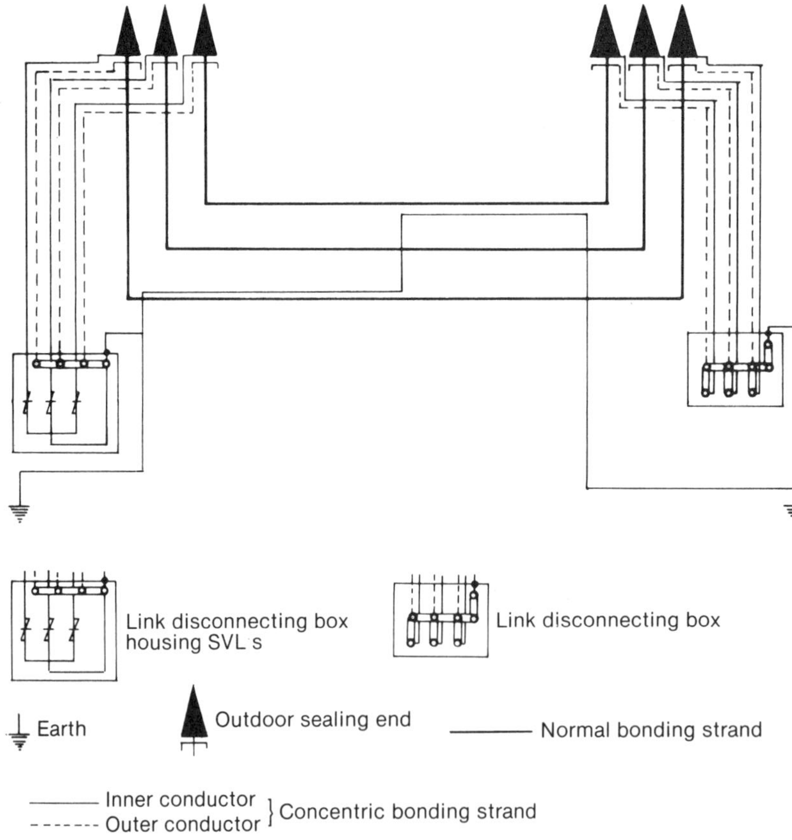

Fig. 37.5 End-point bonding system

end-point bonded system. In this system the cable is earthed at the mid-point of the route and is insulated from ground and provided with SVLs at each termination. It can be seen that this doubles the possible route length, as 65 V can be tolerated at each sealing end.

Cross-bonded system

Either of the foregoing methods of bonding is suitable for comparatively short routes, but for longer routes the cross-bonded system must be used, as shown in fig. 37.6.

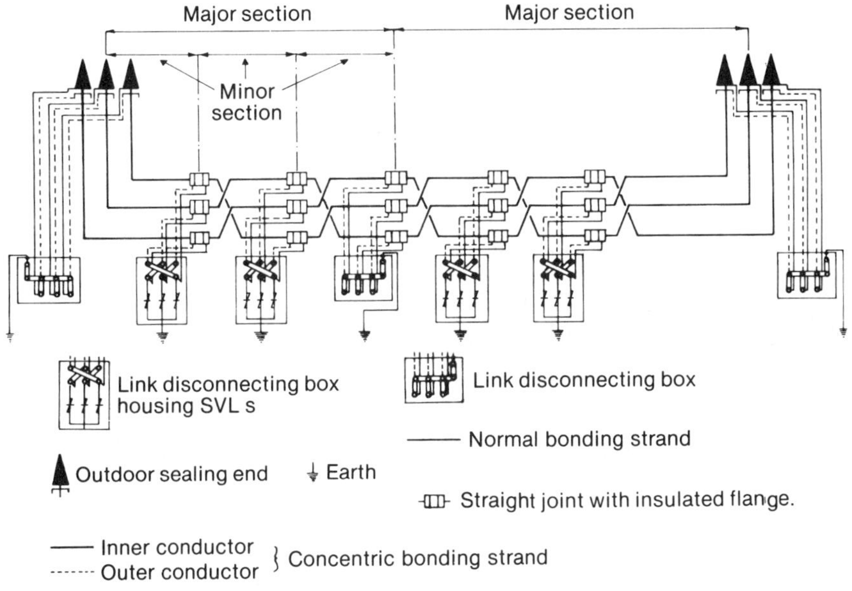

Fig. 37.6 Arrangements in a cross-bonded system

In this system the route is split up into groups of three drum lengths and all joints are fitted with insulated flanges. At each third joint position the sheaths are connected together and at all other positions they are connected so that all sheaths occupying the same position in the cable trench are connected in series. The sheaths at the intermediate positions are also connected to SVLs.

The three sheaths connected in series are associated with conductors of different phases and when the cables are installed in trefoil formation their currents, and hence the sheath voltages, have equal magnitude and phase displacements of 120°. The overall effect is that the resultant voltage across the three sheaths is zero.

When cables are laid in flat formation the voltages induced in the sheaths of the outer cable are greater than that induced on the sheath of the middle cable and the phasor sum is not zero. The cables are therefore transposed at every joint position and the cross-connections are made with a phase rotation opposite to that of transposition so that the sheaths are effectively straight connected, i.e. the sheath of the middle cable of section 1 connects onto the middle cable of section 2 etc. By this method the phasor sum of the sheath voltages over three successive elementary sections is again zero.

The voltages of the sheaths to earth are as shown in fig. 37.7. It can be seen that the maximum voltage is the maximum voltage on each cable length, i.e. 65 V, but the voltage over the three-drum-length section is zero. This pattern can be repeated continuously for any route length without the sheath voltage exceeding 65 V. The system does not require an earth continuity conductor as the sheaths are continuously connected and it is only necessary to earth the sheaths at the ends of each major section. It is to be noted that the voltage induced in the sheaths in the outer position is greater than that induced in the centre sheath.

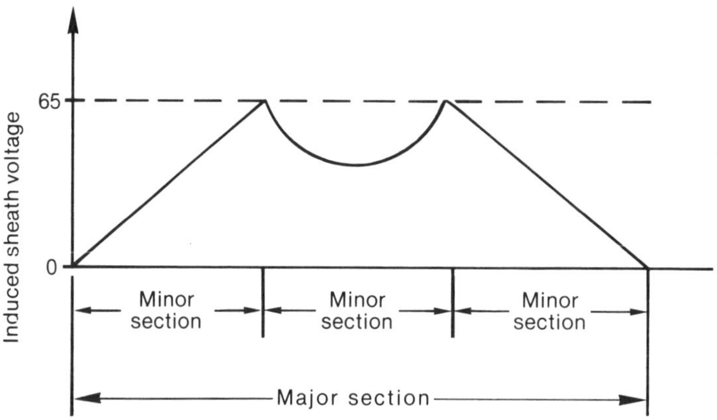

Fig. 37.7 Variation of sheath voltage to earth on a cross-bonded system

Ratings of specially bonded systems

It is apparent from the foregoing that it is possible to increase the current rating of a cable system by improving the heat dissipation through laying the cables in flat spaced formation and eliminating the sheath circulating current losses by employing a special bonding system. This is illustrated in fig. 37.8 where comparison is made between the ratings applicable to 400 kV solid bonded and cross bonded cable systems having lead and corrugated aluminium (CSA) sheaths.

In this case the effect of special bonding is to increase the current rating of the lead sheathed cables by between approximately 15% and 50% and the CSA sheathed cables by between approximately 25% and 80%, depending on conductor size. The bonding system does not, of course, eliminate the sheath eddy current losses but these are reduced by the wider spacing which would be employed.

An improvement in rating is achieved but this is at the expense of having a more complex and costly system due to the provision of SVLs, link boxes and in some cases an earth continuity conductor. It is only economic, therefore, to provide specially bonded systems where the circulating losses are large. Today, specially bonded systems are generally only utilised when conductor sizes greater than 630 mm^2 are required. Although they are cheaper for smaller sizes than this, the saving involved is not usually considered to be worth the additional system complication.

All specially bonded systems must of necessity be fully insulated systems.

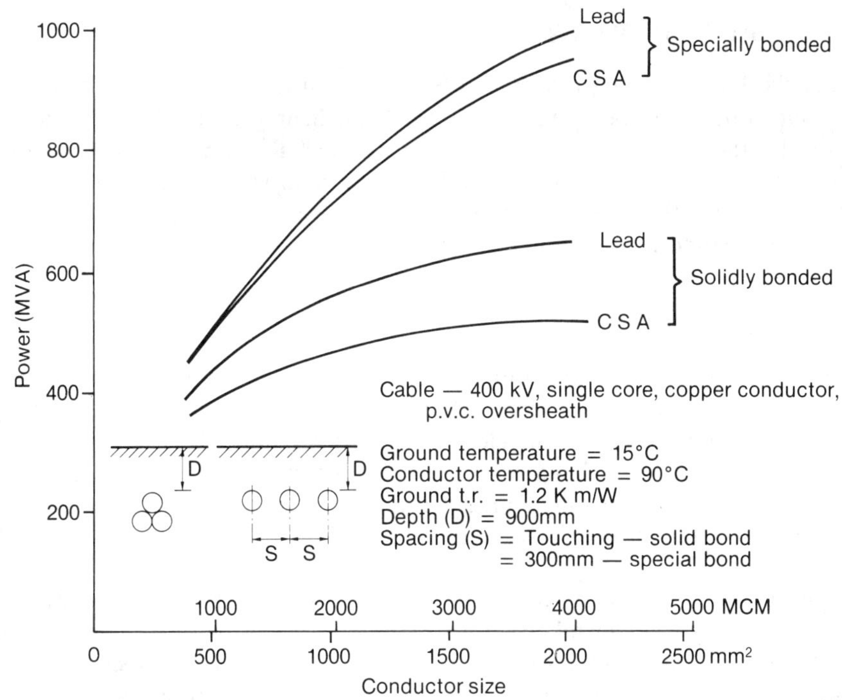

Fig. 37.8 Power ratings for specially bonded cable systems

The fully insulated cable system

To take advantage of the specially bonded cable systems it is necessary to insulate the cable sheath from earth. This is achieved by having an extruded serving of PVC or PE on the cables and housing the joints in compound filled fibreglass boxes to insulate them from the surrounding soil. The sealing ends are also mounted on pedestal insulators to isolate them from their supporting steelwork. The cables are provided with a conducting graphite coating on the external surface so that periodically the serving can be tested for any damage by applying a voltage (usually 10 kV d.c. for 1 min initially and 5 kV for subsequent tests) between the cable sheath and the graphite conducting coating. For ease of testing, bonding and earthing are via removable links in lockable boxes provided at all bonding positions.

Sheath voltage limiters (SVLs)

To limit high voltages appearing on the open-circuited sheaths of specially bonded cable systems under transient voltages, it is necessary to fit SVLs between the sheath and ground. The type of SVL used in the UK is a non-linear resistor having characteristics of a high impedance to current flow when the voltage across it is low but an extremely low resistance when the voltage is high. The SVLs are contained in a sealed box and housed in the associated link box. Concentric bonding leads are used to connect the accessories to the link boxes, the concentric design being used to reduce the surge impedance of the leads to a minimum.

FORCED COOLED CABLE SYSTEMS

To meet the highest rating requirements it is not always possible to design a cable system with one cable per phase, where all the heat generated can be dissipated naturally by the surrounding ground, even if specially bonded systems with very wide phase spacings and special backfills are used. In such circumstances it is only possible to achieve the required rating by the use of multiple cables per phase, or by making use of some form of forced cooling.

Separate pipe cooling

For laid-direct installations the simplest method of forced cooling for self-contained oil-filled cables, and the most commonly used in the UK, has been to pump cooling water through pipes installed in close proximity to the cables. In the UK, high density polyethylene pipes have been used for this purpose. They can be manufactured, transported and installed in the same lengths as the cables. Pipes with a nominal bore up to approximately 85 mm and a pressure rating of 11 bar at 25 °C are used.

A typical arrangement of cables and cooling pipes is shown in fig. 37.9 which shows two cooling pipes installed between the cables and two positioned above the outer cables. Cooling water is normally passed down two of the pipes and returned via the others to cooling stations where the water temperature is reduced by either water–water or water–air heat exchangers before being returned to the inlet pipes. To achieve the highest ratings, the heat extracted by the pipes must be maximised but at the same time cooling section lengths must be made as long as possible to minimise problems in siting heat exchangers. The cooling stations are therefore constructed at suitable positions along the cable route, taking account of the environmental as well as technical requirements. Many such stations have been installed in the suburbs of London and fig. 37.10 shows a typical example. A considerable number of separate pipe cooled systems have been installed in the UK[7,8] and subsequently in Vienna.[9] The thermal design of such systems is complex[10] and, in addition to the normal environmental parameters, several other variables have to be allowed for, e.g.[11]

(a) cable–pipe configurations
(b) water flow patterns
(c) number of pipes
(d) pipe sizes
(e) pipe operating pressure and life
(f) coolant temperature
(g) heat exchanger cooling temperatures

The hydraulic design of the cooling pipe system takes into account such factors as the profile of the route, cooling characteristics of the heat exchangers and availability of cooling station sites.

The problem of obtaining suitable sites for cooling stations along the route (a typical size for an air–water heat exchanger station is 28 m × 11 m × 4 m high and for a water–water heat exchanger station 24 m × 8 m × 4 m high) will frequently

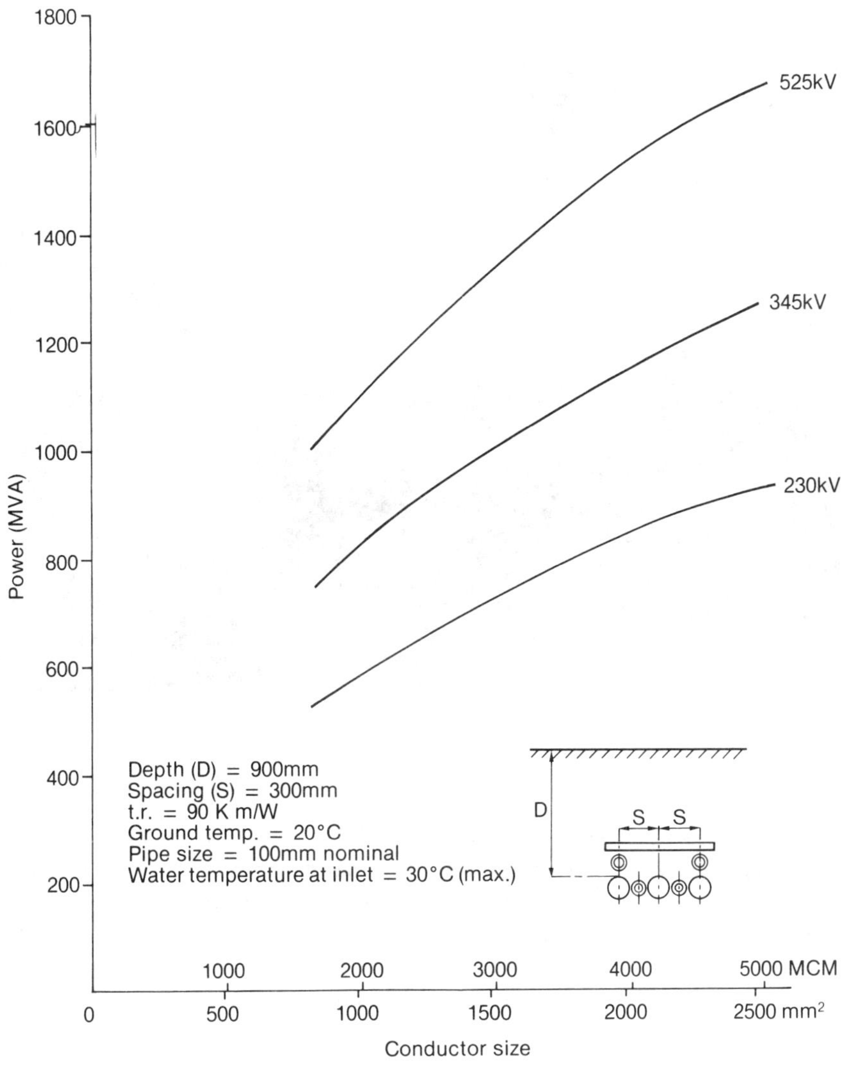

Fig. 37.9 Power ratings for cables installed with separate pipe cooling

limit the possible number of such stations and this can be the limiting design criterion.

Heat transfer relationships in separate pipe cooled systems

If it is assumed that the ground surface is effectively isothermal and that thermal resistivities are not temperature dependent, it is possible to apply the principle of superposition. Thus, at any given position, the cable sheath and water temperature rises (θ°C) and heat emissions (W/m) are governed by a matrix equation of the form

$$[\theta] = [T]\,[H]$$

where the square matrix $[T]$ (K m/W), consisting of 'self' and 'mutual' heating

Fig. 37.10 Typical cooling station in an urban area

coefficients, is dependent on the geometry of the cables and pipes and on the thermal resistivities of the ground, cable oversheaths and pipes. In this equation, whenever the pipe is cooling the system, the pipe heat emission will be negative.

The above, however, is concerned only with radial heat transfer. If water is flowing along the pipes at a rate of q 1/s, then heat will be absorbed to raise the temperature of the water along the route of length L km. The longitudinal heat transfer is governed by the relationship

$$\frac{\mathrm{d}\theta}{\mathrm{d}L} = \frac{-H}{4.18q} \ (^{\circ}\mathrm{C/km})$$

The factors which affect the matrix elements $[\theta]$, $[T]$ and $[H]$ and the influence of water flow rate are many and have to be fully considered in order to design the most economic scheme for any particular installation.

Ratings of separate pipe cooled systems

Typical ratings achievable with 230 kV, 345 kV and 525 kV systems for the conditions specified and a typical cooling section of 3.2 km are included in fig. 37.9. Two cooling sections are normally fed from each heat exchanger and this results in heat exchangers sited every 6.4 km along the route. For comparison, the ratings applicable to the same installation but without forced cooling are shown in fig. 37.11. It will be seen that separate pipe cooling provides very significant improvements in rating, particularly at the higher voltages. For instance at 525 kV the increase in current

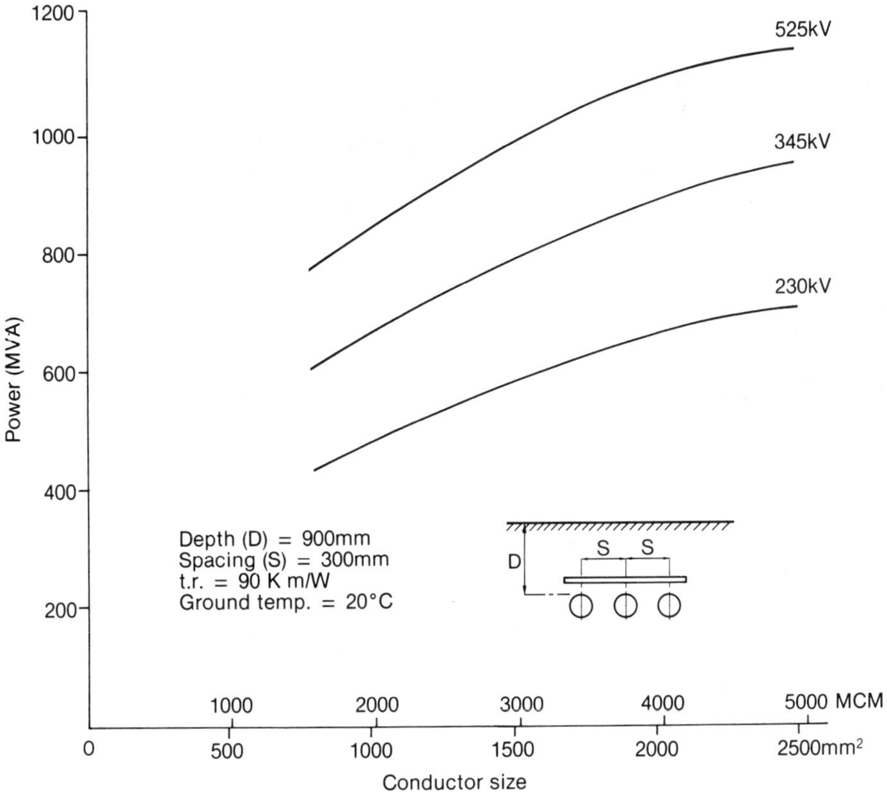

Fig. 37.11 Power ratings for laid-direct installations

rating of a 2500 mm^2 cable is from 1120 MV A to 1700 MV A, an increase of over 50%.

Integral sheath cooling

Integral sheath cooling is an extension of separate water pipe cooling with the difference that, instead of the pipe being laid alongside the cable, the cables are pulled into the water pipes. The pipes are larger than those used for separate pipe cooling and to date systems with one cable per pipe have been used. A circulatory cooling system is normally used, the cooling water being pumped out along one pipe and returned via the other two. The pipe with the outward water flow, which has a flow rate twice that of the other two pipes, can have a larger diameter to reduce pumping pressures. To avoid current induced losses and corrosion problems, non-metallic pipes are preferred. Suitable materials are unplasticised PVC, glass-fibre reinforced PVC or asbestos cement. A corrugated aluminium sheath cable protected with a high density polyethylene oversheath is essential for this application, because this type of cable sheath has a high resistance to fatigue strains arising from thermo-mechanical movements. Where long cooling sections are employed it may be necessary to increase the diameter of the conductor oil duct to allow cooling of the accessories by oil oscillation or circulation.[12]

Ratings of integral cooled cable systems
As the water is in direct contact with the oversheath of the cable and the flow is turbulent, the external thermal resistance is reduced effectively to zero. The rating therefore depends only on the cable characteristics and the maximum water temperature in the system. The latter depends on the inlet water temperature, cable losses, water flow rate and heat exchanger characteristics.

Typical ratings achievable with 230 kV, 345 kV and 525 kV integral sheath cooled systems for the conditions stated are shown in fig. 37.12. The lower thermal resistance between the cable and the cooling water, compared with the separate pipe cooled system, produces a significant improvement in rating and at 525 kV a rating of over 2000 MV A can be achieved, an increase of approximately 80% on the laid-direct rating.

With this type of cable cooling, and to a lesser extent with separate pipe cooling,

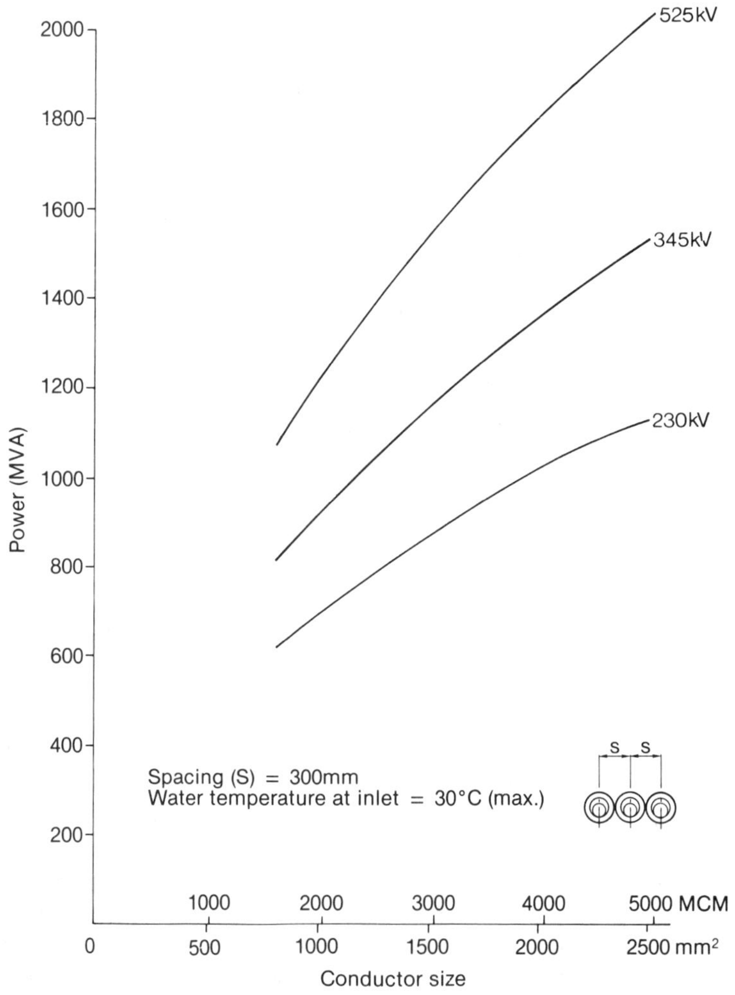

Fig. 37.12 Power ratings for integral sheath cooled cables

significant increases in rating are possible by increasing the insulation design stress. This is illustrated in fig. 37.13 for a 525 kV 2000 mm^2 cable. In the case of naturally cooled cables, the maximum rating is achieved with a design maximum stress of about 13 MV/m for the assumed conditions. For higher design stresses the reduction in cable thermal resistance is not sufficient to offset the increase in dielectric losses, the net effect being a reduction in the current rating of the cable system.

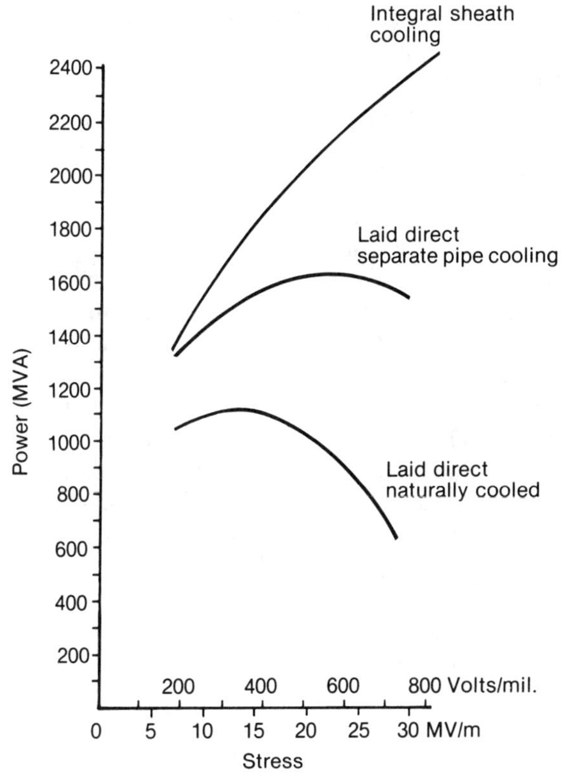

Fig. 37.13 Variation of power rating with cable design stress for a 525 kV, 2000 mm^2 cable

In the case of the integral sheath cooled system, the thermal resistance of the insulation is virtually the total thermal resistance, and hence any reduction will have a far greater effect on rating than in a naturally cooled system. Hence, as shown in fig. 37.13, the rating will increase with design stress and it is desirable to use the highest practical design stress. Fig. 37.13 also illustrates that the rating versus stress characteristic of a separate pipe cooled system lies between those of the naturally cooled and integral sheath cooled systems.

The 400 kV cable system for the Severn Tunnel

An integral sheath cooled cable system has been installed in the UK.[12] It consists of a 400 kV 2600 mm^2 oil-filled cable with a design stress of 15 MV/m installed in resin bonded glass-fibre-reinforced PVC pipes. The installation is in a 3670 m tunnel beneath the River Severn and the River Wye. The design maximum rating is 2600 MVA at a maximum conductor temperature of 95°C.

Internal oil cooling

The most efficient method of obtaining increased rating is to remove the losses at source. This is the principle of the internally oil-cooled cable in which oil is circulated through the conductor, which is itself the main source of the losses. To obtain adequate flow rates the central oil duct is enlarged from the standard 12 mm diameter normally used and oil is fed in and extracted at feed joints situated at intervals along the route. The feed joint is similar in design to the stop joint used with the self-contained oil-filled cable system except that the oil passages are larger to take the greater oil flow.

Ratings of internally cooled cable systems

With internal oil cooling there is virtually no inherent limit on current rating. The practical limitations become the maximum duct size that can be incorporated in the conductor, the spacing of feed joints and the maximum pumping pressure. Fig. 37.14 illustrates the variation in rating of a 525 kV cable system with spacing between feed joints, using a copper conductor of 2000 mm^2 cross-section having a 50 mm oil duct.

A rating of just over 4000 MVA is possible with a spacing between feed joints of 1 km and an advantage of the system is that, because the losses are extracted at the conductor, it can be made virtually independent of its environment. Therefore, such factors as depth of burial and the thermal properties of the ground can be ignored.

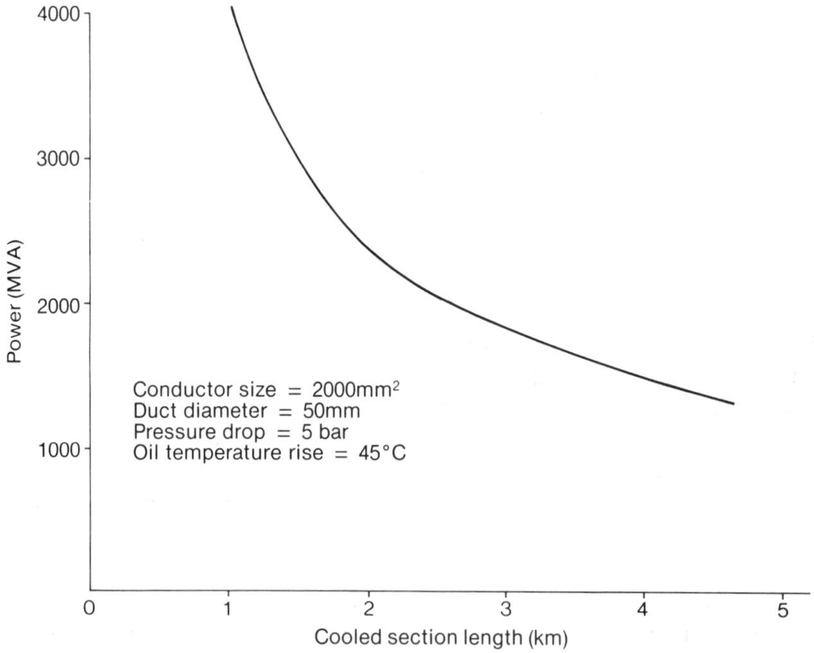

Fig. 37.14 Variation of power rating with cooled section length for 525 kV, 2000 mm^2 cable

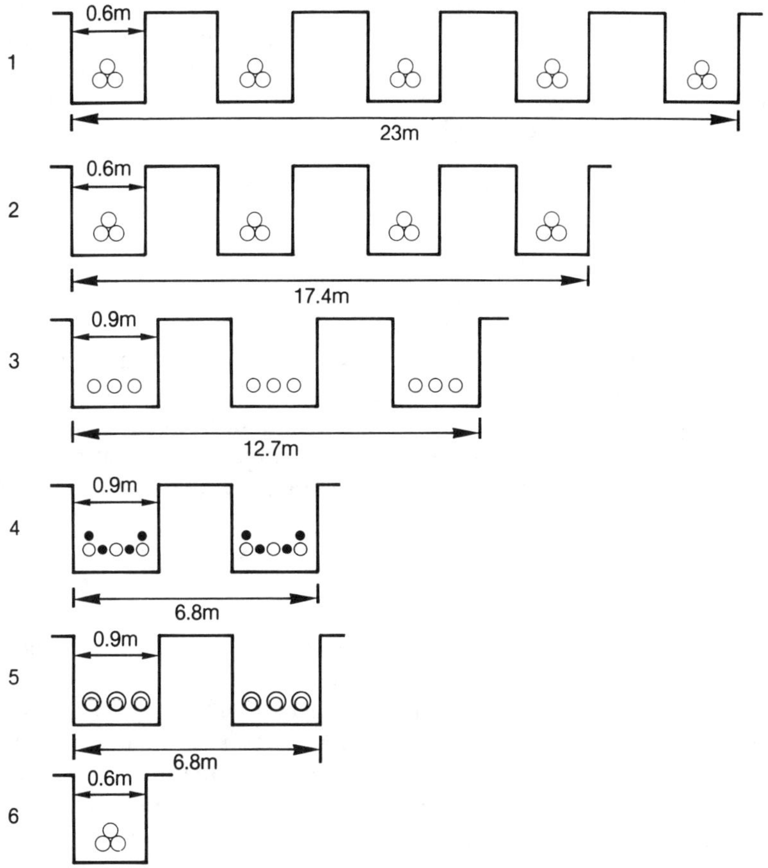

Fig. 37.15 Comparative space requirements for 400 kV circuits of similar rating (copper conductor cable with lead sheath and polyethylene protective finish)

(1) five circuits, 1600 mm^2 – solid bonding, dried-out thermal resistivity of 3.0 K m/W within 50 °C isotherm
(2) four circuits, 2000 mm^2 – solid bonding, stabilised backfill of dried-out thermal resistivity of 1.2 K m/W
(3) three circuits, 1600 mm^2 – 300 mm spacing, cross-bonding, stabilised backfill
(4) two circuits, 2000 mm^2 – separate pipe cooling, cross-bonding, stabilised backfill
(5) two circuits, 1300 mm^2 – integral sheath cooling, cross-bonding, stabilised backfill
(6) one circuit, 2000 mm^2 – internal oil cooling, cross-bonding

Field trials of 400 kV internally oil-cooled cables

To date, although trial installations of internally cooled 400 kV cables have been subjected to extensive tests in the UK,[13] no commercial internally oil-cooled systems appear to have been completed. One of the test installations consisted of 3100 mm^2 aluminium conductor cable with a 35 mm duct and the other of 2000 mm^2 copper conductor cable with a 50 mm duct. The installations included a feed joint, straight joint and sealing ends, together with associated oil pumps and cooling equipment. The tests on the aluminium and copper conductor cables extended over 100 and 200 load cycles respectively, while energised at 1.1 times working voltage. The power factor measurements on the cable system and the circulating oil were stable throughout the trials and examination showed that the condition of the cable after the trial was satisfactory.

SUMMARY

At the beginning of this chapter it was pointed out that many of the advances in supertension cable technology have resulted from the requirement to meet the overhead line ratings given in table 37.1. As a summary, some details are given below to assess how three major developments have contributed towards meeting these ratings and the effect on the economics of underground cable transmission in the UK.

These economic factors are often complex and difficult to quantify[14] but an appreciation can be obtained by considering the cable size and number of circuits required to meet a particular rating, e.g. the normal weather 400 kV, 4 × 400 mm^2, 75 °C overhead line rating, i.e. 2771 MV A.

The effects of the developments can be illustrated by considering them in six separate stages, as shown in fig. 37.15. The first case assumes that special backfills, special bonding and forced cooling had not been developed, but that conductor sizes up to 2000 mm^2 are available. For this case five thermally independent trefoil circuits would be required to meet the rating.

Case 2 shows the effect of using stabilised backfill within the 50 °C isotherm and this results in the number of trefoil cable circuits required being reduced to four. Case 3 illustrates the use of special bonding, with the effect that the number of flat spaced cable circuits required is reduced to three. Cases 4, 5 and 6 demonstrate that by forced cooling using water pipes the number of circuits can be reduced to two and by internal oil cooling to one.

Though quoted in a somewhat arbitrary manner, the above indicates how the reduced costs from the successive developments provide savings resulting from using fewer circuits which are considerably greater than the increased cost due to the extra complexity of the installation.

REFERENCES

(1) Banks, J. (1974) 'Electric power transmission: the elegant alternative'. *Proc. IEE* **121** (1), 419–58.

(2) Cox, H. N., Holdup, H. W. and Skipper, D. J. (1975) 'Developments in U.K. cable-installation techniques to take account of environmental thermal resistivities'. *Proc IEE* **122** (11).

(3) Cox, H. N. and Coates, R. (1965) 'Thermal analysis of power cables in soils of temperature-responsive thermal resistivity'. *Proc. IEE* **112** (12).

(4) Winders, J. J. (1973) 'Computer programme analyzes heat flow cables buried in regions of discontinuous thermal resistivity'. Vancouver: IEEE PES Summer Meeting and EHV/UHV Conf. Paper T 73 502–2.

(5) IEC 287 (1969) 'Calculation of the continuous current rating of cables (100% load factor)'.

(6) CIGRE Study Committee 21, Working Group 07 (May 1973) 'The design of specially bonded cable systems'. *Electra* (28).
(7) Alexander, S. M., Smee, G. J., Stevens, D. F. and Williams, D. E. (Sep. 1979) 'Rating aspects of the 400 kV West Ham–St. John's Wood cable circuits'. *IEE 2nd Int. Conf. on Progress in Cables and Overhead Lines for 220 kV and Above.*
(8) Arkell, C. A., Doughty, D. F. and Skipper, D. J. (Apr. 1979) '400 kV self-contained oil-filled cable installation in South London, UK (Rowdown–Beddington)'. *7th IEEE/PES Transmission and Distribution Conf.*
(9) Arkell, C. A., Bazzi, G., Ernst, G., Schuppe, W.-D. and Traunsteiner, W. (1980) 'First 380 kV bulk power transmission system with lateral pipe external cable cooling in Austria'. Paris: CIGRE Paper No. 21–09.
(10) CIGRE Study Committee 21, Working Group 08 (Oct. 1979) 'The calculation of continuous ratings for forced cooled cables'. *Electra* (66).
(11) Alexander, S. M. and Smee, G. J. (Sep. 1979) 'Future possibilities for separate pipe cooled 400 kV cable circuits'. *IEE 2nd Int. Conf. on Progress in Cables and Overhead Lines for 220 kV and Above.*
(12) Arkell, C. A., Blake, W. E., Brealey, A. D. R., Hacke, K. J. H. and Hance, G. E. A. (Mar. 1977) 'Design and construction of the 400 kV cable system for the Severn Tunnel'. *Proc. IEE* **124** (3).
(13) Brotherton, W., Cox, H. N., Frost, R. F. and Selves, J. (Mar. 1977) 'Field trials of 400 kV internally oil-cooled cables'. *Proc. IEE* **124** (3).
(14) Cherry, D. M. (Mar. 1975) 'Containing the cost of undergrounding'. *Proc. IEE* **122** (3).

Chapter 38

Transmission Cable Accessories and Jointing For Pressure-assisted and Polymeric Cables

The basic accessories are the terminations at the ends of the cable circuit, which seal the cable and provide a connection to other items of transmission plant, and the joints which connect lengths of cable together. Accessories are an integral part of the cable system and are required to exhibit an equal performance to the cable to achieve the highest system rating at the lowest cost.

Unlike the cable, the accessories are assembled on site, often in adverse weather conditions and in confined locations such as joint bays excavated in the ground or located within tunnels and subterranean chambers. The joint insulation is applied by hand without the factory benefits of controlled tape tension, of superclean extruders and of controlled temperature and humidity. Therefore accessory designs and jointing techniques have been developed to reduce the jointing time to a minimum, both to reduce costs and particularly to reduce the contamination of the insulation by the absorption of moisture, air and airborne debris.

GENERAL CRITERIA

Electrical considerations

The concept of designing joint insulation is similar for all types of cable. Compared with the cable, a greater thickness of insulation is applied over the conductor connection so as to reduce the electric stress and thus compensate for the reduction in strength caused by the presence of an interface between the cable and joint and by enlarged gaps between adjacent and overlying insulating tapes. The difference in diameter of insulation between the cable and accessory introduces a component of electric stress along the surface of the insulation, i.e. its weakest direction. The magnitude of this longitudinal stress is an important design parameter, particularly for paper insulated cable, which determines the profiled shape of the conductor connection, the dimension of the cable insulation pencil and the profiled shape of the earth screen, termed the stress control profile. The increase in diameter over the insulation also increases the thermal resistance of the accessory and, unless alleviating steps are taken, it increases the operating temperature of the joint in comparison with that of the adjacent cable. Each accessory has to be thermally designed by limiting the insulation diameter to improve radial heat dissipation and by minimising the length to improve longitudinal dissipation through the conductor.

The type of cable insulation is the determining factor in the design of the accessories and in the techniques of jointing. Oil-impregnated paper insulated cable has been developed to operate at the highest electical design stress and is established at the highest transmission voltage and ratings. Developments to extend the performance of this dielectric further continue to be made to the impregnant, in the form of synthetic hydrocarbon and silicone oils, and to the tape, in the form of low loss laminates of paper and polypropylene. The basis for reliable performance remains unaltered, that the degasified low viscosity oil is both the principal insulant and the means of eliminating gaseous voids. Jointing on OF cables is facilitated by the ease of removal of discrete layers of screening and insulating tapes. The performance of the accessory is tolerant to variations in jointing accuracy because of the inherent resistance of paper to electrical discharging and because the oil is formulated to quench a discharge by the absorption of gas.

Polymeric cable has been made available at transmission voltages by the development of superclean insulation, supersmooth screens and a sophisticated triple extrusion process which employs dry curing under high nitrogen pressure.[1] The quality of the insulation depends on the complete exclusion of sources of electrical discharge such as imperfect screen interfaces, gaseous voids and particulate contamination. Polymeric cable is significantly larger in diameter because of the low design stress and is therefore mainly employed for lower transmission ratings at voltages of 66 kV and 132 kV.[2]

XLPE is the preferred insulant because of its inherent low dielectric loss, although particular EPR compounds are selected for some applications because of increased elasticity and tolerance to moisture. The accessories are similar for both XLPE and EPR cable. The advantage of the polymeric cable is the simplicity of ancillary equipment and of maintenance, because of the absence of a fluid impregnant. This is a disadvantage to the accessory and requires both that the jointer uses a high standard of accuracy and cleanliness and that the designs incorporate other means of eliminating the voids which are inherently associated with the preparation of the surface of the cable dielectric.

Mechanical considerations

The accessories experience increased mechanical loads compared with the cable due to their presence as a mechanical discontinuity in the system. As the cable conductor and sheath generate both tensile and compressive thermomechanical forces in service[3–5] the conductor connection is designed to withstand such loads and the insulated core is reinforced to prevent excessive lateral movement. Polymeric insulation has a memory of the extrusion process in the form of elastic strain, which is released by cutting, and of locked-in strain, which is relieved by heating.[6,7] Retraction of the insulation is confined to be local to the cut end because of the distributed nature of adhesion to the stranded conductor. To prevent retraction from the joint it is important to constrain the insulation additionally and to transfer the tensile loads from one cable to the other.

Straight joints do not experience a differential longitudinal load if the adjacent conductors are of equal area and if the cables are equally constrained. When thermomechanical imbalance is known to be present, an anchor stop joint can be employed to transmit the imbalanced load through the insulated barrier to the joint shell and then through a stanchion to the ground.[4]

Adjacent to cable terminations it is preferred to continue the rigid constraint of the buried cable by close cleating and thus prevent fatigue of the metallic sheath. A rigid insulator is provided for both paper insulated and polymeric supertension cables to constrain conductor movement and to withstand the full thermomechanical conductor load plus the combined effects of busbar loading, short-circuit forces and wind and ice loading. In special circumstances the termination is required to withstand vibrations due to earthquakes and to the operation of the circuit breakers in metal enclosed switchgear.

Pressurised cable systems

The pressure in oil-filled cable systems is maintained by permanently installed tanks of pressurised oil. In gas pressure cable systems, cylinders of compressed gas are connected either to the terminations or to special 'feed joints' installed at predetermined positions along the cable route. In both types of system the function of separating the pressure in adjacent sections of cable is performed by a joint with an insulating barrier which is sealed to the conductor and to the joint shell. This is termed a 'stop joint' in oil-filled cable systems and a 'sectionalising joint' in gas-filled systems. Sectionalising joints are required much less frequently than stop joints. The stop joint and sectionalising joint are also used as feed joints for the oil or gas. In oil-filled systems straight joints predominate and are installed at intervals which are typically 400 m long, whereas stop/feed joints are installed at intervals of 2–5 km, depending on the variation of the static hydraulic pressure along the route. Transition joints are used to connect different types of cable and are similar to stop joints and sectionalising joints in design.

Following manufacture, the joint shells and terminations are submitted to twice the maximum operating pressure, i.e. 10.5 bar for oil-filled cable and up to 34 bar for gas-filled cable.[8] Special accessories have been designed to withstand oil and gas operating pressures of up to 35 bar.[9,10]

Cable ancillaries

The ancillaries are those items of equipment which are permanently installed together with the cables and joints. They provide facilities for maintaining and monitoring pressure and for providing access to the sheath bonding connections to test the cable/accessory sheath insulation.[8] Metal sheaths are fitted to polymeric transmission cables to exclude moisture and as a return conductor for short-circuit current and to paper insulated cables to contain the pressurised impregnant. Single-core cable systems in transmission circuits often employ special sheath bonding to eliminate induced sheath currents and hence increase the current rating.[11,12] This requires that, as with the cable sheath, each accessory shell or sleeve is insulated from ground potential, joint shells being either taped, sleeved or surrounded by bituminous compound and the terminations being mounted on insulated supports. The metallic sheaths of adjacent cables are electrically separated at the joint by an insulated flange in the joint shell and by an insulated gap in the earth screen which covers the joint insulation.

ACCESSORIES FOR SINGLE-CORE OIL-FILLED CABLES (33–525 kV)

Oil flow in single-core cable systems

Oil pressure is maintained in the single-core cable system by a duct located at the centre of the conductor. Terminations and stop joints contain an oil channel which permits the flow of oil between a port in the conductor connection at high voltage to an oil union at low voltage in either the termination sleeve or joint shell and hence to an oil pressure tank. Further details of these are given later. The conductor connection in a straight joint contains a hollow pin which permits oil flow between the adjacent conductor ducts. Additional oil unions are located in the joint shell and termination to permit the accessory to be evacuated from the top union and impregnated with oil through the bottom union. Oil flow from the space between the sheath and cable insulation is prevented during evacuation by a synthetic rubber glove or taped poultice to seal the cable sheath to the core. Oil flow from the conductor connection is sealed during evacuation by an impregnation pin in outdoor terminations and by a drop-out valve in stop joints. These are opened following impregnation, manually in the former case and by oil pressure in the latter.

Outdoor terminations

A 525 kV termination and a 132 kV termination are shown in figs 38.1(a) and 38.1(b) respectively and overall dimensions are given in table 38.1.

Table 38.1 Dimensions of outdoor terminations

U (kV)	BIL (kVp)	Height			Width	
		X[a] (mm)	Y[a] (mm)	Total (mm)	V[a] (mm)	W[a] (mm)
525	1800	5080	1525	6605	1015	840
400	1425	3810	325	4135	585	710
275	1050	2840	290	3130	415	510
161	750	2110	200	2310	255	405
132	650	1710	165	1875	265	405
66	342	1100	310	1410	185	375
33	194	770	185	955	205	230

[a] See fig. 38.1

Insulator
The insulator is made from glazed electrical grade porcelain. The clearance height is determined by the basic impulse level voltage (BIL) specified by standards.[13] Anti-fog sheds are provided in the outer surface to give protection from pollution.[14] The surface creepage length is commonly based on a stress of 0.023 MV/m and the protected to total surface creepage length is based on a ratio of 2. The flashover voltage is reduced at low barometric air pressure and should be calculated for installations at high altitude.[15] Similarly the creepage distance may require to be

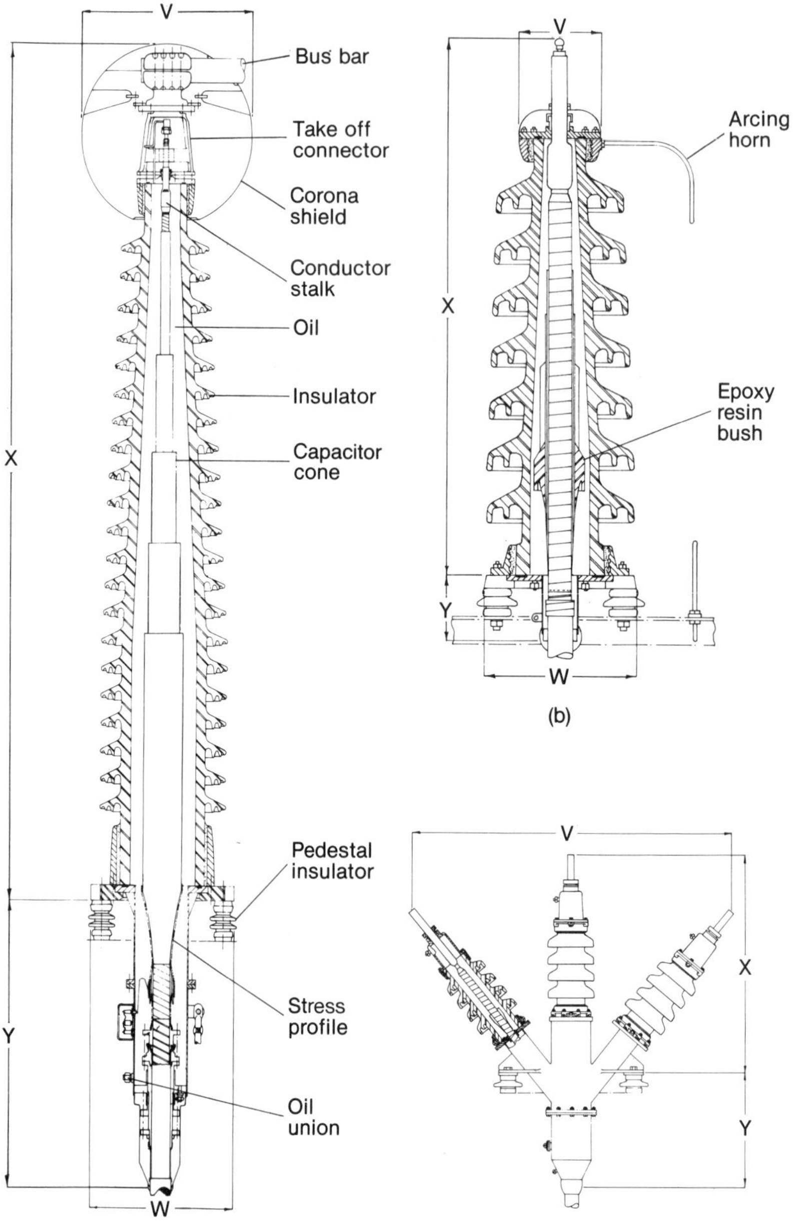

Fig. 38.1 Outdoor terminations for oil-filled cables: (a) 525 kV single-core; (b) 132 kV single-core; (c) 33 kV 3-core

increased in special circumstances for installations adjacent to the sea which are subjected to excessive salt spray or at high altitude when subjected to heavy industrial pollution.

Insulation co-ordination
Arcing horns are provided when required by the user. At 400 kV the gap is formed between two fixed toroids, one suspended from the corona shield and the other supported on the baseplate. For lower voltages an adjustable rod type is used (fig. 38.1(b)). The gap may be reduced by the user to be compatible with the insulation co-ordination policy of the adjacent transmission plant, e.g IEC 71–1[16] recommends that the gap be set to flash over at 80% of the BIL. Table 38.2 gives typical gaps. Account should be taken of the climatic conditions of humidity and barometric pressure.[15,17] The arcing horns should not be set to flash over frequently as power arcs may damage and rupture the porcelain.

Table 38.2 Horn gaps in outdoor terminations

U (kV)	BIL (kVp)	Horn gap	
		At BIL (mm)	At 80% BIL (mm)
400	1425	2540	2080
275	1050	1905	1550
161	750	1370	1090
132	650	990	790
66	342	533	410
33	194	320	220

Take-off connector
The connection to other manufacturers' equipment is made by air insulated flexible or rigid busbars of either aluminium or copper. Copper busbars are connected by a simple clamp directly to the copper stalk joined to the cable conductor and protruding through the top plate of the termination. Aluminium busbars are connected indirectly by a weather protected aluminium/brass take-off connector to avoid the problems of bimetallic corrosion of the conductor stalk (fig. 38.1(a)).

Stress control
Stress control is provided to achieve as uniform a voltage gradient as possible in the air external to the insulator and in the oil channel between the core and the inside of the termination, both of which are electrically weaker than the paper insulation. At voltages of up to 132 kV a simple epoxy resin bush (fig. 38.1(b)) is positioned at the termination of the cable earth screen. A metallic re-entrant of large curvature is set into the bush so that the stress concentration is reduced and contained within the isotropic epoxy resin insulation. At voltages of 161 kV and above, a capacitor cone stress control has advantages (fig. 38.1(a)). This is applied on site and consists of a number of equally spaced cylinders of overlapping aluminium foil insulated from each other and embedded within the paper roll insulation. There is an equal voltage drop between each foil so as to achieve a uniform stress distribution along the insulator. The positions of the outer earth potential foil and the inner conductor potential foil are carefully chosen to achieve optimum flashover withstand level on

both impulse polarities. A corona shield is provided to screen the top metal work, to reduce corona at working voltage and to improve the impulse performance.

Some authorities specify additional electrical proving tests, especially for the cable termination.[17] These can consist of a short time a.c. voltage withstand, both dry and wet under simulated conditions of heavy rainfall, and of radio interference tests. The 525 kV termination shown in fig. 38.1(a), for example, was required to withstand 875 kV r.m.s. for 1 min dry and 690 kV r.m.s. for 10 s wet.[18] The most onerous proving test is the cable system lightning impulse BIL.

Terminations into SF_6 insulated metal-clad equipment

Metal-clad equipment is significantly more compact than that in air insulated substations and outdoor switching yards, thus enabling savings to be made in land utilisation and cost, particularly in urban areas. The equipment has been increasingly employed, to the extent that at some voltages the supply of metal-clad cable terminations has exceeded that of the outdoor type.[19]

A single-phase 400 kV SF_6 termination is shown in fig. 38.2(a) and a 132 kV 3-phase termination in fig. 38.2(b). The leading dimensions are given in table 38.3. These comply with an IEC Publication[20] which was issued to harmonise the dimensional compatibility at the interface between the cable termination and switchgear, thus ensuring interchangeability and elimination of special designs.

Insulator

The external clearance length compared with an outdoor termination (table 38.1) is typically reduced by a factor of 3. A precision cast epoxy resin insulator (fig. 38.2(a)) is employed to withstand the increased radial and longitudinal stresses that occur, both on the outer insulator surface in contact with the SF_6 and on the inner surface in contact with the oil channel. Fig. 38.3 shows a field plot of a 400 kV termination. The SF_6 pressure and chamber diameter are determined by the manufacturer of the metal-clad equipment. The SF_6 working pressure can be up to 8 bar,[20] which is greater than the maximum pressure within the oil-filled cable (5.2 bar) and poses the risk of gas ingress into the oil-filled cable system with the possibility of electrical failure of the termination.

This risk has been eliminated for the designs shown in figs 38.2(a) and 38.2(b) by the introduction of an insulator with a solid embedded electrode (fig. 38.2(c)) which,

Table 38.3 Dimensions of terminations into SF_6 insulated equipment

U (kV)	BIL (kVp)	Length *X* (mm)	Diameter (mm)	
			Trunking, *Y*	Shield, *Z*
66	342	583	300	110
132	650	757	300	110
275	1050	960	480	200
400	1425	1400	540	280
500	1550	1400	630	280

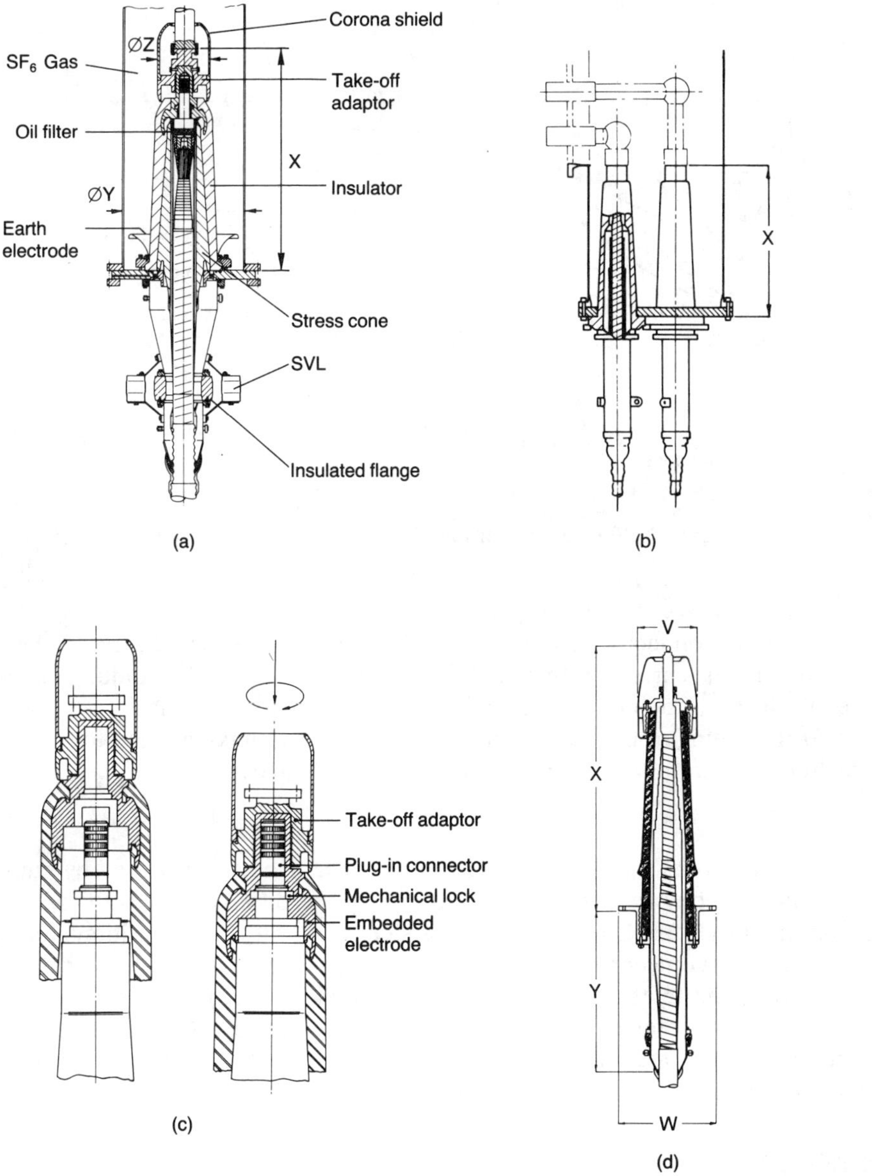

Fig. 38.2 SF_6 and oil-immersed terminations for gas-filled cables: (a) 400 kV SF_6; (b) 132 kV 3-phase SF_6; (c) assembly of plug-in connector; (d) 275 kV oil immersed

being unpierced by seals, completely segregates the SF_6 pressurised switchgear from the cable.[21] The possibility of SF_6 leakage into the cable is eliminated and the need to set the cable oil pressure above the switchgear SF_6 pressure is removed. The solid electrode has been made possible by the development of a plug-in connector with a mechanical lock. At the earthed end of the insulator double O-ring seals are employed with the intermediate gap vented to atmosphere.

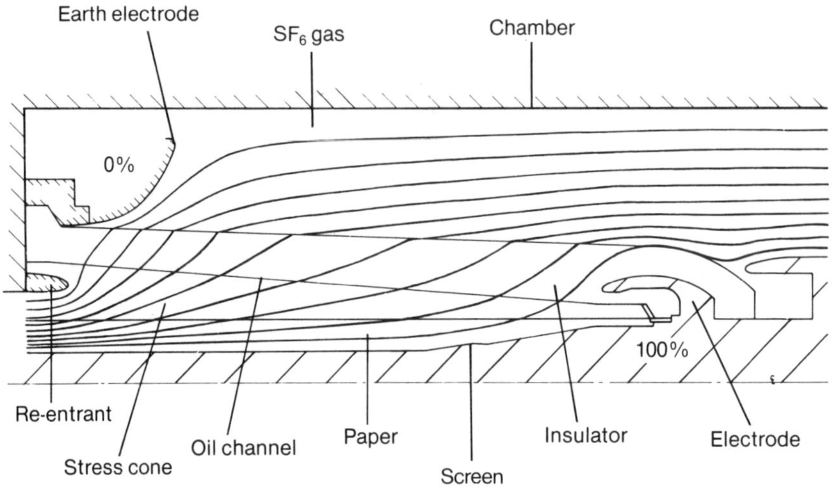

Fig. 38.3 Field plot of 400 kV SF_6 termination showing 10% equipotentials

Take-off connector
The take-off connector is designed to be compatible with the particular type of busbar and its current rating and is therefore designed in conjunction with the manufacturer of the metal-clad equipment. The design shown in fig. 38.2(a) matches the 4000 A rating of the busbar and consists of a plug-in connection to the embedded electrode and a bolted palm connection to the busbar.

Stress control
At 275 and 400 kV particularly short insulator lengths are achieved by employing a close fitting epoxy resin stress cone to reduce the oil channel depth to 1 mm, thus increasing its electric strength. Stainless steel mesh filters are positioned at the ends of the oil channel to prevent the introduction of oil-borne particles. Stress control is achieved by the relative positions of the earth electrode, the stress cone re-entrant, the embedded connector screen and the corona shield (fig. 38.2(a)) which are determined from a computer field plot. At 66 and 132 kV, either cast resin stress cones or capacitor cones can be fitted.

Special performance requirements
The termination is required to withstand lateral thrust from the busbar and vibration from the switchgear breakers in addition to the thermomechanical cable loads and the oil pressure.[19,21] The termination must not exceed either the cable or the busbar operating temperature. Fortunately the dissipation of heat is enhanced by convection in the SF_6 gas and by longitudinal conduction in the conductor and the insulator. The insulated flange in the metal sleeve (fig. 38.2(a)) experiences exceptionally steep fronted voltage transients of the order of $10^{-1}-10^{-2}$ μs due to the close proximity of the switchgear.[22,23] Flashover is prevented by connecting two sheath voltage limiters directly across the flange to present a low surge impedance (figs 38.4(a) and 38.4(c)). The earthing arrangement in fig. 38.4(b) is not recommended as circulating current of high magnitude can flow in the earth loop.[11]

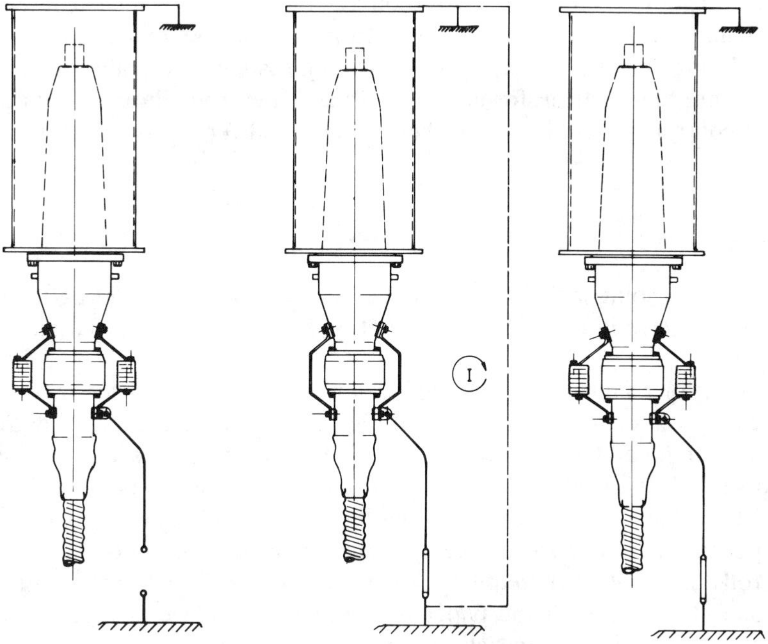

Fig. 38.4 Sheath bonding arrangements: (a) unearthed, end point bonded; (b) direct earthed sheath; (c) direct earthed sheath with SVLs

Oil-immersed terminations

These terminations are in the tanks of oil-filled transformers or switchgear and are used less frequently than outdoor or SF_6 metal clad types. Fig. 38.2(d) shows a 275 kV termination and table 38.4 gives typical dimensions.

Although the transformer oil is fairly similar to cable oil, it exhibits a lower

Table 38.4 Dimensions of oil-immersed terminations

U (kV)	BIL (kVp)	Length (mm)			Diameter (mm)	
		X[a] (mm)	Y[a] (mm)	Total (mm)	V[a] (mm)	W[a] (mm)
400	1425	1640	1210	2850	385	565
275	1050	1345	890	2235	335	530
132	650	1010	905	1915	270	460
66	342	730	450	1180	205	320
33	194	540	320	860	200	300

[a] See fig. 38.2(d)

electrical strength because of its application as a bulk insulator and because it is non-degasified and subject to contamination from debris and oxidation. To prevent flashover during the d.c. voltage commissioning tests on the cable, care must be taken to ensure that the transformer oil is dry and free from fibres. Similar materials and stress control are used in both the oil immersed termination and the outdoor termination.

Straight joints

A typical 400 kV joint without its joint shell insulation is shown in fig. 38.5(a) and dimensions are given in table 38.5. Different types of joint shell insulation are shown in fig. 38.6.

The conductor connections are suitable for conductors of up to 2600 mm^2. The high operating temperature of 90 °C and high conductor retraction loads require a high creep strength and long-term stability. Compression ferrules are used on copper conductors and MIG welded connections on aluminium conductors (figs 38.7(b) and 38.7(c)). To achieve high electric strength, thin pre-impregnated plain paper or crêpe paper tapes are applied adjacent to the conductor connection and pre-shaped profiled rolls are applied thereafter. Crêpe carbon tapes are applied over the conductor connection and over the paper roll profiles to achieve a smooth conducting boundary, free of oil gaps and stress raisers. Slim joints are available for special applications and these employ flush bronze welded and MIG welded connections for copper and aluminium conductors and hand taped insulation, the joint shell being insulated with heat shrink sleeves. Typical dimensions of a slim 400 kV 2000 mm^2 joint are 2800 mm in length and 146 mm in diameter over the shell.

Stop joints

A 400 kV stop joint is shown in fig. 38.5(b) and dimensions are given in table 38.6.

The hydraulic barrier is formed by a cast epoxy resin insulator with an embedded electrode which is clamped to and electrically shields the ferrule. The flange on the insulator is clamped to the joint shell. Two oil feed channels are provided and are

Table 38.5 Dimensions in single-core straight joints

U (kV)	BIL (kVp)	Length X^a (mm)	Maximum diameter V^a (mm)
525	1800	4293	300
400	1425	2718	280
275	1050	2156	265
161	750	1650	215
132	650	1562	205
66	342	1422	190
33	194	600	165

[a] See fig. 38.5

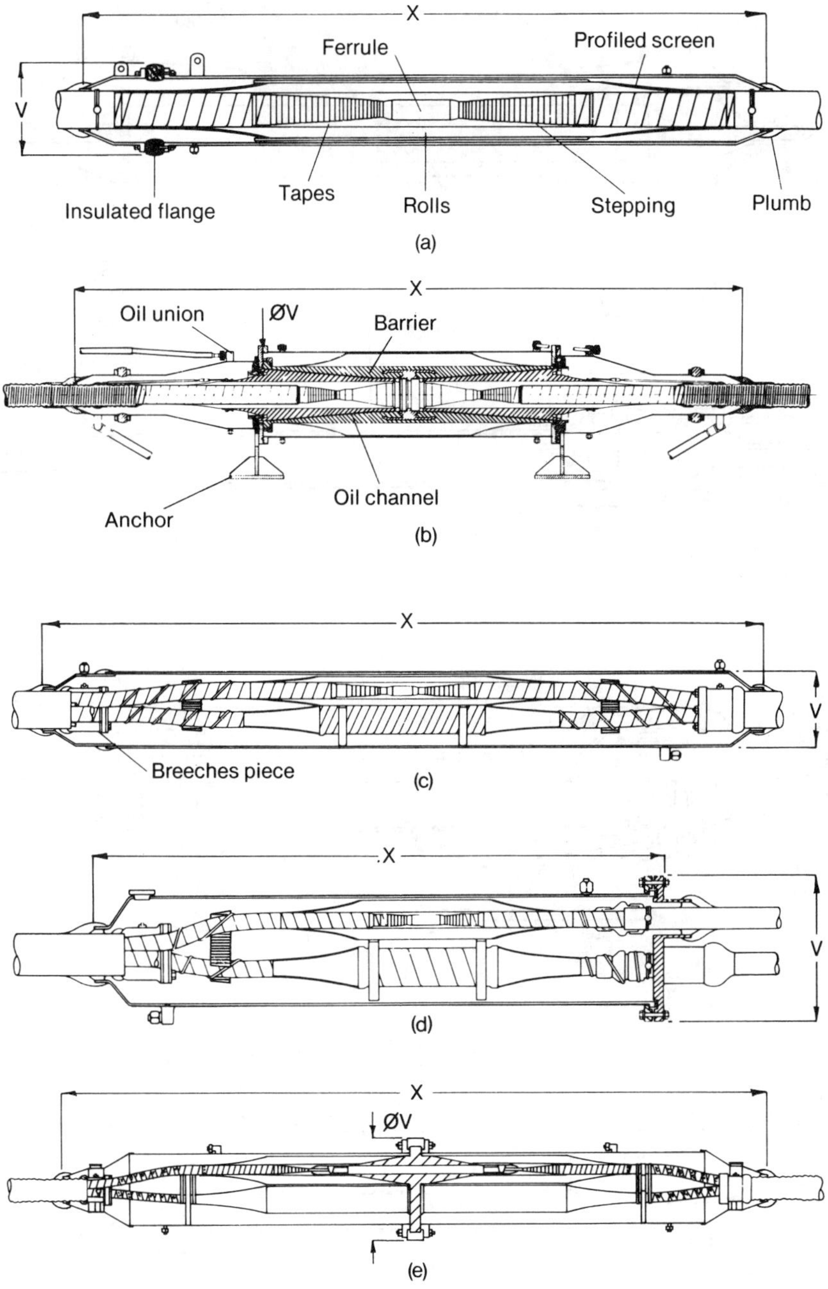

Fig. 38.5 Cable joints for oil-filled cables: (a) 400 kV single-core straight joints; (b) 400 kV single-core stop joint; (c) 132 kV 3-core straight joint; (d) 66 kV 3-core trifurcating joint; (e) 132 kV 3-core stop joint

formed by close-fitting cast epoxy resin stress cones located in the bore on each side of the barrier. At 275 kV and 400 kV the oil channels are sealed at each end by

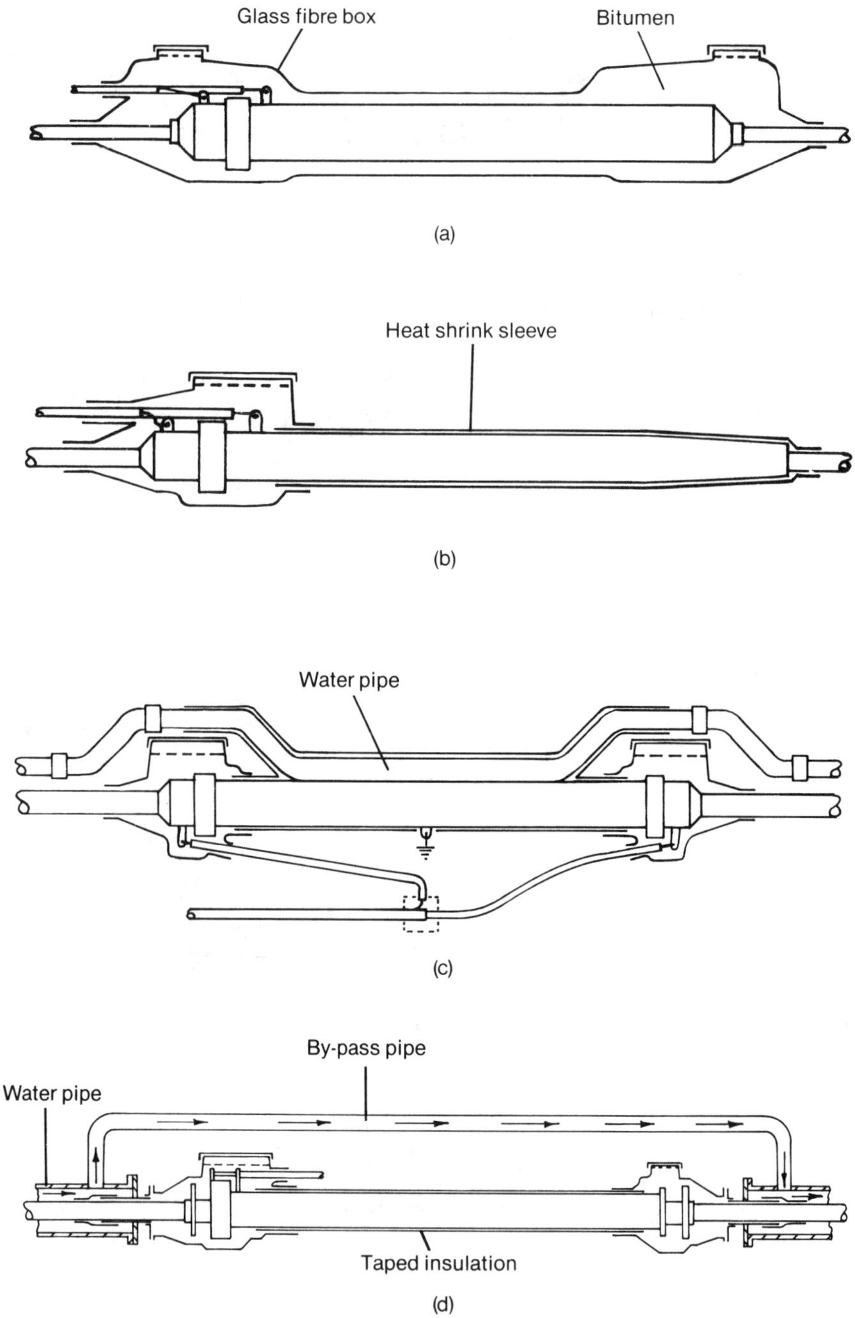

Fig. 38.6 Arrangements for straight joints: (a) 400 kV conventional protection; (b) 275 kV low thermal resistance protection; (c) 400 kV water cooled joint; (d) 400 kV joint in integrally cooled cable

stainless steel filters. Computer field plotting is employed to determine the electrical geometry of the joint, primarily to achieve a uniform stress and dielectrophoretic

Table 38.6 Dimensions of single-core stop joints

U (kV)	BIL (kVp)	Length X^a (mm)	Maximum diameter V^a (mm)
400	1425	4370	530
275	1050	3600	455
161	750	3600	455
132	650	2110	320
66	342	1780	255
33	194	1780	255

[a] See fig. 38.5(b)

force distribution within the oil channel.[24] The latter is the force experienced by an uncharged particle in a non-uniform electric field. A uniform distribution minimises the possibility of the accumulation of microscopic oil-borne particles in the oil channel.

ACCESSORIES FOR 3-CORE OIL-FILLED CABLE SYSTEMS (33–132 kV)

Design principles for conductor connection, insulation and stress control are similar to those for single-core accessories. The 3-core cable differs in that oil pressure is maintained by oil ducts located in the spaces between the three cores. Unlike a single-core cable, the conductor contains no duct and the oil flow is under the sheath at earth potential. The straight joints are required to transmit the oil flow from one cable sheath to the other and the stop joints to form a hydraulic barrier.

Terminations

Fig. 38.1(c) shows a 33 kV pole-mounted 3-phase termination which is unusual in that it permits the 3-core cable to be made off directly into the termination. This termination would be prohibitively large at higher voltages and instead the 3-core cable is divided into three single-core cables at either a trifurcating or a splitter joint. The single-core cable has a corrugated, fluted, or loose sheath to permit the flow of oil between the 3-core cable and the terminations. Standard single-phase terminations are employed with the addition of a special sheath seal containing a drop-out impregnation valve to prevent the ingress of oil during evacuation.

3-core joints

Fig. 38.5(c) illustrates a straight joint. The three insulated and screened cores are bound together and bandaged to form a tight fit in the joint shell to prevent lateral movement and buckling due to thermomechanical expansion of the cable cores. The cores are sealed during jointing by a breeches piece containing a synthetic rubber seal. Following evacuation and impregnation, communication for oil flow between the sheaths is made by inserting a key through a port in the joint shell to operate a

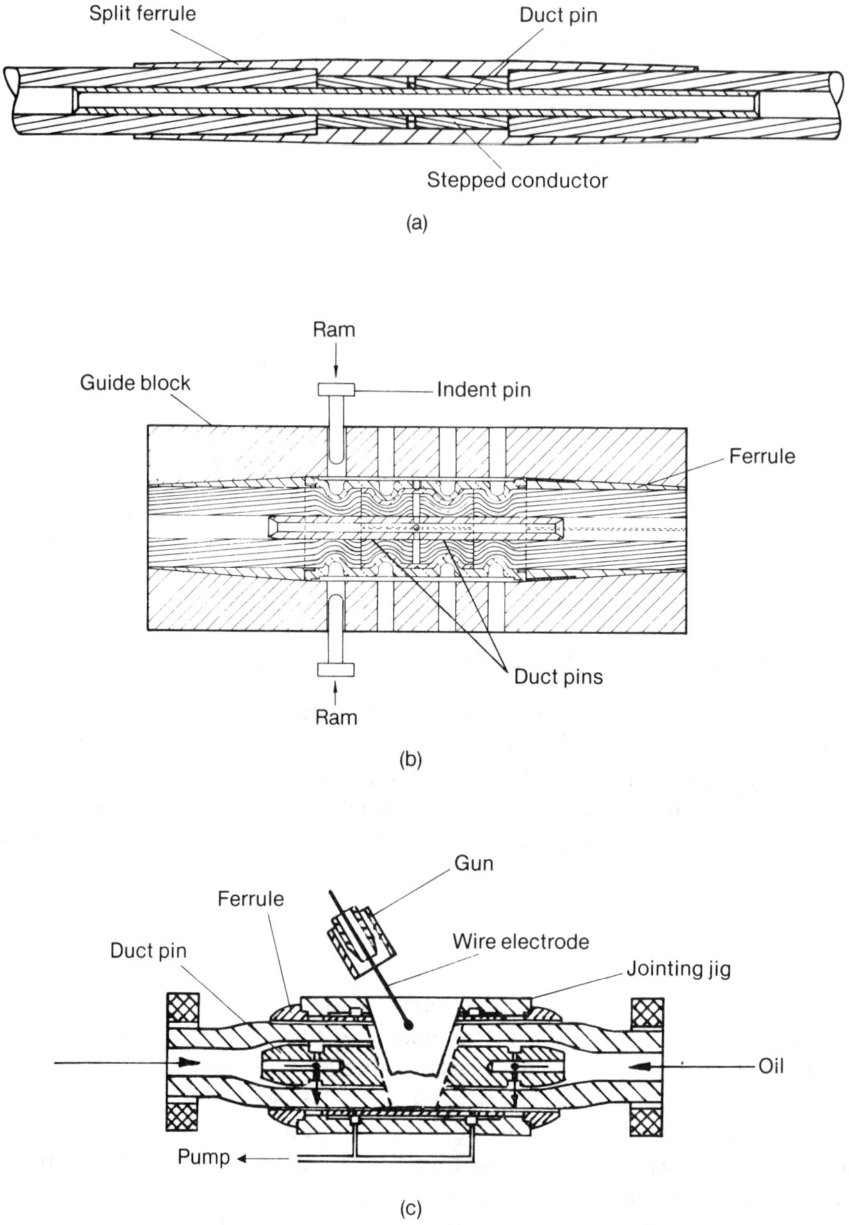

Fig. 38.7 Conductor connectors: (a) soldered; (b) compression; (c) MIG welded

valve in each breeches piece. The sheath cut and breeches piece are designed to permit a small cyclic movement of the cores, of up to 6 mm, without abrasive damage.

Fig. 38.5(d) shows a 66 kV trifurcating joint. This is essentially the same as a straight joint but with the addition of drop-out impregnation valves in each of the single-core tails. A stop joint in which the barrier is formed by an integral epoxy resin casting with three solid conductor rods embedded in separate insulated bushings is illustrated in fig. 38.5(e). Typical dimensions are given in table 38.7.

A slim 132 kV 3-core straight joint with a length of 2185 mm and a joint shell diameter of 140 mm has been employed for submarine crossings.

Table 38.7 Dimensions of 3-core OF joints

U (kV)	Straight		Trifurcating		Stop	
	X[a] (mm)	*V*[a] (mm)	*X*[a] (mm)	*V*[a] (mm)	*X*[a] (mm)	*V*[a] (mm)
132	2335	265	2030	315	3200	440
66	1645	145	1855	300	2130	290
33	1205	140	1415	300	2060	290

[a] See fig. 38.5

ACCESSORIES FOR GAS-FILLED CABLES (33–132 kV)

The predominant type of cable is the pre-impregnated paper type (chapter 34) and the accessories are similar to those for oil-filled cables. Gas pressure is maintained by a central duct in single-core cables of long length and by a duct between the cores in 3-core cables. 3-core cables are manufactured up to 66 kV and single-core cables up to 132 kV. Although the operating temperature is 85 °C the maxium conductor size of 630 mm^2 is comparatively small compared with oil-filled cables and permits the use of soldered conductor connections which are specially elongated to increase the creep strength (fig. 38.7(a)).

Terminations

Fig. 38.8(a) shows a 132 kV outdoor termination. The gas pressure is contained by a high pressure porcelain insulator. The stress is controlled by a pre-shaped stress control profile of pre-impregnated paper rolls, surmounted by a brass toroid insulated with impregnated crêpe paper. A gas entry chamber is sealed to the sheath cut, to which is connected an insulated pressure equalisation pipe of PTFE, which terminates at the conductor stalk. The gas entry chamber permits pressurisation and depressurisation of the cable through the conductor and also under the sheath on both single and 3-core cables. The porcelain is filled with a viscous oil/polyisobutylene compound with a gas space to allow for expansion. At 33 kV an alternative termination is available in which the cable is terminated to a conductor rod embedded in a cast epoxy resin pneumatic barrier. This is sealed to the base of a low pressure porcelain partly filled with compound.

Terminations into SF_6 switchgear employ the same insulator as the oil-filled design (fig. 38.2(b)) and oil immersed terminations are also similar to the oil-filled design (fig. 38.2(d)).

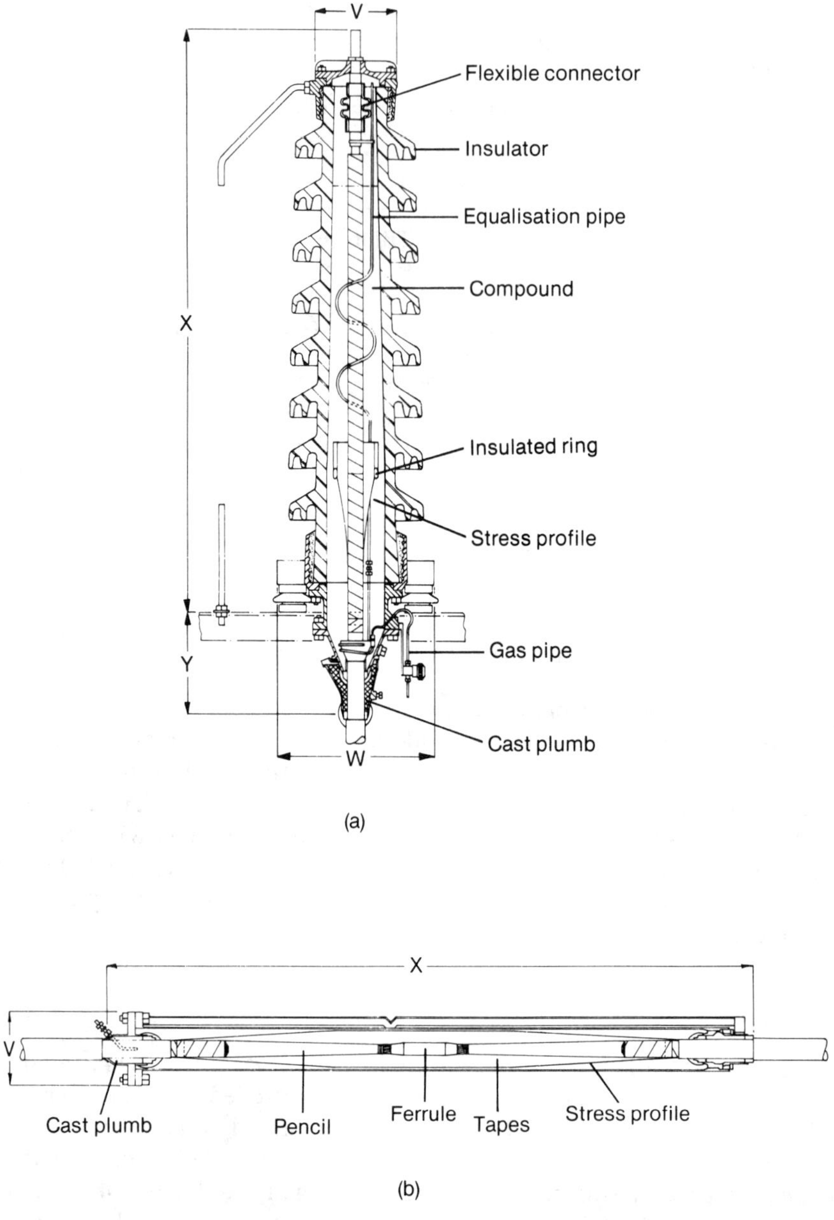

Fig. 38.8 Accessories for gas-filled cable: (a) 132 kV outdoor termination; (b) 132 kV straight joint

Joints

Fig. 38.8(b) shows a 132 kV single-core straight joint of simple construction. The insulation consists of hand applied pre-impregnated tapes. The joint is not filled with compound and sealing of the sheath cut is not required. Gas-filled accessories are not evacuated and the cable can be pressurised from the terminations, thus reducing the need for gas unions in the joint shell. The 3-core straight and trifurcating joints are also similar to simplified versions of the oil-filled joints shown in figs 38.5(c) and 38.5(d). The terminating joints to other types of cable employ a pneumatic barrier and are similar to the stop joint shown in fig. 38.5(e) for 3-core applications up to 66 kV and for single-core applications up to 132 kV (see fig. 38.10(c) later). A low cost single-core straight joint is used and it is contained within a lead sleeve reinforced with epoxy resin impregnated glass fibre tape. A low cost 3-core splitter joint is available which separates and sheaths the cores, thus avoiding the need for a trifurcating joint and special tails.

ACCESSORIES FOR POLYMERIC CABLES (66 AND 132 kV)

The cables are predominantly XLPE insulated and, because of their large diameter, are of single-core construction. A metallic sheath over a water swellable tape is preferred to prevent the radial and longitudinal ingress of water into the cable. Where appropriate the accessories incorporate the service proven features of accessories on pressure-assisted cables, such as compression connectors for copper conductors and MIG connectors for aluminium conductors. Sheath closures to metal glands on joint shells and terminations are similarly reinforced to withstand vertical soil loads and longitudinal oversheath retraction loads.

Outdoor terminations

Fig. 38.9(a) shows a porcelain insulator specifically designed to terminate XLPE cables. The cable core screen is terminated by a slip-on rubber stress cone, which is factory moulded from an insulating compound based on chlorosulphonated polyethylene (CSP). Alternative rubber compounds can be considered such as EPDM and silicone. The increased elastic stretch of CSP reduces the number of mouldings required to cover the cable design range. The high permittivity of CSP gives excellent stress control, depressing the field into the cable dielectric (fig. 38.9(b)) and thus significantly reducing the radial and longitudinal components of stress at the start of the stress cone and at the cable core interface compared with a low permittivity rubber[25] (fig. 38.9(c)). Test experience has shown that the performance of these areas is critically dependent on the finish of the hand-prepared core.

The compact stress cone has enabled the diameter of the porcelains to be reduced in comparison with the anti-fog designs.[13] The long–short (LS) shed profile has the same creepage distance but with a protected creepage reduced from 50% to 40%. The LS profile has a good wet withstand performance and is resistant to the accumulation of wind blown atmospheric pollution.[14] For regions of high pollution and fog the anti-fog design with 50% protected creepage can be employed (fig. 38.1(b)).

The insulator is filled with a viscous grade of silicone oil. Hydrocarbon oils are not recommended as these cause the extruded semiconducting cable screens to swell and to lose conductivity. High oil viscosity enhances the impulse performance and minimises the risk of leaks from seals. An air filled space is provided above the oil to compensate for thermal expansion.

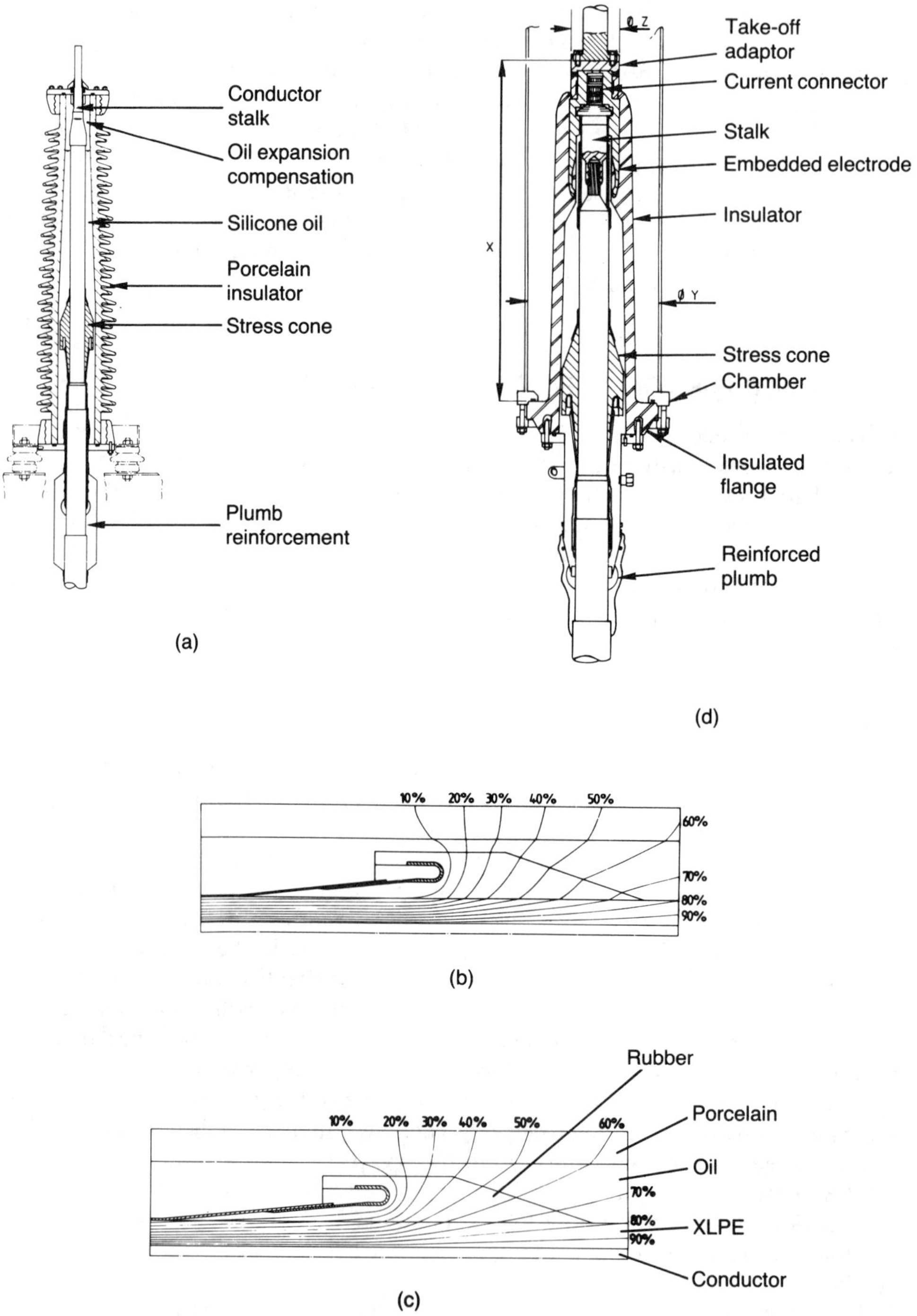

Fig. 38.9 XLPE cable terminations: (a) 132 kV outdoor termination; (b) high permittivity stress cone; (c) low permittivity stress cone; (d) 132 kV SF_6 termination

Terminations into SF_6 insulated metal enclosed equipment

A 132 kV insulator which complies with IEC Publication 859 dimensions[20] is shown in fig. 38.9(d) and dimensions of the 66 kV and 132 kV designs are given in table 38.3. The insulators are cast epoxy resin and are the same as those employed for oil-filled cables with a solid embedded electrode to prevent SF_6 leakage into the insulator and thence to overpressurise the metal glands and enter the cable sheath and conductor. Stress control is achieved by high permittivity CSP rubber stress cones which fit inside the insulators. The insulators can be filled with viscous silicone oil or low pressure SF_6 gas, the former being preferred because of the reduced risk of leakage. Compensation for oil thermal expansion is provided by either a small oil-filled pressure tank or a gravity fed reservoir.

A dry design has been employed which does not need to be filled with oil or gas. The rubber stress cone is designed to be an intimate fit in the bore of the epoxy resin insulator. A spring loaded thrust ring ensures that air is completely excluded from the electrically stressed interface during expansion and contraction in service. This design requires the cable dimensions to be tightly toleranced in manufacture and the jointing to be precise. The dimensions of the range of stress cone bores are required to be compatible with the integral steps in the range of cable diameters.

Terminations into oil immersed terminations

These terminations are seldom required. At 66 kV and 132 kV the terminations for SF_6 insulated metal enclosed equipment are employed as these have an adequate external surface creepage distance for operation in transformer oil.

Straight joints

Three main types of joint are in use at 66 kV and above, being characterised by the method of re-insulating the cable. Compression ferrules are used to connect copper conductors and MIG welds to connect aluminium conductors. The joint design either must be tolerant to longitudinal retraction of the cable insulation[6,7] or must constrain movement. Most designs of joint are encased within a metal shell (fig. 38.10(a)), insulated from earth using the techniques evolved for specially bonded oil-filled cable. It is preferred to fill the shell with a thermosetting resin to constrain movement of the joint and cable insulation and to improve the radial dissipation of heat.[25]

Taped joint

This is the most versatile design and is preferred for general application. The joint in fig. 38.10 has been insulated with self-amalgamating EPR tape and screened with a similar semiconducting grade. The act of stretching the tape activates amalgamation to the underlying layers, this being enhanced by thinning of the tape and by cumulative compressive force. Although joints can be hand insulated it is preferred to use a taping machine to improve speed and quality. This design of joint readily accommodates variations in cable dimensions and can be used to connect different sizes of cable.

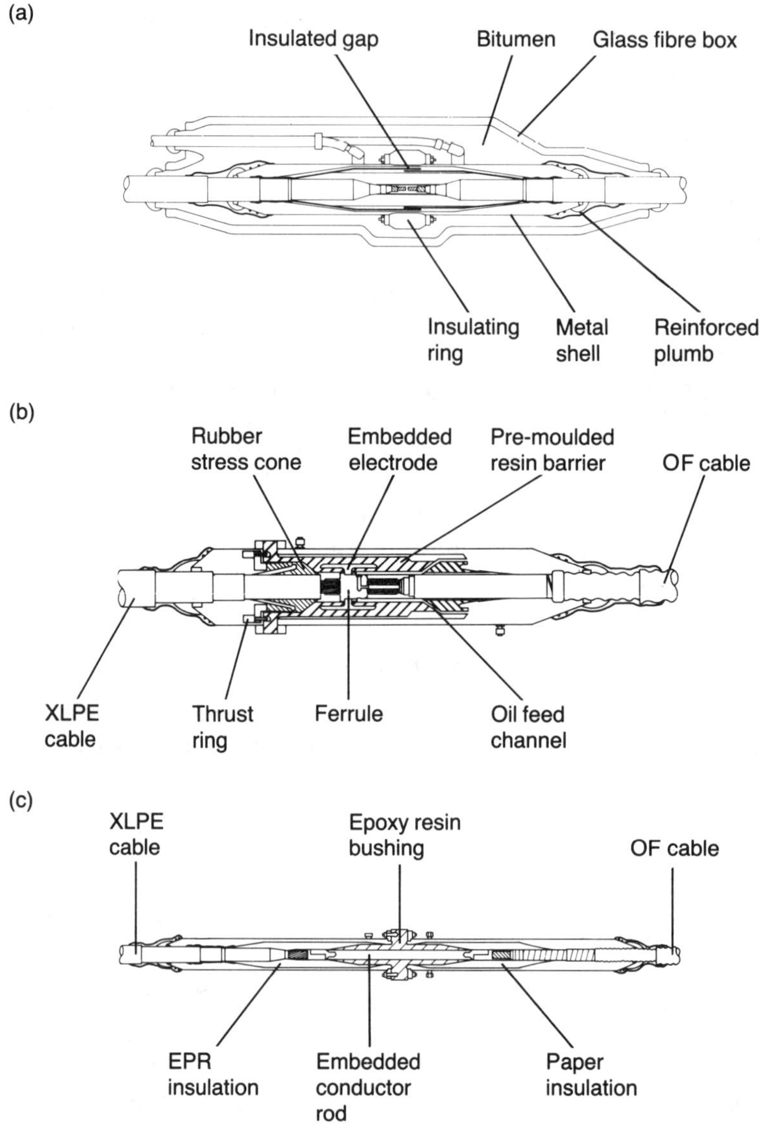

Fig. 38.10 Cable joints for XLPE cable: (a) 132 kV joint with metal sheath and bitumen protection; (b) 132 kV transition joint; (c) 66 kV transition joint

Pre-fabricated joints

This category employs factory moulded and tested insulation, permitting the jointing processes of core penciling and taping to be eliminated. The same high level of skill is required in the removal of the cable core screen and in the smoothing of the core insulation. The joint tends to employ more complex components with special tooling needed to fit them. Dimensional accuracy of manufacture of the cable and accessories and of hand preparation of the cable is paramount. Prefabricated designs are best suited to applications in which the ambient jointing conditions are adverse and time is limited, such as in a confined tunnel under a roadway.

The simplest design is a one-piece elastomeric moulding,[26] usually EPDM rubber, which incorporates an embedded semiconducting rubber electrode to screen the ferrule and the core cuts. The large size of the moulding limits the radial stretch, which requires that a special tool be employed. The tool stretches it onto a hollow mandrel placed over the cable and then extracts the mandrel, so that the moulding tightly grips the two prepared cable cores. The low radial stretch requires that a number of comparatively large mouldings are needed to cover the range of cables. It is necessary to remove the cable sheath for twice the length of the moulded insulation, thus increasing the length of the joint. A more complex design employs one large EPDM centre moulding to fit all cable sizes.[27] This is part pulled and part floated onto two constant-diameter stress cones, which are termed 'cable adaptors'. It is not necessary to remove extra cable sheath, and thus the length of the joint shell is reduced. A range of cable adaptor mouldings needs to be stocked. Another variant with design advantages employs a rigid epoxy resin casting for the centre moulding, similar to that shown in fig. 38.5(b) and 38.10(c). This permits smaller and more flexible rubber stress cones, with better range-taking capability, to be fitted by hand with no special tooling. Spring loaded thrust rings maintain the stress cones in intimate contact with the bore of the epoxy resin casting irrespective of thermal expansion of the cable and of compression set of the rubber.

Site cured joints

The cable factory extrusion and crosslinking process (curing) is emulated on site to reconstitute, consolidate and crosslink the polyethylene joint insulation.[26] This is a sophisticated process which requires a regime of accurately controlled temperature and pressure for in excess of 12 hours, irrespective of conductor size, ambient temperature and variability of the power supply. A disadvantage is that the moulded insulation needs to be shaped, smoothed and screened by hand; this produces a screen interface significantly inferior in quality to the extruded and bonded factory screen. The joint is most suitable for solidly bonded systems because of the problem of forming an insulated gap in the outer screen. The site cured design of joint is suited to applications in which a semi-flush diameter is required, such as for submarine cables or trough installations.

The insulation can be directly injected by a small screw extrusion press bolted to a mould tool around the joint.[28] A simpler method is to apply the polyethylene in tape form and then to constrain it in a mould. The insulation is first heated to melt and consolidate the tapes to each other and to the cable. The temperature is further raised to initiate degradation of the dicumyl peroxide within the tape such that crosslinking is initiated. The temperature is progressively elevated to accelerate the process. Gas is evolved during the reaction and it is essential to keep it in solution by controlling the temperature accurately and by the application of pressure. Pressure can be applied by gas, by liquid or by springs. It is similarly important to control the rate of cooling to prevent the formation of bubbles and of contraction voids.

Transition joints

A prime requirement of the transition joint is that the pressurising medium in an OF or GF cable must not enter the polymeric cable. The low viscosity cable oil will rapidly degrade the polyethylene insulation and screens. The polymeric cable system is not designed to withstand internal pressure. The designs of OF cable stop joint and the GF cable terminating joint are ideal for this application. They also have the capability of withstanding the unbalanced thermomechanical loads arising from the differences in physical size between OF and XLPE cable and in particular between 3-core OF and single-core XLPE cable.[2]

Fig. 38.10(b) shows a 132 kV transition joint. This is based on an OF hollow-core cable stop joint which has the capability of feeding oil to the conductor duct. Hydraulic segregation is formed by a rubber seal, which is clamped between the embedded electrode in the epoxy resin casting and the ferrule. On the XLPE cable side an elastomeric stress cone is held in intimate contact in the bore of the barrier to form a dry dielectric interface.

3-core OF and GF cables do not have conductor ducts and thus a simple through-bushing casting can be employed of the type shown in fig. 38.5(e). It is necessary to increase the creepage length and the diameter of the bushing to match the design parameters of XLPE straight joints; thus transition joints tend to be larger than OF stop joints. On the XLPE side the epoxy resin bushing and cable are insulated with self-amalgamating EPR tape. It is preferred to have three individual bushings which can be insulated without physical interference between cores. The three cores are mounted on a common metal plate. The OF or GF cable side is then insulated with paper in the normal way. For large conductor sizes it is preferable to incorporate the bushings into separate single core joints which connect to the 3-core cable by single-core tails and a splitter joint.

ANCILLARY EQUIPMENT

Sheath bonding equipment

The connections between the cable sheaths (chapter 37, fig. 37.6) are housed within an accessible link box to enable commissioning tests to be conducted.[11] These tests consist of the application of 10 kV d.c. for 1 min to each cable oversheath and the measurement of the imbalanced alternating circulating current through the links. The links may be housed in a street pillar or within a manhole, either in a diving bell box, which is suitable for occasional immersion in water at 1 m depth, or in a watertight sealed box.

Fig. 38.11 illustrates cross-bonding link boxes with the links arranged to transpose the cable sheaths at a minor bonding section. A sheath voltage limiter (SVL) unit is housed in the box to permit disconnection and hence safeguard it from damage during the 10 kV d.c. sheath test. The SVL assembly comprises three non-linear resistors in star connection with each resistor connected to one link so that the insulated flange in each joint shell is bridged by two resistors in series.

The purpose of the SVL is to limit the voltage rise caused by an incident surge on the joint screen gap, insulated flange, cable sheath and bonding lead. Such surges are initiated by normal circuit switching operations, by lightning impulse and, on rare occasions, by flashover of the cable terminations. They travel along the cable in cylindrical mode between the conductor, sheath and earth. At the instant of arrival at the flange, the sheath current is interrupted, thus causing a transfer of energy to

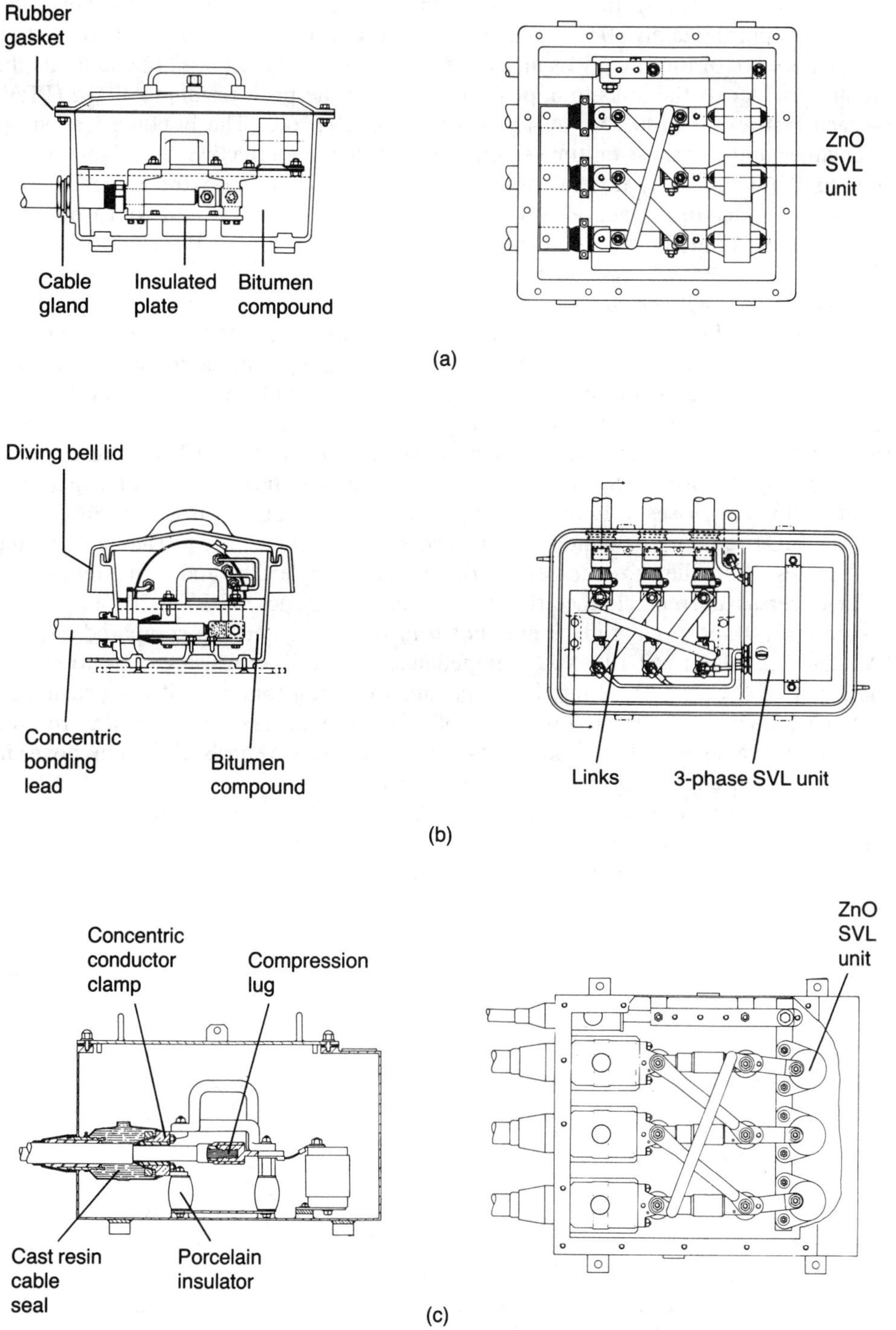

Fig. 38.11 Sheath bonding equipment: (a) cast iron bolted lid design; (b) cast iron diving bell lid design; (c) stainless steel bolted lid design

the electrostatic field by an instantaneous increase in voltage. Across the flange this can reach approximately 40% of the power cable BIL if the SVLs are not connected. The impedance of the two SVLs in series falls to approximately 1–2 Ω and limits the voltage rise across the links to approximately twice the peak residual voltage (PRV) of each resistor, e.g. 40 kVp at 40 kAp for two SVL 60s. The bonding lead surge impedance and transmission time significantly reduce the effectiveness of the protection to the joint. It is normal practice therefore to minimise the impedance by employing concentric leads and the time by restricting the length to 10 m. Such arrangements limit the flange voltage to approximately 8% of the cable BIL, e.g. 125 kVp, for a 400 kV system.[11,12]

Typical SVL voltage versus current characteristics are shown in fig. 38.12. In normal service the maximum induced a.c. sheath voltage is less than 150 V r.m.s. to which the resistor acts as an open circuit. The SVL rating is based upon withstanding the calculated r.m.s. induced sheath voltage, which arises from an external through-fault, for two periods of 1 s each this being the assumed maximum clearance time of the secondary circuit protection. To prevent damage to the SVL and to the link housing it is important that the user ensures that the sheath does not experience additional voltage rises, e.g. due to a high value of substation earth resistance. Zinc oxide (ZnO) resistors have now superseded silicon carbide (SiC). They exhibit the advantages of smaller size, increased rating for a single disc and more repeatable voltage versus current characteristics. The characteristics of SVL 20, 40 and 60 resistors (2, 4 and 6 kV r.m.s.) are shown in fig. 38.12 and are compared with an SVL 28 SiC resistor. At 10 kAp the impedances of the ZnO resistors tend to be less than that of SiC, whilst at rated voltage the ZnO resistors exhibit a much higher impedance. The SVL 60 ZnO unit (fig. 38.13) can withstand the 5 kV d.c. routine test on the oversheath, thus avoiding the need to open two-thirds of the link boxes in a cross-bonded circuit during circuit maintenance work.

Arresters with a spark gap in series with an SiC disc have occasionally been employed, with the advantage that the gap remains open circuit until a surge is seen. A disadvantage is that the effectiveness of protection is reduced by an increase in the

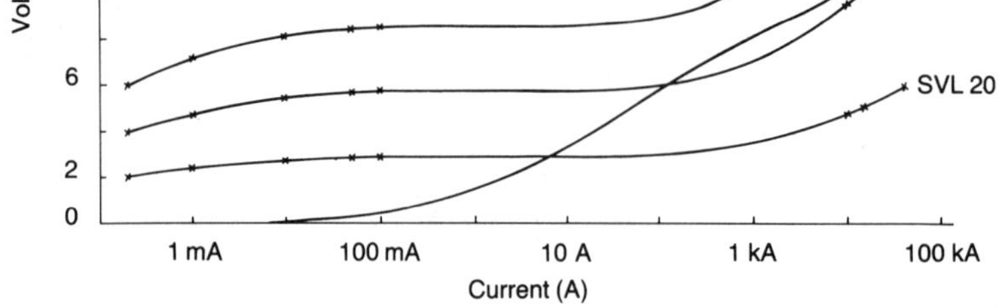

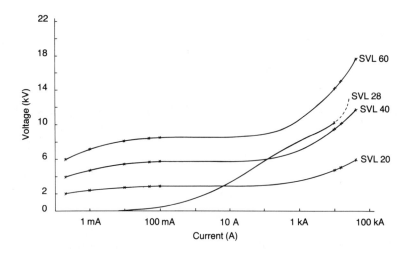

Fig. 38.12 Characteristics of sheath voltage limiters

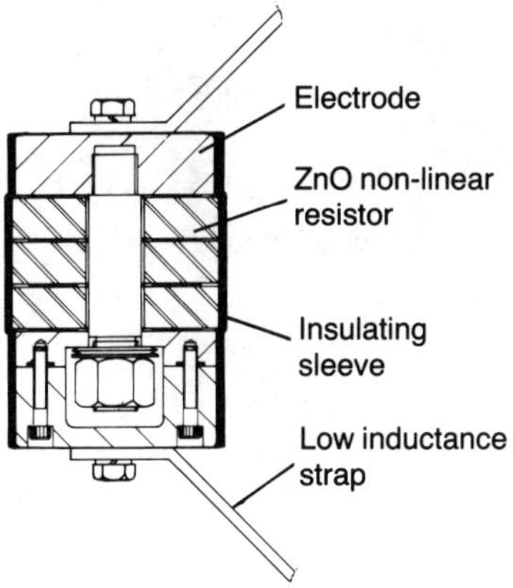

Fig. 38.13 SVL 60 ZnO unit

PRV and in the time to flash over. For these reasons they are not recommended. Capacitors have been employed for special applications but they tend to be prohibitively large and expensive.

Pressure equipment

The pressure in the gas-filled cable is maintained by conventional gas cylinders (BS 5045) pressurised with dry nitrogen to 170 bar. The pressure is reduced to that of the cable by a regulator. The equipment is housed within a surface mounted street pillar.[8]

The pressure in the oil-filled cable is maintained by oil pressure tanks. Fig. 38.14 shows the equipment diagrammatically. The tank contains a number of sealed elements each containing approximately 4.5 litres of CO_2 gas, this gas being used because of its high solubility in cable oil (120% by volume). The faces of the elements are flexible diaphragms (chapter 33, fig. 33.11) either of corrugated tinned mild steel or of stainless steel. The volume around the elements is filled with degasified cable oil. The tank is connected to the cable termination or stop joint by a pipe which contains an insulated link to permit electrical testing of the cable sheath system. The gas in the elements is the source of pressure in the cable system. When the cable carries current, the heated oil expands and flows into the pressure tank and acts upon the diaphragms to compress the gas. The oil in the cable contracts upon cooling and is forced back from the pressure tank by the compressed gas. The pressure tank size is specified by its gas volume in litres and by the pre-pressurisation index (PP), which is the absolute pressure in atmospheres to which the element is pressurised in the factory. Table 38.8 gives typical dimensions of the tanks.

The pressure versus volume characteristic follows the combined gas law and details are given in fig. 38.15 for a 300 litre tank with a range of PP values up to 4. The minimum pressure is the PP level and the maximum pressure is that at which the diaphragms cease to be fully flexible. Mounting of the tanks is discussed in chapter 33.

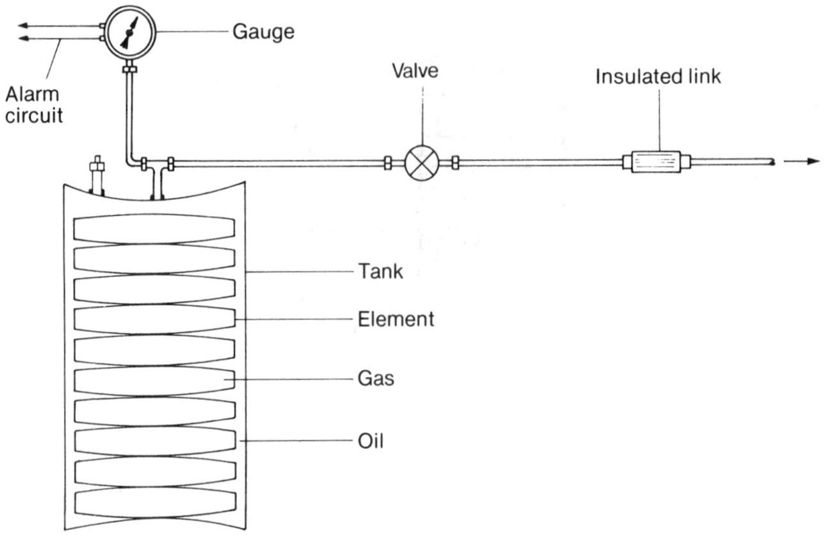

Fig. 38.14 Oil pressure equipment

Table 38.8 Dimensions of OF pressure tanks

Gas volume (litre)	Height (mm)	Diameter (mm)
44	640	565
88	970	565
135	1230	565
180	1500	565
225	1730	565
300	2200	565

Fig. 38.14 also shows a pressure gauge which enables the performance of the system to be checked visually. Two pressure-sensitive contact switches in the gauge sound an alarm if the oil pressure falls, as a result of damage to the cable system, to either the minimum operating pressure or the prescribed emergency minimum pressure. It is usual to locate the pressure gauge and oil pipe connections within manholes in a container similar to that shown in fig. 38.10, or in a street pillar.

JOINTING METHODS

Conductor connections

Fig. 38.7 includes the three main methods of conductor connection. Soldered connections are the simplest but exhibit an inferior hot creep strength as indicated in fig. 38.16, so that they are prone to failure due to the tensile load developed in heavily loaded conductors. Strength can be increased by lengthening the ferrule and

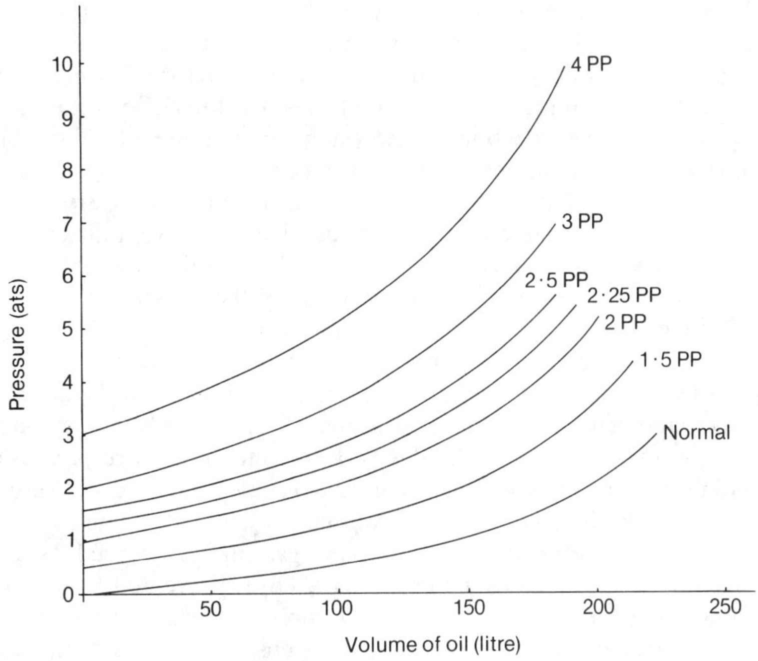

Fig. 38.15 Pressure versus volume characteristics of OF cable pressure tanks

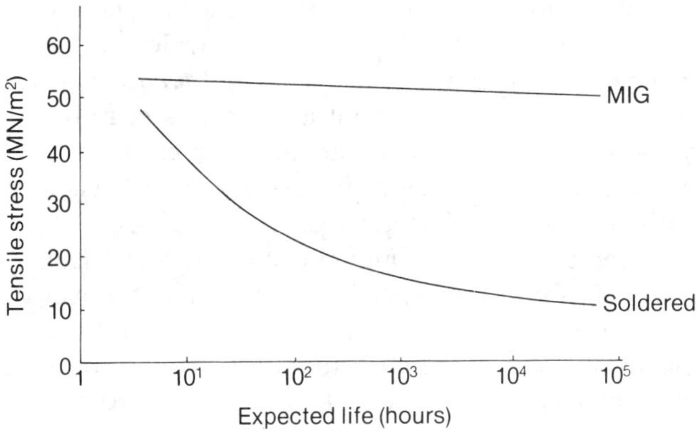

Fig. 38.16 Stress versus life characteristics of conductor connections

by achieving a tight fit to encourage capillary penetration. Such ferrules are employed for gas-filled cables of conductor area up to 630 mm^2. Adequate capillary action is not achieved in larger conductors and for this reason soldered ferrules have been largely superseded for oil-filled cable by compression ferrules and fusion welded connectors. Soldered ferrules are not acceptable for XLPE cable because the conductor is permitted to operate up to 250 °C during short-circuit conditions (OF cable up to 160 °C) and this is significantly higher than the eutectic temperature of solder.

The tensile strength of compression and welded connectors approaches that of the adjacent conductor and is less dependent on jointer proficiency.

The compression ferrule is preferred for copper conductors. For high compaction conductors up to 1000 mm^2, circumferential dies are forced into the ferrule by a hydraulic press, the dies locating either on a circumferential ridge (bump-type compression) or in a circumferential groove (knife-edge compression). For low compaction conductors of the Milliken type, a pin indent compression is used. The ferrule (fig. 38.7(b)) is contained within a guide block to prevent distortion and two diametrically opposed steel pins are forced into the ferrule by 300 kN hydraulic rams. Two rows of indents are made on each side of the ferrule with six indent pins per row. This technique has been applied for ratings up to 4000 A.

Fusion welded connectors are preferred for aluminium conductors and in this case are considered superior to compression ferrules because of the difficulty of breaking the oxide layer and achieving a stable resistance. Fig. 38.7(c) shows a connector for metal–inert gas (MIG) welding. In this process aluminium wire is constantly fed into a welding gun and is used as a consumable electrode. A d.c. arc is struck between the wire and the conductor and continuously propels a fine spray of molten aluminium into the conductor face. The inert gas, argon, is used as a shield to prevent oxidation and to dictate the arc energy. Oil is prevented from reaching the weld by capwelding the conductor faces and applying a vacuum. A voltmeter and ammeter are connected to the welding gun to ensure that the optimum welding parameters are achieved independently of the length of connecting lead and type of welding set. The arc is self-regulating and the method gives a good tolerance for variations in jointer proficiency. A flush connection is produced for conductors in 3-core cables. A ferrule is used for hollow-core conductors and oil communication is formed along a channel in the outer surface of the ferrule and then radially inwards through the conductor to the central oil duct. Another method uses pulsed MIG welding, which permits the weld to be built up around a central hollow duct pin by horizontal spray transfer. However, this method requires greater jointer proficiency and involves an additional compression process which seals each conductor to the pin to prevent oil from entering during welding.

MIG welding is used to connect aluminium conductors in XLPE cable. However, the weld temperature is above the crystalline melting point at which XLPE behaves as a soft elastomer. It is necessary to cool the conductor to prevent distortion and degradation of the insulation. The temperature of the conductor is monitored during welding and heat is extracted by the use of water cooled welding jigs.

Because of its simplicity, thermit welding offers possible attractions for small conductors, but still requires good conductor preparation and oil control. Flush bronze welded connections have been developed for slim 400 kV OF cable joints on copper conductors up to 2000 mm^2 and have been employed in single-core submarine cable joints at 100 and 250 kV d.c. and in 3-core submarine joints at 132 and 150 kV a.c.

Jointing paper insulated cables

Following the completion of the conductor connection the cable insulation is prepared by tearing the paper tapes to form a conical shape, often termed 'pencilling', for gas-filled cable (fig. 38.8(b)) or in a series of steps, i.e. 'stepping', for oil-filled cable (fig.

38.17). The ferrule is screened and the insulation is applied. It is important to minimise moisture absorption and the size of gaps and creases during application of the hand applied insulation. Moisture absorption is minimised by using pre-shaped and pre-impregnated paper rolls which are supplied to site in sealed containers and are stored under hot oil until required by the jointer. Whenever possible, the joint is insulated in a continuous operation. The insulation is basted frequently with hot oil or compound and oil-filled joints are insulated under oil pressure to ensure an outward flow of oil. At voltages above 220 kV it has become practice to employ humidity control in the joint bay to a relative humidity of nominally 50% at 20 °C. This is because moisture significantly increases the dielectric loss angle (DLA) and

Fig. 38.17 Joint bay for 275 kV oil-filled cables

hence the dielectric heating of the paper insulation and also reduces the insulating properties of oil channel surfaces.

Oil channel cleanliness

The oil channels in accessories with electrically stressed short oil channels, such as stop joints, SF_6 terminations and oil-immersed terminations, are carefully washed with oil to remove jointing debris. At 220 kV and above, a high oil pressure flushing probe is used to clean the channels vigorously. These are then visually inspected using an endoprobe and the seepage oil is sampled and checked using either an automatic particle counter or a filter membrane. The cable duct is flushed with filtered oil before jointing and the joint is flushed after impregnation. Hydraulic shears are used to cut the conductor to avoid the generation of swarf. Cleanliness is facilitated by jointing in a well prepared joint bay with good lighting (fig. 38.18).

Jointing XLPE insulated cables

The metal cable sheath is first vented to release gaseous by-products of the crosslinking process, some of which are flammable. A set of specialised tools is required to prepare the insulation. The exposed core is clamped and heated in a cylindrical jig to remove curvature and to encourage the insulation to retract[6,7] before insulation is

Fig. 38.18 Joint bay with 275 kV stop joint for oil-filled cable

applied. A 'screen stripping' tool removes the bonded core screen,[25] it being important to ensure that the tool compensates for the eccentricity of the core, thus avoiding the formation of a stress-raising step into the insulation at the screen termination. An 'end stripping tool' (fig. 38.19) exposes the conductor. For joints which are to be taped or injection moulded a similar 'pencilling tool' is used to form the conical insulation pencil and to expose the conductor screen. The core is smoothed and polished by hand using successive grades of fine abrasive cloth. All traces of indentations and scratches must be removed as these form air filled voids which will electrically discharge in service.

The conductors are joined using a compression ferrule or a MIG welded connection. A stream of ionised air is directed over the insulation to prevent the electrostatic accumulation of airborne debris on the core. The core is finally solvent cleaned and carefully inspected prior to the application of insulation.

For a prefabricated joint the insulating components are pushed back over the prepared core before making the conductor connection. These are pulled over the ferrule using the specialised tooling appropriate to the particular joint, taking care not to contaminate the bore of the insulation by contact with the semiconducting

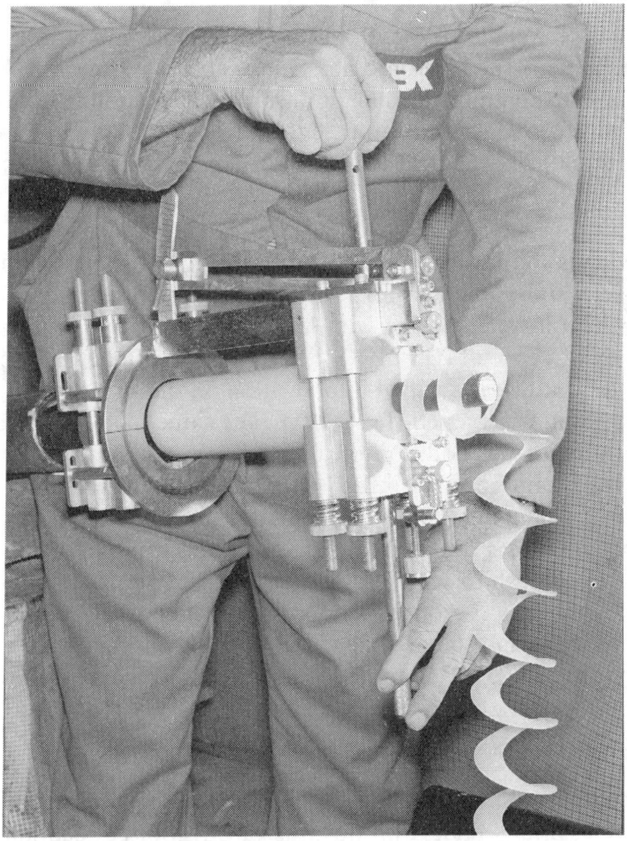

Fig. 38.19 Cutting back XLPE insulation to prepare for conductor jointing

core screen. For an EPR tape joint the screen is hand reconstituted over the conductor connection and a powered taping machine applies the insulation under conditions of pre-set tension and stretch. The core screen and insulated screen gap are formed by hand. The joint shells are slid over, plumbed to the cable sheath, filled with a thermosetting resin compound and encased in the particular type of anticorrosion protection.

Jointing and terminating polymeric cable is a highly skilled process despite the apparent simplicity of the cable. The joint bays are double lined to ensure cleanliness and are well lit to aid visual examination of the prepared core. In temperate climates the bays are heated to achieve consistent properties of the elastomeric components. In tropical climates the bays are air conditioned and ventilated to prevent contamination of the core by perspiration from the jointer. Jointers are required to pass a rigorous training programme culminating in tests of proficiency. For polymeric cable jointing visual adjudication alone is inadequate. A direct way to confirm quality is for the jointer to assemble a joint and termination in the high voltage laboratory (fig. 38.20) and to require the accessories to withstand a 4 hour test at $3U_0$ and to pass a discharge test at $1.5U_0$.

Sheath closure

The joint shell is sealed to the sheath to contain the maximum design pressure within the OF or GF cable.[8] The seal onto an XLPE cable is required to be non-porous so that water is not sucked into the sheath during a cable cooling cycle. Each design of seal is required to conduct the return current during a system short circuit and to withstand the sheath mechanical loads in normal service.

External plumbed wipe

A plumbed wipe is the normal method used with lead or aluminium sheaths for oil-filled cable, for XLPE cable and for some types of gas-filled cable. The cable sheath is tinned and the joint shell sealed with lead strip to exclude oil during plumbing. A lead based alloy of H metal (BS 219) in stick form is softened to a plastic state using a gas torch and is patted and wiped into position on the sheath until a thickness of 15 mm above the gland is achieved (fig. 38.21). The same method is used on aluminium sheathed cables, with the addition of a friction tinning process to break the oxide layer. The sheath is vigorously brushed and heated and a thin stick of metal is rubbed into the surface (fig. 38.22). Aluminium sheaths, unlike lead sheaths, do not readily creep and thus mechanical loads are concentrated on the plumbs which, being of lead alloy, exhibit a low creep strength at the operating temperature of typically 70 °C. For this reason it is now the practice to reinforce all supertension cable plumbs to withstand sheath loads of up to 10 kN using epoxy resin impregnated glass fibre tape (fig. 38.23). Reinforced external plumbs have been used satisfactorily at pressures of up to 17 bar.[29]

Cast plumb

A mould is incorporated into the joint shell (fig. 38.24) or formed around the sheath of pressure cables and is filled with hot wax or oil. Molten lead alloy is poured into the mould to displace the liquid. This method requires careful control of the alloy temperature to avoid porosity and is now employed for high pressure applications in

Fig. 38.20 Preparing cable termination for electrical tests in laboratory

conjunction with a wiped pressure seal. An externally wiped plumb is included in fig. 38.8(a).

Internal plumbed wipe

This is made using the same technique as the external wipe but is reversed in direction so that it is located inside the joint on a plumbing gland (fig. 38.24) and experiences the pressure loads in the stronger mode of compression. The joint shell is mechanically sealed to the plumbing gland. The internal plumb has been employed for oil and gas pressures up to 31 bar,[10] usually in conjunction with external mechanical reinforcement in the form of a cast plumb, a wiped plumb, cast epoxy resin, or a mechanical lock.

Welded closures

Figs 38.25 and 38.1(a) show welded closures for a special application[9] on a smooth

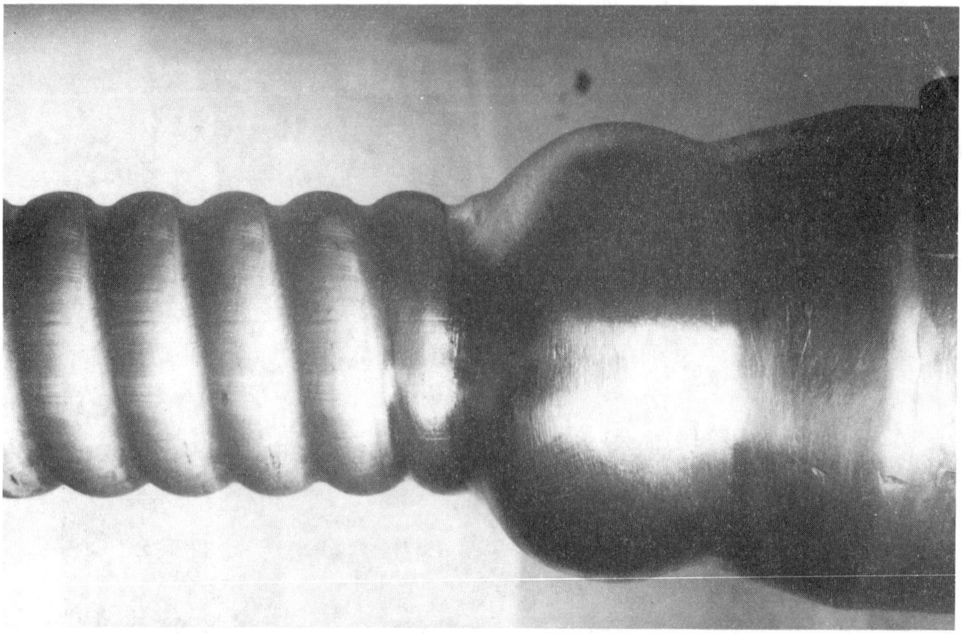

Fig. 38.21 Sheath closure with plumbed wipe

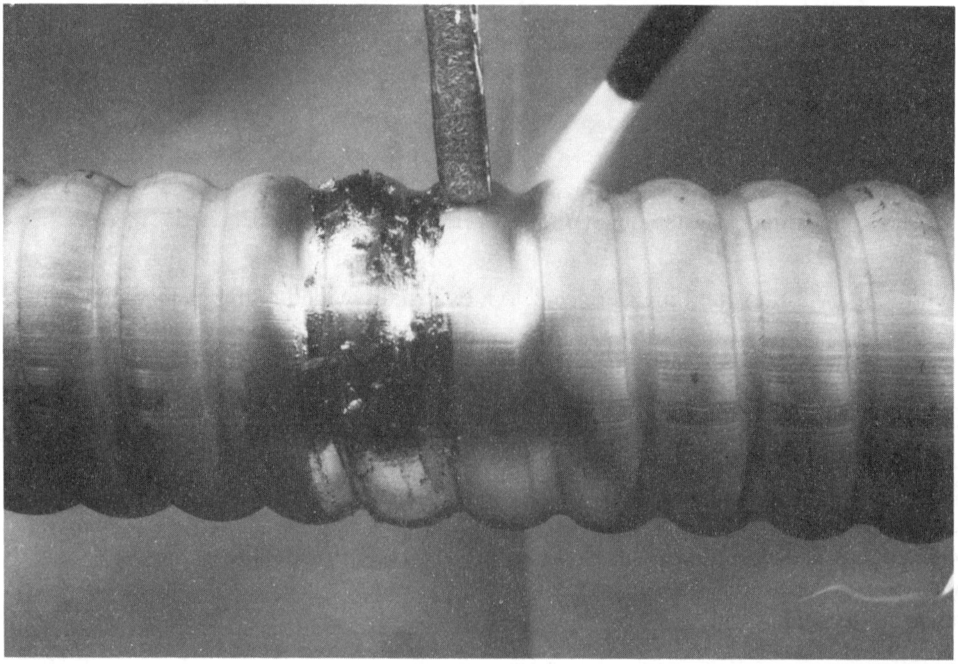

Fig. 38.22 Friction tinning a corrugated aluminium sheath

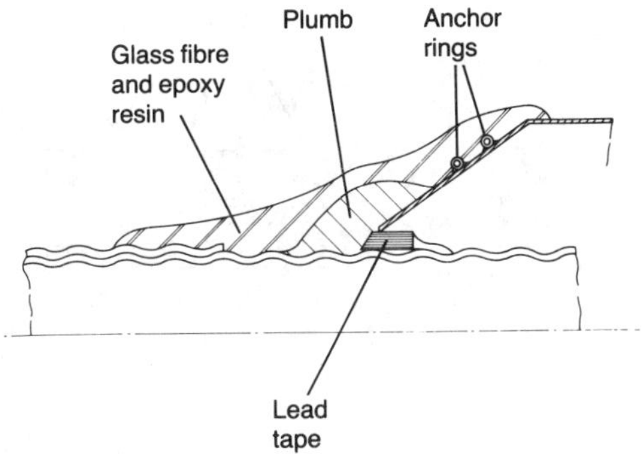

Fig. 38.23 Reinforced plumbed wipe on corrugated aluminium sheath

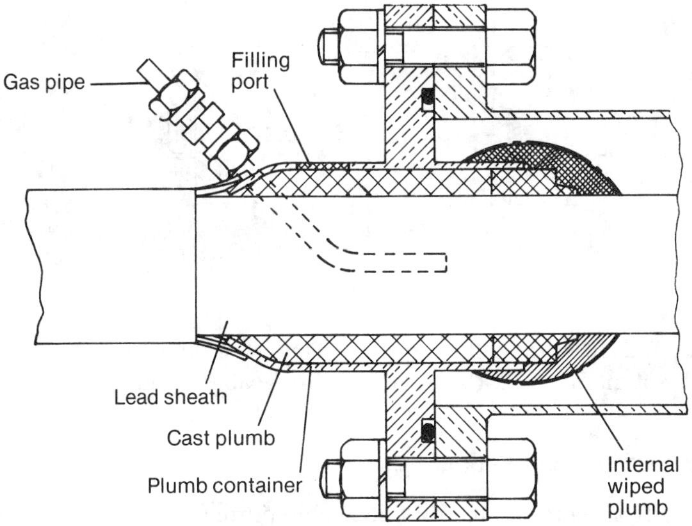

Fig. 38.24 Sheath closure with cast plumb and internal plumbed wipe

non-corrugated) thick wall aluminium sheathed 525 kV cable for operation at a pressure of 25 bar. The sheath is belled out using hydraulic tools and sealed with an O-ring to prevent oil from contaminating the weld. Tungsten–inert gas (TIG) welding, with a shield of helium, is used to fuse the sheath to an aluminium closure plate. Welding has also been employed on non-corrugated aluminium sheathed gas cables at 17 bar. Pulsed MIG welding has been developed for oil-filled cables but has not yet been adopted for cables with thin wall corrugated sheaths because of the risk of puncture of the sheath by the weld pool.

Lead burning

Lead burning is a highly skilled technique used principally for submarine cables to achieve a butted or overlapped flush connection between a lead alloy sleeved joint and the lead alloy sheath of the cable. Oxygen and hydrogen are burnt in a fine

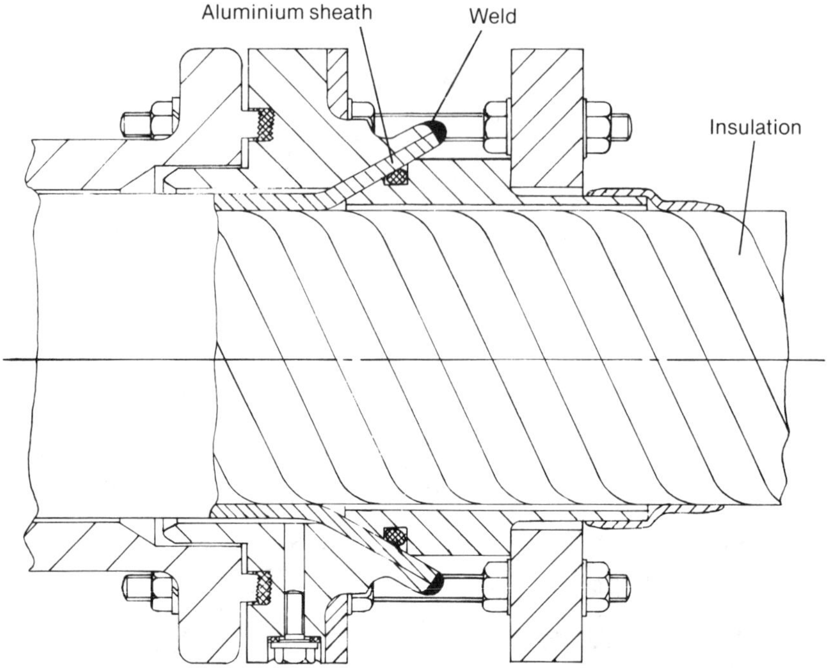

Fig. 38.25 Welded sheath closure

flame to melt and fuse the alloy locally. This technique has been successfully employed with submarine 132 kV 3-core oil-filled cable joints.

Impregnation and pressurisation

Air is prevented from entering the oil-filled cable during jointing by raising the joint above the level of the adjacent cable and by jointing under oil flow. A vacuum drain jar is connected to the bottom of the completed joint to remove seepage oil and a vacuum pump is connected to the top. Evacuation is conducted for a typical period of up to 6 hours for accessories up to 132 kV. At higher voltages, periods of up to 24 hours are required together with a 'pressure rise' test in which the vacuum pump is disconnected and the joint pressure is measured to ensure that it does not exceed typically 0.1 to 0.15 torr in 30 min. The joint is impregnated under vacuum by admitting degasified oil through a bottom union. At 400 kV the residual gas pressure (RGP) of the oil is measured after impregnation to ensure that it is below 5 torr. An oil pressure test at the maximum system pressure (i.e. up to 5.2 bar) is conducted with the oil unions, seals and sheath closures whitewashed to locate possible leaks.

Accessories on gas-filled cable are not evacuated but are simply purged and pressurised with dry oxygen-free nitrogen together with the cable.

Joints on XLPE cable up to 132 kV are not liquid filled. Non-degasified silicone oil is used to fill porcelain insulators on outdoor terminations. A simplified degasifying and evacuation process is necessary for a termination into metal-enclosed equipment to achieve complete filling of the short epoxy resin insulator.

INSULATION AND THERMAL DESIGN

Insulation design for paper cable accessories

The limiting performance of the insulation occurs at the lightning impulse BIL[30]. The maximum radial stress occurs at or adjacent to the ferrule in a straight joint and is chosen in conjunction with the thermal rating and method of insulation. For example, a high radial stress would require the joint to be insulated with paper tapes, thus increasing the jointing time. The reduced diameter would increase the dielectric losses but reduce the radial thermal resistance. Typically the maximum radial stress is 40%–80% of that of the cable. The stress and outer diameter are determined using the formula

$$E = V\left\{r_x\epsilon_x\left[\frac{1}{\epsilon_a}\log_e\left(\frac{r_{oa}}{r_{ia}}\right) + \frac{1}{\epsilon_b}\log_e\left(\frac{r_{ob}}{r_{ib}}\right) + \ldots\right]\right\}^{-1} \qquad (38.1)$$

where r_x = radius at which the stress is required (m)
E = stress (MV/m)
V = voltage (MV)
r_{oa} = outer radius of the material (a, b etc.) (m)
r_{ib} = inner radius of the material (a, b etc.) (m)
ϵ_a = relative permittivity of the material (a, b etc.)

Typical values for relative permittivity are as follows:

Oil impregnated paper	3.5
Oil	2.2
Pre-impregnated paper (gas cable)	3.4
Epoxy resin	4.2
Porcelain	6.0

The maximum radial stress in complex accessories (e.g. stop joints and resin bush terminations) is determined by computer field plotting (fig. 38.3).

The shape of the stress control profile, cable stepping and ferrule is calculated to control the longitudinal component of stress along the surface of the paper insulation. The longitudinal impulse strength of the paper is 0.5%–5% of the radial strength and is influenced by the anisotropic nature of the paper, the presence of oil gaps and creases and the magnitude of the radial stress. For the purpose of design, the longitudinal stress parameters are made a function either of the radial stress or of the longitudinal distance along the profile and incorporate a design margin to allow for jointing variations.

For simple accessories such as straight joints the angle of the stress control profile may be approximated from

$$\theta = \arctan\left(\frac{E_l}{E}\right) \qquad (38.2)$$

where θ = angle of stress control profile
E_l = limiting value of longitudinal stress (MV/m)
E = radial stress at the profile from equation (38.1) (MV/m)

For complex accessories such as SF_6 terminations and stop joints with large profile angles, the above approximation is invalid and longitudinal stress should be measured from a computer field plot. A finite network solution can be employed, complex geometries such as stop joints requiring between 5000 and 15 000 nodes. Finite element solutions offer reductions in preparation and computation time and give greater freedom in the economic positioning of small elements to obtain accuracy in regions where divergent fields are expected; e.g. the number of rectangular elements can be reduced to between 1000 and 2000. The combination of computer aided design, and pre- and post-processing and computation requires a powerful computer. A computer printout of the equipotential distribution allows the solution to be verified visually. Stress and dielectrophoretic force[24] distributions along each interface can be graphically printed and compared with the design parameters.

Insulation design for polymeric cable accessories

The limiting performance of accessories on polymeric cable can be either the hot impulse test or the $3U_0$ 4 hour a.c. withstand test at ambient temperature.[31] The a.c. test is particularly searching in those aspects of design, material and jointing which introduce stress raisers and voids and hence promote electrical discharging. As with pressurised cables the insulation geometry must be designed to control the radial and longitudinal components of stress along the interface with the cable core. Elastomeric insulating materials have the advantages of isotropic design parameters and of greater choice of permittivity (table 38.9) but the disadvantages of a less well defined geometry and a greater temperature-dependent permittivity.

Thermal rating

The rating formulae and parameters are the same as those for the cable (chapter 37) but with the addition of longitudinal heat flow along the conductor and cable sheath. Typical thermal resistivities are given in table 38.10 and typical values of DLA in table 38.11.

To calculate the maximum operating temperature of the joint, the centre joint in the bay is chosen and is assumed to be thermally symmetrical about its centre line. The joint and joint bay are divided transversely into sections of similar radial and longitudinal geometry and these are further subdivided to obtain accuracy of solution. An equivalent thermal network is constructed and solved using a computer. The finite element representation typically requires between 50 and 150 transverse sections and 5–10 radial sections. A graphical printout is obtained of the temperature distribution along the conductor (fig. 38.26(a)). If the temperature exceeds the maximum cable design temperature (typically 90 °C) the spacing between the joints is increased to reduce mutual heating and the solution is repeated to obtain a graph of the variation of maximum temperature with spacing (fig. 38.26(b)).

For directly buried naturally cooled cables, an increase in the joint spacing is usually adequate to limit the temperature. However, this is seldom possible with special cable systems designed with enhanced heat dissipation to achieve increased current density (e.g. shallow trough and water cooled systems). Fig. 38.26(c) shows a comparison of the cable and joint thermal resistances to the ground surface for a 275 kV system. It will be seen that if either the external thermal resistance of the ground around the cable or the mutual heating is significantly reduced, a comparative

Table 38.9 Relative permittivity of materials in accessories for polymeric cable

Material	Relative permittivity[a]
Extruded XLPE	2.5
Extruded EPR	3.0
Tape EPR	2.8
Moulded EPDM	3.5
Moulded CSP	8–10
Stress control elastomer	15–25
Silicone oil (viscous)	2.8

[a] Values are for the average of the ambient and operating temperatures

Table 38.10 Thermal resistivity of materials in accessories

Material	Thermal resistivity (Km/W)
Oil paper/GF paper	5.5
Oil: annular gap	3.5[a]
Extruded XLPE cable	3.5
Extruded EPR	5.0
EPR tape	4.8
Acrylic resin compound	2.0
Polyurethane compound	4.8
Filled epoxy resin	0.9
Porcelain	0.95
Bitumen	6.2
Stabilised backfill	1.2
Copper conductor	0.0026
Aluminium conductor	0.0043

[a] 50% of static value to allow for convection in typical applications

Table 38.11 Dielectric loss angles of materials in accessories used for thermal ratings

Material	DLA[a]
OF cable	0.0024
OF joint	0.003
GF insulation	0.0045
Extruded XLPE	0.001
Extruded EPR	0.005
EPR/EPDM joint insulation	0.005

[a] Values are for the operating temperature

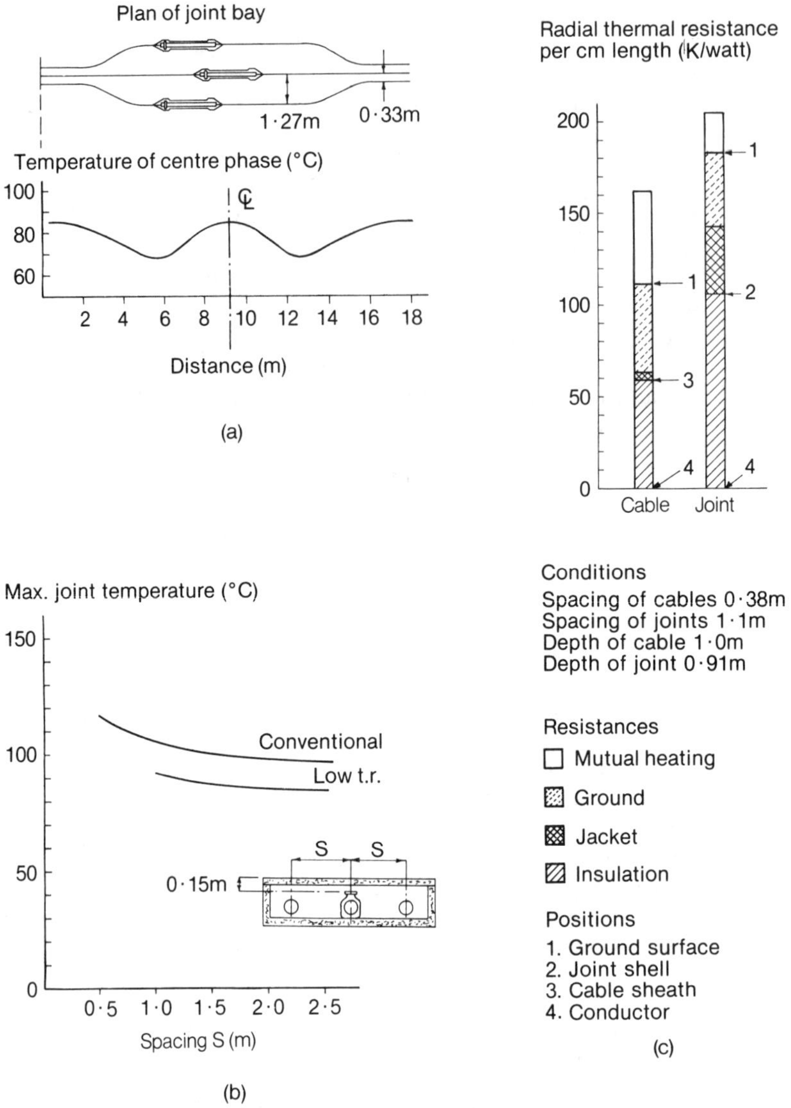

Fig. 38.26 Thermal design characteristics: (a) conductor temperature in a 275 kV straight joint bay; (b) 275 kV joint temperature versus spacing characteristic; (c) comparison of 275 kV cable and joint thermal resistances

reduction in resistance can only be achieved by altering the joint design, e.g. by replacing the bitumen filled glass fibre box by low thermal resistivity insulation of either tape or heat shrink sleeve. Fig. 38.26(b) shows the reduction of temperature achieved with a low thermal resistivity joint shell insulation for a 275 kV trough installation.

Efficient force cooled cable systems require that superior cooling is given to the joints. Fig. 38.6(c) shows a 400 kV straight joint with a water pipe welded to the copper joint shell, the pipe being connected to the cable cooling pipe with the coolest water. Fig. 38.6(d) is a 400 kV straight joint in an integrally water cooled cable system. The heat is dissipated by longitudinal heat flow along the conductor and oil duct to the water cooled cable and to a lesser extent by radial flow to air. The oil within the cable central oil duct is reciprocated at laminar flow velocity. Turbulence is promoted in the joint duct to improve heat transfer by increasing the velocity over a flexible ridged mandrel inserted during jointing.[29]

Terminations and stop joints on OF cable are thermally less critical than straight joints, as the radial dissipation of heat is improved for the former by internal and external convection and for the latter by conduction through the cast epoxy resin barrier.

XLPE cable joints are potentially at a greater thermal disadvantage compared with the cable than are OF cable joints. This is because of the absence of convective heat transfer by oil to the joint shell, the reduced level of dielectric heating in the cable and the increased diameter of some types of joint. It is important to ensure that joint shells are filled with a thermally conductive material, that joint dimensions are minimised and that joint bays are thermally designed.[25]

REFERENCES

(1) Gregory, B. and Nicholls, A. W. (Nov. 1986) '66 kV and 132 kV XLPE supertension cable systems'. *Sixth Conf. on Electric Power Supply Industry. Transmission and Distribution Systems and Equipment.* Paper No. 3.08.
(2) Smee, G. J. and West, R. S. V. (Nov. 1986) 'Factors influencing the choice between paper and XLPE insulated cables in the voltage range 66 kV–132 kV'. *Second Int. Conf. on Power Cables and Accessories 10 kV to 180 kV.* IEE Publication No. 270, pp. 193–197.
(3) Arkell, C. A., Arnaud, U.C. and Skipper, D. J. (1974) 'The thermomechanical design of high power self-contained cable systems'. Paris: CIGRE Paper No. 21–05.
(4) Ball, E. H. and Holdup, H. W. (1984) 'Development of cross-linked polyethylene insulation for high voltage cables. Paris: CIGRE.
(5) Nakagawa, H., Nakabasami, T., Sugiyana, K. and Shimada, A. (Mar. 1984) 'Development of various snaking installation methods of cables in Japan'. Jicable 84 Conference Publication, pp. 413–420.
(6) Aalst, R. J., Laar, A. M. F. J. and Leufkens, P. P. (Aug. 1986) 'Thermomechanical stresses in extruded HV cables'. Paris: CIGRE Paper No. 21–07.
(7) Asada, Y. and Maruyama, Y. (Sep. 1987) 'A study on insulation shrinkback in crosslinked polyethylene cables'. Jicable 87 Conference Publication, pp. 264–269.
(8) ESI Standard 09–4 (Oct. 1979) '66 and 132 kV impregnated paper insulated oil-filled and gas-pressure type power cable systems: Electricity Supply Industry.
(9) Ray, J. J., Arkell, C. A. and Flack, H. W. (Mar.–Apr. 1974) '525 kV self-contained oil-filled cable systems for Grand Coulee third powerplant: design and development'. *IEEE Trans.* **PAS-93**.
(10) Williams, A. L., Davey, E. L. and Gibson, J. N. (Jan. 1966) 'The 250 kV d.c. submarine power cable interconnection between the North and South Islands of New Zealand'. *Proc. IEE* **113** (1).
(11) Engineering Recommendation C55/3 draft (Jul. 1988) 'Insulated sheath power

cable systems'. Electricity Council Chief Engineers Conference, Mains Committee.

(12) CIGRE Study Committee 21, Working Group 07 (Jul. 1976) 'The design of specially bonded cable circuits', part II. *Electra* (47), second report.

(13) ESI Standard 09–10 (Nov. 1976) 'Porcelain insulators for 33, 66, 132, 275 and 400 kV pressure assisted cable outdoor sealing ends'. Electricity Supply Industry.

(14) Looms, J. S. T. (1988) Insulators for High Voltages. *IEE Power Engineering Series 7. Peter Peregrinus.*

(15) IEC 137 (1973) 'Bushings for alternating voltages above 1000 V' (2nd edition).

(16) IEC 71–1 (1976) 'Insulation coordination'. Part 1: 'terms, definitions, principles and rules' (6th edition).

(17) IEEE (1975) 'Standard test procedures and requirements for high voltage a.c. cable terminations'. *IEEE* **48**.

(18) Arkell, C. A., Johnson, D. F. and Ray, J. J. (Mar.–Apr. 1974) '525 kV self-contained oil-filled cable systems for Grand Coulee third powerplant: design proving tests'. *IEEE Trans.* **PAS-93**.

(19) Arkell, C. A., Galloway, S. J. and Gregory, B. (Sep. 1981) 'Supertension cable terminations for metalclad SF_6 insulated substations'. *Eighth IEEE/PES Conf. and Exposition on Overhead and Underground Transmissions and Distribution.*

(20) IEC 859 (1986) 'Cable connections for gas-insulated metal-enclosed switchgear for rated voltages of 72.5 kV and above'.

(21) Gregory, B. and Lindsey, G. P. (Aug. 1988) 'Improved accessories for supertension cable'. Paris: CIGRE Paper No. 21–03.

(22) Sütterlin, K. H. (Mar. 1972) 'Cable lead-ins into 110 kV metal-clad switchgear'. IEE Conference Publication No. 83, pp. 45–52.

(23) Ishikawa, M. *et al.* (Feb. 1981) 'An approach to the suppression of sheath surge involved by switching surges in a GIS power cable connection system'. *IEEE Trans.* **PAS-100** (2).

(24) Gibbons, J. A. M., Saunders, B. L. and Stannett, A. W. (Nov. 1980) 'Role of metal debris in the performance of stop joints as used in 27, kV and 400 kV self-contained oil-filled cable circuits'. *Proc. IEE, Part C* **127** (6).

(25) Gregory, B. and Vail, J. (Nov. 1986) 'Accessories for 66 kV and 132 kV XLPE cables'. *Second Int. Conf. on Power Cables and Accessories 10 kV to 180 kV.* IEE Publication No. 270, pp. 248–256.

(26) Rosevear, R. D., Williams, G. and Parmigiani, (Nov. 1986) 'High voltage XLPE cable and accessories'. *Second Int. Conf. on Power Cables and Accessories 10 kV to 180 kV.* IEE Publication No. 270, pp. 232–237.

(27) Stepniak, F. M., Burghardt, R. R., Boliver, V. J. and Shimshock, J. F. (Jul. 1987) 'Effects of aging on premoulded elastomeric splices for 138 kV XLPE cable'. *IEEE Trans.* **PWRD-2** (3), 632–637. Paper 86 T & D 585–4.

(28) Nakabasami, T. *et al.* (Feb. 1985) 'Investigations for commercial use of 275 kV XLPE cables and development of extrusion type moulded joint'. IEEE/PES 1985 Winter Meeting, Paper 85 WM 007–0.

(29) Arkell, C. A. *et al.* (Mar. 1977) 'Design and construction of the 400 kV cable system for the Seven Tunnel'. *Proc. IEE* **124** (3), 303–316.

(30) Engineering Recommendation C47/1 (Dec. 1975) 'Type approval tests for single core impregnated paper insulated gas pressure and oil filled power cable

systems for 275 kV and 400 kV'. Electricity Council Chief Engineers Conference, Mains Committee.

(31) ESI Standard 09–16 (Aug. 1983) 'Testing specification for metallic sheathed power cables with extruded crosslinked polyethylene insulation and accessories for system voltages of 66 kV and 132 kV'. Electricity Supply Industry, Issue 1.

Chapter 39

Installation of Transmission Cables

PROJECT PLANNING

The installation situations in which cables are used at transmission voltages fall into three main categories:

(a) inside power stations or substations where the use of busbar or overhead line connections would be either a less economic or impracticable solution
(b) to lead overhead line circuits into congested substation areas or to form part of a circuit in an area where overhead transmission is environmentally unacceptable
(c) for the interconnection of substations within urban areas where the use of overhead transmission is neither practical nor environmentally acceptable

The third category is by far the most common for transmission cable, although most of the considerations discussed below apply to all three groups.

Owing to the high cost per unit length of the transmission cable and the great diversity of types and sizes manufactured, it is relatively rare for a manufacturer to be able to supply any new requirements from stock. In general, cables at these voltages are 'made to measure' project by project. In a limited number of applications the standard drum length approach is adopted, where one or more standard drum lengths are selected from experience as typical of the optimum length for installation in such a situation, and manufacture proceeds on this basis.

Such an approach to the installation will yield faster project mobilisation times even where the routes are not cleared and will enable a more flexible approach to the site work, but suffers from the drawback that it inevitably involves a higher level of surplus cable at the end of the project. Such a method is not practicable where joint bay location is in any way difficult due to the size of the joint bays, lack of available space in the roadways, or the need to match cable lengths for cross-bonding. It is rarely encountered, therefore, at voltages above 132 kV or in heavily developed urban environments.

The more commonly used approach is firstly to determine and clear a substantial part or preferably all of the cable route. Once the line of the route is set the position of every joint bay is determined. In principle it is normal to use as long a length of cable between joint bays as possible, i.e. the minimum number of joints practicable. In practice the maximum section length (distance between consecutive joint bays) can be limited by any one or more of a number of different constraints:

(a) local restrictions on the length of continuous trench that can be opened
(b) manufacturing length

(c) transportable length on one drum
(d) handling limitations at the site of installation
(e) induced voltage in the cable sheath
(f) balancing of minor section lengths on cross-bonded systems
(g) positioning of joint bays

In oil-filled cable installations, the need to install stop joints instead of simple straight through joints is identified and all the materials are then put into manufacture, each drum of cable being manufactured to a specific predetermined length. In this type of approach to the installation work, the planning and manufacturing lead times are much greater but wastage is limited and the whole project is fully detailed and programmed prior to work starting at site.

TRANSPORTATION OF CABLES

Although transportation systems are now quite highly developed in most parts of the world, problems are still encountered, even in the most developed countries. The difficulties are usually limited to the road transportation of large cable drums with regard to size rather than weight, since weight limitations are overcome by increasing the number of axles utilised.

As the rated voltage of the cable increases, the diameter and the minimum bending radius become greater. Thus the minimum hub diameter of the drum increases and also the volume of the cable to be added to it. In order to comply with the width limitations contained in most sets of highways regulations, the increase in the bulk of the drums results in larger diameter drums.

A drum carrying 400 m of 400 kV cable will be of the order of 4 m in diameter over the battens. When this is placed on the back of a conventional low loader, bridge clearances in excess of 4.5 m are required and these are not always available. Specialist vehicles have had to be developed to meet these situations, both in the form of heavy duty drum carriers for short haul applications and specialised trailer units for overland transportation, in which the drums are carried very close to the ground.

CABLE TRENCHES

The line of the cable trench and position of the joint bays will have been selected during the planning stage and basically proved at that time by sample trial holes. The extent of the trial holing is determined by experience and moderated in accordance with the extent and accuracy of the available records of existing services and obstructions along the proposed route. A subsurface electronic survey can be particularly accurate in locating existing underground electric services and other metallic services which have an induced 50–60 Hz 'hum'. With major services, water mains for example, where the exact intersection with the cable route is not known, a signal can be injected onto the pipe at a known reference point and its direction and depth can be plotted.

The final line of trench should be selected to have as few changes of line and direction as possible and corners should be taken at a radius preferably greater than the minimum installation radius of the cable. This enables the most efficient cable laying operation to be followed since cables of this size and weight tend to be difficult to bend. An indication of minimum bending radii for oil-filled cables may be obtained from table 39.1, where d_o is the overall cable diameter.

Table 39.1 Minimum bending radii (summary)

Voltage (kV)	Number of cores	Minimum installation bending radii			
		Adjacent to accessories		Laid direct	Laid in ducts
		with former	without former		
Non-pressure-assisted					
33	1	$15d_o$	$20d_o$	$21d_o$	$35d_o$
	3	$12d_o$	$15d_o$	$18d_o$	$30d_o$
Pressure-assisted					
33–132	1	$15d_o$	$20d_o$	$30d_o$	$35d_o$
	3	$12d_o$	$15d_o$	$20d_o$	$30d_o$
275–400	1	$20d_o$	$20d_o$	$30d_o$	$35d_o$
Extruded dielectric (metallic sheath)					
66–132	1	$15d_o$	$20d_o$	$30d_o$	$35d_o$

Cables can be laid in three different ways:

(a) by the traditional open-cut method, buried directly in the ground
(b) by pulling into existing pipes with joint bays in buried underground chambers
(c) in buried concrete troughs which are either pre-cast or cast *in situ*

The method to be employed will depend upon a number of factors, which include economics, inconvenience to the public and the need to provide for the security of the system against external influences.

The traditional open-cut method is by far the most economical and allows great flexibility in installation. This method, however, can cause considerable inconvenience to the public when the whole trench is excavated for the cable to be installed, and security of the system to third party damage is low.

Inconvenience is localised with cables being pulled into existing pipes, the installation of which can be carried out well in advance of cabling, a small portion at a time, by a cut and fill operation. This method of construction, together with the consequent cable derating in long air filled pipes, makes for an expensive installation although the security of the system is good.

The final method that has become increasingly popular, particularly with the installation of cable systems for the transmission of bulk power to load centres and major industrial users where security of the system is a priority, is to lay cables in buried reinforced concrete troughing. Although as inconvenient to the public as the open-cut method, it has major advantages in that it is particularly safe from damage by third party activity and it also retains the selected low thermal resistivity backfill material which otherwise would normally be lost when work is carried out under or adjacent to the cables so that the system would be put at risk of derating. Whilst this method of installation is most secure and retains substantial flexibility, it is comparatively expensive.

The line of trench must also allow for the necessary clearance from other services (usually 300 mm) and other parallel cable circuits (preferably 5 m). Due regard should also be taken of statutory regulations and the rights and interests of landowners, which may also affect the line of trench.

Transmission cables are usually laid deeper than lower voltage cables and standard installation depths of 1.0–2.5 m are quite normal. These cables are frequently of the single-core type and the system design will then specify a minimum spacing of phase centres at standard laying depth to ensure that the cables do not overheat at the design rating. The cables are usually laid at this spacing to minimise induced sheath voltage and enable the narrowest (cheapest) trench to be excavated. When transverse obstructions are met, it may be necessary for the cables to be laid deeper, in which case the need to widen the phase spacing must be considered to ensure that the cables do not overheat. Increased ratings may be achieved by the installation of polyethylene water cooling pipes alongside the cables; by passing water through these pipes, heat may be removed from the cable environment. The pipes are usually installed at a set distance from the cables, the distance being controlled by the use of plastic spacers.

During the design stage, work will have been carried out to measure the normal level of ground thermal resistivity in the area. Once the cable trench is excavated, sample tests should be carried out in the trench wall to ensure that the surrounding ground is at least as good as the standard used for determining the cable rating.

Open-cut trenches are usually excavated to a level about 75 mm below the final position of the bottom of the cable, to allow for a bedding layer of selected backfill to be placed in the trench below the cables.

For buried trough installations the trough is either cast *in situ* or constructed from pre-cast elements which are hoisted into position onto a bedding layer of weak mix concrete. The speed of installation of the cast *in situ* trough can be rapidly increased by the use of plasticiser or quick curing additives in the concrete. After the cables are installed the trough is filled with a selected backfill and a reinforced concrete lid, sufficiently waterproofed, is placed on top.

Selected backfill materials may be divided into three groups: sand, cement bound sand and sand–gravel mix. The importance of using a selected backfill is to achieve the required thermal resistivity demanded by the system design and local conditions (chapter 37). Thermal resistivities are difficult to measure accurately on site, and as the measurement is time consuming it may delay installation work. For a given material, as thermal resistivity is related to dry density, the latter characteristic is used for quality control on site. As a further precaution to eliminate lumps of foreign material from the cable environment, it is quite normal to have transmission cable trenches close timbered where unstable ground is encountered or to use open poling in moderately firm ground.

ROAD CROSSINGS

The most frequent obstacle a trench encounters, other than drains, water or gas pipes, cables etc., is the crossing of side roads where they join the road in which the trench is being excavated. These road junctions must usually be kept open and operational throughout the cable installation period. Thus the trench cannot simply continue across the side road and some special arrangement is required. The most useful method is to install ducts, with one duct for each cable to be installed. The diameter of the inside of the duct is about twice the cable diameter. The ducts are set in a block of concrete at predetermined spacings, dependent on the depth of laying, to ensure that cables do not overheat. The road way, however, is often the location for large services such as high pressure sewer lines and stormwater drainage systems, and it is not always possible for a rigid block of ducts to pass between these services.

A duct block requires careful planning; a trial trench should therefore be excavated across the road to the exact dimensions of the proposed installation. This trench can be either temporarily backfilled or covered with heavy steel plates to allow continuity of traffic flow. Once the trench has been proved any temporary backfill can be removed and the duct block installed, taking account of any adjustments to the trench dimensions which may be necessary due to changes in depth to overcome obstructions.

The ducts themselves are usually made from rigid PVC or equivalent material and are laid in short sections. They require adequate wall thickness to ensure that they do not deform to an oval shape under the pressures exerted during installation and should be installed in such a manner as to ensure a smooth internal surface to prevent damage to the cable oversheath during installation. With the increasing variety of modern materials that are becoming available in the market, an excellent alternative to rigid PVC ducts is the flexible high density polyethylene corrugated pipe. This has advantages for various applications in that its coefficient of friction is much less than rigid PVC pipe and hence the pulling force on the cable is reduced. The flexibility of the pipe also allows for a more flexible installation where the pipe can easily follow the contour of obstructions and return to normal laying depth over a shorter distance, economising on both the dimensions of the trench and the concrete used in constructing the block. This type of pipe is also well suited to undercrossings of rivers and canals that can be dredged, the installation of the pipes being made in one continuous length.

After installing the cable in the ducts they should be filled with a mixture of bentonite, sand and cement. This is kept in position by sealing the annular gap around the cable at each end of the duct. The bentonite mixture improves the conduction of heat away from the cable and supports it thermomechanically in the duct. When duct runs exceeding 50 m are to be filled with bentonite, it is normal to fit a vent pipe near the centre of the duct during installation to facilitate filling from both ends.

An alternative method of road crossing is flush decking. Although mainly superseded by duct blocks this is still used quite satisfactorily in some major cities. This method is based on cutting the trench as usual but going straight across side roads with the trench. As the trench opens across the road, the top 0.3 m is filled in with heavy timbers supported by cross-bearers in such a manner as to reinstate the surface of the road flush. The traffic can then drive on the timbers over the trench. Sufficient room must be left, of course, for men to work under the flush decking which may cause the cables to be laid deeper than otherwise necessary. Plating is another technique to keep traffic flowing. This usually necessitates timbering of the trench prior to the laying of heavy duty steel plates of two to three times the width of the trench.

Thrust boring or pipe jacking and conventional tunnelling, although certainly more costly, is often a practical solution in crossing roads, canals, rivers etc. where other methods are unsuitable.

JOINT BAYS

It is often a requirement that the top of the joint is as deep as the top of the cable at the standard depth of laying, where the top of the joint is taken to be the lid of the fibre glass box. The axis of the joint is thus below that of the cable. In addition there must be adequate clearance under the cable to allow jointing operations to be carried out without difficulty. The joint bay floor tends to be quite deep as a result and certainly deeper than the trench bottom at normal laying depth.

Apart from thermal considerations, the spacing between cables in joint bays may need to be increased to enable the jointers to get between them with their equipment. Joint centre spacing is typically two to four times the cable phase centre spacing at normal depth of laying. In any case, this amount of joint spacing is usually necessary for the thermal integrity of the joint bay. Since space is also required between the outside joints and the joint bay wall, it is often found that the joint bay is two or three times the normal trench width and sometimes greater.

The transition between trench spacing and joint spacing must not take place too sharply after leaving the joints as some straight cable is required during jointing for passing back the joint sleeve and bending radii must meet the specified requirement. Thus although the finished length of the joint may be 1.5–2.0 m, the length over which the trench must be widened may be up to about 16 m.

Certainly at the higher end of the voltage range the joint bays are sizeable constructions, particularly at stop joint positions, for which it can be difficult to find space in congested urban areas. The increasing widths and depths commonly required at the highest voltages have led to the adoption of reinforced concrete floors and side retaining walls as part of the construction. This also ensures a firm flat base for jointing upon, with adequate anchorage for cable cleats should they be required.

The most economic configuration of joints is usually to have all three abreast, but for special requirements, to produce a narrower joint bay, they may be staggered in relation to each other. An arrowhead layout is usually preferable, although an echelon arrangement is not unusual in very confined situations.

SPECIAL CONSTRUCTION

Unless route lengths are very short, special constructions may be required. Typical examples are river crossings, rail crossings, cable tunnels, cable bridges and troughs.

While it is not possible to consider the detailed design of each of these on a general basis, certain aspects of the installation require special attention:

(a) the thermal environment must be satisfactory
(b) any thermomechanical forces that could be experienced must be adequately constrained or dissipated

(c) where cables are in the open, due account must be taken of risks due to fire, vandalism, accidental third party damage and solar radiation
(d) exposure to vibrations
(e) specified installation radii must be observed

CABLE LAYING

The most basic method of laying cable involves pulling the cable from the drum by hand. This technique is still used in many parts of the world today, particularly where labour is cheap and plentiful and the cable is relatively short and lightweight. The drum is mounted to rotate freely and a cable pulling crew is spread along the cable trench at intervals which are determined by the weight per unit length of the cable and the route complexity. The foreman or supervisor of the crew co-ordinates the physical effort made by each individual to move the cable forward, through the use of a whistle or by a shout. This system of cable laying is crude but effective under the right circumstances and is termed 'hand pulling'.

As the need to lay longer cable lengths of heavier cable designs developed, it became clear that some form of motive power should be introduced to act as the prime mover for the cable in the trench. This brought about the use of a power winch at the other end of the trench from the cable drum, with a steel rope, of at least the same length as the cable, paid out from the winch through the trench connected to the end of the cable. When the rope is drawn back by the winch the cable is pulled into the trench. In this method the cable drum must be mounted by a spindle or rim system to allow the cable to be pulled off the drum freely. The frictional forces on the trench bottom are minimised by running the cable over free running rollers spaced at intervals of a few metres. Skid plates are usually installed at bends. If rollers mounted vertically are used the curvature of the roller must match that of the cable to ensure that the cable is not deformed. This method of cable laying is termed 'nose pulling' and probably in one form or another is the most common practice throughout the world.

However, it should be noted that there are limitations in nose pulling cables. The two principal limitations are

(a) the maximum tensile load that can safely be applied to the cable conductor or to the pulling eye fitted to the cable end
(b) the maximum side wall thrust developed on the cable as it traverses directional changes along the cable trench.

These limitations are directly proportional to the complexity of the cable pull and the size and weight etc. of the cable involved; it is therefore necessary to calculate the anticipated loads before installing a cable by the nose pulling method. A dynamometer should be utilised to indicate actual tensions developed whilst pulling in cables by mechanically aided means. Some modern winches are fitted with a tension recording device and an automatic shut-down facility to respond to a pre-set maximum permissible tension.

However, there are many projects which involve extremely heavy cables, very long lengths between joints, tortuous routes involving continuous changes in direction and level, or a mixture of these difficulties in varying degrees. In such circumstances it is often found that the tension or the side thrust would reach an unacceptable level and possibly lead to damage of the cable during installation. To deal with these situations a range of more sophisticated cable pulling techniques has been developed which distribute the pulling force more evenly throughout the cable length. Two of the more widely used methods are described below.

The first method is called 'bond pulling' and is illustrated in fig. 39.1. A wire bond of more than twice the length of the cable route is coiled on a drum mounted on a suitable mobile trailer unit equipped with a braking device to maintain the bond in tension, and this is placed near the cable drum. The bond is run out through the whole length of the trench over cable rollers and attached to the pulling winch. At each change of direction of the route the bond is taken through a snatch block anchored to the side of the trench. These snatch blocks take the full side force on the bond from the change in direction. Initially, some 20–25 m of cable is hand pulled off the drum to allow 10–12 ties of jute yarn and cable. Before applying any ties, the bond wire must be back-tensioned to a load value approximately of 12.5% of the total weight of cable to be pulled. As the cable installation progresses the back tension may be relaxed to hold the load value essentially constant throughout the pull. The bond must not be allowed to relax totally until the cable is in its final position when the ties can be removed. Once the winch has started, the cable is tied to the bond at intervals of approximately 2 m as it is drawn off the cable drum. Prior to each change of direction at snatch block positions the ties are removed whilst the cable is taken round the bend, and the ties are re-attached to the bond immediately after the change of direction. Care must be taken to guide the nose of the cable over the rollers to avoid jamming or displacement of rollers and possible consequential damage to the cable. Once the cable has been pulled into position and the jute ties have been removed the bond is rewound onto the bond carrier ready for the next cable pull.

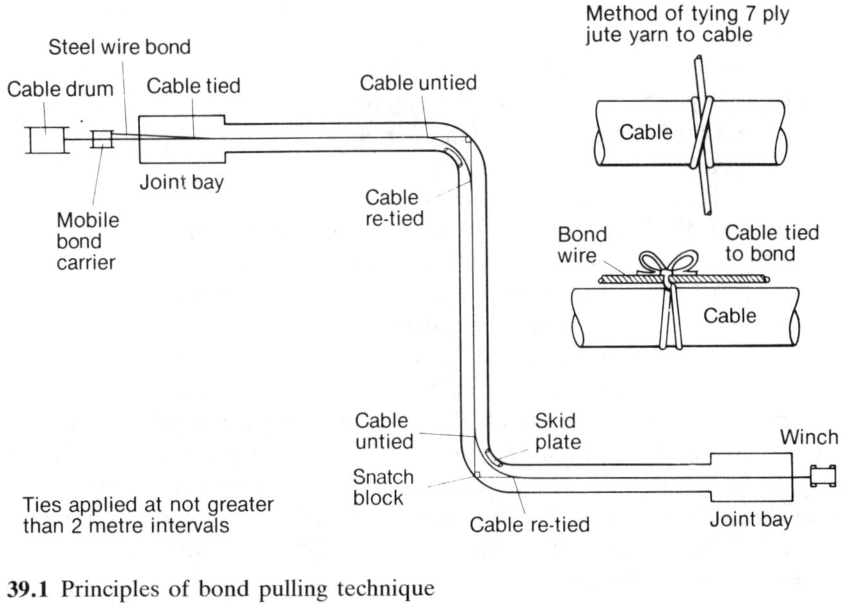

Fig. 39.1 Principles of bond pulling technique

The second method of cable laying is the driven roller technique. At intervals of 10–20 m along the trench, power roller units are installed. Each of these comprises a pair of wheels between which the cable passes and from which it gets the motive force to push it as far as the next roller unit. One wheel is a powered wheel driven by an electric motor through a gear box. It transmits the driving force to the cable by the frictional force between the cable sheath and the pneumatic tyre on the driving wheel. The frictional force is maintained by the physical spacing of the two wheels. The distance between roller units in a straight trench is determined by the weight per unit length of the cable. At corners, ducts etc., extra units are employed to provide the increased power requirements involved in bending the cable. The nose of the cable is guided from one unit to the next by a pulling rope run back from a light capstan winch at the opposite end of the trench to the drum. The forces applied to the cable nose in this system are a small fraction of those involved in the nose pulling method. The roller units and the winch are synchronised by electrical interconnection. Free-running rollers are used to support the cable between driven roller units.

The third method of cable pulling is similar to the driven roller technique except that caterpillar machines are used instead of driven rollers. The caterpillar machines, of similar design to those used in cable manufacturing, have the advantage over motor driven rollers that their surface area in contact with the cable sheath is much greater and hence there is less likelihood of the cable slipping. Both the driven roller and the caterpillar machine have the advantage of being able to position the cable in the trench accurately with both forward and limited backward movement of the cable. This is something which is not easily achieved with the bond pulling system. The caterpillar machine is also recommended when cables are installed in confined spaces such as tunnels and substations where accurate control is required to minimise the risk of damage to the cable from protruding steelwork, concrete beams etc., and also damage to essential equipment already commissioned. The use of pulling blocks, winches, rollers and wire bonds are not always recommended in confined spaces.

The above notwithstanding, the most economic and straightforward method of cable pulling in most situations is the nose pulling method. The basis of safe cable pulling irrespective of the method used is good communication, usually by two-way radio, and a disciplined workforce. Good co-ordination between operators will ensure a satisfactory cable installation. Laying of cables must only take place when cable and ambient temperature have been at or above 0 °C for the previous 24 hours.

Transmission voltage cables are invariably of the insulated sheath type, the cable being covered with an oversheath of either medium density polyethylene or reduced flame propagating PVC depending on its location. Over this sheath a graphite coating is applied to form a conducting layer. For such cables it is common practice to check the integrity of the cable oversheath electrically after cable laying to ensure that the oversheath has not sustained damage. This may be caused by sharp stones or other deleterious matter which had not been removed from the trench, thus necessitating oversheath repairs (for repair methods see chapter 27). The optimum time to carry out this test is immediately following the placing of primary backfill and cable protection tiles. Any faults can then be rectified without re-excavation of the road. The test usually involves applying 25 kV d.c. between the metallic cable sheath and earth where the cable is in ducts or 12 kV d.c. if no ducts are present. The integrity of the oversheath of the auxiliary cables laid with the main feeder cables is also checked, albeit at lower voltages.

After installation it is recommended that all non-pressurised cable ends at joint bays be raised up from the joint bay floor to prevent the possible ingress of water.

JOINTING

At transmission voltages, jointing operations take days in total rather than hours and it is essential to use some form of weather/security protection in the form of a tent over the joint bay and dewatering pumps. At the highest voltages, on the more sophisticated system designs, it is not unusual for joint bay occupation to spread over 5–8 weeks in total and for jointing procedures to demand a clean humidity controlled environment. In these cases complete houses are erected over joint bays. Special air-conditioned enclosures are constructed inside and substantial quantities of electricity have to be provided to power the equipment used. A typical 400 kV straight joint enclosure is shown in fig. 39.2 where the internal tubular frame supports a fire-retardant PVC cover to contain the dehumidified atmosphere required for jointing. Overall protection is provided by a fabricated steel building which also allows adequate space for the dehumidification, jointing and ancillary equipment. The joint bay floor and walls are coated with a special non-slip epoxy paint which seals the concrete and prevents build-up of dust.

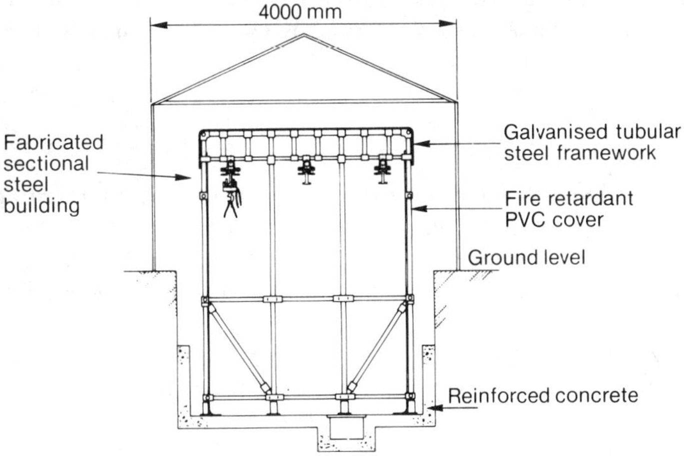

Fig. 39.2 Enclosure for joint bays to obtain atmospheric humidity control

For oil-filled cables, cleanliness during jointing is of paramount importance and it is necessary to replace the oil lost during the jointing operations with processed cable oil. The required quality is achieved by utilising a degasification plant, which filters and heats the raw cable oil under vacuous conditions within defined limits, thus ensuring that the replacement oil is up to the specified standard.

The sequence of jointing is considered at the planning stage to ensure that the effects of profiles and oil feeding requirements on jointing sequence are adequately catered for. This of course affects the cable laying sequence.

Oil-filled cables should be jointed with the cables maintained under a positive oil pressure; however, in some unusual situations where this is not possible, e.g. for cables installed vertically in shafts, special techniques have to be adopted.

On completion of jointing, the joint is evacuated for a specified period to remove all traces of air before it can be impregnated. After satisfactory testing to prove the efficacy of this operation, the joint is filled with clean processed oil and the jointed cable system is returned to its normal pressure. A whitewash test is applied to the plumbs for a period of no less than three days before the outer parts of the joint are placed in position as a final test to prove their integrity.

Cleanliness at joint bays for XLPE installations is also of primary importance and once again a clean controlled dehumidified environment is achieved using air-conditioning and/or heating units. Air deionisers are also used in the jointing area to obviate dust contamination. When the basic cable jointing is completed the cross-bonding link boxes can be made off and other auxiliary work completed.

SF_6 gas immersed switchgear (GIS) designs are becoming increasingly more compact with consequentially higher gas pressures. As a result high differential pressures between SF_6 gas and the cable oil may appear across O-ring seals of the termination into the GIS equipment and failure of these seals could contaminate the cable oil through a transfer of gas. Such contamination could lead to free gas accumulating in the cable termination and result in discharges and subsequent failure of the termination with a serious risk of consequential damage to the GIS. To overcome this problem, gas isolating resin terminations have been introduced which totally encapsulate the cable, thus obviating any O-ring or similar seals between SF_6 gas and cable oil.

SITE TESTS

Tests after installation are made in order to demonstrate the integrity of the cable system and its accessories. Typical tests (other than hydraulic tests on oil-filled cables) are conductor resistance, 10 kV d.c. oversheath tests (on insulated sheath systems), cross-bonding circulating sheath currents (on cross-bonded systems) and high voltage d.c. tests.

The high voltage d.c. test is carried out at a multiple of the a.c. cable voltage varying between 1.7 and 2.6, depending on the cable voltage and test specification used. The cross-bonding check is designed to measure the sheath currents flowing under simulated load conditions in cross-bonded cable systems. This is achieved by applying a low voltage short-circuit current to the three cable conductors and measuring the induced currents in the cable sheaths at the link box locations, from which the full load sheath circulating currents may be calculated to determine the efficacy of the cross-bonding system.

Chapter 40
Thermomechanical Design

A change in the load being carried by a power cable causes a variation in the temperature of the various components and this results in thermal expansion or contraction of these components. The effects of these thermal changes on the insulation have been discussed in chapters 2 and 32. In this chapter the effects of temperature on the metal components of the cable are considered. These effects have a considerable influence on the design of cable installations, bearing in mind that cables installed in air can be subjected to temperature variations of approaching 100 °C under normal loading conditions and even greater excursions when short circuits are taken into account. Thermomechanical design must be considered for all types of power cable installation but it is of special importance in the case of transmission cables where maximum operating temperatures are high and conductor cross-sectional areas up to 2500 mm^2 are used.

Theoretically there are two extremes in installation practice as far as thermomechanical effects are concerned:

(a) where the cable is completely unrestricted and the changes in temperature result in the full expected thermal expansion; in these situations no compressive or tensile forces develop in the cable;
(b) when the cable is fully restrained and no movement of the cable is permitted; in these cases, the thermal expansion or contraction is fully absorbed by internal compressive or tensile forces.

In practice it is not possible to achieve these two extremes as the cable has more than one metallic component. These will be at different temperatures and have different coefficients of thermal expansion. Therefore, if no differential movement of the cable components is permitted, it is impossible to obtain free expansion, i.e. without tensile or compression forces developing over a range of temperature. In practice, the conductor is usually the dominant factor in thermomechanical effects. This is because it experiences the greatest range of temperature change and has a high elastic modulus. An exception to this is the case of smooth (i.e. non-corrugated) aluminium sheaths, particularly when associated with small conductor sizes and thin insulation (i.e. a small difference in conductor and sheath temperatures).

Similarly it is not possible to restrain all the cable components fully. In practical installations only the sheath or pipe is restrained and therefore the conductors are not rigidly held and will have some freedom for movement. This freedom of movement will be extremely small in the case of a single-core self-contained cable but will be of significant proportions in the case of the cores in a pipe type cable.

Thermomechanical design of installations must take into account the movements and forces which develop and ensure that these can safely be withstood by the cable and its accessories. As mentioned earlier, the effects of the thermal expansion depend on how the cable is installed and therefore it is convenient to review the design under the headings of methods of installation.

BURIED CABLES

Considering a single-core cable installed in a well compacted backfill, longitudinal and lateral movement of the complete cable is virtually eliminated, and the only possible movement is longitudinal displacement of the conductor and insulation within the sheath. This movement is resisted by friction between the core and the sheath but can be eliminated if the conductor is firmly held at the cable ends. If it is assumed that no longitudinal movement occurs, then the force developed in the conductor will be

$$F = ES\alpha\theta \tag{40.1}$$

where F = force in conductor (N)
E = effective modulus of elasticity of the conductor (N/m^2)
S = cross-sectional area of the conductor (m^2)
α = coefficient of expansion of the conductor (per degree Celsius at 20 °C)
θ = temperature rise of the conductor (°C)

In this equation it is assumed that the conductor acts as an elastic member. The effective modulus of the conductor will depend on its material, the method of construction and the state of temper of the material. Fig. 40.1 shows a typical initial force versus temperature characteristic of a single-core Milliken conductor cable where no longitudinal movement is permitted. It will be seen that, up to about half the maximum temperature rise, the relationship between temperature rise and force is linear, but for higher temperatures the rate of rise in force decreases.

The reason for this is that the conductor no longer acts as an elastic member and some permanent set occurs. Tested under conditions similar to those experienced in service, a 2000 mm^2 Milliken conductor cable can produce a maximum thrust of some 60 kN.[1] If end movement is permitted, the maximum force will be reduced, the magnitude of the reduction depending on the amount of movement permitted and the frictional force between the core and the sheath. In the case of a fully

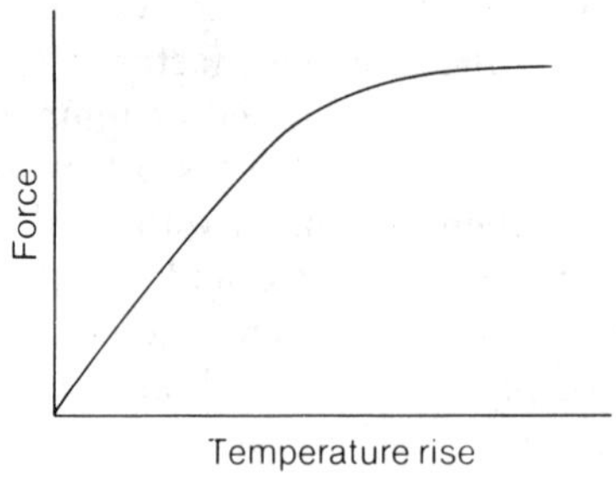

Fig. 40.1 Force versus temperature characteristics for a restrained single-core cable with Milliken conductor

restrained cable, if the cable is allowed to cool to its initial temperature a tensile force will develop in the conductor. This is due to the fact that the conductor has effectively been shortened at the maximum temperature, as a result of creep of the conductor. The effect of repeated heat cycles is illustrated in fig. 40.2 where it will be seen that the cable system progresses to a position where compressive and tensile forces of approximately equal magnitude develop during the respective heating and cooling periods.

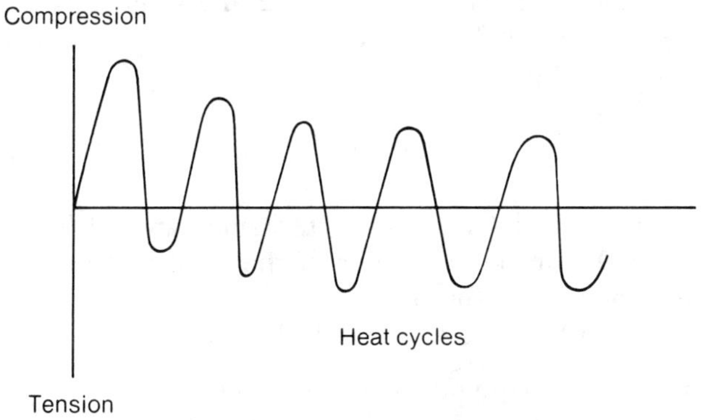

Fig. 40.2 Tensile and compressive forces generated in a single-core cable during loading cycles

CABLES INSTALLED IN AIR

Cables are often installed in air, outdoors and indoors, and it is usually necessary to provide a cleating system to support the cables. Basically two design philosophies are adopted.

Rigid system
With this system, the cables are supported in such a manner that no longitudinal or lateral movement is permitted, i.e. it is similar to a buried cable system.

Flexible system
Lateral expansion of the cable between supports is permitted but it is controlled in such a manner that the cyclic strains imposed on the cable components are kept within acceptable limits. The component most affected by these strains is the cable sheath.

Because expansion is not permitted in the rigid system, the compressive forces will be high. It is therefore necessary to determine the spacing of the cleats so that buckling of the cable will not occur.

The spacing between supports can be calculated using a development of Euler's buckling theory.[2] It should be noted that the theory assumes longitudinal uniformity and therefore is not strictly applicable to corrugated sheaths. However, experimental work has shown that it can be applied to corrugated aluminium sheaths if the values given in the following sections are used.

$$L = \frac{2\pi}{s}\left(\frac{E_{\text{eff}}I}{1000\ F_{\text{p}}}\right)^{1/2} \tag{40.2}$$

where L = maximum spacing between supports (m)
s = factor of safety
E_{eff} = effective modulus of sheath material (N/m^2)
I = second moment of area of sheath (mm^4)
F_{p} = thermomechanical force developed in conductor and sheath (N)

It is usual to take a factor of safety s between 2 and 4. For corrugated aluminium sheath cables, E_{eff} is taken as 25% of that of aluminium. The second moment of area is calculated as follows:

$$I = \frac{\pi(d_0{}^4 - d_{\text{i}}{}^4)}{64}\ (\text{mm}^4)$$

where d_0 = the outside diameter for smooth aluminium and lead sheaths, or the mean of the outside diameter of the crest and trough for corrugated aluminium sheaths (mm)
$d_{\text{i}} = d_{\text{o}} - 2t$ (mm), where t = sheath thickness (mm)

Where cables are installed around bends, it is necessary to reduce the spacing between cleats to 30%–60% of the values used for straight sections.

The most usual forms of flexible system are where cable movement is permitted at right angles to the longitudinal axis of the cable. To ensure that the cyclic strains in the cable are within acceptable limits it is necessary to set up the cable initially with offsets. Two different systems are used: those in which the cable moves in a horizontal plane and those in which the cable is permitted to move in the vertical plane. An example of the latter is shown in fig. 40.3, which shows a 25 kV corrugated aluminium sheathed cable installed along a railway. In the case of the horizontally trained cable it is usually necessary to provide intermediate sliding supports between cleats. This is illustrated in fig. 40.4.

Systems which permit vertical movement usually take the form of widely spaced supports with the cable sagged between them in the manner advocated by Holttum.[3] The initial work has been extended to smooth and corrugated sheath cable and the following formulae may be used.

Lead sheath cable

$$L = \left(\frac{K\ d_{\text{m}}{}^2 t}{W \times 10^3}\right)^{1/2} + 0.2\ (\text{m}) \tag{40.3}$$

where L = spacing (m)
d_{m} = mean diameter of sheath (mm)
t = sheath thickness (mm)
W = cable weight (kg/m)
K = factor as given below:

Material	*K*
Pure lead	5.98
Alloy E	9.5

Fig. 40.3 Railway electrification feed cables suspended on posts

Alloy $\frac{1}{2}$C	9.15
Alloy B	16.19

Aluminium sheath cables

$$L = \left(\frac{0.00244\ Y\ I}{d_r\ W}\right)^{1/2}\ (\mathrm{m}) \tag{40.4}$$

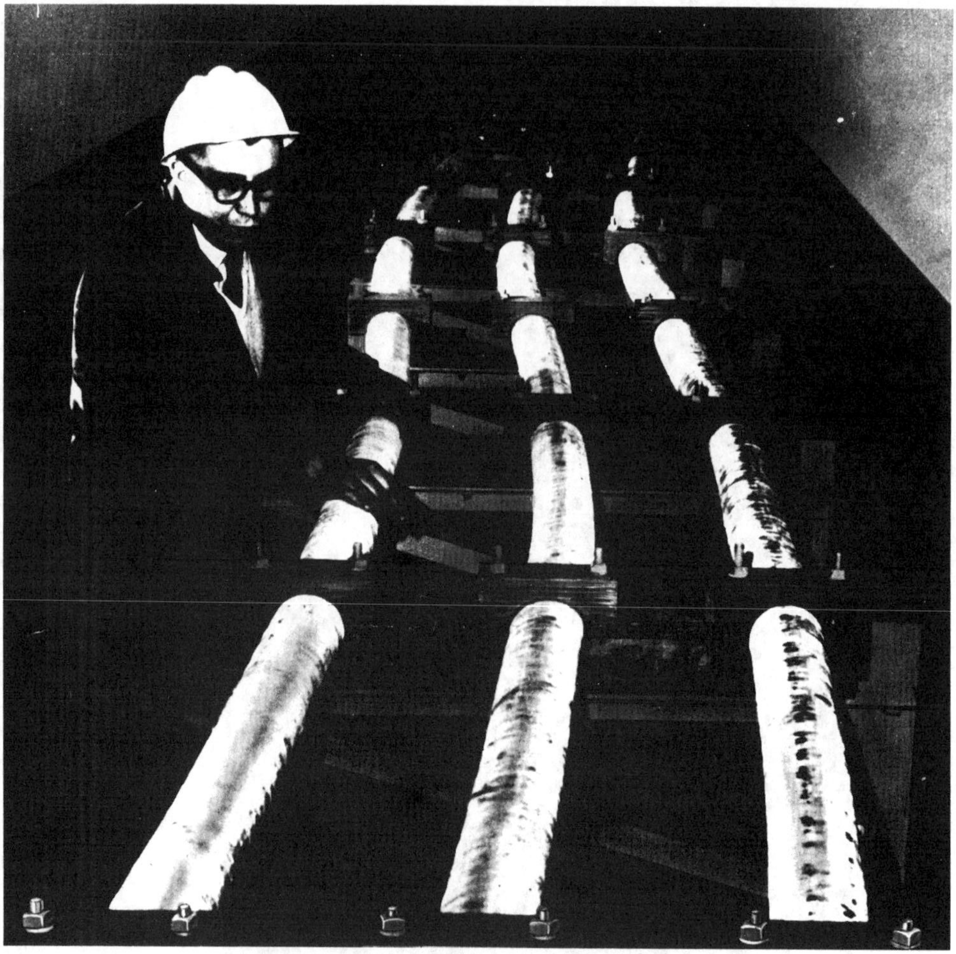

Fig. 40.4 Cables cleated horizontally with allowance for cable movement by sliding at alternate cleat positions

where L = spacing between supports (m)
Y = yield stress of aluminium or effective yield stress in the case of aluminium sheaths (N/m^2)
I = second moment of area of the sheath (mm^4)
d_r = outside diameter for smooth sheaths or root diameter for corrugated sheaths (mm)
W = cable weight (kg/m)

The value for I is calculated in the same manner as for equation (40.2). The effective yield stress for corrugated aluminium sheaths is taken as 25%–30% of the yield stress of aluminium.

The calculated values for spacing are not critical and the distance between supports in a vertically sagged system can be adjusted within limits of 20% to suit load conditions. The initial sag in the vertical direction is chosen so that the bending strain in the sheath, as a result of changes in length due to temperature variations, does not exceed the design limits for the sheath.

In cable systems that accommodate expansion in the horizontal plane, it is usual to train the cables in approximately a sine wave with swivel cleats at the points of inflexion. The distance between cleats and the offset are chosen so that the change in sheath strain due to temperature variations does not exceed the design limit. For simplicity, it is usual to assume that movement of the cable is equal to the unrestrained expansion of the conductor. However, when required, a more accurate calculation is possible which makes allowances for the compressive force in the conductor.

Compared with the rigid system, the flexible system uses fewer cleats and supports and the mechanical forces imposed on the accessories and support system are relatively low. Against this, the cable has to be carefully positioned during installation and allowance must be made for the space occupied by the offsets over the full temperature range. Table 40.1 makes a comparison of the spacing between supports for rigid and vertical sagged systems with self-contained oil-filled cables having a corrugated aluminium sheath.

Table 40.1 Comparison of spacings between cleats for rigid and vertically sagged flexible systems (OF cable with CSA sheath)

Cable type and size	Spacing between cleats on straight sections (m)	
	Rigid	Vertical sagged
Single-core 400 kV 2000 mm^2	1.0	4.0
Single-core 132 kV 300 mm^2	0.55	3.15
3-core 33 kV 185 mm^2	0.7	3.45

Cleats used for cables installed in air can be made of aluminium alloy or of a filled resin. When the cleat is metallic, an elastomeric liner is usually used. In situations where special restraint is required, e.g. when cables are installed in long vertical runs, long cleats manufactured from hardwood are normally used. For cleating cables underground, cleats manufactured from a filled resin are now preferred to the hardwood cleats previously employed.

Polymeric insulated cables without a metallic sheath or with a lead sheath require special consideration. With this type of cable the thermal expansion of the polymeric insulation causes a significant increase in cable diameter. If a normal type of cleat is used it can restrain the insulation from expanding and result in deformation of the insulation. To prevent this, the cleats for this type of cable are designed to permit a limited expansion of the cable and at the same time provide the necessary restraint. This can be achieved by providing a specially resilient liner or by using a bolt assembly which allows a degree of movement, e.g. by the use of specially designed spring washers.

CABLE INSTALLED IN DUCTS

The duct method of installation of self-contained cables is widely adopted in North America and Japan. Traditionally, the thermal expansion of the cables is accommodated by permitting movement of the cable into the manholes in which the joints are situated. Because of the friction between the cable and the duct, the full expansion of the cable is not experienced in the manhole. To cater for the thermal expansion, the joints are offset from the centre line of the ducts as illustrated in fig. 40.5. However, the movement of the cable into the manhole imposes bending strains on the cable adjacent to the joints. Before the mechanism was fully understood, considerable trouble was experienced with fatigue cracks developing in the cables due to cyclic bending. To keep cyclic strains within acceptable limits, it is necessary to adopt generous offsets for the joints and in some cases to allow the joints to move. More information on the layout of cables in manholes is given elsewhere.[4–6] A manhole for a 230 kV cable system is shown in fig. 40.6 in which it will be noted that movement of the joints is catered for by suspending the joints from the manhole ceiling.

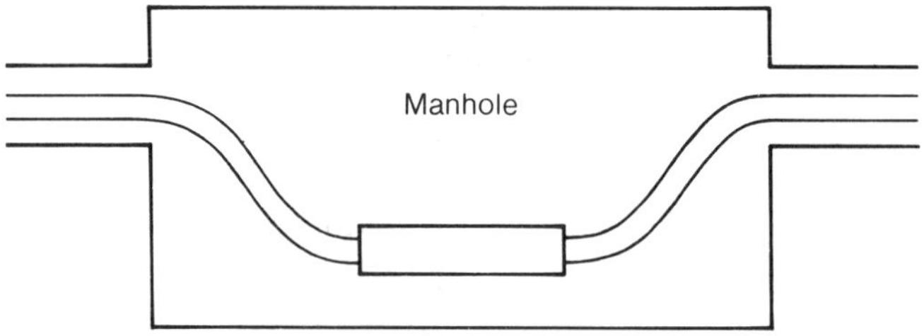

Fig. 40.5 Cable joint installed in a manhole

There are advantages in using aluminium sheathed cables for duct systems because a cyclic strain some 2.5 times greater than for lead alloy sheath can be tolerated. As a result of this, smaller offsets can be employed, and hence smaller manholes.

Even for cables with aluminium sheaths, the manholes for duct installations take up a considerable amount of space and hence are expensive. Attempts have been made to overcome this problem by rigidly cleating the cable and thus preventing movement, instead of permitting movement of cable into the manholes. Thermal expansion of the cable has then to be absorbed by lateral movement of the cable within the duct and the development of compressive forces. Following satisfactory laboratory trials, commercial installations were first undertaken in the late 1960s and the operating experience has been satisfactory.

INSTALLATION DESIGN

The analysis given in the preceding sections assumes that the method of installation is uniform throughout the cable route. In many cases this is not the case. For example short duct runs are often used for road crossings in directly buried systems and terminations are invariably associated with at least short lengths of cable in air. If this transition involves a change from a fully restrained system to a flexible system,

Fig. 40.6 Manhole for 230 kV system with suspended joints to cater for cable expansion

it is possible that core movement from the fully restrained system to the flexible portion will occur on heating and vice versa during cooling. If this movement is excessive there is a possibility of damage to the insulation and its screen and also that excessive sheath strains occur in the flexible part of the system. The importance of these effects increases with conductor size and with maximum conductor operating temperature.

If possible it is best to avoid such transitions. For example where portions of a directly buried system come to the surface, a cleating arrangement which produces a rigid system should be used. Similarly for short duct runs it is possible, after installation of the cable, to fill up the duct with a special pumpable grout which provides similar support to that which the cable experiences in the ground. If it is required to remove the cable at a later stage, the grout can be removed using high pressure water hoses.

If a transition is unavoidable, movement can be restricted by increasing the frictional force between the core and sheath by snaking the cable at the transition. For cables with extremely large conductor sizes and where it is necessary to avoid all movement, a stop joint can be used at the transition position. With this type of accessory, the conductor is effectively connected to the joint sleeve by the epoxy resin moulding.

JOINTS AND TERMINATIONS

The thermomechanical forces developed by the cable have a significant effect on the design of accessories. In fully restrained systems, the conductor connections must be capable of withstanding the maximum compressive and tensile forces. Soldered connections, which are widely used for small conductor cables, are susceptible to slow creep failure under tensile forces. For the larger conductor size used in transmission cables, it is now established practice to use connections with a superior long-term tensile performance, i.e. compression ferrules or welded connections.

The thrust developed by the cable conductors is also important with regard to the electrical insulation of the joint. If the joint is not sufficiently strong in compression there is a possibility of collapse due to buckling. Generally there is no significant problem with single-core joints but 3-core cable joints are significantly weakened by the need to offset the cores due to the requirement to build up the installation over the ferrule. This makes the pitch circle diameter of the conductors in the joint greater than that in the cable and the offset of the cores encourages movement of cable cores into the joint.

The performance of joints is illustrated in fig. 40.7. The full line shows the relationship between movement of the cores from the cable and the force in the conductors for the maximum operating temperature. The broken lines are the movement versus force characteristics of two joints. The latter curves are established by subjecting a joint in the laboratory to an increasing compressive load and noting the movement of the conductor into the joint. The position where the joint characteristics cut the curve of the cable versus force characteristics is the situation which would occur if the joint was installed on a long length of cable. In the case of joint A, it will be seen that relatively little core will move from the cable into the joint and that there is no sign of the joint collapsing. However, in the case of joint B, the two curves do not intersect until significantly more cable core has moved into the joint and the joint characteristic is showing signs of buckling, i.e. a large amount of movement is occurring for virtually no increase in thrust. It is thus important that joints are designed with a mechanical characteristic similar to that of joint A rather joint B.

The joint A characteristic is important not only from an initial thrust point of view but also when consideration is given to the performance of the joint under the compressive and tensile forces developed as a result of load cycles. Repeated local

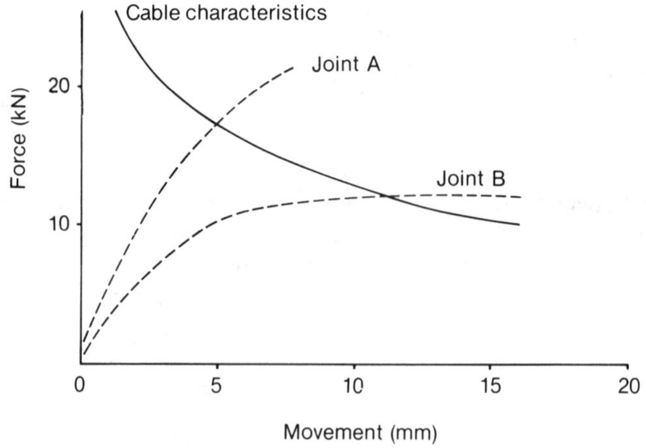

Fig. 40.7 Cable and joint compressive force versus movement characteristics

bending of the cable in the joint can cause soft spots to develop in the paper insulation. These soft spots are caused by the butt gaps between papers enlarging and accumulating at one position. In an extreme form they can lead to cable failure. It is also necessary to ensure that any contact between the cable cores and joint fittings does not cause cable damage as a result of the cyclic movement.

The considerations described above apply both to self-contained and pipe type cables.

Terminations must be capable of withstanding the full conductor thrusts. Generally this presents no problem but in some cases, when large conductor cables are associated with high internal pressure, this can become an important design criterion for the porcelain or epoxy resin moulding.

Terminations into SF_6 insulated metal-clad equipment require special consideration. It is normal practice for the equipment manufacturer to allow small movements of the cable termination chamber to accommodate thermal expansion of the equipment. If the cable adjacent to the equipment is flexibly cleated, it is comparatively simple to arrange the cleating to allow for this movement. The situation is more complicated if the cable is rigidly cleated – this is ofen the case when most of the cable length is directly buried. In this situation, a semi-rigid member such as an I beam can be fixed from the cable termination chamber to the cleat support structure. The length and cross-section of the I beam is chosen to allow the chamber to move without imposing too great a load on it. The cable is then close cleated to the I beam. With this arrangement the cable is prevented from buckling by the close cleating and the flexibility of the I beam allows for the small movements of the metal-clad equipment.

Finally, the connection between the cable sheath and the accessory must be capable of withstanding the thermomechanical forces developed by the cable in addition to any other forces such as those arising from any internal pressure. Generally plumbing is satisfactory for lead and corrugated aluminium sheaths, backed up by resin and glass fibre reinforcement. In the case of non-corrugated aluminium sheaths, the thermomechanical forces are much higher. When these are associated with the high internal pressures used in some designs of pressure-assisted cables, it is necessary to provide a connection with increased mechanical strength, e.g. reinforced plumbs or welded connections.

REFERENCES

(1) Arkell, C. A., Arnaud, V. C. and Skipper, D. J. (1974) 'The thermomechanical design of high power self-contained cable systems'. Paris: CIGRE Paper No. 21–05.

(2) Cavalli, M., Guaktien, G. and Lanfranconi, G. M. (1973) '330 kV oil-filled cable laid in 1600 ft vertical shaft at Kafue Gorge hydro electric plant'. *IEEE* Paper No. T. 73. 126.

(3) Holttum, W. (1955) 'The installation of metal sheathed cables on spaced support'. *Proc. IEE, Part A* **102**, 729–742.

(4) Schifreen, C. S. (1951) 'Thermal expansion effects in power cables'. *Proc. AIEE* **70**. Paper No. 51–22.

(5) Hata, H. (Oct. 1967) 'On the design of cable offsets in manholes'. *Sumitomo Electr. Tech. Rev.* (10), 32–40.

(6) Mochlinski, K. (1961) 'Cables in ducts: arrangement of unarmoured lead covered cables at duct ends and in manholes'. *ERA* Report No. F/T 201.

Chapter 41

D.C. Cables

Although many of the first electrical supply systems were based on d.c. distribution, these were rapidly superseded by a.c. systems which had the desirable feature of easy transformation between generation, transmission and distribution voltages. The development of modern electrical supply systems in the first half of this century was based exclusively on the a.c. transmission system. However, by the 1950s there was a growing demand for long transmission schemes and it became clear that in certain circumstances there could be benefits by adopting a d.c. voltage. These include reduction of system stability problems, more effective use of equipment because the power factor of the system is always unity and the ability to use a given insulation thickness or clearance at a higher operating voltage. Against these very significant advantages has to be weighed the high cost of the terminal equipment to convert the a.c. to d.c. and to invert the d.c. back again to a.c. For a given transmission power, the terminal costs are constant and therefore, for d.c. transmission to be economic, the system must be greater than a certain length so that the saving in the transmission equipment exceeds the cost of the terminal plant.

In the case of submarine transmission cables there is a further factor of importance. The high capacitance of cables results in a comparatively high charging current in a.c. transmission. As capacitance is proportional to length, there is a critical length at which the charging current equals the thermal current rating of the cable and hence the cable system has no capability for useful power. The charging current increases with voltage and hence the critical length reduces as operating voltage increases. In the case of underground cables, the problem can be overcome, albeit at the penalty of significant cost, by the use of shunt reactors at intervals along the route. However, this is not practical for submarine cables and hence a.c. submarine transmission systems have significant length limitations. In d.c. transmission, a charging current only occurs during switching on or off and therefore has no effect on the continuous current rating of the system. Thus the length limitation is eliminated and this explains why d.c. transmission has been so widely used for long submarine crossings.

To date, the same basic types of cable that have been developed for a.c. transmission have been adopted for d.c. transmission. Hence many of the design features are similar and in the following sections it is intended only to discuss features where differences in design occur.

CONDUCTORS

As there are no electromagnetic induction effects, except when switching on and off, there are no skin and proximity effects to be taken into account in the determination of the continuous current rating. As the a.c. resistances of a conductor due to these effects can in practice be up to 20% greater than the d.c. resistance, the use of d.c. results in lower conductor losses. Furthermore there is no need, from a rating point of view, to use the more complex Milliken construction for the larger conductor sizes.

INSULATION

As might be expected, there are considerable differences in the design of the dielectric for d.c. cables in comparison with a.c. operation.[1]

The long-time electrical strength of dielectrics under d.c. conditions is significantly higher than under a.c. This arises from the reduced discharge activity under d.c. As was explained in chapter 2, an important deterioration phenomenon in paper insulated cables is the effect of discharge activity in the butt gaps between adjacent turns of paper. In the case of a.c., multiple discharges can occur during both positive and negative half cycles because, following a discharge, voltage conditions are rapidly re-established by the capacitive current flowing in the insulation. In a d.c. cable, the build-up of voltage following a discharge is much slower, being controlled by the leakage current through the insulation, which is several orders of magnitude lower than the a.c. charging current. Therefore the discharge repetition rate in d.c. cables is very much lower than with a.c. cables and, for equal life, the d.c. cable can be operated at much higher electrical stresses.

This is particularly evident in the case of mass-impregnated solid type cables where the maximum stress under a.c. operation is limited to about 4 MV/m (r.m.s.) but for d.c. operation stresses up to about 25 MV/m have been employed.

The dielectric design of d.c. cables is more complex than that of a.c. cables because of the different stress distribution. In chapter 2 the stress distribution in a.c. cables was derived and the assumption was made that the insulation has a uniform permittivity. This characteristic of the insulation is affected only to a very minor extent by changes in cable temperature and hence the stress distribution does not change significantly as a result of current loading conditions. In the case of a d.c. cable, the stress in the insulation depends on the geometry of the cable and the resistivity of the insulation. It can be shown that, if the resistivity is uniform throughout the insulation, then the stress distribution is the same as that in an a.c. cable. However, the resistivity of the insulation is highly dependent on temperature and to a lesser extent on the electrical stress.

The relationship is given by the following formula:

$$\rho = \rho_0 \exp(-\alpha\beta) \exp(-\beta E) \tag{41.1}$$

where ρ_0 = resistivity at reference temperature (Ω m)
θ = difference in temperature between the actual and reference temperatures (°C)
α = temperature coefficient of electrical resistivity (per °C)
β = stress coefficient of electrical resistivity (per MV/m)
E = electrical stress in the insulation (MV/m)

In the case of oil impregnated paper, a typical value for α is 0.1 and for β 0.03. Hence temperature has the greater influence on resistivity.

The following equation has been derived for the stress distribution in a d.c. cable:[2]

$$E_r = \frac{\delta\, V(r/r_s)^{\delta-1}}{r_s\,[1 - (r_c/r_s)^{\delta}]} \tag{41.2}$$

where E_r = stress at radius r (MV/m)
V = working voltage (MV)
r_c = conductor screen radius (m)
r_s = radius over insulation (m)
W_c = conductor loss (W/m)
T = thermal resistivity of insulation (Km/W)

and

$$\delta = \frac{\alpha W_c T/2\pi + \beta V/(r_s - r_c)}{\beta V/(r_s - r_c) + 1}$$

When the cable is carrying load, there will be a temperature gradient across the insulation and the influence of this is illustrated in fig. 41.1. It will be seen that the effect of the gradient, compared with the isothermal case, is to reduce the stress nearest the conductor and increase it at the outside of the insulation. Increasing the conductor loading will increase the temperature gradient and increase the stress at the outside of the insulation. The current rating of the cable is usually limited so that the stress at the outside of the cable under full load conditions does not exceed that at the conductor under no load.

As in the case of a.c. transmission cables, transient voltages usually determine tne insulation thickness of d.c. cables. It has been found that the most onerous condition

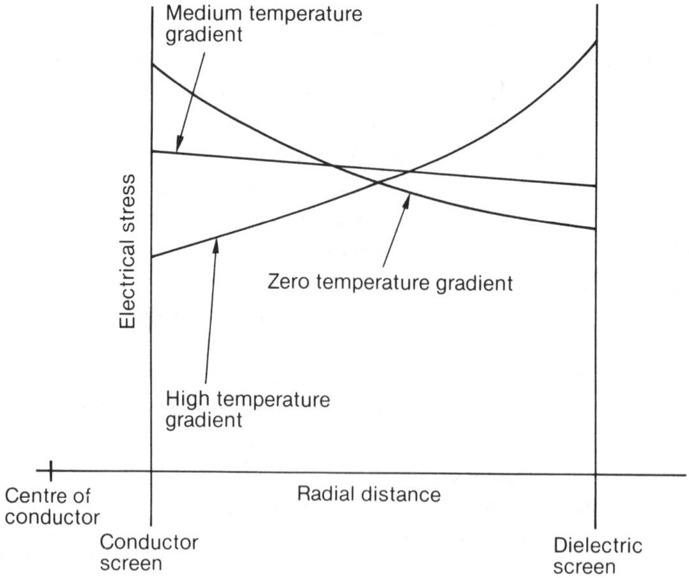

Fig. 41.1 Electrical stress in d.c. cable showing dependence on temperature gradient

occurs when a transient voltage of opposite polarity to the operating voltage is imposed on the system when the cable is carrying full load. If the cable is connected to an overhead line system, this condition usually occurs as a result of lightning transients. The condition is illustrated in fig. 41.2. Its effect on the stress distribution within the cable can be determined using the principle of stress superposition, i.e. the resultant stress at any point in the insulation is that resulting from the summation of the stress due to the operating voltage U_o and that due to a transient voltage equal to the impulse level of the system U_p plus U_o. The overall effect of this is illustrated in fig. 41.3, and it will be seen that the maximum stress appears next to the conductor and decreases through the insulation. The magnitude of the maximum stress will depend on the stress next to the conductor immediately before the

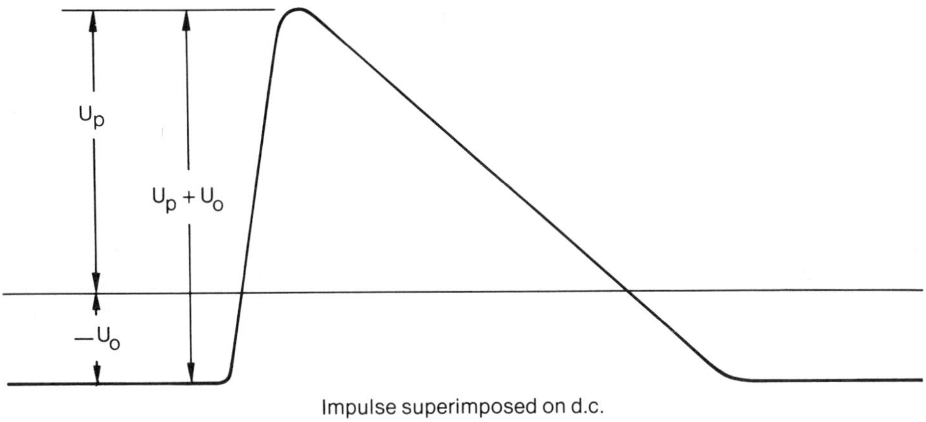

Fig. 41.2 Impulse transient on a d.c. cable

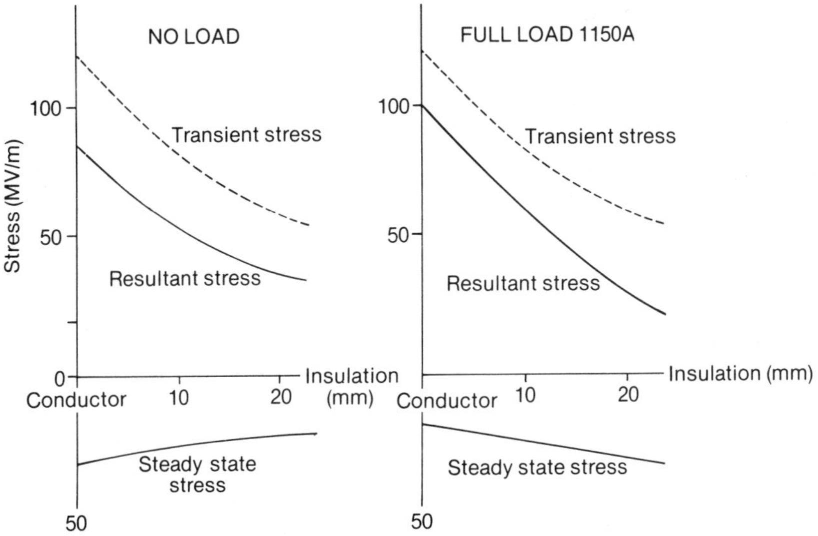

Fig. 41.3 Stress distribution in a 600 kV, 1000 mm^2, d.c. cable with a positive impulse superimposed on negative operating voltage

transient occurs. When the d.c. stress is at its minimum (full load conditions) the resultant stress will be at its maximum, and when the d.c. stress is at its maximum (zero load conditions) the resultant stress will be at its minimum.

It is this requirement which usually determines the insulation thickness necessary and it is an important test requirement which has now been included in international test specifications.[3]

An important benefit of d.c. operation is the virtual elimination of dielectric losses. The d.c. leakage current is of such small magnitude that it can be ignored in current rating calculations, whereas in a.c. cables dielectric losses cause a significant reduction in current rating. This is of considerable importance for higher system voltages. Similarly, high capacitance is not a penalty in d.c. cables. This permits the use of high density papers which have a high electric strength and low thermal resistivity. The latter is of importance in reducing the temperature gradient, which in turn reduces the effect of loading on the stress distribution.

SHEATHS

The absence of continuous electromagnetic induction effects results in the complete absence of sheath and armour losses. This is of particular importance for submarine cables, where in the case of single-core a.c. cables the wide separations required between cables for maintenance purposes result in very high sheath and armour losses.

ACCESSORIES

Designs are very similar to those used for a.c. cable systems. In the case of accessories using a range of materials in the electric field, e.g. stop joints, the electric field analysis under varying load conditions is most complex. Special attention has to be paid to the pollution of terminations where the d.c. field attracts dust particles to the porcelain.

SYSTEMS

The net effects of the differences in design of a.c. and d.c. cables is that, for equal power ratings, d.c. cable systems can be installed at an appreciably lower cost than a.c. cable systems. This is illustrated in fig. 41.4 in which a comparison is made between a.c. and d.c. cable systems. For the a.c. case a naturally cooled cable system using 275 kV 2000 mm^2 oil-filled cables has been considered. This cable, with suitable modification to the dielectric design, can be considered as a d.c. cable rated at 500 kV. For equal power ratings it is obvious that the d.c. cable scheme will be significantly cheaper with respect to both cable and installation costs, as two cables in a single trench can be used for the d.c. scheme whilst six a.c. cables are required in two trenches.

As mentioned earlier, the cost of cable is only part of the total cost and the cost of the converter equipment must be included. The latter is very expensive and at present it is unlikely that a d.c. submarine cable system would be economic for a route length of less than approximately 30 km and a d.c. underground scheme for less than approximately 80 km.

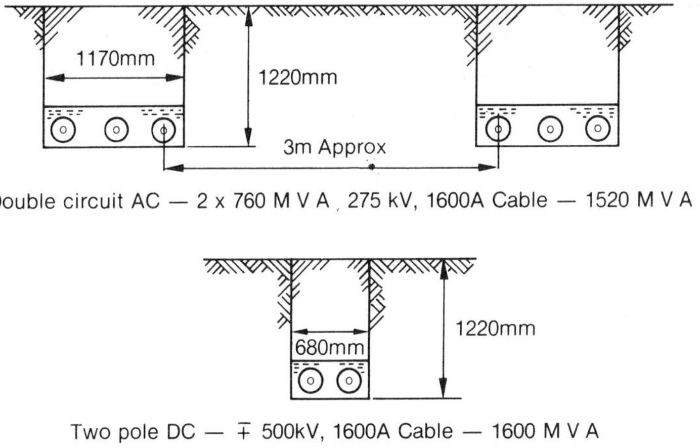

Fig. 41.4 Comparison of a.c. and d.c. transmission capacities, taking as a basis 275 kV, 2000 mm^2, a.c. cable

Several d.c. submarine cables have been installed and some details are included in chapter 45. To date there has been only one major scheme of significance which has been installed totally underground. This is a link from Kingsnorth, east of London, through Beddington in the south to Willesden in northwest London, giving a total route length of approximately 80 km. Between Kingsnorth and Beddington there are two 266 kV d.c. cables with a neutral cable giving a power rating of 640 MW and from Beddington to Willesden there is one 266 kV d.c. cable and a neutral with a rating of 320 MW. The purpose of the neutral cable is to provide a path for return current to flow in the case of single-pole operation so that currents in the earth are avoided. In the case of the section between Kingsnorth and Beddington, this provides a half power capability in the event of the equipment associated with one pole being out of commission.

The pole cables are 266 kV 800 mm^2 oil-filled cables with an insulation thickness of approximately 10 mm and a corrugated aluminium sheath protected by high density polyethylene.

Oil-filled, gas-filled and solid type cables have been used for submarine cable installations, with the latter type now predominating. Trials with polymeric cables to date have been disappointing, a wide scatter in breakdown voltages being obtained. It is suspected that this is due to the presence of space charges that affect the stress distribution in the insulation. Polyethylene has a very high insulation resistivity and any space charges that occur will persist for long periods. This is in contrast with impregnated paper insulation where space charges can disperse more readily, particularly at the higher temperatures, owing to the relatively lower electrical resistivity.

REFERENCES

(1) Arkell, C. A. and Parsons, A. F. (1982) 'Insulation design of self-contained oil-filled cables for D.C. operation'. *IEEE Trans.* **PAS-101**, 1805–1814.

(2) Eoll, K. (Mar. 1975) 'Theory of stress distribution in insulation of high voltage d.c. cables', Part II. *IEEE Trans.* **EI-10** (1).

(3) (Oct. 1980) 'Recommendations for tests on power transmission d.c. cables for a rated voltage up to 600 kV'. *Electra* (72), 105–114.
(4) Casson, W. (1966) 'Kingsnorth–London d.c. transmission interconnector'. *IEE Conf. H.V.D.C. Transmission*, Paper 9. Manchester.

Chapter 42

Testing of Transmission Cable Systems

The testing is dictated primarily by international, national and user specifications with procedures grouped into four categories:

(a) routine tests on cables and accessories
(b) special (sample) tests on cables requested by the purchaser
(c) type tests on cables and accessories
(d) site tests on systems after installation

The information given in this chapter covers the essential tests in IEC specifications and those of the British Electricity Boards for cables of the paper insulated type, primarily self-contained oil-filled cables and cables with polymeric insulation. The test requirements for polymeric insulated cables are similar in many respects to those required for paper insulated cables, but there are significant differences and the main ones are included herein.

The most important IEC and BEB specifications are as follows:

IEC 141 Tests on oil-filled and gas pressure cables and their accessories
Engineering Recommendation C28/4 Type approval tests for impregnated paper insulated gas pressure and oil-filled power cable systems from 33 kV to 132 kV inclusive
Engineering Recommendation C47/1 Type approval tests for single core impregnated paper insulated gas pressure and oil-filled cable systems for 275 and 400 kV
ESI Standard 09-3 33 kV impregnated paper insulated oil-filled and gas pressure type power cable systems
ESI Standard 09-4 66 and 132 kV impregnated paper insulated oil-filled and gas compression type power cable systems
ESI Standard 09-5 275 and 400 kV impregnated paper insulated oil-filled and gas compression type power cable systems
IEC 840 Tests for power cables with extruded insulation for rated voltages above 30 kV (U_m = 36 kV) up to 150 kV (U_m = 170 kV)
ESI Standard 09-16 Testing specification for metallic sheathed power cables with extruded cross-linked polyethylene insulation and accessories for system voltages of 66 kV and 132 kV
IEC 233 Tests on hollow insulators for use in electrical equipment

Other important specifications include the following:

Electra (72), 105–114, October 1980 Recommendations for tests on power transmission d.c. cables for rated voltages up to 600 kV

AEIC C54-79 Specification for impregnated paper insulated low pressure oil-filled cables
AEIC C52-82 Specification for impregnated paper insulated cables – high pressure pipe type
IEEE 48 Test procedures and requirements for high voltage a.c. cable terminations

Many principles are the same as for the testing of distribution cables, as given in chapter 29, and are not repeated here.

PAPER INSULATED CABLES

Routine tests

Most specifications require electrical tests along the lines illustrated below for oil-filled cables, in accordance with IEC 141-1. The examples given vary to some extent in other specifications but are typical of the requirements.

Dielectric loss angle (DLA) and high voltage tests
The DLA is measured at ambient temperature and corrected to 20 °C. The voltage range is from U_0 to $2U_0$ for cables up to a U_0 of 87 kV and $1.67U_0$ for higher voltage cables. Requirements are shown in table 42.1 for cables not screened with carbon-black paper. Slightly higher values are permitted when carbon-black paper screens are used. The test is followed by application of high voltage for 15 min at the level shown in table 42.1

Table 42.1 Test voltage and DLA for OF cables

Cable voltage (U_o/U) (kV)	Highest voltage for DLA test (kV)	Maximum DLA		Maximum difference in DLA from U_0 to highest voltage $\times 10^{-4}$	A.C. withstand test (kV)
		U_0 $\times 10^{-4}$	Highest voltage $\times 10^{-4}$		
19/33	38	35	43	10	53
38/66	76	35	43	10	86
76/132	152	33	40	8	162
160/275	230	30	34	5	275
230/400	385	28	31	4	395

The DLA and high voltage tests for gas-compression and gas-filled cables are carried out at any gas pressure up to 2 bar. These cables normally operate at a pressure of approximately 14 bar and, as the reduced pressure is not representative of normal service conditions, the test voltages are accordingly reduced.

In the case of d.c. cables the high voltage test comprises the application of $2U_0$, with negative polarity, for 15 min, and as with a.c. cables the high voltage test ensures freedom from mechanical defects. For d.c. cables, however, no convenient method is available which is comparable with the a.c. measurement of DLA for monitoring cable quality. It is therefore usual to measure the DLA at reduced test voltage and the results give a good indication of freedom from excessive moisture content and introduction of contamination during processing. For oil-filled d.c. cable with U_0 from 100 to 600 kV, the DLA is measured over a voltage range equivalent to a.c. maximum stress values of 10–20 MV/m. For gas pressure cable and mass-impregnated cable the stress values are reduced.

The application of these high voltages between conductor and sheath necessitates special attention to the provison of suitable cable terminations. Permanent installations require expensive porcelain containers and the services of skilled personnel. It is beneficial to have more simple procedures for temporary terminations for routine testing. For cables of 33 kV and below a test termination may be made by removing the metal sheath and dielectric screen over a length of approximately 1 m and applying a stress cone or other means of electric field control. For higher voltages, a cast resin termination has now been developed. This consists essentially of a reusable cast resin stress cone enclosed in an oil chamber.

Other electrical tests

Conductor resistance and capacitance tests are mandatory. Capacitance is conveniently calculated from Schering bridge or transformer ratio bridge measurements made during the DLA test and is a useful check on cable quality. The figure should not be greater than 8% above the declared value.

Particularly when the cable contains an aluminium sheath and when it is to be installed in an insulated sheath system, it is very important that there are no defects in the corrosion protective finish. This is checked by the application of d.c. with a voltage corresponding to a stress of 8 kV/mm of average thickness of the finish (maximum value 25 kV). To make this test practicable the extruded oversheath is coated with a conducting layer of colloidal graphite during the manufacture of the cable.

Routine tests on accessories

Cable joints and terminations form an integral part of a cable transmission system and to ensure their reliability in service are subjected to rigid inspection and routine test procedures before despatch. Most cable joints and terminations are manufactured from several individual components and to ensure correct assembly and compliance with appropriate standards each item is visually examined and dimensionally checked before being subjected to any further tests. The additional test requirements can be considered in two main groups: (a) hydraulic and pneumatic pressure tests and (b) electrical tests.

Pressure tests

Whenever possible, the various pressure tests required are carried out with all the individual components of the accessory completely assembled, except for the cable. Cable entry positions are sealed with a plate soldered on or by a specially manufactured cover with rubber or similar seals. All accessories for use in oil-filled and gas-filled cable systems, i.e. sealing ends, transformer or switchgear terminations and joints, together with any epoxy resin or other insulating components which form part of the pressure-retaining envelope, are subjected to pressure withstand tests. The following are examples of routine pressure tests carried out on various components.

(a) Porcelain and epoxy resin terminations: each porcelain or epoxy resin termination complete with base plate, bottom extension gland, sheath insulating ring and top plate fitted with the conductor terminal for use on oil-filled cable systems is subjected to a hydraulic pressure test at 11 bar (just over twice the maximum system operating pressure) for a minimum time of 15 min. The same assembly for use on gas-filled cable systems is subjected to a hydraulic pressure test at 34 bar (twice maximum system operating pressure) for a minimum time of 15 min followed by a pneumatic pressure test for 24 hours at the maximum design pressure of 17 bar. To comply with the test specification there should be no evidence of leakage or unacceptable distortion of the metal components during or at the end of the test.

(b) Joint sleeves complete with end bells, insulating rings or resin barriers are subjected to the same pressure test procedures as for porcelain and epoxy resin terminations.

(c) Pressure tanks for all oil-filled cable systems: each pressure tank is subjected to a hydraulic pressure test at a pressure equal to 1.1 times the design pressure for 8 hours. There should be no evidence of leakage. Following this test the pressure versus volume characteristic of the tank is checked.

(d) Auxiliary components for gas-filled cable systems: gas cylinder regulators, safety valves, pressure gauges and gas control cubicles are subjected to pressure tests to ensure their safe and correct operation.

Electrical tests

(a) Cast epoxy resin components incorporating cast-in electrodes or conductors are now widely used in the construction of joints and terminations and require electrical tests to ensure the integrity and material quality of the casting. These components are formed of a homegeneous material which is extremely sensitive to electrical discharge and when subjected to such discharge rapidly erodes, leading to breakdown of the component. If voids are present within the casting, electrical discharge will occur in the void when the voltage across the void reaches a critical value.

    Voids can be caused by cracks in the resin, separation of the resin from the cast-in electrodes or conductors, or gas bubbles. Two high voltage tests are applied to resin components: partial discharge tests to indicate whether voids are present in the casting, and DLA measurements to indicate the quality of the material forming the casting. For both these tests an outer earth screen is applied and the component is installed under oil in an insulated tank. The high voltage is connected to either the cast-in electrode or conductor(s). DLA and partial discharge measurements are made at a test voltage which ensures that the stress imposed on the critical areas of the component is the same as the stress encountered in service.

(b) Joint sleeves: metal joint sleeves are sometimes provided with factory applied external insulation to enable the d.c. voltage site test on the anticorrosion covering of the cable to be carried out. To ensure that the insulation is free from pinholes or mechanical damage the insulation is subjected to a voltage of 10 kV d.c. for 5 min.

(c) Porcelain insulators: to verify the electrical integrity of the wall of porcelain insulators, each insulator is subjected to a high voltage a.c. test, equivalent to a stress of 1.5 kV/mm of wall thickness with a minimum requirement of 35 kV for 5 min. For this test the insulator is filled with water to form the inner electrode and wire or chains are placed around the barrel between the sheds to form the outer electrode. Any insulator which punctures during the test is rejected.

Special tests on cables

Because of the importance of the integrity of expensive transmission cables, careful attention is given to a visual examination of a sample cut from each length and to a check of dimensions. As an additional check on cable quality the customer may request tests to be carried out on cable samples: for example the frequency of taking samples as stipulated in IEC 141-1 is shown in table 42.2.

Table 42.2 Number of samples taken from contract cables

Cable length				Number of samples
3-core cables		Single-core cables		
Above (km)	Up to and including (km)	Above (km)	Up to and including (km)	
2	10	4	20	1
10	20	20	40	2
20	30	40	60	3

In this category the most usual test is a mechanical test, which comprises a bending test followed by the application of high voltage a.c. for 15 min and subsequent detailed examination of the cable.

Bending test

A sample of cable is subjected to severe cycles of bending to demonstrate that it will not suffer from normal cable laying operations.

The bending test is carried out at ambient temperature and consists of winding the cable onto a test drum, unwinding, rotating the cable through 180°, rewinding and unwinding. This cycle is repeated three times, precautions being taken to prevent the sample from twisting. The hub diameter of the test cylinder is given in table 42.3.

After a 15 min application of a.c. at the voltage specified for the routine test, a 1 m sample is cut from the centre of the test length and is examined in detail. IEC specifications prescribe limits for damage and displacement of component parts, including the insulation papers.

Special tests on accessories

IEC 233 requires tests on porcelain insulators and details the rate of sampling.

Table 42.3 Diameter of cylinder for bend test on OF cables

Type of cable	Hub diameter
Single-core cables with lead or corrugated aluminium sheath	$25(d_s + d_c)$
Three-core cables with sheaths as above	$20(d_s + d_c)$
All cables with smooth aluminium sheath	$36(d_s + d_c)$

d_s = measured overall diameter of the metal sheath
d_c = measured diameter over the conductor or the equivalent diameter for shaped conductors

Temperature cycle test
For this test the insulator, at ambient temperature, is immersed for 30 min in a bath of hot water and then withdrawn and immediately immersed in cold water for 30 min. The temperature difference between the two baths is related to the dimensions of the insulator and is generally between 35 and 50 °C. The cycle of operations is repeated three times. The result is satisfactory if there are no cracks or damage to the glaze or loosening of the cemented top and bottom rings.

Porosity tests
For this test freshly broken pieces of porcelain are required which in production have been fired adjacent to the insulator. The samples are immersed in a 1% solution of fuchsine dye in alcohol at a pressure of 150 bar for not less than 12 hours. The samples are then further broken and examined. No sign of dye penetration should be found at the freshly broken surfaces.

Type approval tests

Type tests are tests made in order to demonstrate satisfactory performance characteristics to meet the intended application. They are of such a nature that, after they have been made, they need not be repeated unless changes are made in either the material or the design. A summary of the various forms of test in accordance with IEC 141-1 and British Electricity Boards Engineering Recommendations is given below.

Mechanical tests
A bending test is carried out as previously described and it may be required that a further sample of the bent cable is submitted to a mechanical integrity test of the metal sheath. For this test an internal pressure equal to twice the maximum design pressure is applied for seven days. No leakage should occur.

Loading cycle test
(a) A.C. systems: In this test a cable system is subjected to conditions more severe than encountered in normal operational service. Three miniature cable installations, each consisting of 30 m of cable previously submitted to the conditions of the bending test, and including the accessories designed for use with the

Fig. 42.1 A miniature oil-filled cable installation under test

cable, are subjected to a minimum of 20 loading cycles with a continuously applied voltage between $1.33U_0$ (275 and 400 kV) and $1.5U_0$ (33–132 kV). During each load cycle, circulating current is passed through the conductor and/or sheath for 8 hours so that the conductor temperature is maintained between 5 and 10 °C above the maximum design value for the last 3 hours. There is then a cooling period of 16 hours. The DLA and capacitance of each installation is measured hot and cold during each load cycle. Circulating current is induced in the cable by the use of ring core transformers, independently of the high voltage. The conductor and/or extreme ends of the sheath are connected together to make closed loops which form single-turn secondary windings of the ring core transformers. The magnitude of the induced current is controlled by voltage regulators connected to the transformer primary windings. The result is considered to be satisfactory if there is no breakdown and the measured values of DLA remain stable. Fig. 42.1 shows an installation of oil-filled cable under test.

(b) D.C. systems: in service, d.c. systems may be energised with either positive or negative voltage and under certain conditions may be subjected to rapid polarity reversal due to failure of termination or converter equipment. To simulate this condition the test requirements are similar to those for an a.c. system, with 30 loading cycles, but for the first ten cycles the cable is energised at a voltage of $2U_0$ with positive polarity. The next ten cycles are with $2U_0$ negative polarity and during the last ten cycles the voltage is $1.5U_0$ with polarity reversal every 4 hours. No breakdown should occur in any of the components during this test.

DLA versus temperature test

IEC 141-1 does not include the loading cycle test but specifies requirements for DLA measurement at U_0 on the cable at ambient temperature, 5 °C above maximum operating temperature, 60 °C, 40 °C and again at ambient temperature. The DLA must not exceed specified values.

Thermal stability test

This test comprises an extension to the a.c. loading cycle test to demonstrate stability over a prolonged period. Following the last cycle, current loading is applied continuously to each installation at a voltage of $1.33U_0$ (275 and 400 kV) or $1.5U_0$ (132 kV) until the conductor temperature is steady at a value between 5 and 10 °C above the design operating temperature. The current loading is then held constant for 6–12 hours and the variation of conductor and sheath temperature should not exceed 2 °C after making allowance for any change of ambient temperature. As a further check the DLA is measured at test voltage immediately following the test period.

Impulse tests

(a) A.C. systems: in most cases, underground power transmission cables are connected to overhead lines and must withstand the high transient voltages generated by lightning strokes on or near the overhead line. Switching operations occurring in other parts of the transmission system may also generate high transient voltages. The impulse test is specified to ensure that the cable system will operate satisfactorily under these severe service conditions. For test purposes an impulse voltage can be defined as either positive or negative with respect to earth, rising rapidly to a maximum voltage and decaying less rapidly to zero without any appreciable oscillations. The majority of impulse tests are made using the standard lightning impulse in which the voltage rises to a crest value in 1.2–5 μs and decays to half the crest value in approximately 50 μs.

For system operating voltages of 132 kV and above, an additional impulse test is made using standard switching impulse. In this case the voltage rises to a crest value in 250 μs and decays to half the crest value in approximately 2500 μs.

The recommended method of measuring the voltage wave shapes for impulse tests is given in BS 923: Part 2: 1980. For the lightning or switching impulse test, 20 impulses, ten positive and ten negative, are applied to the test installations submitted previously to the load cycle test or dielectric loss angle versus voltage test. The test is carried out with the cable conductor temperature 5 °C higher than the maximum design operating temperature. Table 42.4 shows the values of lightning impulse and where appropriate switching impulse voltages, for cable system voltages from 33 to 400 kV, specified in British Electricity Boards Engineering Recommendations.

(b) D.C. systems: lightning can also impose high transient voltages on d.c. cable transmission systems and the most severe condition occurs when the polarity of the lightning impulse is of opposite polarity to the cable voltage. This condition is recognised in the type test procedure by the inclusion of a lightning impulse

Table 42.4 Comparison of impulse test and a.c. voltages

Cable voltage (U_0/U) (kV)	Lightning impulse voltage (kV) (crest)	Switching impulse voltage (kV) (crest)
19/33	194	–
38/66	342	–
76/132	640	380
160/275	1050	750
230/400	1425	1050

superimposed on the d.c. test. For this test the cable conductor is heated to 5 °C above its maximum operating temperature and energised at a d.c. voltage of U_0 negative polarity for a minimum time of 2 hours, and then subjected to ten impulses of positive polarity. The test is then repeated with the cable energised at U_0 positive polarity and ten impulses of negative polarity are applied. Specialised equipment is required to enable these tests to be carried out.

Dielectric security test
To ensure that the cable system has an ample safety margin under abnormal a.c. operating conditions, each installation must be submitted successfully to a high voltage a.c. dielectric security test of up to $2.5U_0$ for 24 hours at ambient temperature. A high voltage d.c. test may also be carried out to ensure that cable accessories will withstand the d.c. voltage applied during the routine tests after installation. As an alternative to the dielectric security test, a switching impulse test may be carried out.

Thermal resistivity of dielectric
The thermal resistivity is important in the calculation of current ratings and some specifications require measurement on a minimum length of 11 m of cable at maximum operating temperature. The value obtained should not exceed the design value by more than 5% for 275 kV and 400 kV or 10% for 33–132 kV.

Tests on cable corrosion protective finishes
To demonstrate that cable finishes have adequate properties to meet installation and laying conditions, tests are specified in IEC 229 and BEB C48/1.

A sample of cable is first submitted to the bending test conditions already described, and then abraded by 50 passages along its surface by a length of steel angle with its point at right angles to the cable and loaded with a mass of $0.018D^{1.7}$ kg where D is the overall diameter of the cable. The maximum mass is 55 kg.

To represent possible damage to the surface by stones, a preloaded cycle chain wheel is then passed along the cable diametrically opposite the length abraded, the loading being a mass of $0.2d + 2$ kg (maximum load 18 kg). In this case d is the diameter under the oversheath.

The sample is then placed in a 0.5% saline solution and submitted to 100 daily temperature cycles with 10 V d.c. applied between the metal sheath and the saline solution. The saline solution is heated to a temperature of 75–80 °C for 5 hours and allowed to cool for 19 hours. The leakage current is measured daily for 100 days and the sample is finally subjected for 1 min to a d.c. voltage equivalent to a stress of 2 kV/mm of oversheath thickness (maximum 5 kV).

The finish is deemed to be satisfactory if no failure occurs and an examination of the centre 1 m section reveals no sign of corrosion.

Reference to another test sometimes requested for protective finishes for aluminium sheaths is made in chapter 5. This involves removal of four circular pieces of oversheath 10 mm in diameter and immersion in 1% sodium sulphate solution.

Additional tests for accessories
Additional type tests for outdoor sealing ends may include power frequency voltage withstand – wet and dry – and measurement of radio interference.

Tests after installation

Electrical and hydraulic tests are required on the complete installation to ensure that no damage has occurred during cable laying and assembly of the accessories. In addition to measurement of conductor resistance, typical tests in accordance with IEC 141-1 comprise the following.

High voltage test
For a.c. cables the application for 15 min of a d.c. voltage which is the lower value of either 50% of the specified lightning impulse withstand voltage or $4.5U_0$ for cables with U_0 not exceeding 64 kV, $4U_0$ for U_0 not exceeding 130 kV and $3.5U_0$ for U_0 exceeding 130 kV.

For d.c. cables a voltage of $1.8U_0$ is typical.

Voltage test on cable oversheath
10 kV d.c. is applied as described earlier. To carry out this test all joints must be insulated from earth.

Oil flow test (for OF cables)
Each cable section is subjected to an oil flow test to ensure that no abnormal restriction is present in the cable or accessories. The test is carried out by measuring the pressure drop in the section under measured oil flow.

Pneumatic test on gas pressure cables
Each complete circuit, including joints and terminations, is pressurised to 17 bar for seven days, followed by a further seven days at normal operating pressure to 12 bar. The gas tightness of the circuit is considered satisfactory if there is no leakage of gas during the seven day period at normal pressure.

POLYMERIC CABLES

Many of the routine tests, sample (special) tests and type tests required for cables insulated with polymeric materials (PE, XLPE or EPR) are similar to those required for paper insulated cables, but there are important differences, as shown below. In addition to the electrical tests on complete cable, physical tests are required on samples of the component parts of the cable to check that the materials used have satisfactory properties.

Various countries have produced their own specifications for tests on polymeric cables and the examples given below are those required by ESI Standard 09-16 and IEC Publication 840 for power cables with XLPE insulation for 66 and 132 kV transmission systems.

Routine tests

Partial discharge test and high voltage test

For polymeric cables the partial discharge test has replaced the traditional method of assessing insulation quality applied to paper insulated cables by measurement of the DLA against increasing voltage. This is explained in chapter 29. The partial discharge test is made at ambient temperature. The test voltage is raised initially to $1.73U_0$ for 10 s and then reduced to $1.5U_0$ and the partial discharge is measured. The magnitude of the partial discharge at $1.5U_0$ is required not to exceed 10 pC. The test is followed by the application of a voltage of $2.5U_0$ for 30 min.

Special tests

The frequency of tests is similar to that required for paper insulated cables. The tests include the following.

(a) Conductor examination for compliance with IEC 228.
(b) Measurement of the electrical resistance of the conductor for compliance with IEC 228 or BS 6360 (while classed as a special test in IEC 840, with measurement not required on every length of cable, this is a routine test in ESI Standard 09-16).
(c) Measurement of cable dimensions, including thicknesses of insulation and metallic and non-metallic sheaths and overall diameters.
(d) Hot set tests for XLPE insulation to check that the material has been properly cured to give the required thermal properties (test conditions are given in IEC Publication 811-2-1).
(e) Volume resistivity of semiconducting screens: the values for the inner and outer semiconducting screens are required not to exceed 500 Ω/m a 90 °C.
(f) Test for shrinkage of insulation. Extruded synthetic materials exhibit a degree of shrinkage when heated, which is associated with residual strain in the material resulting from the heating and cooling cycles that take place during manufacture. If excessive, this might cause retraction of the insulation, when it becomes warm, at joints and terminations. For this test a 200 mm length of cable, with the sheath and metallic screens removed, is subjected to a temperature of 130 °C for 1 hour; after the sample has cooled to ambient temperature, the shrinkage is required not to exceed 4%.
(g) Measurement of capacitance: the value of the capacitance is required to be not greater than 8% above the value declared by the manufacturer in his tender.

Type tests

Electrical tests on complete cable

ESI 09-16 requires electrical tests on two miniature cable installations, one being of cable only and the second being of cable together with accessories designed for use with the cable. In both cases each installation must include a minimum of 10 m of cable previously submitted to a bending test. The bending test conditions are the same as those required for single-core paper insulated cables with lead or corrugated aluminium sheaths. IEC 840 does not specifically include tests on accessories and electrical tests are required on cable only.

Sequence of tests

The electrical tests are required successively on the same miniature installations generally in the sequence

(a) partial discharge test
(b) DLA measurement as a function of the voltage and cable capacitance (cable installation only)
(c) DLA measurement as a function of temperature (cable installation only)
(d) loading cycle test
(e) power frequency voltage test
(f) d.c. voltage test (accessory installation only)
(g) examination of cable and accessories

Partial discharge test

The partial discharge test is made at ambient temperature. The voltage is initially raised to $1.73U_0$ for 10 s and then reduced slowly to $1.5U_0$ for the cable installation and to $1.25U_0$ for the accessory installation and partial discharge measurements are made. The magnitude of the partial discharge at $1.5U_0$ and $1.25U_0$ must not exceed 5 pC.

DLA measurement as a function of voltage and capacitance

The DLA and capacitance of the cable is measured at $0.5U_0$, U_0 and $2U_0$ at ambient temperature. The DLA requirements given in ESI 09-16 for XLPE insulated cables are that the value at U_0 should not exceed 0.001 and the difference between the values at $0.5U_0$ and $2U_0$ should not exceed 0.001.

DLA measurement as a function of temperature

The DLA of the cable is measured at U_0 at ambient temperature and the measurement is repeated with the conductor temperature 5 °C higher than the maximum design operating temperature. The maximum DLA at ambient temperature must not exceed 0.001. The maximum DLA at a conductor temperature 5 °C higher than the maximum design operating temperature must not exceed 0.002 (ESI 09-16) or 0.001 (IEC 840).

Loading cycle test

The conditions for the loading test are similar to those for paper insulated cables with the addition of partial discharge measurements. Both miniature test installations must be subjected to 20 loading cycles with a continuously applied test voltage of between $1.5U_0$ and $2U_0$. During the last 2 hours of each loading cycle the conductor temperature must be maintained at temperatures not less than 5–10 °C and not greater than 10–15 °C above the maximum design operating temperature. The test is considered to be satisfactory if there is no breakdown and the measured values of DLA or partial discharge magnitude remain stable.

Impulse test
The test conditions and withstand levels are the same as those required for paper insulated cables.

Power frequency voltage test
This test is made at ambient temperature. Both installations must be submitted successfully to the application of a voltage of $3U_0$ for 4 hours. IEC 840 does not include this test but specifies the application of an a.c. voltage of $2.5U_0$ for 15 min.

D.C. voltage test
To ensure that the cable and accessory will withstand the high voltage test after installation the accessory installation must withstand a d.c. test voltage of $4U_0$ for 15 min.

Physical tests

These tests are required to check that the materials used for the component parts of the cable have satisfactory properties. In addition to those already described under sample tests, IEC 840 and ESI 09-16 include the following:

(a) mechanical properties of the insulation before and after ageing
(b) ageing tests on complete cable samples to test compatibility of materials during operation
(c) insulation/screen moisture content
(d) effect of material compatibility on semiconducting screen resistivity

Tests after installation

The electrical tests required on complete installations are similar to those required for paper insulated cables. Some countries have expressed concern that the high voltage d.c. test can cause failures at places where failures would not occur under a.c. service conditions. IEC 840 provides for alternative a.c. testing in the same way as IEC 502 (see chapter 29). The IEC Standard also indicates that the full d.c. test voltage does not apply to installations which have been in use and that lower values should be negotiated for these, much as in BS 6622, referred to in chapter 29.

Chapter 43
Fault Incidence and Location for Transmission Cables

Transmission cables are laid with greater care and, usually, at greater depth than distribution cables and consequently are less prone to damage by accidental contact. Table 43.1 shows that failures of underground transmission circuits are more often associated with the joints and accessories than with the cable.

Table 43.1 UK transmission cable statistics 1975–80

Voltage (kV)	Average length in service (km)	Number of underground faults			
		Cable	Joints	Oil and gas equipment	Others
132	2400	133	43	75	107
275	433	10	24	11	16
400	58	1	10	1	0

There are three significant differences in the fault location procedures required for transmission cables compared with those required on distribution cables. The first, and obvious, difference is that the voltages which are required, both in testing and fault locating, are much higher, and many of the techniques which can be applied quite easily on distribution cables become impractical. The second difference is that transmission cables are usually installed with their sheaths and joints insulated from the general mass of earth, except at specific points, and special techniques are required for locating faults on this outer insulation (corrosion protective finish, also known as serving). The third difference arises from the fact that until recently all transmission cables used pressure assistance and methods of locating leaks of both gas and oil are essential.

MAIN INSULATION FAULTS

Main insulation faults are usually accompanied by reduction of the cable internal pressure and so the residual electric strength of the insulation is much lower than normal. Even so, the insulation level will often still be too high for the fault to be broken down with a surge generator of manageable proportions. Since most faults on transmission cables will exhibit a 'flashing' characteristic it is possible to use a high voltage test set to break down the fault and to record, using impulse current equipment (chapter 30), the current transients which flow from the faulty phase into a healthy phase. In fig. 43.1 the linear coupler is shown on a bond which connects

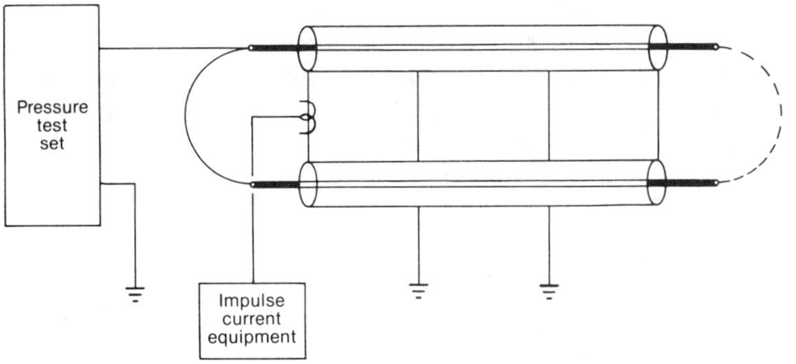

Fig. 43.1 Impulse current method for transmission cables

the sheaths of the single-core cables. It is important that all sheaths are temporarily bonded together during high voltage testing and fault location, both at the cable terminals and at any 'cross-bonding' points.

In order to simplify interpretation of the recorded transients it is useful to obtain recordings with and without a shorting link at the far end of the cable (fig. 43.2). On transmission cables the fault will usually not ionise sufficiently to produce a complete short circuit across the cable insulation and therefore part of the wave reflected from the open circuit at the far end of the cable, when no shorting link is present, will travel 'through' the fault to appear in the linear coupler. As can be seen in fig. 43.2, this only serves to emphasise the point of separation. The time interval T (μs) between the start of the transient and the point of separation gives the distance to the fault, measured from the far end of the cable, using equation (30.6) of chapter 30.

Occasionally the fault resistance may be too low for the high voltage test set to produce a flashover under d.c. stress. In such situations the faulty core can be impulsed via a spark gap from one of the healthy cores which is charged by the high voltage set. It is preferable to charge two healthy cores to provide a source impedance equal to half the surge impedance of the faulty core and thereby obtain a 'voltage

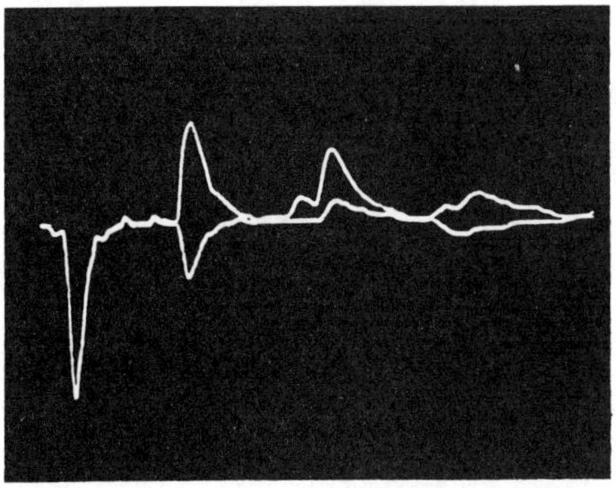

Fig. 43.2 Typical waveform using the circuit of fig. 43.1

efficiency' of 67%. A modified version of the comparison method shown in fig. 43.2 can be used if one of the healthy cores is charged from the pressure test set whilst the other healthy core is connected to the faulty core. The voltage efficiency of this connection, however, is only 33% and it would therefore be necessary to set the spark gap to a greater separation so that the voltage on the charged core can rise to a higher level before the spark gap fires.

FAULTS IN THE PROTECTIVE FINISH

Since the insulated sheath of a transmission cable is in effect a single unscreened buried conductor, it is not possible to use any of the prelocation or pinpointing methods which can be applied to faults in the main insulation. A method of prelocation used for many years and based on a modification of the bridge test is the Hilborn loop, but it is a difficult test to carry out accurately. More recently use has been made of very sensitive magnetometers to trace the current flowing along the sheath of a cable from a transmitter to the fault point. The transmitter used is a modified version of the unit originally developed for pinpointing serving faults by the POPIE method.[1] The principle of operation of both the magnetometer and POPIE instruments is shown in fig. 43.3. The d.c. generator applies an easily recognised characteristic signal between the metallic sheath of the cable and the general mass of earth. The current leaves the cable sheath at the point of fault and returns to the generator by a distributed path creating, around the fault, a voltage gradient which appears at the ground surface as a series of circular equipotential lines. The POPIE detector consists of a sensitive high impedance millivoltmeter connected to a pair of probes which are moved along the cable route until they straddle the fault.

On long cables it would be extremely tedious to survey the whole of the route with the POPIE and so the initial pre-location, or sectionalising, is done using the magnetometer which responds to the magnetic field produced by the sheath current

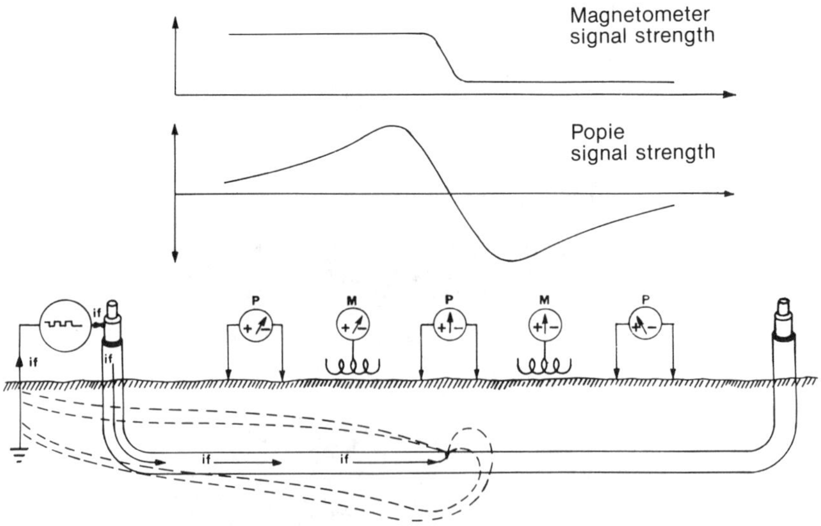

Fig. 43.3 Location of faults in protective finish using the magnetometer and POPIE methods

up to the fault point. The magnetometer does not give as precise a location as the POPIE method but it is extremely quick and easy to use and the two methods are therefore complementary.

OIL AND GAS LEAKS

Locating oil and gas leaks can be extremely time consuming as there are, as yet, no really effective pre-locating techniques. Often it is possible to identify the particular section of a cable route that is faulty if barrier joints are installed with the facility for introducing flowmeters or pressure gauges. A large proportion of leaks on pressurised systems are associated with the pipework of joints and control panels and this should always be checked first before embarking on the very costly exercise of testing along a cable route. Pipework leaks on gas panels can be pinpointed using the simple technique of applying soapy water to valve stems, unions etc. or by probing with suitable gas detectors.

Since the pressurising gas used in cables is nitrogen, it is not readily identified and so it is necessary to introduce a tracer gas into the cable. The two commonest tracer gases are dichlorodifluoromethane (CCl_2F_2) and sulphur hexafluoride (SF_6). Both these gases can be detected very easily, even at minute concentrations, using modern portable gas chromatographs which are used to take samples of 'air' from the ground along the cable route. Although the electric strength of mixtures of nitrogen and CCl_2F_2, or nitrogen and SF_6, is higher than for pure nitrogen, it is normal practice to purge the cable of the tracer gas once the fault has been found in order to facilitate location of the next leak, should it occur.

Whilst gas leaks can normally be pinpointed by probing the cable route from ground level, oil leaks require the cable to be excavated first. The most reliable method of sectionalising oil leaks is to use a freezing sleeve of liquid nitrogen which is applied to the cable to freeze the oil. By measuring the pressure at the joints on either side of the freezing point, it is then possible to identify from which side of the freeze the oil is escaping. This procedure may have to be repeated a number of times before the precise fault position can be pinpointed. Attempts to introduce tracers into the cable oil to allow detection from ground level have had limited success as also have various methods of identifying the direction of flow of the oil from the outside of the cable.

REFERENCES

(1) Gooding, H. T. and Briant, T. A. (1962) 'Location of serving defects in buried cables'. *Proc. IEE, Part A* **109**, 124–125.
(2) Gooding, H. T. and Briant, T. A. (1962) 'Location of gas leaks in buried pressure-cable systems'. *Proc. IEE, Part A* **109**, 126–128.

Chapter 44

Recent Improvements and Development of Transmission Cables

ESSENTIAL REQUIREMENTS

Higher power transmission capability

While in many parts of the industrialised world the late 1970s and early 1980s saw little growth in the demand for electricity, the late 1980s have seen a return to growth, although not at the same rate as in the previous two decades. It is reasonable to assume that this will continue and that in the future there will be a requirement for higher power circuits than are currently used. The improvements in space occupancy achieved by intensively cooling conventional cables is illustrated in fig. 44.1. With space beneath city streets becoming scarcer, the incentive to obtain greater transmission capability through one cable circuit is expected to persist.

Most underground cable systems are part of longer overhead line transmission circuits which determine the operating voltage and load transmission capability. Operating voltages for overhead line systems have already reached 765 kV and research is being carried out on 1000/1100 kV systems. It is reasonable to suppose that, just as has happened in the past, requirements for undergrounding will occur, initially at line terminations and in rural areas of beauty, but later extending to load centres in urban areas.

A demand in the future for underground cable for operating at voltages of 765 kV can reasonably be expected, but the timing of such a requirement is uncertain.

Reduced running losses

With increasing energy costs, there is a greater incentive to develop cable systems with lower losses, the two basic forms of which are current-dependent and voltage-dependent losses. To make significant changes in current-dependent losses it is necessary to use a conductor which has a much lower resistance than the copper or aluminium conductor used at present, e.g. a superconductor. However, there is far more scope for a reduction of the voltage-dependent loss, i.e. the dielectric loss. These losses are far more predictable than current-dependent losses as they exist whenever the circuit is energised. Calculation of current-dependent losses requires assumptions to be made for the daily and seasonal load variations over the complete life of the cable.

The calculation of dielectric losses is dealt with in chapter 2. The magnitude of the losses increases with operating voltage and this is shown in table 44.1. It will be seen that at the higher voltages the losses increase very steeply. There is a growing tendency to take these losses into account when assessing costs of cable systems.

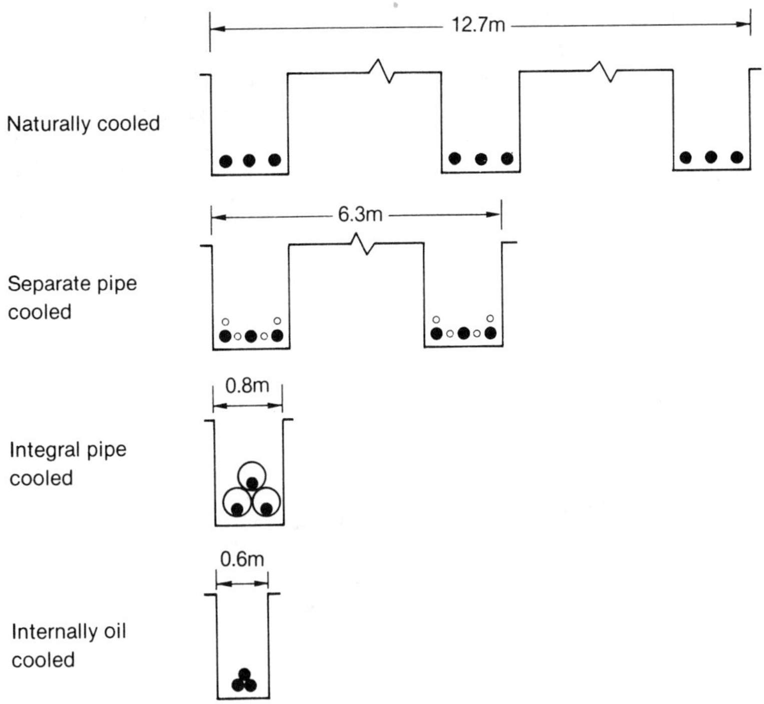

Fig. 44.1 Land requirements for a 400 kV circuit of 2600 MVA capacity

Table 44.1 Dielectric losses for 33–750 kV 2000 mm^2 oil-filled cables[a]

Voltage (kV)	Design stress (MV/m)	Dielectric loss (W/m)
33	4.5	0.4
66	9	1.5
132	10	3.3
275	13	9.0
400	15	15.2
750	20	38.0

[a] Assumptions: DLA = 0.0024; relative permittivity, 3.5; operating frequency, 50 Hz

This is done by adding to the initial cost a notional capital sum of money which would pay for the cost of the losses throughout the life of the cable. The calculation takes into account the magnitude of the losses, the cost of the losses, the life of the cable and interest rates. The latter is important as it is assumed that the sum of money would be invested and that the interest would assist in paying for the losses as well as the capital, which would reduce to zero at the end of the assumed cable life. The same calculation can be used for the current-dependent losses, but as indicated earlier there is some difficulty in predicting the current loading over the life of the cable. A further complication is that the losses are proportional to the square of the current and this makes accurate calculation more difficult.

In addition to the cost effects, the presence of dielectric losses reduces the current rating of the cable. This is illustrated in fig. 44.2, which shows the variation of current rating of a 2500 mm^2 oil-filled cable with operating voltage. It will be seen that the current rating reduces with voltage until at a voltage of about 850 kV the paper insulated cable system has no rating capability. PPL insulation is referred to later in this chapter.

It should be noted that forced cooling can have an effect on the dielectric losses of a cable system. For example, if it is possible to use one cable in place of two in parallel by using cooling, the single cable will have a significantly lower capacitance than the two-cable circuit and the dielectric losses, which are proportional to capacitance, will therefore be reduced.

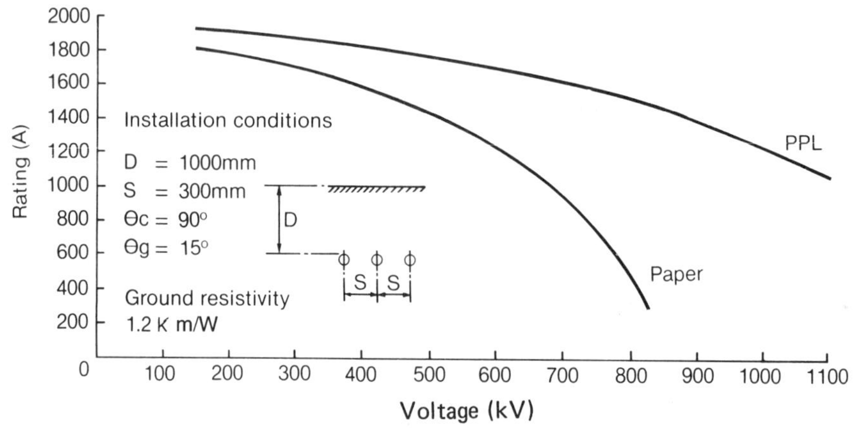

Fig. 44.2 Variation of current rating with operating voltage for paper and PPL insulation; conductor size 2500 mm^2

Reduction of capacitance

Any reduction in capacitance, provided that the dielectric loss angle is not increased, will reduce the dielectric losses. However, capacitance is important in other respects. The charging current of a cable system is proportional to the cable capacitance, the line voltage and the frequency. As the capacitance is proportional to cable length, the charging current will increase with cable length.

In fact there is a critical length at which the charging current equals the thermal rating of the cable, and therefore the cable circuit can carry no useful load. This length decreases with increasing voltage; the effect is illustrated in fig. 44.3 for a 50 Hz system.

In the case of land cables the length effect can be overcome by splitting the cable into sections and fitting shunt reactors. In some situations shunt reactors are used in any case, to compensate for the effect of the cable capacitance on the transmission

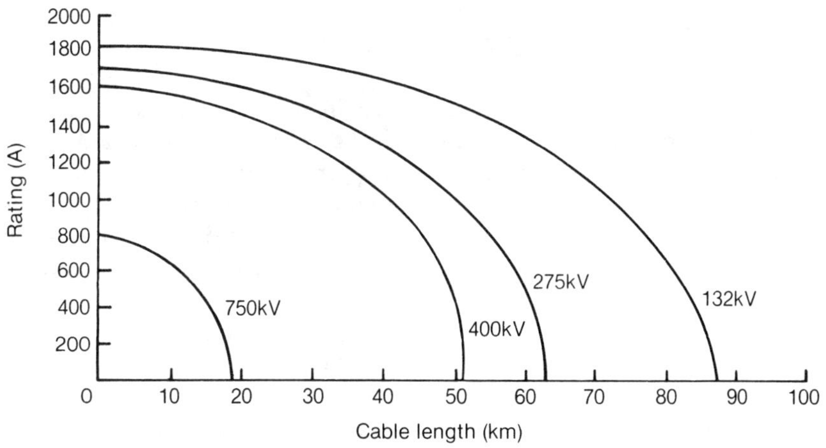

Fig. 44.3 Effect of feeder length on useful current rating for 2500 mm^2 OF cable

system. Use of a reactor involves a capital cost and a running cost due to its losses. These can be taken into account financially in a similar manner to that explained for dielectric losses. Therefore there are economic advantages in lowering the capacitances of cable systems.

Reactors cannot be used to overcome the problem for submarine systems and the reduction of cable capacitance is of great importance on long installations.

Reduced cost of installation and maintenance

A modern pressurised cable system requires very sophisticated installation techniques. For example, both self-contained and high pressure pipe type systems need specialised oil treatment for the installation of the cables and the jointing requires the employment of highly skilled jointers working in air-conditioned enclosures for the higher voltages. While this equipment and expertise is usually readily available in the industrialised nations, it can present problems in other areas. Perhaps of greater significance, is the need for this equipment and expertise for possible maintenance during the life of the cable. With pressurised systems, there is inevitably a possibility of leakage. Although the systems are designed to continue in operation with minor leaks, these are nevertheless an irritation.

Development is thus being carried out to try to simplify existing systems and to improve performance in relation to leakage. The development of systems which do not need pressurisation is also being undertaken.

DEVELOPMENT OF EXISTING CABLE SYSTEMS

The information given in the previous sections outlines the objectives of the developments currently being carried out. In several cases the development covers more than one of the objectives.

Pressurised cable systems

Cooling of conductors

Much work has already been carried out to improve the current rating of low pressure and high pressure oil-filled cables. The area where further developments can be expected is in conductor cooling. In chapter 37 reference was made to the use of oil circulation through the conductor to improve rating and fig. 37.14 illustrated that it is only this type of cooling that would permit the use of one cable per phase to meet a required rating of 4000 MVA at 525 kV. Oil circulation has been used in trials carried out in Italy on a 1100 kV cable system.[1] It is therefore to be expected that development of this system will continue further. Similar developments, but using different fluids, have been carried out in Germany and Japan.

In Germany, water has been used for conductor cooling.[2] Compared with oil, water has several attractions, e.g. its heat capacity is about 2.5 times higher and its viscosity is only about one-tenth of that of oil. Its major disadvantages are that it has to be kept isolated from the oil in the cable and that injection and removal must be through long insulators at the terminations. For the latter purpose the water must be deionised to reduce the losses. Because the injection of water cannot be made at intermediate feed joints along the route, the cooling section must be the full length of the circuit. To achieve this a stainless steel tube approximately 55 mm in internal diameter is incorporated into the conductor and pumping pressures up to 30 bar are employed. The cable system has a very high rating, but the presence of high pressure water inside the conductor of an oil-filled cable means that the integrity of the cooling system must be exceptionally high. A minute leakage could irreparably damage considerable quantities of cable and it is from this aspect that doubts about its practicability arise. In Japan, trials have been made using evaporative conductor cooling.[3] This type of cooling is most efficient and has the advantage that coolant pumps can be eliminated. However, the coolant must be separated from the cable insulation and the coolant duct in the cable must be sufficiently large to permit 2-phase flow, i.e. liquid and gas. Whilst elimination of pumping equipment is a positive advantage, gravity distribution of coolant restricts the length and profile of the cable system. It therefore appears that any applications will be restricted to relatively short lengths.

Alternative tape materials for insulation

From dielectric considerations, work with conventional oil-filled cables has indicated that it is possible to extend the operating voltage to about 1100 kV a.c.[1]

To achieve the highest voltages, an increase in minimum operating pressure to 15 bar is envisaged. While from an electrical strength point of view, it is clear that conventional paper insulation can be extended to these voltages, the problem of high dielectric losses remains. For example, at 1100 kV the dielectric losses of the cable would be so high that unless some form of cooling is employed the cable would be thermally unstable. Thus it would be necessary to employ some form of cooling whenever the cable is energised. At 750 kV in certain favourable installation conditions, it would be possible to operate with natural cooling but the rating would be severely restricted.

It is with these problems in mind that designers have looked for alternatives to paper insulation. Initially much work was carried out on the use of plastic films instead of paper but various restrictions have prevented successful development, e.g. (a) compatibility of the plastic and impregnant; (b) difficulty in obtaining 100% impregnation with oil; (c) relatively low impulse strength; (d) poor bending performance; (e) high cost. A compromise which has found favour is a composite tape consisting of a plastic film sandwiched between layers of Kraft paper. Various forms of laminate have been considered and some of these are described in references (4)–(8). The preferred construction is now considered to be a laminate consisting of a film of polypropylene between two layers of Kraft paper.[9,10] The proportion of paper to polypropylene is approximately 50:50. It has been found that this type of laminate overcomes many of the problems associated with the plastic films. The paper layer provides a good path for impregnation of the insulation and mechanically reinforces the plastic, which results in an improved bending performance and restricted swelling. It also protects the plastic from local discharges, which increases the impulse strength of the insulation.

Table 44.2 compares the properties of paper 100 μm thick, as used for OF cables, and polypropylene paper laminate (PPL).

Table 44.2 Typical properties of 100 μm paper and PPL insulation

Property	PPL	Paper
Tensile strength (MN/m^2)	50	110
Elongation at break (%)	2.0	2.5
Air impermeability (G s)	Infinity	15 000
Density (g/cm^3)	0.9	0.9
*Relative permittivity at 90 °C	2.7	3.4
*Dielectric loss angle at 90 °C	0.0008	0.0023
*Dielectric loss factor at 90 °C (permittivity × DLA)	0.0021	0.0078
*Impulse strength (MV/m)	160	135
*Short time a.c. strength (MV/m)	55	50

* Characteristics from oil-impregnated model cables

Although PPL does not achieve the low loss associated with 100% polymer (i.e. a relative permittivity of 2.3 and a DLA of 0.0003) it nevertheless gives a marked reduction in losses compared with conventional paper insulation. This is illustrated in fig. 44.2 which includes a comparison of the ratings for conventional and PPL insulated oil-filled cables. It will be seen that, at the higher voltages, the rating of the PPL insulated cable is much higher than that of the paper insulated cables. As may be expected, the cost of PPL is significantly higher than that of plain paper. However, at the higher voltages this is outweighed by the possibility of using a smaller conductor size and obtaining lower running losses. For example, using a separate pipe water-cooled system, a 400 kV 1600 mm^2 PPL insulated oil-filled cable has the same current rating as a 2000 mm^2 conventional paper insulated cable.

Under maximum load conditions, the total losses of a PPL insulated cable will be virtually the same as for an impregnated paper cable, as the lower dielectric losses are offset by the smaller conductor size. However, under other loading conditions the use of PPL results in significant savings in losses. This is illustrated in table 44.3,

Table 44.3 Total losses for 400 kV 1600 mm^2 PPL and 2000 mm^2 paper insulated cables

Cable	Total losses (W/m)					
	Two feeders in operation			One feeder in operation		
	Winter	Normal	Summer	Winter[a]	Normal	Summer
PPL	125	103	86	213	168	135
Paper	175	155	141	218	179	150
Ratio PPL: paper	0.71	0.66	0.61	0.98	0.94	0.9

[a] Design condition: winter current, 2038 A; normal current, 1793 A; summer current, 1591 A

which shows the total losses of two parallel separate pipe cooled feeders. Each circuit is capable of carrying a maximum design load of 1410 MVA in winter but in normal operation both feeders are in circuit and sharing the load equally. The conductor size of the impregnated paper cable is 2000 mm^2 and that of the PPL insulated cable is 1600 mm^2.

It will be seen that, with one feeder in operation under winter conditions, the losses of both cables are approximately the same. With both feeders in operation, the ratio of the losses in the PPL cable to those of the paper cable varies from 0.61 to 0.71 depending on the season. It should be noted that the losses quoted in table 44.3 refer to the maximum load on the circuit. For all ratings less than maximum feeder load, the ratio of the PPL to paper losses will be lower than is given in the table.

PPL insulation is now beginning to be used commercially in OF cables up to 500 kV and in HP OF pipe type cables up to 345 kV. The latter application is in the USA where PPL is particularly attractive for the following reasons.

(a) The operating frequency is 60 Hz compared with 50 Hz.
(b) The insulation thicknesses used traditionally for paper insulated cables are conservative, i.e. greater than strictly necessary. By using realistic design stresses for laminate insulated cables, it is possible to use cables with considerable thinner insulation.
(c) Steel pipes are supplied in discrete diameter steps. The ability to use a smaller size pipe can make a considerable reduction in the quantity of oil used in the system.
(d) Dielectric losses are more significant in the determination of the current rating of HP OF cables.
(e) The smaller diameter associated with laminate insulation gives the possibility of re-cabling existing pipe with a higher voltage cable and thus increasing the power transmitting capability of the pipe.

Long-term tests have been successfully completed on a 765 kV HP OF cable insulated with PPL.[10]

Cost of maintenance

Finally, as mentioned previously, work is being carried out to minimise maintenance associated with pressure-assisted cables. In self-contained oil-filled cables, the main source of oil leaks is in accessories. Although welding has been employed on some installations,[11] plumbing remains the most widely used method for making the connection between the cable sheath and the line accessory. Methods have been developed to provide mechanical reinforcement of the plumbs to avoid problems that have been experienced due to slow creep of the plumb under adverse conditions of pressure and longitudinal stress in the sheath. Improved methods of leak detection and location are also being pursued.

Polymeric insulated cables

The use of polymeric insulated cables for transmission requirements has been discussed in chapter 36. Below is a brief outline of the work carried out to date and an indication of future developments.

Ever since the excellent dielectric properties of polyethylene were recognised during the Second World War, it has been predicted that this material would replace paper for the insulation of power cables. Initially its low melting point was an obstacle but this was overcome by the development of crosslinked polyethylene during the 1960s. Rapid progress was made with its use for distribution cable but a setback occurred when it was discovered that water trees could develop within the dielectric of crosslinked or linear polyethylene if a metal sheath was not used. These trees can lower the electrical strength of the insulation.

Investigations showed the presence of microvoids in crosslinked polyethylene insulated cables and how some improvement could be obtained by using dry curing instead of steam curing. However, it was recognised at a very early stage that polyethylene was very susceptible to erosion by electrical discharges and much attention was paid to the elimination of voids within the dielectric. In the event it was found that this alone did not give the anticipated electrical strength. Extensive research indicated that the electrical strength could be seriously affected by contamination and every effort is now made to achieve a high degree of cleanliness both in the polymer and during cable manufacture. The additional compounding process makes this slightly more difficult to achieve in the case of crosslinked polymeric materials.

Initially most progress with cables for the higher voltages was made using linear polyethylene. In 1986 it was reported[12] that some 690 km of 225 kV linear polyethylene cable was in service and that short lengths of 400 kV cable had just been commissioned.

The development of crosslinked polyethylene cables has been somewhat behind that of cables insulated with linear polyethylene. A limited length of 275 kV cable is in service and short lengths of 500 kV cables have been installed.[13] The incentive to use crosslinked insulation is that a maximum operating temperature of 90 °C can be used compared with the value of 70 °C used for low density polyethylene. In France some installations have been made with cables insulated with high density polyethylene. A maximum conductor temperature of 80 °C is used for these cables.

It is now generally accepted that transmission cables insulated with linear or crosslinked polyethylene should be protected against the entry of water by a metallic barrier.

Design stresses up to 10 MV/m have been used for 220/275 kV cables compared with a value of 15 MV/m for OF cables. The polymeric cables are therefore larger and use more material than the comparable OF cable.

The development of extruded polymeric cables is continuing with most countries preferring crosslinked polyethylene insulation. The system has been established for voltages up to and including 132 kV albeit, at present, with lower design stresses than paper insulated cables. However, the advantages of not having a pressurised system has led to its use in significant quantities in certain countries. Extensive use of 220 kV cables insulated with low density polyethylene has been made in France and limited installations of 220–275 kV crosslinked cables have been made elsewhere. Trial installations at 400–500 kV are being made with both materials.

Much work is being carried out around the world to improve the design stresses of linear and crosslinked polyethylene cables and there appears to be reasonable prospect that improvements will be possible, mainly based on reduced contamination and, in the case of crosslinked insulations, by improved curing techniques. It seems likely that further developments in polymer technology will be required before reliable cables without metal barriers can be produced for the highest voltage applications.

NEW DESIGNS OF TRANSMISSION CABLE

Compressed gas insulated cables

It may be argued by some of the supporters of compressed gas insulation that cable designs have already been established. However, although many installations of this type of cable have been completed, principally in the USA, they are all of relatively short length (30–1000 m) and have not been used for main underground transmission links through cities.

The compressed gas insulated (CGI) cables have developed from the metal-clad substations and the initial designs were in effect an extension of the gas-insulated busbar, many of the early installations being associated with switching stations. Fig. 44.4 shows a sample of a typical single-phase rigid CGI cable.

The inner conductor consists of a rigid aluminium tube and is supported in a larger aluminium pipe by means of rigid spacers, usually of filled epoxy resin, which are situated at intervals along the pipe. For burial in the ground, an anticorrosion

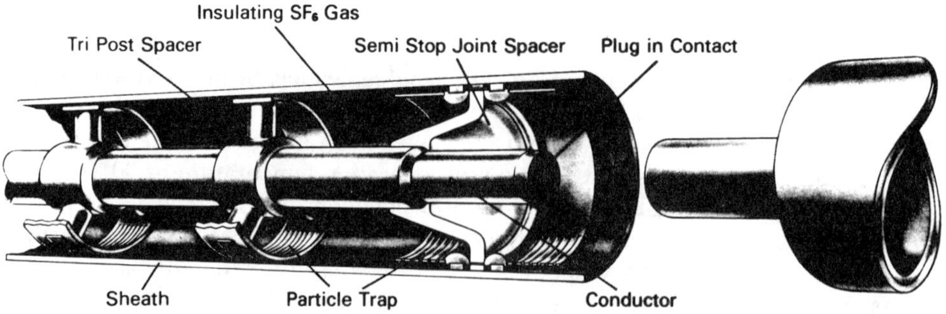

Fig. 44.4 Typical 230 kV single-phase rigid CGI cable (Courtesy of Westinghouse Electric Corporation)

layer is applied over the outer pipe. The space between the conductor and the outer pipe is filled with pressurised SF_6 gas. This is an electronegative gas and at atmospheric pressure has an electrical breakdown strength some 60% greater than nitrogen. To improve the electrical strength of the gas further, it is used under a pressure of 3–5 bar.

Lengths of up to 20 m are pre-assembled in the factory and transported to site. The amount of work in jointing these lengths together on site depends on the precise design. A typical design would include plug-in connections for the conductor connection and a welded joint for the outer pipe. The plug-in connector permits expansion of the conductor to take place and avoids high thermomechanical forces in the conductor system. A key feature of the cable is the design of spacer. The most usual forms are discs, cones or post type insulators. They are designed to minimise their effect on the flashover voltage between the conductor and outer pipe. Metal inserts are usually cast in the spacer to eliminate high electric fields between the spacer and the pipe conductor. The spacer system must be designed to allow longitudinal gas flow during pressurisation.

The electrical strength of the gas–spacer system is very much influenced by the presence of conducting particles and it is of greatest importance that the highest cleanliness standards are maintained during assembly of lengths in the factory and during installation at site. Some designs of cable include special low electrical field regions at the earthed end of the spacer which are designed to trap conducting particles.

At present, most single-phase CGI cables operate with the outer pipes fully bonded and earthed. The dimensions of the cables are such that the sheath currents are very high and an increase in the thickness of the pipe results in a lowering of the losses. The precise thickness is a balance between the cost of the losses and the initial cost of the pipe. An advantage of the fully bonded system is that the electromechanical forces arising on the conductor from short circuits are greatly reduced by the opposing currents induced in the outer pipes.

Terminations for single-phase CGI cables are relatively simple, stress control being achieved by corona rings or shields placed at the top and bottom of the insulator. To cater for changes in direction, factory manufactured elbows are provided. T-joints are also a possibility.

Following the trends of the insulated busbar, 3-phase CGI cables are being developed. The reasons for this development are similar to those which apply to more conventional cable systems, i.e. economy in sheath materials, reduction of space requirements and simpler installation. For this system, post type insulators are used . Systems are in commercial service at voltages up to and including 550 kV. Trials have been made on a 1200 kV cable installation.[14]

In order to reduce the costs of CGI cables further, development of long length flexible designs is being carried out. If possible, this would greatly reduce installation costs as the lengths between joints could be increased by a factor of about 10. The cable consists of a flexible conductor, rigid spacers and a flexible corrugated aluminium sheath.[15] The pressure of SF_6 is similar to that used in rigid systems and hence overall diameters are also similar. Fig. 44.5 shows a cross-section of a 230 kV design.

CGI cables have attractions in terms of current rating, low capacitance and dielectric losses. In the case of the rigid designs, large conductor cross-sections can be employed without the bending complications usually encountered in underground cables. A

Fig. 44.5 Example of flexible CGI cable with rigid spacers (Courtesy of Electrical Power Research Institute, USA)

further advantage is the low internal thermal resistance of the cable. This results from heat transfer by radiation and convection. The high density of SF_6 makes heat transfer by convection most effective. The different mechanisms of heat transfer make a general comparison of the thermal resistance of traditional solid insulations and CGI cable insulations difficult. Furthermore, heat transfer in gaseous insulation is not simply proportional to temperature difference. However, specific comparison at 400 kV indicates that the internal thermal resistance of a CGI cable is approximately 20%–25% of that of a conventional oil-filled cable. Thus the CGI cable will have a superior rating in terms of both the possibility of larger conductor sizes and a lower thermal resistance. In the case of surface cooling, the effect of internal thermal resistance on rating is greater than for natural cooling, as the internal thermal resistance forms the major part of the total thermal resistance. The increase in rating obtained by surface cooling is therefore much greater for CGI cables than for conventional cables.

The relative permittivity of SF_6 is virtually unity and the power factor is virtually zero. Dielectric losses are effectively zero and the low capacitance of the cable arising from the low relative permittivity and large dimensions results in a much longer critical length before the cable system becomes self-loading due to capacitive current.

The CGI cable therefore has many attractive features from an electrical point of view. However, the rigid system is very expensive in terms of material and installation costs. There are considerable practical difficulties in installing such a system in urban areas, owing to the space it occupies and the difficulties that would be encountered at obstructions. The flexible cable is more practical and has potential for a cheaper system, but it has not been proved in normal service.

Superconducting cables

The discovery of superconductivity at temperatures of around 90 K has taken place too recently for its effect on transmission cable design to be evaluated. However, conventional superconducting transmission cable has been under consideration for many years. As originally conceived this was to be a low voltage cable capable of carrying a current of many hundred kiloamps, so eliminating the need for voltage transformation. Unfortunately, research work quickly showed that this dream was not possible. This arises from the fact that in addition to a critical temperature, i.e. a temperature above which the material cannot be superconducting, there is also a critical magnetic field. If the superconductor is placed in a magnetic field above this critical value, the conductor becomes normal, i.e. possesses resistance. The critical field is related to the temperature of the conductor: the lower the temperature, the higher is the critical magnetic field. Conductors which have the above characteristics are known as type 1 superconductors and include pure metals such as lead, mercury and tin. As current produces a magnetic field, for a particular conductor geometry the critical magnetic field can be expressed as a critical current, and hence a current limitation exists for a particular design of superconducting cable.

Further research into the behaviour of conductors at near absolute zero identified a class of materials known as type 2 conductors. These materials were found to have two critical fields: H_{C1}, the field below which the material is truly a superconductor, and a higher field H_{C2} above which the material has normal resistance. In the region between fields H_{C1} and H_{C2} the material is in a mixed state and has some losses. However, these losses are of very small magnitude and type 2 conductors can be used in higher critical fields than type 1 conductors.

Two such type 2 materials which have been considered for superconducting plant are niobium alloys containing either tin or titanium.

The design of superconducting cables is so different from that of conventional cables that the principles will be best understood by describing a design that has been taken to the field trial stage.[16] Fig. 44.6 shows the experimental 138 kV cable designed for a rating of 1000 MV A. It comprises two flexible cores installed in a rigid pipe (commercial cables would have three cores). Each core consists of an inner and outer conductor separated by the main insulation which consists of lapped polypropylene tapes. The conductor is made from niobium–tin strips. The magnetic field from the inner conductor induces a circulating current in the outer conductor almost equal in magnitude but in the opposite direction to the conductor current. This effectively confines the magnetic field to the cable core, thus avoiding eddy currents anywhere is the cable system. The cable was installed in a thermally insulated enclosure to minimise the entry of heat into the system, i.e. a completely opposite situation to conventional cables where the heat generated is dissipated to the surrounds. The enclosure consists of two concentric pipes with diameters of 215 and 405 mm. The inner pipe is held inside the outer by spoke type supports and is thermally insulated by pumping the air out of the space between the two pipes. The

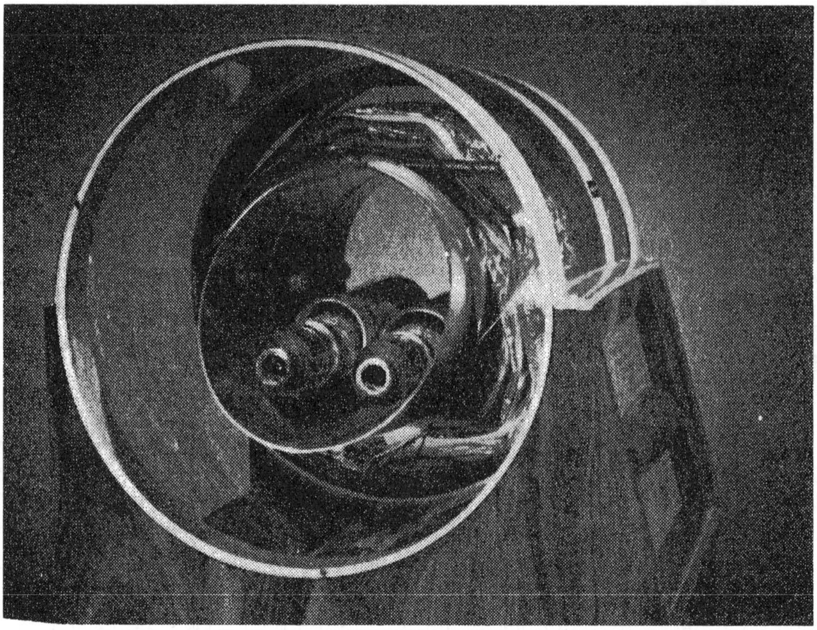

Fig. 44.6 Experimental 138 kV superconducting cable (© 1986 IEEE)

inner pipe is wrapped with multilayer aluminised plastic sheets to minimise the transfer of radiated heat. The cable core is cooled to less than 10 K by the circulation of liquid helium.

The test installation has been operated for extensive periods in the superconducting mode. However, much more development work would be required to make it a practical proposition. Other studies of superconducting cables suggest that they could only become economic compared with conventional 400 kV cables when circuit ratings of 5000 MV A or more are required.[17]

CONCLUSIONS

For load requirements up to about 3 GVA it appears that developments of existing designs of cable will probably be the most economic for the foreseeable future. For ratings in the range 3–5 GVA, compressed gas insulated cables would be capable of meeting the requirements, with superconducting cables coming in at the higher ratings. Compressed gas insulated cables for these ratings will be extremely large and rigid and it remains to be seen whether it is practical to install such systems in the centre of large urban conurbations. A further aspect is the necessity for a high degree of cleanliness both in installation and maintenance. Much more development is required before superconducting cables can be considered as viable alternatives to present designs.

For higher voltage applications, impregnated paper insulation is technically feasible for voltages up to 1100 kV a.c. and d.c. In the case of a.c. systems, the dielectric losses cause severe reductions in current ratings at the higher system voltages and polypropylene/paper laminate insulation is likely to be increasingly used.

REFERENCES

(1) Donazzi, F., Fameti, F., Luoni, G. and Mosca, W. (1984) 'Power transmission of a self-contained oil-filled 1100 kV cable system. Full scale tests and design criteria'. Paris: CIGRE Paper No. 21-09.

(2) Blasius, P., Marjes, B., Henschel, M., Kunisch, H. J. and Martin, W. (1982) 'Testing a 110 kV low-pressure oil-filled cable with a water cooled conductor in Berlin (West)'. Paris: CIGRE Paper No. 21-01.

(3) Kojima, K. and Kubo, H. (1976) 'A study of internally cooled cable systems for bulk power underground transmission'. *IEEE Transmission and Distribution Conference.*

(4) Itoh, H., Nakagawa, M. and Ichino, T. (1979) 'EHV self-contained oil-filled cable insulated with composite paper DCLP'. *IEE Conference on Progress in Cables and Overhead Lines for 220 kV and Above.*

(5) Sakurai, T., Iwata, Z., Shimizu, M., Fujisaki, Y. and Furisawa, H. (1980). '275 kV self-contained oil-filled cable insulated with polymethylpentne laminated paper'. IEEE Paper No. 80 SM 555-3.

(6) Kusano, T., Soda, S., Fujiwara, Y. and Kinoshita, S. (1981) 'Practical use of "Siolap" insulated oil-filled cables'. IEEE Paper No. 81 WM 114-8.

(7) Matsuura, K., Kubo, H. and Miyazaki, T. (1976) 'Development of polypropylene laminated paper insulated EHV power cables'. *IEEE Underground Transmission and Distribution Conference.*

(8) Soda, S., Kojima, T., Fujiwara, Y., Kinoshita, S. and Takeuchi, K. (1979) 'Development of "Siograthene" laminated paper insulated oil-filled cables'. *IEE Conference on Progress in Cables and Overhead Lines for 220 kV and Above.*

(9) Arkell, C. A., Edwards, D. R., Skipper, D. J. and Stannett, A. W. (1980) 'Development of polypropylene paper laminate (PPL) oil-filled cable UHV systems'. Paris: CIGRE Paper No. 21-04.

(10) Allam, E. M., Cooper, J. H. and Shimshock, J. F. (1986) 'Development and long-term testing of a low-loss 765 kV high-pressure oil-filled pipe cable'. Paris: CIGRE Paper No. 21-06.

(11) Ray, J. J., Arkell, C. A. and Flack, H. W. (1974) '525 kV self-contained oil-filled cable systems for Grand Coulee. Third power plant: design and development'. *IEEE Trans.* **PAS-93**, 630–639.

(12) Auclair, H., Dhuicq, B., Favrie, E. and Jocteur, R. (1986) 'Development of 400 kV links with low density polyethylene insulation'. Paris: CIGRE Paper No. 21-09.

(13) Aihara, M., Fujiki, S., Kato, N., Magasaki, S., Nakagaira, M. and Yoshida, N. (1988) 'Philosophy of design and experience on high voltage XLPE cables and accessories in Japan'. Paris: CIGRE Paper No. 21-01.

(14) Bolin, P. C., Cookson, A. M., Corbett, J., Garitty, T. F. and Shimshock, J. F. (1982) 'Development and test installation of a three-conductor and UHV compressed gas insulated transmission line for heavy load transmission'. Paris: CIGRE Paper No. 21-04.

(15) Spencer, E. M., Samm, R. W., Artbauer, J. and Schatz, F. (1980) 'Research and development of a flexible 362 kV compressed gas insulated transmission cable'. Paris: CIGRE Paper No. 21-02.

(16) Forsyth, E. B. and Thomas, R. A. (1986) 'Operational test results of a prototype superconducting power transmission system and their extrapolation to the performance of a large system'. *IEEE Trans.* **PWRD-1** (1).
(17) Maddock, B. J., Cairns, D. H. H., Sutten, J., Swift, D. A., Cotrill, J. E. J., Humphries, M. B. and Williams, D. E. (1976) *'Superconducting a.c. power cables and their application'*. Paris: CIGRE Paper No. 21-05.

PART 5

SUBMARINE DISTRIBUTION AND TRANSMISSION

Chapter 45

Submarine Cables and Systems

Submarine cables are used in three basic types of installation:

(a) river or short route crossings which are generally relatively shallow water installations
(b) between platforms, platforms and sea-bed modules or between shore and a platform in an offshore oil or gas field; these cables are currently laid in depths not exceeding 200 m but it is anticipated that much deeper installations will be required in the future
(c) major submarine cable installations, coast to coast, often laid in deep water and crossing shipping routes and fishing zones; these cables are generally required for bulk power transfer in a high voltage either a.c. or d.c. transmission scheme

Submarine cables are usually subject to much more onerous installation and service conditions than an equivalent land cable and it is necessary to design each cable to withstand the environmental conditions prevailing on the specific route. Subject to certain restrictions, paper insulated solid type cables, oil-filled cables, gas-filled cables and polymeric cables are all suitable for submarine power cable installations. Polymeric and thermoplastic insulated cables are used for control and instrumentation and appropriate action has to be taken in the design and manufacture of the cable to attain the required mechanical characteristics.

Cables for river crossings

Cable routes for river crossings are generally only a few kilometres long and cross relatively shallow water. The length of cable required can often be delivered to site as a continuous length on a despatch drum. Normal methods of installation include laying the cable from a barge into a pre-cut trench and mounting the drum on jacks on one shore and floating the cable across the river on inflatable bags. Installation of the cable is therefore a relatively simple operation which does not involve excessive bending or tension. The cable design is the most similar to land cable practice of all the different types of submarine cable. However, it is considered prudent to improve the mechanical security of the cable by applying slightly thicker lead and anticorrosion sheaths and to increase the diameter of the armour wires. If the cable is to be laid across the river at the entrance to a port, it is recommended that the cable be buried to a depth of at least 1 m. A cheaper but less effective alternative is to protect a surface-laid cable by laying bags of concrete around it.

Should the cable be considered liable to damage due to shipping activities, an alternative solution to direct burial of the cable is to entrench a suitable pipe into the river bed and then pull in the selected type of cable.

Requirements for long cable lengths laid in deep water

Any cable to be laid on the sea bed should have the characteristics given below, the relevant importance of each particular characteristic being dependent on the depth of water and length of cable route.

(a) The cable must have a high electrical factor of safety as repair operations are generally expensive and the loss of service before repairs can be completed is often a serious embarrassment to the utility concerned.
(b) The cable should be designed to reduce transmission losses to a minimum, as submarine cable routes are generally long and the operating power losses are therefore significant in the overall economics of the system.
(c) The cable should preferably be supplied in the continuous length necessary to permit a continuous laying operation without the need to insert joints while at sea. Proven designs of flexible joints are available to permit drum lengths of cable to be jointed together, either during manufacture or prior to loading the continuous cable length onto the laying vessel.
(d) The cable must withstand, without deterioration, the severe bending under tension, twisting and coiling which may occur during the manufacture and installation programmes.
(e) The cable must also withstand, without deformation, the external water pressure at the deepest part of the route.
(f) The cable, and where appropriate the terminal equipment, must be designed to ensure that only a limited length of cable is affected by water ingress if the metal sheath is damaged when in service.
(g) The armour must be sufficiently robust to resist impact damage and severance of the cable if fouled by a ship's anchor or fishing gear.
(h) For deep water installations, the cable must be reasonably torque balanced to avoid uncontrolled twisting as it is lowered to the sea bed.
(i) The weight of the cable in water must be sufficient to inhibit movement on the sea bed under the influence of tidal currents. Movement would cause abrasion and fatigue damage to the cable.
(j) The cable must be adequately protected from all corrosion hazards.
(k) All cable components must have adequate flexural fatigue life.
(l) All paper insulated and some polymeric insulated cables are required to be watertight along their complete lengths. Water ingress impairs the electric strength of these cables.

Requirements for cable to be buried

The requirements for cable laid on the sea bed also largely apply to cables which are to be buried. The bending characteristics of the cable as it passes through the burial device may need further consideration, and the friction of the serving against rollers and skid plates has to be taken into account. It is essential that information be provided on the length of the proposed route, the nature and contour of the sea bed, tidal currents, temperatures etc. before a provisional cable design can be prepared for the proposed installation. Sufficient information can often be obtained from Admiralty charts to enable a tentative cable design to be prepared to complete a feasibility study but in most cases it is necessary to carry out a hydrographic survey before the cable design can be finalised.

A.C. cable schemes

Submarine cable schemes are normally a.c. schemes as land transmission and distribution systems usually operate on a.c. As in the case of land cable circuits, the use of 3-core cables up to and including 150 kV is preferred to single-core cables provided that they can meet the required rating. 3-core cables also offer savings in both cable and installation costs as only two cables compared with four for a 3-phase scheme need be installed when security of supply is required if one cable is damaged. There is a limit, however, to the length of 3-core cable that can be laid and the cost of inserting flexible joints into very long cable lengths has to be taken into account.

If a 3-core submarine cable is damaged externally, e.g. by a ship's anchor or trawling gear, all three cores are liable to be affected. It would therefore be necessary to install two 3-core cables from the outset, preferably separated by 250 m or more to obtain reasonable security of supply. In 3-core solid type cable installations (i.e. for circuits up to 33 kV rating) single lead type cables (i.e. HSL cables) are sometimes preferred, particularly for deep water installations.

For major a.c. power schemes it will probably be necessary to use single-core cables as 3-core cables will be unable to meet the rating. In this case the cables are spaced far apart so that the risk of more than one cable being damaged in a single incident is minimised. The installation of four single-corc cables for one circuit, or one spare cable for two or three circuits, would be expected to provide reasonable assurance of continuity of supply. However, widely spaced single-core magnetically armoured cables give rise to high sheath losses. These losses can be reduced substantially by the use of non-magnetic armour in conjunction with an outer concentric conductor, although this solution increases the initial cost of the cables.

D.C. cable schemes

For major cable installations requiring bulk transfer of large quantities of power, the choice has to be made between an a.c. or a d.c. transmission scheme. The longest submarine transmission schemes are invariably d.c. as their length is not limited by the necessity of supplying the charging current inherent in the a.c. system. Where it is intended to connect two separate power systems, e.g. between different countries, d.c. is again chosen as it is possible to keep the two systems independent, thereby preventing risk of instability. A d.c. system also allows for a greater degree of control of power flowing through the cables. Where the link is relatively short, the a.c. system will be more attractive than the d.c. because of the high capital cost of the converter stations required at both ends of the d.c. route. In a small number of routes it may be possible to position some reactive compensation for the a.c. system on conveniently placed islands, although this solution may affect the economics of the scheme. One additional advantage of a d.c. scheme is that, for major links incorporating single-core cables, only two cables are necessary whereas a minimum of three cables is invariably required for a.c. schemes.

D.C. transmission schemes may consist of one pole cable carrying full circuit power with sea return, or preferably two pole cables each carrying half circuit power. The magnetic field created by a single-pole cable causes compass errors near the cable route which may be unacceptable to the relevant Admiralty authorities as it would create a potential hazard to shipping.[1] The single-pole scheme suffers the further disadvantage that if the submarine cable is damaged there would be no transmission capability until the cable was repaired. In a bipole transmission scheme, if only one pole cable is damaged, the remaining cable will continue to carry half circuit power with sea return. The installation of three single-core cables from the outset provides reasonable assurance of full transmission capability even if one cable is damaged.

ELECTRICAL DESIGN FEATURES OF CABLES

Conductors

The conductor design will be influenced by the choice of transmission scheme in which it is required to operate. Long submarine routes are generally d.c. schemes, which allow for the use of concentrically stranded conductors. As most land cables operate on a.c. there will be no difference in the design of conductor used in a.c. submarine cables. Large a.c. conductors will be of the Milliken type.

Copper is generally preferred to aluminium for the conductors of all submarine cables as its use permits a higher current density, thereby reducing the overall diameter of the cable. In the event of the cable being damaged and sea-water entering it, a copper conductor is much more resistant to corrosion than an aluminium conductor.

Details of the design of conductors are given in a later section dealing with specific types of cable.

Insulation thickness

For a.c. cables the insulation thickness is designed on the same basis as for land cables and for the higher voltages is determined by the lightning impulse test requirement. It is considered prudent, however, to employ slightly lower maximum design stresses for submarine cables than would be adopted for land cables, to compensate for the more severe bending and tension which a submarine cable may need to withstand during the laying operation. The resultant increase in the electric strength of the cable is considered to justify the small increase in cost.

There are as yet no international standards for the thickness of insulation or electrical design stresses of d.c. cables. Past experience of high voltage d.c. cable performance is almost exclusively in submarine cables where maximum stresses of 25 MV/m have been found acceptable for solid type paper insulated cables and up to 30 MV/m for oil-filled paper insulated cable. The insulation may still have an impulse test requirement which gives an insulation thickness designed in the same manner as for a.c. cables. The steady state d.c. stresses above are dictated by transients of internal origin and polarity reversal requirements and are considerably lower than the maximum impulse breakdown strength of the insulation.

All d.c. submarine cables are expected to meet the electrical test requirements specified in the latest CIGRE 'Recommendation for tests for power transmission d.c. cables for a rated voltage up to 600 kV', following mechanical tests carried out in accordance with the CIGRE 'Recommendations for mechanical tests on submarine cables'.[2]

Current ratings

The current rating of submarine cables is mainly dependent on the maximum recommended conductor temperature, the thermal resistivity of the dielectric and the environment in which the cable is laid, and in the case of single-core a.c. cable schemes the axial spacing of the cables on the sea bed and the choice of armouring material.

The thermal resistivity of the environment in which the cables operate is dependent on site conditions and the method of laying. If the cables are laid on the surface of the sea bed, thermal values of 0.3 K m/W have sometimes been assumed. If the cable is to be buried in the sea bed, however, values of up to 1.0 are usually used for cables buried no deeper than 2.0 m.

In single-core a.c. submarine cable schemes, the cables are normally widely spaced on the sea bed and the sheath circuits are bonded at both ends. The wide cable spacing increases the sheath circulating current and reduces the current rating of the cables. Whereas the use of aluminium alloy armour permits the highest current density in the phase conductors at minimum cost, the mechanical properties of the aluminium alloy are often inadequate to protect the cables from external hazards. Galvanised steel wire armour has excellent mechanical characteristics but when applied to single-core a.c. cables gives rise to eddy currents, hysteresis and circulating circuits in the magnetic material.

The current rating of single-core a.c. cables is dependent, *inter alia*, on the effective resistance of the sheath circuit (i.e. the metallic sheath, armour wires and any reinforcing tapes in parallel). One method of reducing the losses and increasing the current rating is to reduce the effective resistance of the sheath circuit. This may be achieved by using an outer concentric conductor which usually consists of a layer or layers of copper wires applied underneath the anticorrosion sheath. This reduces the external magnetic field and permits the use of steel wire armour. When determining the most economic size of outer conductor for use on lead sheathed paper insulated cables where both conductors are copper, a useful rule of thumb is that the return conductor should be approximately half the cross-sectional area of the primary conductor, irrespective of system voltage.

Fig. 45.1 shows the relationship between the effective sheath circuit resistance and the sheath losses in a typical single-core submarine cable with the cables at 1 m spacing.

Protection of anticorrosion sheath against voltage transients

On long submarine cable routes it is necessary to take steps to ensure that the voltage appearing across the anticorrosion sheath, due to voltage transients in the transmission circuit, does not approach the electrical breakdown level of the sheathing material. It is standard practice, therefore, to bond the lead sheath and any associated reinforcing tapes electrically to the armour wires at regular intervals along the cable length.

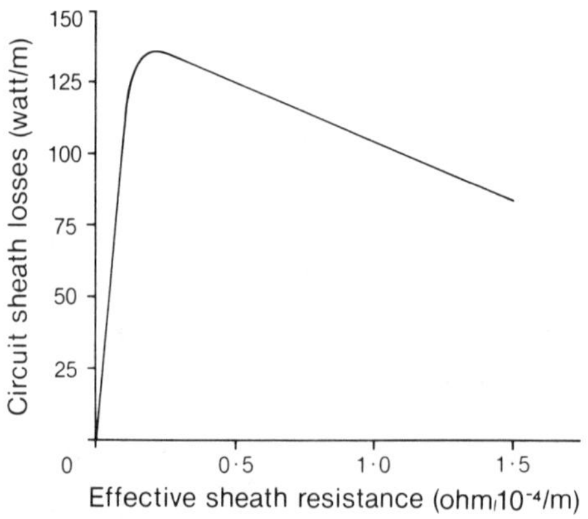

Fig. 45.1 Relationship between effective sheath resistance and sheath losses in 630 mm^2 single-core oil-filled submarine cable

MECHANICAL DESIGN FEATURES OF CABLES

Effect of method of installation

Two alternative techniques are available: transporting the cable to site and then laying from large coils formed in the hold of a suitable vessel (fig. 45.2), or transporting to site and laying from a large turntable or drum mounted on the deck of a purpose designed laying barge.

The choice between the two methods of installation is often dictated by economic considerations, the turntable or drum technique being generally more expensive as there are relatively few turntable or drum barges available and the turntables themselves may need to be constructed. The turntable or drum technique is the technically preferred option as the cable has to withstand only bending with no twisting action which, apart from tension considerations, often imposes a less severe condition on the cable than when it is laid from a despatch drum on a land cable route. Provided that turntables are used in all stages of cable manufacture the angle of lay and tension of application of all helically applied cable components need differ little from those used for land cables.

Winding of the cable into a coil imparts a 360° twist in each complete turn of cable in the coil. In a typical case, coiling a cable of 125 mm overall diameter to a minimum eye of 7.5 m (60 times the overall diameter) causes a twist of 15° per metre, the twist per metre decreasing slightly with each turn coiled outwards. For long cable routes the cable coil may be several metres high when coiled into the holds of the laying vessel. Cable is generally coiled clockwise when viewed from above. This causes all components which have been applied with right-hand lay, i.e. clockwise, to tighten and all components applied with left-hand lay to loosen when the cable is coiled down. It follows that at the interface between a right-hand component applied over a left-hand component the former is under abnormal tension while the latter is slack. These conditions are conducive to the formation of creases in the slack components unless the effect is controlled by careful selection of the angle of lay and the application tension of every helically applied component of the

Fig. 45.2 Coiled lengths of cable awaiting transfer to the laying vessel

cable. Lifting of the cable from the coil immediately prior to laying removes the twist from the cable so that it is in the twist-free condition as it passes outboard from the laying vessel. In a well designed cable every component should be free of creases when uncoiled.

A single wire armoured cable will tolerate coiling provided that the armour wires are applied so that they loosen as the cable is coiled down. It is virtually impossible to coil a double-wire armoured cable as there is no combination of reverse lays in the two layers of armour which will avoid either crushing the cable or creating such interfacial pressure between the two layers of armour that it is physically impossible to cause the cable to lay flat in a coil. When site conditions necessitate the use of a double wire reverse lay armoured cable, the only laying technique available for long continuous cable lengths is from a turntable or pipe laying drum barge which obviates the need for coiling. Double wire armoured cable with both layers applied in the same direction can be coiled and handled in a similar manner to single-wire armoured cable.

Resistance of cable to water pressure

The ability of a submarine cable to withstand the external water pressure is determined by the internal pressure of pressure-assisted cables (i.e. oil- or gas-filled cables), the hardness and coefficient of expansion of non-pressure-assisted cables and the thickness and composition of any metal sheath and metal tapes external to the sheath. The external pressure in sea-water increases by approximately 0.1 bar per metre depth. Distortion of a conventionally designed circular non-pressurised cable does not usually occur at depths less than about 150 m. At greater depths the metal sheath is liable to suffer distortion following the first heating cycle unless the cable is specially reinforced against the external water pressure. Fig. 45.3 shows the cross-section of a solid type cable which withstood an external pressure of 27.5 bar (2.75 MN/m^2) at ambient temperature but which became misshapen when cooling to ambient temperature following a heating cycle to 60°C. Thermal expansion of the impregnant had distended the lead alloy sheath. As the sheath did not cool uniformly, an annulus was created between the inside of the sheath and the outside of the core and the non-supported distended sheath was then deformed by the external water pressure. An adjacent sample of cable withstood an external pressure of 65 bar (6.5 MN/m^2) and repeated heating and cooling when a steel tape 1.5 mm thick was lapped over the lead sheath.

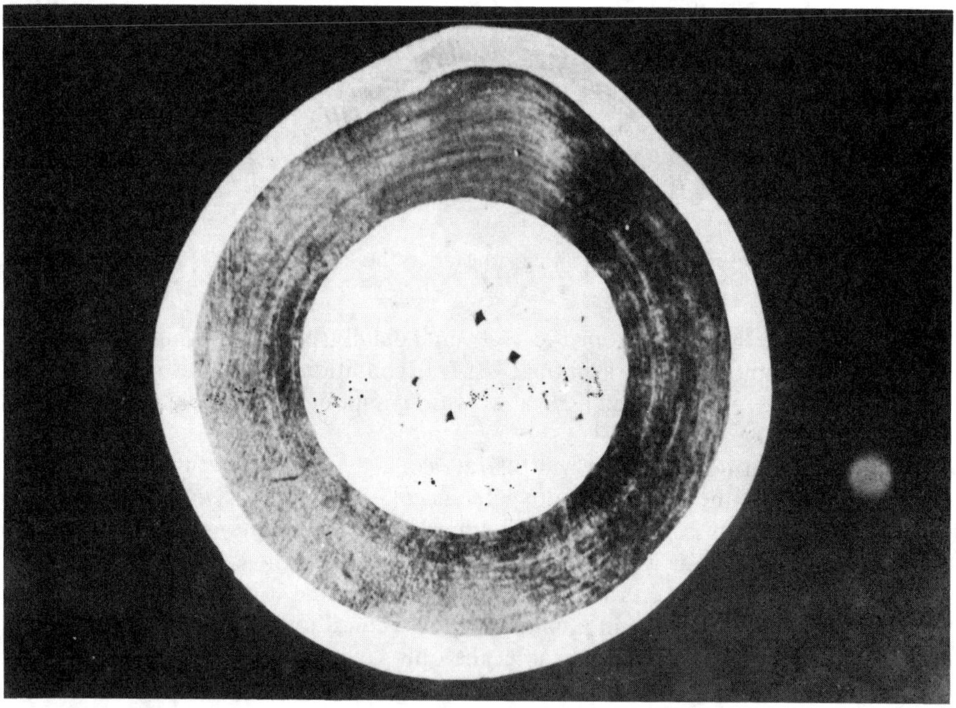

Fig. 45.3 Deformation of solid type PILS cable resulting from a heating cycle to 60°C with hydrostatic pressure of 27.5 bar

The reinforcing tapes over the lead sheath of oil- and gas-filled cables maintain the external diameter of the sheath at practically constant values, the thermal expansion of the dielectric fluid merely increasing the internal pressure of the cable which, in the case of oil-filled cables, causes oil to flow into reservoirs at the cable terminals.

Because of the high coefficient of expansion of XLPE insulation, it may be necessary to restrict the temperature rise and hence the current loading when lead-sheathed XLPE cables are laid in deep water, so as to avoid excessive distension of the lead sheath.

The efficacy of any metal tapes applied external to the lead sheath to reinforce the cable against the external water pressure is proportional to t^3n/d^3 where t is the thickness of one tape, d is the pitch circle diameter of the tapes when applied to the cable and n is the number of tapes applied. A single tape of 1 mm thickness will therefore provide as much resistance to the external water pressure as eight tapes each 0.5 mm thickness. Development tests have shown that optimum results are achieved if a polyethylene sheath is applied over the lead sheath followed by one or more layers of reinforcing tape. In the case of oil- and gas-filled cables these tapes may also be used for anti-twist duties, provided that the tapes are applied with appropriate angle and direction of lay.

An alternative method of combating the external water pressure favoured by some cable manufacturers for deep water single-core cable schemes is to install solid type cables which operate as compression cables. The cable is made slightly oval shaped with a polyethylene sheath applied directly over the lead sheath, followed by one or two layers of reinforcing tapes and appropriate servings. Under current loading conditions the thermal expansion distends the minor axis of the lead sheath, the cable therefore tending towards a circular shape. As the cable cools, the external water pressure causes it to return to its original oval shape, thus maintaining the dielectric under pressure at all times.

Choice of lead alloy sheath

The lead alloy sheath of a submarine cable has a very onerous duty imposed upon it compared with that of land cables. It will probably be subjected to strains and vibrations when the cable is laid and when in service and have to give an unknown fatigue performance due to the motion of the ship if the cable has to be recovered for repair. Tests have shown that lead alloys E (0.4% Sn and 0.2% Sb) and F3 (0.15% As, 0.1% Bi, 0.1% Sn) have adequate fatigue life for this duty.[3] Submarine cables have also given satisfactory service, however, when sheathed with other alloys, e.g. $\frac{1}{2}$B (0.45% Sb) and $\frac{1}{2}$C (0.2% Sn, 0.1% Cd).

Choice of armouring

Submarine cables need to be armoured to withstand the highest tensile loading likely to be encountered when laying and the residual tension left in the cable after laying (typically 1–3 tonnes) and to provide reasonable resistance to impact and abrasion damage from trailing ships' anchors or fishing gear. The armour must be resistant to corrosion as failure of individual wires in service may cause kinks to form followed by electrical failure of the cable. Galvanised mild or high tensile steel wires meet the mechanical and ánticorrosion requirements at lowest material cost but, as described earlier, the use of magnetic armour on single-core cables may cause an unacceptable reduction in the current rating of the cable.

Resistance to impact and abrasion damage may be improved by applying double wire armour. However, if, as is usual, submarine cables are coiled when transported, it is necessary to apply both layers with the same direction of lay. Additionally, the added protection may only be considered necessary over part of the cable route such as the shore ends. Both these factors raise manufacturing difficulties, e.g. in order to produce a cable with acceptable handling and bending performance it is necessary to 'let in' individual armours by welding them to adjacent wires over a distance of a few metres in the transition between single and double wire armour.

When the economics of steel wire armoured a.c. single-core cable schemes is unfavourable, the choice of armouring material is normally limited to non-magnetic stainless steel or aluminium alloys. Several grades of stainless steel have an ultimate tensile strength superior to that of mild magnetic steel, are highly resistant to corrosion and are readily welded, but all grades are relatively expensive.

All aluminium alloys have lower ultimate tensile strength than mild or stainless steel but are sometimes adequate for shallow submarine cable installations. Aluminium alloys cost substantially less than stainless steel but the resistance to corrosion is inferior to magnetic and stainless steel. Aluminium alloy M57S armour wires (complying with BS 1470, type NS4) were applied to the 420 kV a.c. submarine cables laid between Denmark and Sweden,[4] and there has not been any report of chemical corrosion on this circuit. However, there are published reports of chemical and electrolytic corrosion failure of the aluminium alloy armour wires on the cables laid between Connecticut and Long Island.[5]

Torque balance in cable construction

When a single wire armoured cable is suspended from the bow sheave of the laying vessel, a high proportion of the tensile load is carried by the helically applied armour wires. This loading produces a torque in the armour wires which, unless appropriate precautions are taken in the design of the cable, tends to cause the cable to twist so that the lay of the armour wires straightens towards the axis of the cable and thereby transfers strain to the core(s). The twisting action cannot pass backwards through the brakes of the cable laying gear to the cable yet to be laid, nor forward to the cable already laid on the sea bed. The twisting action therefore tends to concentrate in the suspended cable between the bow sheave and the sea bed. The problems become more severe with increasing immersed weight per unit length and increasing depth of laying. Fig. 45.4 shows a submarine cable which has developed a kink due to lack of torque balance.

The twisting action can be nullified by applying a second layer of armour wires which under tensile loading conditions produces an equal and opposite torque to that of the inner layer of wires. Alternatively, the twisting action can be reduced to acceptable levels by the application of metal anti-twist tapes below a single layer of armour wires to produce a counter torque, as shown in fig. 45.5. The requirements may be expressed mathematically.

The torque produced by the armour is

$$Tr_{\mathrm{a}} \sin \theta \text{ (kg m)}$$

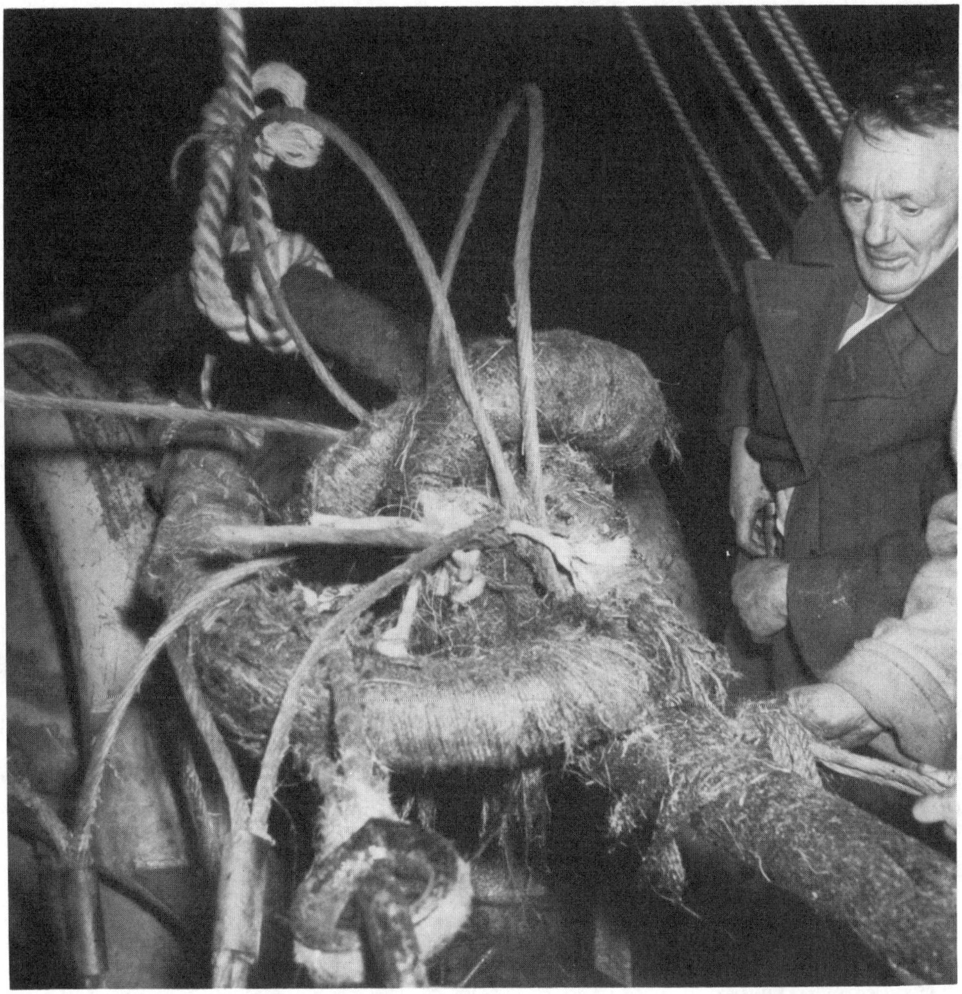

Fig. 45.4 Recovered sample of submarine cable containing kink due to lack of torque balance

and the torque produced by the anti-twist tapes is

$$Tr_{at} \sin \phi \text{ (kg m)}$$

where T = tension in cable (kg)
θ = angle of armour wires to cable axis
ϕ = angle of anti-twist tapes
r_a = pitch circle radius of armour wires (m)
r_{at} = pitch circle radius of anti-twist tapes (m)

The torque is balanced when

$$Tr_a \sin \theta = Tr_{at} \sin \phi$$

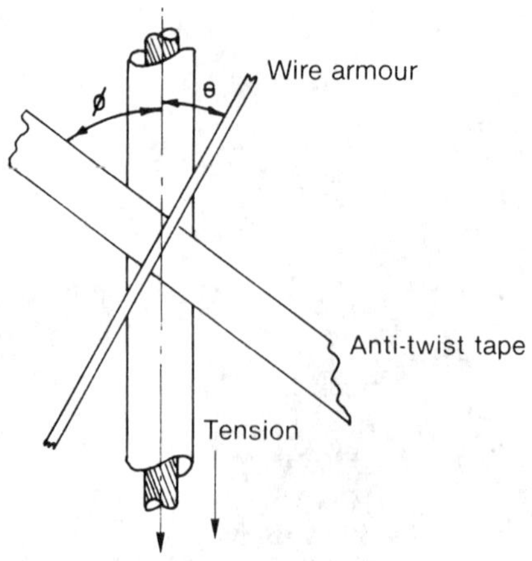

Fig. 45.5 Torque balance in single-core cable by using single wire armour and anti-twist tapes

i.e. when

$$r_a \sin \phi = r_{at} \sin \phi$$

Although it is difficult to achieve complete torque balance with a single layer of armour and anti-twist tapes, the solution is economically attractive as the anti-twist tapes make a significant contribution to reinforcing the cable against internal pressure and hydrostatic and other pressures to which the cable may be subjected when laying or in service.

Avoidance of cable movement on sea bed

Any cable which is subject to movement across the sea bed due to tidal currents is liable to premature failure due to abrasion damage. It is therefore important that the submerged weight of the cable is adequate to resist the maximum tidal sea-bed currents expected, even under storm conditions. The resistance to movement is proportional to the square root of the coefficient of friction of the cable with respect to the sea bed multiplied by the W/D ratio of the cable, where W is the submerged weight of the cable and D is the overall diameter. The coefficient of friction may be as low as 0.2 if the cable is laid across smooth rock but a value of 0.5 is typical of a cable laid on sand or shingle.

Although in many cases the cable may ultimately be silted over, so inhibiting cable movement, it would be unwise to rely on this occurring uniformly along the complete length of the cable. Therefore, standard practice when designing a submarine cable is to calculate the water velocity likely to cause movement. Should this velocity be less than the maximum expected tidal current at the sea bed, including the shore approaches where tidal currents may be the highest, it would be necessary to increase the weight of the cable. For lead sheathed cables an increase in the weight of the cable is achieved at minimum cost by increasing the thickness of the sheath. For non-metallic sheathed cables it may be necessary to apply lead tapes or to insert lead fillers in the cable to attain an adequate weight-to-diameter ratio.

Mechanical performance of submarine cables

All a.c. and d.c. submarine cables are required to comply with the requirements of the CIGRE 'Recommendations for mechanical tests on submarine cables.[2] This specification requires that the cable, including flexible joints, should be subjected to tension tests, bending under tension, external pressure withstand tests and, in the case of pressure-assisted cables, an internal pressure withstand test. If the cable is to be coiled, either during manufacture or for transporting to site, all the tests listed above are preceded by a coiling test. The cable is required to withstand a voltage test following the mechanical tests. The cable should be free of damage or untoward features when subjected to visual examination following the mechanical and electrical tests.

PROTECTION AGAINST CORROSION

The service life of a submarine cable will be dependent, *inter alia*, on the efficacy of the anticorrosion protection, as sea-water is an aggressive environment in which to operate. Should the metal sheath of a non-pressure-assisted cable suffer corrosion damage, water would enter the cable and a voltage failure would ultimately occur. In the case of internal pressure-assisted cables, i.e. gas- and oil-filled cables, a leak in the pressure-retaining sheath would cause the pressure alarms to operate. Small leaks can be tolerated for a short time by maintaining the gas or oil feed until it is convenient to undertake cable repairs. Corrosion or failure of the sheath reinforcing tapes would cause the sheath to burst. This would necessitate taking the cable out of service and undertaking emergency action to avoid water entering the cable.

Lead alloy sheaths are preferred to aluminium sheaths for submarine cables because of the vastly superior resistance of lead to corrosion when immersed in sea-water. If an aluminium sheath is used, any defect or damage to the anticorrosion sheath would be liable to cause rapid corrosion failure of the metal sheath.

Extruded polyethylene provides the most impermeable barrier to moisture ingress and is used practically universally for the anticorrosion sheath.

The provision of an anticorrosion sheath external to the armour wires of an a.c. submarine cable is generally unnecessary and technically undesirable. In all but the simplest cable installations it would be impossible to guarantee that any extruded thermoplastic or elastomeric oversheath would be undamaged during the cable laying operation, particularly if laying over rocks. Should the oversheath survive the laying operation without damage, it would still be subject to damage while in service from marine borers, sometimes by fish and invariably by shipping activity. If the oversheath were damaged, some of the current in the cable sheath/armour circuit would flow to the sea at the point of damage to the oversheath, causing electrolytic corrosion of the armour wires.

If the cable is served overall with textile tapes instead of an extruded oversheath, the armour wires are uniformly in contact with the sea-water along the complete cable route and the resultant distributed electrolytic action on the armour wires is very small. Some manufacturers recommend that each individual armour wire should be sheathed with a thermoplastic anticorrosion covering. Severe problems have sometimes been experienced when this solution was adopted on single-core a.c. cables because the corrosion by-products formed following corrosion of one damaged wire caused corrosion damage to adjacent but previously undamaged wires. The use of individually sheathed armour wires reduces the number of armour wires which can be applied to the cable, renders the cable subject to damage between adjacent wires and reduces the ultimate tensile strength of the cable.

Experience has shown that the zinc coating of galvanised steel armour wires may deteriorate after a few year's immersion, thus displaying small areas of non-protected steel. Slight corrosion pitting has been observed in such areas, but in a typical 138 kV a.c. single-core cable installation the diameter of individual armour wires merely decreased from 5.89 to 5.86 mm after 24 years service.[1] Although there is no longer term experience available for stainless steel armour wires, laboratory tests indicate that the corrosion resistance will be superior to that of galvanised steel armour wires. As previously stated there is contradictory evidence concerning the long-term corrosion resistance of aluminium alloy armour wire.

Making the assumptions that (a) it is impossible to guarantee throughout the service life of the cable the integrity of an anticorrosion sheath applied external to the armour wires, (b) it is imperative that the lead alloy sheath and any reinforcing tapes are protected from corrosion and (c) the correct choice of armouring material will ensure adequate resistance of the non-protected wires to corrosion, it follows that the anticorrosion sheath should be applied below the armour wires. It is therefore standard practice to apply the anticorrosion sheath directly above the lead alloy sheath and any pressure-reinforcing tapes. The anticorrosion sheath should be at least 0.5 mm thicker than would be applied to an equivalent land cable.

If anti-teredo protection is required, one or two layers of brass or copper tape are applied between the anticorrosion sheath and the armour wires.

Overall finishes

When laying a submarine cable it is necessary to brake the cable as it is paid out over the bow or stern skid in order to maintain control of the disposition of the cable on the sea bed (chapter 46). The amount of compression applied to the cable for braking purposes is dependent on the coefficient of friction between the finish of the cable and the braking gear. Apart from the disadvantages of a plastic oversheath on an a.c. cable, to which reference has been made, plastic materials have a low coefficient of friction which necessitates undesirably high pressure on the cable to attain the required braking effort, particularly for deep water installations. For these reasons a bitumen coated jute or polypropylene string serving is preferred, both of which have a high friction coefficient with respect to the braking gear. A string serving also has the advantage of being sufficiently elastic to permit an increase in the pitch circle diameter of the armour wires resultant on coiling the cable without adverse effect on the serving. If a plastic oversheath were applied and the bursting force of the armour wires or other mechanical incident caused rupture of the plastic oversheath, bird-caging of the armour wires would be expected at that position when coiling the cable.

SOLID TYPE PAPER INSULATED CABLES

Solid type paper insulated cables have been used for submarine installations up to 34.5 kV a.c. or 400 kV d.c. This type of cable has become established as the most economic and practical cable for use on very long high voltage d.c. transmission links. For these the use of oil-filled cable is restricted for hydraulic reasons.

Three-core cables

The 3-core HSL type of cable has certain technical advantages over the 3-core H type cable, particularly for deep water installations as the construction is inherently more resistant to external water pressure.

The conductors of 3-core HSL and H type cables are normally circular, of compacted construction, and are compound filled by the impregnating process to reduce the interstitial spaces to a minimum, thus restricting possible water penetration in the event of damage to the cable when in service. The paper insulation, conductor and core screens are applied in a similar manner to that of comparable land cables except that if the cable is to be coiled down, either during manufacture or for transport to site, it may be necessary to modify the paper lapping tensions to attain satisfactory coiling characteristics. In all cases the core is produced in the longest lengths attainable with the production facilities available. The cores of 3-core H type cables are laid up and padded circular to produce a hard circular cable. The 3 cores of H type mass-impregnated cables and the single cores for HSL mass-impregnated cables are dried and impregnated in conventional cable vessels. The impregnant is usually a viscous fluid compound or occasionally a non-draining compound. The individual impregnated cores for HSL cable, or laid-up cores for H type cable, are sheathed with a lead alloy and served with an anticorrosion sheath. Thc three served cores for HSL cables are laid up and padded circular with bitumen impregnated jute or polypropylene string fillers. If the cable is to be delivered to site in drum lengths for jointing at sea, the appropriate armouring and serving is applied and the cable is wound onto a despatch drum. If multiple lengths of non-armoured cable are to be jointed together, prior to armouring as a continuous length, the drum lengths of non-armoured cable are either coiled down or wound onto a turntable and flexible joints are inserted between adjacent drum lengths. After armouring and serving, the cable is coiled down or wound onto a turntable to await pre-despatch tests and transfer to the laying vessel.

Single-core cables

The conductors of single-core cables are circular and of high occupancy. No duct is required in the centre of a conductor of a solid cable and high occupancy may be achieved by stranding layers of segments around a central circular rod. An occupancy of 96% is claimed for the ± 270 kV d.c. cross channel interconnection.[6] High occupancy in the conductor has the advantage of presenting excellent resistance to water penetration in the event of cable damage especially when used in conjunction with a viscous impregnating compound. Although the construction of the single-core solid cable is intrinsically very resistant to external pressure, where the cable is required to operate in very deep water it may be necessary to control the sheath movement due to load cycles. One method which has been used to provide increased control of sheath deformation under these conditions is to manufacture the cable using an oval conductor, although oval shaped cables are difficult to manufacture and to control when laying.

The design of the insulation and screens is similar to that of the cores of the 3-core cables previously described. It is possible to manufacture much longer lengths of single-core cable without joints than 3-core cable, the restriction on the length of 3-core cables being the capacity of the core drums on the laying-up machine. Some cable manufacturers have special drying and impregnating vessels capable of processing 40 or 50 km lengths of single-core cable. This process requires the core to be wound onto a turntable within the drying vessel as it leaves the insulating machine, thereby avoiding the restrictions on maximum drum lengths resultant on the use of drums. Flexible joints may be inserted between lengths of core usually at the lead or anticorrosion sheath stage in order to create even longer lengths. This type of joint may be used without any reduction in cable electrical or mechanical strength which makes the maximum length attainable limited only by the size of the storage space or the capacity of the laying vessel.

The lead sheathing, anticorrosion sheathing, armouring and serving processes differ little from standard production techniques for land cable. However, the lead sheathing and plastic sheathing of very long cable lengths necessitate continuous processes, often lasting several days, and require the highest standards of extruder performance to achieve satisfactory product quality.

Water penetration through damaged sheath

If the lead sheath of a single-core or 3-core HSL paper insulated solid type submarine cable is damaged, or the cable is severed, the sea-water causes the paper insulation to swell rapidly, so forming a partial blockage to further water ingress. Further cable beyond the blockage will be affected by moisture, however, owing to the vacuous conditions in the cooling cable and by wick action in the insulating papers. Because of its high occupancy, the conductor has excellent resistance to water penetration.

The interstitial fillers in 3-core H type cable form a low resistance path for water to enter the cable following damage to the sheath. It may be necessary to replace a substantial amount of cable to eliminate moisture should this type of cable be damaged after laying.

OIL-FILLED CABLES

Oil-filled paper insulated cables are suitable for use up to the highest voltages and they were the type of cable chosen for the 525 kV link between British Columbia mainland and Vancouver Island installed in 1984. Oil-filled cables have the advantage of requiring the smallest insulation thickness for a given voltage so that it is possible in some cases to use a 3-core cable where three single-core cables would otherwise have been necessary. This presents advantages from a manufacturing and installation point of view as well as making the installation less prone to damage when in service.

Hydraulic design

It is an essential feature of any oil-filled submarine cable installation that, if the pressure-retaining sheath is damaged, the internal oil pressure under leak conditions should exceed the external water pressure at that position, so that water does not enter the cable. The worst possible condition would be for the cable to be severed near one terminal during a period when the cable was carrying full load current, as the rate of cooling would then be at a maximum. Whereas under normal operating conditions the oil reservoirs at each end of the route effectively feed oil to the mid-point of the route, if the cable is severed near one terminal the seaward length of cable would be dependent on the oil reservoir at the remote end of the route. This reservoir would be required to feed oil at a sufficient rate to compensate for the thermal contraction of the oil within the complete cable length and also to maintain a positive pressure with respect to the external water pressure where the cable was severed. The oil feed length would therefore be nearly twice the normal length and the pressure drop nearly four times that which would occur if the cable was severed at the mid-point. It is therefore necessary to incorporate within the cable oil channels having sufficiently low hydraulic impedance that a positive oil pressure can be maintained under oil leak conditions, without the need to operate the cable at an excessive internal pressure.

The calculation of the hydraulic parameters of the cable system is similar to that detailed in chapter 31 for oil-filled cables installed on land, but for submarine cable installations it may be necessary to calculate many alternative solutions to obtain the optimum size of the oil duct(s) and the feed pressure of the oil pumps. There are practical limits to the size of the oil channels which can be incorporated in a cable and this limits the maximum length of route over which an oil-filled cable can be operated to about 35–40 km. On long cable routes and in deep water installations oil-filled cables are required to operate at higher internal pressure than a conventional land cable and it is therefore necessary to apply additional reinforcing tapes to enable the lead alloy sheath to withstand the internal oil pressure.

Further details regarding calculation of oil pressure transients may be obtained by reference to the CIGRE report 'Transient pressure variations in submarine cables of the self contained oil filled type'.[7] This document also explains how to allow for pressure transients encountered during the laying operation.

Fig. 45.6 shows the internal oil pressures in a typical 1000 mm^2 275 kV single-core cable operating to a maximum conductor temperature of 80 °C on a cable route having a maximum depth of 90 m. The cable concerned has an oil duct of 23 mm bore. The graph shows the variation in maximum oil pressure along the cable route when the cable is heating, the minimum pressure when cooling and the transient pressures if the cable is severed near one end of the route following a period of full current loading. It will be noted that, in order to maintain an internal oil pressure of 1 bar at the severed end of the cable, it is necessary to operate the oil pumps at 11 bar, the pressure drop along the complete route from the remote oil pump being approximately 10 bar. The graph also shows that the cable would need to be reinforced to withstand an internal oil pressure of 30 bar.

It is sometimes necessary to restrict the temperature rise of oil-filled submarine cables to reduce the oil pressure transients to acceptable levels. This necessitates the use of larger conductors than would otherwise be justified by the current loading requirement.

3-core cables

3-core oil-filled submarine cables can be manufactured for voltages up to 150 kV a.c.

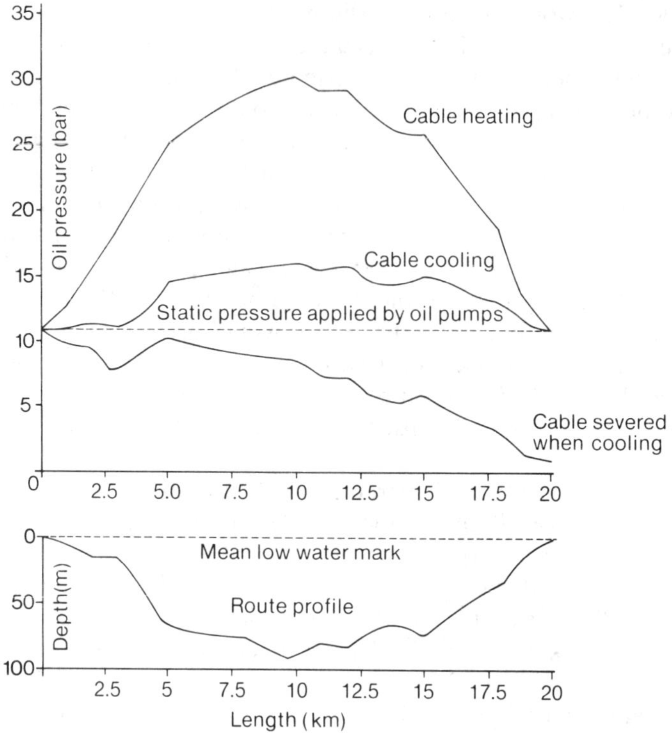

Fig. 45.6 Variation in oil pressure in 1000 mm^2 275 kV oil-filled single-core cable under operational and fault conditions

subject to certain restrictions on the maximum cross-sectional area of the conductors. As with all types of 3-core cable the capacity of the laying-up machine limits the maximum length which can be manufactured without the need to insert flexible joints in at least the conductors and insulation. In some cases the manufacturer has the option of inserting flexible joints in the laid-up cores before the lead sheathing process, but in most cases the drum lengths of cable are jointed together in the lead sheathed stage, all subsequent processes being carried out on the continuous length. Alternatively, large drum lengths of completed cable may have flexible joints inserted between drum lengths before they are installed.

Flexible joints are technically acceptable in oil-filled cables. Comprehensive laboratory testing by several cable manufacturers has shown that the electrical characteristics of a well designed flexible joint can be as good as the machine-made cable and the mechanical performance completely adequate. Flexible joints have additionally given satisfactory service in single and 3-core 132 kV a.c. oil-filled cables for many years.

The design and construction of the conductors, insulation and screens is similar to that for land cables except that the angle of lay and application tension of the paper tapes may need to be modified if the cable is to be coiled down either during manufacture or on the laying vessel. When laying-up the cores, oil ducts are usually included in the interstitial spaces between the cores. The maximum bore of the ducts which can be accommodated within the spaces available may impose a restriction on the length of route over which a 3-core cable can be laid.

The laid-up cable is generally sheathed with a lead alloy and reinforced against the internal oil pressure by two or more layers of metal tape. Tin-bronze, non-magnetic steel and aluminium alloy tapes have been used for reinforcement. As the transient oil pressure in submarine cables is often much greater than is normally permitted in land cables, the total thickness of reinforcement is correspondingly increased. The finished cable is either coiled down or wound onto a drum or turntable for pre-despatch testing prior to loading onto the cable laying vessel.

Oil feed tanks are connected to the cable ends immediately after sheathing and a positive oil flow is maintained from the cable ends on every occasion that the cable is cut, so that no air or moisture can enter the cable. The oil tanks remain connected to the cable throughout all subsequent manufacturing and laying operations.

Single-core cables

Single-core oil-filled cables are not subject to the same restrictions on maximum unjointed manufacturing lengths as 3-core cables are, because the maximum lengths attainable are only dependent on the size of the impregnating and drying vessels available. Some cable manufacturers are equipped with very large vessels capable of drying and impregnating 40–50 km lengths of core.

Single-core cables are required to have a central oil duct in the conductor and the maximum length which can be installed is limited by the impedance to oil flow which this duct presents. Significant improvements can be made by increasing the bore of the duct as its impedance varies with the fourth power of the radius. This improvement has to be balanced against the impact of having to increase the diameter of the cable. Additionally it may be possible to employ a low viscosity impregnant. The single-core conductor may be stranded around a helically wound steel duct or alternatively be formed of interlocking segments which form a self-supporting oil channel with shaped wires stranded over it. If the cable is to be coiled at any stage during manufacture or installation, special attention needs to be given to the length and direction of wire lays to achieve satisfactory coiling characteristics.

All manufacturing processes are carried out on conventional plant, apart from the use of turntables or coiling down processes if the length of cable required exceeds the capacity of the largest drums which can be handled. If flexible joints are to be made prior to despatch, these are normally inserted after lead sheathing or after any subsequent process, as convenient. Oil pressure tanks are connected to the cable after lead sheathing and at all subsequent stages of manufacture.

The sheath reinforcing tapes are non-ferrous for a.c. cables but steel tapes offer the cheapest reinforcement for d.c. cables. The anticorrosion sheath, armour and servings generally comply with the details previously quoted.

Oil pressure supply systems

For short length oil-filled submarine cable installations, conventional oil pressure tanks and appropriate alarm equipment, as used for land cables, are often adequate for maintaining the oil pressure within the cable. On longer cable routes it is often necessary to provide pumping plant and oil storage tanks at both ends of the route because of the much larger oil flow under pressure transient conditions. The pumps are normally duplicated and alarm circuits are provided to signal any malfunction of the pumping equipment. As these pumps are usually energised from the public electricity supply it may be necessary to install auxiliary power generators to ensure the security of the oil-filled cables in the event of a failure of the electricity supply.

Facilities are generally provided to restrict the rate of oil flow to maintain the minimum acceptable oil leak to the sea should the lead sheath of the cable be damaged.

Prevention of water penetration through damaged sheath

If the lead sheath of an oil-filled cable is perforated when in service, the internal pressure causes oil to leak to the sea and water does not enter the cable. The oil tanks or pumps at the cable terminals replace the oil lost and operate alarms to indicate an abnormal rate of oil flow. In the event of a major oil leak the standard procedure is then for the cable to be taken out of service and a restrictor actuated in the hydraulic circuit to limit the oil feed to the minimum necessary to ensure a positive oil leak to the sea at all states of the tide. Ideally, the oil leak should be located at an early stage, the cable cut and lifted and the ends checked for moisture and cut back if necessary. End caps would be fitted and the capped ends lowered to the sea bed with marker buoys attached. Experience has shown that after removing the lengths of cable damaged during the lifting operation the remaining cable is generally free of moisture and suitable for jointing to the new piece of cable required to link the cut ends.

GAS-FILLED CABLE

Cable of the pre-impregnated paper gas-filled type has many advantages from a manufacturing and system design point of view. As manufacture of this type of cable requires no large tank in which to impregnate the core, the possible length of joint-free cable is entirely dependent on the capacity of the laying-up machine or, for single-core cables, the amount of storage space available. The general construction of the conductor, screens and insulation follows solid cable practice except that for the longest length of single-core cable a gas duct is required in the centre of the conductor.

The metal sheath is of lead alloy which is heavily reinforced with steel tapes followed by a conventional anticorrosion sheath, beddings, armour and serving.

The static pressure in the gas-filled cable system is maintained higher than the external water pressure to prevent ingress of moisture should the cable be damaged. The minimum design operating pressure is 14 bar but in one installation the pressure had to be raised to 28 bar to fulfil this condition.[8] This places an onerous duty on the cable reinforcement and the accessories. Once the cable is charged with gas there is no longitudinal gas flow within the cable which means that there is not the pressure restriction on cable length inherent in oil-filled systems, but gas feed and alarm equipment is still required at the cable ends.

Factory flexible joints have been installed into gas-filled cables and have given satisfactory service for many years.

Although the gas-filled submarine cable system has seemingly several advantages, no new systems have been installed since the 1960s. Nevertheless one major transmission link operating at ±250 kV d.c. is still in operation and can boast an availability of over 90% for 15 years of its life.[8] The gas-filled cable system has been gradually phased out for land cable systems as other types of cable are usually more economic and this has ultimately led to utilities looking to other designs of cable for new submarine cable systems.

POLYMERIC INSULATED CABLES

Design limitations

Polymeric insulated submarine cables (usually XLPE) are in increasing demand for use in offshore oil fields and inter-island links. Considerable experience in land cable installations in many parts of the world has indicated that the service life of polymeric cables may be limited unless steps are taken to prevent moisture ingress into the insulation. It is therefore necessary to provide an impermeable moisture barrier over the insulation, and for submarine installations this is best achieved by the application of a lead alloy sheath.

The immersed weight-to-diameter ratio of non-sheathed polymeric submarine cables is generally low and the cable is therefore liable to movement over the sea bed when subjected to even modest tidal currents. The application of a lead sheath of appropriate thickness inhibits cable movement, apart from ensuring that the core insulation is maintained in a dry condition.

Submarine cables insulated with EPR require no metal sheath and are installed as a 'wet' construction. Provided that special formulations are used, this type of cable is suitable for use up to 33 kV. Owing to the increased insulation thickness required for polymeric designs over paper insulated cables, the highest voltage for which a practical 3-core cable can be manufactured is 34.5 kV. Some 3-core designs incorporate optical fibres or other communication cables in the interstices.

Many cable manufacturers have the capability to manufacture long continuous lengths of polymeric insulated core although the increased insulation thickness over paper insulated cables will make the core size much greater than for a comparable paper design. For example, the insulation thickness at 132 kV is about twice that of the equivalent oil-filled cable. Laboratory proved techniques are available for the construction of flexible joints in the insulation although there is limited operating experience of these joints.

Cable design and manufacture

The thickness of the screens and insulation applied to polymeric cables up to 30 kV rating should not be less than the appropriate value quoted in IEC 502, although, as with all submarine cables, a slight increase in the insulation thickness may be justified to enhance the factor of safety. The thickness of insulation for cables above 30 kV is subject to agreement between the customer and the cable manufacturer, there being as yet no internationally agreed standard for the insulation thicknesses for the higher transmission voltages.

The economics of the insulating procedure for polymeric cores favour the production of the longest continuous core lengths which can be accommodated on a turntable or core drum. As with all types of 3-core cable the capacity of the laying-up machine limits the maximum length of cable which can be manufactured without inserting flexible joints.

When a lead sheath is applied over a single- or 3-core cable the external protection normally comprises a polyethylene anticorrosion sheath, armour bedding, one or two layers of armour wires and a bituminised textile serving overall.

Effects of damage to lead sheath

Polymeric materials have a relatively high coefficient of expansion which may cause a permanent distension of the lead sheath after an XLPE or PE insulated cable has been on load. Should the lead sheath be damaged after it has been distended, water would enter the annulus between the core(s) and the inside of the lead sheath. The penetration can be minimised by the use of water-swellable tapes over the cable insulation. If the damage is sufficiently severe to reach the conductor, then water penetration can be inhibited by filling the conductor with compound. It is important that a lead sheathed polymeric insulated cable should be cut back far enough to eliminate all traces of moisture before a repair joint is inserted. The length of cable to be scrapped may be much longer than would be necessary for a paper insulated cable.

PILOT, CONTROL AND COMPOSITE CABLES

There is a demand in offshore oil and gas fields for submarine pilot, control and composite cables which are laid between platforms or between a platform and a sea-bed unit for the remote control and monitoring of equipment. In each case the cable needs to be designed for the specific project, the number and type of cores varying considerably. Generally there are requirements for some pilot cores, speech circuits or TV cores together sometimes with optical fibres, power cores and hydraulic hoses within the same cable envelope. The cable needs to be designed and manufactured to have a high factor of safety, as the failure of a control cable may necessitate closing down an oil well with the consequent loss of production until the cable is repaired or replaced.

Thermoplastic polyethylene (PE) or sometimes crosslinked polyethylene (XLPE) is favoured for the insulation of speech circuits, PE for TV cores and either PE, XLPE or EPR for pilot and power cores. Flexible hydraulic hoses normally comprise a polyester elastomer inner core which is reinforced with aramid fibre and sheathed with a polyester elastomer jacket.

The individual cable pairs, cores and hoses are laid up with a relatively short lay to reduce the risk that these components are subjected to a significant strain when the cable is under tension. The optical fibre is generally laid up near the centre of the assembly to give maximum protection against damage. Fillers are normally laid up with the cable components to achieve a compact circular shaped cable. Providing there is no severe restriction on the mutual capacitance of the speech pairs it is considered advantageous to inject a thixotropic compound into the remaining interstices of the laid-up cable to restrict water penetration in the event of sheath damage after installation. In most cases a polyethylene sheath is applied over the laid-up cores followed by the appropriate armour and serving, the finish being generally similar to that applied to lead sheathed submarine power cables.

If the cable is required to hang in a catenary from a platform to the sea bed, it is essential that the cable be torque balanced. In these circumstances it is sometimes advantageous to lay up the cable around a central tensile member and to dispense with the external armour wires. If the cable is to be laid on the sea bed it may be necessary to apply a lead sheath to attain an adequate weight to diameter ratio to inhibit movement on the sea bed under the influence of tidal currents. Alternatively, in order to avoid the need for a lead sheath, it may be possible to bury the cable using a 'remote operated vehicle'. Such vehicles are usually equipped with sonar or TV systems and bury the cable using a plough technique.

FLEXIBLE JOINTS FOR CABLES

Techniques have been developed for constructing flexible joints in all types of cable commonly used in submarine cable installations. Most existing major submarine cable circuits contain one or more flexible joints. These joints have generally given trouble-free service. Individual cable manufacturers have developed different techniques for constructing flexible joints but all are expected to meet the mechanical test requirements recommended by CIGRE Committee 21-06.[2] Fig. 45.7 shows a typical design of flexible joint in a solid type submarine cable.

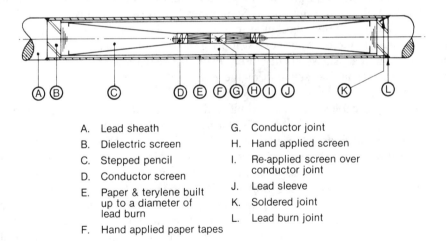

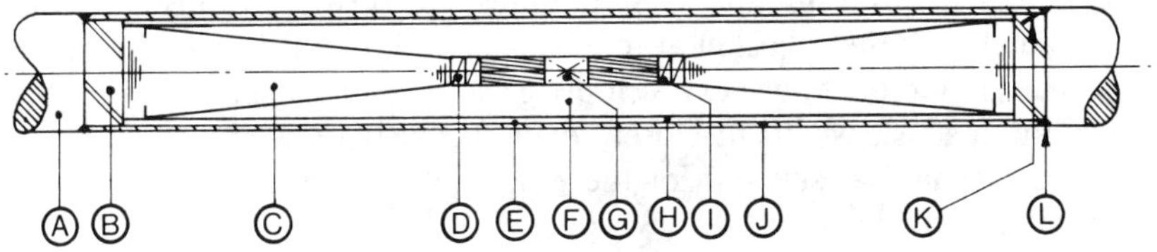

A. Lead sheath
B. Dielectric screen
C. Stepped pencil
D. Conductor screen
E. Paper & terylene built up to a diameter of lead burn
F. Hand applied paper tapes
G. Conductor joint
H. Hand applied screen
I. Re-applied screen over conductor joint
J. Lead sleeve
K. Soldered joint
L. Lead burn joint

Fig. 45.7 Construction of flexible joint in single-core solid type submarine cable up to the lead sheath stage

Conductors

Submarine cables are generally laid with a certain amount of tension in the system. This is either unavoidable because of the length of cable suspended underneath the laying ship or is deliberate in order to prevent kinking. The tensile strength of the conductor connection is therefore of paramount importance. Two alternative methods are used for the jointing of conductors. The individual wires of the conductor may be butt-brazed in a staggered configuration so that the conductor retains its original diameter and flexibility. Alternatively, the multiwire conductor may be butt-brazed to form a solid joint which complies with the original diameter but restricts the flexibility of the conductor over a short distance.

Paper insulation and semiconductive paper screens

In all types of paper insulated cable the conductor screen and insulation are profiled on both sides of the joint in the conductor, the length of profile being designed to ensure a controlled electrical stress along the profile when the cable is energised. The insulation is then reconstituted over the jointed conductor, pre-impregnated paper tapes being applied by hand or machine under very carefully controlled conditions often in a humidity-controlled atmosphere. Each paper tape is accurately terminated on the steps of the profiles of the two cables being jointed. The re-application by hand can be a fairly lengthy process and it is possible to design a joint with shorter profiles which are quicker to re-insulate but it is then necessary to restrict the number of bends to which the joints will be subjected. This extra speed in completing a joint may be very useful indeed where a cable is being repaired at sea and the weather forecast has turned unfavourable!

The outside diameter of the joint is determined by service performance and electrical test requirements applicable to the system. The use of a flush brazed conductor connection and graded paper tape insulation enables the diameter of the dielectric to be kept to a minimum. Sometimes it is possible to insulate the joint to the same diameter as the adjacent core but usually the joint is insulated to a greater diameter. This diameter, however, is rarely greater than the lead sheath of the cable and allows the lead sleeve to fit closely over the insulation and cable sheath. This enhances the mechanical strength of the joint and is convenient for the process of sealing the sleeve to the sheath.

For solid type cables it is usual to baste the reconstituted insulation with impregnating compound at regular intervals during the insulating process. When making flexible joints in oil-filled cables two alternative techniques are available for preventing air or moisture from entering the cable during the jointing operation. The joint may be made under a continuous flow of oil fed from pressure tanks located at the remote ends of the cables being jointed, or the cable may be frozen on either side of the joint and the papers applied without an oil feed. In both cases the joint is required to be impregnated with oil after the re-insulation process. This is achieved either via special oil fittings in the lead sleeve which will need to be sealed afterwards or by impregnating using a temporary sleeve and then swaging down a lead sleeve over the insulation with continuous oil flow.

Polymeric insulation

The insulation of PE, XLPE and EPR cores is pencilled down to a smooth controlled profile often using special tools. The cable core is then reconstituted with special insulating and screening tapes which can also be applied with specially designed machines. Application by machine ensures even tension and correct geometric shape. The insulation is applied over the pencilled cable and is then profiled up to a greater diameter than the cable. Temporary binder tapes are applied to the reconstituted

Table 45.1 Some typical submarine cable installations

Year cables installed	Site	Type of cable	Maximum depth (m)	Longest cable length (km)
1956	British Columbia mainland to Vancouver Island	138 kV a.c. gas filled	183	25.3
1965	England–France cross channel link (abandoned 1983)	±100 kV d.c. solid type	58	24
1965	Sardinia–Corsica (Italy)	±200 kV d.c. solid type	450	104
1965	Cook Strait (New Zealand)	±250 kV d.c. gas filled	245	40
1969	British Columbia mainland to Vancouver Island	±300 kV d.c. solid type	170	26
1973	Denmark–Sweden	420 kV a.c. oil filled	37	7.3
1976	British Columbia mainland to Vancouver Island	±300 kV d.c. oil filled	170	36
1976–7	Denmark–Norway (Skaggerak)	±250 kV d.c. solid type	550	127
1977	Margareta Island to mainland Venezuela	115 kV a.c. oil filled	30	25
1978	Tsugaru Strait (Japan)	±250 kV d.c. oil filled	300	45
1981	Lamma (Hong Kong)	275 kV a.c. oil filled	45	3.2
1983	Sweden–Gotland	150 kV d.c. solid type	160	90
1984	British Columbia to Vancouver Island	525 kV a.c. oil filled	400	30
1985	England–France cross channel link	±270 kV d.c. solid type	60	45
1985	Jersey–France	90 kV a.c. 3-core OF	25	27.5
1985	Morcote–Brusino, Switzerland	150 kV a.c. XLPE in PE conduit	68	2.3
1986	Lamma (Hong Kong), phase 2	275 kV a.c. oil filled	45	2
1986	Pulau Langkawi	132 kV a.c. oil filled	20	26
In Progress	Sweden–Finland	±400 kV d.c. solid type	117	200
Planned	Hawaii–Maui Alenuihaha Channel	±300 kV d.c. oil filled	2000	61

joint to compress the hand applied tapes while the joint is pressurised and heated under carefully controlled conditions to bond the PE tapes and to vulcanise the insulation in the case of XLPE or EPR cores.

An alternative procedure is to use a proprietary injection moulding machine for all types of core.

Lead sheaths

Prior to the start of jointing lead sheathed cables, a lead sleeve is passed over the lead sheath of one of the cable lengths being jointed. After completing the application of the core insulation and screens, the lead sheath is positioned over the core joint and progressively swaged down until it is a close fit over the insulated core. If the diameter of the reconstituted core insulation is equal to that of the original core, the lead sleeve is swaged down and cut to length to permit butt joints to be made to the cut ends of the lead sheath of the cables being jointed. However, if excess insulation has been applied over the joint, the lead sleeve is swaged down to be a close fit over the original lead sheath.

A fusion technique known as lead burning is the conventional method of sealing the lead sleeve to the cable sheath and lead burns have given excellent service over many years. The technique requires highly skilled operators and is very time consuming. More modern methods based on a TIG welding technique are under development.

Other components

Metal tapes such as reinforcing tapes or anti-teredo tapes are jointed by brazing or welding. Polymeric anticorrosion sheaths are reconstituted using polyolefin heat-shrinkable sleeves passed over one of the cable cores prior to jointing.

Armour wires in joints between drum lengths of completed cable or in repair joints may be jointed by welding or by the use of threaded turnbuckles. Both these methods give more than adequate mechanical strength. For factory-made joints it is sometimes possible to pass the joint through the armouring machine and armour the cable and joint as one continuous process. This solution is adopted where continuous lengths of cable are specifically required but it may impose an onerous condition on the flexible joint if it is to be wound onto a drum before being armoured.

TYPICAL INSTALLATIONS

Table 45.1 gives details of some representative installations. Further information may be obtained from the Bibliography in appendix A18.

REFERENCES

(1) Buseman, F. (1963) 'The magnetic compass errors caused by d.c. single-core sea cables'. ERA Report No. B/T 116.

(2) CIGRE Study Committee 21, Working Group 06 (Jan. 1980) 'Recommendations for mechanical tests on submarine cables'. *Electra* (68), 31–36.

(3) Anelli, P., Donazzi, F. and Lawson, W. C. (Jan. 1988) 'The fatigue life of alloy E as a sheathing material for submarine power cables'. *IEEE Trans.* **PD-3** (1).
(4) Gazzana Prioroggia, P. and Maschio, G. (Sep–Oct. 1973) 'Continuous long length a.c. and d.c. submarine h.v. power cables'. *IEEE Trans.* **PAS-92** (5), 1744–1749.
(5) Chamberland, D. M., Margolin, S. and Shelley, M. (Apr. 1979), 'The Long Island Sound submarine cable interconnection'. *7th IEEE Transmission and Distribution Conf.*
(6) Arkell, C. A., Ball, E. H., Hacke, K. J. H., Waterhouse, N. H. and Yates, J. B. (1986) 'Design and installation of the U.K. part of the 270 kV d.c. cable connection between England and France, including reliability aspects'. Paris: CIGRE Paper No. 21–02.
(7) CIGRE Study Committee 21, working Group 02 (1983) 'Transient pressure variations in submarine cables of the oil-filled type'. *Electra* (89), 23–29.
(8) Crabtree, I. M. and O'Brian, M. T. (1986) 'Performance of the Cook Strait ±250 kV d.c. submarine cables, 1964–1985'. Paris: CIGRE Paper No. 21–01.

Chapter 46
Submarine Cable Installation

A submarine power cable project includes a series of stages:

(a) feasibility study
(b) survey
(c) cable laying vessel selection
(d) cable handling equipment design or selection
(e) shore end site work
(f) provision of moorings
(g) cable laying
(h) terminating the cable
(i) testing
(j) maintenance
(k) repair

Although all the above are not necessarily carried out by the same organisation, this is very frequently the case. In any case, it is essential that there should be close co-operation between the cable supplier, the survey team and the installation organisation so that the work can be carried out in the most effective and efficient way. Although it is often thought that difficulties in defining responsibility are likely to arise if separate organisations are employed for the cable supply and for the installation work, this is not borne out in practice. The best installation results from a combination of the most experienced cable manufacturer and the most competent installation organisation working in close liaison or as a joint venture.

FEASIBILITY STUDY

The initial stages of the investigation into the feasibility of a submarine power cable interconnection will normally rely on published survey data given in such publications as UK Admiralty Charts and Pilots and other similar sources of information.

In order to estimate the cost of the installation work it is necessary to work with provisional cable designs which specify the cable diameter, weight per unit length and the number of cables required. Taking into account alternative operating voltages, conductor sizes, cable construction, types of insulation and possible route variations, this may give rise to a large number of combinations which have to be evaluated in terms of shipping and cable handling requirements.

The feasibility study should result in a positive proposal which defines the type of system to be installed and indicates the preferred location of the interconnection. The precise route of the cables is then determined from the data collected by a full survey of the area.

SURVEY

A preliminary site survey may be included in the feasibility study or as the first stage of the full survey. The objectives are to obtain information concerning local conditions and to confirm the choice of areas to be surveyed in detail. The following features will be investigated:

(a) possible landing points for cables
(b) local support facilities
(c) possible practical cable routes
(d) hazards in the vicinity
(e) land access to landing points and identity of landowners who may be involved
(f) selection of station sites for the navigation system to be used for the survey and for the installation

The extent of the full survey will depend upon the band width required to accommodate the cables at a separation adequate to enable one cable to be repaired without a risk of damage to adjacent cables of the interconnection. If the cables are to be buried in the sea bed to protect them from fishing activities, it is essential to include a sub-bottom investigation using seismic methods and core sampling at enough locations to enable the seismic recordings to be interpreted correctly.

A close-up visual survey may also be required to identify the minor sea-bed features which would be indistinguishable by other means but would influencc the design of the trench cutting and cable burying machinery. The physical and mechanical properties of the sea-bed material can become the most significant features in the determination of the best route for a buried cable system.

If the cable is to be laid on the sea bed, the survey will be planned to obtain data principally concerned with the water currents and the surface of the sea bed in the area. In particular, it is essential to obtain accurate bathymetric data and to identify areas of exposed rock, wrecks and other hazards so that either the cable route can be planned to avoid the hazards or alternatively the sections of cable requiring armour to resist these conditions can be specified.

A substantial amount of the basic data required can be obtained from official sources, and the Hydrographic Department of the country concerned can usually provide assistance with more detailed information concerning the area than that shown on published charts. Available information may include adequate figures concerning tidal conditions, weather statistics and water temperature so that only a limited number of current and tidal measurements are needed to verify that the data apply to the precise location of the selected route. It is normal for power cables to link island to island or islands to a mainland by as short a route as is practical and consequently the crossing of a narrow channel can also involve working in an area of relatively high tidal currents, which could cause movement of the cable with consequential damage, and so it is essential to know the maximum velocity close to the sea bed.

When the prospective routes have been selected it is necessary to prepare profiles, and if possible it is advantageous to make a recording of an echo sounding run along each of the specific routes to confirm the correct interpretation of the survey data obtained. A survey of the landing points, to determine the conditions and distance between the underwater section of the route and the actual cable terminal on land, completes the overall picture required.

From the full survey data it is possible to determine the exact length of each route and other features which enable an accurate estimate of the cable requirements to be made, which will include allowances for contouring and navigational deviations etc. The method of cable installation can also be determined together with the requirements for the cable laying vessel and other equipment needed to carry out the installation. It is preferable to aim at the installation of single continuous lengths of cable to reach from shore to shore without joints, but it may be necessary to allow the inclusion of flexible reconstitutions in long route lengths.

CABLE LAYING VESSEL AND CABLE HANDLING EQUIPMENT

As submarine cable laying projects vary from small river crossings to major international system interconnections, the cable laying vessel has to be selected to suit the particular circumstance of each individual contract. In general the cable laying and repair vessels designed for handling telecommunication cables are only suited to the installation of power cables on comparatively rare occasions. This is because their cable handling machinery is normally designed with smaller bending radii than are required for high voltage cables and their high operating costs make them uneconomic for lower voltage installations, which generally tend to be of short route length. The vessel is selected such that it is as small as is compatible with all the requirements for the installation work. The principal features to be considered are as follows:

(a) suitable hold dimensions for the storage of cable coils, drums or a turntable
(b) suitability of the deck layout for fitting cable handling equipment
(c) overall dimensions including minimum operating draught
(d) adequate manoeuvrability
(e) navigational and communications equipment and facilities for fitting additional items as necessary
(f) power supplies available for additional equipment
(g) accommodation and messing facilities and space for fitting temporary additions if necessary
(h) age and general condition of the vessel such that specially constructed items may be of use for future operations
(i) charter terms and conditions

The manoeuvrability of the vessel at relatively low speeds is of considerable importance since this may determine the accuracy with which the cable can be laid on the selected route. The fitting of a bow propeller can assist when leaving or entering moorings but a full dynamic positioning (DP) system enables the vessel to be controlled at very low speeds and, if necessary, to remain stationary without the use of moorings. The use of DP to avoid the use of mooring anchors is virtually essential for a vessel employed in installing cables between offshore platforms.

Cable can be laid over the stern or over the bow of the vessel and the selection of the direction of pay-out depends upon the proposed method of handling the shore ends of the cable as well as upon the navigational problems of the main crossing.

Although opinions differ about the best arrangement, cable repair work is almost invariably carried out over the bow of the vessel. Naturally, the deck layout of the vessel selected for an operation needs to be compatible with the planned scope of the work, which may include the capability for repairing any accidental damage which may occur during installation. Fig. 46.1 shows the arrangement of the MV *Photinia* as adapted for the installation of the Cook Strait cables in 1964.

The cable handling equipment includes all the items necessary for the transfer of cable from its stowage in the vessel to its planned position on the sea bed. The main items included in this are the cable storage facility, tension control equipment, tension measuring instrumentation and bow or stern gear.

Single wire armoured cables can be coiled down into the hold or onto the deck of the vessel and very long lengths of cable can be stowed in this way with the minimum amount of equipment. Although coiling may require a relatively large labour force to stow the cable, this can be minimised by the use of a suitable rotating mechanical arm which guides the cable into position. Coiled cable may be laid at any speed up to about 8 knots although it is usual to lay at an average of not more than about 3 knots.

Cables with double wire armouring, where the two layers of wire have the same direction of lay, may be coiled in the same way as single wire armoured cables. If the two layers of wires have the opposite hand lay then the cable cannot be coiled and it is necessary to use either a turntable or a drum onto which the cable can be wound. The former is usually preferred for handling long lengths. The use of either arrangement, however, involves the requirement for a system to control the rotation of the mass of the stored cable plus that of the turntable or drum which must be braked or accelerated to match the laying speed. Nevertheless, for short cable lengths the use of a drum, on which cable has been supplied from the factory, reduces the transport and loading costs and only requires the provision of secure drum stands and a braking system to enable cable to be paid out under control at modest speeds.

The cable tension must be changed from the low value at which it leaves the storage system to the laying tension which supports the cable suspended between the vessel and the sea bed. This must be done by a braking system which subjects the insulation of the cable to negligible damage from creasing, crushing or other disturbance. To achieve this, the radius of bends round which the cable passes must be as large as practical consistent with the size and weight of plant which can be accommodated on the vessel.

The energy to be dissipated in the braking system is a function of cable laying tension and cable speed, and so when a heavy cable is being laid in deep water it is essential to provide adequate cooling for both normal and emergency braking systems. If the energy to be dissipated is not too great it is possible to use simple friction brakes which act directly on the cable servings, and cooling can be provided by water applied to the cable as it enters the brake blocks.

Cable engines, which may be of the capstan, caterpillar or multiple-wheel linear type, grip the cable and enable the energy to be dissipated in a mechanical, hydraulic or electrical braking system. They enable cable to be paid out with much more positive control over a wide tension and speed range and may provide the means of recovering cable for repair work.

Although slack cable coming from storage to the tension control equipment may be passed round bends formed from groups of relatively small diameter rollers to

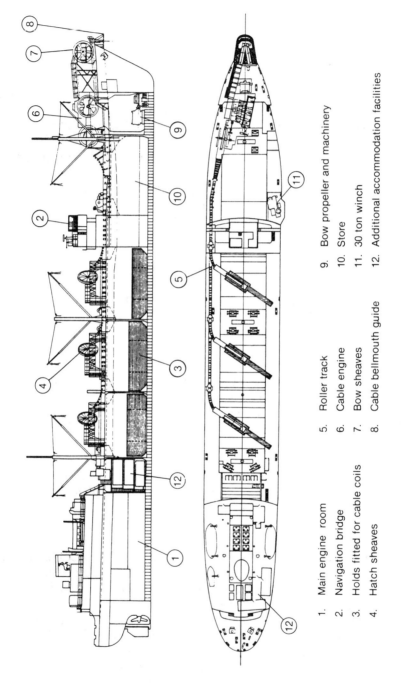

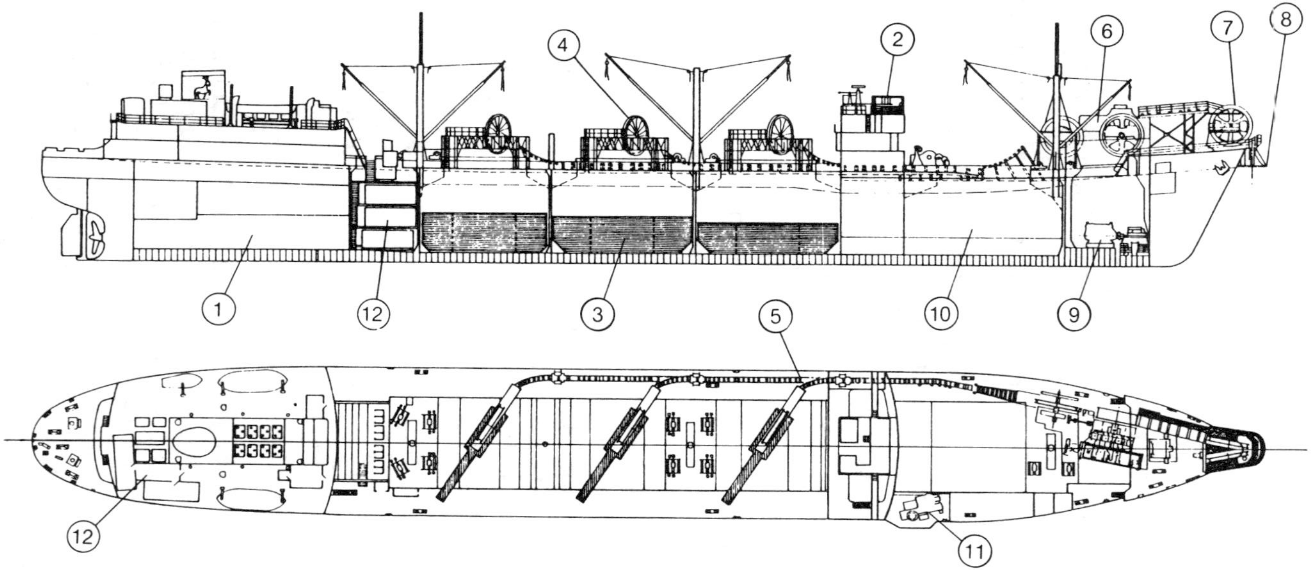

1. Main engine room
2. Navigation bridge
3. Holds fitted for cable coils
4. Hatch sheaves
5. Roller track
6. Cable engine
7. Bow sheaves
8. Cable bellmouth guide
9. Bow propeller and machinery
10. Store
11. 30 ton winch
12. Additional accommodation facilities

Fig. 46.1 MV *Photinia* equipped for laying the Cook Strait cables

reduce friction, cable under tension must bend round the smooth curved surface of a wheel or skid. All guides on the cable engine and along the cable run to the bow or stern gear should be of large radius.

The degree of sophistication required from the cable tension measuring instrumentation depends upon a number of factors. For slow cable laying in water less than 80 m deep and with tidal currents of, say, less than 1 knot, it may be adequate to observe the angle at which the cable enters the water in order to estimate the tension and no direct tension measurement is essential. In deeper water and in conditions where the relative velocity of the water to the cable is significant, the laying angle becomes inadequate to determine whether cable is being laid slack or with the proper residual tension, and so it is essential to use an instrument to measure the tension at the braking equipment, at the bow or stern gear, or at an intermediate point along the cable run. If cable is laid over a skid, it is necessary to know the angle of wrap round the curved surface and the coefficient of friction of the cable servings on this surface in order to calculate the required inboard cable tension.

The cable tension is sensed by either hydraulic or electrical load cells which need to be robust and resistant to salt water, vibration and shock loads. Similarly, the associated amplifiers, recorders and indicators need to be suitable for use in a marine environment and robust reliability is more appropriate than sophistication and high sensitivity.

Although the indication of tension is of prime importance, the measurement of cable speed and of the length paid out are also valuable aids to the control and provision of records of the operation.

The final equipment over which the cable passes on its way out of the vessel is the bow or stern gear which may be in the form of a large sheave wheel or a skid. Although the latter is cheaper, lighter and easier to fit to a vessel it has the inherent disadvantage of causing a change in the cable tension by a factor of $\exp(\mu\theta)$, which makes tension control less sensitive during laying and increases the tension required to recover cable during repair operations. One of the difficulties is in compensating for variations in the angle of wrap (θ) and the other is in achieving a stable known value for the coefficient of friction (μ).

The basic navigational instrumentation for cable laying is that required for measuring the water depth and that for plotting the position of the vessel along the route. Additional features which may usefully be provided are measurements of the speed of the vessel through the water and of speed over the ground, which can be used to assist and verify the correctness of the control being applied during the cable laying operation.

The use of modern position fixing systems, together with a track plotter or a visual display unit, make navigation along the main part of the route a simple matter and enable records of the operation to be obtained with minimal effort. If the cable tension, speed and length instruments are suitably grouped, it is possible to record these on the same time base so that they can be readily related to the navigational record and the trace from the echo sounder which shows the profile of the sea bed along the route actually traversed by the vessel while laying the cable.

PRELIMINARY SITE WORK

Bow and stern moorings are usually required close to the shore at each end of the route to hold the vessel securely whilst the ends of the cable are pulled ashore. Their distance offshore should be the minimum compatible with the safety of the vessel and their spacing must be adequate to enable all the cables of the system to be handled without the need to reposition anchors between laying operations. As the handling of the shore ends is the most hazardous part of a cable laying operation, it is desirable to minimise the length of cable involved and the time taken in effecting this at each end of the route.

To prevent cable from being damaged by surf action or by impact from floating logs, small boats etc., it is normal to bury the cable from some distance below the low water mark across the beach to the terminal position, which may be at a joint pit or at the terminal of an overhead line. The trench should be prepared before cable laying is commenced so that the cable can be protected as soon as possible after it has been laid.

If the cable is landed over a rocky area where it is difficult to cut a trench of adequate depth, protection may be provided by fitting cast iron cable protectors or concrete bags.

On arrival of the cable vessel on site, the normal procedure is for the ship to enter moorings at the starting end and to practice leaving moorings, navigation along the cable route at cable laying speed and entering moorings at the finishing end. During this practice useful records of the sea-bed profile can be obtained and the Master of the vessel can become familiar with the special requirements for handling his vessel during cabling operations.

CABLE LAYING

The cable laying operation is not commenced until an adequate period of favourable weather is predicted and the sea conditions are seen to be suitable for the laying of the complete length of cable in one uninterrupted operation. A discontinuity in cable laying can readily result in damage to the insulation of a high voltage cable and result in the need to insert one or more repair joints to remedy the defect. On rare occasions the weather conditions may change unexpectedly and prevent the vessel from entering moorings to land the finishing end of the cable. In this event the balance of the length of cable is laid off on an escape route near the shore in moderately shallow water where it can remain safely on the sea bed until conditions are favourable for its recovery and re-laying on the planned route. Only in the last resort would a power cable be cut to enable the laying vessel to escape from some disastrous situation since this makes the expense of a repair or of the replacement of a length of cable inevitable.

Landing the starting end of the cable by pulling it ashore on floats is a simple and fairly short operation but landing the finishing end is more complex and also more vulnerable if the weather deteriorates. It is therefore usual to arrange the direction of cable laying so that the finishing end is at the more sheltered and secure location. Nevertheless, there may be other overriding considerations, such as the requirement for landing a very long length of cable to reach the terminal, which then makes that site the better location for starting.

With the ship in the moorings at the starting end of the route, the required length of cable is pulled ashore. The end of the cable is secured and the floats are removed from the cable progressively from the shore towards the ship. This operation is timed to take place when the floating cable is as directly over the route as possible with minimal deviation caused by tidal currents or wind. If the cable is floated on twin inflatable floats which are linked together into a continuous string by tack lines between them and all the filler plugs on one side are secured to a rip cord, it is possible to deflate the floats in sequence on that side so that the inflated floats pull the deflated ones clear as the cable sinks to the sea bed. By this means it is possible to release floats very quickly, even though some will be pulled beneath the surface in the deeper water near the ship.

During this operation it is essential to maintain adequate tension control so that the cable is held straight without an excessive pull being exerted as the last floats are released. If the released floats are connected together by tack lines, they are readily recovered for subsequent operations.

As the vessel commences cable laying on the main part of the crossing, it is normal for control of the cable laying operation to be initially by the visual judgement of the Cable Officer while the vessel's moorings are slipped and the ship manoeuvres onto her course along the cable route. Once the vessel is clear of obstructions, the responsibility for handling the cable is handed over to the cable laying control centre and the responsibility for the navigation of the vessel along the desired route and for the maintenance of a steady speed reverts to the bridge.

In the cable laying control centre, the correct cable tension appropriate to the conditions is determined from observation of the ship's position, ship's speed, the water depth and the distance traversed. Instructions are given directly to the cable engine driver or brake operator to adjust the cable tension accordingly. Laying control is simplified if tables relating the ship's position and the required tension are prepared in advance for a range of speeds adequate to cover all likely contingencies.

In shallow water and at relatively low speeds, it is possible to effect laying control adequately by observation of the angle at which cable leaves the vessel and this is frequently the method used when cable is paid out over a stern skid.

The objectives of laying control are twofold. The first is to ensure that no slack cable is laid because this could form a loop on the sea bed which might subsequently be pulled into a kink and damage the insulation. The second is to ensure that the residual tension in the cable on the sea bed is as low as practical to permit it to follow the contours without bridging hollows and this will also ensure that the tension applied to the cable as it leaves the ship is minimised. The value of residual tension employed in the calculation of the laying control figures will vary with the weight per unit length of the cable and also with the sensitivity of the tension measuring equipment. Its value is usually in the range of 250 kg for a light cable and 1000 kg for a heavy cable in deep water.

The speed at which power cables are laid is usually set by the lowest speed at which the cable laying vessel can safely maintain steady progress accurately along the desired route, which in turn is related to the maximum tidal currents predicted for the duration of the cable laying operation. A cable laying speed of between 2 and 3 knots is usually aimed at, with a maximum of about 5 knots. If it is necessary to maintain the speed at less than 2 knots, as for example when laying from a turntable, it is generally considered essential to use a vessel with a DP system or to have tugs available to assist in controlling the movement of the vessel. The former of these with its centralised controls is much the more effective arrangement.

If the cable is being buried as it is laid and the laying speed has to be reduced to below 1 knot, a DP system or a system of moorings moved as required by one or more anchor handling vessels is necessary to control the vessel.

Having traversed the main part of the cable route, the cable laying vessel arrives at moorings which are designed to hold her securely while the finishing end of the cable is landed.

The method used for landing the cable end depends upon the type of cable and to some extent upon the length of cable to be handled. Cables operating at 33 kV or below are frequently 'turned over' by taking a bight of cable over to an adjacent coiling area and transferring the balance of the length into a coil or figure eight formation in which the end becomes available for pulling ashore on floats. The operation is completed by lowering the final bight of cable to the sea bed while the shore winch takes away the slack and finally the floats are removed between the ship and the shore.

Other methods which may be used for handling long finishing shore ends employ either a barge onto which cable is transferred[1] or a floating head which enables a bight of cable to be pulled out and laid without necessitating the carrying out of a coiling operation. Fig. 46.2 illustrates diagrammatically the floating head, which, being amphibious, enables the cable to be landed on the beach in one continuous operation. This was the method employed in handling the Cook Strait 250 kV d.c. cables.[2]

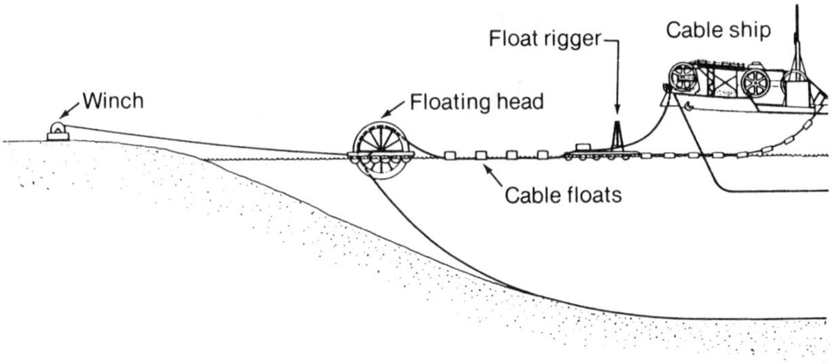

Fig. 46.2 Floating head landing a cable end

Since it is essential to ensure that the length of cable supplied is certain to reach the terminal position, the allowances for contouring on the sea bed and for navigational deviations, plus a small safety margin, tend to be generous and are seldom totally utilised. During the shore end handling operation it is preferable to cut the cable on the ship to the correct length with only a small safety margin and seal the ends with temporary end caps. The surplus cable can then remain in the vessel until it is convenient to offload it for storage as maintenance cable for possible future repairs.

With the cable end landed, the cable is moved into its final position and secured by a ground anchor before jointing to a section of land cable or terminating on a suitable structure. On completion of the jointing work the cable is finally subjected to the appropriate commissioning tests. The installation is completed by fitting cast iron cable protectors or other means of securing the cable against damage in the surf zone if it is not adequately protected by trenching.

MAINTENANCE AND REPAIR

The most frequent cause of failure in the submarine sections of power cable systems is mechanical damage by ships' anchors or by fishing gear. Other faults may arise from abrasion, sometimes coupled with fatigue of the lead sheath, which is the result of movement of the cable on the sea bed caused by tidal currents. More rarely, faults may be associated with joints in the cable since these tend to involve a discontinuity in the mechanical or electrical properties of the cable.

In the event of an electrical fault, a series of tests is carried out which may include measurements of resistance and capacitance and testing by pulse-echo methods. The position of the fault is identified by reference to the installation records of the actual route and length installed in conjunction with technical data of the cable characteristics. However, if the cable has been hooked by an anchor it may have been dragged a considerable distance away from its original route. In this case it may be necessary to find the cable either by using a search coil or towed electrodes to detect a signal injected into the cable or by using side-scan sonar or divers to search for it. If the fault is not electrical and is only leakage of gas or oil from the cable, the position of the leak is located by pneumatic flow, hydrostatic pressure or hydraulic measurements with reference to the route profile. Leaks may be difficult to locate accurately although, on occassions, gas leaks have been found by the use of an echo sounder and should be identifiable by side-scan sonar.

Having found the fault it can be marked by a float attached to a sinker and a pattern of moorings is then laid round the fault position to secure the vessel during subsequent jointing operations. Access to the faulty section of cable is obtained either by using a grapnel to hook the cable or by picking up cable from one end and recovering it until the fault is reached. In the former case if the cable was not severed at the time of the fault, it may be necessary to cut it by a mechanical cutter or by explosives to enable it to be lifted to the surface without subjecting it to excessive tension. The damaged section can then be replaced with a new length by using two joints to connect it to the original cable. If the cable is picked up from one end, the damaged section of cable is cut out and it is only necessary to lay a single joint in the fault area, with new cable being jointed in near the shore in order to complete the length required to reach the terminal position.

The method adopted depends upon the location of the fault, the depth of water, tidal currents, weather conditions, equipment and vessels available and also upon the age of the cable. Although recovery of the cable from one end out to the fault area may appear simpler, it nevertheless may result in damage to a considerable length of cable if the cable is old or if weather and tidal conditions make it difficult to control the repair vessel during a long slow recovery operation. However, the two joint method not only involves finding and lifting the cable out at sea, which generally involves cutting it well below the surface, but also involves lowering the final joint and a bight of cable to the sea bed without the formation of kinks. The latter method does have the advantage of minimising the disturbance caused to the original cable, although it also involves staying in position at sea for a longer period.

Whichever method is adopted, it is essential to have a mooring system which enables the vessel to be held with minimal variations of position during the jointing operations and also provides a method of controlling movement of the vessel as the joint or joints are laid. Since the expansion of the offshore oil industry, the development of deep water moorings and the availability of anchor handling vessels make it possible to effect cable repairs which were impractical at the time of the 250 kV d.c. Cook Strait installation in 1964–5.

FUTURE DEVELOPMENTS

Because of the increasing interest in large submarine power cable interconnections, and for their greater security against mechanical damage, more emphasis is being placed on their burial in the sea bed. In relatively soft or non-cohesive material it is possible to use either a plough or a jetting device to create a trench into which the cable can be introduced in a simultaneous operation, or subsequently after the cable laying operation.

In rock areas, however, it is necessary to use either a mechanical trench cutting machine or explosives. Both these methods are slow, and although it may be possible to cut a trench after cable laying or simultaneously with that activity, it is preferable to complete the trench cutting operation before cable laying is commenced. The patented Guide Line System and cable laying and embedding machine CLEM have been designed and developed for the installation of cables into a pre-cut trench. The method of operation is to install a robust steel wire rope in the bottom of the trench during the trench cutting operation and at this stage any deviation of route can be made. This wire rope is subsequently used as a guide wire for the guidance and traction of the cable handling machine which traverses the trench on

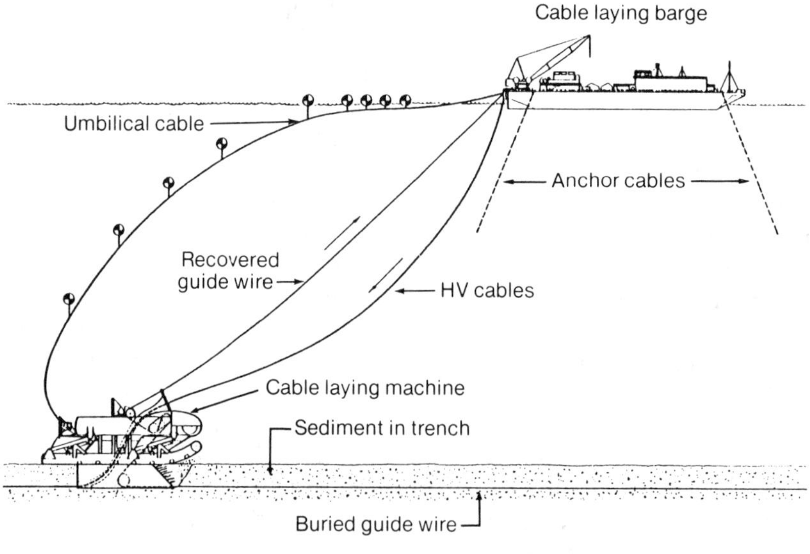

Fig. 46.3 Guide line method of embedding cables in a pre-cut trench

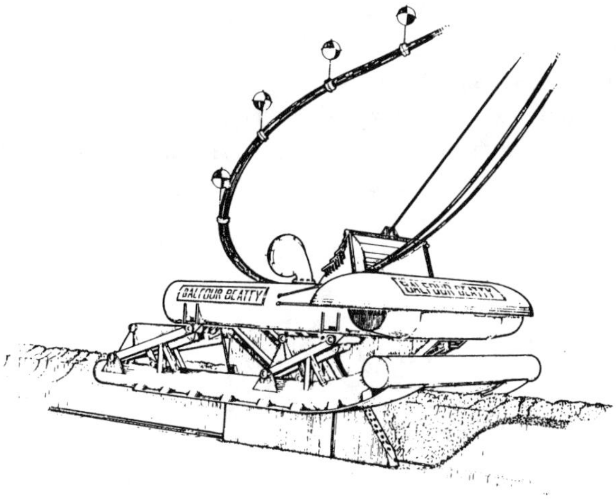

Fig. 46.4 Prototype cable embedding machine: CLEM

the route which has been proved in the previous operation. As the cable machine winches itself along the wire rope, any debris and sediment is cleared out of the trench by water jets and the cables are guided into position in the bottom of the trench as illustrated in fig. 46.3.

In 1979 the prototype machine CLEM, shown in fig. 46.4, was constructed and tested during a series of sea trials for the CEGB. These trials demonstrated the suitability of both the method and the machine for guiding twin 270 kV d.c. cables into a trench 1.5 m deep by 0.6 m wide in preparation for the installation of the 2000 MW Cross Channel Cable Scheme.[3,4] A more powerful and fully instrumented contract machine, CLEM II, was designed, built and tested before being used in 1985 for the successful installation of two pairs of cables from England to France.[5]

Even buried submarine cables may be subject to damage and this requires the development of new techniques for carrying out repairs. In order to minimise the amount of cable which has to be excavated and later reburied, a sea-bed repair habitat has been built and proved by sea trials for maintenance work, if necessary, on the 270 kV cross channel cables.

REFERENCES

(1) Ingledow, T., Fairfield, R. M., Davey, E. L., Brazier, K. S. and Gibson, J. N. (1957) 'British Columbia–Vancouver Island 138 kV submarine power cable'. *Proc. IEE, Part A* **104** (18).

(2) Williams, A. L., Davey, E. L. and Gibson, J. N. (1966) 'The 250 d.c. submarine power cable interconnection between the North and South Islands of New Zealand'. *Proc. IEE* **113** (1).

(3) Baldwin, D. S. F., Giles, E. G., Hacke, K. J. H., Seamans, J. W. S. and Waterhouse, N. H. (1979) 'Methods for installing buried submarine cables for a 2 GW d.c. cross channel link'. *Proc. Conf. on Progress in Cables and Overhead Lines for 220 kV and above*. IEE.

(4) Goddard, S. C., Yates, J. B., Urwin, R. J., Le Du, A., Marechal, P. and Michel, R. (1980) 'The new 2000 MW interconnection between France and the United Kingdom'. CIGRE Paper No. 14–09.
(5) Arkell, C. A., Ball, E. H., Hacke, K. J. H., Waterhouse, N. H. and Yates, J. B. (1986) 'Design and installation of the UK part of the 270 kV d.c. cable connection between England and France including reliability aspects'. CIGRE Paper No. 21–02.

APPENDICES

Appendix A1

Abbreviations

MATERIALS

CGI	compressed gas insulation
CPE	chlorinated polyethylene
CR	*see* PCP
CSM	*see* CSP
CSP	chlorosulphonated polyethylene
EPDM	ethylene–propylene terpolymer rubber
EPM	*see* EPR
EPR	ethylene–propylene rubber
ETFE	ethylene–tetra fluroethylene
EVA	ethylene–(vinyl acetate)
FEP	fluorinated ethylene propylene
HDPE	high density polyethylene
HEPR	hard EPR
IIR	isoprene isobutylene (butyl) rubber
LDPE	low density polyethylene
MEPR	medium hardness EPR
NBR	acrylonitrile–butadiene copolymer rubber
NR	natural rubber
PC	polycarbonate
PCP	polychloroprene rubber
PE	polyethylene
PETP	polyethylene terephthalate
PIB	polyisobutylene
PP	polypropylene
PPL	polypropylene paper laminate
PTFE	polytetrafluoroethylene
PVA	poly(vinyl acetate)
PVC	poly(vinyl chloride)
SBR	styrene–butadiene rubber
SR	silicone rubber
TPR	thermoplastic rubber
VR	vulcanised rubber
XLPE	crosslinked polyethylene

ASSOCIATIONS AND INSTITUTIONS

ABS	American Bureau of Shipping

AEIC	Association of Edison Illuminating Companies (USA)
ASTM	American Society for Testing Materials
BASEC	British Approvals Service for Electric Cables
BASEEFA	British Approvals Service for Electrical Equipment for Flammable Atmospheres
BC	British Coal
BCMC	British Cable Makers' Confederation
BCS	British Coal Specification
BR	British Rail
BRB	British Railways Board
BS	British Standard
BSI	British Standards Institution
BT	British Telecom
BV	Bureau Veritas
CEE	International Commission for Conformity Certification of Electrical Equipment
CEGB	Central Electricity Generating Board (UK)
CENELEC	European Committee for Electrotechnical Standardisation
CIGRE	Congrès International des Grands Réseaux Electriques (International Conference on Electric Transmission Systems)
CIRED	Congrès International des Réseaux Electriques de Distribution (International Conference on Electric Distribution Systems)
CMA	Cable Makers' Association (UK)
DNV	Det Norske Veritas (Norway)
ECMC	Electric Cable Makers' Confederation (UK)
EEC	European Economic Community
EEMUA	Engineering Equipment and Materials User's Association
EFTA	European Free Trade Association
EPRI	Electric Power Research Institute (USA)
ERA	Electrical Research Association (now ERA Technology Ltd)
GL	Germanische Lloyds (Germany)
ICEA	Insulated Cable Engineers' Association (USA)
IEC	International Electrotechnical Commission
IEE	Institution of Electrical Engineers (UK)
IEEE	Institute of Electrical and Electronics Engineers (USA)
IPCEA	Insulated Power Cable Engineers' Association (USA) (now ICEA)
ISO	International Standards Organisation
LRS	Lloyd's Register of Shipping
LTE	London Transport Executive
LUL	London Underground Limited
MOD(N)	Ministry of Defence (Navy)
NAC	National Accreditation Council
NAO	National Approval Organisation (EEC)
NCB	National Coal Board (UK)
NEMA	National Electrical Manufacturers' Association (USA)
OCMA	Oil Companies Materials Association

UL	Underwriter's Laboratories (USA)
VDE	Verband Deutscher Electrotechniker

CABLES AND CONSTRUCTIONS

CNE	combined neutral and earth
CPC	circuit protective conductor
CSA	corrugated seamless aluminium (sheath)
CTS	cab tyre sheath
DCO	ductless circular (conductor) OF cable
DSO	ductless shaped (conductor) OF cable
DWA	double wire armour
ECC	earth continuity conductor
GSW	galvanised steel wire
HOFR	heat and oil resisting-and flame retardant
HP OF	high pressure oil-filled
HR	heat retardant
HSA	Hochstadter (screened) separately aluminium sheathed
HSL	Hochstadter (screened) separately lead sheathed
LFH	limited fire hazard
LSF	low smoke and fume
MI	mineral insulated
MIND	mass-impregnated non-draining
NR	nitrile rubber
OF	oil-filled
OFR	oil resisting and flame retardant
PIAS	paper insulated aluminium sheathed
PILS	paper insulated lead sheathed
PME	protective multiple earthed
PWA	pliable wire armour
RNN	rubber/neoprene/neoprene
RP	reduced flame propagation
RPS	reduced flame propagation sheath
SAC	solid aluminium conductor
SC OF	self-contained oil-filled
SL	separately lead sheathed
SNE	separate neutral and earth
STA	steel tape armour
SWA	single wire armour
TRS	tough rubber sheath
ZH	zero (negligible) halogen

MISCELLANEOUS

AWG	American wire gauge
BIL	basic impulse level

CCV	continuous catenary vulcanising
CRT	cathode ray tube
CV	continuous vulcanising
DLA	dielectric loss angle
EHV	extra high voltage (imprecise)
HCV	horizontal continuous vulcanising
HV	high voltage (imprecise)
LV	low voltage (imprecise)
MCM	thousand circular mils (also kc mil)
MFI	melt flow index
MIG	metal–inert gas
MV	medium voltage (imprecise)
PLCV	pressurised liquid continuous vulcanising
PP	pre-pressurisation index
SSI	solid state interlock (signalling)
SVL	sheath voltage limiter
UD	underground distribution (USA)
UHV	ultra high voltage (imprecise)
URD	underground residential distribution (USA)
VCV	vertical continuous vulcanising
VTB	voltage time breakdown

Appendix A2

Symbols Used

A = volume resistivity
C = electrostatic capacitance per core (F/m)
D = dielectric loss (W/m)
E = effective modulus of elasticity (N/m^2)
E = electric stress in insulation (MV/m)
F = force (N)
G = geometric factor
I = current (A)
I = second moment of area of sheath (mm^4)
K = temperature interval (°C) (used in preference to degree Celsius)
K = constant (chapters 2, 4, 9, 10, 27 and 40)
L = length (m)
L = distance between supports (mm)
L = depth of burial (mm)
L = inductance (mH/m)
M = mutual inductance (mH/km)
N = electrical loss in cable component (W/m)
P = thermomechanical force (N)
Q = discharge magnitude (pC)
R = resistance (Ω)
S = axial spacing between conductors (mm)
S = eddy current loss (W/m)
S = conductor area (mm^2)
T = torque in cable (kg m)
T = thermal resistance (K m/W)
T = time (s)
T = pulling tension (kgf)
U = rated voltage between any two conductors (V)
U_m = maximum voltage for equipment (V)
U_o = rated voltage between conductor and earth (V)
V = volume of oil in OF cable (litre)
V = constant (chapter 27)
W = weight of cable (kg/km)
X = reactance (Ω)
Y = yield stress (N/m^2)
Z = impedance (Ω/m)

a = diameter of armour wire (mm)

b = hydraulic impedance (OF cable duct)
d = diameter (mm)
f = supply frequency (Hz)
h = heat dissipation coefficient
k = conductor/insulant factor for protection calculation (chapter 10)
m = number of armour wires
n = number of conductors in cable
n = number of wires in conductor
q = rate of flow (l/s)
r = radius (mm)
s = factor of safety
t = thickness (mm)
t = temperature
v = velocity (m/s)
x = duty cycle (welding) (%)
y = skin or proximity effect constant

α = coefficient of expansion
α = temperature coefficient of resistance
β = stress coefficient of electrical resistivity
δ = dielectric loss angle (tan δ)
ϵ = relative permittivity
η = viscosity of oil (cP)
θ = temperature difference (°C)
θ = angle of armour wire to cable axis (°)
λ = ratio of loss in component to loss in conductor
μ = coefficient of friction
ρ = resistivity (Ω m)
ρ = thermal resistivity (K m/W)
ϕ = angle of anti-twist tape to cable axis (°)

Note
The unit 'bar' is used for pressure rather than 'bar g'. Gauge pressure is always quoted and not absolute pressure.

Appendix A3

Conversion Factors and Multiple Metric Units

CONVERSION FACTORS

From	*To*	*Factor*	*Reciprocal*
mm	in	0.0394	25.4
m	ft	3.2808	0.3048
m	yard	1.0936	0.9144
km	mile	0.6214	1.6093
mm^2	in^2	0.00155	645.16
mm^2	circular mil	1973.5	5.0671×10^{-4}
N	lbf	0.2248	4.4482
N	kgf	0.1020	9.8067
bar	N/m^2	10^5	10^{-5}
bar	lbf/in^2	14.5	68.9476×10^{-3}
N/m^2	torr (mmHg)	7.501×10^{-3}	133.32
N/m^2	lbf/in^2	1.450×10^{-4}	6894.76
kgf/cm^2	lbf/in^2	14.223	0.07031
kg	ton	9.8421×10^{-4}	1016.05
kg	lb	2.2046	0.4536
t (tonne)	lb	2204.6	0.4536×10^{-3}
1 (litre)	gal (UK)	0.2202	4.541
1 (litre)	gal (US)	0.2642	3.785

MULTIPLE AND SUB-MULTIPLE METRIC UNITS

Multiple	*Prefix*	*Symbol*	*Sub-multiple*	*Prefix*	*Symbol*
10^{12}	tera	T	10^{-1}	deci	d
10^9	giga	G	10^{-2}	centi	c
10^6	mega	M	10^{-3}	milli	m
10^3	kilo	k	10^{-6}	micro	μ
10^2	hecto	h	10^{-9}	nano	n
10	deca	da	10^{-12}	pico	p

Appendix A4

Conductor Data

Table A4.1 Metric conductor sizes and resistances (20 °C) for fixed wiring

Conductor size (mm^2)	Maximum d.c. resistance: Plain copper (Ω/km)	Metal-coated copper (Ω/km)	Aluminium[a] (Ω/km)	Conductor size (mm^2)	Maximum d.c. resistance: Plain copper (Ω/km)	Metal-coated copper (Ω/km)	Aluminium*[a] (Ω/km)
0.5	36.0	36.7		500	0.0366	0.0369	0.0605
0.75	24.5	24.8		630	0.0283	0.0286	0.0469
1	18.1	18.2		800	0.0221	0.0224	0.0367
1.5	12.1	12.2		1000	0.0176	0.0177	0.0291
2.5	7.41	7.56		1200	0.0151	0.0151	0.0247
4	4.61	4.70	7.41	1400[b]	0.0129	0.0129	0.0212
6	3.08	3.11	4.61	1600[b]	0.0113	0.0113	0.0186
10	1.83	1.84	3.08	1800[c]	0.0101	0.0101	0.0165
16	1.15	1.16	1.91	2000[c]	0.0090	0.0090	0.0149
25	0.727	0.734	1.20	1150[c]	0.0156		0.0258
35	0.524	0.529	0.868	1300[c]	0.0138		0.0228
50	0.387	0.391	0.641	380[d]			0.0800
70	0.268	0.270	0.443	480[d]			0.0633
95	0.193	0.195	0.320	600[d]			0.0515
120	0.153	0.154	0.253	740[d]			0.0410
150	0.124	0.126	0.206	960[d]			0.0313
185	0.0991	0.100	0.164	1200[d]			0.0250
240	0.0754	0.0762	0.125				
300	0.0601	0.0607	0.100				
400	0.0470	0.0475	0.0778				

[a] Includes metal-coated and metal-clad
[b] Non-preferred sizes in IEC 228
[c] Sizes used for OF cables (not in IEC 228)
[d] Solid sectoral conductors (not in IEC 228 but standard for British practice, BS 6360)
Except where stated, the data are in accordance with IEC 228 and British Standards.

Table A4.2 Metric sizes and resistances (20 °C) for flexible conductors

Conductor size (mm^2)	Maximum d.c. resistance		Conductor size (mm^2)	Maximum d.c. resistance	
	Plain copper (Ω/km)	Metal-coated copper (Ω/km)		Plain copper (Ω/km)	Metal-coated copper (Ω/km)
0.5	39.0	40.1	70	0.272	0.277
0.75	26.0	26.7	95	0.206	0.210
1	19.5	20.0	120	0.161	0.164
1.5	13.3	13.7	150	0.129	0.132
2.5	7.98	8.21	185	0.106	0.108
4	4.95	5.09	240	0.0801	0.0817
6	3.30	3.39	300	0.0641	0.0654
10	1.91	1.95	400	0.0486	0.0495
16	1.21	1.24	500	0.0384	0.0391
25	0.780	0.795	630	0.0287	0.0292
35	0.554	0.565			
50	0.386	0.393			

The data are in accordance with IEC 228 and British Standards.

Table A4.3 USA stranded conductor sizes and resistances (20 °C) for fixed wiring

Nominal area (AWG or MCM[a])	Equivalent metric area[b] (mm^2)	Nominal d.c. resistance			Maximum d.c. resistance[c]			
		Copper (Ω/km)	Coated copper (Ω/km)	Aluminium (Ω/km)	Copper single-core (Ω/km)	Aluminium single-core (Ω/km)	Copper multicore (Ω/km)	Aluminium multicore (Ω/km)
20	0.519	33.9	36.0		34.6		35.3	
18	0.823	21.4	22.7		21.8		22.2	
16	1.31	13.4	14.3		13.7		14.0	
14	2.08	8.45	8.78		8.62		8.79	
13	2.63	6.69	6.96		6.82		6.96	
12	3.31	5.32	5.53	8.71	5.43	8.88	5.54	9.06
11	4.17	4.22	4.39	6.92	4.30	7.06	4.39	7.20
10	5.26	3.34	3.48	5.48	3.41	5.59	3.48	5.70
9	6.63	2.65	2.76	4.35	2.70	4.44	2.75	4.53
8	8.37	2.10	2.19	3.45	2.14	3.52	2.18	3.59
7	10.6	1.67	1.73	2.73	1.70	2.78	1.73	2.84
6	13.3	1.32	1.38	2.17	1.35	2.21	1.38	2.25
5	16.8	1.05	1.09	1.72	1.07	1.75	1.09	1.79
4	21.2	0.832	0.865	1.36	0.849	1.39	0.866	1.42
3	26.7	0.660	0.686	1.08	0.673	1.10	0.686	1.12
2	33.6	0.523	0.544	0.857	0.533	0.874	0.544	0.891
1	42.4	0.415	0.431	0.680	0.423	0.694	0.431	0.708
1/0	53.5	0.329	0.342	0.539	0.336	0.550	0.343	0.561
2/0	67.4	0.261	0.271	0.428	0.266	0.437	0.271	0.446
3/0	85.0	0.207	0.215	0.339	0.211	0.346	0.215	0.353
4/0	107	0.164	0.169	0.269	0.167	0.274	0.170	0.279
250	127	0.139	0.144	0.228	0.142	0.233	0.145	0.238
300	152	0.116	0.120	0.190	0.118	0.194	0.120	0.198
350	177	0.0992	0.103	0.163	0.101	0.166	0.103	0.169
400	203	0.0868	0.0893	0.142	0.0885	0.145	0.0903	0.148

450	228	0.0771	0.0794	0.126	0.0786	0.129	0.0802	0.132
500	253	0.0694	0.0714	0.114	0.0708	0.116	0.0722	0.118
550	279	0.0631	0.0656	0.103	0.0644	0.105	0.0657	0.107
600	304	0.0578	0.0602	0.0948	0.0590	0.0967	0.0602	0.0986
650	329	0.0534	0.0550	0.0875	0.0545	0.0893	0.0556	0.0911
700	355	0.0496	0.0510	0.0813	0.0506	0.0829	0.0516	0.0846
750	380	0.0463	0.0476	0.0759	0.0472	0.0774	0.0481	0.0789
800	405	0.0434	0.0447	0.0711	0.0443	0.0725	0.0452	0.0740
900	456	0.0386	0.0397	0.0632	0.0394	0.0645	0.0402	0.0658
1000	507	0.0347	0.0357	0.0569	0.0354	0.0580	0.0361	0.0592
1100	557	0.0316	0.0325	0.0517	0.0322	0.0527	0.0328	0.0538
1200	608	0.0289	0.0298	0.0474	0.0295	0.0483	0.0301	0.0493
1250	633	0.0278	0.0286	0.0455	0.0284	0.0464	0.0290	0.0473
1300	659	0.0267	0.0275	0.0438	0.0272	0.0447	0.0277	0.0456
1400	709	0.0248	0.0255	0.0406	0.0253	0.0414	0.0258	0.0422
1500	760	0.0231	0.0238	0.0379	0.0236	0.0387	0.0241	0.0395
1600	811	0.0217	0.0223	0.0356	0.0221	0.0363	0.0225	0.0370
1700	861	0.0204	0.0210	0.0335	0.0208	0.0342	0.0212	0.0349
1750	887	0.0198	0.0204	0.0325	0.0202	0.0332	0.0206	0.0339
1800	912	0.0193	0.0198	0.0316	0.0197	0.0322	0.0201	0.0328
1900	963	0.0183	0.0188	0.0300	0.0187	0.0306	0.0191	0.0312
2000	1013	0.0174	0.0179	0.0285	0.0177	0.0291	0.0181	0.0297
2500	1267	0.0140	0.0144	0.0230	0.0143	0.0235	0.0146	0.0240
3000	1520	0.0117	0.0120	0.0192	0.0119	0.0196	0.0121	0.0200
3500	1773	0.0101	0.0104	0.0166	0.0103	0.0169	0.0105	0.0172
4000	2027	0.00885	0.00911	0.0145	0.00903	0.0148	0.00921	0.0151
4500	2280	0.00794	0.00817	0.0130	0.00810	0.0133	0.00826	0.0136
5000	2534	0.00715	0.00735	0.0117	0.00729	0.0119	0.00744	0.0121

[a] AWG up to 4/0, MCM from 250 upwards
[b] Based on nominal area and incorrect for equivalent resistance
[c] Taken as 2% above nominal resistance for single-core cable and 2% above single-core cable for multicore cable
The data are based on IPCEA 5–66–524, NEMA WC7, and IPCEA 5–19–81, NEMA WC3, for concentric stranded and compact stranded conductors. Different values apply to solid conductors.

Table A4.4 Temperature correction factors for conductor resistance

Temperature of conductor (°C)	Factor to convert to 20 °C	Reciprocal to convert from 20 °C
5	1.064	0.940
6	1.059	0.944
7	1.055	0.948
8	1.050	0.952
9	1.046	0.956
10	1.042	0.960
11	1.037	0.964
12	1.033	0.968
13	1.029	0.972
14	1.025	0.976
15	1.020	0.980
16	1.016	0.984
17	1.012	0.988
18	1.008	0.992
19	1.004	0.996
20	1.000	1.000
21	0.996	1.004
22	0.992	1.008
23	0.988	1.012
24	0.984	1.016
25	0.980	1.020
26	0.977	1.024
27	0.973	1.028
28	0.969	1.032
29	0.965	1.036
30	0.962	1.040
35	0.943	1.060
40	0.926	1.080
45	0.909	1.100
50	0.893	1.120
55	0.877	1.140
60	0.862	1.160
65	0.847	1.180
70	0.833	1.200
75	0.820	1.220
80	0.806	1.240
85	0.794	1.260
90	0.781	1.280

Table A4.5 Maximum diameters (mm) of circular copper conductors (BS 6360)

Cross-sectional area (mm^2)	Conductors in cables for fixed installations		
	Solid (class 1)	Stranded (class 2)	Flexible conductors (classes 5 and 6)
0.5	0.9	1.1	1.1
0.75	1.0	1.2	1.3
1	1.2	1.4	1.5
1.5	1.5	1.7	1.8
2.5	1.9	2.2	2.6
4	2.4	2.7	3.2
6	2.9	3.3	3.9
10	3.7	4.2	5.1
16	4.6	5.3	6.3
25	5.7	6.6	7.8
35	6.7	7.9	9.2
50	7.8	9.1	11.0
70	9.4	11.0	13.1
95	11.0	12.9	15.1
120	12.4	14.5	17.0
150	13.8	16.2	19.0
185		18.0	21.0
240		20.6	24.0
300		23.1	27.0
400		26.1	31.0
500		29.2	35.0
630		33.2	39.0
800		37.6	
1000		42.2	

Notes

(a) For circular copper conductors, maximum diameters only are given and for the stranded (class 2) conductors these are based on uncompacted conductors. The reason for this is that connectors will cope with a wider range of diameters with copper than with aluminium and therefore with copper it is generally only necessary to recommend the maximum diameters to be accommodated. Moreover, circular stranded copper conductors are more frequently used in the uncompacted form than are aluminium conductors.

(b) If minimum diameters for circular copper conductors class 1 and class 2 are needed, reference can be made to the minimum diameters for solid and stranded compacted circular aluminium conductors indicated in table A4.6.

Table A4.6 Minimum and maximum diameters (mm) of circular aluminium conductors (BS 6360)

Cross-sectional area (mm^2)	Solid conductors (class 1)		Stranded compacted conductors (class 2)	
	Minimum diameter	Maximum diameter	Minimum diameter	Maximum diameter
16	4.1	4.6	4.6	5.2
25	5.2	5.7	5.6	6.5
35	6.1	6.7	6.6	7.5
50	7.2	7.8	7.7	8.6
70	8.7	9.4	9.3	10.2
95	10.3	11.0	11.0	12.0
120	11.6	12.4	12.5	13.5
150	12.9	13.8	13.9	15.0
185	14.5	15.4	15.5	16.8
240	16.7	17.6	17.8	19.2
300	18.8	19.8	20.0	21.6
400	–	–	22.9	24.6
500	–	–	25.7	27.6
630	–	–	29.3	32.5

Notes

(a) In the exceptional case of uncompacted circular stranded aluminium conductors the maximum diameters should not exceed the corresponding values for copper conductors given in column 3 of table A4.5.

(b) The dimensional limits of aluminium conductors with cross-sectional areas smaller than 16 mm^2 are not given because of the variations in dimensions that exist depending on the wide range of materials and combinations of materials used.

(c) The dimensional limits of aluminium conductors with cross-sectional areas above 630 mm^2 are not given as the compaction technology is not generally established.

Appendix A5

Industrial Cables for Fixed Supply

PVC ARMOURED POWER OR CONTROL CABLES 600/1000 V to BS 6346
Main application: factory wiring

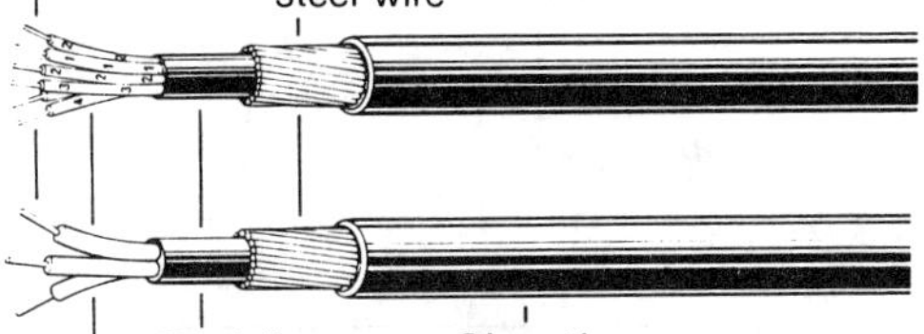

For sizes above 16 mm^2 see appendix A13: The current ratings tabulated are in accordance with the fifteenth edition of the IEE Regulations. If these do not apply, reference should be made to ERA Report 69–30, Part 3. The ratings are for a single circuit only. Rating factors and other details are given in chapters 8 and 10.

Table A5.1 Current ratings and volt drop

Conductor size (mm^2)	2-core cable, d.c. or single-phase a.c.		3- or 4-core cable, 3-phase a.c.	
	Rating (A)	Volt drop per A/m (mV)	Rating (A)	Volt drop per A/m (mV)
In air, clipped direct (ambient temperature 30°C, maximum conductor temperature 70°C)				
1.5	21	29	18	25
2.5	28	18	25	15
4	38	11	33	9.5
6	49	7.3	42	6.4
10	67	4.4	58	3.8
16	89	2.8	77	2.4
Direct in ground at 0.5 m depth (ground temperature 15°C, conductor temperature 70°C)				
1.5	32	29	27	25
2.5	41	18	35	16
4	55	12	47	9.6
6	69	7.4	59	6.3
10	92	4.3	78	3.8
16	119	2.7	101	2.3

PVC ARMOURED POWER OR CONTROL CABLES

600/1000 V to BS 6346

Table A5.2 Dimensions and weights (2-, 3- and 4-core cables)

Conductor size (mm^2)	Armour wire diameter (mm)	Approximate diameter (mm)	Approximate weight (kg/km)
2-core (ref 6942X)			
1.5[a]	0.9	11.7	280
1.5	0.9	12.3	298
2.5[a]	0.9	13.1	350
2.5	0.9	13.6	355
4	0.9	15.1	460
6	0.9	16.5	550
10	1.25	20.1	880
16	1.25	21.9	930
3-core (ref. 6943X)			
1.5[a]	0.9	12.3	310
1.5	0.9	12.8	344
2.5[a]	0.9	13.6	390
2.5	0.9	14.1	413
4	0.9	15.8	520
6	1.25	18.0	730
10	1.25	21.2	1010
16	1.25	23.1	1220
4-core (ref. 6944X)			
1.5[a]	0.9	13.0	350
1.5	0.9	13.5	383
2.5[a]	0.9	14.5	440
2.5	0.9	15.0	470
4	1.25	17.8	710
6	1.25	19.2	850
10	1.25	22.8	1200
16	1.6	26.3	1700

[a] Solid conductor

PVC ARMOURED AUXILIARY MULTICORE CABLES
600/1000 V to BS 6346

Table A5.3 Dimensions and weights (5- to 48-core cables)

Number of cores	Solid conductors			Stranded conductors		
	Armour wire diameter (mm)	Approximate diameter (mm)	Approximate weight (kg/km)	Armour wire diameter (mm)	Approximate diameter (mm)	Approximate weight (kg/km)
1.5 mm² conductor						
5	0.9	13.8	390	0.9	14.3	
7	0.9	14.5	445	0.9	15.2	470
8	0.9	15.4	490	0.9	16.5	
10	1.25	18.1	685	1.25	19.0	
12	1.25	18.6	740	1.25	19.4	784
14	1.25	19.2	800	1.25	20.3	
16	1.25	20.1	920	1.25	21.3	
19	1.25	21.1	965	1.25	22.2	1023
22	1.6	25.0	1330	1.6	26.2	
27	1.6	25.4	1420	1.6	26.7	1506
30	1.6	26.1	1510	1.6	27.4	
37	1.6	27.8	1730	1.6	29.2	1834
40	1.6	28.7	1970	1.6	30.2	
48	1.6	30.8	2080	1.6	32.9	
2.5 mm² conductor						
5	0.9	15.4	495	0.9	16.3	
7	0.9	16.6	590	1.25	18.0	729
8	1.25	18.5	760	1.25	19.2	
10	1.25	20.9	895	1.25	21.9	
12	1.25	21.4	975	1.25	22.4	1049
14	1.6	22.3	1070	1.6	24.6	
16	1.6	23.2	1170	1.6	25.5	
19	1.6	25.4	1500	1.6	26.6	

(*cont.*)

PVC ARMOURED AUXILIARY MULTICORE CABLES
600/1000 V to BS 6346

Table A5.3 cont.

Number of cores	Solid conductors			Stranded conductors		
	Armour wire diameter (mm)	Approximate diameter (mm)	Approximate weight (kg/km)	Armour wire diameter (mm)	Approximate diameter (mm)	Approximate weight (kg/km)
22	1.6	28.8	1770	1.6	30.2	
27	1.6	29.3	1910	1.6	30.7	2043
30	1.6	30.1	2050	1.6	32.0	
37	1.6	32.4	2360	1.6	34.0	2517
40	1.6	33.5	2520	2.0	36.6	
18	2.0	37.5	3200	2.0	39.5	
Multicore: 4 mm² conductor (stranded)						
5				1.25	19.0	795
7				1.25	20.5	940
8				1.25	21.5	1050
10				1.6	26.1	1420
12				1.6	26.8	1560
14				1.6	27.4	1730
16				1.6	28.7	1880
19				1.6	30.5	2080
22				1.6	34.5	2490
27				2.0	37.1	3040
30				2.0	38.2	
37				2.0	40.8	
40				2.0	42.5	
48				2.0	46.0	
Multicore: 6 mm² conductor (stranded)						
5				1.25	20.3	980
7				1.25	21.7	1160

XLPE ARMOURED POWER OR CONTROL CABLES
600/1000 V to BS 5467 and 6724

Cable design is as shown above table A5.1 for PVC cables but 'low smoke and fire cable' to BS 6724 has special material for the bedding and oversheath.
For sizes above 16 mm^2 see appendix A14.

The ratings are for a single circuit only. Rating factors and other details are given in chapters 8 and 9.

Table A5.4 Current ratings and volt drop

Conductor size (mm^2)	2-core cable, d.c. or single phase a.c.		3- or 4-core cable, 3-phase a.c.	
	Rating (A)	Volt drop per A/m (mV)	Rating (A)	Volt drop per A/m (mV)
In air, clipped (ambient temperature 30°C, conductor temperature 90°C)				
1.5	26	31	22	27
2.5	37	19	31	17
4	49	12	42	10
6	63	7.9	54	6.8
10	86	4.7	74	4.1
16	115	2.9	99	2.6

XLPE ARMOURED POWER OR CONTROL CABLES
600/1000 V to BS 5467 and 6724

Table A5.5 Dimensions and weights (2-, 3- and 4-core cables)

Conductor size (mm^2)	Armour wire diameter (mm)	Approximate diameter (mm)	Approximate weight (kg/km)
2-core (stranded conductor)			
1.5	0.9	12.5	310
2.5	0.9	13.6	360
4	0.9	14.7	430
6	0.9	15.9	500
10	0.9	18.0	800
16	1.25	20.0	940
3-core (stranded conductor)			
1.5	0.9	13.0	340
2.5	0.9	14.1	410
4	0.9	15.3	500
6	1.25	16.6	770
10	1.25	19.5	900
16	1.25	21.2	1180
4-core (stranded conductor)			
1.5	0.9	14.0	390
2.5	0.9	15.0	470
4	1.25	16.4	580
6	1.25	18.7	820
10	1.25	21.1	1060
16	1.25	22.9	1410

XLPE ARMOURED POWER OR CONTROL CABLES
600/1000 V to BS 5467 and 6724

Table A5.6 Dimensions and weights (multicore auxiliary cables)

Number of cores	Armour wire diameter (mm)	Approximate diameter (mm)	Approximate weight (kg/km)
1.5 mm^2 conductor (stranded)			
7	0.9	15.9	490
12	1.25	20.2	830
19	1.25	23.2	1070
27	1.6	27.9	1580
37	1.6	30.6	1880
2.5 mm^2 conductor (stranded)			
7	0.9	17.1	600
12	1.25	22.4	1020
19	1.6	26.6	1530
27	1.6	30.7	1960
37	1.6	33.8	2370

Appendix A6

Cables for Fixed Installation in Buildings

PVC WIRING CABLES 300/500 V and 450/750 V to BS 6004
Main application: wiring in buildings

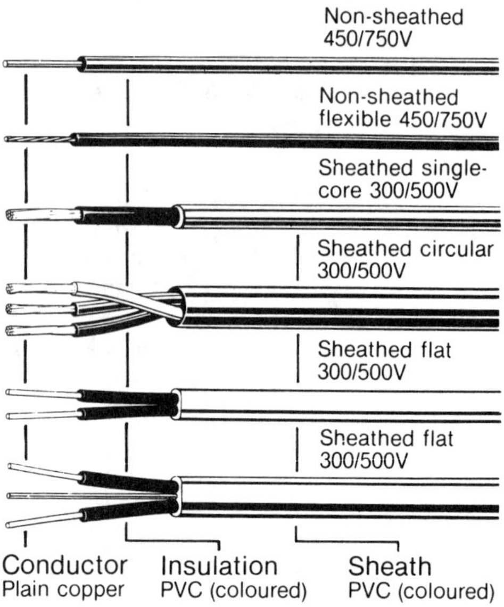

Current rating conditions

The ratings given in tables A6.1 and A6.2 are for a single circuit and are in accordance with the June 1987 amendment to the fifteenth edition of the IEE Regulations for Electrical Installations. They correspond to continuous loading at a maximum conductor temperature of 70 °C and are based on an ambient temperature of 30 °C. When the protection is by semi-enclosed fuse the cable should be selected with a rating not less than 1.38 times the rating of the fuse.

Further information on current ratings is given in chapters 8 and 10. Rating correction factors are included in chapter 8.

Details of the methods of installation applicable to the column headings are in appendix 9 of the IEE Regulations for Electrical Installations.

PVC WIRING CABLES
300/500 V and 450/750 V
to BS 6004

Table A6.1 Current ratings for single-core non-sheathed conduit cables and single-core sheathed cables

Conductor size (mm^2)	Bunched and enclosed in conduit or trunking[a]		Clipped direct		On perforated tray (horizontal or vertical)	
	2 cables, single-phase a.c. or d.c. (A)	3 or 4 cables, 3-phase a.c. (A)	2 cables, single-phase a.c. or d.c. (A)	3 or 4 cables, 3-phase a.c. (A)	2 cables, single-phase a.c. or d.c. (A)	3 or 4 cables, 3-phase a.c. (A)
1.0	13.5	12	15.5	14		
1.5	17.5	15.5	20	18		
2.5	24	21	27	25		
4	32	28	37	33		
6	41	36	47	43		
10	57	50	65	59		
16	76	68	87	79		
25	101	89	114	104	126	112
35	125	110	141	129	156	141
50	151	134	182	167	191	172
70	192	171	234	214	246	223
95	232	207	284	261	300	273
120	269	239	330	303	349	318
150	300	262	381	349	404	369
185	341	296	436	400	463	424
240	400	346	515	472	549	504
300	458	394	594	545	635	584

[a] Non-sheathed cables are not suitable for conduits or trunking etc. buried underground

PVC WIRING CABLES
300/500 V and 450/750 V
to BS 6004

Table A6.2 Voltage drop (per A/m) for single-core non-sheathed conduit cables and single-core sheathed cables

Conductor size (mm^2)	Bunched and enclosed in conduit or trunking[a]		Clipped direct		On perforated tray (horizontal or vertical)	
	2 cables, single-phase a.c. or d.c. (mV)	3 or 4 cables, 3-phase a.c. (mV)	2 cables, single-phase a.c. or d.c. (mV)	3 or 4 cables, 3-phase a.c. (mV)	2 cables, single-phase a.c. or d.c. (mV)	3 or 4 cables, 3-phase a.c. (mV)
1.0	4.4	38	44	38		
1.5	29	25	29	25		
2.5	18	15	18	15		
4	11	9.5	11	9.5		
6	7.3	6.4	7.3	6.4		
10	4.4	3.8	4.4	3.8		
16	2.8	2.4	2.8	2.4		
25	1.8	1.55	1.75	1.5	1.75	1.5
35	1.3	1.10	1.25	1.1	1.25	1.1
50	1.0	0.85	0.95	0.82	0.95	0.82
70	0.72	0.61	0.66	0.57	0.66	0.57
95	0.56	0.48	0.50	0.43	0.50	0.43
120	0.47	0.41	0.41	0.36	0.41	0.36
150	0.41	0.36	0.34	0.30	0.34	0.30
185	0.37	0.32	0.28	0.26	0.29	0.26
240	0.33	0.29	0.25	0.22	0.25	0.22
300	0.31	0.27	0.22	0.19	0.22	0.19

[a] Non-sheathed cables are not suitable for conduits or trunking etc. buried underground

PVC WIRING CABLES
300/500 V and 450/750 V
to BS 6004

Table A6.3 Current ratings and volt drop for flat cables

Conductor size (mm^2)	Bunched and enclosed in conduit or trunking[a]		Clipped direct		On perforated tray (horizontal or vertical)	
	2-core cable, single-phase a.c. or d.c.	3- or 4-core cable, 3-phase a.c.	2-core cable, single-phase a.c. or d.c.	3- or 4-core cable, 3-phase a.c.	2-core cable, single-phase a.c. or d.c.	3- or 4-core cable, 3-phase a.c.
Current ratings (A)						
1.0	13	11.5	15	13.5	17	14.5
1.5	16.5	15	19.5	17.5	22	18.5
2.5	23	20	27	24	30	25
4	30	27	36	32	40	34
6	38	34	46	41	51	43
10	52	46	63	57	70	60
16	69	62	85	76	94	80
Volt drop per A/m (mV)						
1.0	44	38	44	38	44	38
1.5	29	25	29	25	29	25
2.5	18	15	18	15	18	15
4	11	9.5	11	9.5	11	9.5
6	7.3	6.4	7.3	6.4	7.3	6.4
10	4.4	3.8	4.4	3.8	4.4	3.8
16	2.8	2.4	2.8	2.4	2.8	2.4

The data apply to one cable, with or without a protective conductor.

PVC WIRING CABLES
300/500 V and 450/750 V
to BS 6004

Table A6.4 Dimensions and weights (non-sheathed single-core cables)

Conductor size (mm^2)	300/500 V solid conductor (ref. H05V-U)		450/750 V solid or stranded conductor (ref. 6491X, H07 V)		450/750 V flexible conductor (ref. H07V-K)	
	Maximum diameter (mm)	Approximate weight (kg/km)	Maximum diameter (mm)	Approximate weight (kg/km)	Maximum diameter (mm)	Approximate weight (kg/km)
1.0	2.8[a]	17[a]				
1.5			3.3[a]	21[a]		
1.5			3.4	21	3.5	21
2.5			3.9[a]	33[a]		
2.5			4.2	35	4.2	33
4			4.8	50	4.8	50
6			5.4	71	6.3	70
10			6.8	120	7.6	120
16			8.0	180	8.8	180
25			9.8	280	11.0	290
35			11.0	380	12.5	400
50			13.0	510	14.5	570
70			15.0	720	17.0	770
95			17.0	990	19.0	1000
120			19.0	1200	21.0	1300

150	21.0	1500	23.5	1600
185	23.5	1900	26.0	1900
240	26.5	2500	29.5	2500
300	29.5	3000		
400	33.5	4000		
500	37.0	5000		
630	41.0	6300		

[a] Solid conductor

PVC WIRING CABLES
300/500 V
to BS 6004

Table A6.5 Dimensions and weights (300/500 V, single-core sheathed, flat 2-core and 3-core cables without CPC)

Conductor size (mm^2)	Mean diameter or dimensions		Approximate weight (kg/km)
	Lower limit (mm)	Upper limit (mm)	
Single-core sheathed (ref. 6181Y)			
1.0[a]	3.8	4.5	28
1.5[a]	4.2	4.9	36
2.5[a]	4.8	5.8	51
4	5.4	6.8	75
6	6.0	7.4	98
10	7.2	8.8	150
16	8.4	10.5	220
25	10.0	12.5	340
35	11.0	13.5	440
2-core flat (ref. 6192Y)			
1.0[a]	4.0 × 6.2	4.7 × 7.4	53
1.5[a]	4.4 × 7.0	5.4 × 8.4	71
1.5	4.5 × 7.2	5.6 × 8.8	78
2.5[a]	5.2 × 8.4	6.2 × 9.8	100
2.5	5.2 × 8.6	6.6 × 10.5	112
4	5.6 × 9.6	7.2 × 11.5	150
6	6.4 × 10.5	8.0 × 13.0	204
10	7.8 × 13.0	9.6 × 16.0	305
16	9.0 × 15.5	11.0 × 18.5	469
3-core flat (ref. 6193Y)			
1.0[a]	4.0 × 8.4	4.7 × 9.8	78
1.5[a]	4.4 × 9.8	5.4 × 11.5	105
2.5[a]	5.2 × 11.5	6.2 × 13.5	155
4	5.8 × 13.5	7.4 × 16.5	230
5	6.4 × 15.0	8.0 × 18.0	300
10	7.8 × 19.0	9.6 × 22.5	480
16	9.0 × 22.0	11.0 × 26.5	700

[a] Solid conductor

PVC WIRING CABLES
300/500 V
to BS 6004

Table A6.6 Dimensions and weights (300/500 V, flat 2-core and 3-core with protective conductor)

Conductor size (mm^2)	Protective conductor (mm^2)	Mean dimensions: Lower limit (mm)	Mean dimensions: Upper limit (mm)	Approximate weight (kg/km)
2-core flat (ref. 6242Y)				
1.0[a]	1.0	4.0 × 7.2	4.7 × 8.6	69
1.5[a]	1.0	4.4 × 8.2	5.4 × 9.6	88
1.5	1.0	4.5 × 8.4	5.6 × 10.0	95
2.5[a]	1.5	5.2 × 9.8	6.2 × 11.5	130
2.5	1.5	5.2 × 9.8	6.6 × 12.0	136
4	1.5	5.6 × 10.5	7.2 × 13.0	176
6	2.5	6.4 × 12.5	8.0 × 15.0	243
10	4	7.8 × 15.5	9.6 × 19.0	390
16	6	9.0 × 18.0	11.0 × 22.5	567
3-core flat (ref. 6243Y)				
1.0[a]	1.0	4.0 × 9.6	4.7 × 11.0	92
1.5[a]	1.0	4.4 × 10.5	5.4 × 12.5	120
2.5[a]	1.0	5.2 × 12.5	6.2 × 14.5	173
4	1.5	5.8 × 14.5	7.4 × 18.0	255
6	2.5	6.4 × 16.5	8.0 × 20.0	340
10	4	7.8 × 21.0	9.6 × 25.5	550
16	6	9.0 × 24.5	11.0 × 29.5	730

[a] Solid conductor

ELASTOMERIC INSULATED CABLES

300/500 V and 450/750 V
to BS 6007

Main application: single-core for wiring in buildings and 2-core for festoon lighting

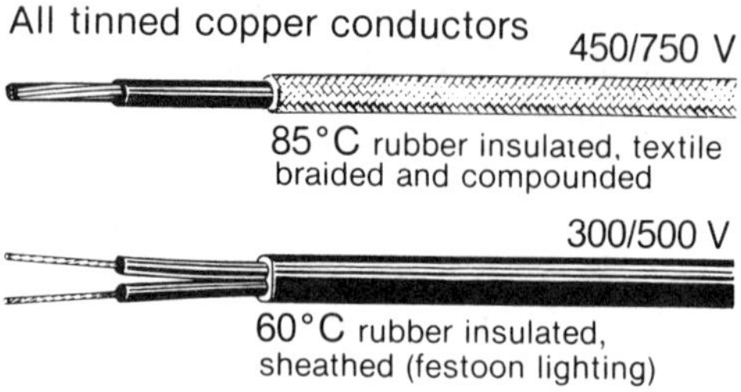

Table A6.7 Current ratings and volt drop

Conductor size (mm^2)	Enclosed				Clipped direct			
	2 cables d.c. or single-phase a.c.		3 or 4 cables, 3-phase a.c.		2 cables d.c. or single-phase a.c.		3 or 4 cables, 3-phase a.c.	
	Rating (A)	Volt drop per A/m[a] (mV)	Rating (A)	Volt drop per A/m (mV)	Rating (A)	Volt drop per A/m[a] (mV)	Rating (A)	Volt drop per A/m (mV)
Single-core cables								
1.0	17	46	15	40	19	46	17	40
1.5	22	31	19	26	25	31	23	26
2.5	30	18	27	16	34	18	31	16
4	40	12	36	10	45	12	42	10
6	52	7.7	46	6.7	59	7.7	54	6.7
10	72	4.6	63	4.0	81	4.6	75	4.0
16	96	2.9	85	2.5	108	2.9	100	2.5
25	127	1.9	112	1.65	143	1.85	133	1.6
35	157	1.4	138	1.2	177	1.35	164	1.15
50	190	1.05	167	0.91	215	0.99	199	0.88
70	242	0.74	213	0.65	274	0.69	254	0.62
95	293	0.58	258	0.51	332	0.52	308	0.48
Flat twin cable								
2.5					24	18		

[a] A.C. only

Note

The ratings are based on an ambient temperature of 30 °C and a maximum conductor temperature of 85 °C for single-core cable and 60 °C for twin cable. They apply to a single circuit only.

The ratings for single-core cables are in accordance with the IEE Wiring Regulations and those for twin cable are given for guidance. When the protection is by a semi-enclosed fuse the cable should be selected with a rating not less than 1.38 times the rating of the fuse. Rating factors are given in chapter 8.

ELASTOMERIC INSULATED CABLES
300/500 V and 450/750 V
to BS 6007

Table A6.8 Dimensions and weights

Conductor size (mm^2)	Maximum diameter (mm)	Approximate weight (kg/km)
Single-core, braided 450/750 V (ref. 6101T)		
1[a]	4.3	19
1.5[b]	4.6	24
2.5[b]	5.0	35
4	6.4	57
6	7.0	84
10	8.6	133
16	9.6	194
25	11.5	292
35	13.0	396
50	14.5	530
70	16.5	741
95	19.0	1030
Flat twin 300/500 V (festoon lighting)		
2.5	6.8 × 11.0	116

[a] Solid conductor
[b] Solid or stranded conductor

XLPE INSULATED FLOORWARMING CABLES
230 to 380 V (BICC designs)

Main application: heating of buildings and soil warming

Type X

Type XS

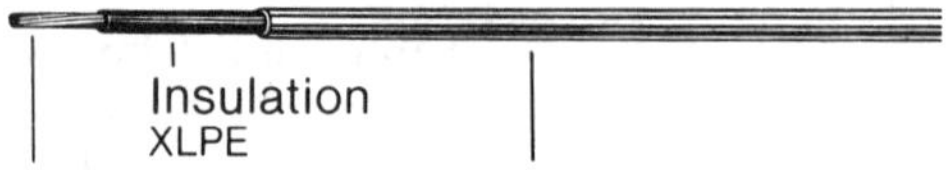

Type XSBV

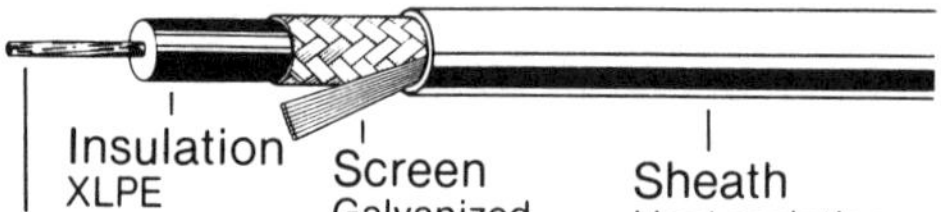

Type XB

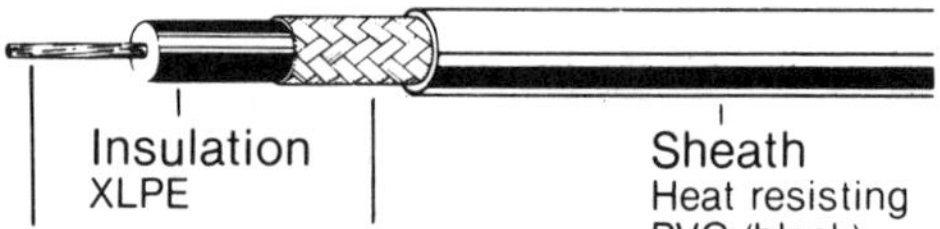

Table A6.9 General data

Types	X: XLPE core, insulated only XJ: with heat resisting PVC sheath XB: with tinned copper wire braid and sheath as XJ XSBV: with galvanised steel wire braid, 1.0 mm² drain wire and sheath as XJ				
Cable sizes	18 standard conductor resistances from 12.2 to 0.013 Ω/m				
Voltages	220, 230, 240 and 380 V				
Lengths and output of heating units	16 standard wattages covering				
	Voltage (V)	Heat output (W)		Length (m)	
		minimum	maximum	minimum	maximum
	220	250	3500	15	230.5
	230	260	3750	16.5	235
	240	275	4000	17	236
	380	450	6300	27	382

Appendix A7

Cables for Fixed Installation (Shipwiring and Offshore)

ELASTOMERIC SHIPWIRING POWER CABLES 600/1000 V to BS 6883
Main application: shipwiring and offshore

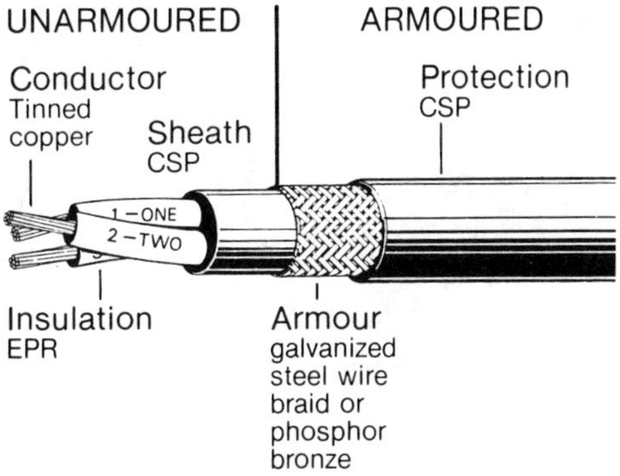

Table A7.1 Maximum a.c. continuous current ratings in ships

Conductor size (mm^2)	Single core (A)	2-core (A)	3- or 4-core (A)	Conductor size (mm^2)	Single core (A)	2-core (A)	3- or 4-core (A)
1.0	16	13	11	70	225	190	160
1.5	20	17	14	95	275	235	195
2.5	28	24	20	120	320	270	225
4	38	32	27	150	365	310	255
6	48	41	34	185	415	350	290
10	67	57	47	240	490	415	345
16	90	76	63	300	560	475	390
25	120	100	84	400	630		
35	145	125	100	500	680		
50	180	155	125	630	740		

Note

The ratings are based on an ambient temperature of 45 °C and a maximum conductor operating temperature of 85 °C. They apply to a single circuit in which up to six cables may be bunched together. If there are more than six cables a derating factor of 0.85 should be applied. Considerably higher ratings may be possible for offshore installations where regulations for ships do not apply, e.g. ambient temperature of 30 °C and maximum conductor temperature of 90 °C (table A7.2).

Rating factor for ambient temperature

Ambient temperature (°C)	35	40	45	50	55	60	65	70	75
Rating factor	1.12	1.06	1.00	0.94	0.87	0.79	0.71	0.61	0.50

ELASTOMERIC SHIPWIRING POWER CABLES
600/1000 V to BS 6883

Table A7.2 Maximum a.c. continuous current ratings – offshore

Conductor size (mm^2)	In free air or on a perforated cable tray[a]				Clipped to a non-metallic surface[a]			
	Single-core cable		Multicore cable		Single-core cable		Multicore cable	
	Two cables single-phase or three or four cables 3-phase spaced (A)	Three cables 3-phase, flat and touching or trefoil (A)	One 2-core cable, single-phase (A)	One 3- or 4- core cable, 3-phase (A)	Two cables, single-phase (A)	3 or 4 cables, 3-phase (A)	One 2-core cable, single phase (A)	One 3-core cable, 3-phase (A)
1	20	18	20	18	20	18	19	17
1.5	26	24	26	23	26	24	24	21
2.5	36	33	35	31	35	32	33	29
4	49	44	48	42	47	44	45	38
6	64	58	62	54	62	56	58	50
10	88	80	84	74	84	78	80	68
16	120	105	115	98	110	105	105	92
25	160	140	150	130	150	140	140	120
35	200	175	185	155	185	170	175	150
50	245	215	220	195	225	205	210	180
70	315	275	285	245	285	265	265	230
95	385	335	340	300	345	320	320	280
120	450	390	395	345	400	370	375	325

150	520	450	455	400	460	425	430	375
185	595	515	520	455	540	490	490	425
240	710	610	610	535	630	575	575	500
300	820	710	700	620	720	660	660	575
400	970	830			860	790		
500	1120	960			980	900		
630	1310	1100			1130	1040		
800	1490	1240			1270	1170		
1000	1680	1390			1420	1300		

[a] See below for conditions applicable

Rating factor for ambient temperature

Ambient temperature (°C)	25	30	35	40	45	50	60	70	80
Rating factor	1.04	1	0.96	0.91	0.87	0.82	0.71	0.58	0.41

NOTES ON CURRENT RATINGS FOR OFFSHORE APPLICATIONS

Ambient and maximum cable temperature

Certain authorities do not regard the regulations governing shipwiring cables, e.g. the IEE Regulations for the Electrical and Electronic Equipment of Ships, and the current ratings so prescribed, as applicable to offshore applications. Consequently, higher ratings may be adopted which exploit the full thermal capabilities of the cable materials. Instead of an ambient temperature of 45 °C and a maximum conductor temperature of 85 °C, the ratings in table A7.2 are based on temperatures of 30 °C and 90 °C respectively.

General installation conditions

The current ratings in table A7.2 are based on the following installation conditions.

Metallic protection
As cables on platforms at sea are chiefly used in flameproof installations, they have a metallic protection layer which assists glanding and earthing arrangements. The ratings assume that the metallic covering is bonded at both ends, as required in hazardous locations. The covering is usually a galvanised steel wire braid but single-core cables have a non-magnetic (phosphor bronze) wire braid.

Iron or steel surfaces
The ratings assume that single-core cables are installed remotely from iron or ferrous concrete (other than cable supports) and that cables which carry 250 A or more are spaced from any steel deck or bulk head by a distance of at least 50 mm.

Isolation of circuits
One circuit is isolated from other circuits or groups of cables as follows:

(a) horizontal clearances of not less than the overall width of an individual circuit, except that the distance need not exceed 150 mm
(b) horizontal clearances of not less than six times the overall diameter of an individual cable
(c) vertical distance between circuits not less than 150 mm
(d) if the number of circuits exceeds four they are installed in a horizontal plane

Cables in free air or on a cable tray

The ratings given in columns 2–5 of table A7.2 are calculated assuming the following.

Single-core cables flat spaced (column 2)
(a) Cables are fixed by supports to the vertical surface of a wall, any supporting metalwork under the cables occupying less than 10% of the plan area.
(b) They are installed either vertically one above the other, or horizontally, the distance between cables being not less than the cable diameter D_e and the distance from the wall to the nearest cable not less than $0.5D_e$.*

Single-core cables touching (column 3)
Three single-core cables are installed in contact with one another in flat formation on a perforated cable tray or in trefoil formation either on a perforated cable tray or fixed to a vertical wall. When fixed to a wall condition (a) above for spaced cables applies. The distance from the wall to the nearest cable should be not less than $0.5D_e$ or, where two cables are equidistant from the wall, not less than $0.75D_e$.*

Multicore cables (columns 4 and 5)
Cables are installed singly either on a perforated cable tray or fixed to a vertical wall. When fixed to a wall, condition (a) above for spaced single-core cables applies, and the minimum distance between cable and wall is $0.3D_e$.*

Cables clipped to a surface (columns 6–9)

Cables are clipped direct to or lying on a non-metallic surface. Single-core cables are in contact with one another, and may be installed in trefoil formation.

Group rating factors

For rating factors of groups of cables other than those covered in table A7.2, reference should be made to other published data or to the cable manufacturer.

* See general installation conditions above relating to iron or steel surfaces.

ELASTOMERIC SHIPWIRING POWER CABLES
600/1000 V to BS 6883

Table A7.3 Dimensions and weights

Numbers of cores × conductor size (mm^2)	Circular conductors			
	Unarmoured		Armoured	
	Approximate diameter (mm)	Approximate weight (kg/km)	Approximate diameter (mm)	Approximate weight (kg/km)
1 × 1.0	5.3	40	9.1	135
1 × 1.5	5.5	47	9.3	145
1 × 2.5	6.0	58	9.8	165
1 × 4	6.9	84	10.8	195
1 × 6	7.5	110	11.4	225
1 × 10	9.0	170	13.1	320
1 × 16	10.1	235	14.2	395
1 × 25	12.4	375	16.7	565
1 × 35	13.3	455	17.8	670
1 × 50	15.2	670	19.7	855
1 × 70	17.2	825	22.1	1120
1 × 95	19.2	1100	24.4	1440
1 × 120	21.4	1410	26.6	1770
1 × 150	23.5	1890	28.9	2120
1 × 185	26.0	2350	32.5	2700
1 × 240	29.2	3050	36.0	3410
1 × 300	32.3	3700	39.4	4160
1 × 400	36.4	4470	43.9	5280
1 × 500	40.2	5360	48.1	6480
1 × 630	44.1	6680	52.3	7830
2 × 1.0	8.2	86	12.3	240
2 × 1.5	8.9	105	13.0	260
2 × 2.5	9.8	147	13.9	320
2 × 4	12.0	225	16.3	440
2 × 6	13.1	290	17.6	530
2 × 10	16.0	440	20.7	750
2 × 16	18.3	645	23.4	990
2 × 25	22.9	1020	28.1	1480
2 × 35	24.7	1230	30.1	1710
2 × 50	28.4	1640	35.1	2400
2 × 70	32.3	2200	39.3	3110
2 × 95	37.0	2940	44.4	4000

ELASTOMERIC SHIPWIRING POWER CABLES
600/1000 V to BS 6883

Table A7.3 cont.

Numbers of cores × conductor size (mm^2)	Circular conductors			
	Unarmoured		Armoured	
	Approximate diameter (mm)	Approximate weight (kg/km)	Approximate diameter (mm)	Approximate weight (kg/km)
2 × 120	40.8	3680	48.5	4860
2 × 150	45.1	4500	53.4	5870
2 × 185	50.0	5600	58.8	7170
2 × 240	56.6	7260	65.8	9090
2 × 300	62.7	9050	72.7	11140
3 × 1.0	8.9	100	13.0	270
3 × 1.5	9.4	130	13.5	300
3 × 2.5	10.4	180	14.7	370
3 × 4	12.7	270	17.0	500
3 × 6	13.9	355	18.4	610
3 × 10	17.2	560	22.1	890
3 × 16	19.5	790	24.6	1630
3 × 25	24.4	1290	29.8	1790
3 × 35	26.5	1590	33.1	2290
3 × 50	30.3	2120	37.2	2930
3 × 70	34.7	2900	41.9	3860
3 × 95	39.7	3790	47.6	5000
3 × 120	43.8	4790	52.0	6150
3 × 150	48.4	5860	57.0	7410
3 × 185	53.9	7310	62.9	9110
3 × 240	61.1	9500	70.6	11630
3 × 300	67.6	11960	77.9	14290
4 × 1.0	9.6	130	13.7	300
4 × 1.5	10.3	160	14.6	340
4 × 2.5	11.4	200	15.7	430
4 × 4	13.9	340	18.4	600
4 × 6	15.4	450	20.1	750
4 × 10	18.9	710	24.0	1080
4 × 16	21.7	1020	26.9	1450
4 × 25	27.1	1630	33.6	2380
4 × 35	29.4	2058	36.2	2880
4 × 50	33.9	2740	41.0	3670

(*cont.*)

ELASTOMERIC SHIPWIRING POWER CABLES
600/1000 V to BS 6883

Table A7.3 cont.

Numbers of cores × conductor size (mm^2)	Circular conductors			
	Unarmoured		Armoured	
	Approximate diameter (mm)	Approximate weight (kg/km)	Approximate diameter (mm)	Approximate weight (kg/km)
4 × 70	38.5	3730	46.1	4840
4 × 95	44.4	4946	52.6	6300
4 × 120	48.9	6240	57.4	7770
4 × 150	54.1	7640	63.1	9410
4 × 185	60.0	9510	69.6	11520
4 × 240	68.0	12410	78.3	14840
4 × 300	75.5	15000	86.6	18260
5 × 1.0	10.5	150	14.7	300
5 × 1.5	11.3	190	15.5	370
5 × 2.5	12.6	275	16.9	470
5 × 4	15.3	425	20.0	680
6 × 1.0	11.4	180	15.7	360
6 × 1.5	12.4	235	16.7	420
6 × 2.5	13.7	330	18.2	545
6 × 4	16.7	505	21.6	765

ELASTOMERIC SHIPWIRING POWER CABLES 1.9/3.3 kV and 3.3/3.3 kV to BS 6883
Main application: shipwiring and offshore

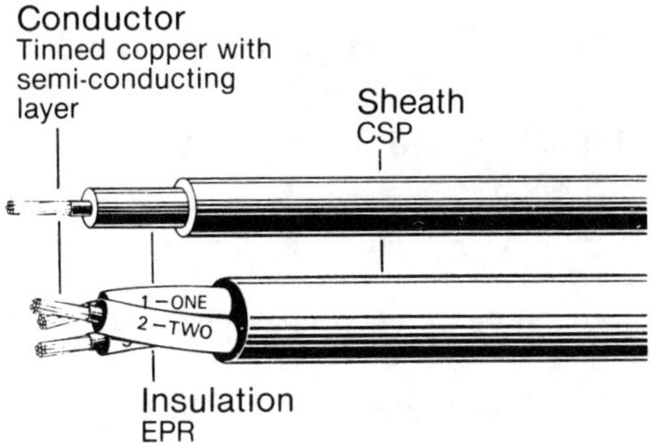

Current ratings

All the relevant data for current ratings, conditions applicable to the ratings and rating factors are the same as for the lower voltage cables as given in tables A7.1 and A7.2.

ELASTOMERIC SHIPWIRING POWER CABLES
1.9/3.3 kV and 3.3/3.3 kV to BS 6883

Table A7.4 Dimensions and weights

Conductor size (mm^2)	Single-core		3-core	
	Approximate diameter (mm)	Approximate weight (kg/km)	Approximate diameter (mm)	Approximate weight (kg/km)
1900/3300 V				
16	14.0	330	28.8	1260
25	15.8	475	32.6	1770
35	16.7	560	34.8	2110
50	18.2	710	37.7	2620
70	20.2	950	42.1	3480
95	22.0	1210	46.1	3990
120	24.0	1490	50.3	4990
150	25.7	1800	53.9	5940
185	27.6	2180	58.4	7240
240	30.4	2780	64.5	9150
300	33.1	3410	70.2	11260
400	36.8	4210		
500	40.2	5310		
630	44.1	6720		
3300/3300 V				
16	16.2	400	33.6	1580
25	18.0	550	37.4	2130
35	18.9	645	39.5	2490
50	20.4	800	42.5	3030
70	22.3	1040	46.6	3910
95	24.2	1310	50.9	4400
120	26.2	1620	54.9	5390
150	27.7	1910	58.6	6400
185	29.8	2310	63.0	7700
240	32.7	2920	69.2	9850
300	35.3	3570	75.0	11860
400	39.0	4480		
500	42.5	5500		
630	46.3	6930		

ELASTOMERIC HIGH VOLTAGE CABLES

1.8/3 kV to 8.7/15 kV to IEC 502

Main application: shipwiring and offshore

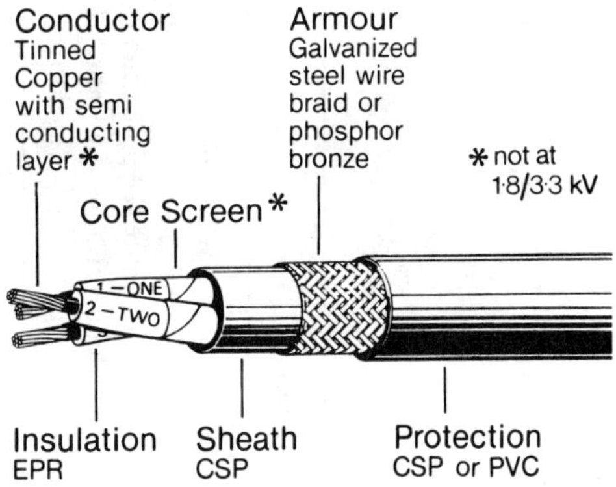

Current ratings

All the relevant data for current ratings, conditions applicable to the ratings and rating factors are the same as for the lower voltage cables as given in table A7.1 and A7.2.

ELASTOMERIC HIGH VOLTAGE CABLES
1.8/3 kV to IEC 502

Table A7.5 Dimensions and weights

Conductor size (mm^2)	Unarmoured				Armoured			
	PVC sheath		CSP sheath		PVC sheath		CSP sheath	
	Approximate diameter (mm)	Approximate weight (kg/km)	Approximate diameter (mm)	Approximate weight (kg/km)	Approximate diameter (mm)	Approximate weight (kg/km)	Approximate diameter (mm)	Approximate weight (kg/km)
1.8/3 kV single-core cables								
16	12.9	346	12.9	348	17.2	479	18.1	530
25	14.3	472	14.3	474	19.3	651	20.3	708
35	15.6	560	15.6	562	20.1	749	21.2	813
50	16.7	698	16.7	699	21.3	901	22.4	969
70	19.0	951	19.0	952	23.5	1147	24.6	1219
95	20.9	1263	20.9	1264	25.9	1507	27.4	1589
120	22.8	1555	22.8	1557	27.6	1843	29.2	1937
150	24.7	1859	24.7	1860	29.2	2149	30.8	2245
185	28.6	2244	26.6	2245	31.0	2564	32.7	2674
240	29.5	2866	29.5	2868	33.8	3197	35.5	3315
300	31.5	3521	31.5	3523	37.2	3974	38.9	4113
400	35.3	4431	35.3	4433	41.2	4964	43.1	5124
500	39.0	5497	39.0	5499	45.0	6098	46.9	6270
630	43.3	6990	43.3	6993	49.0	7669	51.0	7866
800	47.3	8780	47.3	8782	54.9	9761	57.0	9993
1000	53.3	10968	53.3	10974	60.0	12037	62.3	12328

1.8/3 kV 3-core cables								
16	25.6	1164	25.6	1165	29.7	1984	31.4	2096
25	28.6	1595	23.6	1597	32.9	2534	34.6	2664
35	30.5	1363	30.5	1869	35.0	2914	36.7	3048
50	33.3	2360	33.3	2361	39.0	3810	40.8	3982
70	38.5	3205	38.5	3207	43.8	4762	45.7	4942
95	42.0	4210	42.0	4212	47.9	5893	49.8	6098
120	46.3	5200	46.3	5202	53.1	7657	55.2	7896
150	50.0	6198	50.0	6201	56.6	8837	58.7	9084
185	54.3	7499	54.3	7505	60.7	10385	63.1	10687
240	60.5	9556	60.5	9562	67.2	12802	69.6	13118
300	66.3	11672	66.3	11691	72.7	15287	75.3	15658

For the unarmoured cables core screens are included

ELASTOMERIC HIGH VOLTAGE CABLES
3.6/6 kV to IEC 502

Table A7.6 Dimensions and weights

Conductor size (mm^2)	Unarmoured				Armoured			
	PVC sheath		CSP sheath		PVC sheath		CSP sheath	
	Approximate diameter (mm)	Approximate weight (kg/km)	Approximate diameter (mm)	Approximate weight (kg/km)	Approximate diameter (mm)	Approximate weight (kg/km)	Approximate diameter (mm)	Approximate weight (kg/km)
3.6/6 kV single-core cables								
16	17.2	475	17.0	469	22.0	726	23.1	792
25	18.6	616	18.3	608	23.3	937	24.4	1015
35	19.5	726	19.2	718	24.2	1081	25.3	1159
50	21.4	1011	21.0	1002	25.6	1285	26.7	1374
70	23.1	1160	22.7	1149	28.1	1559	29.7	1653
95	25.0	1439	24.6	1426	29.8	1854	31.5	1959
120	26.9	1766	26.3	1751	31.5	2210	33.2	2322
150	28.5	2061	28.0	2044	33.0	2528	34.7	2643
185	30.5	2475	30.0	2457	35.0	3073	36.7	3200
240	33.5	3122	32.7	3101	37.8	3815	39.6	3958
300	36.0	3781	35.3	3763	41.6	4527	43.5	4688
400	39.2	4692	38.4	4662	44.7	5490	46.6	5661
500	43.1	5792	42.2	5759	48.4	6817	50.3	7005
630	47.1	7316	46.2	7276	53.4	8482	55.5	8708
800	51.7	9169	50.6	9122	58.2	10443	60.3	10683

1000	56.6	11339	55.5	11282	63.0	12765	65.4	13066
3.6/6 kV 3-core cables								
16	34.3	1823	34.4	1789	39.3	2675	41.1	2860
25	37.5	2352	37.6	2311	43.9	3067	45.8	3269
35	39.5	2757	39.6	2702	45.7	3342	47.6	3548
50	42.9	3414	43.0	3360	49.0	4302	51.0	4569
70	46.8	4315	46.9	4249	52.9	4942	55.0	5193
95	50.7	5315	50.8	5230	58.4	5701	60.5	5886
120	54.7	6458	54.8	6358	62.3	6408	64.7	6753
150	58.1	7523	58.2	7409	65.7	7073	68.1	7430
185	62.3	9029	62.5	8866	70.2	7941	72.8	8358
240	68.2	11297	68.5	11135	76.2	9287	78.9	9728
300	73.5	13661	73.7	13440	81.6	11700	84.3	12170

ELASTOMERIC HIGH VOLTAGE CABLES
6/10 and 8.7/15 kV to IEC 502

Table A7.7 Dimensions and weights

Conductor size (mm^2)	6/10 kV armoured				8.7/15 kV armoured			
	PVC sheath		CSP sheath		PVC sheath		CSP sheath	
	Approximate diameter (mm)	Approximate weight (kg/km)	Approximate diameter (mm)	Approximate weight (kg/km)	Approximate diameter (mm)	Approximate weight (kg/km)	Approximate diameter (mm)	Approximate weight (kg/km)
Single-core cables								
16	23.5	769	24.6	850				
25	24.8	1013	26.3	1090	27.3	1246	28.9	1287
35	25.9	1163	27.4	1244	28.1	1363	29.7	1408
50	27.1	1340	28.7	1430	29.3	1643	30.9	1698
70	28.9	1616	30.5	1712	31.4	1849	33.1	1910
95	30.9	1947	32.6	2045	33.3	2188	35.0	2260
120	32.5	2271	34.2	2385	35.7	2612	37.4	2698
150	34.2	2608	35.9	2728	37.9	3016	39.7	3115
185	37.5	3191	39.2	3320	39.7	3468	41.6	3582
240	40.0	3889	41.9	4035	42.5	4178	44.4	4316
300	42.7	4619	44.6	4783	45.1	4892	47.0	5053
400	45.7	5676	47.6	5749	49.1	6040	51.0	6239
500	50.0	6700	52.1	6898	52.8	7201	54.9	7438
630	54.4	8533	56.5	8749	56.9	8820	59.0	9111
800	59.0	10501	61.1	10723	61.4	11752	63.8	12140

1000	64.0	12819	66.4	13111	66.5	13095	68.9	13527
3-core cables								
16	43.0	3602	44.9	3797				
25	46.0	4294	47.9	4499	53.0	5775	55.1	5965
35	50.1	5389	52.2	5632	55.1	6273	57.2	6480
50	52.9	6084	55.0	6337	57.9	7298	60.0	7539
70	56.9	7265	59.0	7531	62.3	8291	64.7	8564
95	60.8	8383	63.2	8809	66.4	9574	68.8	9890
120	65.1	9894	67.5	10232	70.2	10877	72.6	11236
150	68.5	11136	70.9	11487	73.7	12230	76.3	12633
185	72.7	12874	75.3	13281	79.1	13937	81.8	14397
240	79.8	15394	82.5	15846	85.5	17634	88.2	18215
300	85.7	19198	88.4	19831				

Appendix A8

Flexible Cords and Cables

PVC INSULATED FLEXIBLE CORDS

300/300 V and 300/500 V
to BS 6500 and BS 6141

Main application: internal wiring and external connection of appliances

Insulated only 300/300 volt parallel twin

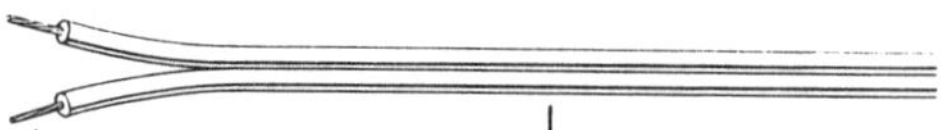

Insulated only 300/500 volt single core

Sheathed 300/300 volt, light cord

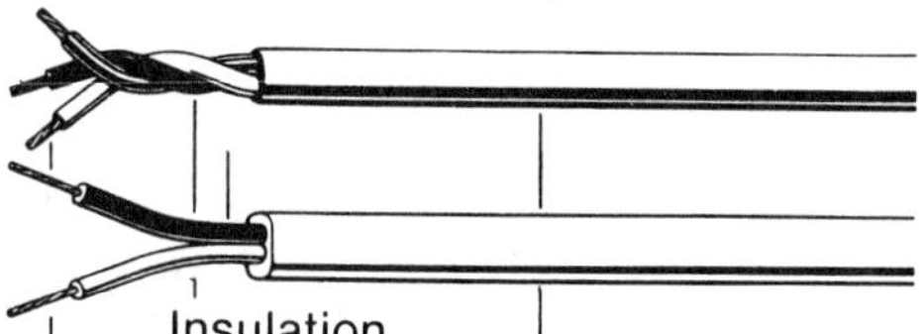

Sheathed 300/500 volt ordinary cord

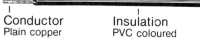

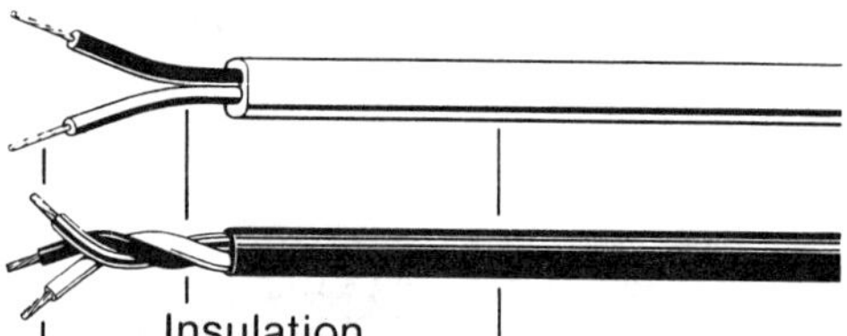

Note: the 300/300 V parallel twin cable is not to a British Standard.

Table A8.1 Current ratings

Conductor size (mm^2)	Rating	
	D.C. or single-phase a.c. (A)	3-phase a.c. (A)
0.5	3	3
0.75	6	6
1.0	10	10
1.25	13	–
1.5	16	16
2.5	25	20

Note: The ratings are based on an ambient temperature of 30 °C and are in accordance with IEE Regulations. They are only applicable to cords laid straight, not to coils.

Rating factors for ambient temperature

Ambient temperature (°C)	30	35	40	45	50	55	60	70
General purpose cords	1.00	0.92	0.82	0.71	0.58	0.41		
Heat-resisting cords	1.00	1.00	1.00	1.00	1.00	0.96	0.83	0.47

PVC INSULATED FLEXIBLE CORDS

300/300 V and 300/500 V
to BS 6500 and BS 6141

Table A8.2 Dimensions and weights (PVC insulated only – 300/300 V and 300/500 V – BS 6500)

Conductor		300/300 V parallel twin (ref. 2812X) (not to BS)			300/500 V circular single-core (ref. 2491X)	
Size (mm^2)	Maximum diameter of wires (mm)	Mean dimensions Minimum (mm)	Mean dimensions Maximum (mm)	Approximate weight (kg/km)	Maximum diameter (mm)	Approximate weight (kg/km)
0.5	0.21	2.5 × 5.0	3.0 × 6.0	25		
0.5	0.21				2.6	10
0.75	0.21	2.7 × 5.4	3.2 × 6.4	33		
0.75	0.21				2.8	13
1.0	0.21				3.0	16

PVC INSULATED FLEXIBLE CORDS
300/300 V and 300/500 V
to BS 6500 and BS 6141

Table A8.3 Dimensions and weights (PVC insulated, PVC sheathed, 300/300 V, light cord — BS 6500 and BS 6141[a])

Conductor		Mean dimensions		Approximate weight (kg/km)	
Size (mm^2)	Maximum diameter of wires	Minimum (mm)	Maximum (mm)		
Flat 2-core (ref. 2192Y)					
0.5	0.21	3.0 × 4.8	3.6 × 6.0	30	
0.75	0.21	3.2 × 5.2	3.9 × 6.4	37	
Circular 2-core (ref. 2182Y and 2092Y[a])					
				2182Y	2092Y[a]
0.5	0.21	4.8	6.0	43	39
0.75	0.21	5.2	6.4	51	47
Circular 3-core (ref. 2183Y and 2093Y[a])					
				2183Y	2093Y[a]
0.5	0.21	5.0	6.2	51	45
0.75	0.21	5.4	6.8	63	57
Circular 4-core (ref. 2184Y)					
0.5	0.21	5.6	6.8	61	
0.75	0.21	6.0	7.4	73	

[a] Heat-resisting circular to BS 6141; others to BS 6500

PVC INSULATED FLEXIBLE CORDS

300/300 V and 300/500 V
to BS 6500 and BS 6141

Table A8.4 Dimensions and weights (PVC insulated, PVC sheathed, 300/500 V ordinary cord) BS 6500, BS 6141[a] and BICC Polarflex[b]

Conductor		Dimensions		Approximate weight (kg/km)		
Size (mm^2)	Maximum diameter of wires (mm)	Minimum (mm)	Maximum (mm)			
Flat 2-core (ref. 3192Y)						
0.75	0.21	3.8 × 6.0	5.2 × 7.6		46	
Circular 2-core (ref. 3182Y, 3092Y[a] and 3182Y AG[b])						
				3182Y	3092Y[a]	3182Y AG[b]
0.5	0.21	5.6	7.0	50	49	–
0.75	0.21	6.0	7.6	64	58	64
1.0	0.21	6.4	8.0	74	68	74
1.25	0.21	7.0	8.6	90	83	–
1.5	0.26	7.4	9.0	99	90	99
2.5	0.26	8.9	11.0	144	136	144
Circular 3-core (ref. 3183Y, 3093Y[a] and 3183Y AG[b])						
				3183Y	3093Y[a]	3183Y AG[b]
0.5	0.21	5.8	7.2	–	58	–
0.75	0.21	6.4	8.0	76	72	76
1.0	0.21	6.8	8.4	89	85	89
1.25		7.6	9.4	112	103	–
1.5		8.0	9.8	125	112	129
2.5		9.6	12.0	180	171	180
Circular 4-core (ref. 3184Y, 3094Y[a] and 3184Y AG[b])						
				3184Y	3094Y[a]	3184Y AG[b]
0.5	0.21	6.4	7.8	–	60	–
0.75	0.21	6.8	8.6	84	74	84
1.0	0.21	7.6	9.4	104	92	104
1.5	0.26	9.0	11.0	150	141	150
2.5	0.26	10.5	13.0	220	213	220
Circular 5-core (ref. 3185Y)						
0.75	0.21	7.8	9.6	107		
1.0	0.21	8.3	10.0	126		
1.5	0.26	10.0	12.0	183		
2.5	0.26	11.5	14.0	268		

[a] Heat resisting to BS 6141
[b] BICC Polarflex

ELASTOMERIC INSULATED FLEXIBLE CORDS

300/300 V, 300/500 V and 450/750 V to BS 6500

Sheathed and braided designs

Main application: mains supply or extension leads to appliances

Braided 300/300 volt
All tinned copper conductors

Fig. 1

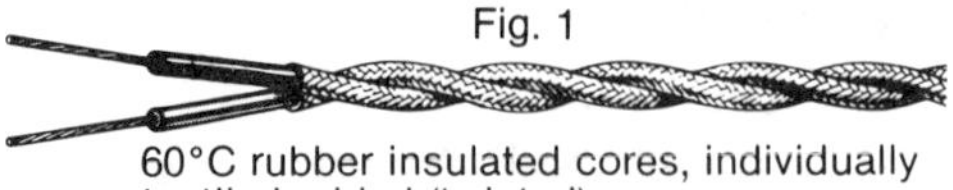

60°C rubber insulated cores, individually textile braided (twisted)

Fig. 2

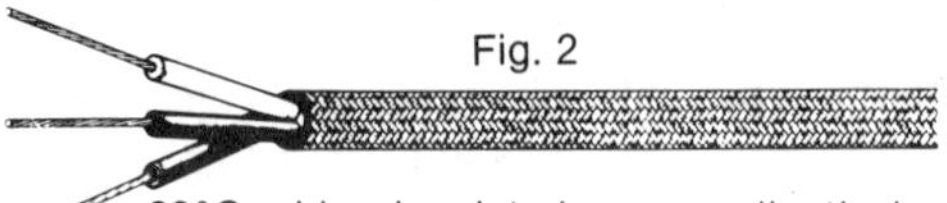

60°C rubber insulated cores, collectively textile braided.

Fig. 3

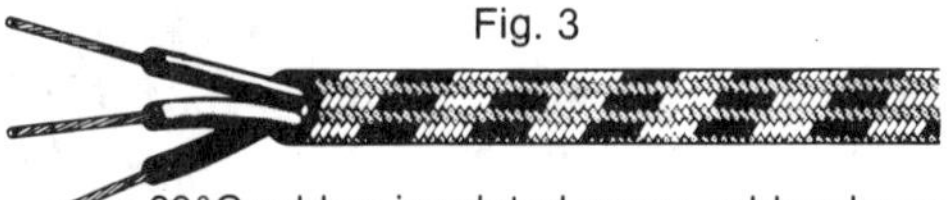

60°C rubber insulated cores, rubber layer, collectively textile braided (UDF) semi-embedded

Braided 300/500 volt

Fig. 4

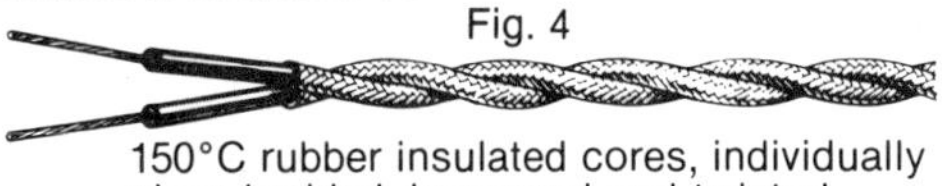

150°C rubber insulated cores, individually glass braided, lacquered and twisted

Fig. 5

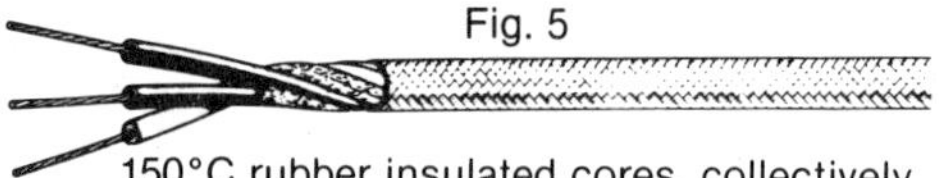

150°C rubber insulated cores, collectively glass braided and lacquered.

Sheathed 450/750 volt

Fig. 9

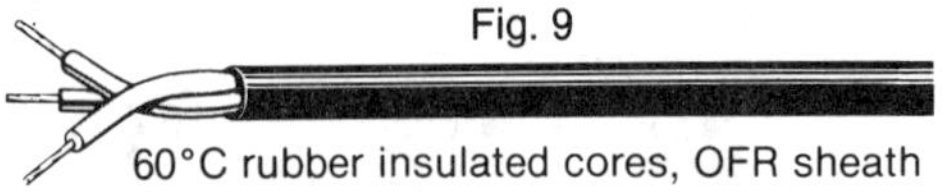

60°C rubber insulated cores, OFR sheath

Sheathed 300/500 volt

Fig. 6

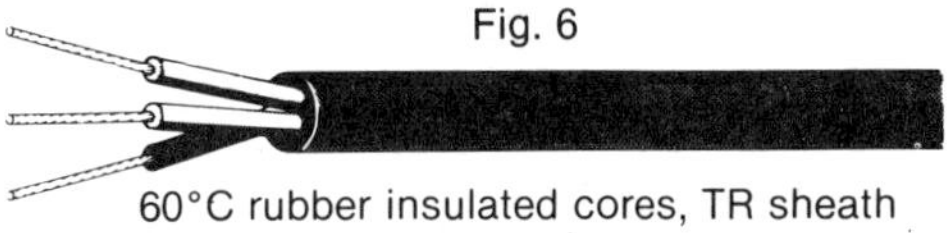

60°C rubber insulated cores, TR sheath

Fig. 7

60°C rubber insulated cores, TR inner sheath, tinned copper wire braid, OFR outer sheath

Fig. 8

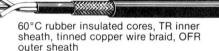

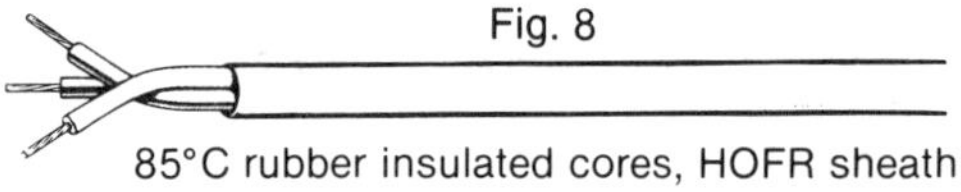

85°C rubber insulated cores, HOFR sheath

Cords to fig. 5 are not supplied to BS 6500.

Current ratings

The ratings for PVC insulated cords in table A8.1 are applicable.

Rating factors for ambient temperature

Ambient temperature (°C)	30	35	40	45	50	55	60	70
60 °C rubber	1.00	0.92	0.82	0.71	0.58	0.41		
85 °C rubber	1.00	1.00	1.00	1.00	1.00	0.96	0.83	0.47

Ambient temperature (°C)	35–120	125	130	135	140
150 °C rubber	1.0	0.96	0.85	0.74	0.60

ELASTOMERIC INSULATED FLEXIBLE CORDS

300/300 V, 300/500 V and 450/750 V to BS 6500

Table A8.5 Dimensions and weights (60 °C insulation, braided, 300/300 V)

Conductor size (mm^2)	Twisted twin (fig. 1) (ref. 2022)		Circular (fig. 2)				Circular (fig. 3)			
			2-core (ref. 2042)		3-core (ref. 2043)		2-core (ref. 2212)		3-core (ref. 2213)	
	Maximum diameter[a] (mm)	Approximate weight (kg/km)	Maximum diameter (mm)	Approximate weight (kg/km)	Maximum diameter (mm)	Approximate weight (kg/km)	Maximum diameter (mm)	Approximate weight (kg/km)	Maximum diameter (mm)	Approximate weight (kg/km)
0.5	3.2	24	7.6	33	8.0	37	6.4	41	6.8	51
0.75	3.4	30	8.0	44	8.6	58	6.8	49	7.2	59
1.0	3.6	37	8.4	49	9.0	69	7.2	57	7.6	70
1.5			9.0	62	9.6	88	8.6	78	9.2	101

[a] For each braided core

ELASTOMERIC INSULATED FLEXIBLE CORDS
300/300 V, 300/500 V and 450/750 V to BS 6500

Table A8.6 Dimensions and weights (150 °C insulation, glass braided, 300/500 V)

Conductor size (mm^2)	Circular single-core (ref. 2771D)		Twisted twin (fig. 4) (ref. 2782D)		Circular (fig. 5)[a]			
					2-core (ref. 2792D)		3-core (ref. 2793D)	
	Maximum diameter (mm)	Approximate weight (kg/km)	Maximum diameter (mm)	Approximate weight (kg/km)	Maximum diameter (mm)	Approximate weight (kg/km)	Maximum diameter (mm)	Approximate weight (kg/km)
0.5	3.4	10	6.8	22	5.3	29	5.8	37
0.75	3.6	13	7.2	28	5.8	37	6.2	47
1.0	3.8	16	7.4	34	6.2	45	6.6	58
1.5	4.3	23	8.6	50	7.6	60	8.1	83
2.5	5.0	35	10.0	76	8.8	85	9.4	135

[a] Not included in BS 6500

ELASTOMERIC INSULATED FLEXIBLE CORDS
300/300 V, 300/500 V and 450/750 V to BS 6500

Table A8.7 Dimensions and weights (60 °C insulation, TRS sheathed ordinary cord, 300/500 V)

Conductor size (mm^2)	Circular (fig. 6)							
	2-core (ref. 3182)		3-core (ref. 3183)		4-core (ref. 3184)		5-core (ref. 3185)	
	Maximum diameter (mm)	Approximate weight (kg/km)	Maximum diameter (mm)	Approximate weight (kg/km)	Maximum diameter (mm)	Approximate weight (kg/km)	Maximum diameter (mm)	Approximate weight (kg/km)
0.5	7.8	50	8.2	59				
0.75[a]	8.2	61	8.8	75	9.6	90	11.0	112
1.0[a]	8.8	74	9.2	87	10.0	106	11.5	131
1.5	10.5	109	11.0	130	12.5	163	13.5	197
2.5	12.5	155	13.0	187	14.0	236	15.5	280

[a] Also available (2- and 3-core) with OFR sheath (cable reference 3182P, 3183P)

ELASTOMERIC INSULATED FLEXIBLE CORDS

300/300 V, 300/500 V and 450/750 V to BS 6500

Table A8.8 Dimensions and weights (60 °C insulation, sheathed, screened, OFR sheathed, 300/500 V)

Conductor size (mm^2)	Circular, screened (fig. 7)					
	2-core (ref. 3802P)		3-core (ref. 3803P)		4-core (ref. 3804P)	
	Maximum diameter (mm)	Approximate weight (kg/km)	Maximum diameter (mm)	Approximate weight (kg/km)	Maximum diameter (mm)	Approximate weight (kg/km)
0.5	11.0	139	11.5	155	12.5	189
0.75	12.0	169	12.5	178	13.0	202
1.0	12.5	188	13.0	193	14.0	239
1.5	14.0	248	15.0	275	16.0	324
2.5	16.0	314	16.5	352	18.0	417

Table A8.9 Dimensions and weights (85 °C insulation, HOFR sheathed, 300/500 V)

Conductor size (mm^2)	Circular (fig. 8)					
	2-core (ref. 3182TQ)		3-core (ref. 3183TQ)		4-core (ref. 3184TQ)	
	Maximum diameter (mm)	Approximate weight (kg/km)	Maximum diameter (mm)	Approximate weight (kg/km)	Maximum diameter (mm)	Approximate weight (kg/km)
0.5	7.8	40	8.2	57		
0.75	8.2	50	8.8	74	9.6	80
1.0	8.8	61	9.2	88	10.0	107
1.5	10.5	89	11.0	113	12.5	151
2.5	12.5	129	13.0	165	14.0	217

ELASTOMERIC INSULATED FLEXIBLE CORDS
300/300 V, 300/500 V and 450/750 V to BS 6500

Table A8.10 Dimensions and weights (60 °C insulation, OFR sheathed, 450/750 V)

Conductor size (mm^2)	Circular (fig. 9)									
	Single-core (ref. 3981)		2-core (ref. 3982)		3-core (ref. 3983)		4-core (ref. 3984)		5-core (ref. 3985)	
	Maximum diameter (mm)	Approximate weight (kg/km)	Maximum diameter (mm)	Approximate weight (kg/km)	Maximum diameter (mm)	Approximate weight (kg/km)	Maximum diameter (mm)	Approximate weight (kg/km)	Maximum diameter (mm)	Approximate weight (kg/km)
1.0			10.5	109	11.5	125	12.5	163	13.5	188
1.5	7.2	60	11.5	138	12.5	168	13.5	206	15.0	249
2.5	8.0	78	13.5	194	14.5	233	15.5	280	17.0	355

PVC INSULATED FLEXIBLE CORDS

300/500 V with metal braid to BS 6500

Main application: mains supply or extension leads to appliances in mechanically arduous conditions

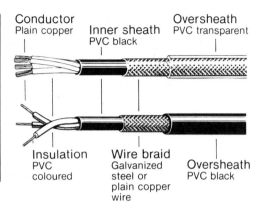

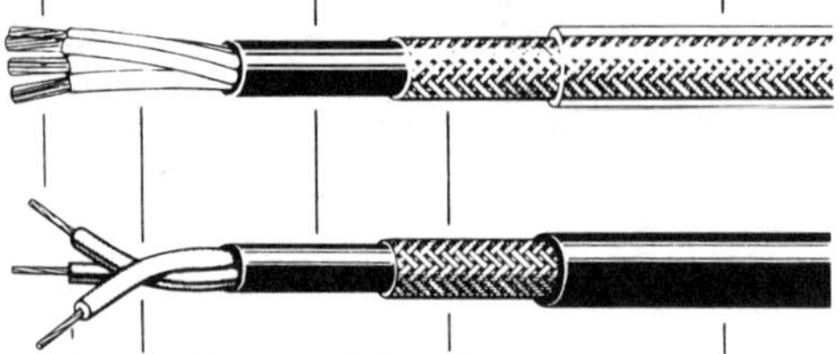

Table A8.11 Conductors and ratings

Conductor details				
Size (mm^2)	0.75	1.0	1.5	2.5
Maximum diameter (mm)	0.21	0.21	0.26	0.26
Current ratings				
All the data given in table A8.1 are applicable.				

PVC INSULATED FLEXIBLE CORDS

300/500 V with metal braid to BS 6500

Table A8.12 Dimensions and weights

Conductor size (mm^2)	2-core		3-core		4-core		5-core[a]	
	Approximate diameter (mm)	Approximate weight (kg/km)	Approximate diameter (mm)	Approximate weight (kg/km)	Approximate diameter (mm)	Approximate weight (kg/km)	Approximate diameter (mm)	Approximate weight (kg/km)
Plain copper wire braid								
	(reference 3802Y)		(reference 3803Y)		(reference 3804Y)		(reference 3805Y)	
0.75	9.6	146	10.1	167	10.7	196	11.6	225
1.0	10.1	161	10.5	184	11.6	223	12.0	246
1.5	11.2	217	11.9	237	13.2	289	14.3	341
2.5	13.1	270	14.1	333	15.3	396	15.8	439
Galvanised steel wire braid (not to BS 6500)								
	(reference 3262Y)		(reference 3263Y)		(reference 3264Y)		(reference 3265Y)	
0.75	10.0	156	10.5	174	11.1	200	12.0	244
1.0	10.5	188	10.9	197	12.0	232	12.4	264
1.5	11.6	212	12.3	247	13.6	292	14.7	364
2.5	13.5	280	14.5	335	15.7	386	16.3	471

[a] Cords of both constructions with up to 12 cores are also available

ELASTOMERIC INSULATED FLEXIBLE CABLES

450/750 V to BS 6007

Main application: services or mains supply where flexibility is required

60 °C rubber insulated, PCP sheathed flexible cable and 85 °C rubber insulated, HOFR sheathed flexible cable

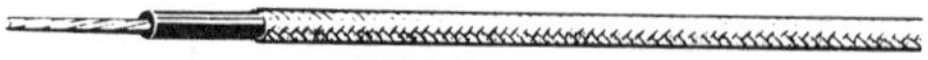

150 °C rubber insulated, glass braided, laquered

Table A8.13 Current ratings and volt drop (60 °C rubber insulated)

Conductor		Ratings		Volt drop per A/m		
Size (mm^2)	Maximum diameter of wires (mm)	One 2- or 3-core cable single-phase (A)	One 3-, 4- or 5-core cable, 3-phase (A)	D.C. (mV)	Single-phase-a.c. (mV)	3-phase a.c. (mV)
4	0.31	30	26	12	12	10
6	0.31	39	34	7.8	7.8	6.7
10	0.41	54	47	4.6	4.6	4.0
16	0.41	73	63	2.9	2.9	2.5
25	0.41	97	83	1.80	1.85	1.55
35	0.41		102			1.15
50	0.41		124			0.84
70	0.51		158			0.58
95	0.51		192			0.44
120	0.51		222			0.36
150	0.51		255			0.30
185	0.51		291			0.26
240	0.51		343			0.21
300	0.51		394			0.19

Guidance on the ratings of single core 60 °C rubber insulated cables may be obtained by multiplying the ratings in columns 6 and 7 of table A7.2 by a factor of 0.67.

Note
For details of the conditions on which the ratings are based and the rating factors see under table A8.14.

ELASTOMERIC INSULATED FLEXIBLE CABLES

450/750 V to BS 6007

Table A8.14 Current ratings and volt drop (85 °C and 150 °C rubber insulated)

Conductor		Ratings		Volt drop per A/m		
Size (mm^2)	Maximum diameter of wires (mm)	One 2- or 3-core cable, single-phase (A)	One 3-, 4- or 5-core cable, 3-phase (A)	D.C. (mV)	Single-phase a.c. (mV)	3-phase a.c. (mV)
4	0.31	41	36	13	13	11
6	0.31	53	47	8.4	8.4	7.3
10	0.41	73	64	5.0	5.0	4.3
16	0.41	99	86	3.1	3.1	2.7
25	0.41	131	114	2.0	2.0	1.7
35	0.41		140			1.2
50	0.41		170			0.91
70	0.51		216			0.63
95	0.51		262			0.48
120	0.51		303			0.39
150	0.51		348			0.32
185	0.51		397			0.27
240	0.51		467			0.22
300	0.51		537			0.20

Guidance on the ratings of single core 85 °C and 150 °C rubber insulated cables may be obtained by multiplying the ratings in columns 6 and 7 of table A7.2 by a factor of 0.95.

Note

The rating given in tables A8.13 and A8.14 are for a single circuit and are based on an ambient temperature of 30 °C. They are in accordance with the fifteenth edition of the IEE Wiring Regulations.

The ratings are for cables in free air but may also be used for cables resting on a surface. They are not applicable to cables in coils or wound on a drum.

Ratings factors for ambient temperature

Ambient temperature (°C)	35	40	45	50	55	60	70
Factor for 60 °C rubber insulation	0.91	0.82	0.71	0.58	0.41		
Factor for 85 °C rubber insulation	0.95	0.90	0.85	0.80	0.74	0.67	0.52

Ambient temperature (°C)	35–85	90	100	110	120	130	140
Factor for 150 °C rubber insulation	1.0	0.96	0.88	0.78	0.68	0.55	0.39

Group rating factors

For the rating factors of groups of cables other than those given in the tables, reference should be made to the cable manufacturer or to other published data.

ELASTOMERIC INSULATED FLEXIBLE CABLES
450/750 V to BS 6007

Table A8.15 Dimensions and weights (60 °C rubber insulated, circular, OFR sheathed cables, 450/750 V)

Conductor size (mm^2)	Number of cores			
	One (ref. 6381P)		Two (ref. 6382P)	
	Maximum diameter (mm)	Approximate weight (kg/km)	Maximum diameter (mm)	Approximate weight (kg/km)
4	9.0	101	15.0	264
6	11.0	142	18.5	367
10	12.5	202	24.0	559
16	14.5	284	27.5	760
25	16.5	406	31.5	1160
35	18.5	553		
50	21.0	754		
70	23.5	957		
95	26.0	1308		
120	28.5	1610		
150	31.5	1960		
185	34.5	2370		
240	38.0	3078		
300	41.5	3775		
400	46.5	4875		
500	51.5	5980		
630	56.5	7450		

(cont.)

Table A8.15 cont.

Conductor size (mm^2)	Number of cores					
	Three (ref. 6383P)		Four (ref. 6384P)		Five (ref. 6385P)	
	Maximum diameter (mm)	Approximate weight (kg/km)	Maximum diameter (mm)	Approximate weight (kg/km)	Maximum diameter (mm)	Approximate weight (kg/km)
4	16.0	330	18.0	406	19.5	509
6	20.0	470	22.0	560	24.5	673
10	25.5	764	28.0	947	30.5	1119
16	29.5	1035	32.0	1292	35.5	1568
25	34.0	1491	37.5	1872	41.5	2420
35	38.0	1940	42.0	2415		
50	44.0	2680	48.5	3419		
70	49.5	3564	54.5	4462		
95	54.0	4860	60.5	6066		
120	59.0	5832	65.6	7367		
150	66.5	7223	74.0	9470		
185	71.5	8667	78.0	11261		
240	81.0	11448	90.0	14756		
300	89.5	14148	99.5	18367		

Notes
(a) For flexible cords below 4 mm^2 see tables A8.7 and A8.10.
(b) For conductor details see table A8.13.

ELASTOMERIC INSULATED FLEXIBLE CABLES
450/750 V to BS 6007

Table A8.16 Dimensions and weights (85 °C rubber insulated, circular, HOFR sheathed cables, 450/750 V)

Conductor size (mm^2)	Number of cores			
	One (ref. 6381TQ)		Two (ref. 6382TQ)	
	Maximum diameter (mm)	Approximate weight (kg/km)	Maximum diameter (mm)	Approximate weight (kg/km)
4	9.0	99	15.0	262
6	11.0	140	18.5	360
10	12.5	200	24.0	550
16	14.5	280	27.5	750
25	16.5	400	31.5	1150
35	18.5	550		
50	21.0	750		
70	23.5	950		
95	26.0	1300		
120	28.5	1600		
150	31.5	1950		
185	34.5	2350		
240	38.0	3050		
300	41.5	3750		
400	46.5	4850		
500	51.5	5950		
630	56.5	7400		

(*cont.*)

ELASTOMERIC INSULATED FLEXIBLE CABLES
450/750 V to BS 6007

Table A8.16 cont.

Conductor size (mm^2)	Number of cores					
	Three (ref. 6383TQ)		Four (ref. 6384TQ)		Five (ref. 6385TQ)	
	Maximum diameter (mm)	Approximate weight (kg/km)	Maximum diameter (mm)	Approximate weight (kg/km)	Maximum diameter (mm)	Approximate weight (kg/km)
4	16.0	330	18.0	390	19.5	500
6	20.0	440	22.0	550	24.5	660
10	25.5	700	28.0	900	30.5	1086
16	29.5	950	32.0	1250	35.5	1508
25	34.0	1400	37.5	1800	41.5	2350
35	38.0	1800	42.0	2300		
50	44.0	2500	48.5	3200		
70	49.5	3300	54.5	4250		
95	54.0	4500	60.5	5750		
120	59.0	5400	65.6	6950		
150	66.5	6750	74.0	8850		
185	71.5	8100	78.0	10400		
240	81.0	10600	90.0	13600		
300	89.5	13100	99.5	16850		

Notes
(a) For flexible cords below 4 mm^2 see table A8.9
(b) For conductor details see table A8.13.

ELASTOMERIC INSULATED FLEXIBLE CABLES
450/750 V to BS 6007

Table A8.17 Dimensions and weights (150 °C rubber insulated, glass braided, 300/500 V)

Conductor size (mm^2)	Single-core circular		Two-core twisted	
	Maximum diameter (mm)	Approximate weight (kg/km)	Maximum diameter (mm)	Approximate weight (kg/km)
4	5.6	51	11.2	105
6	6.2	77	12.4	159
10	8.2	126	16.4	260
16	9.6	188	19.2	388

Notes
(a) For sizes of 0.5 to 2.5 mm^2 see table A8.6.
(b) For conductor details see table A8.13.

HEAT RESISTING FLEXIBLE CABLES FOR 250 °C OPERATION (BICC Intemp 250*)

600/1000 V

* Registered trade mark

Main application: flexible cables for industrial control and supply circuits

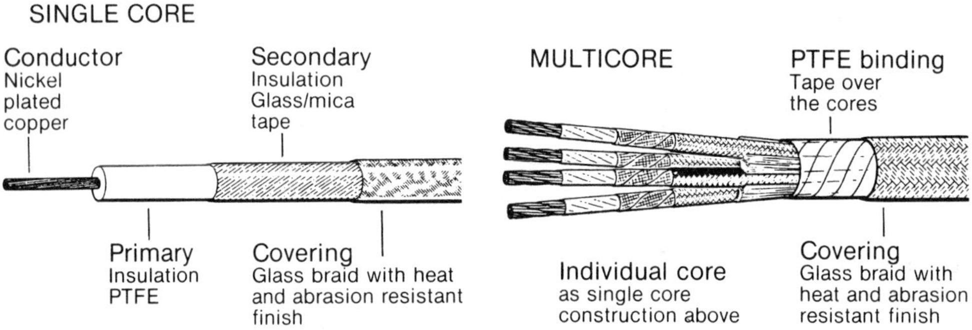

Table A8.18 Range and dimensions

Conductor		Single-core cable			Maximum number of cores in multicore cable
Size (mm^2)	Nominal wires (number/mm)	Approximate diameter (mm)	Approximate weight (kg/km)	Minimum bending radius (mm)	
1.0	32/0.20	3.58	25	38	28
1.5	30/0.25	3.86	32	41	25
2.5	50/0.25	4.26	44	45	21
4	56/0.30	4.86	59	51	16
6	84/0.30	5.56	84	58	12
10	80/0.40	6.46	123	67	9
16	126/0.40	8.75	207	87	5
25	196/0.40	10.15	299	105	4

The above are standard sizes and other sizes up to 150 mm^2 are also produced.

For situations where mechanical protection is required, a range of stainless steel wire braided Intemp single and multicore cables is available.

HEAT RESISTING FLEXIBLE CABLES FOR 250 °C OPERATION

Table A8.19 Current ratings

Conductor size (mm^2)	Resistance at 20 °C (Ω/km)	Maximum continuous current (A)
1.0	19.1	25
1.5	13.0	40
2.5	7.82	54
4	4.85	74
6	3.23	98
10	1.85	135
16	1.18	180
25	0.757	240

Notes

(a) The above ratings are based on an ambient temperature of 30 °C and a maximum continuous conductor temperature of 250 °C.

(b) It is assumed that the cables cannot be touched and are not in contact with heat sensitive materials.

(c) Because the current rating is high, volt drop and power loss in the cable will be high and special fusing may be required.

(d) The ratings apply to single cables freely ventilated in air. See below for group rating factors.

(e) If the high current approach is not desirable, the ratings for a temperature rise of 50 °C may be taken as 48% of the figures in table A8.19. Such ratings need not be corrected for ambient temperature up to 200 °C.

Rating factors for ambient temperature

Ambient temperature (°C)	40	80	120	160	200	240
Rating factor	0.98	0.88	0.77	0.64	0.48	0.20

Group rating factors

Number of cables	2	5	10	15	20	25
Rating factor	0.8	0.6	0.45	0.4	0.36	0.33

'BICC ARMAFLEX'*
PROTECTED FLEXIBLE CORDS
300/500 V
* Registered trademark

Main application: industrial power supply leads

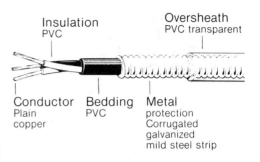

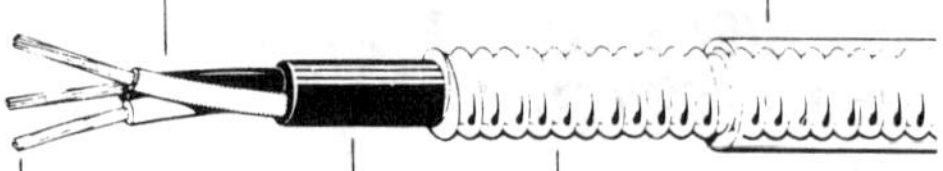

Table A8.20 Current ratings (A)

Conductor size (mm^2)	D.C. or single phase a.c.	3-phase a.c.
0.75	6	6
1.0	10	10
1.5	16	16
2.5	25	20
4	32	25

Rating factor for ambient temperature

Ambient temperature (°C)	35	40	45	50	55
Rating factor	0.92	0.82	0.71	0.58	0.41

Notes

(a) The current ratings are based on an ambient temperature of 30 °C and a maximum conductor operating temperature of 70 °C in accordance with the fifteenth edition of the IEE Wiring Regulations. They apply to a single circuit only.

(b) When the protection is by a semi-enclosed fuse, the cable should be selected with a current rating not less than 1.38 times the rating of the fuse (see chapter 10).

'BICC ARMAFLEX'* PROTECTED FLEXIBLE CORDS

300/500 V

* Registered trade mark

Table A8.21 Dimensions and weights

Conductor size (mm^2)	2-core (ref. 3222Y)		3-core (ref. 3223Y)		4-core (ref. 3224Y)		5-core (ref. 3225Y)	
	Nominal diameter over metal protection (mm)	Approximate weight (kg/km)	Nominal diameter over metal protection (mm)	Approximate weight (kg/km)	Nominal diameter over metal protection (mm)	Approximate weight (kg/km)	Nominal diameter over metal protection (mm)	Approximate weight (kg/km)
0.75	9.1	178	9.4	195	10.1	219	10.9	249
1.0	9.5	194	9.9	214	10.8	249	11.5	301
1.5	10.4	240	11.1	265	12.1	320	13.2	354
2.5	12.0	280	12.8	362	13.9	418	15.1	495
4.0	13.4	366	14.4	453	15.8	677	16.9	631

EPR INSULATED LINAFLEX FLAT FLEXIBLE CORDS (300/500 V) AND CABLES (450/750 V)
(BICC designs)

Main application: industrial installations and supply to mobile equipment particularly if required to be wound on reeling drums or festooned

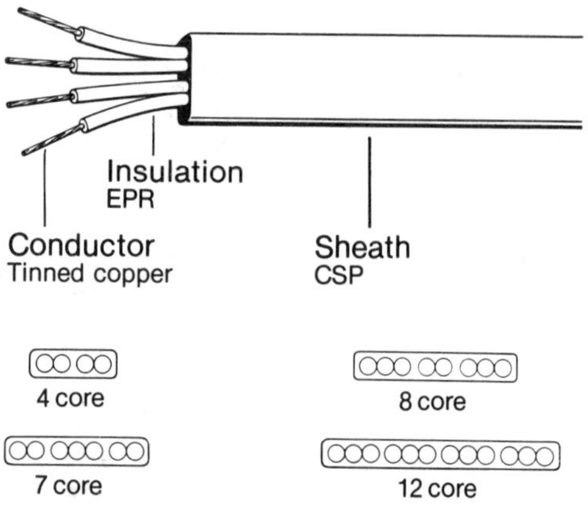

Table A8.22 Current ratings

Conductor size (mm²)	Current rating (A)
Flexible cords	
1.5	21
2.5	28
4	39
Flexible cables	
6	50
10	70
16	92
25	125
35	150
50	185
70	235
95	280
120	325

The ratings quoted are based on an ambient temperature of 30 °C and a maximum operating temperature of 85 °C with three conductors loaded. They are for cables in free air, but may also be used for cables resting on a surface. They are not applicable to cable in coils or wound on a drum. Rating factors for ambient temperature other than 30 °C are given under table A8.14 (85 °C rubber).

EPR INSULATED LINAFLEX FLAT FLEXIBLE CORDS (300/500 V) AND CABLES (450/750 V)

(BICC designs)

Table A8.23 Range and dimensions

Conductor		Dimensions			
Size (mm^2)	Maximum diameter of wires (mm)	Minor (mm)	Major (mm)	Minor (mm)	Major (mm)
Flexible cords					
		4-core		7-core	
1.5	0.26			6.4	31.2
2.5	0.26	7.8	22.3	8.0	37.0
4	0.31	9.0	25.6	9.2	42.3
		8-core		12-core	
1.5	0.26			7.4	51.4
2.5	0.26	8.0	41.2	9.0	60.8
Flexible cables					
		4-core		7-core	
6	0.31	9.8	28.7	10.2	48.1
10	0.41	12.2	35.9	14.0	61.4
16	0.41	13.5	41.2	16.1	71.4
25	0.41	15.6	47.8		
35	0.41	17.7	53.8		
50	0.41	20.9	64.0		
70	0.51	23.0	71.6		
95	0.51	26.5	81.6		
120	0.51	29.5	91.6		

Appendix A9

Industrial Cables for Special Applications

WELDING CABLES
to BS 638, Part 4

Main application: low voltage leads for connection to automatic or hand-held metal arc welding electrodes and for the earthing return leads

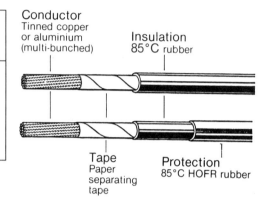

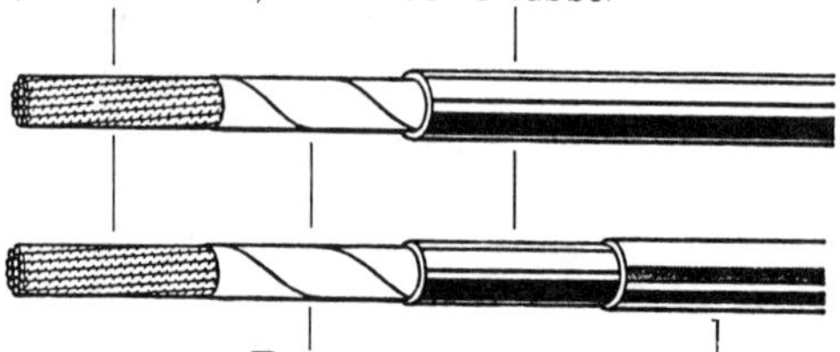

Table A9.1 Range and dimensions

Conductor size (mm^2)	Diameter		Approximate weight		
	Minimum (mm)	Maximum (mm)	Design[a] (kg/km)	Design[a] (kg/km)	Design[a] (kg/km)
Copper conductor			*0361T*	*0361TQ*	*0361H*
16	8.8	11.5	225	230	231
25	10.0	13.0	320	325	320
35	11.0	14.5	430	440	437
50	13.0	17.0	590	600	601
70	15.0	19.5	820	830	832
95	17.0	22.0	1090	1110	1108
120	19.0	24.0	1350	1370	1370
185	23.0	29.0	2030	2050	2057
Aluminium conductor			*0361T (A1)*	*0361TQ (A1)*	*0361H (A1)*
25	10.0	13.0	165	170	168
35	11.0	14.5	210	215	213
50	13.0	17.0	285	295	289
70	15.0	19.0	370	385	381
95	17.0	21.5	480	500	507
120	19.0	24.5	620	640	626
150	21.0	26.5	740	760	756
240	26.0	33.0	1150	1180	1151

[a] T signifies 85 °C rubber insulation; TQ signifies 85 °C rubber insulation and 85 °C HOFR covering; H signifies 85 °C HOFR covering

WELDING CABLES
to BS 638, Part 4

Table A9.2 Resistance and volt drop

Conductor size (mm^2)	Maximum resistance (Ω/km) at 20 °C		Voltage drop – d.c. (V/100 A/10 m of cable)		
	Tinned	Plain	20 °C	60 °C	85 °C
Copper conductor					
16	1.24	1.21	1.24	1.43	1.56
25	0.795	0.780	0.80	0.92	1.00
35	0.565	0.554	0.57	0.65	0.71
50	0.393	0.386	0.39	0.46	0.49
70	0.277	0.272	0.28	0.32	0.35
95	0.210	0.206	0.21	0.24	0.26
120	0.164	0.161	0.16	0.19	0.21
185	0.108	0.106	0.11	0.13	0.14
Aluminium conductor					
25		1.248	1.25	1.45	1.58
35		0.886	0.89	1.03	1.12
50		0.616	0.62	0.72	0.78
70		0.440	0.44	0.51	0.56
95		0.326	0.33	0.38	0.41
120		0.254	0.25	0.30	0.32
150		0.208	0.21	0.24	0.26
240		0.126	0.13	0.15	0.16

Notes

(a) Excessive voltage drop may occur if long lengths of cable are required. Under such circumstances much larger conductors are required than dictated by rating but for flexibility the final length to the electrode may revert to the size appropriate to rating.

(b) The corresponding voltage drops when using a.c. may be much higher depending on the configuration of the cables.

WELDING CABLES
to BS 638, Part 4

Table A9.3 Current ratings

Conductor size (mm^2)	Duty cycle			
	100% (A)	85% (A)	60% (A)	30% (A)
Copper conductor (tinned)				
16	135	145	175	245
25	180	195	230	330
35	225	245	290	410
50	285	310	370	520
70	355	385	460	650
95	430	470	560	790
120	500	540	650	910
185	660	715	850	1200
Aluminium conductor				
25	140	150	180	255
35	175	190	225	320
50	225	245	290	410
70	275	300	355	500
95	335	365	430	610
120	390	425	500	710
150	455	495	590	830
240	600	650	770	1110

Notes

(a) The above ratings are based on an ambient temperature of 25 °C and a maximum conductor operating temperature of 85 °C.

(b) High operating temperatures make the cable too hot to handle and reduce the expected service life. Under severe conditions, if a long service life is not expected, e.g. because of the possibility of mechanical damage, or where a high surface temperature can be tolerated, the current ratings for 25 °C ambient may be used up to 40 °C.

Rating factors

Ambient temperature (°C)	25	30	35	40	45
Rating factor	1.0	0.96	0.91	0.87	0.82

Duty cycle

Current ratings have to be related to the period of the operating cycle, defined as the percentage time per 5 min period that the cable is operated. The classification of duty cycles adopted is as follows:

Automatic	up to 100%
Semi-automatic	30%–85%
Manual	30%–60%
Intermittent or occasional	up to 30%

X-RAY CABLES AND FLEXIBLE SUPPLY LEADS
(BICC designs)

Main application: supply to X-ray tubes for medical, industrial and research uses

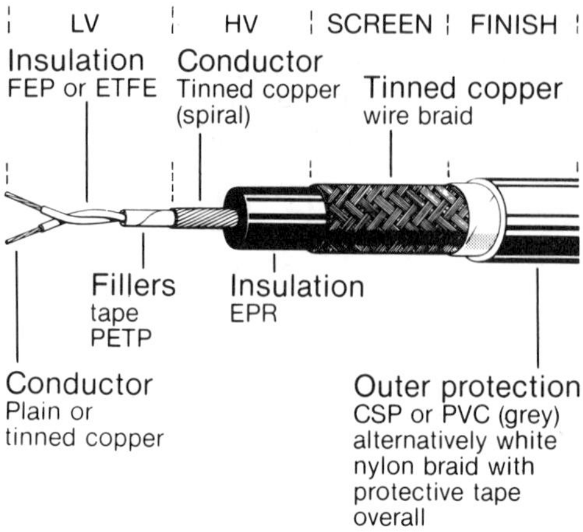

Table A9.4 Range and dimensions

Cable type	Conductor: nominal number of wires and size		Operating voltage[a] (rectified d.c.) (kV)	Approximate diameter		
	LV conductor (mm)	HV conductor (mm)		CSP sheath (mm)	PVC sheath (mm)	Nylon braid (mm)
E	3-core 7/0.45	54/0.25	120	25.3	24.8	
G	2-core 7/0.45	52/0.25	100	22.0	21.5	19.2
J	2-core 7/0.45	52/0.25	150	29.6	29.1	
K	2-core 7/0.45	52/0.25	75		15.6	

[a] The operating voltages in the table are for one cable to earth. They may be doubled if two cables are used.

Note
Low voltage conductors are rated at 5 A for a.c. operation at 240 V (r.m.s.) and will withstand 5 kV d.c. between the LV conductor and the HV conductor.

Appendix A10

Mining Cables

UNARMOURED FLEXIBLE TRAILING CABLES
640/1100 V

Main application: supplies to machinery at underground coal faces (British Coal Specification 188)

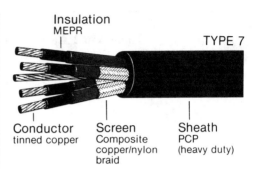

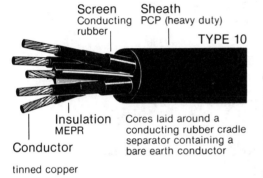

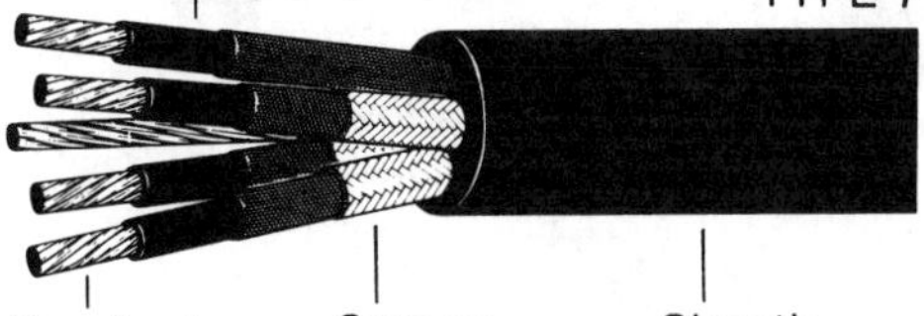

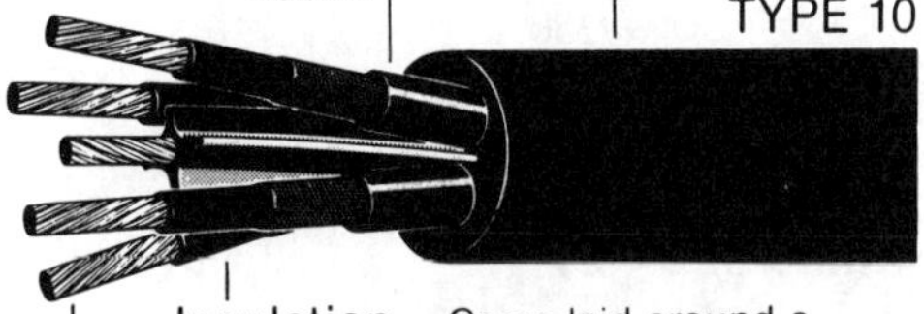

Table A10.1 Construction

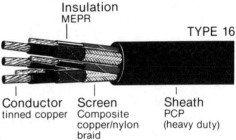

Type	Power cores		Pilot cores		Earth conductor	
	Number	Screen	Number	Screen	Number	
7	3	Copper/nylon	1	Unscreened	1	Bare (in centre)
7M	3	Copper/nylon	1	Copper/nylon	1	Bare (in centre)
7S	3	Copper/nylon	1 unit[a]	Unscreened	1	Bare (in centre)
10	3	Condg rubber	1	Condg rubber	1	In cradle
11[b]	3	Copper/nylon	1	Copper/nylon	–	–
14	3	Copper/nylon	1	Unscreened	1	Insulated
16	3	Copper/nylon	1	Unscreened	2	Insulated

[a] This sheathed pilot unit contains three unscreened cores
[b] A PETP tape is applied over the conductors

UNARMOURED FLEXIBLE TRAILING CABLES

640/1100 V

Table A10.2 Current ratings

Power conductor size (mm^2)	Continuous rating (A)	Intermittent rating (A)
16	85	90
25	110	120
35	135	150
50	170	190
70	205	235
95	250	295
120	295	350

Ambient temperature

The ratings are based on an ambient temperature of 25 °C.

Intermittent rating

The ratings assume cyclic operation with conditions not more severe than

full current for 40 min
no current for 10–15 min
half current for 40 min
no current for 10–15 min
and repetitive cycles of the above

Rating factors for ambient temperature

Ambient temperature (°C)	30	35	40	45	50	55	60
Rating factor	0.93	0.87	0.80	0.73	0.66	0.57	0.48

Note

The above ratings are not applicable to cables in coils or on drums or where circumstances reduce heat dissipation from the cable.

UNARMOURED FLEXIBLE TRAILING CABLES
640/1100 V

Table A10.3 Range and dimensions

Power conductor size (mm^2)	Conductor formation			Diameter		Approximate weight (kg/km)
	Power (number/diameter)	Pilot (number/diameter)	Earth (number/diameter)	Minimum (mm)	Maximum (mm)	
Type 7						
16	126/0.40	126/0.40	126/0.40	35.8	38.6	2310
25	196/0.40	126/0.40	126/0.40	39.7	42.6	2960
35	276/0.40	126/0.40	147/0.40	43.1	46.3	3550
50	396/0.40	196/0.40	196/0.40	48.5	51.8	4600
70	360/0.40	276/0.40	276/0.40	55.1	58.8	6040
95	475/0.50	396/0.40	396/0.40	62.4	66.1	7880
120	608/0.50	360/0.50	396/0.40	68.0	72.5	10500
Type 7M						
16	126/0.40	126/0.40	126/0.40	35.8	38.6	2548
25	196/0.40	196/0.40	126/0.40	39.7	42.9	3163
34	276/0.40	276/0.40	147/0.40	43.1	46.3	3841
50	396/0.40	396/0.40	196/0.40	48.5	51.8	5019
70	360/0.50	360/0.50	276/0.40	55.1	58.8	6498
95	475/0.50	475/0.50	396/0.40	62.4	66.1	8222
120	608/0.50	608/0.50	396/0.50	68.0	72.5	9951
Type 7S						
50	396/0.40	56/0.30	196/0.40	48.5	51.8	4551
70	360/0.50	84/0.30	276/0.40	55.1	58.8	5916
95	475/0.50	84/0.30	396/0.40	62.4	66.1	7576
120	608/0.50	80/0.40	396/0.40	68.0	72.5	9099

(cont.)

UNARMOURED FLEXIBLE TRAILING CABLES
640/1100 V

Table A10.3 cont.

Power conductor size (mm^2)	Conductor formation			Diameter		Approximate weight (kg/km)
	Power (number/diameter)	Pilot (number/diameter)	Earth (number/diameter)	Minimum (mm)	Maximum (mm)	
Type 10						
25	196/0.40	126/0.40	126/0.40	45.7	49.0	3250
35	276/0.40	126/0.40	196/0.40	51.1	54.9	4160
50	396/0.40	196/0.40	276/0.40	58.9	62.6	5600
70	360/0.40	276/0.40	396/0.40	66.7	71.3	7320
95	475/0.50	396/0.40	396/0.40	73.8	78.3	9620
Type 11						
16	126/0.40	126/0.40	–	30.9	33.0	1958
Type 14						
25	196/0.40	126/0.40	196/0.40	43.2	46.5	3450
35	276/0.40	126/0.40	276/0.40	47.3	50.7	4210
50	396/0.40	196/0.40	396/0.40	53.7	57.6	5550
70	360/0.50	276/0.40	360/0.50	61.2	65.0	7270
95	475/0.50	396/0.40	475/0.50	69.3	73.9	9560
Type 16						
25	196/0.40	80/0.40	80/0.40	36.5	39.2	2700
35	276/0.40	80/0.40	80/0.40	39.5	42.7	3170
50	396/0.40	126/0.40	126/0.40	43.9	47.0	4120
70	360/0.50	196/0.40	196/0.40	49.6	53.3	5490
95	475/0.50	276/0.40	276/0.40	56.2	63.0	8200

PLIABLE ARMOURED FLEXIBLE TRAILING CABLES

320/550 V to 3800/6600 V

Main application: supplies to underground services and equipment moved occasionally (British Coal Specification 504)

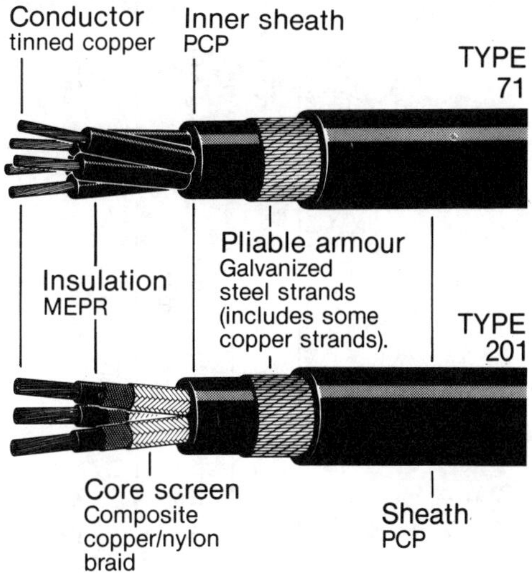

Table A10.4 Construction

Type	Voltage	Insulation	Number of cores	Number and screen on power cables	Earth core
62	640/1100	MEPR	2	2, copper/nylon	–
63	640/1100	MEPR	3	3, copper/nylon	–
64	640/1100	MEPR	4	4, copper/nylon	–
70	320/ 550	MEPR	4	3, unscreened	Unscreened
71	320/ 550	MEPR	5	4, unscreened	Unscreened
201	640/1100	MEPR	3	3, copper/nylon	–
211	640/1100	MEPR	4	3, copper/nylon	Unscreened
321	1900/3300	MEPR	4	3, unscreened	Unscreened
331	1900/3300	MEPR	4	3, copper/nylon	Unscreened
631	3800/6600	MEPR	4	3, copper/nylon	Unscreened

Table A10.5 Current ratings

Conductor size (mm^2)	10	16	25	35	50	70	95	120
Continuous rating (A)	63	85	110	135	170	205	250	295

Note

These ratings do not apply to types 62–71 which are control and lighting cables with a rating of 28 A. For rating factors for ambient temperature see table A10.2.

PLIABLE ARMOURED FLEXIBLE TRAILING CABLES
320/550 V to 3800/6600 V

Table A10.6 Range and dimensions

Power conductor size (mm^2)	Conductor formation		Armour[a]	Diameter		Approximate weight (kg/km)
	Power (number/mm)	Earth (number/mm)	(number/mm)	Minimum (mm)	Maximum (mm)	
Type 62						
4	56/0.30	–	7/0.45	23.9	26.4	1070
Type 63						
4	56/0.30	–	7/0.45	24.8	27.3	1230
Type 64						
4	56/0.30	–	7/0.45	26.4	28.9	1430
Type 70						
4	56/0.30	–	7/0.45	23.5	26.0	1060
Type 71						
4	56/0.30	–	7/0.45	24.9	27.4	1220
Type 201						
10	80/0.40	–	7/0.71	37.3	39.8	2780
16	126/0.40	–	7/0.71	40.6	43.4	3310
25	196/0.40	–	7/0.71	44.6	47.4	4050
35	276/0.40	–	7/0.71	48.3	51.1	4780
50	396/0.40		7/0.71	53.6	57.4	6080

70	360/0.50	–	7/0.90	60.7	64.5	7740
95	475/0.50	–	7/1.25	71.8	75.8	10940
120	608/0.50	–	7/1.25	76.7	81.0	12690
Type 211						
10	80/0.40	80/0.40	7/0.71	39.8	42.3	3160
16	126/0.40	126/0.40	7/0.71	44.0	46.8	3860
25	196/0.40	126/0.40	7/0.71	48.5	51.3	4680
35	276/0.40	196/0.40	7/0.71	52.7	56.5	5590
50	396/0.40	276/0.40	7/0.90	59.7	63.5	7330
70	360/0.50	396/0.40	7/0.90	68.8	72.8	9620
95	475/0.50	360/0.50	7/1.25	80.6	84.9	13450
120	608/0.50	360/0.50	7/1.25	86.2	90.5	16460
Type 321						
35	276/0.40	196/0.40	7/0.90	60.3	64.1	6860
50	396/0.40	276/0.40	7/0.90	68.3	72.3	8700
70	360/0.50	396/0.40	7/0.90	74.4	78.4	10400
95	475/0.50	360/0.50	7/1.25	84.9	89.2	14950
120	608/0.50	360/0.50	7/1.25	89.4	93.7	15950
Type 331						
25	196/0.40	126/0.40	7/0.90	57.8	61.6	6440
35	276/0.40	196/0.40	7/0.90	64.6	68.4	8010
50	396/9.40	276/0.40	7/0.90	69.8	73.8	9170
70	360/0.50	396/0.40	7/1.25	80.3	84.6	12740
95	475/0.50	360/0.50	7/1.25	86.4	90.7	14800
120	608/0.50	360/0.50	7/1.25	90.9	95.2	16850
Type 631						
50	396/0.40	276/0.40	7/1.25	86.7	91.0	13830
70	360/0.50	396/0.40	7/1.25	92.8	97.1	16220

[a] Some sizes have copper wires in the armour

PLIABLE ARMOURED FLEXIBLE MULTICORE AUXILIARY CABLES
320/550 V

Main application: interconnections between sections of large mining machines or between machine sections and associated auxiliary equipment (British Coal Specification 653)

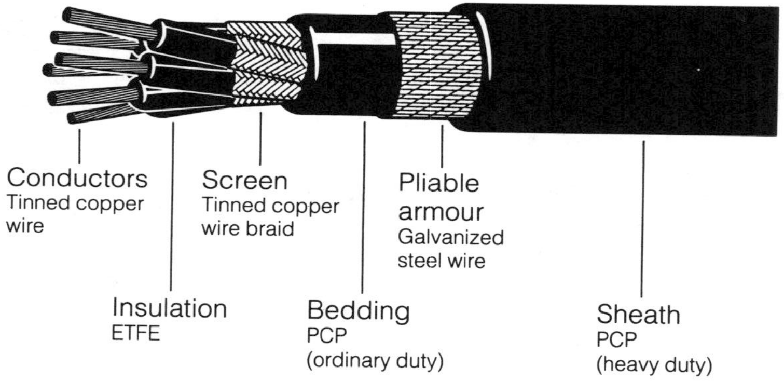

Table A10.7 Range and dimensions

Cable type	Conductor		Number of cores	Armour (number/mm)	Diameter		Approximate weight (kg/km)
	Area (mm^2)	Formation (number/mm)			Minimum (mm)	Maximum (mm)	
506	1.34	19/0.30	6	7/0.45	21.1	23.6	876
512	1.34	19/0.30	12	7/0.45	21.1	23.6	960
518	1.34	19/0.30	18	7/0.45	22.8	25.3	1136
524	0.93	19/0.25	24	7/0.45	24.2	26.7	1219

UNARMOURED FLEXIBLE CABLES
600/1000 V

Main application: highly flexible and robust cables for supply to portable equipment (British Coal Specification 505)

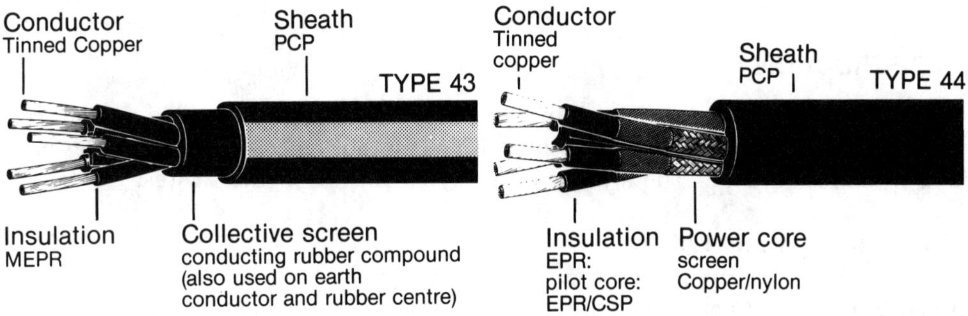

CURRENT RATINGS

These cables normally carry currents below their thermal capacity. Where applicable the current rating for types 43 and 44 is 46 A.

Table A10.8 Range and dimensions

Conductor		Diameter		Approximate weight (kg/km)
Size (mm^2)	Formation (number/mm)	Minimum (mm)	Maximum (mm)	
Type 43 (conducting rubber screen)				
6	84/0.30	25.6	27.6	967
Type 44 (copper/nylon screen)				
6	84/0.30	24.7	26.7	1180

PLIABLE ARMOURED FLEXIBLE CABLES

600/1000 V to 3800/6600 V to BS 6116

Main application: trailing cables for power supply in open-cast and miscellaneous mines and quarries

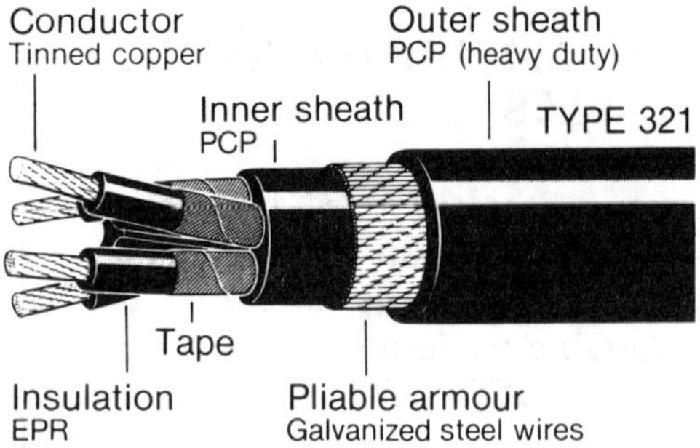

CONSTRUCTION

PETP tape is applied over the conductors for all sizes of type 321 cable and all sizes of types 20 and 21 except 2.5 and 4 mm^2 which are not taped. Type 621 cables have a semiconducting tape. The armour consists of bunches of seven wires.

Table A10.9 Current ratings

Conductor size (mm^2)	Continuous rating[a] D.C. or single-phase a.c. (A)	Continuous rating[a] 3-phase a.c. (A)	Conductor size (mm^2)	Continuous rating[a] D.C. or single-phase a.c. (A)	Continuous rating[a] 3-phase a.c. (A)
2.5	31	27	35	145	125
4	40	35	50	185	160
6	51	44	70	225	195
10	70	60	95	270	235
16	93	81	120	305	270
25	120	105	150	355	305

[a] Not applicable to cables in coils or on drums

Rating factors for ambient temperature

Ambient temperature (°C)	30	35	40	45	50	60	70
Rating factor	1.0	0.93	0.86	0.80	0.72	0.54	0.31

PLIABLE ARMOURED FLEXIBLE CABLES
600/1000 V to 3800/6600 V

Table A10.10 Range and dimensions

Conductor		Armour wires (number/mm)	Diameter		Approximate weight (kg/km)
Size (mm^2)	Formation (number/mm)		Minimum (mm)	Maximum (mm)	
Type 20, 600/1000 V 3-core					
2.5	50/0.25	7/0.45	24.5	26.9	1060
4	56/0.30	7/0.45	25.8	28.2	1200
6	84/0.30	7/0.71	34.3	36.5	2130
10	80/0.40	7/0.71	36.2	38.4	2450
16	126/0.40	7/0.71	38.6	40.8	2930
25	196/0.40	7/0.90	43.6	48.4	3960
35	276/0.40	7/0.90	46.6	50.6	4660
50	396/0.40	7/0.90	51.3	56.7	5740
70	360/0.50	7/0.90	56.6	62.7	7060
95	475/0.50	7/0.90	68.4	72.1	9200
120	608/0.50	7/0.90	72.2	77.0	10750
150	756/0.50	7/1.25	83.3	87.3	14240
Type 21, 600/1000 V 4-core					
2.5	50/0.25	7/0.45	26.2	28.6	1210
4	56/0.30	7/0.45	27.7	30.1	1380
6	84/0.30	7/0.71	36.7	38.8	2440
10	80/0.40	7/0.71	38.8	41.0	2820
16	126/0.40	7/0.71	41.5	44.0	3430
25	196/0.40	7/0.71	46.1	49.8	4310
35	276/0.40	7/0.90	51.0	56.1	5560
50	396/0.40	7/0.90	56.1	61.8	6900
70	360/0.50	7/0.90	64.8	71.4	9150
95	475/0.50	7/0.90	74.9	78.6	11090
120	608/0.50	7/1.25	83.8	89.0	14880
150	756/0.50	7/1.25	91.4	95.3	17230
Type 321, 1900/3300 V 4-core					
16	126/0.40	7/0.71	51.5	55.8	4640
25	196/0.40	7/0.90	56.7	60.1	5810
35	276/0.40	7/0.90	60.7	64.1	6852
50	396/0.40	7/0.90	68.6	72.3	8790
70	360/0.50	7/0.90	74.7	78.4	10390

(*cont.*)

PLIABLE ARMOURED FLEXIBLE CABLES
600/1000 V to 3800/6600 V

Table A10.10 cont.

Conductor		Armour wires (number/mm)	Diameter		Approximate weight (kg/km)
Size (mm^2)	Formation (number/mm)		Minimum (mm)	Maximum (mm)	
95	475/0.50	7/1.25	85.3	89.2	14040
120	608/0.50	7/1.25	88.5	93.7	15950
150	756/0.50	7/1.25	95.4	99.3	18280
Type 621, 3800/6600 V 4-core					
16	126/0.40	7/0.90	67.2	70.4	7460
25	196/0.40	7/0.90	71.4	74.6	8410
35	276/0.40	7/0.90	75.4	78.6	9570
50	396/0.40	7/1.25	85.1	88.6	12920
70	360/0.50	7/1.25	91.2	94.6	14880
95	475/0.50	7/1.25	97.4	100.9	17120
120	608/0.50	7/1.25	100.5	105.2	19000
150	756/0.50	7/1.25	107.5	111.0	21390

PVC INSULATED ARMOURED MINING POWER CABLES

635/1000 V to 6.35/11 kV

Main application: fixed cables for power distribution in coal mines (British Coal Specification 295)

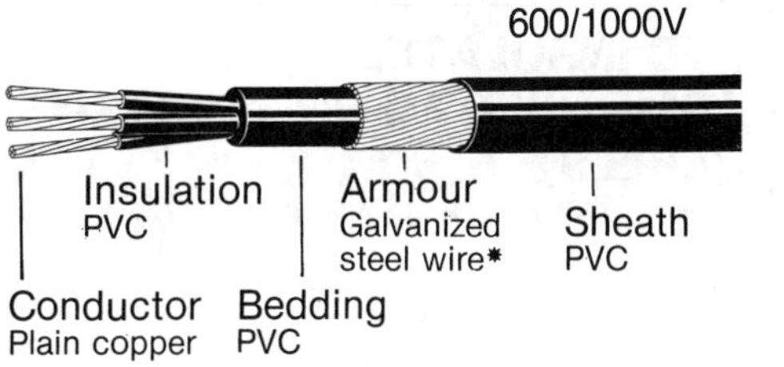

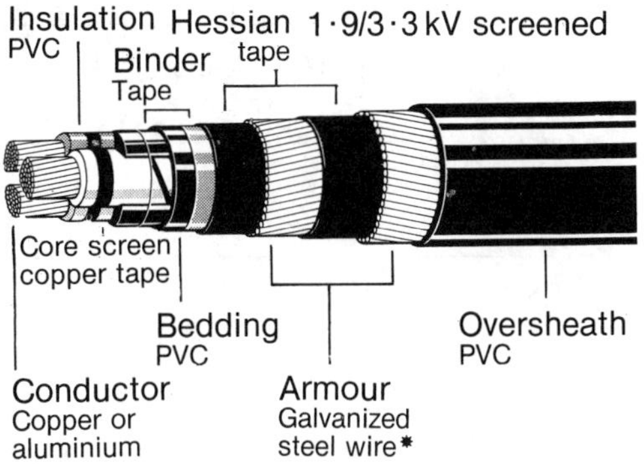

* The armour may contain copper wires and may be SWA or DWA

Specification
British Coal Specifications: 295 for 635/1000 V and 1.9/3.3 kV cables and 656 for 3.8/6.6 kV and 6.35/11 kV cables.

Number of cores
635/1000 V: 2-, 3- and 4-core.
Other voltages: 3-core only.

Conductors
All conductors are stranded. For voltages up to and including 3.8/6.6 kV conductors are shaped except as indicated in the tables. For 6.35/11 kV all conductors are circular.

Insulation
PVC for 635/1000 V and 1.9/3.3 kV cables.
EPR for 3.8/6.6 kV and 6.35/11 kV cables.

Core screens
1.9/3.3 kV cables may be screened or unscreened.

3.8/6.6 kV and 6.35/11 kV cables
These cables have conductor and core screens. Conductor screens consist of extruded semiconducting compound. Insulation screens comprise a layer of semiconducting material plus a copper tape.

PVC INSULATED ARMOURED MINING POWER CABLES

635/1000 V to 6.35/11 kV

Table A10.11 Current ratings

Conductor size (mm²)	635/1100 V (copper)		1.9/3.3 kV[a]		3.8/6.6 kV and 6.35/11 kV	
	2-core (A)	3- and 4-core (A)	Copper (A)	Aluminium (A)	Copper (A)	Aluminium (A)
1.5	24	21				
2.5	33	28				
4	44	38				
6	56	48				
10	77	66				
16	102	87	90		94	73
25		116	118		125	96
35		142	143		150	115
50		172	173		175	135
70		218	217	155	220	170
95		268	266	190	265	205
120			308		305	240
150			351	250	345	270
185			403	290	390	310
240			474		460	365
300			540		520	415
400			620			

[a] Applies to screened and unscreened

Note

These ratings are based on an ambient temperature of 25 °C and a maximum continuous conductor temperature of 70 °C.

Rating factors for ambient temperature

Ambient temperature (°C)	25	30	35	40	45
Rating factor	1.0	0.94	0.88	0.82	0.75

PVC INSULATED ARMOURED MINING POWER CABLES
635/1000 V

Table A10.12 Range and dimensions (635/1000 V cables, SWA and DWA with copper conductors)

Conductor size (mm^2)	Armour		Approximate diameter (mm)	Approximate weight (kg/km)
	Wire diameter (mm)	Copper wires (number)		
2-core SWA				
1.5	0.9	0	11.7	280
2.5	0.9	0	13.1	350
4	0.9	0	15.1	450
6	0.9	2	16.5	545
10	1.25	1	20.1	870
16	1.25	4	21.9	980
3-core SWA				
1.5	0.9	0	12.3	310
2.5	0.9	0	13.6	390
4	0.9	0	15.8	510
6	1.25	0	18.0	720
10	1.25	1	21.2	1000
16	1.25	4	23.1	1130
25[a]	1.6	4	25.0	1650
35[a]	1.6	7	27.3	2050
50[a]	1.6	11	30.5	2600
70[a]	2.0	10	35.0	3610
95[a]	2.0	15	39.3	4750
4-core SWA				
1.5	0.9	0	13.0	350
2.5	0.9	0	14.5	445
4	1.25	0	17.8	715
6	1.25	0	19.2	855
10	1.25	1	22.8	1190
16	1.6	1	26.3	1520
25[a]	1.6	4	27.8	2050
35[a]	1.6	6	30.5	2540
50[a]	2.0	5	35.4	3480
70[a]	2.0	9	39.2	4490
95[a]	2.0	14	44.3	5890

(cont.)

PVC INSULATED ARMOURED MINING POWER CABLES
635/1000 V

Table A10.12 cont.

Conductor size (mm^2)	Armour		Approximate diameter (mm)	Approximate weight (kg/km)
	Wire diameter (mm)	Copper wires (number)		
3-core DWA				
1.5	0.9	0	17.0	690
2.5	0.9	0	18.3	795
4	0.9	0	20.6	985
6	1.25	0	23.4	1380
10	1.25	0	26.5	1760
4-core DWA				
1.5	0.9	0	17.6	745
2.5	0.9	0	19.1	870
4	1.25	0	23.2	1360
6	1.25	0	24.8	1550
10	1.25	0	28.2	2110

[a] Shaped conductors

PVC INSULATED ARMOURED MINING POWER CABLES
1.9/3.3 kV

Table A10.13 Range and dimensions (3-core 1.9/3.3 kV cables)

Conductor size (mm^2)	Armour		Approximate diameter (mm)	Approximate weight (kg/km)
	Wire diameter (mm)	Copper wires (number)		
Unscreened, copper conductor, DWA				
16[a]	1.6	0	37.2	3210
25[a]	1.6	0	40.1	3420
35	1.6	0	39.1	3900
50	2.0	1	43.8	5090
70	2.0	5	47.0	6140
95	2.0	11	50.4	7220
120	2.5	7	56.4	9370
150	2.5	12	59.2	10570
185	2.5	17	62.5	12020
240	2.5	25	67.9	14540
300	2.5	35	73.4	17060
400	2.5	48	79.7	20790
Unscreened, aluminium conductor, DWA				
70	2.0	0	47.0	4780
95	2.0	0	50.4	5410
150	2.5	1	59.2	7710
185	2.5	4	62.5	8450
Unscreened, aluminium conductor, SWA				
70	2.0	3	41.8	3270
95	2.0	6	45.2	3710
150	2.5	6	52.8	5230
185	2.5	9	56.1	5840
Screened, copper conductor, DWA				
16[a]	1.6	0	38.1	3400
25[a]	1.6	0	40.9	3630
35	1.6	0	39.9	4140
50	2.0	0	44.6	5400
70	2.0	5	47.9	6390
95	2.0	10	51.3	7520
120	2.5	7	57.2	9720
150	2.5	11	60.0	10900

(cont.)

PVC INSULATED ARMOURED MINING POWER CABLES
1.9/3.3 kV

Table A10.13 cont.

Conductor size (mm^2)	Armour		Approximate diameter (mm)	Approximate weight (kg/km)
	Wire diameter (mm)	Copper wires (number)		
185	2.5	17	63.4	12370
240	2.5	25	68.8	14920
300	2.5	35	74.2	17520
400	2.5	48	80.6	21170
Screened, aluminium conductor, DWA				
70	2.0	0	47.9	5090
95	2.0	0	51.3	5720
150	2.5	1	60.0	8100
185	2.5	4	63.4	8860
Screened, aluminium conductor, SWA				
70	2.0	2	42.7	3380
95	2.0	5	46.1	3900
150	2.5	6	53.6	5470
185	2.5	9	57.0	6090

[a] Circular conductor; remainder shaped

EPR INSULATED ARMOURED MINING POWER CABLES
3.8/6.6 kV

Table A10.14 Range and dimensions (3.8/6.6 kV cables)

Conductor size (mm^2)	Armour wire diameter (mm)	Copper wires in armour (number)	Approximate diameter (mm)	Approximate weight (kg/km)
Copper conductor, DWA				
16[a]	2.0	0	47.7	4830
25[a]	2.0	0	50.8	5450
35[a]	2.0	0	53.4	6030
50[a]	2.0	0	57.0	6660
70	2.5	0	58.4	8580
95	2.5	1	61.6	9790
120	2.5	5	65.3	11150
150	2.5	9	68.1	12570
185	2.5	14	71.4	14120
Aluminium conductor, DWA				
50[a]	2.0	0	57.0	5780
70	2.5	0	58.4	7230
95	2.5	0	61.6	8660
120	2.5	0	65.3	8890
150	2.5	0	68.1	9760
185	2.5	1	71.4	10580
Copper conductor, SWA				
16[a]	2.0	0	44.0	3130
25[a]	2.0	0	47.0	3620
35[a]	2.0	0	50.0	4140
50	2.0	2	53.0	4660
70	2.5	3	52.0	5970
95	2.5	6	55.2	7050
120	2.5	10	58.9	8080
150	2.5	13	61.7	9440
185	2.5	18	65.0	10810
Aluminium conductor, SWA				
50[a]	2.0	0	53.0	3760
70	2.5	0	52.0	4660
95	2.5	1	55.2	5230
120	2.5	3	58.9	5760
150	2.5	5	61.7	6610
185	2.5	7	65.0	7260

[a] Circular conductors; remainder shaped

EPR INSULATED ARMOURED MINING POWER CABLES
6.35/11 kV

Table A10.15 Range and dimensions (6.35/11 kV cables)

Conductor size[a] (mm[a])	Armour wire diameter (mm)	Copper wires in armour (number)	Approximate diameter (mm)	Approximate weight (kg/km)
Copper conductor, DWA				
25	2.0	0	53.1	5600
35	2.5	0	58.6	7340
50	2.5	0	60.9	7995
70	2.5	0	64.5	9090
95	2.5	0	68.5	10365
120	2.5	2	72.7	11770
150	2.5	6	75.9	13240
185	2.5	12	79.9	15090
Aluminium conductor, DWA				
25	2.0	0	52.8	5120
35	2.5	0	58.3	6580
50	2.5	0	60.9	7100
70	2.5	0	64.5	7805
95	2.5	0	68.5	8580
120	2.5	0	72.7	9515
150	2.5	0	75.9	10460
185	2.5	0	79.9	11610
Copper conductor, SWA				
25	2.0	0	47.9	3755
35	2.5	0	52.2	4785
50	2.5	0	54.7	5380
70	2.5	2	58.3	6315
95	2.5	5	62.3	7440
120	2.5	8	66.5	8600
150	2.5	12	69.5	9715
185	2.5	16	73.5	11145

EPR INSULATED ARMOURED MINING POWER CABLES
6.35/11 kV

Table A10.15 cont.

Conductor size[a] (mm[a])	Armour wire diameter (mm)	Copper wires in armour (number)	Approximate diameter (mm)	Approximate weight (kg/km)
Aluminium conductor, SWA				
25	2.0	0	47.6	3275
35	2.5	0	51.9	4125
50	2.5	0	54.7	4490
70	2.5	0	58.3	5025
95	2.5	0	62.2	5650
120	2.5	2	66.5	6345
150	2.5	3	69.5	6935
185	2.5	6	73.5	7665

[a] Conductors are circular

Appendix A11

Mineral Insulated Wiring Cables

Cable design

Copper conductor, copper sheathed, 500 V light duty and 750 V heavy duty cables to BS 6207, Part 1.

Main application

Fixed installations in factories and other buildings.

Data in tables

(a) Current ratings, volt drop and rating factors for cables with up to 7 cores:
   (i) exposed to touch or covered
   (ii) with bare sheath, not exposed to touch or in contact with combustible material
(b) Dimensions and weights

Notes on current ratings

(a) The current ratings are based on an ambient temperature of 30 °C with a sheath temperature rise of 40 °C for cables exposed to touch or covered and 75 °C for cables with bare sheath not exposed to touch or in contact with combustible material.
(b) Where protection is provided by means of semi-enclosed (rewireable) fuses to BS 3036, the cable should be selected with a current rating not less than 1.38 times the rating of the fuse (see chapter 10).
(c) The 'free air' ratings apply to a cable or trefoil group spaced at least half of a cable diameter from the wall or other surface to which it is attached. In addition, for single-core cables in flat formation the spacing between cables is one cable diameter (i.e. two diameters between centres).

Notes on volt drop

(a) The volt drops for 500 V light duty cables with conductor sizes up to 4 mm^2 are the same as for the corresponding 750 V cables, as given in tables A11.6 and A11.7.
(b) The values of volt drop for 'spaced' single-core cables apply to cables spaced as for the 'free air' current ratings.

500 V LIGHT DUTY M.I. CABLE

Table A11.1 Current ratings for cables exposed to touch or covered

Conductor size (mm²)	Two single-core cables or one 2-core cable, single phase a.c. or d.c.		Three single-core cables in trefoil or one 3-core cable, 3-phase a.c.		Three single-core cables in flat formation, 3-phase a.c.		
	Clipped direct (A)	Free air (A)	Clipped direct (A)	Free air (A)	Clipped direct (A)	Free air	
						Horizontal	Vertical (A)
1	18.5	19.5	15	16.5	17	23	20
1.5	23	25	19	21	21	29	26
2.5	31	33	26	28	29	39	34
4	40	44	35	37	38	51	45

Conductor size (mm²)	One 4-core cable, three cores loaded, 3-phase a.c.		One 4-core cable, all cores loaded		One 7-core cable, all cores loaded	
	Clipped direct (A)	Free air (A)	Clipped direct (A)	Free air (A)	Clipped direct (A)	Free air (A)
1	15	16	13	14	10	11
1.5	19.5	21	16.5	18	13	14
2.5	26	28	22	24	17.5	19

Rating factors for ambient temperature and for groups of cables are given in chapter 8.

500 V LIGHT DUTY M.I. CABLE

Table A11.2 Current ratings for cables with bare sheaths not exposed to touch or in contact with combustible material

Conductor size (mm^2)	Two single-core cables or one 2-core cable, single phase a.c. or d.c.		Three single-core cables in trefoil or one 3-core cable, 3-phase a.c.		Three single-core cables in flat formation, 3-phase a.c.		
	Clipped direct (A)	Free air (A)	Clipped direct (A)	Free air (A)	Clipped direct (A)	Free air Horizontal	Free air Vertical (A)
1	22	24	19	21	21	29	26
1.5	28	31	24	26	27	37	33
2.5	38	41	33	35	36	49	43
4	51	54	44	46	47	64	56

Conductor size (mm^2)	One 4-core cable, three cores loaded, 3-phase a.c.		One 4-core cable, all cores loaded		One 7-core cable, all cores loaded	
	Clipped direct (A)	Free air (A)	Clipped direct (A)	Free air (A)	Clipped direct (A)	Free air (A)
1	18.5	20	16.5	18	13	14
1.5	24	26	21	22	16.5	18
2.5	33	35	28	30	22	24

Rating factors for ambient temperature are given in chapter 8.
No rating factors for groups need be applied.

500 V LIGHT DUTY M.I. CABLE

Table A11.3 Dimensions and weights

Conductor size (mm^2)	Diameter of bare cable (mm)	Diameter of PVC sheathed cable (mm)	Conductor diameter (nominal) (mm)	Approximate weight	
				Bare cable (kg/km)	PVC sheathed cable (kg/km)
2 × 1.0	5.1	6.6	1.13	105	126
2 × 1.5	5.7	7.2	1.38	131	154
2 × 2.5	6.6	8.1	1.78	180	205
2 × 4.0	7.7	9.4	2.25	248	282
3 × 1.0	5.8	7.3	1.13	136	159
3 × 1.5	6.4	7.9	1.38	168	194
4 × 1.0	6.3	7.8	1.13	162	187
4 × 1.5	7.0	8.5	1.38	203	230
7 × 1.0	7.6	9.3	1.13	173	207
7 × 1.5	8.4	10.1	1.38	294	331

The above are the most commonly used sizes; other sizes are available.

Table A11.4 Current ratings for cables exposed to touch or covered

Conductor size (mm^2)	Two single-core cables or one 2-core cable, single-phase a.c. or d.c.		Three single-core cables in trefoil or one 3-core cable, 3-phase a.c.		Three single-core cables in flat formation, 3-phase a.c.		
	Clipped direct (A)	Free air (A)	Clipped direct (A)	Free air (A)	Clipped direct (A)	Free air Horizontal (A)	Free air Vertical (A)
1	19.5	21	16	17.5	18	25	22
1.5	25	26	21	22	23	32	28
2.5	34	36	28	30	31	43	37
4	45	47	37	40	41	56	49
6	57	60	48	51	52	71	62
10	77	82	65	69	70	95	84
16	102	109	86	92	92	125	110
25	133	142	112	120	120	162	142
35	163	174	137	147	147	197	173
50	202	215	169	182	181	242	213
70	247	264	207	223	221	294	259
95	296	317	249	267	264	351	309
120	340	364	286	308	303	402	353
150	388	416	327	352	346	454	400
185	440	472	371	399	392	507	446
240	514	552	434	466	457	565	497

Conductor size (mm²)	One 4-core cable, three cores loaded, 3-phase a.c.		One 4-core cable, all cores loaded		One 7-core cable, all cores loaded	
	Clipped direct (A)	Free air (A)	Clipped direct (A)	Free air (A)	Clipped direct (A)	Free air (A)
1	16.5	18	14.5	16	11.5	12
1.5	21	23	18	20	14.5	15.5
2.5	28	30	25	27	19.5	21
4	37	40	32	35	26	28
6	47	51	41	44	–	–
10	64	68	55	59	–	–
16	85	89	72	78	–	–
25	110	116	94	101	–	–

Rating factors for ambient temperature and for groups of cables are given in chapter 8.

Table A11.5 Current ratings for cables with bare sheaths not exposed to touch or in contact with combustible material

Conductor size (mm^2)	Two single-core cables or one 2-core cable, single-phase a.c. or d.c.		Three single-core cables in trefoil or one 3-core cable, 3-phase a.c.		Three single-core cables in flat formation, 3-phase a.c.		
	Clipped direct (A)	Free air (A)	Clipped direct (A)	Free air (A)	Clipped direct (A)	Free air Horizontal (A)	Free air Vertical (A)
1	24	26	20	22	24	32	28
1.5	31	33	26	28	30	40	35
2.5	42	45	35	38	41	54	47
4	55	60	47	50	53	70	61
6	70	76	59	64	67	89	78
10	96	104	81	87	91	120	105
16	127	137	107	115	119	157	137
25	166	179	140	150	154	204	178
35	203	220	171	184	187	248	216
50	251	272	212	228	230	304	266
70	307	333	260	279	280	370	323
95	369	400	312	335	334	441	385
120	424	460	359	385	383	505	441
150	485	526	410	441	435	565	498
185	550	596	465	500	492	629	557
240	643	697	544	584	572	704	624

Conductor size (mm^2)	One 4-core cable, three cores loaded, 3-phase a.c.		One 4-core cable, all cores loaded		One 7-core cable, all cores loaded	
	Clipped direct (A)	Free air (A)	Clipped direct (A)	Free air (A)	Clipped direct (A)	Free air (A)
1	20	22	17.5	19	14	15
1.5	26	28	22	24	17.5	19
2.5	35	37	30	32	24	26
4	46	49	40	43	32	34
6	58	63	50	54	–	–
10	78	85	68	73	–	–
16	103	112	90	97	–	–
25	134	146	117	126	–	–

Ratings factors for ambient temperature are given in chapter 8.
No rating factor for groups need be applied.

750 V HEAVY DUTY M.I. CABLE

Table A11.6 Volt drops for cables exposed to touch or covered (sheath operating temperature 70 °C)

Conductor size (mm^2)	Single-phase operation		3-phase operation			
			Three single-core cables			
	Two single-core cables touching (mV/A/m)	Multicore cables (mV/A/m)	Trefoil (mV/A/m)	Flat touching (mV/A/m)	Flat spaced (mV/A/m)	Multicore cables (mV/A/m)
1	42	42	36	36	36	36
1.5	28	28	24	24	24	24
2.5	17	17	14	14	14	14
4	10	10	9.1	9.1	9.1	9.1
6	7	7	6.0	6.0	6.0	6.0
10	4.2	4.2	3.6	3.6	3.6	3.6
16	2.6	2.6	2.3	2.3	2.3	2.3
25	1.65	1.65	1.45	1.45	1.5	1.45
35	1.2	–	1.05	1.1	1.1	–
50	0.91	–	0.80	0.83	0.87	–
70	0.64	–	0.56	0.60	0.65	–
95	0.49	–	0.43	0.47	0.53	–
120	0.41	–	0.36	0.40	0.46	–
150	0.34	–	0.30	0.36	0.42	–
185	0.29	–	0.26	0.32	0.39	–
240	0.25	–	0.22	0.29	0.36	–

750 V HEAVY DUTY M.I. CABLE

Table A11.7 Volt drops for cables with bare sheaths not exposed to touch or in contact with combustible material (sheath operating temperature 105 °C)

Conductor size (mm^2)	Single-phase operation		3-phase operation			
	Two single-core cables touching (mV/A/m)	Multicore cables (mV/A/m)	Three single-core cables: Trefoil (mV/A/m)	Three single-core cables: Flat touching (mV/A/m)	Three single-core cables: Flat spaced (mV/A/m)	Multicore cables (mV/A/m)
1	47	47	40	40	40	40
1.5	31	31	27	27	27	27
2.5	19	19	16	16	16	16
4	12	12	10	10	10	10
6	7.8	7.8	6.8	6.8	6.8	6.8
10	4.7	4.7	4.1	4.1	4.1	4.1
16	3.0	3.0	2.6	2.6	2.6	2.6
25	1.85	1.85	1.65	1.65	1.65	1.6
35	1.35	–	1.2	1.2	1.25	–
50	1.0	–	0.88	0.91	0.95	–
70	0.71	–	0.62	0.65	0.70	–
95	0.54	–	0.47	0.50	0.56	–
120	0.44	–	0.38	0.42	0.48	–
150	0.36	–	0.32	0.37	0.43	–
185	0.31	–	0.27	0.33	0.39	–
240	0.26	–	0.22	0.29	0.36	–

750 V HEAVY DUTY M.I. CABLE

Table A11.8 Dimensions and weights

Conductor size (mm^2)	Diameter of bare cable (mm)	Diameter of PVC sheathed cable (mm)	Conductor diameter (nominal) (mm)	Approximate weight	
				Bare cable (kg/km)	PVC sheathed cable (kg/km)
1 × 2.5	5.3	6.8	1.78	114	136
1 × 6	6.4	7.9	2.76	178	203
1 × 10	7.3	9.0	3.57	241	274
1 × 16	8.3	10.0	4.51	326	363
1 × 25	9.6	11.3	5.64	456	498
1 × 35	10.7	12.4	6.68	586	632
1 × 50	12.1	13.8	7.98	777	813
1 × 70	13.7	15.4	9.44	1027	1086
1 × 95	15.4	17.7	11.00	1326	1416
1 × 120	16.8	19.1	12.36	1614	1712
1 × 150	18.4	20.7	13.82	1966	2073
1 × 185	20.4	23.2	15.35	2425	2570
1 × 240	23.3	26.1	17.48	3146	3312
2 × 1.5	7.9	9.6	1.38	223	259
2 × 2.5	8.7	10.4	1.78	275	313
2 × 4	9.8	11.5	2.25	355	389
2 × 6	10.9	12.6	2.76	446	493
2 × 10	12.7	14.4	3.57	619	674
2 × 16	14.7	16.4	4.51	852	914
2 × 25	17.1	19.4	5.64	1175	1275
3 × 1.5	8.3	10.0	1.38	253	290
3 × 2.5	9.3	11.0	1.78	324	365
3 × 4	10.4	12.1	2.25	415	461
3 × 6	11.5	13.2	2.76	525	575
3 × 10	13.6	15.3	3.57	753	811
3 × 16	15.6	17.9	4.51	1035	1126
3 × 25	18.2	20.5	5.64	1442	1548
4 × 1.5	9.1	10.8	1.38	303	343
4 × 2.5	10.1	11.8	1.78	385	429
4 × 4	11.4	13.1	2.25	506	555
4 × 6	12.7	14.4	2.76	645	700
4 × 10	14.8	16.5	3.57	912	975
4 × 16	17.3	19.6	4.51	1290	1391
4 × 25	20.1	22.9	5.64	1800	1943

750 V HEAVY DUTY M.I. CABLE

Table A11.8 cont.

Conductor size (mm^2)	Diameter of bare cable (mm)	Diameter of PVC sheathed cable (mm)	Conductor diameter (nominal) (mm)	Approximate weight	
				Bare cable (kg/km)	PVC sheathed cable (kg/km)
7 × 1.5	10.8	12.5	1.38	431	478
7 × 2.5	12.1	13.8	1.78	561	613
12 × 2.5	15.6	17.9	1.78	909	1001
19 × 1.5	16.6	18.9	1.38	989	1086

The above are the most commonly used sizes, other sizes are available.

Appendix A12

Paper Insulated Distribution Cables

CONTENTS

Tables are included for dimensions and weights, sustained ratings and electrical characteristics. Notes on the cable designs and conditions applicable are given before the tables.

CABLE DESIGNS

Typical constructions are shown in figs A12.1–A12.3.

Tabulated figures are included for unarmoured single-core cables together with unarmoured and armoured multicore cables to BS 6480 with the following constructions.

Fig. A12.1 Paper insulated 4-core 600/1000 V steel tape armoured cable

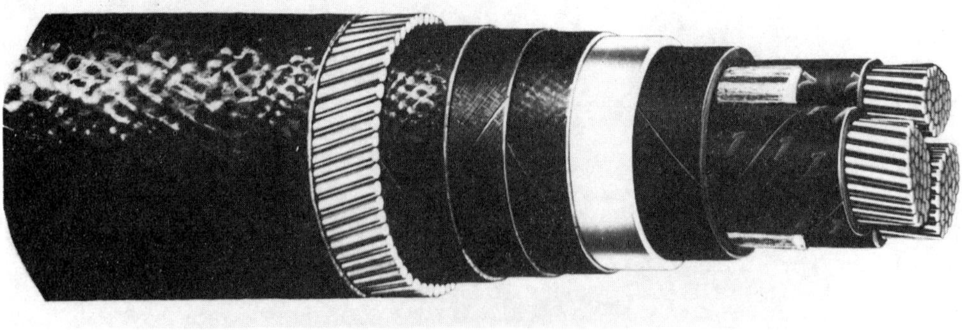

Fig. A12.2 Paper insulated 3-core 6.35/11 kV belted wire armoured cable

Fig. A12.3 Paper insulated 3-core 19/33 kV screened SL cable

Conductors
Stranded copper and aluminium, single-core circular and multicore sector shaped. Conductors for 12.7/22 kV and 19/33 kV 3-core cables are oval and for SL cables are circular.

Armour bedding
Bituminised textiles.

Armour
Steel tape and galvanised steel wire.

Finish
Extruded PVC oversheath for unarmoured cables and bituminised textile serving for armoured cables.

SUSTAINED RATINGS

The maximum ratings in the tables are for a single circuit and are based on ERA Technology Ltd Report ERA 69-30, Part 1, which is in general conformity with IEC 287.

If compared with the ratings published in the fifteenth edition of the IEE Regulations for the Electrical Equipment of Buildings it will be found that the values in the tables for cables in air are higher. This is only because they are based on an ambient temperature of 25 °C instead of the 30 °C used by the IEE. For any specific temperature both values are the same after application of the appropriate temperature correction factor.

The standard conditions on which the ratings are based are given below. For other conditions the rating factors included in chapter 8 should be applied.

Maximum conductor temperature

80 °C	0.6/1, 1.9/3.3 and 3.8/6.6 kV
65 °C	6.35/11 kV belted
70 °C	6.35/11 and 8.7/15 kV screened
65 °C	12.7/22 and 19/33 kV screened

Cables laid direct in ground

Ground temperature
15 °C

Ground thermal resistivity
1.2 K m/W

Adjacent circuits
At least 1.8 m apart.

Depth of laying
For voltages up to 1000 V, 0.5 m and for higher voltages 0.8 m (measured from ground surface to centre of cable or trefoil group).

Single-core cables

The data apply to three or four single-core cables operating 3-phase.

Bonding
It is assumed that the sheaths will be solidly bonded, i.e. bonded at both ends of the run. For very short runs it may be found possible to bond at one end only but consideration must be given to the value of the standing voltage which can occur along the cable length under both normal and fault conditions.

Trefoil
A close trefoil is assumed with the cables touching.

Flat formation
The ratings and technical data are based on horizontal installation with a spacing between cable centres of twice the overall diameter for sizes up to and including 185 mm^2 and 90 mm for 240 mm^2 and above.

Installation in air

An ambient air temperature of 25 °C.

It is assumed that the cables are shielded from direct rays from the sun and that air circulation is not restricted significantly, e.g. if fastened to a wall the cables are spaced at least 20 mm from it; if in a trench they are not covered.

The data cover adjacent circuits which are spaced apart (chapter 8) and suitably disposed to prevent mutual heating.

ELECTRICAL CHARACTERISTICS

The standard conditions given for sustained ratings are equally applicable to the electrical characteristics. A.C. resistances are tabulated. D.C. resistances are given in table 4.1 of chapter 4.

PAPER INSULATED DISTRIBUTION CABLES (BS 6480)

600/1000 V

Table A12.1 Dimensions and weights

Conductor size (mm^2)	Approximate diameter			Approximate weight, stranded copper conductors			Approximate weight, stranded aluminium conductors		
	PVC sheath unarmoured (mm)	STA and textile finish (mm)	SWA and textile finish (mm)	PVC sheath unarmoured (kg/m)	STA and textile finish (kg/m)	SWA and textile finish (kg/m)	PVC sheath unarmoured (kg/m)	STA and textile finish (kg/m)	SWA and textile finish (kg/m)
Single-core cables									
50	17.0			1.12			0.83		
70	18.8			1.42			0.99		
95	20.9			1.77			1.18		
120	22.7			2.15			1.41		
150	24.4			2.51			1.60		
185	26.5			3.03			1.89		
240	29.5			3.76			2.26		
300	32.4			4.59			2.71		
400	35.7			5.68			3.27		
500	39.7			7.01			3.97		
630	44.1			8.75			4.82		
800	48.8			10.86			5.84		
1000	53.8			13.33			7.00		

(*cont.*)

PAPER INSULATED DISTRIBUTION CABLES (BS 6480)
600/1000 V

Table A12.1 cont.

Conductor size (mm^2)	Approximate diameter			Approximate weight, stranded copper conductors			Approximate weight, stranded aluminium conductors		
	PVC sheath unarmoured (mm)	STA and textile finish (mm)	SWA and textile finish (mm)	PVC sheath unarmoured (kg/m)	STA and textile finish (kg/m)	SWA and textile finish (kg/m)	PVC sheath unarmoured (kg/m)	STA and textile finish (kg/m)	SWA and textile finish (kg/m)
2-core cables									
25	19.0	24.9	26.1	1.24	1.92	2.13	0.93	1.61	1.82
35	20.7	26.7	27.9	1.51	2.25	2.48	1.08	1.82	2.05
50	22.7	28.6	29.8	1.91	2.70	2.95	1.32	2.11	2.36
70	25.5	31.4	33.4	2.51	3.35	3.87	1.67	2.51	3.03
95	28.4	34.3	36.3	3.24	4.16	4.74	2.07	2.99	3.57
120	31.1	36.8	38.8	3.98	4.98	5.61	2.50	3.50	4.13
150	34.5	40.0	43.0	4.83	5.91	6.95	3.02	4.10	5.14
185	37.6	42.8	45.8	5.86	7.00	8.11	3.58	4.72	5.83
240	42.3	48.6	50.4	7.49	9.19	10.02	4.50	6.20	7.03
300	46.4	52.2	54.0	9.10	10.89	11.79	5.35	7.14	8.04
400	51.5	56.8	58.6	11.41	13.32	14.30	6.61	8.52	9.50
3-core cables									
25	20.9	26.8	28.0	1.62	2.38	2.61	1.15	1.91	2.14
35	23.2	29.1	30.3	2.07	2.91	3.16	1.42	2.26	2.51
50	25.5	31.4	32.6	2.61	3.47	3.79	1.73	2.59	2.91
70	28.5	34.4	36.4	3.37	4.33	4.92	2.10	3.06	3.65
95	32.1	37.8	39.8	4.40	5.45	6.10	2.65	3.70	4.35
120	35.3	40.8	42.8	5.39	6.51	7.21	3.18	4.30	5.00
150	39.3	44.6	47.6	6.69	7.90	9.08	3.97	5.18	6.36
[illegible]	[illegible]	[illegible]	[illegible]	[illegible]	[illegible]	[illegible]	[illegible]	[illegible]	[illegible]

240	48.4	54.4	56.2	10.37	12.27	13.21	5.88	7.78	8.72
300	53.1	58.7	60.5	12.64	14.64	15.66	7.01	9.01	10.03
400	59.0	64.1	65.9	15.85	17.98	19.10	8.65	10.78	11.90
4-core cables									
25	23.5	29.4	30.6	2.04	2.87	3.13	1.41	2.24	2.50
35	26.0	31.9	33.1	2.53	3.39	3.71	1.67	2.53	2.85
50	28.7	34.6	36.6	3.21	4.16	4.74	2.05	3.00	3.58
70	32.7	38.4	40.4	4.31	5.35	6.01	2.63	3.67	4.33
95	37.0	42.5	44.5	5.65	6.79	7.51	3.31	4.45	5.17
120	40.6	45.9	48.9	6.94	8.16	9.35	3.99	5.21	6.40
150	45.3	51.5	53.3	8.60	10.37	11.24	4.97	6.74	7.61
185	49.5	55.5	57.3	10.44	12.33	13.27	5.89	7.78	8.72
240	56.3	61.8	63.6	13.51	15.57	16.62	7.54	9.60	10.65
300	61.6	66.9	68.7	16.43	18.64	19.78	8.92	11.13	12.27
400	68.6	73.3	76.4	20.61	22.93	24.99	11.02	13.34	15.40
4-core with reduced neutral[a]									
25	23.3	29.2	30.4	1.88	2.70	3.00	1.31	2.13	2.43
35	25.3	31.2	32.4	2.37	3.25	3.57	1.62	2.50	2.82
50	27.9	33.8	35.8	2.98	3.94	4.53	1.95	2.91	3.50
70	31.6	37.6	39.6	3.95	5.04	5.70	2.47	3.56	4.22
95	36.2	42.0	44.0	5.14	6.35	7.09	3.10	4.31	5.05
120	40.3	45.8	48.8	6.35	7.66	8.90	3.72	5.03	6.27
150	43.6	48.8	51.8	7.62	8.98	10.31	4.47	5.83	7.16
185	48.0	54.3	56.1	9.30	11.27	12.22	5.31	7.28	8.23
240	54.2	60.0	61.8	12.03	14.16	15.22	6.80	8.93	9.99
300	59.4	65.0	66.8	14.60	16.89	18.04	8.05	10.34	11.49
300	61.4	66.7	68.5	14.91	17.25	18.43	8.16	10.50	11.68
400	66.0	71.1	74.2	18.25	20.70	21.97	9.91	12.36	13.63

[a] Size of reduced neutral

Phase (mm^2)	25	35	50	70	95	120	150	185	240	300	300	400
Neutral (mm^2)	16	16	25	35	50	70	70	95	120	150	185	185

PAPER INSULATED DISTRIBUTION CABLES (BS 6480)
1.9/3.3 kV

Table A12.2 Dimensions and weights

Conductor size (mm^2)	Approximate diameter			Approximate weight, stranded copper conductors			Approximate weight, stranded aluminium conductors		
	PVC sheath unarmoured (mm)	STA and textile finish (mm)	SWA and textile finish (mm)	PVC sheath unarmoured (kg/m)	STA and textile finish (kg/m)	SWA and textile finish (kg/m)	PVC sheath unarmoured (kg/m)	STA and textile finish (kg/m)	SWA and textile finish (kg/m)
Single-core cables									
50	18.2			1.22			0.93		
70	20.0			1.52			1.10		
95	21.9			1.87			1.28		
120	23.7			2.25			1.51		
150	25.2			2.59			1.68		
185	27.3			3.13			1.99		
240	29.9			3.82			2.31		
300	32.6			4.63			2.75		
400	35.9			5.73			3.32		
500	39.7			7.04			4.00		
630	44.1			8.78			4.86		
800	48.8			10.90			5.88		
1000	53.8			13.37			7.04		

3-core cables									
25	23.4	29.3	30.5	1.90	2.74	3.00	1.43	2.27	2.53
35	25.5	31.4	32.6	2.29	3.16	3.48	1.65	2.52	2.84
50	27.8	33.7	35.7	2.86	3.80	4.38	1.98	2.92	3.50
70	31.0	37.0	39.0	3.73	4.77	5.41	2.47	3.51	4.15
95	34.7	40.4	42.4	4.81	5.94	6.64	3.05	4.18	4.88
120	37.8	43.3	46.3	5.82	7.01	8.16	3.61	4.80	5.95
150	40.8	47.3	49.1	6.93	8.60	9.40	4.21	5.88	6.68
185	44.4	50.7	52.5	8.38	10.15	11.02	4.97	6.74	7.61
240	49.5	55.3	57.1	10.58	12.48	13.44	6.10	8.00	8.96
300	54.2	59.8	61.6	13.01	15.05	16.09	7.39	9.43	10.47
400	60.0	65.2	68.3	16.26	18.43	20.30	9.07	11.24	13.11

PAPER INSULATED DISTRIBUTION CABLES (BS 6480)
3.8/6.6 kV

Table A12.3 Dimensions and weights

Conductor size (mm^2)	Approximate diameter			Approximate weight, stranded copper conductors			Approximate weight, stranded aluminium conductors		
	PVC sheath unarmoured (mm)	STA and textile finish (mm)	SWA and textile finish (mm)	PVC sheath unarmoured (kg/m)	STA and textile finish (kg/m)	SWA and textile finish (kg/m)	PVC sheath unarmoured (kg/m)	STA and textile finish (kg/m)	SWA and textile finish (kg/m)
Single-core cables									
50	19.6			1.33			1.04		
70	21.4			1.64			1.21		
95	23.5			2.06			1.47		
120	25.1			3.38			1.64		
150	26.8			2.82			1.91		
185	28.7			3.28			2.13		
240	31.5			4.07			2.57		
300	34.0			4.80			2.91		
400	37.4			5.91			3.49		
500	40.7			7.19			4.15		
630	45.1			8.94			5.01		
800	49.8			11.07			6.04		
1000	55.0			13.57			7.24		

3-core cables									
25[a]	31.1	37.0	39.0	2.39	3.61	4.25	1.92	3.10	3.74
35	30.1	36.0	38.0	2.91	3.93	4.56	2.27	3.29	3.92
50	32.4	38.1	40.1	3.44	4.51	5.18	2.56	3.63	4.30
70	35.9	41.4	43.4	4.39	5.54	6.27	3.12	4.27	5.00
95	39.5	44.8	47.8	5.53	6.75	7.95	3.77	4.99	6.19
120	42.7	48.9	50.7	6.61	8.33	9.17	4.39	6.11	6.95
150	45.4	51.7	53.5	7.73	9.56	10.45	5.01	6.84	7.73
185	49.1	55.1	56.9	9.24	11.16	12.12	5.83	7.75	8.71
240	54.3	59.9	61.7	11.70	13.76	14.81	7.21	9.27	10.32
300	58.8	64.2	66.0	14.05	16.23	17.39	8.42	10.60	11.76
400	64.7	69.6	72.7	17.40	19.71	21.72	10.21	12.52	14.53

[a] Circular conductors

PAPER INSULATED DISTRIBUTION CABLES (BS 6480)
6.35/11 kV

Table A12.4 Dimensions and weights

Conductor size (mm^2)	Approximate diameter			Approximate weight, stranded copper conductors			Approximate weight, stranded aluminium conductors		
	PVC sheath unarmoured (mm)	STA and textile finish (mm)	SWA and textile finish (mm)	PVC sheath unarmoured (kg/m)	STA and textile finish (kg/m)	SWA and textile finish (kg/m)	PVC sheath unarmoured (kg/m)	STA and textile finish (kg/m)	SWA and textile finish (kg/m)
Single-core cables									
50	21.1			1.47			1.18		
70	23.1			1.85			1.43		
95	25.0			2.21			1.63		
120	26.8			2.64			1.90		
150	28.3			2.99			2.08		
185	30.4			3.55			2.41		
240	33.0			4.27			2.76		
300	35.7			5.12			3.23		
400	39.0			6.26			3.84		
500	43.3			7.53			4.49		
630	47.7			9.32			5.40		
800	52.4			11.48			6.45		
1000	57.6			14.18			7.85		
960[a]	58.2			13.82					
1200[a]	63.7			16.98					

3-core cables, belted									
25[b]	35.5	41.4	43.4	3.25	4.44	5.11	2.78	3.97	4.64
35[b]	38.6	44.3	46.3	3.51	5.02	5.73	3.07	4.33	5.04
50	37.2	42.6	45.6	4.18	5.37	6.45	3.31	4.50	5.58
70	40.6	45.9	48.9	5.20	6.46	7.62	3.94	5.20	6.36
95	44.2	50.5	52.3	6.41	8.19	9.00	4.66	6.44	7.25
120	47.2	53.2	55.0	7.40	9.26	10.12	5.19	7.05	7.91
150	50.2	56.0	57.8	8.61	10.54	11.45	5.89	7.82	8.73
185	53.8	59.4	61.2	10.18	12.21	13.18	6.77	8.80	9.77
240	58.8	64.2	66.0	12.70	14.89	15.95	8.22	10.41	11.47
300	63.3	68.5	71.6	15.13	17.44	19.36	9.50	11.81	13.73
400	69.2	73.9	77.0	18.57	21.00	23.08	11.38	13.81	15.89
3-core cables, screened									
25[b]	35.3	41.2	43.2	3.24	4.43	5.12	2.76	3.95	4.64
35[b]	38.2	43.9	45.9	3.39	4.89	5.60	3.10	4.19	4.90
50	37.1	42.5	44.5	4.15	5.24	5.94	3.17	4.36	5.06
70	40.3	45.8	48.8	5.04	6.32	7.48	3.78	5.06	6.22
95	44.0	50.4	52.2	6.23	8.03	8.84	4.48	6.28	7.09
120	47.2	53.4	55.2	7.36	9.25	10.11	5.15	7.04	7.90
150	50.2	56.2	58.0	8.56	10.53	11.44	5.84	7.81	8.72
185	53.8	59.6	61.4	10.13	12.20	13.17	6.72	8.79	9.76
240	58.9	64.3	66.1	12.48	14.67	15.73	8.00	10.19	11.25
300	63.7	68.8	71.9	15.10	17.42	19.35	9.48	11.80	13.73
400	69.6	74.3	77.4	18.55	20.97	23.08	11.35	13.77	15.88

[a] Milliken conductors
[b] Circular conductors

PAPER INSULATED DISTRIBUTION CABLES (BS 6480)
8.7/15 kV

Table A12.5 Dimensions and weights

Conductor size (mm^2)	Approximate diameter			Approximate weight, stranded copper conductors			Approximate weight, stranded aluminium conductors		
	PVC sheath unarmoured (mm)	STA and textile finish (mm)	SWA and textile finish (mm)	PVC sheath unarmoured (kg/m)	STA and textile finish (kg/m)	SWA and textile finish (kg/m)	PVC sheath unarmoured (kg/m)	STA and textile finish (kg/m)	SWA and textile finish (kg/m)
Single-core cables									
50	22.9			1.68			1.39		
70	24.7			2.00			1.57		
95	26.8			2.46			1.87		
120	28.4			2.80			2.06		
150	30.1			3.26			2.35		
185	32.0			3.74			2.59		
240	34.8			4.57			3.07		
300	37.5			5.35			3.46		
400	40.9			6.50			4.09		
500	45.1			7.91			4.87		
630	49.5			9.74			5.81		
800	54.2			11.93			6.91		
1000	59.4			14.52			8.19		
960[a]	60.0			14.32					
1200[a]	65.5			17.34					

3-core cables, screened									
25[b]	39.2	44.9	46.9	3.79	5.07	5.82	3.32	4.60	5.35
35[b]	42.3	47.8	50.8	4.50	5.85	7.08	3.84	5.19	6.42
50	42.2	47.4	50.4	4.77	6.05	7.23	3.90	5.18	6.36
70	45.6	51.8	53.6	5.70	7.49	8.31	4.43	6.22	7.04
95	49.5	55.5	57.3	7.10	9.00	9.88	5.35	7.25	8.13
120	52.6	58.4	60.2	8.12	10.09	11.02	5.91	7.88	8.81
150	55.7	61.3	63.1	9.36	11.42	12.40	6.64	8.70	9.68
185	59.4	64.8	66.6	10.98	13.12	14.16	7.57	9.71	10.75
240	64.7	69.8	72.9	13.59	15.89	17.80	9.10	11.40	13.31
300	69.4	74.3	77.4	16.07	18.48	20.52	10.44	12.85	14.89
400	75.4	79.9	83.0	19.60	22.13	24.33	12.41	14.94	17.14

[a] Milliken conductors
[b] Circular conductors

PAPER INSULATED DISTRIBUTION CABLES (BS 6480)
12.7/22 kV

Table A12.6 Dimensions and weights

Conductor size (mm^2)	Approximate diameter			Approximate weight, stranded copper conductors			Approximate weight, stranded aluminium conductors		
	PVC sheath unarmoured (mm)	STA and textile finish (mm)	SWA and textile finish (mm)	PVC sheath unarmoured (kg/m)	STA and textile finish (kg/m)	SWA and textile finish (kg/m)	PVC sheath unarmoured (kg/m)	STA and textile finish (kg/m)	SWA and textile finish (kg/m)
Single-core cables									
50	26.2			2.03			1.74		
70	28.0			2.36			1.94		
95	30.1			2.85			2.26		
120	31.7			3.21			2.47		
150	33.4			3.69			2.78		
185	35.3			4.19			3.05		
240	38.4			5.07			3.56		
300	41.0			5.86			3.98		
400	44.2			7.05			4.64		
500	48.3			8.52			5.48		
630	52.7			10.38			6.46		
800	57.4			12.63			7.61		
1000	62.4			15.28			8.95		
960[a]	63.2			15.07					
1200[a]	68.5			18.14					

3-core cables, screened									
25[b]	46.1	51.3	54.4	4.93	6.37	7.70	4.45	5.89	7.22
35[b]	49.2	55.4	57.2	5.72	7.71	8.61	5.07	7.06	7.96
50[b]	52.1	58.1	59.9	6.44	8.51	9.46	5.55	7.62	8.57
70	52.6	58.4	60.2	7.00	9.00	9.94	5.74	7.74	8.68
95	56.3	61.9	63.7	8.29	10.38	11.38	6.54	8.63	9.63
120	59.4	64.9	66.7	9.49	11.68	12.73	7.29	9.43	10.53
150	62.5	67.8	69.6	10.79	13.04	14.13	8.09	10.34	11.43
185	66.2	71.4	74.5	12.45	14.79	16.74	9.05	11.39	13.34
240	71.6	76.4	79.4	15.14	17.57	19.65	10.68	13.11	15.19
300	76.4	80.8	83.9	17.65	20.17	22.37	12.06	14.53	16.78
400	82.4	86.5	89.6	21.25	23.86	26.21	14.10	16.71	19.06
3-core cables, screened SL type									
25[b]		58.2	60.0		7.46	8.41		6.98	7.93
35[b]		60.8	62.6		8.17	9.16		7.52	8.51
50[b]		64.0	65.8		9.26	10.31		8.37	9.42
70[b]		67.9	69.7		10.52	11.64		9.23	10.35
95[b]		72.4	74.2		12.30	13.51		10.52	11.73
120[b]		75.9	77.7		13.63	14.90		11.39	12.66
150[b]		79.6	81.4		15.37	16.70		12.61	13.94
185[b]		83.7	86.8		17.18	19.55		13.71	16.08
240[b]		89.8	92.9		20.28	22.84		15.73	18.29
300[b]		95.0	98.1		23.02	25.73		17.30	20.01
400[b]		101.9	105.0		27.14	30.06		19.83	22.75

[a] Milliken conductors
[b] Circular conductors

PAPER INSULATED DISTRIBUTION CABLES (BS 6480)
19/33 kV

Table A12.7 Dimension and weights

Conductor size (mm²)	Approximate diameter			Approximate weight, copper conductors			Approximate weight, aluminium conductors		
	PVC sheath unarmoured (mm)	STA and textile finish (mm)	SWA and textile finish (mm)	PVC sheath unarmoured (kg/m)	STA and textile finish (kg/m)	SWA and textile finish (kg/m)	PVC sheath unarmoured (kg/m)	STA and textile finish (kg/m)	SWA and textile finish (kg/m)
Single-core cables									
50	31.4			2.73			2.44		
70	33.2			3.04			2.64		
95	34.9			3.49			2.94		
120	36.7			3.89			3.18		
150	37.8			4.29			3.44		
185	39.7			4.82			3.75		
240	42.8			5.77			4.31		
300	45.4			6.57			4.75		
400	48.8			7.81			5.49		
500	52.8			9.33			6.35		
630	57.1			11.31			7.38		
800	61.8			13.75			8.79		
1000	66.8			16.49			10.17		
960[a]	67.6			15.85					
1200[a]	72.9			18.98					

3-core cables, screened									
50[b]	63.7	69.3	71.1	9.07	11.53	12.53	8.16	10.82	11.62
70	64.4	69.7	71.5	10.05	12.57	13.49	8.74	11.40	12.18
95	67.2	72.4	75.5	11.36	14.03	15.75	9.55	12.29	13.94
120	70.5	75.4	78.5	12.76	15.60	17.31	10.47	13.29	15.03
150	72.3	77.0	80.1	14.08	16.90	18.71	11.27	14.14	15.90
185	76.0	80.5	83.6	16.04	18.93	20.85	12.51	15.46	17.32
240	81.1	85.3	88.4	18.76	21.86	23.83	14.12	17.22	19.19
300	85.8	89.8	92.9	21.67	24.81	26.96	15.85	19.08	21.14
400	91.8	95.4	98.5	25.95	29.10	31.49	18.34	21.68	23.88
3-core cables, screened SL type									
50		75.2	77.0		11.87	13.04		11.00	12.16
70		79.1	80.9		13.01	14.20		11.86	13.07
95		82.8	85.9		14.62	16.82		13.01	15.23
120		86.2	89.4		16.00	18.29		13.90	16.21
150		88.7	91.8		17.38	19.72		14.83	17.20
185		92.8	95.9		19.22	21.66		16.09	18.58
240		98.9	102.0		22.50	25.19		18.15	20.79
300		104.1	107.2		25.30	28.04		19.81	22.59
400		111.0	114.1		29.51	32.43		22.50	25.46

[a] Milliken conductors
[b] circular conductors

PAPER INSULATED DISTRIBUTION CABLES (BS 6480)
600/1000 V

Table A12.8 Sustained ratings

Conductor size (mm^2)	In air				In ground			
	Single-core		2-core (A)	3- or 4-core (A)	Single-core		2-core (A)	3- or 4-core (A)
	Trefoil (A)	Flat (A)			Trefoil (A)	Flat (A)		
Copper conductors								
16			105	91			120	105
25			145	120			160	135
35			175	150			195	165
50	215	235	210	180	220	230	230	195
70	275	300	265	230	270	280	285	240
95	335	370	325	280	320	335	345	290
120	390	430	380	325	365	380	395	335
150	445	490	430	375	410	430	445	375
185	520	570	495	430	460	485	500	425
240	620	710	590	510	530	560	580	490
300	710	810	670	590	600	620	650	550
400	820	930	780	680	680	700	740	620
500	940	1040			760	770		
630	1080	1170			850	860		
800	1220	1300			940	930		
1000	1350	1410			1010	980		
Aluminium conductors								
16			81	70			94	80
25			110	93			125	105
35			135	115			150	125
50	165	180	165	140	170	175	180	150
70	210	230	205	175	210	220	220	185
95	260	285	255	220	250	260	270	225
120	305	335	295	255	285	300	305	255
150	350	385	335	290	320	335	345	290
185	405	445	390	335	360	380	395	330
240	485	560	460	400	420	440	455	380

PAPER INSULATED DISTRIBUTION CABLES (BS 6480)
600/1000 V

Table A12.8 cont.

Conductor size (mm^2)	In air				In ground			
	Single-core		2-core (A)	3- or 4-core (A)	Single-core		2-core (A)	3- or 4-core (A)
	Trefoil (A)	Flat (A)			Trefoil (A)	Flat (A)		
300	560	640	530	460	475	495	520	430
400	650	740	620	540	540	560	590	500
500	760	840			610	630		
630	880	970			690	710		
800	1020	1090			780	780		
1000	1150	1220			860	850		

For relevant conditions see the notes at the beginning of this appendix.
Single-core cables are PVC sheathed unarmoured. Multicore cables are armoured.

PAPER INSULATED DISTRIBUTION CABLES (BS 6480)
1.9/3.3 and 3.8/6.6 kV

Table A12.9 Sustained ratings

Conductor size (mm^2)	In air			In ground		
	Single-core		3-core (A)	Single-core		3-core (A)
	Trefoil (A)	Flat (A)		Trefoil (A)	Flat (A)	
Copper conductors						
16			93			99
25			125			130
35			150			155
50	215	235	180	205	215	185
70	275	295	230	255	265	230
95	335	365	280	305	315	275
120	390	425	325	345	360	315
150	445	490	370	385	400	355
185	520	570	430	435	455	400
240	610	700	510	510	520	460
300	710	800	590	570	590	520
400	820	920	680	640	660	580
500	940	1030		720	720	
630	1080	1170		800	800	
800	1220	1290		880	860	
1000	1350	1410		950	910	
Aluminium conductors						
16			72			78
25			95			100
35			115			120
50	170	185	140	160	165	145
70	210	230	175	195	205	180
95	260	285	215	235	245	215
120	305	335	255	270	280	250
150	350	380	290	300	315	280
185	405	440	335	340	355	315
240	480	560	400	395	410	370

PAPER INSULATED DISTRIBUTION CABLES (BS 6480)

1.9/3.3 and 3.8/6.6 kV

Table A12.9 cont.

Conductor size (mm^2)	In air			In ground		
	Single-core		3-core (A)	Single-core		3-core (A)
	Trefoil (A)	Flat (A)		Trefoil (A)	Flat (A)	
300	560	640	460	445	465	415
400	650	740	540	510	530	470
500	750	840		580	590	
630	880	960		650	660	
800	1020	1090		730	730	
1000	1150	1210		810	790	

For the relevant conditions see the notes at the beginning of this appendix.
Single-core cables are PVC sheathed, unarmoured. 3-core cables are armoured.

PAPER INSULATED DISTRIBUTION CABLES (BS 6480)

6.35/11 and 8.7/15 kV

Table A12.10 Sustained ratings

Conductor size (mm²)	In air				In ground			
	Single-core		3-core		Single-core		3-core	
	Trefoil (A)	Flat (A)	Belted[a] (A)	Screened (A)	Trefoil (A)	Flat (A)	Belted[a] (A)	Screened (A)
Copper conductors								
16			80	95			89	100
25			105	120			115	125
35			130	145			140	150
50	200	215	155	175	190	200	165	180
70	250	270	195	220	235	245	205	220
95	305	330	240	265	280	290	245	265
120	355	385	275	310	320	330	280	300
150	405	440	315	350	360	370	315	340
185	465	510	360	400	405	420	355	380
240	550	620	425	475	470	480	410	435
300	630	700	490	540	530	540	460	485
400	730	800	560	620	600	600	520	550
500	840	900			660	660		
630	960	1010			740	730		
800	1080	1120			810	780		
1000	1190	1220			880	820		
960[b]	1270	1260			930	840		
1000[b]	1420	1370			1010	880		
Aluminium conductors								
16			62	74			69	79
25			82	94			89	99
35			100	110			110	115
50	155	165	120	135	150	155	130	140
70	195	210	150	170	180	190	160	170
95	235	260	185	205	220	225	190	205
120	275	300	215	240	250	260	220	235
150	315	340	245	270	280	290	245	265
185	360	395	280	315	315	330	280	300
240	435	490	335	370	370	380	325	345

PAPER INSULATED DISTRIBUTION CABLES (BS 6480)

6.35/11 and 8.7/15 kV

Table A12.10 cont.

Conductor size (mm^2)	In air				In ground			
	Single-core		3-core		Single-core		3-core	
	Trefoil (A)	Flat (A)	Belted[a] (A)	Screened (A)	Trefoil (A)	Flat (A)	Belted[a] (A)	Screened (A)
300	500	560	385	430	415	430	365	390
400	580	640	450	495	475	485	415	440
500	670	730			530	540		
630	780	840			600	610		
800	900	950			680	670		
1000	1020	1050			750	720		

[a] 6.35/11 kV only
[b] Milliken conductors

For the relevant conditions see the notes at the beginning of this appendix. Single-core cables are PVC sheathed unarmoured. 3-core cables are armoured.

PAPER INSULATED DISTRIBUTION CABLES (BS 6480)
12.7/22 kV

Table A12.11 Sustained ratings

Conductor size (mm^2)	In air				In ground			
	Single-core		3-core		Single-core		3-core	
	Trefoil (A)	Flat (A)	Screened (A)	SL (A)	Trefoil (A)	Flat (A)	Screened (A)	SL (A)
Copper conductors								
25			115	115			120	120
35			135	140			140	145
50	185	200	165	170	180	190	165	170
70	235	255	210	210	225	230	210	210
95	290	310	255	255	265	275	250	250
120	330	360	290	295	305	315	285	285
150	380	410	330	335	340	350	320	315
185	435	470	380	380	385	395	360	355
240	510	560	445	445	445	455	415	410
300	590	640	510	510	500	510	465	455
400	680	730	580	580	570	570	520	510
500	780	820			630	620		
630	890	920			710	680		
800	1000	1020			780	730		
1000	1110	1110			840	770		
960[a]	1170	1150			880	780		
1200[a]	1310	1250			950	820		
Aluminium conductors								
25			88	91			92	93
35			105	110			110	110
50	145	155	125	130	140	145	130	130
70	180	195	160	165	175	180	165	160
95	225	240	195	200	210	215	195	195
120	260	280	225	230	235	245	225	220
150	295	320	255	260	265	275	250	250
185	340	370	295	300	300	310	285	280
240	405	445	350	355	350	360	330	325
300	465	510	400	405	395	405	370	365

PAPER INSULATED DISTRIBUTION CABLES (BS 6480)

12.7/22 kV

Table A12.11 cont.

Conductor size (mm^2)	In air				In ground			
	Single-core		3-core		Single-core		3-core	
	Trefoil (A)	Flat (A)	Screened (A)	SL (A)	Trefoil (A)	Flat (A)	Screened (A)	SL (A)
400	540	590	465	465	450	460	420	415
500	620	670			510	510		
630	730	760			580	570		
800	830	860			650	630		
1000	940	960			710	670		

[a] Milliken conductors

For the relevant conditions see the notes at the beginning of this appendix. Single-core cables are PVC sheathed unarmoured. 3-core cables are armoured.

PAPER INSULATED DISTRIBUTION CABLES (BS 6480)

19/33 kV

Table A12.12 Sustained ratings

Conductor size (mm^2)	In air				In ground			
	Single-core		3-core		Single-core		3-core	
	Trefoil (A)	Flat (A)	Screened (A)	SL (A)	Trefoil (A)	Flat (A)	Screened (A)	SL (A)
Copper conductors								
50	190	205	165	175	180	190	165	170
70	240	255	215	215	225	230	210	210
95	290	315	260	260	265	275	250	250
120	335	360	295	300	305	315	285	285
150	380	410	335	340	340	350	320	320
185	440	470	385	385	385	395	360	355
240	520	560	450	455	445	450	415	410
300	590	630	510	515	500	500	465	455
400	690	720	580	580	570	560	520	510
500	780	810			630	620		
630	890	910			710	670		
800	1010	1010			780	720		
1000	1110	1100			840	760		
960[a]	1170	1130			870	770		
1200[a]	1300	1240			950	800		
Aluminium conductors								
50	150	160	130	135	140	145	130	135
70	185	200	165	170	175	180	165	165
95	225	245	200	205	205	215	195	195
120	260	280	230	235	235	245	225	225
150	300	320	260	265	265	275	250	250
185	340	370	300	305	300	310	285	280
240	405	440	355	360	350	360	330	325
300	465	500	405	410	395	405	370	365
400	540	580	470	470	450	455	420	415
500	620	660			510	510		
630	730	750			580	570		
800	830	850			650	620		
1000	940	950			710	670		

[a] Milliken conductors

For the relevant conditions see the notes at the beginning of this appendix. Single-core cables are PVC sheathed, unarmoured. 3-core cables are armoured.

PAPER INSULATED DISTRIBUTION CABLES (BS 6480)

600/1000 V

Table A12.13 Voltage drop (50 Hz, per A/m)

Conductor size (mm^2)	Copper				Aluminium			
	Single-core[a]		2-core (mV)	3- or 4-core (mV)	Single-core[a]		2-core (mV)	3- or 4-core (mV)
	Trefoil (mV)	Flat (mV)			Trefoil (mV)	Flat (mV)		
16			2.8	2.5			4.7	4.1
25			1.8	1.6			3.0	2.6
35			1.3	1.1			2.2	1.9
50	0.85	0.89	0.95	0.82	1.4	1.4	1.6	1.3
70	0.60	0.66	0.66	0.58	0.97	1.0	1.1	0.95
95	0.44	0.52	0.49	0.43	0.71	0.76	0.81	0.70
120	0.36	0.45	0.40	0.35	0.57	0.62	0.64	0.55
150	0.31	0.40	0.33	0.28	0.47	0.54	0.53	0.46
185	0.26	0.37	0.28	0.24	0.38	0.46	0.43	0.38
240	0.22	0.34	0.24	0.20	0.31	0.40	0.34	0.31
300	0.20	0.32	0.21	0.18	0.26	0.36	0.29	0.26
400	0.18	0.31	0.20	0.17	0.22	0.34	0.24	0.22
500	0.16	0.30			0.19	0.32		
630	0.15	0.29			0.17	0.30		
800	0.15	0.29			0.16	0.30		
1000	0.14	0.29			0.15	0.29		

[a] Data for three unarmoured cables

For the relevant conditions see the notes at the beginning of this appendix.

PAPER INSULATED DISTRIBUTION CABLES (BS 6480)
600/1000 V and 1.9/3.3 kV

Table A12.14 Electrical characteristics

Conductor size (mm^2)	Single-core[a]					Multicore			
	A.C. resistance at 80 °C		Reactance (50 Hz)		Capacitance (μF/km)	A.C. resistance at 80 °C		Reactance (50 Hz) (Ω/km)	Capacitance (μ/km)
	Copper (Ω/km)	Aluminium (Ω/km)	Trefoil (Ω/km)	Flat (Ω/km)		Copper (Ω/km)	Aluminium (Ω/km)		
600/1000 cables									
16						1.42	2.37	0.080	0.56
25						0.898	1.49	0.076	0.62
35						0.648	1.08	0.074	0.69
50	0.478	0.796	0.102	0.189	0.77	0.479	0.796	0.073	0.79
70	0.330	0.552	0.097	0.183	0.91	0.332	0.551	0.071	0.93
95	0.239	0.397	0.093	0.180	0.98	0.239	0.398	0.069	1.06
120	0.190	0.315	0.090	0.177	1.10	0.190	0.315	0.068	1.20
150	0.155	0.257	0.088	0.175	1.13	0.155	0.257	0.069	1.09
185	0.124	0.205	0.086	0.173	1.25	0.124	0.205	0.068	1.21
240	0.0954	0.156	0.084	0.197	1.26	0.0954	0.157	0.068	1.23
300	0.0771	0.125	0.083	0.190	1.32	0.0771	0.126	0.067	1.37
400	0.0616	0.0988	0.081	0.182	1.40	0.0617	0.0989	0.067	1.54
500	0.0495	0.0778	0.080	0.175	1.42				
630	0.0404	0.0617	0.079	0.167	1.60				
800	0.0340	0.0501	0.077	0.159	1.80				
1000	0.0295	0.0417	0.075	0.152	2.01				

1.9/3.3 kV cables									
16						1.42	2.37	0.091	0.38
25						0.898	1.49	0.083	0.47
35						0.648	1.08	0.081	0.52
50	0.478	0.796	0.106	0.164	0.61	0.479	0.796	0.079	0.59
70	0.330	0.552	0.100	0.158	0.71	0.332	0.551	0.076	0.68
95	0.239	0.397	0.096	0.154	0.82	0.239	0.398	0.073	0.78
120	0.190	0.315	0.092	0.150	0.92	0.190	0.315	0.072	0.88
150	0.155	0.257	0.090	0.148	1.01	0.155	0.257	0.071	0.96
185	0.124	0.205	0.088	0.146	1.12	0.124	0.205	0.070	1.06
240	0.0954	0.156	0.085	0.168	1.27	0.0954	0.157	0.069	1.20
300	0.0771	0.125	0.083	0.161	1.41	0.0771	0.126	0.068	1.33
400	0.0616	0.0988	0.081	0.153	1.50	0.0616	0.0988	0.068	1.49
500	0.0495	0.0778	0.080	0.146	1.59				
630	0.0404	0.0617	0.078	0.137	1.80				
800	0.0340	0.0501	0.077	0.130	2.02				
1000	0.0295	0.0417	0.076	0.123	2.26				

[a] Three unarmoured cables

For the relevant conditions see the notes at the beginning of this appendix.

PAPER INSULATED DISTRIBUTION CABLES (BS 6480)
3.8/6.6 kV

Table A12.15 Electrical characteristics

Conductor size (mm^2)	Single-core[a]					Multicore			
	A.C. resistance at 80 °C		Reactance (50 Hz)		Capacitance (μF/km)	A.C. resistance at 80°C		Reactance (50 Hz) (Ω/km)	Capacitance (μF/km)
	Copper (Ω/km)	Aluminium (Ω/km)	Trefoil (Ω/km)	Flat (Ω/km)		Copper (Ω/km)	Aluminium (Ω/km)		
16						1.42	2.37	0.106	0.26
25						0.899	1.49	0.096	0.32
35						0.648	1.08	0.092	0.35
50	0.478	0.796	0.111	0.169	0.48	0.479	0.796	0.089	0.39
70	0.330	0.551	0.105	0.163	0.56	0.332	0.550	0.085	0.46
95	0.239	0.397	0.100	0.158	0.64	0.239	0.398	0.081	0.51
120	0.190	0.315	0.096	0.154	0.71	0.190	0.315	0.079	0.57
150	0.155	0.257	0.094	0.151	0.78	0.154	0.257	0.078	0.62
185	0.124	0.205	0.091	0.149	0.86	0.124	0.205	0.076	0.69
240	0.0953	0.156	0.088	0.168	0.97	0.0952	0.156	0.074	0.77

300	0.0769	0.125	0.086	0.161	1.08	0.0768	0.126	0.073	0.85
400	0.0614	0.0987	0.084	0.153	1.21	0.0613	0.0986	0.072	0.95
500	0.0504	0.0793	0.082	0.146	1.34				
630	0.0410	0.0629	0.080	0.137	1.52				
800	0.0345	0.0509	0.078	0.130	1.70				
1000	0.0299	0.0423	0.077	0.123	1.90				

[a] Three unarmoured cables

For the relevant conditions see the notes at the beginning of this appendix.

PAPER INSULATED DISTRIBUTION CABLES (BS 6480)
6.35/11 kV

Table A12.16 Electrical characteristics

Conductor size (mm^2)	Single-core[a]					Multicore			
	A.C. resistance at 70 °C		Reactance (50 Hz)		Capacitance (μF/km)	A.C. resistance at operating temperature[b]		Reactance (50 Hz) (Ω/km)	Capacitance (μ/km)
	Copper (Ω/km)	Aluminium (Ω/km)	Trefoil (Ω/km)	Flat (Ω/km)		Copper (Ω/km)	Aluminium (Ω/km)		
						Belted cables			
16						1.35	2.26	0.112	0.24
25						0.856	1.42	0.105	0.28
35						0.617	1.03	0.098	0.31
50	0.463	0.770	0.113	0.173	0.37	0.456	0.757	0.094	0.34
70	0.320	0.533	0.107	0.167	0.42	0.316	0.524	0.090	0.39
95	0.232	0.384	0.102	0.162	0.48	0.228	0.378	0.086	0.44
120	0.184	0.305	0.098	0.158	0.53	0.181	0.299	0.083	0.48
150	0.150	0.249	0.095	0.155	0.57	0.147	0.244	0.082	0.52
185	0.120	0.198	0.093	0.152	0.63	0.118	0.195	0.080	0.57
240	0.0992	0.151	0.090	0.168	0.71	0.0907	0.149	0.078	0.64
300	0.0745	0.121	0.088	0.161	0.78	0.0732	0.120	0.076	0.70
400	0.0595	0.0956	0.085	0.153	0.87	0.0585	0.0939	0.075	0.78
500	0.0477	0.0752	0.085	0.146	0.96				
630	0.0389	0.0596	0.083	0.137	1.00				
800	0.0329	0.0483	0.081	0.130	1.20				

1000	0.0284	0.0400	0.080	0.123	1.34				
960[c]	0.0243		0.079	0.121	1.36				
1200[c]	0.0201		0.078	0.114	1.51				
							Screened cables		
16						1.38	2.29	0.113	0.31
25						0.870	1.44	0.106	0.36
35						0.627	1.04	0.099	0.41
50						0.463	0.770	0.095	0.46
70						0.321	0.533	0.091	0.53
95						0.232	0.385	0.087	0.60
120						0.184	0.305	0.084	0.67
150						0.149	0.248	0.082	0.73
185						0.120	0.198	0.081	0.80
240						0.0921	0.151	0.078	0.90
300						0.0743	0.122	0.077	1.00
400						0.0593	0.0954	0.075	1.11

[a] Three unarmoured cables
[b] 65 °C for belted and 70 °C for screened cables
[c] Milliken conductors

For the relevant conditions see the notes at the beginning of this appendix.

PAPER INSULATED DISTRIBUTION CABLES (BS 6480)
8.7/15 and 12.7/22 kV

Table A12.17 Electrical characteristics

Conductor size (mm^2)	Single-core[a]					Multicore			
	A.C. resistance at operating temperature[b]		Reactance (50 Hz)		Capacitance (μF/km)	A.C. resistance at operating temperature[b]		Reactance (50 Hz) (Ω/km)	Capacitance (μ/km)
	Copper (Ω/km)	Aluminium (Ω/km)	Trefoil (Ω/km)	Flat (Ω/km)		Copper (Ω/km)	Aluminium (Ω/km)		
8.17/15 kV cables									
25						0.870	1.44	0.114	0.30
35						0.627	1.04	0.106	0.34
50	0.463	0.770	0.118	0.178	0.37	0.463	0.770	0.102	0.38
70	0.320	0.533	0.111	0.172	0.42	0.321	0.533	0.097	0.43
95	0.232	0.384	0.107	0.166	0.48	0.232	0.385	0.092	0.49
120	0.184	0.305	0.102	0.162	0.53	0.184	0.305	0.089	0.54
150	0.150	0.248	0.099	0.159	0.57	0.149	0.248	0.087	0.59
185	0.120	0.198	0.096	0.156	0.63	0.120	0.198	0.085	0.64
240	0.0921	0.151	0.093	0.168	0.71	0.0920	0.151	0.082	0.72
300	0.0744	0.121	0.091	0.161	0.78	0.0742	0.122	0.080	0.80
400	0.0594	0.0955	0.088	0.153	0.87	0.0592	0.0953	0.078	0.89
500	0.0476	0.0751	0.087	0.146	0.96				
630	0.0387	0.0595	0.085	0.137	1.08				
800	0.0324	0.0482	0.083	0.130	1.20				
1000	0.0281	0.0400	0.082	0.123	1.34				

960[c]	0.0243		0.081	0.121	1.36				
1200[c]	0.0202		0.080	0.114	1.51				
12.7/22 kV cables									
25						0.856	1.42	0.125	0.25
35						0.617	1.03	0.116	0.28
50	0.455	0.757	0.126	0.187	0.30	0.456	0.757	0.111	0.31
70	0.315	0.524	0.119	0.180	0.34	0.316	0.524	0.106	0.35
95	0.227	0.377	0.114	0.174	0.39	0.228	0.378	0.100	0.39
120	0.181	0.299	0.109	0.169	0.42	0.181	0.299	0.097	0.43
150	0.148	0.244	0.106	0.165	0.46	0.147	0.244	0.094	0.47
185	0.118	0.195	0.102	0.162	0.50	0.118	0.195	0.091	0.51
240	0.0906	0.148	0.099	0.168	0.56	0.0904	0.149	0.088	0.57
300	0.0730	0.119	0.096	0.161	0.61	0.0728	0.119	0.086	0.62
400	0.0582	0.0937	0.093	0.153	0.68	0.0581	0.0936	0.083	0.69
500	0.0466	0.0737	0.092	0.146	0.75				
630	0.0379	0.0584	0.089	0.137	0.84				
800	0.0317	0.0472	0.087	0.130	0.93				
1000	0.0275	0.0392	0.085	0.123	1.03				
960[c]	0.0239		0.084	0.121	1.05				
1200[c]	0.0197		0.083	0.114	1.16				

[a] Three unarmoured cables
[b] 70 °C for 8.7/15 kV and 65 °C for 12.7/22 kV
[c] Milliken conductors

For the relevant conditions see the notes at the beginning of this appendix.

PAPER INSULATED DISTRIBUTION CABLES (BS 6480)
19/33 kV

Table A12.18 Electrical characteristics

Conductor size (mm^2)	Single-core					Multicore			
	A.C. resistance at 65 °C		Reactance (50 Hz)		Capacitance (μF/km)	A.C. resistance at 65 °C		Reactance (50 Hz) (Ω/km)	Capacitance (μ/km)
	Copper (Ω/km)	Aluminium (Ω/km)	Trefoil (Ω/km)	Flat (Ω/km)		Copper (Ω/km)	Aluminium (Ω/km)		
50[a]	0.447	0.742	0.138	0.200	0.23	0.456	0.758	0.126	0.24
70	0.309	0.514	0.130	0.193	0.26	0.316	0.524	0.119	0.27
95	0.223	0.370	0.124	0.185	0.30	0.228	0.379	0.112	0.30
120	0.178	0.294	0.118	0.180	0.32	0.181	0.300	0.107	0.33
150	0.145	0.240	0.114	0.175	0.36	0.147	0.244	0.103	0.37
185	0.116	0.191	0.114	0.171	0.39	0.118	0.195	0.101	0.40
240	0.0886	0.145	0.110	0.168	0.43	0.0902	0.149	0.097	0.44
300	0.0714	0.117	0.106	0.161	0.47	0.0727	0.120	0.094	0.48
400	0.0569	0.0918	0.103	0.153	0.52	0.0582	0.0935	0.090	0.53
500	0.0464	0.0736	0.098	0.146	0.57				

630	0.0376	0.0582	0.097	0.138	0.63
800	0.0314	0.0470	0.092	0.130	0.70
1000	0.0271	0.0389	0.089	0.123	0.78
960[b]	0.0238		0.089	0.121	0.79
1200[b]	0.0196		0.087	0.114	0.87

[a] Circular conductors in multicore cables
[b] Milliken conductors

For the relevant conditions see the notes at the beginning of this appendix. Except for 50 mm^2, multicore cables have oval conductors.

Appendix A13
PVC Insulated Distribution Cables

CONTENTS

Tables are included for dimensions and weights, sustained ratings and electrical characteristics. Notes on the cable designs and conditions applicable are given before the tables.

The data given apply to cables to BS 6346 in sizes from 16 mm^2 upwards. For smaller sizes see appendix A5.

CABLE DESIGNS

Typical designs are shown in figs A13.1 and A13.2.

Fig. A13.1 PVC insulated 3-core 600/1000 V wire armoured cable with solid aluminium conductor

Fig. A13.2 PVC insulated single-core 600/1000 V, unarmoured cable with sectoral aluminium conductor

Values are provided for unarmoured and armoured cables to BS 6346 with the following characteristics:

Conductors
Stranded copper and solid aluminium circular conductors for single-core cables and shaped for multicore cables. Cables with stranded aluminium conductors are also available and the dimensions are the same as for cables with copper conductors.

Armour bedding
Extruded PVC for single-core cables, extruded or taped PVC for multicore cables.

Armour
Armoured cables are assumed to have SWA, aluminium for single-core cables and galvanised steel for multicore cables.

Oversheath
Extruded PVC.

SUSTAINED RATINGS

The maximum ratings in the tables are for a single circuit and are based on ERA Technology Ltd Report 69-30, Part III, which is in general conformity with IEC 287. However, the ratings tabulated in ERA Report 69-30 are based on an ambient air temperature of 25 °C whereas the ratings given in this appendix are based on a temperature of 30 °C to align with the ratings for 600/1000 V cables tabulated in the IEE Regulations for Electrical Installations. When temperature correction factors are applied, the ratings become identical.

The standard conditions on which the tabulated ratings are based are given below. For other conditions the rating factors included in chapter 8 should be applied.

Maximum conductor temperature

70 °C.

Circuit protection

The cable should be selected with a rating of not less than the nominal current of the device providing protection against overload, or not less than 1.38 times this value if the device will not operate within 4 hours at 1.45 times its nominal current.

Installation in air

An ambient air temperature of 30 °C.

The cables are shielded from the direct rays of the sun. Air circulation is not restricted significantly, e.g. if fastened to a wall the cables are spaced at least 20 mm from it; if in a trench they are not covered.

Adjacent circuits are spaced apart (chapter 8) and suitably disposed to prevent mutual heating.

Cables laid direct in ground

Ground temperature
15 °C.

Ground thermal resistivity
1.2 K m/W.

Adjacent circuits
At least 1.8 m apart.

Depth of laying
0.5 m for voltages up to 1000 V and 0.8 m for 1.9/3.3 kV cables (measured from ground surface to centre of cable or trefoil group).

Single-core cables

The data apply to three or four single-core cables operating 3-phase.

Bonding
It is assumed that the armour will be solidly bonded, i.e. bonded at both ends of the run. For very short runs it may be found possible to bond at one end only but consideration must be given to the value of the standing voltage which can occur along the cable length under normal and fault conditions.

Trefoil
A close trefoil is assumed with the cables touching.

Flat formation
The ratings and technical data are based on horizontal installation with a spacing between cable centres of twice the overall diameter. Cables installed vertically will have somewhat lower ratings.

ELECTRICAL CHARACTERISTICS

The standard conditions given for sustained ratings are equally applicable to the electrical characteristics. A.C. resistances are tabulated. D.C. resistances are given in table 4.1 of chapter 4.

PVC INSULATED DISTRIBUTION CABLES (BS 6346)

600/1000 V – copper

Table A13.1 Dimensions and weights

Conductor size (mm^2)	Approximate diameter			Approximate weight		
	Unarmoured (mm)	Armoured (SWA)		Unarmoured (kg/m)	Armoured (SWA)	
		Tape bedding (mm)	Extruded bedding (mm)		Tape bedding (kg/m)	Extruded bedding (kg/m)
Single-core (aluminium wire armoured)						
50	15.1		19.1	0.60		0.78
70	16.9		21.1	0.81		1.03
95	19.4		23.4	1.10		1.33
120	21.0		26.3	1.35		1.68
150	23.2		28.3	1.65		2.00
185	25.8		30.8	2.06		2.43
240	29.0		34.1	2.67		3.09
300	32.1		37.0	3.32		3.77
400	35.8		42.0	4.19		4.83
500	39.6		45.6	5.23		5.92
630	43.8		49.7	6.63		7.42
800	48.3		55.8	8.33		9.50
1000	53.7		61.0	10.44		11.76
2-core cables (shaped)						
16[a]	18.6	21.9	21.9	0.54	0.98	0.99
25	18.4	22.6	23.0	0.69	1.26	1.28
35	20.1	24.5	24.9	0.95	1.59	1.61
50	22.8	27.4	27.8	1.26	1.99	2.01
70	25.5	30.0	30.4	1.70	2.50	1.52
95	29.3	34.7	35.5	2.31	3.46	3.52
120	31.8	37.2	38.0	2.88	4.12	4.20
150	35.1	40.5	41.3	3.52	4.89	4.96
185	39.1	45.2	46.4	4.39	6.25	6.39
240	43.9	50.0	51.2	5.76	7.86	8.02
300	48.7	54.8	56.4	7.16	9.48	9.71
400	54.2	60.3	61.9	9.04	11.60	11.85

(cont.)

PVC INSULATED DISTRIBUTION CABLES (BS 6346)
600/1000 V – copper

Table A13.1 cont.

Conductor size (mm^2)	Approximate diameter			Approximate weight		
	Unarmoured (mm)	Armoured (SWA)		Unarmoured (kg/m)	Armoured (SWA)	
		Tape bedding (mm)	Extruded bedding (mm)		Tape bedding (kg/m)	Extruded bedding (kg/m)
3-core cables (shaped)						
16[a]	19.7	23.1	23.1	0.73	1.20	1.21
25	20.4	24.6	25.0	1.00	1.65	1.67
35	22.4	26.9	27.3	1.30	2.03	2.05
50	25.5	30.1	30.5	1.72	2.56	2.58
70	28.7	34.2	35.0	2.36	3.52	3.59
95	33.3	38.5	39.3	3.33	4.64	4.71
120	36.3	41.4	42.2	4.10	5.51	5.59
150	40.0	46.3	47.5	5.02	6.97	7.11
185	44.6	50.7	51.9	6.26	8.39	8.54
240	50.1	56.2	57.8	8.15	10.55	10.79
300	55.6	61.6	63.2	10.14	12.79	13.04
400	62.2	68.0	69.6	12.86	15.76	16.02
4-core cables (sector shaped)						
16[a]	21.6	25.9	26.3	0.92	1.58	1.62
25	22.9	27.4	27.8	1.29	2.03	2.05
35	25.4	30.1	30.5	1.69	2.51	2.53
50	29.2	34.6	35.4	2.25	3.41	3.48
70	33.0	38.4	39.2	3.10	4.40	4.47
95	38.3	43.5	44.3	4.36	5.83	5.90
120	41.8	48.1	49.3	5.38	7.40	7.54
150	46.3	52.4	53.6	6.63	8.81	8.97
185	51.3	57.4	59.0	8.25	10.66	10.89
240	58.0	64.1	65.7	10.73	14.43	13.69
300	64.6	70.4	72.0	13.38	16.33	16.61
400	72.0	79.3	81.3	16.93	21.07	21.48
4-core cables with reduced neutral[b]						
25	22.9	27.4	27.8	1.26	2.00	2.02
35	24.7	29.1	29.5	1.59	2.41	2.43
50	28.3	32.7	33.1	2.12	3.03	3.05

PVC INSULATED DISTRIBUTION CABLES (BS 6346)

600/1000 V – copper

Table A13.1 cont.

Conductor size (mm^2)	Approximate diameter			Approximate weight		
	Unarmoured (mm)	Armoured (SWA)		Unarmoured (kg/m)	Armoured (SWA)	
		Tape bedding (mm)	Extruded bedding (mm)		Tape bedding (kg/m)	Extruded bedding (kg/m)
70	32.0	37.2	38.0	2.89	4.15	4.22
95	37.5	42.9	43.7	3.92	5.38	5.46
120	41.4	47.8	49.0	4.89	6.85	6.99
150	44.7	50.8	52.0	5.90	8.03	8.18
185	49.9	56.0	57.2	7.40	9.75	9.91
240	56.0	62.1	63.7	9.59	12.23	12.47
300	62.2	68.2	69.8	11.91	14.81	15.08
300	64.2	70.2	71.8	12.19	15.09	15.36
400	69.9	76.6	78.6	15.07	19.07	19.47

[a] Circular conductors

[b] Size of reduced neutral conductor

Phase conductor (mm^2)	25	35	50	70	95	120
Neutral conductor (mm^2)	16	16	25	35	50	70
Phase conductor (mm^2)	150	185	240	300	300	400
Neutral conductor (mm^2)	70	95	120	150	185	185

All cables have stranded conductors.
See appendix A5 for smaller sizes of armoured cables.
The phase conductors are shaped, but for some sizes the neutral conductors are circular.

PVC INSULATED DISTRIBUTION CABLES (BS 6346)

600/1000 V – aluminium

Table A13.2 Dimensions and weights

Conductor size (mm^2)	Approximate diameter,[a] solid aluminium conductor			Approximate weight		
	Unarmoured (mm)	Armoured (SWA)		Unarmoured (kg/m)	Armoured (SWA)	
		Tape bedding (mm)	Extruded bedding (mm)		Tape bedding (kg/m)	Extruded bedding (kg/m)
Single-core (aluminium wire armoured)						
50	13.8		17.8	0.28		0.46
70	15.4		19.6	0.36		0.57
95	17.6		21.6	0.48		0.70
120	19.0		24.3	0.57		0.89
150	21.0		26.1	0.69		1.03
185	23.3		28.3	0.86		1.22
240	26.1		31.2	1.09		1.50
300	28.9		33.7	1.34		1.77
380[b]	32.4		38.4	1.67		2.25
480[b]	35.7		41.7	2.06		2.70
600[b]	38.7		44.6	2.44		3.13
740[b]	42.2		49.5	2.94		3.89
960[b]	47.4		54.9	3.75		4.79
1200[b]	52.0		59.7	4.58		5.78
2-core cables (shaped)						
16[c]	17.4	20.7	20.7	0.34	0.34	0.62
25	16.6	20.9	21.3	0.38	0.92	0.94
35	18.0	22.5	22.9	0.49	1.09	1.11
50	20.4	25.1	25.5	0.62	1.31	1.33
70	22.8	27.3	27.7	0.81	1.56	1.58
95	26.2	31.6	32.4	1.08	2.16	2.22
3-core cables (sector shaped)						
16[c]	18.4	21.8	21.8	0.42	0.86	0.86
25	19.2	23.5	23.9	0.51	1.14	1.16
35	21.0	25.4	25.8	0.63	1.32	1.34
50	23.8	28.5	28.9	0.81	1.61	1.62
70	26.8	32.2	33.0	1.06	2.16	2.22

PVC INSULATED DISTRIBUTION CABLES (BS 6346)

600/1000 V – aluminium

Table A13.2 cont.

Conductor size (mm^2)	Approximate diameter,[a] solid aluminium conductor			Approximate weight		
	Unarmoured (mm)	Armoured (SWA)		Unarmoured (kg/m)	Armoured (SWA)	
		Tape bedding (mm)	Extruded bedding (mm)		Tape bedding (kg/m)	Extruded bedding (kg/m)
95	31.1	36.3	37.1	1.49	2.73	2.80
120	33.7	38.9	39.7	1.78	3.11	3.19
150	37.2	43.5	44.7	2.16	4.00	4.14
185	41.4	47.5	48.7	2.69	4.69	4.84
240	46.5	52.6	54.2	3.44	5.68	5.90
300	51.6	57.6	59.2	4.25	6.72	6.96
4-core cables (sector shaped)						
16[c]	20.4	24.4	24.8	0.50	1.13	1.17
25	21.5	25.9	26.3	0.65	1.36	1.38
35	23.6	28.2	28.6	0.78	1.59	1.61
50	27.1	32.5	33.3	1.05	2.17	2.24
70	30.6	36.0	36.8	1.38	2.62	2.69
95	35.5	40.6	41.4	1.95	3.35	3.42
120	38.6	44.9	46.1	2.32	4.22	4.36
150	42.8	48.9	50.1	2.84	4.90	5.05
185	47.4	53.5	55.1	3.52	5.79	6.01
240	53.5	59.6	61.2	4.53	7.07	7.31
300	59.6	65.4	67.0	5.62	8.39	8.65

[a] The diameter of cables with stranded conductors is the same as for copper (see table A13.1)
[b] Solid sectoral aluminium conductors
[c] Circular conductors

PVC INSULATED DISTRIBUTION CABLES (BS 6346)
1.9/3.3 kV

Table A13.3 Dimensions and weights (armoured cables, SWA)

Conductor size (mm^2)	Approximate diameter		Approximate weight	
	Stranded copper or aluminium conductor (mm)	Solid aluminium conductor (mm)	Stranded copper conductor (kg/m)	Solid aluminium conductor (kg/m)
Single-core (aluminium wire armour)				
50	21.0	19.8	0.87	0.55
70	22.8	21.3	1.11	0.65
95	26.0	24.3	1.49	0.85
120	27.6	25.6	1.77	0.97
150	29.4	27.1	2.07	1.10
185	31.3	28.8	2.47	1.25
240	34.1	31.2	3.09	1.50
300	37.0	33.7	3.77	1.77
400	42.0		4.83	
500	45.6		5.92	
630	49.7		7.42	
800	55.8		9.50	
1000	61.0		11.76	
380[a]		38.4		2.25
480[a]		41.7		2.70
600[a]		44.6		3.13
740[a]		49.5		3.89
960[a]		54.9		4.79
1200[a]		59.7		5.78
3-core cables (sector shaped)				
16[b]	30.3	29.0	1.80	1.47
25[b]	33.1	31.3	2.25	1.68
35	32.1	30.6	2.57	1.82
50	35.6	33.9	3.33	2.32
70	38.9	36.9	4.14	2.72

PVC INSULATED DISTRIBUTION CABLES (BS 6346)

1.9/3.3 kV

Table A13.3 cont.

Conductor size (mm^2)	Approximate diameter		Approximate weight	
	Stranded copper or aluminium conductor (mm)	Solid aluminium conductor (mm)	Stranded copper conductor (kg/m)	Solid aluminium conductor (kg/m)
95	42.3	40.0	5.11	3.19
120	46.6	44.0	6.45	4.01
150	49.4	46.5	7.43	4.45
185	52.8	49.6	8.73	5.03
240	57.8	54.2	10.83	5.95
300	63.2	59.2	13.09	7.00
400	69.6		16.09	

[a] Solid sectoral aluminium conductors
[b] Circular conductors

The data apply to cables with extruded PVC bedding.

PVC INSULATED DISTRIBUTION CABLES (BS 6346)
600/1000 V – armoured

Table A13.4 Sustained ratings

Conductor size (mm²)	In air				In ground			
	Single-core[a]		2-core (A)	3- or 4-core (A)	Single-core[a]		2-core (A)	3- or 4-core (A)
	Trefoil (A)	Flat (A)			Trefoil (A)	Flat (A)		
Copper conductors								
16			97	83			119	101
25			128	110			158	132
35			157	135			190	159
50	181	230	190	163	203	211	225	188
70	231	286	241	207	248	257	277	233
95	280	338	291	251	297	305	332	279
120	324	385	336	290	337	341	377	317
150	373	436	386	332	376	377	422	355
185	425	490	439	378	423	417	478	401
240	501	566	516	445	485	469	551	462
300	567	616	592	510	542	515	616	517
400	657	674	683	590	600	549	693	580
500	731	721			660	586		
630	809	771			721	627		
800	886	824			756	648		
1000	945	872			797	679		
Aluminium conductors								
16			72	61			91	77
25			92	80			118	100
35			113	98			142	120
50	131	169	136	120	154	160	168	143
70	168	213	173	151	188	197	209	176
95	205	255	213	188	226	235	250	213
120	238	293		218	257	267		243
150	275	335		248	288	298		272
185	315	379		288	326	332		309
240	372	443		344	377	380		360
300	430	505		396	424	423		407

PVC INSULATED DISTRIBUTION CABLES (BS 6346)

600/1000 V – armoured

Table A13.4 cont.

Conductor size (mm^2)	In air				In ground			
	Single-core[a]		2-core (A)	3- or 4-core (A)	Single-core[a]		2-core (A)	3- or 4-core (A)
	Trefoil (A)	Flat (A)			Trefoil (A)	Flat (A)		
380[b]	497	551			475	457		
480[b]	568	604			532	501		
600[b]	642	656			586	540		
740[b]	715	707			648	582		
960[b]	808	770			701	608		
1200[b]	880	822			755	644		

[a] Single-core cables with aluminium wire armour
[b] Solid sectoral aluminium conductors

For the relevant conditions see the notes at the beginning of this appendix.

PVC INSULATED DISTRIBUTION CABLES (BS 6346)

600/1000 V – unarmoured

Table A13.5 Sustained ratings

Conductor size (mm^2)	In air				In ground			
	Single-core[a]		2-core (A)	3- or 4-core (A)	Single-core[a]		2-core (A)	3- or 4-core (A)
	Trefoil (A)	Flat (A)			Trefoil (A)	Flat (A)		
Copper conductors								
16			94	80			117	100
25			119	101			157	131
35			148	126			189	158
50	167	219	180	153	200	210	225	188
70	216	281	232	196	246	258	276	231
95	264	341	282	238	294	310	332	277
120	308	396	328	276	335	354	379	316
150	356	456	379	319	376	397	425	355
185	409	521	434	364	424	451	480	401
240	485	615	514	430	491	524	559	466
300	561	709	593	497	553	594	631	525
400	656	852	715	597	627	679	718	595
500	749	982			706	774		
630	855	1138			790	883		
800	971	1265			872	995		
1000	1079	1420			948	1103		
Aluminium conductors								
16			73	61			89	76
25			89	78			118	100
35			111	96			142	120
50	128	163	135	117	152	160	169	143
70	165	210	173	150	187	197	209	176
95	203	256	210	183	224	236	250	211
120	237	298		212	256	269		241
150	274	344		245	287	302		271
185	316	394		280	325	343		307
240	375	466		330	377	399		357

PVC INSULATED DISTRIBUTION CABLES (BS 6346)

600/1000 V – unarmoured

Table A13.5 cont.

Conductor size (mm^2)	In air				In ground			
	Single-core[a]		2-core (A)	3- or 4-core (A)	Single-core[a]		2-core (A)	3- or 4-core (A)
	Trefoil (A)	Flat (A)			Trefoil (A)	Flat (A)		
300	435	538		381	426	453		404
380[a]	507	625			484	515		
480[a]	590	726			549	587		
600[a]	680	837			613	658		
740[a]	776	956			690	745		
960[a]	907	1125			787	860		
1200[a]	1026	1293			870	963		

[a] Solid sectoral aluminium conductors

For the relevant conditions see the notes at the beginning of this appendix.

PVC INSULATED DISTRIBUTION CABLES (BS 6346)
1.9/3.3 kV – armoured

Table A13.6 Sustained ratings

Conductor size (mm^2)	In air			In ground		
	Single-core [a]		3-core (A)	Single core[a]		3-core (A)
	Trefoil (A)	Flat (A)		Trefoil (A)	Flat (A)	
Copper conductor						
16			85			97
25			111			125
35			134			151
50	183	226	163	193	199	178
70	229	281	204	236	242	219
95	284	339	250	282	285	264
120	348	386	290	319	320	299
150	371	433	330	357	354	336
185	426	489	379	401	393	379
240	500	558	446	459	441	436
300	571	620	508	513	483	488
400	649	667	583	566	513	548
500	729	720		621	546	
630	817	780		678	582	
800	881	821		708	599	
1000	949	874		744	626	
Aluminium conductors						
16			64			74
25			84			95
35			102			114
50	134	167	122	147	152	136
70	169	210	154	180	186	168
95	208	256	189	215	222	201
120	240	295	219	244	252	230
150	273	335	249	273	281	257
185	317	380	287	309	313	292
240	375	443	339	357	358	338

PVC INSULATED DISTRIBUTION CABLES (BS 6346)

1.9/3.3 kV – armoured

Table A13.6 cont.

Conductor size (mm^2)	In air			In ground		
	Single-core [a]		3-core (A)	Single core[a]		3-core (A)
	Trefoil (A)	Flat (A)		Trefoil (A)	Flat (A)	
300	431	499	388	402	397	381
380[b]	497	548		450	429	
480[b]	569	607		503	469	
600[b]	637	661		553	504	
740[b]	719	719		610	541	
960[b]	803	763		658	564	
1200[b]	884	819		707	595	

[a] Single-core cables with aluminium wire armour
[b] Solid sectoral aluminium conductors

For the relevant conditions see the notes at the beginning of this appendix.

PVC INSULATED DISTRIBUTION CABLES (BS 6346)
600/1000 V

Table A13.7 Voltage drop (50 Hz, per A/m)

Conductor size (mm^2)	Copper				Aluminium			
	Single-core[a]		2-core (mV)	3- or 4-core (mV)	Single-core[a]		2-core (mV)	3- or 4-core (mV)
	Trefoil (mV)	Flat (mV)			Trefoil (mV)	Flat (mV)		
Armoured cables								
16			2.8	2.4			4.5	3.9
25			1.75	1.5			2.9	2.5
35			1.25	1.1			2.1	1.8
50	0.82	0.86	0.94	0.81	1.35	1.35	1.55	1.35
70	0.58	0.68	0.65	0.57	0.93	1.00	1.05	0.92
95	0.45	0.57	0.50	0.43	0.70	0.80	0.79	0.68
120	0.37	0.50	0.41	0.35	0.57	0.68		0.55
150	0.32	0.45	0.34	0.29	0.47	0.58		0.44
185	0.27	0.41	0.29	0.25	0.39	0.51		0.37
240	0.23	0.37	0.24	0.21	0.32	0.44		0.30
300	0.21	0.34	0.21	0.185	0.27	0.40		0.25
400	0.195	0.32	0.185	0.16				
500	0.18	0.30						
630	0.17	0.28						
800	0.16							
1000	0.155							
380[b]					0.24	0.38		
480[b]					0.22	0.35		
600[b]					0.20	0.32		
740[b]					0.185	0.30		
960[b]					0.175	0.27		
1200[b]					0.17	0.25		
Unarmoured cables								
16			2.8	2.4			4.5	3.9
25			1.75	1.5			2.9	2.5
35			1.25	1.1			2.1	1.8
50	0.82	0.86	0.94	0.81	1.35	1.4	1.55	1.35
70	0.57	0.63	0.65	0.57	0.92	0.96	1.05	0.92

PVC INSULATED DISTRIBUTION CABLES (BS 6346)

600/1000 V

Table A13.7 cont.

Conductor size (mm^2)	Copper				Aluminium			
	Single-core[a]		2-core (mV)	3- or 4-core (mV)	Single-core[a]		2-core (mV)	3- or 4-core (mV)
	Trefoil (mV)	Flat (mV)			Trefoil (mV)	Flat (mV)		
95	0.42	0.47	0.49	0.42	0.67	0.70	0.79	0.68
120	0.35	0.40	0.40	0.35	0.54	0.58		0.54
150	0.29	0.35	0.34	0.29	0.45	0.49		0.45
185	0.25	0.33	0.29	0.25	0.37	0.42		0.37
240	0.21	0.32	0.24	0.21	0.30	0.36		0.29
300	0.19	0.31	0.21	0.18	0.25	0.32		0.25
400	0.17	0.28	0.19	0.17				
500	0.16	0.27						
630	0.15	0.25						
800	0.15	0.23						
1000	0.14	0.22						
380[b]					0.22	0.33		
480[b]					0.20	0.30		
600[b]					0.18	0.28		
740[b]					0.16	0.26		
960[b]					0.15	0.24		
1200[b]					0.15	0.23		

[a] Data for aluminium wire armoured cables
[b] Solid sectoral aluminium conductors

For the relevant conditions see the notes at the beginning of this appendix.

PVC INSULATED DISTRIBUTION CABLES (BS 6346)
600/1000 V

Table A13.8 Electrical characteristics

Conductor size (mm^2)	Armoured single-core cables[a]				Armoured or unarmoured multicore cables		
	A.C. resistance at 70 °C		Reactance (50 Hz)		A.C. resistance at 70 °C		Reactance (50Hz) (Ω/km)
	Copper (Ω/km)	Aluminium (Ω/km)	Trefoil (Ω/km)	Flat[b] (Ω/km)	Copper (Ω/km)	Aluminium (Ω/km)	
16					1.38	2.27	0.087
25					0.870	1.44	0.084
35					0.627	1.04	0.081
50	0.464	0.770	0.112	0.198	0.464	0.770	0.081
70	0.321	0.553	0.107	0.193	0.321	0.533	0.079
95	0.232	0.385	0.103	0.189	0.232	0.385	0.077
120	0.184	0.305	0.103	0.188	0.184	0.305	0.076
150	0.150	0.248	0.101	0.186	0.150	0.248	0.076
185	0.121	0.198	0.099	0.184	0.121	0.198	0.076
240	0.0927	0.152	0.096	0.182	0.0929	0.152	0.075
300	0.0751	0.122	0.094	0.181	0.0752	0.122	0.074
400	0.0600		0.091	0.178	0.0604		0.074
500	0.0484		0.089	0.176			
630	0.0398		0.086	0.173			
800	0.0334		0.086				
1000	0.0290		0.084	0.181			
380[c]		0.0976	0.094	0.179			
480[c]		0.0779	0.092	0.176			
600[c]		0.0643	0.089				
740[c]		0.0522	0.089				
960[c]		0.0415	0.087				
1200[c]		0.0348	0.085				

[a] Aluminium wire armoured
[b] Twice cable diameter spacing between centres
[c] Solid sectoral aluminium conductors

For the relevant conditions see the notes at the beginning of this appendix.

PVC INSULATED DISTRIBUTION CABLES (BS 6346)

1.9/3.3 kV

Table A13.9 Electrical characteristics

Conductor size (mm^2)	A.C. resistance at 70 °C		Reactance (50 Hz)		Capacitance[a]	
	Copper (Ω/km)	Aluminium (Ω/km)	Trefoil (Ω/km)	Flat[b] (Ω/km)	Copper (μF/km)	Aluminium (μF/km)
Single-core, aluminium wire armoured						
50	0.463	0.770	0.115	0.173	0.86	0.77
70	0.321	0.533	0.109	0.167	1.00	0.89
95	0.232	0.385	0.107	0.165	1.08	0.96
120	0.184	0.305	0.102	0.160	1.20	1.05
150	0.150	0.248	0.099	0.157	1.30	1.15
185	0.120	0.198	0.096	0.154	1.44	1.26
240	0.0929	0.152	0.093	0.151	1.62	1.41
300	0.0752	0.122	0.091	0.149	1.69	1.48
400	0.0600		0.091	0.149	1.71	
500	0.0484		0.089	0.147	1.81	
630	0.0398		0.086	0.144	2.03	
800	0.0334		0.086	0.137	2.17	
1000	0.0290		0.084	0.142	2.32	
380[c]		0.0976	0.094	0.152		1.51
480[c]		0.0779	0.092	0.150		1.59
600[c]		0.0643	0.089	0.147		1.74
740[c]		0.0522	0.089	0.147		1.85
960[c]		0.0415	0.087	0.145		2.00
1200[c]		0.0343	0.086	0.143		2.13
3-core, armoured or unarmoured						
16	1.38	2.27	0.107		0.54	0.50
25	0.870	1.44	0.097		0.65	0.57
35	0.627	1.04	0.094		0.71	0.64
50	0.463	0.770	0.090		0.78	0.70
70	0.321	0.533	0.086		0.90	0.80
95	0.232	0.385	0.082		1.01	0.91
120	0.184	0.305	0.080		1.10	0.97
150	0.150	0.248	0.079		1.20	1.06
185	0.121	0.198	0.077		1.32	1.16
240	0.0929	0.152	0.075		1.45	1.27

(*cont.*)

PVC INSULATED DISTRIBUTION CABLES (BS 6346)
1.9/3.3 kV

Table A13.9 cont.

Conductor size (mm^2)	A.C. resistance at 70°C		Reactance (50 Hz)		Capacitance[a]	
	Copper (Ω/km)	Aluminium (Ω/km)	Trefoil (Ω/km)	Flat[b] (Ω/km)	Copper (μF/km)	Aluminium (μF/km)
300	0.0752	0.122	0.075		1.50	1.32
400	0.0604		0.074		1.58	

[a] Not applicable to unarmoured cables
[b] Twice cable diameter spacing between centres
[c] Solid sectoral aluminium conductors

The characteristics apply to cables with extruded PVC bedding.
For the relevant conditions see the notes at the beginning of this appendix.

Appendix A14
XLPE Insulated Distribution Cables

CONTENTS

Tables are included for dimensions and weights, sustained ratings and electrical characteristics. Notes on the cable designs and conditions applicable are given before the tables.

The data included cover cables up to 3.3 kV to BS 5467 and BS 6724, cables for 6 kV to 33 kV to BS 6622 and 66 and 132 kV cables. The size range for the 600/1000 V cables is from 16 mm^2 upwards. For smaller cables to BS 5467 and BS 6724 see appendix A5.

CABLE DESIGNS

600/100 V and 1.9/3.3 kV, to BS 5467 and BS 6724

Fig. A14.1 XLPE insulated 4-core 600/1000 V armoured cable

Conductors
Stranded copper and solid aluminium circular conductors for single-core and shaped conductors for multicore cables. Stranded aluminium conductors can also be supplied. The dimensions are the same as for cables with copper conductors.

Armour bedding
Extruded PVC for cables to BS 5467. Extruded special synthetic material for cables to BS 6724.

A design with PVC tapes is also available for cables to BS 5467 but dimensions are not included in the tables.

Armour
The tabulated data apply to

(a) unarmoured and armoured cables to BS 5467
(b) armoured only cables to BS 6724

The armour consists of galvanised steel SWA on multicore cables and aluminium wire SWA on single-core cables.

Oversheath
Extruded PVC for cables to BS 5467. Special synthetic material for cables to BS 6724.

Fig. A14.2 XLPE insulated single-core, 6.35/11 kV cable with copper wire screen

Fig. A14.3 XLPE insulated 3-core, 6.35/11 kV wire armoured cable

3.8/6.6 kV to 19/33 kV inclusive, to BS 6622 and to IEC 502

Conductors
Stranded copper and stranded aluminium circular conductors for single-core and 3-core cables. Solid aluminium conductors are also available up to and including 11 kV.

The tabulated data only cover circular conductor cables but shaped conductors are also available up to 11 kV.

Screens
Extruded semiconducting layer over conductor and taped or extruded layer over insulation.

Metallic screen component
Copper wires over screen on single-core cables, copper tape on 3-core cables.

Bedding under armour
Extruded PVC on 3-core cables.

Armour
Galvanised steel SWA on 3-core cables.

The tabulated data apply to unarmoured single-core cables and armoured 3-core cables. Aluminium wire armoured single-core cables and unarmoured 3-core cables are also available.

Oversheath
Extruded PVC.

Conductor size range
Ratings are given in the tables for a range of voltages but, particularly at the higher voltages, the smallest conductor sizes may not be manufactured. A footnote indicates when reference should be made to the table of dimensions to check that the size is available.

66 kV and 132 kV cables – BICC designs

Conductors
Single-core cables only, with circular stranded copper or stranded aluminium conductors.

Screens
Extruded semiconducting layer over conductor and also over the insulation.

Metallic screen component
The main component is the metallic sheath but a copper tape is also applied over the insulation screen on cables with corrugated aluminium sheath.

Metallic sheath
The tabulated data cover cables with lead and corrugated aluminium sheaths. Smooth aluminium sheathed cables are also available.

Armour
Armour is not usually provided on these cables but aluminium wire armour may be applied on lead sheathed cables.

Oversheath
Extruded PVC or polyethylene.

SUSTAINED RATINGS

The tabulated ratings have been determined in accordance with IEC 287. They are for a single circuit with the standard conditions given below. For other conditions the rating factors included in chapter 8 should be applied.

For cables to BS 5467 and BS 6724 (up to 3.3 kV) the ratings given in this appendix are in accordance with ERA Report 69–30, Part V (which is in conformity with IEC 287). For cables in air the ratings are based on an ambient temperature of 30 °C to align with the IEE Regulations for Electrical Installations. The ratings actually tabulated in ERA 69–30 are based on 25 °C but after application of temperature correction factors the ratings become identical.

Maximum conductor temperature

90 °C

Circuit protection

600/1000 V cables should be selected with a rating of not less than the nominal current of the device providing protection against overload, or not less than 1.38 times this value if the device will not operate within 4 hours at 1.45 times its nominal current.

Installation in air

An ambient temperature of 30 °C for cables up to 1.9/3.3 kV and 25 °C for higher voltage cables.

The cables are shielded from the direct rays of the sun. Air circulation is not restricted significantly, e.g. if fastened to a wall the cables are spaced at least 20 mm from it; if in a trench they are not covered.

Adjacent circuits are spaced apart (chapter 8) and suitably disposed to prevent mutual heating.

Cables laid direct in ground

Ground temperature
15 °C

Ground thermal resistivity
1.2 K m/W.

Adjacent circuits
At least 1.8 m apart.

Depth of laying
0.5 m for voltages up to 1000 V and 0.8 m for higher voltage cables (measured from ground surface to centre of cable or trefoil group).

Single-core cables

The data apply to three or four single-core cables operating 3-phase.

Bonding
For trefoil installation it is assumed that the armour will be solidly bonded, i.e. bonded at both ends of the run. For very short runs it may be found possible to bond at one end only but consideration must be given to the value of thc standing voltage which can occur along the cable length under both normal and fault conditions.

For flat formation the ratings for 600/1000 V cables are based on bonding at both ends and for higher voltage cables on single point bonding.

Trefoil
A close trefoil is assumed with the cables touching.

Flat formation
The ratings and technical data are based on horizontal installation with a spacing between cable centres of twice the overall diameter. Cables installed vertically will have somewhat lower ratings.

ELECTRICAL CHARACTERISTICS

The standard conditions given for sustained ratings are equally applicable to the electrical characteristics. A.C. resistances are tabulated. D.C. resistances are given in table 4.1 of chapter 4.

XLPE INSULATED DISTRIBUTION CABLES (BS 5467 or BS 6724)

600/1000 V—copper

Table A14.1 Dimensions and weights

Conductor size (mm^2)	Approximate diameter		Approximate weight	
	Unarmoured (mm)	Armoured (mm)	Unarmoured (kg/m)	Armoured (kg/m)
Single-core (aluminium wire armour)				
50	14.2	17.5	0.54	0.80
70	16.2	20.2	0.75	0.94
95	18.3	22.3	1.01	1.22
120	20.2	24.2	1.25	1.49
150	22.4	27.4	1.53	1.87
185	24.7	30.0	1.90	2.29
240	27.7	32.8	2.47	2.88
300	30.6	35.6	3.08	3.52
400	34.2	40.4	3.89	4.52
500	38.0	44.2	4.97	5.68
630	42.9	48.8	6.37	7.12
800	47.8	55.4	8.07	9.15
1000	53.0	60.6	10.08	11.27
2-core cables				
16[a]	17.2	20.0	0.49	0.90
25[a]	20.8	24.1	0.66	1.05
35[a]	23.2	27.9	0.88	1.48
50	21.0	25.8	1.11	1.80
70	24.0	29.0	1.52	2.32
95	26.9	33.1	2.04	3.16
120	29.9	36.1	2.57	3.79
150	33.4	39.3	3.13	4.50
185	37.1	44.7	3.92	5.82
240	41.7	49.0	5.05	7.22
300	45.8	53.5	6.35	8.71
400	51.6	59.0	8.00	10.65
3-core cables				
16[a]	18.3	21.2	0.64	1.07
25[a]	22.1	26.7	0.92	1.55
35[a]	24.8	29.6	1.19	1.94
50	23.6	28.5	1.58	2.37
70	27.4	32.2	2.22	3.12
95	30.8	37.0	2.98	4.31

Table A14.1 cont.

Conductor size (mm^2)	Approximate diameter		Approximate weight	
	Unarmoured (mm)	Armoured (mm)	Unarmoured (kg/m)	Armoured (kg/m)
120	34.2	40.4	3.73	5.16
150	37.9	45.5	4.58	6.61
185	42.5	49.8	5.74	7.92
240	47.8	55.1	7.45	9.93
300	52.6	60.2	9.23	11.97
400	59.2	66.6	11.72	14.77
4-core cables				
16[a]	20.0	22.9	0.82	1.30
25[a]	24.3	28.9	1.17	1.88
35[a]	27.3	32.1	1.55	2.35
50	26.9	32.0	2.05	2.95
70	31.5	37.7	2.90	4.24
95	35.6	41.7	3.92	5.40
120	39.5	47.1	4.94	7.00
150	44.1	51.4	6.04	8.30
185	49.3	56.6	7.58	10.07
240	55.5	63.0	9.86	12.68
300	61.4	68.8	12.28	15.38
400	68.8	78.1	15.60	19.95
4-core cables with reduced neutral[b]				
25[a]	23.3	28.0	1.11	1.80
35[a]	25.7	30.5	1.39	2.18
50	26.1	31.2	1.85	2.77
70	30.4	36.6	2.55	3.82
95	34.8	41.0	3.46	4.86
120	39.4	45.3	4.41	5.97
150	42.5	50.0	5.28	7.53
185	47.7	55.3	6.67	9.08
240	53.4	61.0	8.70	11.50
300	59.0	66.7	10.75	13.76
300	61.2	68.6		14.10
400	66.4	73.8	13.82	17.27

[a] Circular conductors

[b] Size of reduced neutral conductor

Phase conductor (mm^2)	25	35	50	70	95	120
Neutral conductor (mm^2)	16	16	25	35	50	70
Phase conductor (mm^2)	150	185	240	300	300	400
Neutral conductor (mm^2)	70	95	120	150	185	185

All cables have stranded conductors. The phase conductors are shaped, but for some sizes the neutral conductors are circular.

XLPE INSULATED DISTRIBUTION CABLES (BS 5467 or BS 6724)
600/1000 V – aluminium (solid)

Table A14.2 Dimensions and weights

Conductor size (mm^2)	Approximate diameter		Approximate weight	
	Unarmoured (mm)	Armoured (mm)	Unarmoured (kg/m)	Armoured (kg/m)
Single-core (aluminium wire armour)				
50	12.9	16.2	0.24	0.47
70	14.7	18.7	0.32	0.50
95	16.6	20.6	0.41	0.62
120	18.1	22.1	0.50	0.73
150	20.1	25.2	0.61	0.93
185	22.2	27.4	0.75	1.11
240	24.8	29.9	0.95	1.34
300	27.3	32.4	1.17	1.60
380[a]	30.8	37.1	1.45	2.06
480[a]	34.2	40.4	1.81	2.47
600[a]	37.6	43.8	2.19	2.91
740[a]	41.7	49.1	2.71	3.68
960[a]	46.9	54.4	3.47	4.56
1200[a]	52.0	59.7	4.30	5.52
2-core cables				
16[b]	16.0	19.2	0.24	0.72
25[b]	19.1	22.4	0.34	0.75
35[b]	21.1	25.7	0.42	0.95
50	18.7	23.5	0.50	1.12
70	21.3	26.3	0.69	1.42
95	23.8	30.0	0.88	1.92
3-core cables				
16[b]	17.0	20.4	0.32	0.81
25[b]	20.3	24.9	0.42	1.00
35[b]	22.4	27.3	0.57	1.23
50	22.0	26.8	0.70	1.43
70	25.4	30.2	0.94	1.78
95	28.6	34.8	1.21	2.42
120	31.7	37.8	1.48	2.81
150	35.1	42.7	1.81	3.66
185	39.4	46.7	2.30	4.32

XLPE INSULATED DISTRIBUTION CABLES (BS 5467 or BS 6724)

600/1000 V – aluminium (solid)

Table A14.2 cont.

Conductor size (mm^2)	Approximate diameter		Approximate weight	
	Unarmoured (mm)	Armoured (mm)	Unarmoured (kg/m)	Armoured (kg/m)
240	44.2	51.5	2.73	5.17
300	48.6	56.2	3.56	6.10
4-core cables				
16[b]	18.6	21.9	0.40	0.85
25[b]	22.3	26.9	0.53	1.17
35[b]	24.7	29.5	0.67	1.39
50	24.9	30.0	0.90	1.73
70	29.1	35.3	1.22	2.46
95	32.8	39.0	1.58	2.93
120	36.4	44.0	1.94	3.84
150	40.6	47.9	2.38	4.44
185	45.5	52.7	2.96	5.24
240	51.1	58.5	3.85	6.45
300	56.4	63.8	4.71	7.53

[a] Solid sectoral conductors
[b] Circular conductors

XLPE INSULATED DISTRIBUTION CABLES (BS 5467 or BS 6724)

1.9/3.3 kV

Table A14.3 Dimensions and weights

Conductor size (mm^2)	Approximate diameter		Approximate weight	
	Copper (mm)	Solid aluminium (mm)	Copper (kg/m)	Solid aluminium (kg/m)
Single-core (aluminium wire armour)				
50	20.6	19.4	0.81	0.49
70	22.4	20.9	1.04	0.59
95	24.3	22.5	1.33	0.70
120	27.2	25.2	1.68	0.88
150	28.8	26.5	1.97	1.00
185	30.8	28.3	2.37	1.16
240	33.4	30.5	2.96	1.38
300	36.1	32.8	3.61	1.62
400	40.4		4.60	
500	44.2		5.68	
630	48.8		7.16	
800	55.4		9.15	
1000	60.6		11.27	
380[a]		37.1		2.06
480[a]		40.4		2.47
600[a]		43.8		2.91
740[a]		49.1		3.68
960[a]		54.4		4.56
1200[a]		59.7		5.52
3-core cables				
16[b]	28.9	26.0	1.60	1.31
25[b]	32.2	28.4	2.06	1.47
35[b]	35.0	31.5	2.32	1.56
50	34.7	31.0	3.04	2.02
70	38.0	34.0	3.80	2.38
95	41.4	37.9	4.73	2.79
120	45.7	40.9	6.07	3.59
150	48.5	43.4	7.01	4.02
185	51.9	46.5	8.27	4.54
240	56.9	51.8	10.31	5.39
300	61.2	55.8	12.30	6.21
400	66.6		14.77	

[a] Solid sectoral conductors [b] Circular conductors

XLPE INSULATED DISTRIBUTION CABLES (BS 6622)

3.8/6.6 kV

Table A14.4 Dimensions and weights

Conductor size (mm^2)	Approximate diameter	Approximate weight	
	Stranded copper or aluminium (mm)	Copper (kg/m)	Stranded aluminium (kg/m)
Single-core (copper wire screened, unarmoured)			
50	23.3	0.9	0.6
70	25.2	1.1	0.7
95	26.9	1.4	0.8
120	28.8	1.7	1.0
150	30.2	2.1	1.2
185	32.2	2.4	1.3
240	34.8	3.0	1.5
300	37.7	3.7	1.8
400	41.6	4.8	2.2
500	45.3	5.7	2.6
630	49.2	7.1	3.1
800	55.4	8.8	3.7
1000	60.1	10.9	4.5
3-core (circular conductors, armoured, SWA)			
25	43.3	3.1	2.7
35	46.1	3.5	3.0
50	50.3	4.5	3.8
70	54.2	5.4	4.3
95	58.3	6.5	5.0
120	62.1	7.6	5.6
150	65.3	8.6	5.9
185	69.6	10.1	6.8
240	75.8	12.4	8.1
300	83.8	15.6	10.0

XLPE INSULATED DISTRIBUTION CABLES (BS 6622)
6.35/11 kV

Table A14.5 Dimensions and weights

Conductor size (mm^2)	Approximate diameter	Approximate weight	
	Stranded copper or aluminium (mm)	Copper (kg/m)	Stranded aluminium (kg/m)
Single-core (copper wire screened, unarmoured)			
50	25.3	1.0	0.7
70	27.0	1.2	0.8
95	29.0	1.5	0.9
120	30.6	1.8	1.1
150	32.2	2.2	1.3
185	34.0	2.6	1.4
240	36.6	3.2	1.7
300	39.1	3.8	1.9
400	42.4	4.7	2.3
500	45.7	5.8	2.7
630	49.6	7.3	3.3
800	55.8	8.9	3.8
1000	60.5	10.9	4.5
3-core cables (circular conductors, armoured, SWA)			
25	48.8	4.0	3.6
35	51.6	4.4	3.9
50	54.6	5.0	4.4
70	58.5	5.9	4.8
95	62.6	7.1	5.6
120	66.6	8.2	6.2
150	69.8	9.2	6.6
185	74.1	10.7	7.4
240	81.2	13.8	9.5
300	86.8	16.2	10.6

XLPE INSULATED DISTRIBUTION CABLES (BS 6622)

8.7/15 kV

Table A14.6 Dimensions and weights

Conductor size (mm^2)	Approximate diameter	Approximate weight	
	Stranded copper or aluminium (mm)	Copper (kg/m)	Stranded aluminium (kg/m)
Single-core (copper wire screened, unarmoured)			
50	27.5	1.1	0.8
70	29.5	1.3	0.9
95	31.4	1.6	1.0
120	33.0	2.2	1.2
150	34.6	2.4	1.4
185	36.4	2.7	1.5
240	39.0	3.3	1.6
300	41.5	3.9	2.0
400	44.9	5.0	2.6
500	48.1	5.9	2.8
630	52.0	7.4	3.4
800	58.2	9.1	4.0
1000	62.9	11.1	4.7
3-core cables (circular conductors, armoured, SWA)			
25	54.2	4.5	4.1
35	57.0	5.0	4.5
50	60.0	5.7	4.9
70	63.8	6.6	5.5
95	67.9	7.8	6.3
120	71.8	8.9	6.9
150	75.0	10.0	7.3
185	80.0	12.3	9.0
240	86.6	14.7	10.4
300	91.9	17.1	11.4

XLPE INSULATED DISTRIBUTION CABLES (BS 6622)
12.7/22 kV

Table A14.7 Dimensions and weights

Conductor size (mm^2)	Approximate diameter	Approximate weight	
	Stranded copper or aluminium (mm)	Copper (kg/m)	Stranded aluminium (kg/m)
Single-core (copper wire screened)			
50	29.8	1.2	0.9
70	31.7	1.4	1.0
95	33.4	1.7	1.1
120	35.2	2.3	1.4
150	36.6	2.5	1.5
185	38.6	2.8	1.6
240	41.2	3.4	1.9
300	43.5	4.0	2.1
400	46.9	5.4	3.0
500	50.1	6.2	3.1
630	54.0	7.7	3.6
800	60.4	9.3	4.2
1000	65.2	11.3	4.9
3-core cables (circular conductors, armoured, SWA)			
35	61.7	5.6	5.1
50	64.5	6.3	5.6
70	68.6	7.2	6.1
95	72.8	8.6	6.9
120	77.8	10.4	8.4
150	81.2	11.6	8.9
185	85.7	13.2	9.8
240	91.3	15.6	11.0
300	96.6	18.0	12.3
400	100.6	21.3	14.3

XLPE INSULATED DISTRIBUTION CABLES (BS 6622)

19/33 kV

Table A14.8 Dimensions and weights

Conductor size (mm^2)	Approximate diameter	Approximate weight	
	Stranded copper or aluminium (mm)	Copper (kg/m)	Stranded aluminium (kg/m)
Single-core (copper wire screened, unarmoured)			
50	35.2	1.5	1.2
70	36.9	1.7	1.3
95	38.8	2.0	1.4
120	40.4	2.4	1.7
150	42.0	2.7	1.8
185	43.8	3.1	1.9
240	46.5	3.9	2.4
300	49.0	4.6	2.7
400	52.3	5.6	3.2
500	55.5	6.6	3.5
630	59.4	8.0	3.9
800	65.7	9.9	4.8
1000	70.6	12.1	5.7
3-core cables (circular conductors, armoured, SWA)			
50	78.2		
70	82.1	10.3	9.1
95	86.1	11.7	10.1
120	90.0	12.9	10.8
150	93.2	14.1	11.4
185	97.5	16.1	12.7
240	103.3	18.3	13.8
300	108.8	21.5	15.9
400	116.0	24.4	17.4

XLPE INSULATED DISTRIBUTION CABLES
66 kV and 132 kV

Table A14.9 Dimensions and weights

Conductor size (mm^2)	Approximate diameter		Approximate weight			
			Copper conductors		Aluminium conductors	
	Lead sheath (mm)	Aluminium sheath (mm)	Lead sheath (kg/m)	Aluminium sheath (kg/m)	Lead sheath (kg/m)	Aluminium sheath (kg/m)
66 kV single-core cables, unarmoured						
150	54	59	6.59	3.88	5.66	2.95
185	56	61	7.33	4.36	6.17	3.20
240	58	65	8.20	5.13	6.67	3.60
300	61	67	9.27	5.87	7.35	3.95
400	64	71	10.65	6.91	8.16	4.42
500	69	75	12.35	8.24	9.20	5.09
630	73	79	14.48	9.84	10.48	5.84
800	77	84	16.98	11.86	11.87	6.75
1000	82	90	20.13	14.23	13.69	7.79
132 kV single-core cables, unarmoured						
300	85	92	15.00	8.95	13.08	7.03
400	86	94	15.88	9.86	13.39	7.37
500	88	96	17.33	10.90	14.18	7.75
630	92	100	19.70	12.73	15.70	8.73
800	94	103	21.98	14.50	16.86	9.39
1000	99	108	25.07	16.97	18.63	10.53

XLPE INSULATED DISTRIBUTION CABLES (BS 5467 or BS 6724)

600/1000 V – armoured

Table A14.10 Sustained ratings

Conductor size (mm^2)	In air				In ground			
	Single-core[a]		2-core (A)	3- or 4-core (A)	Single-core		2-core (A)	3- or 4-core (A)
	Trefoil (A)	Flat (A)			Trefoil (A)	Flat (A)		
Copper conductors								
16			118	101			141	119
25			154	132			183	152
35			190	162			219	182
50	217	279	229	196	231	241	259	217
70	277	350	288	247	284	295	317	266
95	340	425	355	305	340	350	381	319
120	395	488	411	353	386	395	433	363
150	454	543	469	404	431	434	485	406
185	522	610	541	465	485	482	547	458
240	615	700	639	549	558	545	632	529
300	700	775	728	626	623	597	708	592
400	800	834	838	720	691	637	799	667
500	905	910			765	688		
630	1019	986			841	737		
800	1107	1032			888	760		
1000	1202	1098			942	797		
Aluminium conductors								
16			90	76			108	91
25			114	100			138	116
35			141	122			165	139
50	162	209	169	147	177	185	196	165
70	208	264	213	186	218	227	240	203
95	255	322	263	229	260	270	288	244
120	295	370		266	296	306		278
150	340	417		305	331	339		311
185	392	473		352	374	380		353
240	464	550		417	433	435		409
300	532	619		478	486	483		461

* single-core cables with aluminium wire armour

For relevant conditions see the notes at the beginning of this appendix.

XLPE INSULATED DISTRIBUTION CABLES (BS 5467)
600/1000 V – unarmoured

Table A14.11 Sustained ratings

Conductor size (mm^2)	In air			
	Single-core[a]		2-core (A)	3- or 4-core (A)
	Trefoil (A)	Flat (A)		
Copper conductors				
16			117	101
25			147	126
35			181	155
50	210	272	221	189
70	267	344	280	241
95	331	425	346	297
120	387	495	403	347
150	446	568	462	398
185	518	657	535	460
240	619	784	637	547
300	716	907	736	632
400	834	1059	856	733
500	965	1233		
630	1115	1437		
800	1266	1655		
1000	1413	1874		
Aluminium conductors (solid)				
16			88	76
25			109	95
35			133	116
50	155	202	162	142
70	198	256	206	180
95	245	315	253	223
120	286	367		260
150	330	438		298
185	384	487		346
240	460	580		412
300	533	670		477

[a] Single-core cables with aluminium wire armour

For relevant conditions see the notes at the beginning of this appendix.

XLPE INSULATED DISTRIBUTION CABLES (BS 5467 or BS 6724)

1.9/3.3 kV — armoured

Table A14.12 Sustained ratings

Conductor size (mm²)	In air: Single-core[a] Trefoil (A)	In air: Single-core[a] Flat (A)	In air: 3-core (A)	In ground: Single-core[a] Trefoil (A)	In ground: Single-core[a] Flat (A)	In ground: 3-core (A)
Copper conductors						
16			106			114
25			140			147
35			166			175
50	226	285	201	222	232	207
70	282	358	252	271	284	254
95	346	440	309	324	341	305
120	402	512	359	366	388	347
150	457	585	409	409	436	390
185	523	673	471	460	493	441
240	616	801	556	528	573	510
300	702	925	639	589	648	576
400	800	1081	740	651	741	653
500	905	1255		720	844	
630	1019	1461		789	961	
800	1107	1683		831	1085	
1000	1202	1902		880	1203	
Aluminium conductors						
16			80			87
25			105			113
35			125			134
50	169	214	151	170	178	158
70	212	268	190	208	217	194
95	259	328	233	248	260	233
120	302	382	270	282	297	266
150	343	434	307	315	332	298
185	394	501	355	355	377	338
240	465	595	420	410	438	392
300	533	686	484	460	495	444

[a] Single-core cables with aluminium wire armour

For relevant conditions see the notes at the beginning of this appendix.

XLPE INSULATED DISTRIBUTION CABLES (BS 6622)

3.8/6.6 kV to 8.7/1.5 kV

Table A14.13 Sustained ratings

Conductor size (mm²)	In air			In ground		
	Single-core[a]		3-core (A)	Single-core[a]		3-core (A)
	Trefoil (A)	Flat (A)		Trefoil (A)	Flat (A)	
Copper conductors						
25[b]			145			140
35[b]			175			170
50[b]	235	295	220	220	230	210
70	285	370	270	270	280	255
95	360	455	330	320	335	300
120	415	520	375	360	380	340
150	470	600	430	410	430	380
185	540	690	490	455	485	430
240	640	820	570	520	560	490
300	740	940	650	580	640	540
400	840	1100	740	650	730	600
500	940	1280		710	830	
630	1110	1500		760	940	
800	1270	1740		810	1070	
1000	1400	1960		860	1180	
Aluminium conductors						
25[b]			115			115
35[b]			140			135
50[b]	180	230	170	170	175	160
70	225	290	210	210	215	195
95	260	350	250	250	260	230
120	320	410	295	280	295	265
150	365	465	330	315	330	300
185	425	530	385	355	375	335
240	500	640	450	405	440	380
300	580	730	510	455	495	435
400	670	860	590	510	570	490
500	790	1010		570	650	
630	910	1190		640	750	
800	1052	1400		769		

[a] Copper wire screened, unarmoured
[b] Not applicable to all voltages. See dimension tables for availability

For cable designs and relevant conditions see the notes at the beginning of this appendix.

XLPE INSULATED DISTRIBUTION CABLES (BS 6622)

12.7/22 kV and 19/33 kV

Table A14.14 Sustained ratings

Conductor size (mm^2)	In air			In ground		
	Single-core[a]		3-core (A)	Single-core[a]		3-core (A)
	Trefoil (A)	Flat (A)		Trefoil (A)	Flat (A)	
Copper conductors						
35			180			170
50	245	295	225	220	230	210
70	300	365	275	270	280	255
95	360	450	330	320	335	295
120	425	520	380	360	380	335
150	485	590	430	410	430	375
185	550	670	490	460	485	420
240	650	800	570	530	560	480
300	740	920	650	600	640	530
400	850	1070	740	690	730	590
500	980	1250		760	830	
630	1130	1450		850	950	
800	1290	1690		930	1070	
1000	1430	1910		1010	1190	
Aluminium conductors						
35			145			135
50	190	230	175	170	175	160
70	235	285	215	210	215	195
95	280	345	260	250	260	230
120	330	400	300	280	295	260
150	375	455	335	320	330	290
185	430	520	390	360	375	330
240	510	620	460	415	440	380
300	580	710	520	475	495	425
400	680	840	600	550	570	480
500	790	980		610	650	
630	920	1080		690	750	
800	1070	1360		780	860	
1000	1210	1560		860	970	

[a] Copper wire screened, unarmoured

For cable designs and relevant conditions see the notes at the beginning of this appendix.

XLPE INSULATED DISTRIBUTION CABLES
66 kV

Table A14.15 Sustained ratings

Conductor size (mm^2)	Lead sheathed cable				Aluminium sheathed cable			
	In air		In ground		In air		In ground	
	Trefoil (A)	Flat (A)	Trefoil (A)	Flat (A)	Trefoil (A)	Flat (A)	Trefoil (A)	Flat (A)
Copper conductors								
150	500	570	400	430	425	445	360	395
185	570	660	460	490	485	510	405	445
240	680	790	525	570	565	600	465	520
300	760	890	585	640	640	690	515	590
400	870	1040	660	730	730	800	575	670
500	995	1210	740	825	825	905	630	765
630	1130	1400	830	940	930	1070	700	865
800	1280	1510	910	1050	1025	1220	760	965
1000	1400	1810	990	1150	1150	1360	810	1055
Aluminium conductors								
150	390	460	310	335	340	345	285	305
185	445	510	350	375	380	395	320	350
240	525	600	410	445	450	470	370	405
300	595	695	460	500	510	555	415	460
400	690	755	525	575	585	625	470	525
500	800	950	590	650	675	730	525	600
630	930	1090	670	745	770	855	580	690
800	1060	1240	755	840	870	985	650	780
1000	1180	1420	830	940	965	1090	710	850

For cable designs and relevant conditions see the notes at the beginning of this appendix.

XLPE INSULATED DISTRIBUTION CABLES
132 kV

Table A14.16 Sustained ratings

Conductor size (mm^2)	Lead sheathed cable				Aluminium sheathed cable			
	In air		In ground		In air		In ground	
	Trefoil (A)	Flat (A)	Trefoil (A)	Flat (A)	Trefoil (A)	Flat (A)	Trefoil (A)	Flat (A)
Copper conductors								
300	750	840	575	635	645	695	495	570
400	860	990	650	725	735	810	555	651
500	970	1160	725	820	850	945	615	745
630	1120	1345	815	940	975	1090	675	845
800	1255	1550	890	1040	1100	1260	750	950
1000	1380	1680	960	1150	1220	1420	800	1030
Aluminium conductors								
300	585	665	455	490	485	540	400	445
400	680	780	515	565	560	635	455	510
500	780	895	580	640	650	745	510	590
630	900	1050	655	730	745	870	570	675
800	1030	1230	735	830	845	1015	630	770
1000	1160	1415	810	930	970	1155	680	850

For cable designs and relevant conditions see the notes at the beginning of this appendix.

XLPE INSULATED DISTRIBUTION CABLES (BS 5467 or BS 6724)
600/1000 V

Table A14.17 Voltage drop (50 Hz per A/m)

Conductor size (mm^2)	Copper				Aluminium			
	Single-core[a]		2-core (mV)	3- or 4-core (mV)	Single-core[a]		2-core (mV)	3- or 4-core (mV)
	Trefoil (mV)	Flat[b] (mV)			Trefoil (mV)	Flat[b] (mV)		
16			2.9	2.5			4.8	4.2
25			1.9	1.65			3.1	2.7
35			1.35	1.15			2.2	1.95
50	0.87	0.90	1.00	0.87	1.4	1.4	1.65	1.45
70	0.62	0.70	0.69	0.60	0.98	1.05	1.15	0.97
95	0.47	0.58	0.52	0.45	0.74	0.83	0.84	0.72
120	0.39	0.51	0.42	0.37	0.60	0.70		0.58
150	0.33	0.45	0.35	0.30	0.49	0.60		0.47
185	0.28	0.41	0.29	0.26	0.41	0.53		0.39
240	0.24	0.37	0.24	0.21	0.34	0.46		0.31
300	0.21	0.34	0.22	0.185	0.29	0.41		0.26
400	0.195	0.33						
500	0.18	0.31						
630	0.17	0.29						

[a] Data for aluminium wire armoured cables
[b] Twice cable diameter spacing between cores

For the relevant conditions see the notes at the beginning of this appendix.

XLPE INSULATED DISTRIBUTION CABLES (BS 5467 or BS 6724)

600/1000 V armoured

Table A14.18 Electrical characteristics

Conductor size (mm^2)	A.C. resistance at 90 °C		Reactance (50 Hz)		
	Copper (Ω/km)	Aluminium (Ω/km)	Armoured single-core[a]		Armoured or unarmoured multicore (Ω/km)
			Trefoil (Ω/km)	Flat[b] (Ω/km)	
16	1.47	2.45			0.080
25	0.927	1.54			0.079
35	0.668	1.11			0.077
50	0.494	0.822	0.106	0.145	0.076
70	0.342	0.568	0.103	0.162	0.075
95	0.247	0.411	0.098	0.157	0.073
120	0.197	0.325	0.096	0.155	0.073
150	0.160	0.265	0.097	0.156	0.073
185	0.128	0.211	0.096	0.155	0.073
240	0.0989	0.162	0.092	0.151	0.073
300	0.0802	0.130	0.090	0.149	0.072
400	0.0640		0.090	0.148	
500	0.0515		0.089	0.146	
630	0.0420		0.086	0.144	
800	0.0363		0.086	0.144	
1000	0.0316		0.084	0.142	

[a] Aluminium wire armoured
[b] Twice cable diameter spacing between centres

For the relevant conditions see the notes at the beginning of this appendix.

XLPE INSULATED DISTRIBUTION CABLES (BS 5467 or BS 6724)

1.9/3.3 kV armoured

Table A14.19 Electric characteristics

Conductor size (mm^2)	Single-core cables[a]					3-core cables			
	A.C. resistance at 90 °C		Reactance (50 Hz)		Capacitance (μF/km)	A.C. resistance at 90 °C		Reactance (50 Hz) (Ω/km)	Capacitance (μF/km)
	Copper (Ω/km)	Aluminium (Ω/km)	Trefoil (Ω/km)	Flat[b] (Ω/km)		Copper (Ω/km)	Aluminium (Ω/km)		
16						1.47	2.42	0.104	0.18
25						0.972	1.54	0.095	0.22
35						0.668	1.11	0.092	0.25
50	0.494	0.822	0.116	0.172	0.31	0.494	0.822	0.088	0.27
70	0.342	0.568	0.110	0.165	0.36	0.342	0.568	0.084	0.31
95	0.247	0.411	0.104	0.160	0.42	0.247	0.411	0.081	0.35
120	0.195	0.325	0.104	0.159	0.45	0.195	0.325	0.079	0.38
150	0.160	0.265	0.100	0.156	0.49	0.160	0.265	0.077	0.42
185	0.128	0.211	0.098	0.154	0.54	0.128	0.211	0.076	0.46
240	0.098	0.162	0.094	0.150	0.63	0.098	0.162	0.074	0.51
300	0.080	0.130	0.091	0.147	0.70	0.080	0.130	0.073	0.57
400	0.064		0.090	0.147	0.77				
500	0.051		0.089	0.145	0.80				
630	0.042		0.086	0.143	0.84				

[a] Aluminium wire armoured   [b] Twice cable diameter spacing between centres

For the relevant conditions see the notes at the beginning of this appendix.

XLPE INSULATED DISTRIBUTION CABLES (BS 6622)

3.8/6.6 kV and 6.35/11 kV

Table A14.20 Electrical characteristics

Conductor size (mm^2)	Single-core cables[a]					3-core cables			
	A.C. resistance at 90 °C		Reactance (50 Hz)		Capacitance (μF/km)	A.C. resistance at 90 °C		Reactance (50 Hz) (μ/km)	Capacitance (μF/km)
	Copper (Ω/km)	Aluminium (Ω/km)	Trefoil (Ω/km)	Flat[b] (Ω/km)		Copper (Ω/km)	Aluminium (Ω/km)		
3.8/6.6 kV cables									
16						1.47	2.45	0.126	0.26
25						0.927	1.54	0.117	0.30
35						0.668	1.11	0.109	0.33
50	0.493	0.822	0.121	0.181	0.34	0.493	0.822	0.105	0.36
70	0.343	0.568	0.115	0.174	0.38	0.343	0.568	0.100	0.41
95	0.247	0.411	0.109	0.167	0.43	0.247	0.411	0.095	0.46
120	0.196	0.325	0.105	0.162	0.47	0.196	0.325	0.092	0.50
150	0.159	0.265	0.102	0.159	0.51	0.159	0.265	0.090	0.55
185	0.128	0.211	0.099	0.156	0.56	0.128	0.211	0.087	0.60
240	0.0980	0.162	0.096	0.153	0.61	0.0986	0.162	0.085	0.65
300	0.0791	0.130	0.094	0.151	0.62	0.0798	0.130	0.084	0.67
400	0.0632	0.102	0.092	0.149	0.65	0.0641	0.102	0.082	0.70
500	0.0510	0.804	0.089	0.147	0.69				
630	0.0417	0.0639	0.086	0.144	0.77				

(cont.)

XLPE INSULATED DISTRIBUTION CABLES (BS 6622)
3.8/6.6 kV and 6.35/11 kV

Table A14.20 cont.

Conductor size (mm^2)	Single-core cables[a]					3-core cables			
	A.C. resistance at 90 °C		Reactance (50 Hz)		Capacitance (μF/km)	A.C. resistance at 90 °C		Reactance (50 Hz) (μ/km)	Capacitance (μF/km)
	Copper (Ω/km)	Aluminium (Ω/km)	Trefoil (Ω/km)	Flat[b] (Ω/km)		Copper (Ω/km)	Aluminium (Ω/km)		
6.35/11 kV cables									
16						1.47	2.45	0.134	0.21
25						0.927	1.54	0.124	0.24
35						0.668	1.11	0.116	0.26
50	0.493	0.821	0.127	0.185	0.27	0.493	0.822	0.111	0.28
70	0.342	0.569	0.120	0.177	0.31	0.342	0.568	0.106	0.32
95	0.247	0.410	0.114	0.171	0.34	0.247	0.410	0.100	0.86
120	0.196	0.325	0.109	0.166	0.37	0.196	0.325	0.097	0.39
150	0.159	0.265	0.106	0.163	0.40	0.159	0.265	0.094	0.42
185	0.128	0.211	0.103	0.160	0.44	0.128	0.211	0.092	0.46
240	0.0980	0.161	0.099	0.156	0.49	0.0984	0.161	0.089	0.51
300	0.0790	0.130	0.096	0.153	0.52	0.0797	0.130	0.086	0.56
400	0.0632	0.102	0.093	0.150	0.59	0.0639	0.102	0.083	0.62
500	0.0510	0.0804	0.090	0.147	0.66				
630	0.0416	0.0639	0.087	0.145	0.74				

[a] Copper wire screened, unarmoured   [b] Twice cable diameter spacing between centres

For cable designs and relevant conditions see the notes at the beginning of this appendix.

XLPE INSULATED DISTRIBUTION CABLES (BS 6622)

8.7/15 kV and 12.7/22 kV

Table A14.21 Electrical characteristics

Conductor size (mm²)	Single-core cables[a]					3-core cables			
	A.C. resistance at 90 °C		Reactance (50 Hz)		Capacitance (μF/km)	A.C. resistance at 90 °C		Reactance (50 Hz) (Ω/km)	Capacitance (μF/km)
	Copper (Ω/km)	Aluminium (Ω/km)	Trefoil (Ω/km)	Flat[b] (Ω/km)		Copper (Ω/km)	Aluminium (Ω/km)		
8.7/15 kV cables									
16						1.47	2.45	0.143	0.17
25						0.927	1.54	0.132	0.19
35						0.668	1.11	0.124	0.21
50	0.493	0.822	0.132	0.190	0.22	0.493	0.822	0.118	0.23
70	0.343	0.568	0.125	0.183	0.25	0.343	0.568	0.112	0.26
95	0.247	0.410	0.119	0.176	0.27	0.247	0.410	0.106	0.29
120	0.196	0.325	0.114	0.171	0.29	0.196	0.325	0.102	0.31
150	0.159	0.264	0.111	0.168	0.32	0.159	0.264	0.100	0.34
185	0.128	0.211	0.107	0.164	0.34	0.128	0.211	0.097	0.37
240	0.0979	0.161	0.103	0.160	0.38	0.0982	0.161	0.093	0.41
300	0.0789	0.130	0.100	0.156	0.42	0.0794	0.130	0.090	0.45
400	0.0630	0.102	0.097	0.153	0.47	0.0636	0.102	0.087	0.50
500	0.0507	0.0802	0.093	0.151	0.51				
630	0.0414	0.0636	0.090	0.147	0.57				

(cont.)

XLPE INSULATED DISTRIBUTION CABLES (BS 6622)
8.7/15 kV and 12.7/22 kV

Table A14.21 cont.

Conductor size (mm²)	Single-core cables[a]					3-core cables			
	A.C. resistance at 90 °C		Reactance (50 Hz)		Capacitance (μF/km)	A.C. resistance at 90 °C		Reactance (50 Hz) (Ω/km)	Capacitance (μF/km)
	Copper (Ω/km)	Aluminium (Ω/km)	Trefoil (Ω/km)	Flat[b] (Ω/km)		Copper (Ω/km)	Aluminium (Ω/km)		
12.7/22 kV cables									
16									
25						0.927	1.54	0.139	0.17
35						0.668	1.11	0.130	0.18
50	0.494	0.821	0.138	0.192	0.19	0.493	0.822	0.124	0.20
70	0.342	0.569	0.131	0.185	0.22	0.342	0.568	0.118	0.22
95	0.247	0.409	0.124	0.178	0.24	0.247	0.410	0.111	0.24
120	0.196	0.324	0.119	0.173	0.26	0.196	0.325	0.107	0.26
150	0.159	0.265	0.116	0.170	0.28	0.159	0.264	0.104	0.28
185	0.128	0.211	0.113	0.165	0.30	0.127	0.211	0.101	0.31
240	0.098	0.160	0.108	0.161	0.34	0.098	0.161	0.097	0.34
300	0.079	0.129	0.104	0.158	0.37	0.079	0.130	0.094	0.37
400	0.063	0.101	0.101	0.155	0.40	0.063	0.102	0.090	0.41
500	0.051	0.080	0.097	0.152	0.44				
630	0.041	0.064	0.094	0.149	0.49				

[a] Copper wire screened, unarmoured
[b] Twice cable diameter spacing between centres

For cable designs and relevant conditions see the notes at the beginning of this appendix.

XLPE INSULATED DISTRIBUTION CABLES (BS 6622)

19/33 kV

Table A14.22 Electrical characteristics

Conductor size (mm²)	A.C. resistance at 90 °C		Reactance (50 Hz)		Capacitance (μF/km)
	Copper (Ω/km)	Aluminium (Ω/km)	Trefoil (Ω/km)	Flat[a] (Ω/km)	
single-core cables[b]					
70	0.342	0.568	0.143	0.194	0.16
95	0.247	0.411	0.134	0.189	0.18
120	0.196	0.324	0.129	0.184	0.19
150	0.160	0.264	0.125	0.178	0.21
185	0.128	0.211	0.121	0.174	0.22
240	0.0977	0.160	0.116	0.169	0.25
300	0.0785	0.129	0.112	0.166	0.27
400	0.0624	0.101	0.107	0.162	0.29
500	0.0500	0.0797	0.104	0.158	0.32
630	0.0405	0.0630	0.099	0.155	0.35
800	0.0388	0.0509	0.095	0.151	0.40
3-core cables					
70	0.342	0.568	0.135		0.16
95	0.247	0.411	0.127		0.18
120	0.196	0.325	0.122		0.19
150	0.159	0.265	0.118		0.21
185	0.128	0.211	0.114		0.22
240	0.0978	0.161	0.109		0.24
300	0.0788	0.130	0.105		0.26

[a] Twice cable diameter spacing between centres
[b] Copper wire screened, unarmoured

For cable designs and relevant conditions see the notes at the beginning of this appendix.

XLPE INSULATED CABLES
66 kV and 132 kV

Table A14.23 Electrical characteristics

Conductor size (mm^2)	A.C. resistance at 90 °C		Reactance (50 Hz)		Capacitance (μF/km)
	Copper (Ω/km)	Aluminium (Ω/km)	Trefoil (Ω/km)	Flat[a] (Ω/km)	
66 kV cables					
150	0.159	0.265	0.142	0.220	0.150
180	0.128	0.211	0.137	0.215	0.160
240	0.097	0.161	0.131	0.205	0.175
300	0.078	0.130	0.126	0.198	0.190
400	0.062	0.101	0.122	0.190	0.205
500	0.049	0.079	0.118	0.182	0.225
630	0.040	0.061	0.112	0.173	0.250
800	0.033	0.050	0.108	0.165	0.270
1000	0.028	0.041	0.105	0.158	0.295
132 kV cables					
300	0.078	0.129	0.147	0.198	0.130
400	0.062	0.099	0.140	0.190	0.140
500	0.049	0.078	0.132	0.182	0.160
630	0.039	0.062	0.127	0.173	0.170
800	0.032	0.050	0.121	0.165	0.195
1000	0.028	0.041	0.117	0.158	0.210

[a] Twice cable diameter spacing between centres

Appendix A15
PVC Insulated House Service Cables

CABLE DESIGNS

Typical designs are shown in fig. A15.1. The split concentric single-phase copper conductor cables are covered by BS 4553. Some types of these cables are also available with XLPE insulation – see chapter 19.

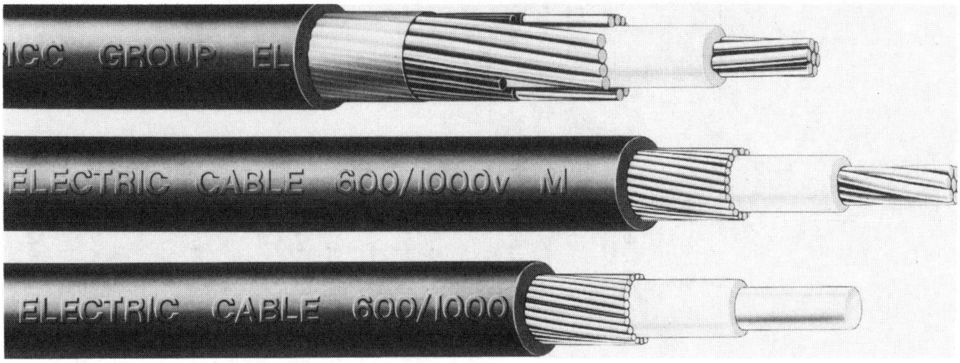

Fig. A15.1 PVC insulated 600/1000 V service cables: split concentric with copper phase conductor (*top*); CNE concentric with copper phase conductor (*middle*); CNE concentric with solid aluminium phase conductor (*bottom*)

Current ratings

The values in the tables are based on

Maximum sustained conductor temperature	70 °C
Ambient air temperature	25 °C
Standard ground temperature	15 °C
Soil thermal resistivity	1.2 K m/W
Depth of laying	0.5 m

PVC INSULATED SERVICE CABLES
600/1000 V

Table A15.1 Dimensions and weights

Conductor size (mm^2)	Number and diameter of copper wires				Approximate diameter (mm)	Approximate weight (kg/m)
	Centre phase conductor (number/mm)	Concentric layer				
		Neutral conductor (number/mm)	Earth conductor (number/mm)	CNE conductor (number/mm)		
Split concentric, copper phase conductor (BS 4553)						
4	7/0.85	7/0.85	3/1.5		10.4	0.206
6	7/1.04	7/1.04	4/1.53		11.3	0.281
10	7/1.35	7/1.35	4/1.78		12.7	0.394
16	7/1.70	7/1.70	4/2.25		14.7	0.583
25	7/2.14	11/1.70	4/2.25		18.2	0.843
35	19/1.53	15/1.70	6/2.25		22.7	1.248
Split concentric, solid aluminium phase conductor						
6		7/0.85	3/1.35		10.1	0.182
10		8/1.04	3/1.70		12.1	0.273
16		7/1.35	3/2.03		13.7	0.365
25		8/1.53	5/2.03		15.2	0.512
35		10/1.70	4/2.25		17.5	0.662
50		13/1.70	6/2.25		21.6	0.968

CNE concentric, copper phase conductor				
4	7/0.85	15/0.67	8.7	0.151
6	7/1.04	18/0.67	9.3	0.185
10	7/1.35	18/0.85	11.0	0.280
16	7/1.70	28/0.85	12.1	0.397
25	7/2.14	25/1.13	14.4	0.596
35	19/1.53	24/1.35	16.1	0.789
CNE concentric, solid aluminium phase conductor				
6		16/0.67	8.9	0.137
10		21/0.67	10.2	0.182
16		19/0.85	11.5	0.244
25		27/0.85	13.0	0.334
35		25/1.04	14.4	0.430
50		33/1.04	16.1	0.562

PVC INSULATED SERVICE CABLES
600/1000 V

Table A15.2 Ratings and characteristics

Conductor size (mm^2)	Current rating		Impedance (50 Hz) (Ω/km)	Approximate volt drop per A/m (mV)
	In air (A)	In ground (A)		
Split concentric, copper phase conductor				
4	42	53	5.41	11.0
6	54	66	3.61	7.2
10	74	88	2.14	4.3
16	97	115	1.36	2.7
25	130	150	0.86	1.7
35	160	185	0.62	1.2
Split concentric, solid aluminium phase conductor				
6	42	51	5.90	12.0
10	58	69	3.53	7.1
16	73	88	2.22	4.4
25	97	115	1.42	2.8
35	120	140	1.02	2.0
50	140	165	0.76	1.5
CNE concentric, copper phase conductor				
4	42	53	5.41	11.0
6	54	66	3.61	7.2
10	74	88	2.14	4.3
16	97	115	1.36	2.7
25	130	150	0.86	1.7
35	160	185	0.62	1.2
CNE concentric, solid aluminium phase conductor				
6	42	51	5.90	12.0
10	58	69	3.53	7.1
16	73	88	2.22	4.4
25	97	115	1.42	2.8
35	120	140	1.02	2.0
50	140	165	0.76	1.5

Appendix A16

Self-contained Oil-filled Cables

The information in this appendix covers the following.

(a) Technical data: dimensions, weights, charging current, capacitance, a.c. resistance and reactance (tables A16.2–A16.8).
(b) Power ratings: for single- and 3-core cables, laid direct and in air (figs A16.1–A16.8).
(c) Electrical losses: representative values for a small and large conductor size of single and 3-core cable, with lead and aluminium sheaths, laid direct in the ground (fig. A16.9).
(d) Conditions applicable: see table A16.1.

Table A16.1 Conditions applicable

Cables laid direct	
Depth to top of cable[a]	900 mm
Spacing between cable centres (flat)[a]	230 mm
Ground temperature	15 °C
Soil thermal resistivity	1.2 K m/W
Conductor operating temperature	90 °C
Cables in air	
Spacing between cable centres (flat)[a]	230 mm
Air temperature	25 °C
Conductor operating temperature	90 °C
(Protection from solar radiation)	

[a] For sketches see figs A16.1–A16.8.

(e) Cable design: the data are based on cables described and illustrated in chapter 33 with the following characteristics.
  (i) *Conductors*: circular, except for 33 kV cables with corrugated aluminium sheath, in which case they are oval.
  (ii) *Oil ducts*: 3-core cables have aluminium ducts but 33 kV cables with aluminium sheath have no ducts or fillers.
  (iii) *Oversheath*: PVC

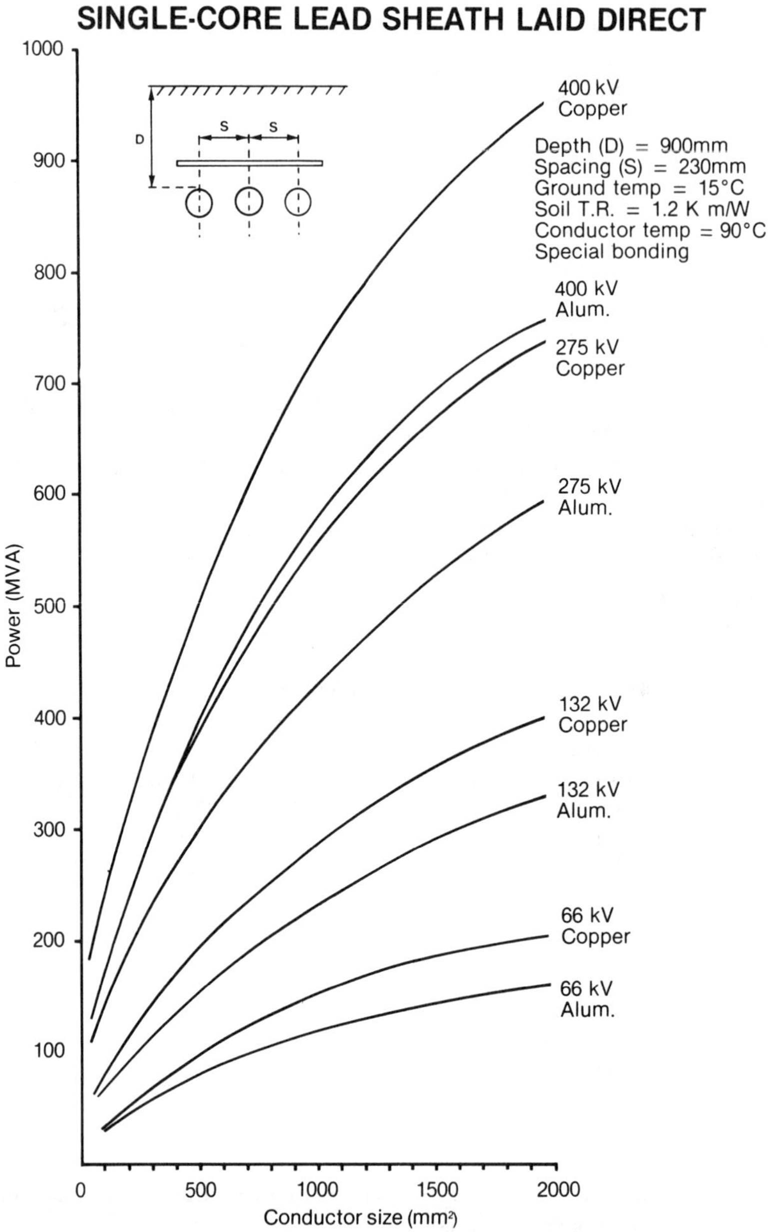

Fig. A16.1 Power ratings for single-core lead sheathed OF cables, laid direct

SINGLE-CORE ALUMINIUM SHEATH LAID DIRECT

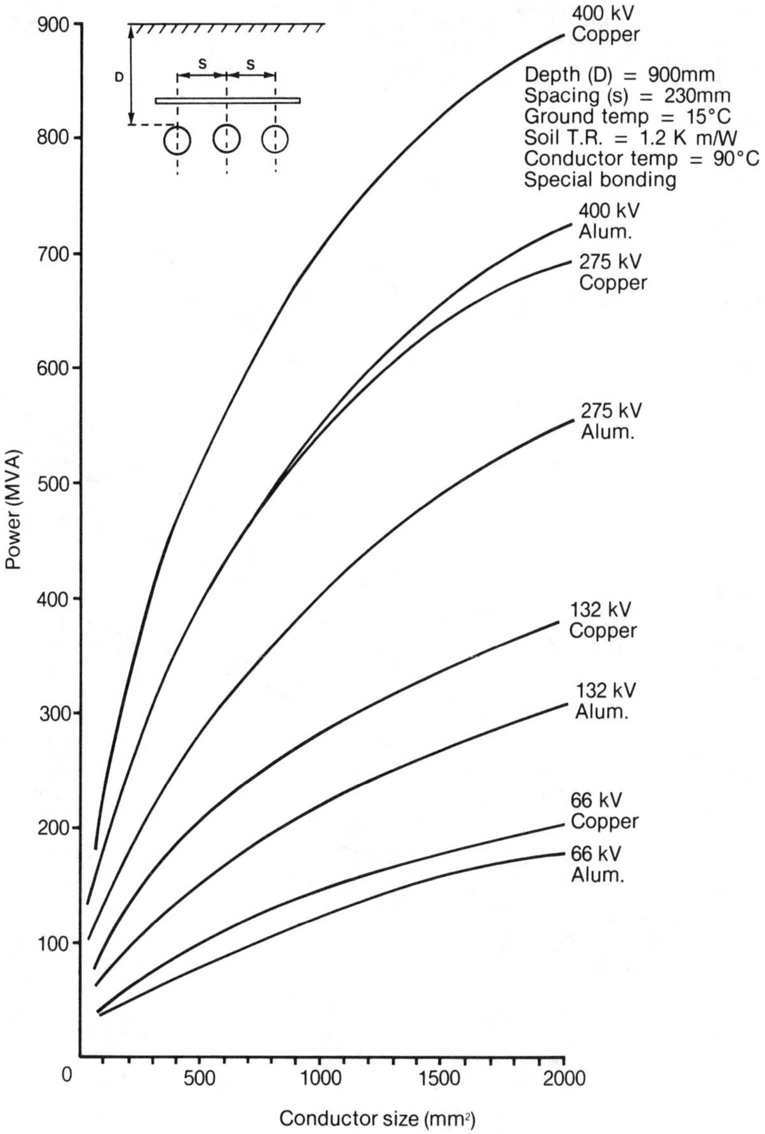

Fig. A16.2 Power ratings for single-core aluminium sheathed OF cables, laid direct

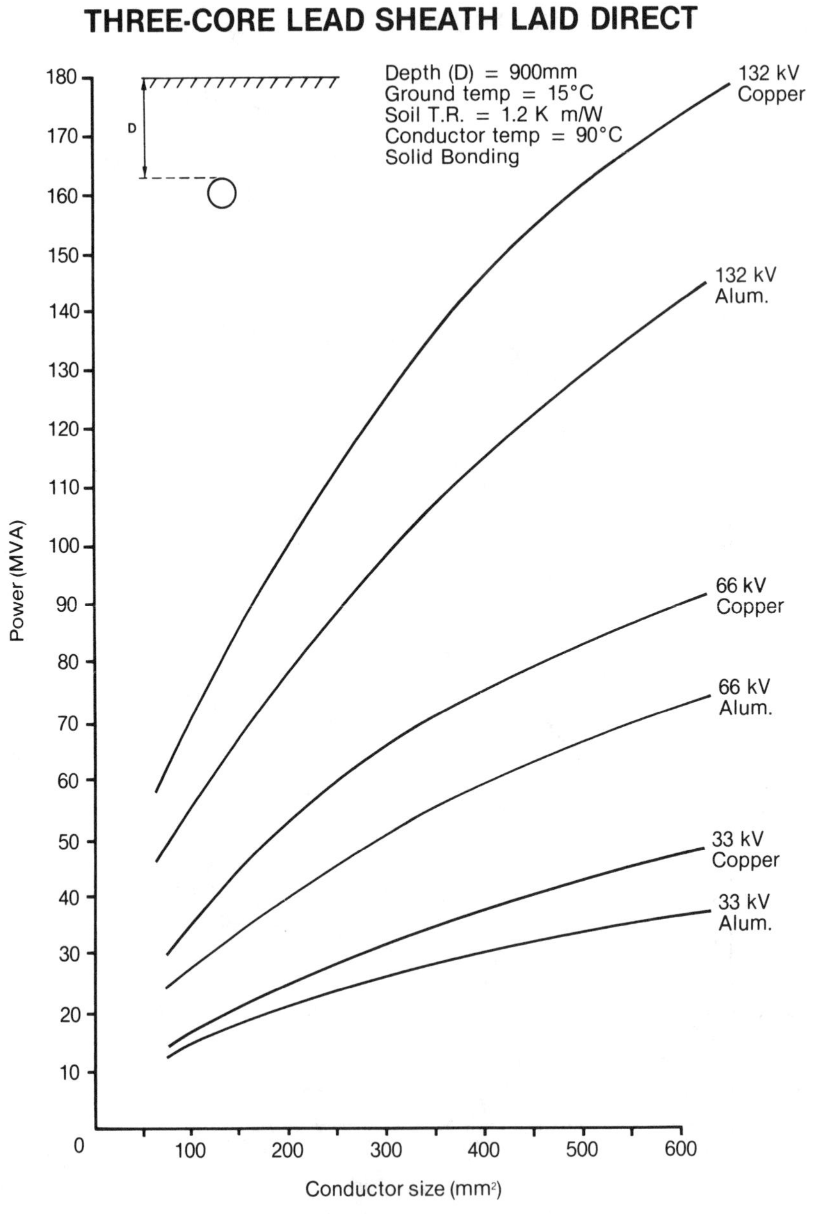

Fig. A16.3 Power ratings for 3-core lead sheathed OF cables, laid direct

THREE-CORE ALUMINIUM SHEATH LAID DIRECT

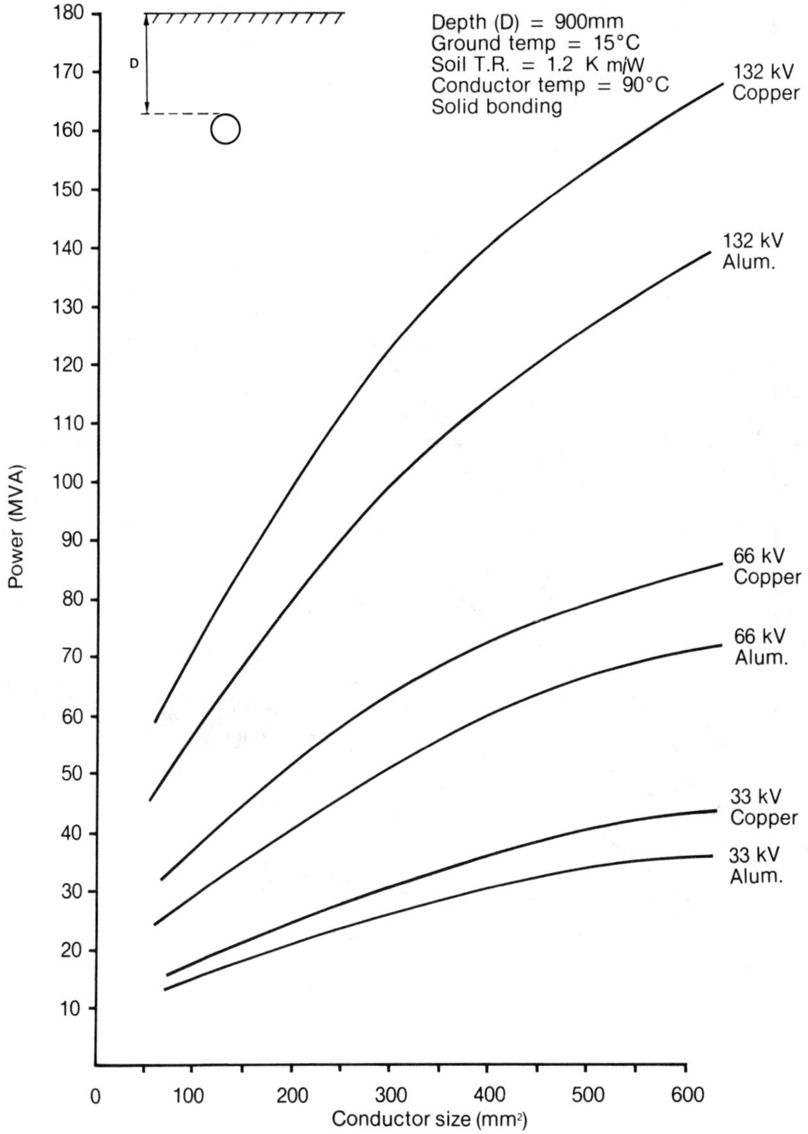

Fig. A16.4 Power ratings for 3-core aluminium sheathed OF cables, laid direct

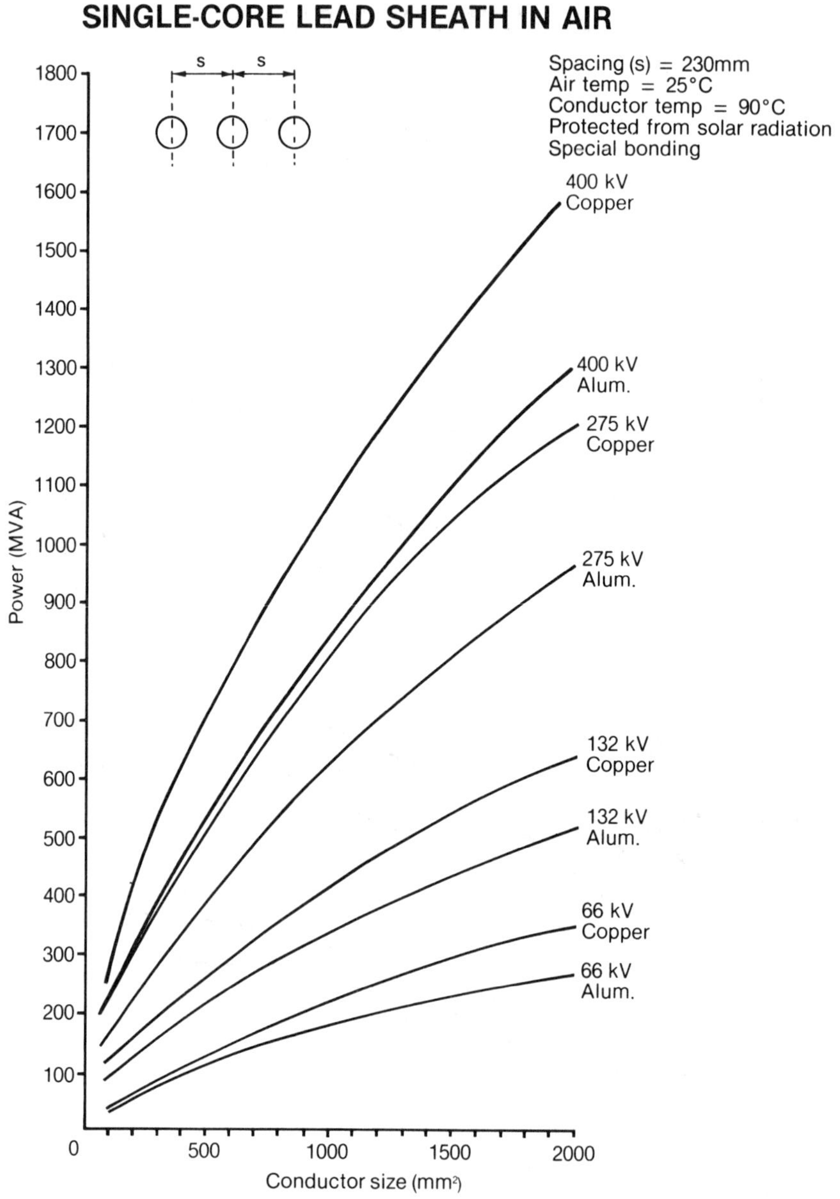

Fig. A16.5 Power ratings for single-core lead sheathed OF cables in air

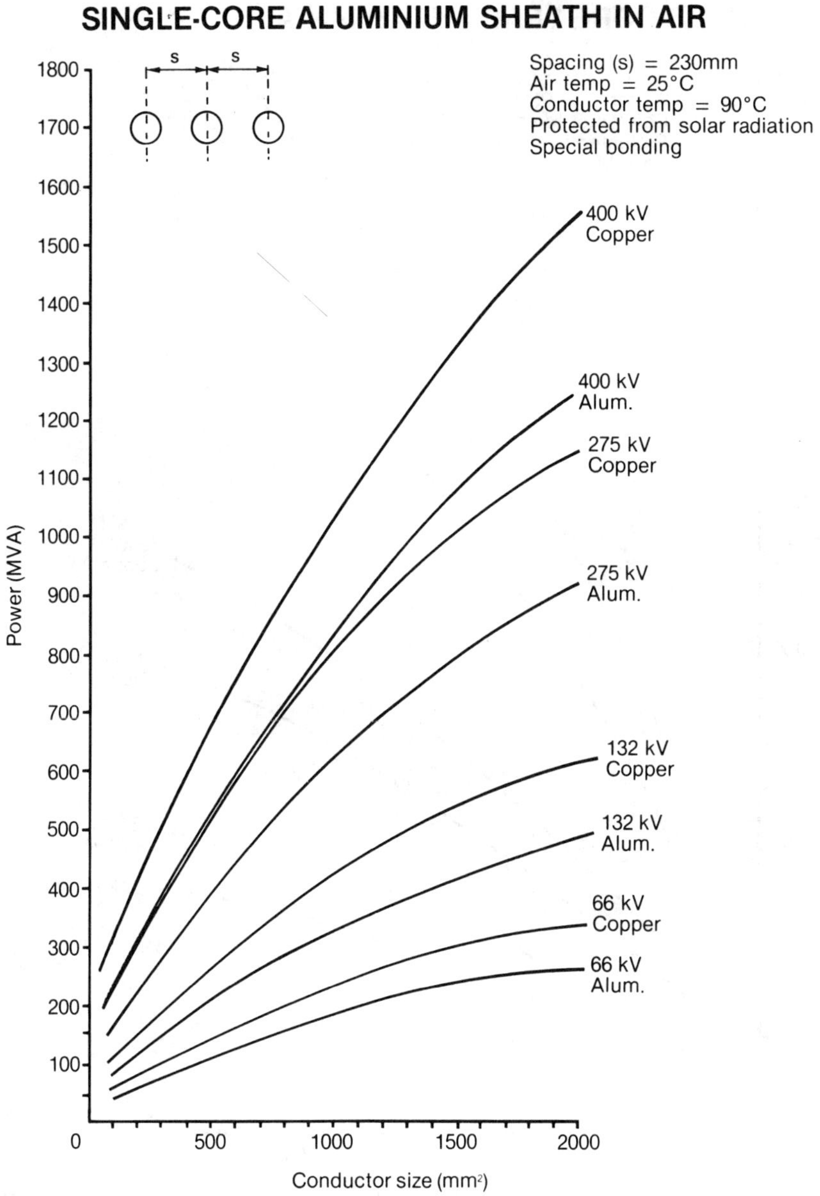

Fig. A16.6 Power ratings for single-core aluminium sheathed OF cables in air

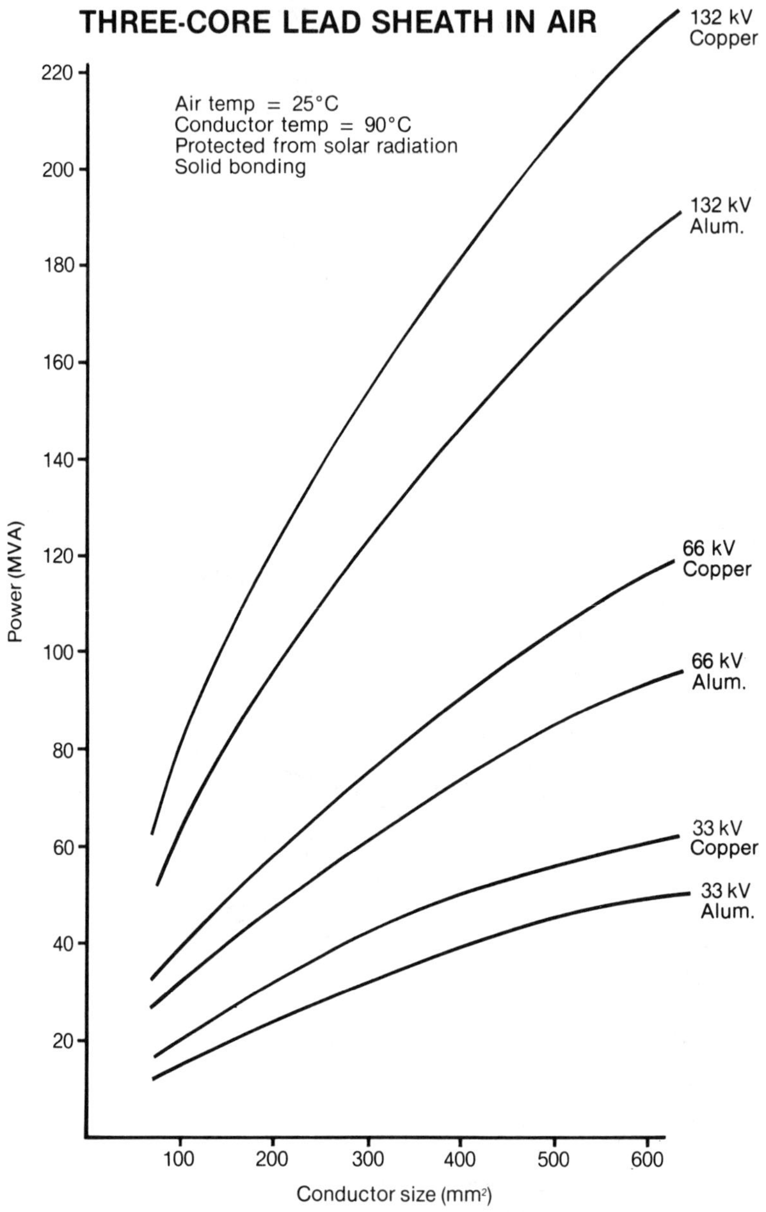

Fig. A16.7 Power ratings for 3-core lead sheathed OF cables in air

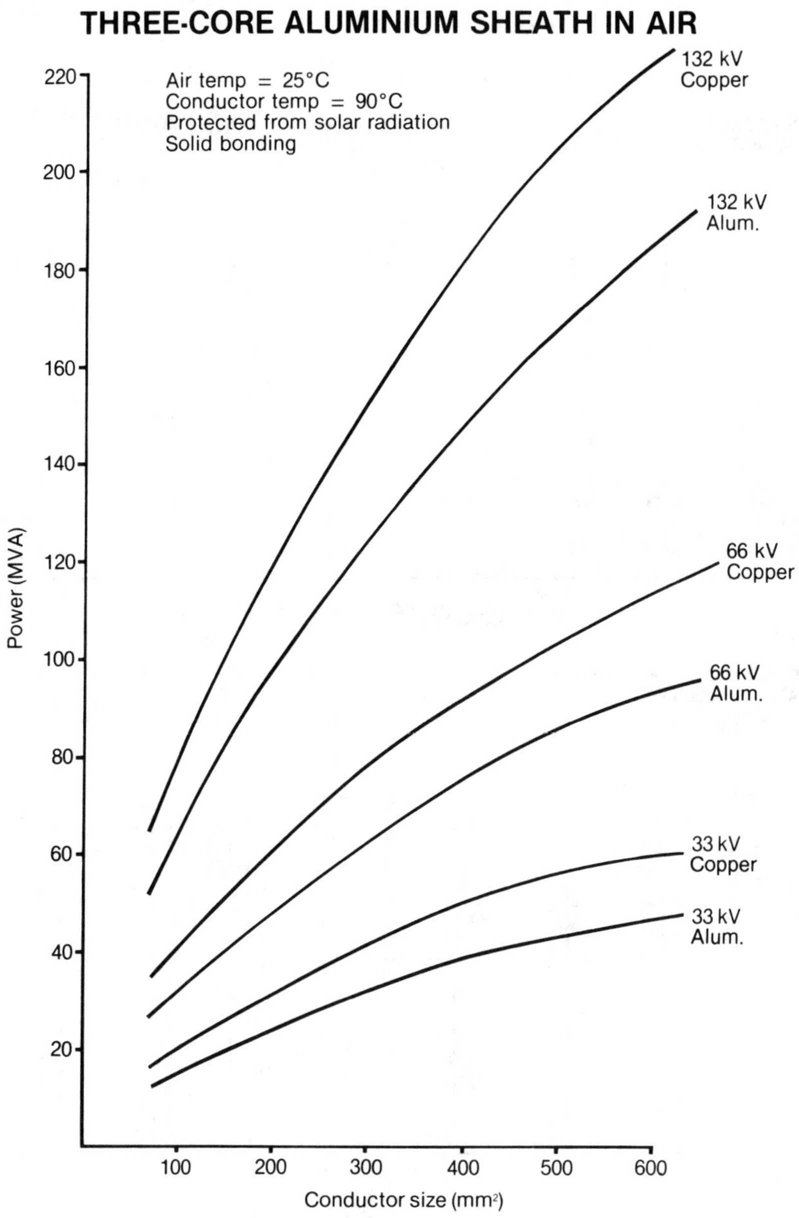

Fig. A16.8 Power ratings for 3-core aluminium sheathed OF cables in air

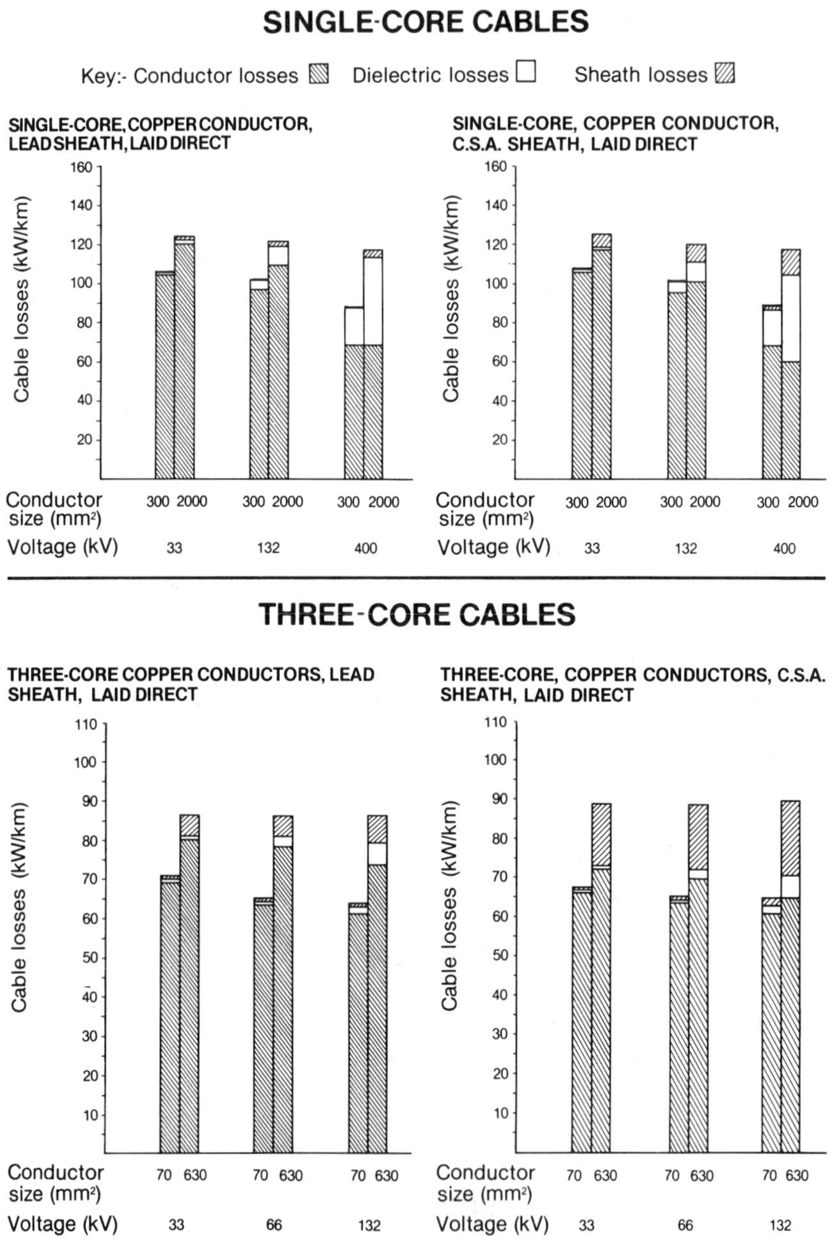

Fig. A16.9 Comparative electrical losses for OF cables with copper and aluminium conductors, laid direct

Table A16.2 Technical data 33 kV 3-core cables

Conductor size (mm^2)	Approximate diameter (mm)	Charging current (mA/m)	Capacitance per core (pF/m)	Reactance (μΩ/m)	Copper conductor		Aluminium conductor	
					A.C. (90 °C) resistance (μΩ/m)	Approximate weight (kg/m)	A.C. (90 °C) resistance (μΩ/m)	Approximate weight (kg/m)
33 kV 3-core, lead sheathed								
70	51	2.4	410	98	342	7.0	555	6.0
95	55	2.8	465	94	247	8.4	411	7.0
120	61	3.0	500	90	196	10.5	325	8.0
150	64	3.2	540	88	160	12.0	265	9.0
185	68	3.5	590	86	128	13.5	212	10.0
240	74	4.0	660	83	98	16.0	162	12.0
260	76	4.2	700	83	91	17.5	149	12.5
300	79	4.4	730	81	80	19.0	130	13.5
350	82	4.7	780	80	70	21.5	113	15.0
400	85	4.9	810	79	64	23.0	102	16.0
500	93	5.4	900	77	52	28.0	82	18.5
630	101	6.0	1010	75	43	34.0	65	22.0
33 kV 3-core, corrugated aluminium sheath								
70	54	2.3	390	95	342	4.5	555	3.0
95	57	3.0	470	92	247	5.5	411	3.5
120	59	3.1	520	90	196	6.5	325	4.0
150	62	3.4	560	88	159	7.5	265	4.5
185	65	3.7	610	86	128	9.0	211	5.5

(*cont.*)

Table A16.2 cont.

Conductor size (mm^2)	Approximate diameter (mm)	Charging current (mA/m)	Capacitance per core (pF/m)	Reactance (μΩ/m)	Copper conductor		Aluminium conductor	
					A.C. (90 °C) resistance (μΩ/m)	Approximate weight (kg/m)	A.C. (90 °C) resistance (μΩ/m)	Approximate weight (kg/m)
240	71	4.1	690	83	98	10.5	161	6.0
260	73	4.2	710	83	91	11.5	148	6.5
300	75	4.6	760	81	79	12.5	130	7.0
350	78	4.9	810	80	70	14.0	113	7.5
400	81	5.0	840	79	63	15.5	101	8.0
500	88	5.6	940	77	51	19.0	81	9.5
630	95	6.3	1050	75	42	23.0	64	11.0

For designs and applicable conditions of installation and operation see the introduction to this appendix.

Table A16.3 Technical data 66 kV single-core cables

Conductor size (mm^2)	Approximate diameter (mm)	Charging current (mA/m)	Capacitance per core (pF/m)	Reactance (μΩ/m)	Copper conductor		Aluminium conductor	
					A.C. (90 °C) resistance (μΩ/m)	Approximate weight (kg/m)	A.C. (90 °C) resistance (μΩ/m)	Approximate weight (kg/m)
66 kV single-core lead sheath								
120	41	6.3	530	220	191	4.7	318	4.0
150	42	6.7	560	217	156	5.2	259	4.2
185	41	6.2	520	220	124	5.1	206	4.0
240	43	6.9	575	216	95	5.9	157	4.4
260	43	7.0	585	215	88	6.2	145	4.5
300	45	7.4	620	211	76	6.7	125	4.8
350	46	7.9	660	208	66	7.4	109	5.2
400	47	8.3	690	206	59	7.8	98	5.4
500	51	9.0	755	200	48	9.3	78	6.0
630	54	10.0	835	194	37	11.0	61	7.0
800	58	11.1	930	188	30	13.2	48	8.1
1000	62	12.3	1025	182	25	15.8	39	9.3
1150	71	13.0	1090	173	21	18.4	34	11.4
1300	73	13.6	1140	171	18	20.5	30	12.5
1600	79	15.0	1250	164	15	24.1	24	14.4
2000	85	16.5	1380	158	13	29.0	20	16.4

(*cont.*)

OIL-FILLED TRANSMISSION CABLES

Table A16.3 cont.

Conductor size (mm^2)	Approximate diameter (mm)	Charging current (mA/m)	Capacitance per core (pF/m)	Reactance (μΩ/m)	Copper conductor		Aluminium conductor	
					A.C. (90 °C) resistance (μΩ/m)	Approximate weight (kg/m)	A.C. (90 °C) resistance (μΩ/m)	Approximate weight (kg/m)
66 kV single-core corrugated aluminium sheath								
120	44	6.3	530	220	191	3.2	318	2.5
150	45	6.7	560	217	156	3.5	259	2.6
185	44	6.2	520	220	124	3.6	206	2.5
240	46	6.9	575	216	95	4.2	157	2.8
260	47	7.0	585	215	88	4.5	145	2.9
300	48	7.4	620	211	76	4.9	125	3.0
350	50	7.9	660	208	66	5.4	109	3.2
400	51	8.3	690	206	59	5.8	98	3.4
500	54	9.0	755	200	48	6.9	78	3.8
630	58	10.0	835	194	37	8.6	61	4.6
800	61	11.1	930	188	30	10.3	48	5.3
1000	65	12.3	1025	182	25	12.6	39	6.1
1150	75	13.0	1090	173	21	14.7	34	7.7
1300	76	13.6	1140	171	18	16.3	30	8.2
1600	82	15.0	1250	164	15	19.3	24	9.6
2000	89	16.5	1380	158	13	23.8	20	11.0

For designs and applicable conditions of installation and operation see the introduction to this appendix.

OIL-FILLED TRANSMISSION CABLES

Table A16.4 Technical data 66 kV 3-core cables

Conductor size (mm^2)	Approximate diameter (mm)	Charging current (mA/m)	Capacitance per core (pF/m)	Reactance (μΩ/m)	Copper conductor		Aluminium conductor	
					A.C. (90 °C) resistance (μΩ/m)	Approximate weight (kg/m)	A.C. (90 °C) resistance (μΩ/m)	Approximate weight (kg/m)
66 kV 3-core, lead sheathed								
70	62	3.4	280	113	342	9.5	555	8.3
95	65	3.9	325	106	247	10.6	411	9.2
120	67	4.3	360	101	196	11.8	325	9.8
150	70	4.8	400	97	159	12.9	265	10.6
185	74	5.3	445	93	128	14.7	211	11.7
240	79	6.1	510	89	98	17.5	161	13.5
260	81	6.3	530	88	91	18.7	149	14.0
300	84	6.8	570	86	79	20.3	130	15.2
350	88	7.3	610	85	70	22.6	113	16.5
400	90	7.7	645	83	63	24.4	102	17.5
500	97	8.6	720	81	52	28.9	82	20.6
630	105	9.8	815	79	42	35.3	65	23.9
66 kV 3-core, corrugated aluminium sheathed								
70	67	3.4	280	113	342	6.2	555	5.0
95	70	3.9	325	106	247	7.3	411	5.6
120	73	4.3	360	101	196	8.2	325	6.0
150	75	4.8	400	97	159	9.1	265	6.4
185	79	5.3	445	93	128	10.4	211	7.2

(cont.)

Table A16.4 cont.

Conductor size (mm^2)	Approximate diameter (mm)	Charging current (mA/m)	Capacitance per core (pF/m)	Reactance (μΩ/m)	Copper conductor		Aluminium conductor	
					A.C. (90°C) resistance (μΩ/m)	Approximate weight (kg/m)	A.C. (90°C) resistance (μΩ/m)	Approximate weight (kg/m)
240	84	6.1	510	89	98	12.6	161	8.3
260	86	6.3	530	88	91	13.6	149	8.8
300	90	6.8	570	86	79	14.9	130	10.4
350	93	7.3	610	85	70	16.7	113	11.0
400	96	7.7	645	83	63	18.0	102	
500	103	8.6	720	81	52	21.6	82	12.8
630	112	9.8	815	79	42	26.8	65	15.3

For designs and applicable conditions of installation and operation see the introduction to this appendix.

OIL-FILLED TRANSMISSION CABLES

Table A16.5 Technical data 132 kV single-core cables

Conductor size (mm^2)	Approximate diameter (mm)	Charging current (mA/m)	Capacitance per core (pF/m)	Reactance (μΩ/m)	Copper conductor		Aluminium conductor	
					A.C. (90 °C) resistance (μΩ/m)	Approximate weight (kg/m)	A.C. (90 °C) resistance (μΩ/m)	Approximate weight (kg/m)
132 kV single-core lead sheath								
120	50	7.7	320	220	191	6.4	314	5.6
150	52	8.1	340	217	156	6.9	259	6.0
185	50	7.7	320	220	124	6.8	206	5.7
240	52	8.3	345	216	95	7.7	157	6.2
260	53	8.5	355	215	88	7.9	145	6.3
300	54	9.1	380	211	76	8.4	125	6.5
350	55	9.6	400	208	66	9.0	109	6.8
400	56	9.9	415	206	59	9.6	98	7.2
500	59	10.9	455	200	48	10.9	78	7.9
630	62	12.1	505	194	37	12.8	61	8.8
800	66	13.4	560	188	30	15.0	48	10.0
1000	70	14.7	615	182	25	17.8	39	11.0
1150	81	14.6	610	173	21	21.4	34	14.4
1300	83	15.1	630	171	18	23.1	30	15.1
1600	88	16.8	700	164	15	26.9	24	17.2
2000	94	18.4	770	158	13	32.0	20	19.4

(*cont.*)

OIL-FILLED TRANSMISSION CABLES

Table A16.5 cont.

Conductor size (mm^2)	Approximate diameter (mm)	Charging current (mA/m)	Capacitance per core (pF/m)	Reactance (μΩ/m)	Copper conductor		Aluminium conductor	
					A.C. (90 °C) resistance (μΩ/m)	Approximate weight (kg/m)	A.C. (90 °C) resistance (μΩ/m)	Approximate weight (kg/m)
132 kV single-core corrugated aluminium sheath								
120	54	7.7	320	220	191	4.3	314	3.5
150	55	8.1	340	217	156	4.6	259	3.7
185	54	7.7	320	220	124	4.7	206	3.5
240	56	8.3	345	216	95	5.3	157	3.8
260	56	8.5	355	215	88	5.5	145	3.9
300	58	9.1	380	211	76	6.0	125	4.1
350	59	9.6	400	208	66	6.5	109	4.4
400	60	9.9	415	206	59	6.9	98	4.5
500	62	10.9	455	200	48	8.0	78	5.0
630	65	12.1	505	194	37	9.6	61	5.6
800	69	13.4	560	188	30	11.4	48	6.3
1000	73	14.7	615	182	25	13.7	39	7.3
1150	84	14.6	610	173	21	16.3	34	9.3
1300	87	15.1	630	171	18	18.0	30	10.0
1600	92	16.8	700	164	15	21.2	24	11.4
2000	98	18.4	770	158	13	25.5	20	12.9

For designs and applicable conditions of installation and operation see the introduction to this appendix.

Table A16.6 Technical data 132 kV 3-core cables

Conductor size (mm^2)	Approximate diameter (mm)	Charging current (mA/m)	Capacitance per core (pF/m)	Reactance (μΩ/m)	Copper conductor		Aluminium conductor	
					A.C. (90 °C) resistance (μΩ/m)	Approximate weight (kg/m)	A.C. (90 °C) resistance (μΩ/m)	Approximate weight (kg/m)
132 kV 3-core lead sheath								
120	93	5.2	215	124	196	19.4	325	17.2
150	94	5.6	235	119	159	20.6	265	17.8
185	96	6.5	270	112	127	21.8	211	18.6
240	99	7.3	305	106	98	24.4	161	20.1
260	101	7.8	325	104	91	25.3	148	20.6
300	103	8.3	345	101	78	26.9	129	21.8
350	106	8.8	370	98	69	29.1	113	22.9
400	108	9.2	385	97	62	31.0	101	24.1
500	116	9.9	415	94	51	36.2	81	28.0
630	123	11.2	470	91	41	42.9	64	31.5
132 kV 3-core corrugated aluminium sheath								
120	99	5.2	215	124	196	12.2	325	10.8
150	100	5.6	235	119	159	13.9	265	11.1
185	102	6.5	270	112	127	15.1	211	11.8
240	104	7.3	305	106	98	17.1	161	12.7
260	107	7.8	325	104	91	17.9	148	13.2
300	110	8.3	345	101	78	19.4	129	13.9
350	113	8.8	370	98	69	21.0	113	14.9
400	115	9.2	385	97	62	22.5	101	15.5
500	123	9.9	415	94	51	26.6	81	18.0
630	131	11.2	470	91	41	32.1	64	20.4

For designs and applicable conditions of installation and operation see the introduction to this appendix.

OIL-FILLED TRANSMISSION CABLES

Table A16.7 Technical data 275 kV single-core cables

Conductor size (mm^2)	Approximate diameter (mm)	Charging current (mA/m)	Capacitance per core (pF/m)	Reactance (μΩ/m)	Copper conductor		Aluminium conductor	
					A.C. (90 °C) resistance (μΩ/m)	Approximate weight (kg/m)	A.C. (90 °C) resistance (μΩ/m)	Approximate weight (kg/m)
275 kV single-core lead sheath								
120	73	9.5	190	220	191	11.5	318	10.8
150	73	10.0	200	217	156	11.7	259	10.8
185	73	9.5	190	220	124	11.9	206	10.8
240	73	10.5	210	216	95	12.4	157	10.9
260	74	10.7	215	215	88	12.6	145	10.9
300	74	11.5	230	211	76	12.9	125	11.1
350	74	12.0	240	208	66	13.4	109	11.3
400	75	12.5	250	206	59	14.1	98	11.6
500	76	13.7	275	200	48	15.2	78	12.1
630	78	15.2	305	194	37	16.8	61	12.7
800	88	14.7	295	188	30	20.9	48	15.8
1000	91	16.2	325	182	25	23.6	39	17.1
1150	96	19.0	380	173	21	26.2	34	19.6
1300	98	20.0	400	171	18	28.0	30	20.0
1600	103	22.0	440	164	15	31.7	24	22.0
2000	108	23.9	480	158	13	36.9	20	24.2

275 kV single-core corrugated aluminium sheath								
120	77	9.5	190	220	191	7.3	318	6.6
150	77	10.0	200	217	156	7.5	259	6.6
185	77	9.5	190	220	124	7.8	206	6.6
240	77	10.5	210	216	95	8.2	157	6.7
260	78	10.7	215	215	88	8.4	145	6.7
300	78	11.5	230	211	76	8.7	125	6.9
350	78	12.0	240	208	66	9.2	109	7.0
400	79	12.5	250	206	59	9.5	98	7.1
500	80	13.7	275	200	48	10.5	78	7.5
630	82	15.2	305	194	37	12.0	61	8.0
800	92	14.7	295	188	30	15.0	48	10.0
1000	95	16.2	325	182	25	17.2	39	10.8
1150	101	19.0	380	173	21	19.3	34	12.3
1300	103	20.0	400	171	18	20.9	30	12.9
1600	107	22.0	440	164	15	24.1	24	14.3
2000	113	23.9	480	158	13	28.6	20	16.0

For designs and applicable conditions of installation and operation see the introduction to this appendix.

Table A16.8 Technical data 400 kV single-core cables

Conductor size (mm^2)	Approximate diameter (mm)	Charging current (mA/m)	Capacitance per core (pF/m)	Reactance (μΩ/m)	Copper conductor		Aluminium conductor	
					A.C. (90 °C) resistance (μΩ/m)	Approximate weight (kg/m)	A.C. (90 °C) resistance (μΩ/m)	Approximate weight (kg/m)
400 kV single-core lead sheath								
120	111	9.4	130	220	191	23.7	318	22.9
150	108	10.2	140	217	156	23.1	259	22.2
185	111	9.4	130	220	124	24.2	206	23.0
240	107	10.9	150	216	95	23.5	157	21.5
260	106	10.9	150	215	88	23.0	145	21.3
300	105	11.6	160	211	76	22.7	125	20.9
350	103	12.3	170	208	66	22.7	109	20.6
400	103	12.3	170	206	59	22.5	98	20.5
500	102	13.8	190	200	48	23.0	78	20.0
630	102	15.2	210	194	37	24.2	61	20.3
800	103	17.0	235	188	30	26.1	48	20.8
1000	104	18.5	255	182	25	28.3	39	21.9
1150	109	21.8	300	173	21	30.7	34	23.7
1300	110	23.2	320	171	18	32.5	30	24.6
1600	114	25.4	350	164	15	36.3	24	26.6
2000	119	27.9	385	158	13	41.5	20	28.8

400 kV single-core corrugated aluminium sheath								
120	116	9.4	130	220	191	14.6	318	13.9
150	113	10.2	140	217	156	14.3	259	13.4
185	116	9.4	130	220	124	15.2	206	14.0
240	112	10.9	150	216	95	14.8	157	13.2
260	111	10.9	150	215	88	14.8	145	13.0
300	109	11.6	160	211	76	14.5	125	12.7
350	108	12.3	170	208	66	14.6	109	12.5
400	107	12.3	170	206	59	14.8	98	12.4
500	106	13.8	190	200	48	15.4	78	12.4
630	106	15.2	210	194	37	16.5	61	12.6
800	107	17.0	235	188	30	18.0	48	13.1
1000	109	18.5	255	182	25	20.1	39	13.7
1150	114	21.8	300	173	21	22.0	34	15.0
1300	115	23.2	320	171	18	23.6	30	15.6
1600	119	25.4	350	164	15	26.6	24	16.9
2000	124	27.9	385	158	13	31.1	20	18.5

For designs and applicable conditions of installation and operation see the introduction to this appendix.

Appendix A17
Minimum Installation Bending Radii

BASIS

The various types of cable covered are divided into sections in accordance with the descriptions given in parts 2–4 of the book. The radii quoted are in accordance with British Standards or, for cables not covered by British Standards, represent accepted practice.

Symbols: d_o = cable overall diameter or the major axis for flat cables
d_s = diameter over metal sheath

PART 2: GENERAL WIRING CABLES

Table A17.1 Cables for fixed wiring

Insulation	Conductors	Construction	Overall diameter (mm)	Minimum radius
PVC or rubber	Aluminium or copper, solid circular or stranded	Unarmoured	Up to 10	$3d_o$[a]
			10–25	$4d_o$[b]
			Above 25	$6d_o$
		Armoured	Any	$6d_o$
Mineral	Copper		Any	$6d_o$

[a] $2d_o$ for single-core cables
[b] $3d_o$ for single-core cables

Table A17.2 PVC and EPR insulated cables for installation in ships

Voltage	Construction	Diameter (mm)	Minimum radius
150/240 V 440/750 V 600/1000 V	Unarmoured	Up to 10 10 to 25 Above 25	$3d_o$ $4d_o$ $6d_o$
150/240 V 440/750 V 600/1000 V	Armoured	Any	$6d_o$
150/240 V 440/750 V 600/1000 V	Shaped conductor	Any	$8d_o$
1.9/3.3 kV 3.3/3.3 kV	Unarmoured Unscreened	Any	$6d_o$
1.9/3.3 kV to 6.35/11 kV	Unarmoured Armoured	Any Any	$8d_o$ $12d_o$

Table A17.3 PVC and EPR insulated wire armoured mining cables (to BCS 295)

Voltage	Construction	Minimum radius
600/1000 V		$8d_o$
1.9/3.3 kV	Unscreened	$8d_o$
1.9/3.3 kV	Screened	$12d_o$
3.8/6.6 kV		$12d_o$

PART 3: DISTRIBUTION CABLES

Table A17.4 Paper insulated cables

Voltage	Minimum radius			
	Single-core	Multicore	Adjacent to joints and terminations	
			Without former	With former
Up to and including 6.35/11 kV	$15d_o$	$12d_o$		
Above 6.35/11 kV and up to and including 12.7/22 kV	$18d_o$	$15d_o$		
19/33 kV single-core	$21d_o$	$18d_o$	$20d_o$	$15d_o$
19/33 kV 3-core screened	$21d_o$	$18d_o$	$15d_o$	$12d_o$
19/33 kV 3-core SL	$21d_o$	$18d_o$	$15d_o$	$12d_o$
19/33 kV cores of SL	$21d_o$		$20d_s$	$15d_s$

Table A17.5 PVC and XLPE insulated cables up to 3.3 kV

Conductor	Construction	Overall diameter (mm)	Minimum radius
Solid aluminium or stranded copper	Armoured or unarmoured	Any	$8d_o$

Table A17.6 XLPE insulated cables for 6.6–33 kV

Type of cable	Minimum radius	
	During laying	Adjacent to joints or terminations
Single-core		
(a) unarmoured	$20d_o$	$15d_o$
(b) armoured	$20d_o$	$12d_o$
3-core		
(a) unarmoured	$15d_o$	$12d_o$
(b) armoured	$12d_o$	$10d_o$

PART 4: TRANSMISSION CABLES

Table A17.7 Oil-filled cables

Voltage	Number of cores	Minimum radius		
		Cable	Adjacent to joints and terminations	
			With former	Without former
33–132 kV	1	$30d_o$	$15d_o$	$20d_o$
	3	$20d_o$	$12d_o$	$15d_o$
275–400 kV	1	$30d_o$	$20d_o$	$20d_o$

Table A17.8 XLPE insulated cables

Type of cable	Minimum radius			
	Cable placed into position adjacent to joints or terminations		Laid direct or in air	Laid in ducts
	Without former	With former		
33 kV non-metallic sheathed single-core	$15d_o$	$15d_o$	$20d_o$	$20d_o$
3-core	$12d_o$	$12d_o$	$15d_o$	$15d_o$
66 kV and 132 kV single-core metal sheathed	$20d_o$	$15d_o$	$30d_o$	$35d_o$

Appendix A18
Bibliography

PART 1: THEORY AND COMMON ASPECTS

Electrical theory

Starr, A. T. (1957) *Transmission and Distribution of Electric Power*. Pitman.

Buchan, M. F. (1967) *Electricity Supply*. Edward Arnold.

Heinhold, L. (1970) *Power Cables and their Applications*. Siemens Aktiengesellschaft.

Cotton, H. and Barber, H. (1975) *Transmission and Distribution of Electrical Energy*. English Universities Press.

Graneau, P. (1980) *The Science, Technology and Economics of High Voltage Cables*. Wiley.

Weedey, B. M. (1980) *Underground Transmission of Electric Power*. Wiley.

Black, R. M. (1986) *The History of Electric Wires and Cables*. Peter Peregrinus.

Materials

Aluminium

McDonald, F. G. (17 Aug. 1967) 'The hedgehog joint and story of 50 year old aluminium cable'. *Electr. Times*.

(2 July 1970) 'New wiring cable has copper-clad conductors'. *Electr. Times*.

McAllister, D. (10 Sep. 1971) 'Aluminium cables accepted by industry'. *Electr. Times*.

McAllister, D. (Aug. 1976) 'Terminations for aluminium conductor power cable'. *BSI News*.

Chattergee, S. (Aug. 1977) 'Failure of terminations of aluminium conductor cables in house-service meters and domestic wiring installations'. Indian Copper Information Centre and Electrical Contractors' Association of India Paper No. 6.

Lead

Hiscock, S. A. (15 Apr., 29 Apr., 13 May 1960) 'American lead alloy cable sheaths'. *Electr. J.*

Hiscock, S. A. (1961) *Lead and Lead Alloys for Cable Sheathing*. Ernest Benn.

Betzer, C. E. (Jun. 1962) 'Determination of the life to fracture by bending of lead sheaths on underground power cable'. *AIEE Summer Meeting*.

Lead Development Association (1964) *Lead Cable Sheathing in N. America*. London.

Lead Development Association (1964) *Lead Alloys for Pressurised Cable Sheaths*. London.

Ball, E. H. and McAllister, D. (Sep. 1968) 'Influence of lead sheath thickness on service performance of cables'. *3rd Int. Conf. on Lead*.

Harvard D. G. (Jan. 1975) 'Selection of cable sheath lead alloys for fatigue resistance'. *IEEE Power Eng. Soc.*

Impregnated paper

Robinson, D. M. (1936) *Dielectric Phenomena in High Voltage Cables*. Chapman and Hall.

Bennett, G. E. (1957) 'Paper cable saturants: European preferences and selection'. *IEEE Trans.* **PAS-81**.

Kelk, E. and Wilson, I. O. (1965) 'Constitution and properties of paper for high-voltage dielectrics'. *Proc. IEE* **112** (3).

Sloat, T. K. (1979) 'Characteristics of insulating oil for electrical application'. EPRI Report No. 577–1, EL-1300.

Chan, J. C. and Hiivala, L. J. (1986) 'Electrical characteristics of synthetic dielectric liquids for oil–paper power cables. *2nd IEE Int. Conf. on Power Cables 10 kV–180 kV.*

Polymeric materials

Blow, C. M. (1975) *Rubber Technology and Manufacture*. London: Newnes-Butterworths.

Brydson, J. A. (1975) *Plastics Materials*. London: Newnes-Butterworths.

Town, W. L. (23 Feb. 1979) 'Using extrudable materials for cable insulation'. *Electr. Times*.

Mason, J. H. (Apr. 1981) 'Assessing the resistance of polymers to electrical treeing'. *Proc. IEE, Part A* **128** (3), 193–201.

Epstein, M. M., Bernstein, B. S. and Shaw, M. T. (1982) 'Ageing and failure in solid dielectric materials'. Paris: CIGRE Paper No. 15–01.

EPRI (1983) 'Examination of distribution cables for chemical and physical changes upon ageing in the field and laboratory'. EPRI Final Report No. EL-3011, Project RP 1357–03.

Occini, E. *et al.* (1983) 'Thermal, mechanical and electrical properties of EPR insulation in power cable'. *IEEE/PES 1983 Winter Meeting*.

Azaroff, L. V. (1984) 'Materials research on extruded power cables'. Jicable Conference Paper No. B2–3.

Fisher, E. J. (1984) 'Advances in cross-linking polyethylene insulation for medium and high voltage cables'. Jicable Conference Paper A6–6.

Fothergill, J. C. *et al.* (1984) 'Structure of water trees and their relation to breakdown'. *4th IEE Int. Conf. on Dielectric Materials*.

Swingler, S. G. *et al.* (1984) 'The dielectric response of polyethylene cable containing water trees'. *4th IEE Int. Conf. on Dielectric Materials*.

Billing, J. (1986) 'Effect of cross-linking residue on the electric strength of XLPE cable insulation'. *5th BEAMA Int. Elect. Ins. Conf., Brighton*.

Simons, M. A. and Gale, P. S. (1986) 'Factors affecting the electric strength of XLPE cable insulation'. *5th BEAMA Int. Elect. Ins. Conf., Brighton*.

Given, M. J. *et al.* (1987) 'The role of ions in the mechanism of water tree growth'. *IEEE Trans.* **E1–22**, 151–156.

Saure, M. and Kalkner, W. (1987) 'On water tree testing of materials'. *CIGRE 1987*.

Billing, J. W. (1988) 'Thermal history of cable insulation revealed by DSC examin-

ation'. *5th IEE Int. Conf. on Dielectric Materials.*
Das-Gupta, D. K. *et al.* (1988) 'Measurement of polarisation in XLPE insulated HV cables'. *5th IEE Int. Conf. on Dielectric Materials.*
Head, J. G. *et al.* (1988) 'Modification of the dielectric properties of polymeric materials'. *5th IEE Int. Conf. on Dielectric Materials.*
Patsch, R. (1988) 'Water treeing in cable insulation'. *5th IEE Int. Conf. on Dielectric Materials.*
Rowland, S. M. and Dissado, L. A. (1988) Measurement of water tree growth in cross-linked polyethylene cables'. *5th IEE Int. Conf. on Dielectric Materials.*
Warren, L. and Paterson, J. R. (1988) 'Studies of irradiation on elastomeric insulation by gamma and neutron flux and thermal radiation degradation'. *5th IEE Int. Conf. on Dielectric Materials.*
Warren, L. and Paterson, J. R. (1988) 'The development of elastomeric insulating materials for use under extreme service conditions'. *5th IEE Int. Conf. on Dielectric Materials.*
Wasilenko, E. (1988) 'Electrical ageing of polyethylene at impulse and a.c. test voltages'. *5th IEE Int. Conf. on Dielectric Materials.*

Conductors

Griesser, E. E. (Dec. 1966) 'Sodium as an electrical conductor'. *Wire.*
Humphrey, L. E. *et al.* (Nov. 1966) 'Insulated sodium conductors – a future trend'. *IEEE Spectrum.*
Steeve, E. J. and Schneider, J. A. (1966) 'Field tests on 15 kV and 600 V sodium cable'. IEEE Paper No. 66–447 (Summer meeting).
Humphrey, L. E. *et al.* (1967) 'Insulated sodium conductors'. *IEEE Trans.* **PAS–86.**
Watson, P. E. and Ventura, R. M. (Apr. 1967) 'Sodium cables used for all secondaries in URD development'. *Trans. Distr.*
Ball, E. H. and Maschio, G. (1968) 'The a.c. resistance of segmented conductors as used in power cables'. *IEEE Trans.* **PAS–87.**
Kalsi, S. S. and Minnich, S. H. (Mar.–Apr. 1980) 'Calculation of circulating current losses in cable conductors'. *IEEE Trans.* **PAS–99.**
Takaoka, M. *et al.* (1982) 'Manufacturing method and characteristics of compact segmental conductors with strands insulated with cupric oxide film'. *Proc. 52nd Annual Convention of Wire Associated Int. Inc. 1982.*
Edwards, D. R. (1988) 'Supertension or superconducting cables'. *Proc. IEE, Part C* **135** (1), 9–23.

Protective finishes

Giblin, J. F. and King, W. T. (May 1954) 'The damage to lead-sheathed cables by rodents and insects'. *Proc. IEE, Part 1* **101**, 129.
Hollingsworth, P. M. (9 Jan., 23 Jan. 1959) 'Protective coverings for lead and aluminium sheathed cables'. *Electr. J.*, 82–87; 221–224.
McAllister, D. (14 May 1965) 'Protection of power cables against corrosion'. *Electr. Rev.*
Gay, F. S. and Wetherley, A. H. (1969) 'Laboratory studies of termite resistance', Part 5, 'The termite resistance of plastics'. Australia: Dept. of Entomology Technical Paper No. 10, Commonwealth Scientific Research Organization.
Shiga, T. and Inagaki, Y. (Mar. 1969) 'Termite damage to cable and its prevention'.

Sumitomo Electr. Techn. Rev. (12).

Bultman, J. D., Leonard, J. M. and Southwell, C. R. (1972) 'Termite resistance of PVC in southern temperate and tropical environments'. Nat. Res. Lab. (Washington) Report No. 7417.

Beal, R. H., Bultman, J. D. and Southwell, C. R. (1973) 'Resistance of polymeric cable coverings to subterranean termite attack'. *Int. Biodeterior, Bull.* **9** (1–2), 28–34.

Beal, R. H. and Bultman, J. D. (1978) 'Resistance of polymeric cable coverings to subterranean termite attack after 8 years of field testing in the tropics'. *Int. Biodeterior Bull.* **14** (4), 123–127.

Bow, K. E. and Snow, J. H. (1982) 'Chemical/moisture barrier cable for underground systems'. *IEEE Trans.* **PAS–101**, 1942–1949.

Bow, K. E. (1984) 'Moisture barrier power cable with a plastic–metal laminate sheath'. Jicable Conference Paper No. B1.1.

Stoget, H. *et al.* (1985) 'Stresses and behaviour of polyethylene sheaths'. CIRED Paper No. 3.14.

Bungay, E. W. G. (1986) 'Protection of MV underground power cables'. *Electron. Power*, 221–225.

Swingler, S. G. (1986) 'Ensuring satisfactory mechanical performance from power cable sheathing'. *5th BEAMA Int. Elect. Ins. Conf., Brighton.*

Cables in fires – special designs and finishes

Day, A. G. (1975) 'Oxygen index tests: temperature effect and comparisons with other flammability tests'. *Plast. Polym.* **43** (164), 64.

Punderson, J. O. (Sep.–Oct. 1977) 'Toxicity and safety of wire insulation: a state of the art review'. *Wire Tech.*

White, T. M. (Feb. 1977) 'Cable fires in power stations'. *Electron. Power.*

Kourtides, D. A., Gilwee, W. J. and Hilado, C. J. (Jun. 1978) 'Relative toxicity of the pyrolysis products from some thermoset polymers'. *Polym. Eng. Sci.* **18** (8), 674.

National Materials Advisory Board (1978) *Flammability, Smoke, Toxicity and Corrosive Gases of Electric Cable Materials.* Washington: National Academy of Sciences Publication No. NMAB–342.

Sullivan, T. and Willis, A. J. (17 Nov. 1978) 'Reducing the hazards from cables in fires'. *Electr. Times.*

Einhorn, I. N. and Grunnet, M. L. (1979) 'The physiological and toxicological aspects of the degradation products produced during the combustion of polyvinyl chloride polymers; flammability of solid polymer cable dielectrics'. EPRI Report No. EL-1263, TPS 77–738.

Smith, V. H. (7 Sep. 1979) 'Fire resistant cables for underground railways'. *Electr. Rev. Int.* **205** (9), 54.

Kingsbury, E. R. *et al.* (Sep. 1980) 'Selection of flame retarded wire and cable for industrial applications'. *Proc. 27th Ann. Pet. Chem. Ind. Conf.*, pp. 55–58. Houston: IEEE.

Barber, M. D., Partridge, P. F. and Gibbons, J. A. M. (1984) 'Reduced fire propagation and low smoke emission requirements for power station cables'. Jicable Conference Paper No. A9–3.

Berry, D. L. and Klamerus, L. J. (1984) 'Cable fire testing to meet realistic design criteria'. Jicable Conference Paper No. A7–1.

Bessei, H. and John, G. (1984) 'Halogen free fire–resistant joints for LV and MV cables'. Jicable Conference Paper No. C–12.

Beyersdorfer, K. W. and Tamplin, P. (1984) 'Accessories for halogen free fire–retardant and fire–resistant cables'. Jicable Conference Paper No. C–13.

Kirchner, F., Guerzio, M. and Villagrasa, F. (1984) 'New cables designed for limiting the risks proceeding from a fire'. Jicable Conference Paper No. A7–3.

Sabiston, A. D. (1984) 'Cables with reduced smoke, toxicity and fire propagation'. Jicable Conference Paper No. A8–2.

Stevens, G. C. and Gibbons, J. A. M. (1984) 'Assessing smoke and gas emission hazards from burning electric cables'. *4th IEE Int. Conf. on Dielectric Materials.*

Beretta, G. (1985) 'Behaviour of cables versus fire risks'. CIRED Paper No. 3.16.

Pays, M. and Simon, C. (1985) 'Improved fire resistant cables'. CIRED Paper No. 3.11.

Dabusti, V. *et al.* (1986) 'Development and prospects of cables with reduced smoke, toxic and corrosive gas emission'. *5th BEAMA Int. Elect. Ins. Conf., Brighton.*

Day, A. G. (1986) 'Examination of combustion products of electrical insulation using the NES 713 test'. *5th BEAMA Int. Elect. Ins. Conf., Brighton.*

Philbrick, S. E., Bungay, E. W. G., Barber, M. D. and Williamson, A. E. (1986) 'Cables for new power stations'. *2nd IEE Int. Conf. on Power Cables 10 kV–180 kV.*

Stevens, G. C. (1986) 'The appraisal and significance of acidic gas emissions from burning electric cable materials'. *5th BEAMA Int. Elect. Ins. Conf., Brighton.*

Stevens, G. C. *et al.* (1988) 'Acidic gas emissions from electrical insulation and their influence on electronic components'. *5th IEE Int. Conf. on Dielectric Materials.*

Stevens, G. C. *et al.* (1988) 'Chemical evaluation of combustion gas toxicity tests applied to electric cable materials'. *5th IEE Int. Conf. on Dielectric Materials.*

Swingler, S. G. *et al.* (1988) 'Small-scale assessment of flame propagation and heat release rate of electric cable materials'. *5th IEE Int. Conf. on Dielectric Materials.*

Sustained ratings

Goldenberg, H. (1958) 'Methods for the calculation of cyclic rating factors and emergency loading for cables direct in ground or in duct's. ERA Report No. F/T 186.

Orchard, R. S., Barnes, C. C., Hollingsworth, P. M. and Mochlinski, K. (1960) 'Soil thermal resistivity: a practical approach to its assessment and its influence on the current rating of buried cables'. Paris: CIGRE Paper No. 214.

Arman, A. N., Cherry, D. M., Gosland, L. and Hollingsworth, P. M. (1964) 'Influence of soil moisture migration on power rating of cables in h.v. transmission systems'. *Proc. IEE* **111** (5).

Milne, A. G. and Mochlinski, K. (1964) 'Characteristics of soil affecting cable ratings'. *Proc. IEE* **111** (5).

ERA Technology Ltd (Aug. 1974) 'Heat emission from cables in air'. ERA Report No. 74–27.

Gosden, J. H., and Kendall, P. G. (May 1976) 'Current ratings of 11 kV cables'. *IEE Conf. on Distribution Cables and Jointing Techniques.*

Mochlinski, K. (Jan. 1976) 'Assessment of the influence of soil thermal resistivity on the ratings of distribution cables'. *Proc. IEE* **123** (1), 60–72.
Electricity Council (1977) *Engineering Recommendation P17 – Current Rating Guide for Distribution Cables*. London.
Parr, R. G. (Sep. 1980) 'Heat emission from cables on perforated steel trays'. ERA Report 74–28, ERA Technology Ltd.
Deschamps, L. *et al.* (1983) Thermal and mechanical behaviour of 20 kV cables under overload conditions'. CIRED Paper No. d.08.
Parr, R. G. (1983) 'Circuit protection for cables in groups'. ERA Report No. 83–0078.
Van Hove, C. *et al.* (1983) 'Overloadability of cable systems'. CIRED Paper No. d.07.
Hutchings, E. and Coates, M. (1984) 'Tests to determine data for rating cables in randomly laid stacks on trays'. ERA Report No. 84–0172.
Coates, M. (1985), 'Temperature rise of cables passing through short lengths of thermal insulation'. ERA Report No. 85–0111.

Short-circuit ratings

Gosland, L. and Parr, R. G. (Jan. 1960) 'A basis for short circuit ratings for paper-insulated, lead-sheathed cables up to 11 kV'. ERA Report No. F/T 195.
Buckingham, G. S. (Jun. 1961) 'Short-circuit ratings for mains cables'. *Proc. IEE, Part A* **108**.
Gosland, L. and Parr, R. G. (Jun. 1961) 'A basis for short-circuit ratings for paper-insulated cables up to 11 kV'. *Proc. IEE, Part A* **108**.
Thomas, A. G. (10 Nov. 1961) 'Short-circuit ratings of aluminium cables'. *Electr. Rev.*
Parr, R. G. (1962) 'Bursting currents of 11 kV, 3-core, screened cables (paper-insulated, lead-sheathed)'. ERA Report No. F/T 202.
Parr, R. G. (1964) 'Short-circuit ratings for 11 kV 3-core paper-insulated screened cables'. ERA Report No. 5057.
Parr, R. G. and Yap, J. S. (1965) 'Short-circuit ratings for PVC insulated cables'. ERA Report No. 5056.
Foulsham, N., Metcalfe, J. C. and Philbrick, S. E. (Oct. 1974) 'Proposals for installation practice of single-core cables'. *Proc IEE* **121** (10).

PART 2: WIRING AND INDUSTRIAL TYPE CABLES

General wiring cables

Town, W. L. (22 Jun., 6 Jul. 1972) 'Wiring cables'. *Electr. Times* **161** (25), 25–26; **162** (1), 33–34.
Hollingsworth, P. M. and Town, W. L. (11 May 1973) 'Trends in wiring cable design and installation'. *Electr. Rev.* **192** (19), 666–669.
Taylor, F. G. (Mar. 1973) 'Cables for electronics'. *Electrotechnology* **1** (2), 3–10.
Town, W. L. (Apr. 1974) 'A guide to the selection of electrical and electronics wires and cables'. *OEM Design*.
Seccombe, G. H. (2 Jan. 1975) 'EEC and cable standards – where are we going?'

Electr. Times (4312), 6, 13.
Todd, D. (Sep. 1975) 'Electric cable for signalling and track-to-train communications'. *Railw. Eng. J.* **4** (5), 71–73.
Bungay, E. W. G. and Hollingsworth, P. M. (2 Apr. 1976) 'Progress with harmonisation of cables standards within CENELEC'. *Electr. Times* (4373), 7–8.
(18 Nov. 1977) 'Selecting the correct cable conductor size based on voltage drop, short-circuit capacity and strength'. *Electr. Times*.
(2 Dec. 1977) 'Selecting cables for the hostile conditions on construction sites'. *Electr. Times* (4454), 12–14.
(4 Aug. 1978) 'Compatibility of PVC cables'. *Electr. Times* (4485), 3.
Town, W. L. (23 Feb. 1979) 'Using extrudable materials for insulating cables'. *Electr. Times* (4511), 10–12.

Mineral insulated cables

Tomlinson, F. W. and Wright, H. M. (Aug. 1946) 'Mineral-insulated metal-sheathed conductors'. *IEE J., Part II* **93** (34).
Jordan, C. A. and Eager, G. S. (Jan.–Feb. 1955) 'Mineral-insulated metallic-sheathed cables'. *AIEE Winter Meeting*.
(9 Jun. 1967) 'Protective multiple earthing – economic advantages of sheath return concentric wiring'. *Elect. Rev.* **180** (23).
Lorch, H. R. (11 Sep. 1969) 'Earthed concentric wiring – M.I. cable suitable for factory distribution'. *Electr. Times*.
Latham, W. B. (2 Apr. 1976) 'Mineral insulated cables in hazardous areas'. *Electr. Times*.
Milles, E. (May 1976) 'Mineral insulated metal sheathed cables'. *Wire Ind.*
Wilson, I. O. (Sep. 1979) 'Magnesium oxide as a high temperature insulant in insulated cables'. *Proc. 3rd Int. Conf. on Dielectric Materials*, pp. 78–81.
Wilson, I. O. (Apr. 1981) 'Magnesium oxide as a high temperature insulant'. *Proc. IEE, Part A* **128** (3), 159–164.

PART 3: DISTRIBUTION-SYSTEMS AND CABLES

Distribution systems

Taylor, H. G. (1937; 1941) 'The use of protective multiple earthing and ELCBs in rural areas'. *Proc. IEE* **81**; **88** (2).
(9 Jun. 1967) 'Protective multiple earthing – general principles and economic advantages of sheath return concentric wiring'. *Electr. Rev.*
Brown, F. J. and Fisher, J. (1971) *The Development of Interconnected Networks in the City of Liverpool and its Environs*. Liège: CIRED.
Cole, J. E. H. (Sep. 1972) 'Standardisation of plant and equipment for public electricity supply'. *Proc. IEE* **119** (9), 1319–1328.
Ford, D. V. (1972) 'The British Electricity Board's national fault and interruption reporting scheme – objectives, development and operating experience'. *IEEE Power Eng. Soc. Winter Meeting, New York*. Paper No. T72 082–1.
Gosden, J. H. (1973) *Reliability of Overhead Line and Cable Systems in Great Britain*. London: CIRED.

Milne, A. G. (Jan. 1974) 'Distribution of electricity (presidential address)'. *Proc. IEE* **121** (1).

Ross, A. (Nov. 1974) 'Cable practice in electricity board distribution networks: 132 kV and below', *Proc. IEE (IEE Rev).* **121** (11 R).

Cridlin, J. M., Stevens, R. H. and Thue, W. A. (1978) 'Performance of URD primary cable'. *USA Reliability Conference Electric Power Industry*, pp. 80–91.

Dickie, R. A. *et al.* (Jul. 1978) 'An examination of underground electric power distribution in residential areas'. *IEEE PES Summer Meeting, Los Angeles.*

Freund, A. (Apr. 1979) 'Distribution systems – grounded or ungrounded?' *Electr. Constr. Maint.* 67–71.

Minsart, G. and Steyaert, R. (1985) 'New trends in the planning of MV supply systems'. CIRED Paper No. 6.11.

Atkinson, W. C. and Ellis, F. E. (1987) 'Electricity distribution – asset replacement considerations'. *Electron Power.*

Power cables (general)

Wanser, G. (Feb. 1969) 'Experience with plastic-insulated cables in Germany'. *Wire* (99), 10–15.

Lacoste, A., Lagarde, R. and Michel, R. (1970) 'LV cables used in the French distribution system'. *Proc. IEE/ERA Distribution Cable Conf.*, pp. 341–349.

Bax, H. (1971) *Modern LV Cables for the Distribution Networks of Power Supply Companies and Industry (Germany).* Liège: CIRED.

McAllister, D. and Cox, E. H. (Apr. 1972) 'Behaviour of MV power distribution cables when subjected to external damage'. *Proc. IEE* **119** (4), 479–486.

Lacoste, A., Lemainque, H. and Schmeltz, J. (1973) *French Distribution Cable Techniques – Present Practices and Future Trends*, Part 1, pp. 92–101, London: CIRED.

Ross, A. (Nov. 1974) 'Cable practice in electricity board distribution. 132 kV and below'. *Proc. IEE (IEE Rev.)* **121** (11 R), 1307–1344.

Wanser, G. (May–Jun. 1974) 'Power cables – present and future'. *Wire* **24** (E3/74), 135–138.

Blechschmidt, H. H. and Goedecke, H. P. (1975) 'Cables with synthetic insulation in the Federal Republic of Germany'. Liège: CIRED Paper No. 36.

Bungay, E. W. G., Philbrick, S. E., Morgan, A. M. and Sloman, L. M. (1975) 'The development of ll kV cable systems'. Liège: CIRED Paper No. 37.

Giusseni, A., Maciotta, G., Portineri, G. and Leonardi, E. (1975) 'Present trends and modern design criteria for low and medium voltage distribution cables with extruded insulation in Italy'. Liège: CIRED Paper No. 35.

Gosden, J. H. (1975) 'Reliability of overhead lines and cable systems in Great Britain'. Liège: CIRED Paper No. 40.

Gosden, J. H. and Walker, A. J. (May 1976) 'The reliability of cable circuits for 11 kV and below'. *IEE Conf. on Distribution Cables, and Jointing Techniques, etc.*, pp. 1–4.

Paper insulated cables

Reynolds, E. H. and Rogers, E. C. (Oct. 1961) 'Discharge damage and failure in 11 kV belted cables'. *Trans. S. Afr. Inst. Electr. Eng.* **52** (10).

Terramosi, P. and Couppe, G. L. (May 1971) 'Developments in non-draining cables'. *Wire Wire Prod.* 95–107.

Swarbrick, P. (14 Dec. 1973) 'Developments in 11 kV underground cable systems. Paper-insulated aluminium-sheathed cables and resin filled joints'. *Electr. Rev.*

Bungay, E. W. G. and Philbrick, S. E. (May 1976) 'Paper insulated 11 kV aluminium sheathed cables'. *IEE Conf. on Distribution Cables.*

Bulens, R. *et al.* (1983) 'Ageing and permissible load of paper insulated medium voltage cables'. CIRED Paper No. 4.06.

Domun, M. (1986) 'Prediction of remaining life of H. V. cables', Part 2, 'Accelerated life tests in the laboratory'. *2nd IEE Int. Conf. on Power Cables, 10 kV–180 kV.*

Harrison, B. J. (1986) 'Some aspects of failure of 33 kV H-type oil–rosin impregnated cables'. *2nd IEE Int. Conf. on Power Cables, 10 kV–180 kV.*

Polymeric cables below 6 kV

Oestreich, U. (May 1959) 'High voltage Protodur cables for rated voltages above 10 kV'. *Siemens-Z.* **33**, 341–345.

Booth, D. H., Hollingsworth, P. M. and Lythgoe, W. H. (Nov. 1962) 'PVC power cables. Their design and manufacture'. *IEE Symp. on Plastic Insulated Mains Cable Systems.*

Swarbrick, P. (28 Jan. 1977) 'Development in the manufacture of XLPE cables'. *Electr. Rev.*

Cables with combined neutral and earth

Booth, D. H. (1970) 'Some considerations relevant to the design of underground power cable systems for use with PME'. *IEE/ERA Conf. on Distribution, Edinburgh.*

Henderson, J. T. and Swarbrick, P. (1970) 'The Consac cable system'. *IEE/ERA Conf. on Distribution, Edinburgh.*

Hughes, O. I. and Bramley, G. E. A. (1970) 'Development and production of a PME elastomeric insulated MV cable'. *IEE/ERA Conf. on Distribution, Edinburgh.*

Majewski, H. A. (1970) 'Special design features with aluminium-sheathed MV power cables'. *IEE/ERA Conf. on Distribution, Edinburgh.*

Rockcliffe, R. H., Hill, E. and Booth, D. H. (1971) 'Protective earthing practices in the UK and their associated underground cable systems'. *IEEE Conf. on Power Distribution*. Paper No. 71C 42–PWR.

McAllister, D. and Cox, E. H. (Apr. 1972) 'Behaviour of MV power distribution cables when subjected to external damage'. *Proc. IEE* **119** (4), 479–486.

Radcliffe, W. S. and McAllister, D. (24 Mar. 1972) 'Cables and joints for PME distribution systems'. *Electr. Rev.*

Garmory, T. H. (15 Nov. 1974) 'Efficiency in electricity distribution. Experience with wave form cables'. *Electr. Rev.*

Baldock, A. T. and Hambrook, L. G. (May 1976) 'Regulations relevant to the design and utilisation of distribution cables for the Electrical Supply Industry and the consumer'. *IEE Conf. on Distribution Cables up to 11 kV.*

Burton, J. M. (May 1976) 'Consac cable system development in the Midlands Electricity Board'. *IEE Conf. on Distribution.*

Geer, P. K. and Sloman, L. M. (May 1976) 'Cables for PME distribution systems'.

IEE Conf. on Distribution.

Kerney, J. M. (May 1976) 'Experience in Ireland with four-core unscreened elastomeric cables'. *IEE Conf. on Distribution.*

Polymeric insulated cables – 6 kV to 60 kV

Devaux, A., Oudin, J. M., Rerolle, Y., Jocteur, R., Noirclerc, A. and Osty, M. (1968) 'Reliability and development towards high-voltage synthetic insulated cables'. CIGRE Paper No. 21–20 (in two parts).

Tabata, T., Nagai, H., Fukuda, T. and Iwata, Z. (Jul.–Aug. 1972) 'Sulphide attack and treeing of polyethylene insulated cables – cause and prevention'. *IEEE Trans.* **PAS–91** (4), 1354–1360.

Vahlstrom, W. (May–Jun. 1972) 'Investigations of insulation deterioration in 15 kV and 22 kV polyethylene cables removed from service'. *IEEE Trans.* **PAS–91** (3), 1023–1035.

Lawson, J. H. and Vahlstrom, W. (Mar.–Apr. 1973) 'Investigation of insulation deterioration in 15 kV and 22 kV cables removed from service' Part 2. *IEEE Trans.* **PAS–92** (2), 824–835.

Bahder, G., Katz, C. and Lawson, J. H. (May–Jun. 1974) 'Electrical and electrochemical treeing effect in polyethylene and crosslinked polyethylene cables'. *IEEE Trans.* **PAS–93** (3), 977–991.

Tanaka, T., Fukuda, S., Suzuki, Y., Nitta, Y., Goto, H. and Kubato, K. (Mar.–Apr. 1974) 'Water trees in crosslinked polyethylene power cables'. *IEEE Trans.* **PAS–93** (2), 693–702.

Hyde, H. B., Philbrick, S. E., Roberts, B. E. and Smith, T. (May 1976) 'Earth fault spiking tests at system voltage on 11 kV polymeric cables'. *IEE Conf. on Distribution Cables and Jointing Techniques*, pp. 83–86.

McKean, A. L. *et al.* (Jul. 1976) 'Investigation of mechanism of breakdown in XLPE cables'. EPRI Report No. TD–138 (Final Report).

Eichhorn, R. M. (Feb. 1977) 'Treeing in solid extruded electrical insulation'. *IEEE Trans.* **EI–12** (1), 2–18.

Bernstein, B. S. (Nov. 1978) 'Research to determine the acceptable emergency operating temperatures for extruded dielectric cables'. EPRI Report No. EL–938.

Chan, J. C. (Dec. 1978) 'Electrical performance of oven-dried XLPE cables'. *IEEE Trans.* **EI–13** (6), 444–447.

Densley, R. J. (Oct. 1978) 'The impulse strength of naturally aged XLPE cables containing water trees'. *IEEE Trans.* EI–13 (5), 389–391.

Jacobsen, C. T., Attermo, R. and Dellby, B. (1978) 'Experience of dry-cured XLPE-insulated high voltage cables'. Paris: CIGRE Paper No. 21–06.

Srinivas, N. N. and Doepken, H. C. (Jun. 1978) 'Electrochemical treeing in PE and XLPE insulated cables – frequency effects and impulse degradation'. *IEEE Int. Symp. on Electrical Insulation.* pp. 106–109.

Yoshimitsu, T. and Nakakita, T. (Jun. 1978) 'New findings on water tree in high polymer insulating materials'. *IEEE Int. Symp. on Electrical Insulation*, pp. 116–121.

Bernadelli, P., Bolognesi, F., Nosca, W. and Zanetti, O. (1979) '*Significance and problems concerned with laboratory tests on power cables and relevant accessories for distribution systems'*. Liège: CIRED Paper No. 30.

Bruggemann, H., Schuppe, W.-D. and Wichmann, H. (1979) *Polymeric insulated LV cables with XLPE as insulant used in public distribution networks in Germany'*. Liège: CIRED Paper No. 32.

Densley, R. S. *et al.* (Jun. 1979) 'The surge characteristics of XLPE insulation containing water trees'. *IEEE Symp. on Electrical Insulation*, pp. 204–207.

Doepken, H. C., McKean, A. L. and Singer, M. L. (Apr. 1979) 'Treeing, insulation material and cable life'. *IEEE Power Engineering Society 7th Transmission and Distribution Conf.*, pp. 299–304.

Ferran, J. and Pinet, A. (1979) 'Development of a new 20 kV cable with synthetic insulation and of its fitting'. Liège: CIRED Paper No. 31.

Horton, W. F. and St. John, A. N. (Apr. 1979) 'The failure rate of polyethylene-insulated cable'. *IEEE Power Engineering Society 7th Transmission and Distribution Conf.*, pp. 324–328.

Lanctoe, T. P., Lawson, J. H. and McVey, W. L. (May–Jun. 1979) 'Investigation of insulation deterioration in 15 kV and 22 kV polyethylene cables removed from service', Part 3. *IEEE Trans.* **PAS–98** (3), 912–925.

Naybour, R. D. (Sep. 1979) 'The growth of water trees in XLPE at operating stresses and their influence on cable life'. *IEE 3rd Int. Conf. on Dielectric Materials*, pp. 238–241.

Pinet, A. and Paris, M. (1979) 'New 20 kV cable of the French MV power system'. *IEEE PES Summer Meeting, Vancouver*. Paper No. A79408–6.

Silver, D. A. and Martin, M. A. (Apr. 1979) 'Progress in overcoming electrochemical treeing'. *Transm. Distr.* **31** (4).

Sletbak, J. (Jul.–Aug. 1979) 'A theory of water tree initiation and growth'. *IEEE Trans.* **PAS–98** (4), 1358–1366.

Doepken, H. C. and Klinger, Y. (Jun. 1980) 'Correlation of water tree theories with experimental data'. *IEEE Symp. on Electrical Insulation*, pp. 208, 211.

Fukuda, T. *et al.* (Jun. 1980) 'Factors governing the voltage breakdown of insulating materials for XLPE insulated cables'. *IEEE Symp. on Electrical Insulation*, pp. 118–121.

Lawson, J. H. and Thue, W. A. (Jun. 1980) 'Summary of service failure of high voltage extruded dielectric insulated cables in the USA'. *IEEE Symp. on Electrical Insulation*, pp. 100–103.

Martin, M. A. and Hartlein, R. A. (1980) 'Correlation of electrochemical treeing in power cables removed from service and in cables tested in the laboratory'. *IEE Trans.* **PAS–99**, 1597–1605.

Namiki, Y., Shimanuki, H., Aida, F. and Morita, M. (Dec. 1980) 'A study of microvoids and their filling in crosslinked polyethylene insulated cables'. *IEEE Trans.* **EI–15** (6), 473–480.

Nunes, S. L. and Shaw, M. T. (Dec. 1980) 'Water treeing in polyethylene – a review of mechanisms'. *IEEE Trans.* **EI–5** (6), 437–450.

Wartusch, J. (Jun. 1980) 'Increased voltage endurance of polyolefine insulating materials by means of voltage stabilisers'. *IEEE Symp. on Electrical Insulation*, pp. 216–221.

Bahder, G., Katz, C. *et al.* (1981) 'Life expectancy of XLPE cables rated 15 to 35 kV'. *IEE Trans.* **PAS–100**, 1581–1590.

Bulinski, A. and Densly, R. (1981) 'The voltage breakdown characteristics of miniature XLPE cables containing water trees'. *IEE Trans.* **EI–16** (4), 319–326.

Lanfranconi, G. M., Metra, P. and Vecellio, B. (1981) 'MV power cables with extruded insulation. A comparison between XLPE and EPR'. CIRED Paper.

Bahder, G., Garrity, T. *et al.* (1982) 'Physical model of electric ageing and breakdown of extruded polymeric insulated power cables'. *IEE Trans.* **PAS–100**, 1379–1390.

Hayami, T. *et al.* (1982) 'Relation between water content and bow-tie tree generation in XLPE cables'. *15th Symp. on Electrical Insulating Materials*, pp. 4–7.

Ball, E. H., Bungay, E. W. G. and Sloman, L. M. (1983) 'Polymeric cables for high voltage distribution systems'. CIRED Paper No. d.11.

Bloemer, B. (1983) 'Experiences with 20 kV single-core plastic (XLPE) cables'. CIRED Paper No. d.10.

Brown, M. (1983) 'Performance of EPR in medium and high voltage power cable'. *IEE Trans.* **PAS-102** (2).

Cochini, E. *et al.* (1983) 'Thermal, mechanical and electrical properties of EPR insulation in power cables'. *IEE Trans.* **PAS–102** (7).

Laar, A. V. D. *et al.* (1983). 'Experience with XLPE insulated cable with solid aluminium conductors'. CIRED Paper No. d.13.

Occini, E. *et al.* (1983) 'Thermal, mechanical and electrical properties of EPR insulations in power cables'. *IEE Winter Meeting 1983*. Paper No. WM 00.

Sletbak, J. and Ildstad, E. (1983) 'Effect of service and test conditions on water tree growth in XLPE cables'. *IEE Trans.* **PAS–102** (7), 2069–2074.

Travers, R. and Reidy, P. (1983) 'Medium voltage distribution cables using XLPE insulation – Irish experience'. CIRED Paper No. d.12.

Brown, M. (1984) 'Performance of EPR insulation in medium and high voltage power cables'. Jicable Conference Paper No. B1–2.

Farneti, F. *et al.* (1984) 'Performance of EPR insulated cables under different laying conditions and unusual thermal stresses'. Jicable Conference Paper No. A3–3.

Franke, H. *et al.* (1984) 'Testing possibilities and results regarding water ageing of PE/XLPE insulated MV cables'. Jicable Conference Paper No. A6–3.

Katz, C., Eager, G. S., Leber, E. R. and Fischer, F. E. (1984) 'Influence of water on dielectric strength and rejuvenation of in-service aged URD cables'. Jicable Conference Paper No. A6-5.

Nagasaki, S. *et al.* (1984) 'Life estimation and improvement of water-tree resistivity of XLPE cables'. Jicable Conference Paper No. A6–2.

Ratra, M. C. (1984) 'Some aspects of compatibility and short circuit characteristics of MV polymeric cables'. Jicable Conference Paper No. A3–1.

Ross, A. (1984) 'Developments in medium voltage polymeric cables'. Jicable Conference Paper No. A1–4.

Schuppe, W. F. (1984) 'Progress with XLPE medium voltage cables in the Federal Republic of Germany'. Jicable Conference Paper No. A2–1.

Silver, D. A. and Lukac, R. G. (1984) 'Factors affecting the dielectric strength of extruded dielectric cables in wet environments'. Jicable Conference Paper No. A6–1.

Takenouch, K. *et al.* (1984) 'Experience in service of 66 kV XLPE power cables'. Jicable Conference Paper No. B6–1.

Tanabe, T. *et al.* (1984) 'Water tree deterioration and counter measure of medium voltage XLPE cables'. Jicable Conference Paper No. A6–4.

Ball, E. H., Metra, P. and Ortiz, M. R. (1986) 'Extruded cable insulation for wet

locations'. *2nd IEE Int. Conf. on Power Cables 10 kV–180 kV.*
Bergin, T. E. *et al.* (1986) 'Review of 66 kV XLPE cables in the State of Bahrein'. *2nd IEE Int. Conf. on Power Cables 10 kV–180 kV.*
Billing, J. W. (1986) 'Diagnostic investigation into XLPE HV cable insulation'. *2nd IEE Int. Conf. on Power Cables 10 kV–180 kV.*
Field, A. W., Nicholls, A. W. and Marsh, G. C. (1986) 'Effect of water on the life of extruded dielectric cables'. *2nd IEE Int. Conf. on Power Cables 10 kV–180 kV.*
Howard, R. S., Jenkins, T. and Brook, R. T. (1986) 'Operating experience with 11 kV polymeric cable systems in one U.K. Area Board'. *2nd IEE Int. Conf. on Power Cables 10 kV–180 kV.*
Hyde, H. B., Poideven, G. J. and Philbrick, S. E. (1986) 'Development of a single-core polymeric cable for 33 kV distribution systems'. *2nd IEE Int. Conf. on Power Cables 10 kV–180 kV.*
Naybour, R. D. (1986) 'Influence of water on the life of polymeric insulated cables'. *2nd IEE Int. Conf. on Power Cables 10 kV–180 kV.*
Pinet, A. and Ferron, J. (Nov. 1986) 'Operating experience with the 20 kV cable used in the French network'. *2nd IEE Int. Conf. on Power Cables 10 kV–180 kV.*
Steenis, E. F. and Boone, W. (1986) 'Water treeing in service aged and accelerated aged XLPE cables'. *2nd IEE Int. Conf. on Power Cables 10 kV–180 kV.*
White, T. M., Bungay, E. W. G. *et al.* (1986) '11 kV polymeric insulated triplex cable'. *2nd IEE Int. Conf. on Power Cables 10 kV–180 KV.*
Fernetti, F. *et al.* (1987) 'Characterisation of extruded insulation cables with respect to water'. Jicable Conference Paper.
Harasawa, K. *et al.* (1987) 'Influence of d.c. voltage application on dielectric performance of XLPE cables'. Jicable Conference Paper.
Jinno, M. *et al.* (1987) 'Present conditions of XLPE cables used in Japan and cable fault analysis'. Jicable Conference Paper.
Ortiz, M. R. *et al.* (1987) 'EPR high voltage cables'. Jicable Conference Paper.

Manufacture

Thomas, B. and Bowrey, M. (May 1977) 'Cross-linked polyethylene insulations using the Sioplas technology'. *Wire J.*
Altonen, M. (Jun 1978) 'Completely dry curing and cooling process'. *Wire J.*
Smart, G. (May 1978) 'PLCV system: pressurised liquid salt continuous vulcanisation'. *Wire J.*
Bickel, H. D., Hellmann, K. and Wiedermann, R. (1980) 'Peroxidal crosslinking procedure for PE insulated cores of 1 kV cables without pressure (salt bath)'. *Wire* **29** (2), 75–80.
Kertscher, E. (Jan.–Feb. 1980) 'Continuous methods of polyethylene insulation of conductors'. *Wire World Int.* **22**.
Hochstrasser, U. P. (1984) 'A new one-step crosslinking process for MV cables'. Jicable Conference Paper No. All–3.

Installation

Holttum, W. (1955) 'The installation of metal sheathed cables on spaced supports'. *Proc. IEE, Part A* **102** 729–742.
Muhleman, C. E. (5 May 1976) 'Cable pulling'. *IEEE Conf. Rec., Pulp and Paper Industry Tech. Conf., Boston* pp., 15–21.
Hazard, M. T. (Jan. 1980) 'Installation of long lengths (of coal mining cables)'. *Min. Tech.*
Ferron, J., Pinet, A. and Pichon, L. (1985) 'Use of mechanical devices in France for narrow trenches and the laying of underground cables'. CIRED Paper No. 3.08.

Jointing and accessories

Crossland, J. (May 1976) 'Joints on 3-core 11 kV paper insulated cables'. *IEE Conf. on Distribution.*
McAllister, D. and Radcliffe, W. S. (May 1976) 'Joints incorporating mechanical connectors and cast resin filling for 600/1000 V cables'. *IEE Conf. on Distribution.*
Ross, A. (May 1976) 'Jointing trials and tests on 11 kV aluminium sheathed cables'. *IEE Conf. on Distribution.*
Radcliffe, W. S. and Roberts, B. E. (May 1978) 'Resin-filled joints for 11 kV paper insulated cables'. *IEE Conf. on Distribution.*
Jorgensen, J. and Nielsen, O. J. (1979) *Straight Joints for Solid Dielectric Insulated Cables, 12–170 kV.* Liège: CIRED.
Naybour, R. D. and Brailsford, J. R. (1979) 'A new type of test for connectors to be used on aluminium conductors'. *Proc. IEE* **126** (10), 991–994.
Ross, A. and Philbrick, S. E. (1981) 'Development of joints for polymeric distribution cables. IEE Conference Publication No. 197, CIRED.
Steckel, R. D. and Eertig, K. (1981) 'Joint boxes for transition from paper to plastic MV cables'. IEE Conference Publication No. 197, CIRED.
Wilk, M., Rupprecht, W. and Bottcher, B. (1981) 'Heat shrinkable terminations and joints for HV power cables'. IEE Conference Publication No. 197, CIRED.
Chatterjee, S. (1984) 'Premoulded cable connector system for today and tomorrow'. Jicable Conference Paper No. C–6.
Sander, D. (1984) 'New solutions in connecting, tap-off, energising and measuring in MV networks'. Jicable Conference Paper No. C–1.
Varner, W. F. (1984) 'Development of factory moulded splices to meet the requirements of advanced synthetic insulated MV cable designs'. Jicable Conference Paper No. C–9.
Bruggemann, H. *et al.* (1985) 'State of the art of plug-in cable connectors for MV cables in the Federal Republic of Germany'. CIRED Paper No. 3.12.
Philbrick, S. E. *et al.* (1985) 'Elastic rubber terminations for MV cables'. CIRED Paper No. 3.13.
Bartle, J. and Parr, J. C. (1986) 'Review of installation and service experience of resin joints on 11 kV paper cable'. *2nd IEE Int. Conf. on Power Cables 10 kV–180 kV.*
Franks, R. (1986) 'MV elastic accessories up to 36 kV'. *2nd IEE Int. Conf. on Power Cables 10 kV–180 kV.*
Friday, A. and Banks, V. A. A. (1986) 'Performance of joint designs for 11 kV and

33 kV polymeric cable'. *2nd IEE Int. Conf. on Power Cables 10 kV–180 kV.*
Hey, S. A. and Weatherley, J. W. (1986) 'New separable plant terminations for paper and polymeric cables up to 24 kV'. *2nd IEE Conf. on Power Cables 10 kV–180 kV.*
Ross, A. (1986) 'Practical jointing for medium voltage polymeric cables'. *2nd IEE Int. Conf. on Power Cables 10 kV–180 kV.*
Weatherley, J. W., Parry, M. H. and Hey, S. A. (1986) 'Advances in jointing systems up to 36 kV using heat shrinkable components'. *2nd IEE Int. Conf. on Power Cables 10 kV–180 kV.*
Weatherley, J. W. *et al.* (1986) 'Heat shrinkable terminations for 66 kV polymeric cables'. *2nd IEE Int. Conf. on Power Cables 10 kV–180 kV.*

Testing

Kreuger, F. H. (1964) *Discharge Detection in High Voltage Equipment.* Heywood.
Working Group 21–01 (1968) 'Discharge measurements in long lengths of cable; prevention of errors due to superposition of travelling waves'. Paris: CIGRE Paper No. 21–01, Appendix 4, pp. 23–25.
Mole, G. (Feb. 1970) 'Measurement of the magnitude of internal corona in cables'. *Trans. IEEE* **PAS–89** (2), 204–212.
Working Group 21–03 (Aug. 1970) 'Elimination of interference in discharge detection'. Paris: CIGRE.
Black, I. A. (Mar. 1973) 'A pulse discrimination system for discharge measurements on equipment operating in a power system'. *IEE Diagnostic Testing Conf.*, pp. 1–7.
Bowdler, G. W. (1973) *Measurements in High Voltage Test Circuits.* Oxford: Pergamon.
Wilson, A. (Mar. 1973) 'The application of correlation analysis in partial discharge measurements'. *IEE Diagnostic Testing Conf.* pp. 8–12.
Wilson, A. (Sep. 1974) 'Discharge detection under noisy conditions'. *Proc. IEE* **121** (9), 993–996.
Mason, J. H. (Jul. 1975) 'Discharge detection and measurements'. *Proc. IEE* **112** (7), 1407–1423.
Smith, A. P. (1984) 'Location of partial discharges in drum length cables'. Jicable Conference Paper No. C–20.
Szaloky, G. and Schwarz, M. (1984) 'Measuring and locating of partial discharges in power cables'. Jicable Conference Paper No. C–21.
Wilson, A. and Swingler, S. G. (1984) 'A.c. test methods used for 11 kV extruded cable in CEGB power stations'. Jicable Conference Paper No. A4–3.
Herstad, K. and Sletbak, J. (1985) 'Effect of increased test voltage on the performance of MV XLPE cables'. CIRED Paper No. 3.16.
Hilder, D. A. and Black, I. A. (1988) 'Noise suppression methods for partial discharge measurements on cables'. *5th IEE Int. Conf. on Dielectric Materials.*
Kearley, S. S. and Mackinley, R. R. (1988) 'Discharge measurements in cables using a solid state 30 kV bipolar low frequency generator'. *5th IEE Int. Conf. on Dielectric Materials.*
Mackinley, R. R. and Peters, G. (1988) 'New methods of partial discharge detection and location'. *5th IEE Conf. on Dielectric Materials.*

Fault incidence and location

Gooding, H. T. and Briant, T. A. (1962) 'Location of serving defects in buried cables'. *Proc. IEE, Part A* **109**, 124–125.

Gooding, H. T. and Briant, T. A. (1962) 'Location of gas leaks in buried pressure cable systems'. *Proc. IEE, Part A* **109**, 126–128.

Gooding, H. T. (1963) 'Cable fault location on power systems'. *Proc. IEE* **113** (1), 111–119.

Gale, P. F. (Apr. 1975) 'Cable fault location by impulse current method'. *Proc. IEE* **122**, 403–408.

Gosden, J. H. (1975) 'Reliability of overhead lines and cable systems in Great Britain'. Liège: CIRED.

Gosden, J. H. and Walker, A. J. (May 1976) 'The reliability of cable circuits for 11 kV and below'. *IEE Conf. on Distribution*.

PART 4: TRANSMISSION CABLES AND SYSTEMS

Transmission cables (general)

Thornton, E. P. G. and Booth, D. H. (Jun. 1959) 'The design and performance of the gas-filled cable system'. *Proc. IEE, Part A* **106** (27).

Burrel, R. W. and Young, F. S. (1971) 'EEI and manufacturers 500/550 kV cable research project, Waltz Mill test facility'. *IEEE Trans.* **PAS–90**.

Endacott, J. D. (1973) 'Underground power cables'. *Phil. Trans. R. Soc. A* **275**, 193–203.

Ray, J. J., Arkell, C. A. and Flack, H. W. (1973) '525 kV self-contained oil-filled cable systems for Grand Coulee third powerplant – design and development'. IEEE Paper No. T73, pp. 492–496.

Endacott, J. D., Arkell, C. A., Cox, H. N. and Roulston, R. J. (1974) 'Progress in the use of aluminium in duct and direct buried installations of power transmission cable'. *IEEE Underground Transmission and Distribution Conf.*, pp. 466–474.

Bahder, G., Corry, A. F., Blodgett, R. B., McIlveen, E. E. and McKean, A. L. (1976) '500 kV HPOF pipe cable development in the USA'. Paris: CIGRE Paper No. 21–11.

Miranda, F. J. and Gazzana Prioroggia, P. (Mar. 1976) 'Self-contained oil-filled cables, a review of progress'. *Proc. IEE* **123** (3), 229–238.

Arkell, C. A., Blake, W. E., Brealy, A. D. R., Hacke, K. J. H. and Hance, G. E. A. (May 1977) 'Design and construction of the 400 kV cables system for the Severn Tunnel'. *Proc. IEE* **124** (3), 303–316.

Miranda, F. J. and Gazzana Prioroggia, P. (Feb. 1977) 'Recent advances in self-contained oil-filled cable systems'. *IEE Electr. Power*, 136–140.

Occhini, E., Tellarini, M. and Maschio, G. (1978) 'Self-contained oil-filled cable systems for 750 kV and 1100 kV. Design and tests'. Paris: CIGRE Paper No. 21–03.

Shimshock, J. F. (Nov. 1978) 'Installed cost comparison for self-contained and pipe-type cable'. EPRI Report No. EL–935.

Beale, H. K. (June 1979) 'Underground cables for HV power transmission'. *CEGB Res.*, 24–32.

Bossi, A., Sesto, E., Luoni, G. and Dechini, E. (Sep. 1979) 'The oil-filled cable for the 1000 kV project – ratings and field tests'. *2nd IEE Conf. Progress Cables for 220 kV and Above.*

Head, J. G., Gale, P. S. and Lawson, W. G. (1979) 'Effects of high temperature and electric stress on the degradation of oil-filled cable insulation'. *3rd Int. Conf. on Dielectric Materials.*

Heumann, H., Oppermann, G., Arkell, C. A. and Mayhew, P. L. (Sep. 1979) '380 kV oil-filled cable for municipal power supply of Vienna'. *2nd IEE Int. Conf. Progress Cables for 220 kV and Above.*

Itoh, H., Nakagawa, M. and Ichino, T. (Sep. 1979) 'EHV self-contained oil-filled cable insulated with composite paper, DCLP'. *2nd IEE Int. Conf. Progress Cables for 220 kV and Above.*

Lawson, W. G. (Sep. 1979) 'Fatigue and creep phenomena in oil-filled supertension cables'. *2nd IEE Int. Conf. Progress Cables for 220 kV and Above.*

Rosevear, R. D. and Vecellio, B. (Sep. 1979) 'Cables for 750/1100 kV transmission'. *2nd IEE Int. Conf. Progress Cables for 220 kV and Above.*

Gibbons, J. A. M., Saunders, S. A. and Stannett, A. W. (Nov. 1980) 'Role of metal debris in the performance of stop-joints as used in 275 kV and 400 kV self-contained oil-filled cable circuits'. *Proc. IEE, Part C* **127** (6), 406–419.

Skipper, D. J. and Arrighi, R. (Jan. 1981) 'Progress report of CIGRE Study Committee 21 – HV insulated cables'. *Electra* (54), 9–18.

Hance, G. E. A. (1986) 'The modern self-contained OF cable system for voltages up to 180 kV'. *2nd IEE Int. Conf. on Power Cables 10 kV–180 kV.*

Smee, G. J. and West, R. S. V. (1986) 'Factors influencing the choice between paper and XLPE insulated cables'. *2nd IEE Int. Conf. on Power Cables 10 kV–180 kV.*

Leufkens, P. P. and Wegbrans, B. H. M. (1988) 'Cross-bonding and a special interruption joint for HV XLPE cable'. Paris: CIGRE Paper No. 21–04.

D.C. transmission cables

Maschio, G. and Occhini, E. (1974) 'High voltage d.c. cables – the state of the art'. Paris: CIGRE Paper No. 21.

Bahder, G. *et al.* (1978) 'Development of ± 400 kV/± 600 kV and medium pressure OF paper insulated d.c. power cable systems'. *IEEE Trans.* **PAS–97**.

Allam, E. M. and McKean, A. L. (Sep.–Oct. 1980) 'Design of an optimised ± 600 kV d.c. cable system'. *IEEE Trans.* **PAS–99** (5).

Allam, E. M. and McKean, A. L. (Mar. 1981) 'Laboratory developments of ± 600 kV d.c. pipe type cable'. *IEEE Trans.* **PAS–100** (3), 1219–1225.

Arkell, C. A. and Parsons, A. F. (1981) 'Insulation design of self-contained OF cables for d.c. operation'. *IEEE Trans.* **PAS–101**, 1805–1813.

Fukagawa, H. *et al.* (1981) 'Insulation properties of 250 kV d.c. XLPE cables'. *IEE Trans.* **PAS–100** (7), 3175.

Sakamoto, Y. *et al.* (1981) 'Development of 500 kV d.c. self-contained OF cable'. *IEE Trans.* **PAS–100** (4), 1949.

Fukagawa, H. *et al.* (1984) 'Development of a new insulating material for d.c. XLPE cables'. Jicable Conference Paper No. B3–2.

Pays, M. *et al.* (1988) 'Behaviour of extruded HVDC power transmission cables: tests on materials and cables'. Paris: CIGRE Paper No. 21–07.

Polymeric insulated transmission cables

Mott, R. P. (1975) 'Status of 138 kV solid dielectric cables being evaluated at Waltz Mill'. *IEEE Winter Meeting*. Paper No. C75 007–0.

Corbett, J. T. (May 1976) 'Experience with 138 kV XLPE insulated cable'. *Transm. Distrib.*

Bahder, E. *et al.* (1978) 'Development of extruded cables for EHV applications in the range 138–400 kV'. Paris: CIGRE Paper No. 21–11.

Jacobsen, C. T. *et al.* (1978) 'Experience of dry-cured XLPE insulated high voltage cables'. Paris: CIGRE Paper No. 21–06.

Dellby, B. *et al.* (Sep. 1979) 'Design and experience of PEX cables and accessories rated 220 kV'. *2nd IEE Int. Conf. Progress Cables for 220 kV and Above.*

Dorison, E. and Legall, Y. (Sep. 1979) 'French experience with polyethylene insulated high voltage cables'. *2nd IEE Int. Conf. Progress Cables for 220 kV and Above.*

Favrie, E. and Auclair, H. (Sep. 1979) '225 kV low density polyethylene insulated cables'. *2nd IEE Int. Conf. Progress Cables for 220 kV and Above.*

Kojima, K. *et al.* (1980) 'Development and commercial use of 275 kV XLPE power cable'. *IEEE Winter Meeting*, Paper No. F80, pp. 220–224.

Kojima, K. *et al.* (Jan. 1981) 'Development and commercial use of 275 kV XLPE power cable'. *IEEE Trans.* **PAS–100** (1), 203–210.

Shinoda, S. *et al.* (Mar. 1981) '275 kV XLPE insulated aluminium sheathed power cable for Oknyahagi No. 2 power station', *IEEE Trans.* **PAS–100** (3), 1298–1306.

Hosokawa, K. *et al.* (1982) 'Present situation of XLPE high voltage cables in Japan'. Paris: *CIGRE Paper* No. 21–09.

Nakagawa, H. *et al.* (1983) 'Installation of 275 kV XLPE cables in the long and steep slope tunnel'. *IEEE Summer Meeting*. Paper No. 83 SM 310.0.

Takoka, M. *et al.* (1983) 'Development of 275 kV cable system and prospect of 500 kV cable'. *IEEE Trans.* **PAS–102**, 3254–3264.

Ball, E. H. *et al.* (1984) 'Development of cross-linked polyethylene insulation for high voltage cables'. Paris: CIGRE Paper No. 21–01.

Nakagawa, H. *et al.* (1984) 'Development and installation of 154 kV XLPE cables'. Jicable Conference Paper No. B6–2.

Takaoka, M. *et al.* (1984) 'Development of 500 kV bulk power XLPE cables and accessories'. Jicable Conference Paper No. B7–3.

Watanabe, Y. *et al.* (1984) 'Actual installation of short distance 275 kV XLPE cables and technical development of long distance cables'. Jicable Conference Paper No. B6–3.

Wretemark, S. and Nelin, G. (1984) 'XLPE cable after long time service at EH voltage levels'. Jicable Conference Paper No. B7–1.

Kobayshi, T. *et al.* (1985) 'Development of 275 kV internally water-cooled XLPE cable'. *IEEE Trans.* **PAS–104**, 775–784.

Nakabasami, T. *et al.* (1985) 'Investigations of commercial use of 275 kV XLPE cables'. *IEEE Trans.* **PAS–104**, 1938.

Ball, E. H. *et al.* (1986) 'Development of XLPE insulation for high voltage cables'. Paris: CIGRE Paper No. 21–01.

Benford, D. F. and Ball, E. H. (1986) 'Use of 66 and 132 kV XLPE insulated cables for long circuit connections in London'. *2nd IEE Int. Conf. on Power Cables 10 kV–180 kV.*

Gregory, B. and Vail, J. (1986) 'Accessories for 66 kV and 132 kV XLPE cables'. *2nd IEE Int. Conf. on Power Cables 10 kV–180 kV.*

Harasawa, K. (1986) 'Studies on the application of 275 kV cables to long distance underground transmission in Japan'. Paris: CIGRE Paper No. 21–03.

Jocteur, R. (1986) 'Development of 400 kV links with low density polyethylene insulation'. Paris: CIGRE Paper No. 21–09.

Rosevear, R. D. *et al.* (1986) 'High voltage XLPE cable and accessories'. *2nd IEE Int. Conf. on Power Cables 10 kV–180 kV.*

Ghindes, H. *et al.* (1988) '161 kV HDPE insulated cable for Tel Aviv'. Paris: CIGRE Paper No. 21–02.

Head, J. G. *et al.* (1988) 'Thermo-mechanical characteristics of XLPE HV cable insulation'. *5th IEE Int. Conf. on Dielectric Materials.*

Nagasaki, S. *et al.* (1988) 'Philosophy of design and experience on high voltage XLPE cables and accessories in Japan'. Paris: CIGRE Paper No. 21–01.

Taralli, C. *et al.* (1988) 'High voltage EPR insulation cable system – manufacturing and installation characteristics'. Paris: CIGRE Paper No. 21–09.

Ratings and forced cooling

Arman, A. N., Cherry, D. M., Gosland, L. and Hollingsworth, P. M. (May 1964) 'The influence of soil moisture migration on power rating of cables in HV transmission systems'. *Proc. IEE* **111**, 1000–1016.

Ball, E. H., Occini, E. and Luoni, G. (Oct. 1965) 'Sheath overvoltages on high voltage cables resulting from special sheath bonding connections'. *IEEE Trans.* **PAS–84**.

Cox, H. N. and Coats, R. (Dec. 1965) 'Thermal analysis of power cables in soils of temperature responsive thermal resistivity'. *Proc. IEE* **112** (12).

Glick, D. *et al.* (1968) 'Design considerations on the current rating of joints for 275 and 400 oil-filled cables'. *IEE Conf. Progress Cables for 220 kV and Above.*

Gosling, C. T. *et al.* (1968) 'Practical considerations associated with cable systems cooled by external pipes'. *IEE Conf. Progress Cables for 220 kV and Above.*

Endacott, J. A. *et al.* (1970) 'Thermal design parameters used for high capacity EHV circuits in Great Britain'. Paris: CIGRE Paper No. 21–03.

Brooks, E. J., Gosling, C. H. and Holdup, W. (Jan. 1973) 'Moisture control of cable environments with particular reference to surface troughs'. *Proc. IEE* **120** (1).

Cox, H. N. *et al.* (1975) 'Developments in UK cable installation techniques to take account of enviromental thermal resistivity'. *Proc. IEE* **122** (11).

Arkell, C. A. *et al.* (1976) 'The development and application of forced cooling techniques to EHV cable systems in the UK'. Paris: CIGRE Paper No. 21–02.

Kojima, K. and Kubo, H. (1976) 'A study of internally cooled cable systems for bulk power underground transmission'. *IEEE Transmission and Distribution Conf.*

Mochlinksi, K. (1976) 'Assessment of the influence of soil thermal resistivity on the ratings of distribution cables'. *Proc. IEE* **123** (1), 60–72.

Williams, R. W. *et al.* (1976) 'Comprehensive force cooled tests on pipe cables at Waltz Mill'. Paris: CIGRE Paper No. 21–07.

Arkell, C. A. Blake, W. E., Brearley, A. D. R., Hacke, K. J. H. and Hance, G. E. A. (Mar. 1977) 'The design and construction of the 400 kV cable system for the Severn Tunnel'. *Proc. IEE* **124** (3).

Arkell, C. A., Hutson, R. B. and Nicholson, J. A. (Mar. 1977) 'Development of internally oil-cooled cable systems'. *Proc. IEE* **124**(3), 317–325.

Arnaud, U. G., Burton, J., Crockett, A. E. and Nicholson, J. A. (Mar. 1977) 'Development and trials of the integral pipe cooled e. h. v. cable system'. *Proc. IEE* **124** (3), 286–293.

Ball, E. H., Endacott, J. D. and Skipper, D. J. (Mar. 1977) 'UK requirements and future for force-cooled cable systems'. *Proc. IEE* **124** (3), 334–338.

Brotherton, W., Cox, H. N., Frost, R. F. and Selves, J. (Mar. 1977) 'Field trials of 400 kV internally oil-cooled cables'. *Proc. IEE* **124** (3), 326–333.

Albrecht, C. V., Mainka, G., Brakelmann, H. and Rasquin, W. (1978) 'High power transmission with conductor cooled cables'. Paris: CIGRE Paper No. 21–10.

Arkell, C. A., Ball, E. H., Barton, A. H., Beale, H. K. and Williams, D. E. (1978) 'The design and installation of cable systems with separate pipe water cooling'. Paris: CIGRE Paper No. 21–01.

Arkell, C. A., Gregory, B. and Smee, G. J. (Mar.–Apr. 1978) 'Self-contained oil-filled cables for high power circuits'. *IEEE Trans.* **PAS–97**.

Mainka, A. G., Brakelmann, H. and Rasquin, W. (1978) 'High power transmission with conductor-cooled cables'. Paris: CIGRE Paper No. 21–10.

Alexander, S. M. and Smee, G. J. (1979) 'Future possibilities for separate pipe cooled 400 kV cable circuits'. *2nd IEE Int. Conf. Progress Cables for 220 kV and Above*. IEE Conference Publication 176.

Alexander, S. M., Smee, G. S., Stevens, D. F. and Williams, D. E. (1979) 'Rating aspects of the 400 kV West Ham – St. Johns Wood cable circuits'. *2nd Int. Conf. Progress Cables for 220 kV and Above*. IEE Conference Publication No. 176.

Arkell, C. A. *et al.* (Apr. 1979) '400 kV self-contained oil-filled cable installation in South London UK (Rowdown Beddington)'. *7th IEEE/PES Transmission Distribution Conf.*

Arkell, C. A., Burton, J., Donelan, J. A. and Nicholson, J. A. (1979) 'Stainless steel sheaths for very heavy duty supertension cables'. *2nd IEE Int. Conf. Progress Cables 220 kV and Above*. IEE Conference Publication No. 176, pp. 208–212.

Bacon, P. E. and Morello, A. (1979) 'Upper limits of power rating of self-contained oil-filled cables'. *2nd IEE Int. Conf. Progress Cables for 200 kV and Above*. IEE Conference Publication No. 176.

Ball, E. H., Reilley, M., Skipper, D. J. and Yates, J. B. (Mar. 1979) 'Connecting Dinorwic pumped storage power station to the grid system by 400 kV underground cables'. *Proc. IEE* **126** (3), 239–245.

Boone, W., Templeaar, H. G., Voss, C. W. M. and Wiel, G. M. (1979) 'Some results of trials of an externally cooled 400 kV cable system'. *2nd IEE Int. Conf. Progress Cables for 220 kV and Above*. IEE Conference Publication No. 176.

Crockett, A. E. and Yates, G. (1979) 'Cooling of accessories of high voltage cable systems'. *2nd IEE Int. Conf. Progress Cables 220 kV and Above*. IEE Conference Publication No. 176, pp. 256–261.

Donazzi, F., Occhini, R. and Seppi, A. (1979) 'Soil thermal and hydrological characteristics in designing underground cables'. *Proc. IEE* **126** (6), 505–516.

Head, J. G., Gale, P. S. and Lawson, W. G. (Sep. 1979) 'Effects of high temperatures and electric stresses on the degradation of OF cable insulation'. *IEE 3rd Int. Conf. on Dielectric Materials*.

Preece, R. J. and Hitchcock, J. A. (1979) 'Simultaneous diffusion of heat and moisture around a normally buried e.h.v. cable system'. *2nd IEE Int. Conf. Progress Cables 220 kV and Above*. IEE Conference Publication No. 176, pp. 262–267.

Skipper, D. J. (Oct. 1979) 'The calculation of continuous ratings for forced cooled cables'. *Electra* (66).

Beale, H. K. (1980) 'Underground cables for high voltage power transmission'. Central Electricity Research Laboratory, Report No. EE 55/T 79–5590.

CIGRE Committee 21. (Mar. 1981) 'Recommendations for tests on anti-corrosion coverings of self-contained pressure cables and accessories for specially bonded circuits'. *Electra* (75), 41–61.

Kuenisch, H. J. *et al.* (1982) 'Testing a 110 kV LP OF cable with a water-cooled conductor in Berlin (West). Paris: CIGRE Paper No. 21–01.

CIGRE Study Committee 21, Working Group 7 (1988) 'Guide to the protection of specially bonded cable systems against sheath overvoltages'. Paris: CIGRE.

CIGRE Study Committee 21, Working Group 21–02 (1988) 'Survey of position on the calculation of cyclic ratings with partial drying of the soil'. Paris: CIGRE.

CIGRE Study Committee 21, Working Group 21–08 (1988) 'The steady state thermal behaviour of accessories for cooled cable systems'. Paris: CIGRE.

Thermomechanical design aspects

Arkell, C. A., Arnaud, U. G. and Skipper, D. J. (1974) 'The thermomechanical design of high power, self-contained cable systems'. CIGRE Paper No. 21–05.

Lawson, W. G., Head, J. G., Lombardi, A. and Anelli, P. (Sep. 1979) 'Fatigue and creep phenomena in oil-filled supertension cables'. *2nd IEE Int. Conf. Progress Cables for 220 kV and Above*.

Installation

Arkell, C. A. and Blake, W. E. (1968) 'Installation of EHV of cables in deep shafts'. *IEE Conf. Progress Overhead Lines and Cables for 220 kV and Above*.

Arkell, C. A. (1976) 'Self-contained oil-filled cable: installation and design techniques'. *IEEE Underground and Transmission Conf.*

Rodenbaugh, T. J. (Jan. 1979) 'Improvement of civil engineering techniques for buried transmission cables'. EPRI Report No. EL–969.

Ohhata, K., Ohno, H. *et al.* (1980) 'Study on vertical installation methods for high voltage XLPE cables'. *Sumitomo Electrl. Tech. Rev.* (116), 27–41.

Smith, D. G. (Oct. 1980) 'Calculating pipe cable pulling tensions'. *Transm. Distrib.* **34** (10), 40–44.

Nakagawa, H. *et al.* (1984) 'Development of various snaking installation methods of cables in Japan'. Jicable Conference Paper No. B7–5.

Jointing and accessories

Ohata, K. *et al.* (1983) 'Development of XLPE moulded joint for high voltage XLPE cable'. *IEEE Trans.* **PAS–103** (7).

Hedman, L. (1984) 'High voltage accessories for XLPE insulated cables 52–170 kV. Stress cones in EPDM rubber'. Jicable Conference Paper No. B5–2.

Gregory, B. and Lindsey, G. P. (1988) 'Improved accessories for supertension cable'. Paris: CIGRE Paper No. 21–03.

Park, J. *et al.* (1988) 'Application of prefabricated joint on 132 kV XLPE cable for power transmission'. Paris: CIGRE Paper No. 21–05.

Parmigiani, B. (1988) 'Premoulded accessories for high voltage extruded insulation cables'. Paris: CIGRE Paper No. 21–08.

Future development

Superconductivity

Graneau, P. (1970) 'Economics of underground transmission with cryogenic cables'. *IEEE Trans.* **PAS–89** (8).

Long, H. M. and Notaro, J. (Jan. 1971) 'Design features of a.c. superconducting cables'. *J. Appl. Phys.* **42** (1).

Rogers, E. C., Slaughter, R. J. and Swift, D. A. (Oct. 1971) 'Design for a superconducting a.c. power cable'. *Proc. IEE* **118** (10), 1493.

Forsyth, E. B. *et al.* (1973) 'Flexible superconducting power cables'. *IEEE Trans.* **PAS–92**, 494–505.

Nagano, H. *et al.* (Apr. 1973) 'Field test of liquid nitrogen cooled cryogenic power cable'. *Cryogenics* **13** (4).

Furuto, Y. *et al.* (1974) 'Electrical tests on a superconducting model cable'. *Int. Cryogenic Engineering Conf.*

Horigome, T. (1975) 'The present state of R&D for superconducting transmission in Japan'. *Cryogenics* **15**, 91–95.

Rogers, E. C. (Sep. 1975) 'Internally force cooled power cables: optimum working temperature in the range 70–358 K'. *Proc. IEE* **122**, 908–914.

Forsyth, E. B. *et al.* (1976) 'Long distance bulk transmission using helium cooled cables'. *Proc. IEEE Conf. Underground Transmission and Distribution*, pp. 446–453.

Graneau, P., Thompson, L. B. and Hoenig, M. O. (1976) 'High power transmission tests of short vacuum insulated liquid nitrogen cryocable loop'. *IEEE Transmission and Distribution Conf.*

Maddock, B. J. *et al.* (1976) 'Superconducting power cables and the applications'. Paris: CIGRE Paper No. 21–05.

Iwata, Z., Ichiyanagi, N. and Kawai, E. (1977) 'Cryogenic cable insulated with oil-impregnated paper'. *IEEE Winter Meeting.*

Mitzukami, T., Fukasawa, M., Sugiyama, K., Kuma, S. and Nagano, H. (Mar.–Apr. 1980) 'Prototype test of EHV cryoresistive cable'. *IEEE Trans.* **PAS–99**.

Pearman, A. J. *et al.* (1980) 'Preliminary ageing tests on a superconducting cable dielectric'. *IEEE Symp. on Electrical Insulation*, pp. 132–135.

Klandi, P. A. and Gerhold, J. (1983) 'Practical conclusions from field trials of a superconducting cable'. *IEEE Trans.* **MAG–19**.

Koyama, K. (1984) 'Research and development of superconductivity for energy technology in electrotechnical laboratory'. *Energy Development in Japan*, pp.101–122.

Rabinowitz, M. and Sosnowski, M. (1984) 'The potential of extruded XLPE for cryogenic power cable'. Jicable Conference Paper No. 133–4.

Forsyth, E. B. and Thomas, R. A. (1986) 'Performance summary of the Brookhaven superconducting power transmission system'. *Cryogenics* **126**.

Schaner, F. *et al.* (Jun. 1987) 'Prototype of a semiflexible multilayer insulated enclosure for cryogenic cables'. *Cryogenic Engineering Conf. Illinois, USA.*

Wu, M. K. *et al.* (1987) 'Superconductivity at 93 K in a new mixed phase Y–Ba–Cu–O compound system at ambient pressure'. *Phys. Rev. Lett.* **58**, 908–910.

Edwards, D. R. (Jan. 1988) 'Supertension or superconducting cables'. *Proc. IEE, Part C* **135** (1), 9–23.

Cable design and construction

Soda, S., Kojima, T., Fujiwara, Y., Kinoshita, S. and Takeuchi, K. (1969) 'Development of "Siograthene" laminated paper insulated oil-filled cables'. *IEE Conf. Progress in Cables and Overhead Lines for 220 kV and Above.*

Edwards, D. R. *et al.* (1972) 'Polymer and polymer/paper laminated tapes for E.H.V. OF cables'. Paris: CIGRE Paper No.15–05.

Doepken, H. C. (1974) 'Compressed gas-insulated cables with increased ampacity and reduced cost'. *IEEE Conf. on Underground Transmission and Distribution.*

Kreuger, F. H. and Van Deventer, G. C. (1974) 'Spacer cable'. Paris: CIGRE Paper No. 21–04.

Ray, J. J., Arkell, C. A. and Flack, H. W. (1974) '525 kV self-contained oil-filled cable systems for Grand Coulee, third power plant: design and development'. *IEEE Trans.* **PAS–93**, 630–639.

Erdinger, A. and Dobsa, J. (1976) 'Efficiency of direct and indirect cooling of underground transmission systems having solid or gaseous insulation. Paris: CIGRE Paper No. 21–04.

Hampten, B. F., Browning, D. N. and Mayes, R. M. (1976) 'Outline of a flexible SF_6 insulated EHV cable'. *Proc. IEE* **123**, 159–165.

Matsuura, K., Kubo, H. and Miyazaki, T. (1976) 'Development of polypropylene laminated paper insulated EHV power cables'. *IEEE Underground Transmission and Distribution Conf.*

Cooksen, A. H., Garrity, T. F. and Samm, R. W. (1978) 'Research and development in the United States on three conductor and UHV compressed gas insulated transmission lines for heavy load transmission'. Paris: CIGRE Paper No. 21–09.

Occhini, E., Lanfranani, G. M., Tellorini, M. and Maschio, G. (1978) 'Self-contained oil-filled cable systems for 750 and 1100 kV design and tests'. Paris: CIGRE Paper No. 21–08.

Takagi, T. *et al.* (1978) 'Development of 500 kV gas spacer cable'. *IEEE Trans.* **PAS–97**.

Watanabe, T. and Tsuda, H. (1978) 'Technical development and practical use of bulk power transmission cable systems in Japan'. Paris: CIGRE Paper No. 21–03.

Allam, E. M. *et al.* (Nov.–Dec. 1979) 'Low-loss 765 kV pipe-type power cable (Part 2)'. *IEEE Trans.* **PAS–98** (6).

Counsell, J. A. H. and Boardman, A. (1979) 'The relationship between molar polarisation and the swelling of polypropylene in organic liquids'. *3rd Int. Conf.*

on Dielectric Materials.

Gibbons, J. A. M., Nicholson, J. A., Parsons, A. F. and Bellote, A. J. (1979) 'Gas pressurised lapped-polyethylene cable developed for 400 kV transmission'. *2nd IEE Int. Conf. Progress Cables for 200 kV and Above.*

Itoh, H. *et al.* (1979) 'A novel type of paper for use in EHV underground cable insulation'. *3rd Int. Conf. on Dielectric Materials.*

Itoh, H., Nakagawa, M. and Ichino, T. (1979) 'EHV self-contained oil-filled cable insulated with composite paper, DCLP'. *IEE Conf. Progress in Cables and Overhead Lines for 220 kV and Above.*

Arkell, C. A., Edwards, D. R., Skipper, D. J. and Stannett, A. W. (1980) 'Development of polypropylene paper laminate (PPL) oil-filled cable UHV systems'. Paris: CIGRE Paper No. 21–04.

Sakurai, T., Iwata, Z., Shimizu, M., Fujisaki, Y. and Furisawa, H. (1980) '275 kV self-contained oil-filled cable insulated with polymethylpentene laminated paper'. IEEE Paper No. 80 SM 555–3.

Spencer, E. M., Samm, R. W., Artbauer, J. and Schatz, F. (1980) 'Research and development of a flexible 362 kV compressed gas insulated transmission cable'. Paris: CIGRE Paper No. 21–02.

Kusano, T., Soda, S., Fujiwara, Y. and Kinoshita, S. (1981) 'Practical use of "Siolap" insulated oil-filled cables'. IEEE Paper No. WM 114–8.

Mori, S. *et al.* (1981) 'Characteristics of gas insulated transmission lines at both ends in relation to short-circuit forces'. *IEEE Trans.* **PAS–97**, 1740–1748.

Watenabe, Y. *et al.* (1981) 'Construction of first gas insulated transmission line in Japan'. *IEEE Trans.* **PAS–100**, 4319–4329.

Allam, E. M. *et al.* (1982) 'Development of low loss 765 kV pipe type cable'. EPRI Report EL–2196, Project RP 7812.

Mori, S. *et al.* (1983) 'Effects of internal conductor to enclosure areas on SF_6 gas insulated transmission line'. *IEEE Trans.* **PAS–103**, 860–869.

Nemita, N. *et al.* (1983) 'Development and installation of 275 kV SF_6 gas insulated transmission line'. *IEEE/PES Summer Meeting.* Paper No. 83 SM307–6.

Dorison, E. *et al.* (1984) 'Evolutions in the specifications of HV and EHT cables associated with installation and operating conditions'. Paris: CIGRE Paper No. 21–03.

Farneti, F. *et al.* (1984) 'Testing of a 1100 kV 3 to 9 GV A underground transmission system'. *IEEE Winter Meeting.*

Tsuda, H. *et al.* (1984) 'Development and actual use of 275 kV low loss self-contained OF cable with laminated paper insulation'. *IEEE Trans.* **PAS–103**, 744–753.

Morello, A. *et al.* (1985) 'Supertension cables for transmission of large power'. *CIGRE Symp. 06–85.* Paper Nos. 230–04 and 230–05.

Suzuki, K., Saito, S. and Yoshida, S. (1986) 'Power cable insulation'. *IEEE Trans.* **EI–21** (6).

PART 5: SUBMARINE CABLES

Buseman, F. (1953) 'The magnetic compass errors caused by d.c. single-core sea cables'. ERA Report No. B/T 116.

Ingledow, T., Fairfield, R. M., Davey, E. L., Brazier, K. S. and Gibson, J. N.

(Dec. 1957) 'British Columbia–Vancouver Island 138 kV submarine power cable'. *Proc. IEE, Part A* **104** (18), 485–499.

Barnes, C. C., Coomber, J. C. E., Rollin, J. and Clavreul, L. (1962) 'The British–French direct current submarine link'. Paris: CIGRE Paper No. 210.

Bjurstrom, B. and Jacobsen, K. (Feb. 1964) 'D.C. cables for the Knoti–Skan transmission scheme'. *Direct Curr.* **9** (1), 12–17.

Williams, A. L., Davey, E. L. and Gibson, J. N. (Jan. 1966) 'The 250 kV d.c. submarine power-cable interconnection between the North and South Islands of New Zealand'. *Proc. IEE* **113** (1), 121–133. (Discussion 1363–1366, 2016).

Gazzana Prioroggia, P. and Patlandri, G. L. (1968) '200 kV d.c. submarine cable interconnection between Sardinia and Corsica and between Corsica and Italy'. Paris: CIGRE Paper No. 21–05.

Eyraud, I., Horne, L. R. and Oudin, J. M. (1970) 'The 300 kV d.c. submarine cables transmission between British Columbia mainland and Vancouver Island'. Paris: CIGRE Paper No. 21–07.

Gazzana Prioroggia, P., Piscioheri, J. and Margolin, S. (Jul.–Aug. 1971) 'The Long Island Sound submarine cable interconnection'. *IEE Trans.* **PAS–90**(H).

Oudin, J. M., Eyraud, I. and Constantin, L. (1972) 'Some mechanical problems of submarine cables'. Paris: CIGRE Paper No. 21–08.

Gazzana Prioroggia, P. and Maschio, G. (Sep.–Oct. 1973) 'Continuous long length a.c. and d.c. submarine HV power cables'. *IEEE Trans.* **PAS–92** (5), 1744–1749.

Eigh, L., Jacobsen, C. T., Bjurstrom, B., Hjalmarsson, G. and Olsson, S. O. (1974) 'The 420 kV a.c. submarine connection between Denmark and Sweden'. Paris: CIGRE Paper No. 21–02.

Hauge, O. and Johnsen, J. N. (1974) 'HV D.C. cable for crossing the Skaggerak Sea between Denmark and Norway'. Paris: CIGRE Paper No. 21–07.

Barnes, C. C. (1977) 'Submarine telecommunication and power cables'. Stevenage: Peter Peregrinus.

Baldwin, D. S. F., Giles, E. G., Hacke, K. J. H., Seamans, J. W. S. and Waterhouse, N. W. (1979) 'Methods for installing buried submarine cables for a 2 GW d.c. cross-channel link'. IEE Conference Publication No. 176, pp. 318–323.

Johnsen, J. N. and Bjorlow-Larsen, K. (1979) 'HVDC submarine cables'. *Progess in Cables and Overhead Lines for 220 kV and Above*. IEE Conference Publication No. 176.

Ledezma, O., Gomez, J. L. and Tsumoto, M. (Feb. 1979) 'Installation of 115 kV oil-filled submarine cable between Margarita Island and mainland Venezuela'. *IEEE Power Engineering Society Winter Meeting*. Paper No. A 79 002–7.

Goddard, S. C. *et al.* (Aug. 1980) 'The new 2000 MW interconnection between France and the UK'. Paris: CIGRE Paper No. 14–09.

Minemura, S. *et al.* (1980) '250 kV d.c. submarine cable for Hokkaido Honshn link'. Paris: CIGRE Paper No. 21–03.

Study Committee 21, Working Group 0.6 (Jan. 1980) 'Recommendations for mechanical tests on submarine cables'. *Electra* (68), 31–36.

Brown, P. V. (Oct. 1983) 'Protection of submarine cables'. *British Telecom. Eng.* **2**.

Foxall, R. G. *et al.* (1984) 'Design, manufacture and installation of 525 kV a.c. submarine cable from mainland Canada to Vancouver Island'. Paris: CIGRE Paper No. 21–04.

Giussani, A. and Bracco, G. (1984) 'Review of Italian experience on MV submarine cables insulated with extruded materials'. Jicable Conference Paper No. B4–1.

Rebuffat, L. *et al.* (1984) 'Installation of submarine power cables in difficult environmental environments. Experience with 400 kV Messina cables'. Paris: CIGRE Paper No. 21–10.

Suden, J. E., Traut, R. T. *et al.* (1984) 'Testing of a high voltage XLPE cable for dynamic submarine application'. Jicable Conference Paper No. B4–3.

Arkell, C. A. *et al.* (1985) 'OF land and submarine/land cable transition joints for the cross channel projects'. *IEE A.C. and D.C. Power Transmission Conf., London.*

Yates, J. B. (1985) '2000 MW link England–France submarine cable laying'. *IEE A.C. and D.C. Power Transmission Conf., London.*

Arkell, C. A. and Ball, E. H. (1986) 'Design and installation aspects of 270 kV d.c. cable connections – England to France'. Paris: CIGRE Paper No. 21–02.

Arnold, R. J. *et al.* (1986) 'Habitat repair facility for the cross channel cable'. Paris: CIGRE.

McConnell, J. *et al.* (1986) 'Long submarine cables for medium voltage connections'. *2nd IEE Int. Conf. on Power Cables 10 kV–180 kV.*

Voyatzakis, Y. *et al.* (1986) 'Installation of 150 kV OF submarine cable for Ionion Islands'. *2nd IEE Int. Conf. on Power Cables 10 kV–180 kV.*

Index